COMBUSTION ENGINEERING

COMBUSTION ENGINEERING

A REFERENCE BOOK ON FUEL BURNING AND STEAM GENERATION

GLENN R. FRYLING, M.E.

Editor

REVISED EDITION
FIRST IMPRESSION

PUBLISHED BY
COMBUSTION ENGINEERING, INC.
277 PARK AVENUE, NEW YORK 10017
1966

The Riverside Press
CAMBRIDGE · MASSACHUSETTS
PRINTED IN THE U.S.A.

PREFACE TO FIRST EDITION

The subject matter of this book deals with the various methods and equipment used for fuel burning, steam generation, and heat recovery. It represents an effort to cover the subject comprehensively, within the limits of one treatment, and thereby to provide answers to many questions that continually arise in the classroom, the engineering office, and the boiler plant.

The information and data from which the text has been prepared were contributed by a number of outstanding fuel technologists, combustion engineers, and specialists. Their collective experience includes design, application, and operation of equipment for thousands of installations and the use of virtually all commercially available fuels, including many so-called waste fuels.

Combustion Engineering is the science of burning fuel to liberate heat and make it available to perform useful work. The *Combustion Engineer* is one who is skilled in the art of burning fuel, and frequently is also a designer of fuel-burning, steam-generating, and related equipment.

The great improvement achieved, during the past quarter-century, in efficiency of steam generation is due primarily to the work of the combustion engineer in developing better methods and equipment for burning fuels. As a result, his field of activity has logically expanded and now includes the process of heat utilization and all equipment related thereto — in other words, all components of the complete steam-generating unit.

Brief outlines of early developments, as contrasted with modern designs, are included in many chapters. It is hoped that this treatment may aid in picturing the evolution of present-day equipment, and thus perhaps be helpful in pointing the way to even more efficient utilization of fuel in the future.

Replacement of much of the older equipment still in use throughout the country with more efficient modern designs is justified, not only from the standpoint of individual plant economy, but also as a measure of national conservation of fuel — our most valuable natural resource. This objective becomes more important each year, in the light of factors such as our accelerating rate of usage of all fuels and our seriously depleted reserves of oil and gas, as well as some of our high-quality coals.

The solution — in addition to replacement of obsolete equipment as rapidly as possible — is to design new installations that can utilize a wide range in fuel quality, instead of only one or two specific high-quality fuels as has commonly been the case in the past. With coal-burning installations, special consideration should be given to the grades of coal that are still abundantly available. A careful study of the fuel economically available to the locality of a particular plant will indicate the primary, as well as the alternate, fuels that should be considered. All these fuels, including any industrial wastes that can be economically burned, should become the basis for selection of equipment and the development of overall design. By following this procedure, the individual plant will be assured of its fuel supply at lowest cost, and under any likely market conditions, and will also be enabled to make a maximum contribution to fuel conservation.

The foregoing comments, considered in conjunction with the Table of Contents and the data presented in the Appendix and elsewhere, will make evident the different ways in which this book may be used by the student engineer, the teacher, and the practicing engineer. In the case of the last named, it is believed that the book will prove to be a useful reference for those engaged in designing, operating, or consulting work, as well as for those who occupy executive posts and have the responsibility of evaluating recommendations for equipment selection and purchase.

The book has been planned so that each chapter is self-contained, and there is therefore some repetition in text and illustrations. . . .

In the preparation of the text, many sources were drawn on for data and other material. . . . Acknowledgment has been given, and any omissions that may have occurred are unintentional.

Our special thanks are due to *Combustion* magazine for the use of material that appeared in many of its issues. . . .

OTTO DE LORENZI

PREFACE TO REVISED EDITION

Since publication of the First Edition of COMBUSTION ENGINEERING in 1947 there has been an extremely rapid rate of change in both the technology of power plants and the teaching of undergraduate engineering students. This Revised Edition represents a cooperative effort to recognize these changes within the general framework of *steam generation* and the *combustion and use of fossil fuels*. The published result is a volume that is completely rewritten and reorganized.

What is known as *engineering science* has received greatly increased emphasis in many fields and at all levels of engineering education. However, the desirable addition of scientific rigor sometimes obscures the relationship between a functioning power plant and its underlying engineering science. Hence a concerted effort has been made in the Revised Edition to stimulate interest in conventional steam power plants by showing that many fundamentals of engineering science are directly applicable to *power plant design*.

COMBUSTION ENGINEERING is primarily intended as a supplementary *reference* textbook for upper level undergraduate and beginning graduate students of engineering. Discussion of power plant cycles in an elementary engineering thermodynamics course provides one suggested use. Other courses that it might supplement, apart from the obvious application to specialized power plant design studies, include structural and machine design, applied mechanics, control technology, systems engineering, heat transfer, fluid mechanics and manufacturing processes. Examples based on realistic engineering experience in industrial settings are incorporated to show ties to all of these academic disciplines. A related suggestion is that the Revised Edition may have additional reference and pedagogical value in undergraduate and graduate courses in engineering design, particularly those which are intended to utilize and integrate knowledge from many professional specialties.

No attempt has been made to engage in detailed repetition of subject matter covered more expertly and adequately in widely adopted textbooks, and the revision itself is essentially directed to examples and information not generally available without seeking out numerous specialized and proprietary sources. It is assumed that the reader has an academic background equivalent to mastery of basic courses in physics, chemistry, mathematics at least through differential equations, mechanics, materials, electrical circuits and electronics. Some sections of the book presume more advanced studies in heat transfer, fluid flow, control theory and systems engineering.

Both the student and the interested practicing engineer will find numerous footnote citations and bibliographical references which treat in greater depth many of the topics discussed at a more elementary level in the text. A special effort has been made to incorporate what may be described as "landmark references", that is technical papers, articles and books which present original or definitive accounts of continuing value and lasting interest. It is also hoped that inclusion of many items originating from international sources will result in greater awareness of the outstanding technical contributions to the art and science of power plant design that have been made by engineers from many nations.

Relevant historical information has been introduced at many points to give some sense of time perspective in technical development and to show the degree of interdependence of many specialized fields. Since the nature of most engineering advances is from the simple to the complex with the advance of time, historical material can contribute to an understanding of the mental processes of creativity and technical innovation as exemplified in steam power technology.

The Editor wishes to acknowledge the generous assistance and continuing co-operation of his engineering colleagues in many organizational sectors of Combustion Engineering, Inc. Many outside the Corporation have likewise contributed services ranging from the simplest but nonetheless vital chores to the highest levels of intellectual activity. Some but regrettably not all of these individuals have been recognized in credit lines and acknowledgments within the text.

Although he may not recognize it as such, A. R. Mumford stimulated much of the thinking embodied in the approach to the Revised Edition in the course of conversations dating back to 1948. I owe personal debts of gratitude to my editorial mentor, A. D. Blake, for his understanding tutelage, and to a truly creative pioneer in corporate public relations and industrial advertising, Charles McDonough, for his management support and guidance over many years.

GLENN R. FRYLING

TABLE OF CONTENTS

APPENDIXES

Artist's conception of Keystone Generating Station

1

Visualizing the Steam Power Plant

Engineering is an art as well as a science. Neither phase can long endure without the other. Much of the art is best understood through written and pictorial descriptions of equipment and by visits to operating installations. The science is often expressed in terms of mathematical equations and physical concepts.

In keeping with the educational trend toward more emphasis on fundamental engineering science, this edition is properly concerned with the basic sciences underlying the design of boilers and nuclear reactors. But an engineer must understand science within a context of application. He must know the meaning of engineering terms and be able to visualize the appearance and function of equipment.

Basically a power plant provides a mechanism to transform *energy*. The input to a power plant may be in the form of the *potential energy* of an elevated body of water, the *chemical energy* that may be released from hydrocarbons in fossil fuels, *solar energy* from the sun, *fission energy* obtained by disintegration of elements at the upper end of the atomic scale or *fusion energy* from appropriate combination of elements at the lower end of the atomic scale. Power plant output may take the form of *heat*

for process or comfort, *electricity* which may be converted into other forms of energy as desired or *thrust* for transportation ranging from automobiles, locomotives and ships to interplanetary space vehicles.

The basic elements of power plants are at least outwardly familiar to everyone who grows up in a complex material civilization that is highly dependent upon power for its conveniences, transportation and economic well-being. Yet the seeming simplicity of the basic elements of power plants may mask the complexity of the actual *systems* of power generation. Each power plant is composed of many interacting systems. Those in a steam power plant include fuel and ash handling; transport of air, products of combustion, feedwater, steam and condensing water; control functions; and transmission and distribution of electrical power output.

Visualization is an important aid to understanding. Extensive knowledge of individual power plant components is important to the engineer, but this is not enough. He must be able to see beyond the detailed construction drawing to the actual physical equipment. He must understand the relationship of the individual parts to the power plant as a whole. He should be able to relate his theoretical engineering knowledge to the actual operating equipment.

One can visualize in many ways. Words, pictures, diagrams and familiar concepts of the mathematical and physical sciences are all aids to visualization. But power plants also involve men and economics, and so what one sees must also be related to the capabilities of individuals who design and operate power plants and to the decisions that must be made on the basis of economic alternatives.

A primary objective of this chapter is to make the reader aware that materials, men and money are always involved in the power plant processes of controlled release of energy. This is to be accomplished by a combined word and pictorial tour of one of the most advanced steam installations, a contrast of the functions and appearance of conventional and nuclear power plants, an exploration of mathematics as applied to power plants and an interpretation of some of the qualities of engineering leadership that have resulted in the remarkable improvements in power generation since 1882 when the pioneering Edison central station was placed in service on Pearl Street in New York City.

What Is a Boiler?

Language is a living and evolving means of communication, and the word "boiler" may not convey the same meaning to all engineers. The primary function of a boiler is to generate steam, and this naturally suggests the use of the terms "steam generator" and "steam generating unit" as equivalent to boiler. There have been some attempts to restrict the meaning of the word boiler to that portion of a steam generator in which water is transformed to the vapor phase, but these have only led to confusion without gaining widespread acceptance. In a similar sense, many have advocated the phrase steam generator or steam generating unit as a more universal designation than boiler, but usage of the latter persists in both lay and engineering circles. In fact, there is much evidence to support the view that the word boiler is gaining ascendancy. Throughout this book, however, the terms *boiler* and *steam generator* or *steam generating* *unit* will be used interchangeably and synonymously.[1]

In simplest terms a boiler is a mechanical device to convert water to steam. Every kitchen contains the basic elements of the largest boiler. These include a heat source in the form of a stove, a tea kettle which acts as a pressure vessel and water which may be heated to form steam. In journeying from this familiar concept to the actual installation in a central station for generating electric power, the engineer is likely to have his imagination challenged. How complex can a simple idea become? Is it really possible to fill the equivalent of a modern skyscraper with flame that will transform water into steam at temperatures at which piping glows like a piece of steel emerging from a blacksmith's forge?

Eddystone Station of Philadelphia Electric Company provides a very vivid contrast of the familiar and the unfamiliar. Here there is in operation a boiler which

[1] See Appendix B, A Glossary of Boiler and Electric Utility Terms.

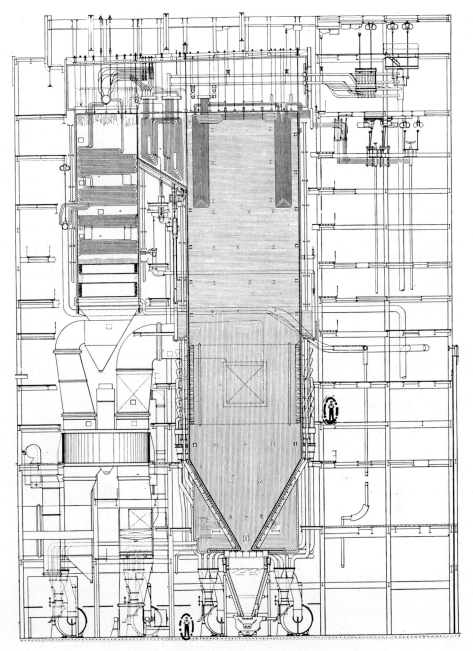

Fig. 1–1. Boiler cross section — note size of men.

produces 2,000,000 lb of steam per hour at a supercritical pressure of 5000 psig and a temperature of 1200 F. Like the kitchen scene to which it may be compared, this boiler has a heat source — this time internal in the form of the combustion of minute particles of coal. Hundreds of miles of tubing and piping are interconnected to constitute a pressure vessel, and there is an intricate water treatment plant to furnish a product of the highest purity for steam generation.

Now the usual way to show a boiler is by means of an engineering drawing known as a *cross section*. Useful though this drawing may be to those familiar with boiler design and construction, it has a sort of deceptive simplicity that needs interpretation for engineers who are just becoming acquainted with size relationships in the power industry. To go from the printed cross section of Fig. 1–1 to the actual physical construction

of the boiler, it seems appropriate to ask the reader to join in a pictorial visit to Eddystone Station.

We enter the station grounds from the industrial highway which connects Philadelphia and Chester in southeastern Pennsylvania. The scene is one of attractive landscaping, and portions of the large structure might well be mistaken for an industrial laboratory or a college classroom building. Only the stacks, Fig. 1–2, are a reminder that we are visiting one of the most efficient steam power plants ever built. Our guide joins us in the station lobby, and then the sound level intensifies slightly as he leads us into a lengthy ground floor enclosure, Fig. 1–3, in which can be seen pumps, piping, sampling lines, electrical conduit and instruments. Walking about in this area we observe more pumps and motors, the pulverizers which prepare finely ground coal for the boiler and a variety of other

Fig. 1–2.   Entrance to Eddystone Station of Philadelphia Electric Company

Fig. 1–3. Pump, sampling piping and instruments at the ground floor level

auxiliary equipment necessary for the operation of a modern steam power plant.

We are fortunate that our visit is timed to coincide with the annual inspection outage of one of the Eddystone boiler-turbine-generator units. Our guide points to the ashpits of one of the boilers, and we ask him if we could look inside to confirm the notion of great size of which we have become conscious. His reply is that we can do better than that, for by climbing several flights of stairs it is possible to enter the bottom of one of the two furnaces which make up each boiler.

Now a boiler may be manufactured and erected from many hundreds of tons of steel, but no matter how large it becomes, access is extremely limited, as shown in Fig. 1–4. As we crawl in after the guide, the inconvenience of entry is more than counterbalanced by the unusual sight of the interior of the furnace, Fig. 1–5. "Tubes, tubes everywhere" becomes our theme song as we view the four furnace walls, each 32 ft in width, and the furnace roof located some 130 ft

above the temporary platform on which we are standing. Portions of these steel walls are covered with a light colored substance known as slag, a fraction of the fuel ash that becomes molten when

Fig. 1–4. Entering a boiler is not always easy

Fig. 1–5. Looking up at miles of tubing — note technician inspecting the burner on the left

fired but transforms to a solid adherent material when the boiler is not operating.

Once again we are reminded of our kitchen analogy when our guide points out a workman, Fig. 1–5, bottom left, who is inspecting one of the four burners located in each corner of the furnace. These burners far outstrip their domestic counterparts, rising to a height of 20 ft and being composed of many nozzles whose angle of direction may be varied so that the resulting flame can encom-

pass as much or as little of the furnace as necessary to maintain the desired steam temperature.

As we are ready to leave the bottom of the furnace, our guide points to the superheater tube assemblies suspended from two sides of the roof. He makes a statement that sounds paradoxical and contrary to engineering logic: "If you think it is a long way from here to the top, just wait until you look down through the furnace to the ashpit." Surprised by the inference that the distance down could possibly appear to be greater than the distance up, we crawl out of the furnace and accompany the guide to the station elevator, a subtle reminder of the height of a large boiler. Elevators, we muse, are for office buildings and apartment houses — and in the age of space, for rocket launching pads. But as the guide pushes the button for the eleventh floor, 153 ft above the ground level, Fig. 1–6, we come to the realization that a modern central station boiler, in terms of physical size, ranks among modern man's most massive creations.

After we leave the elevator the guide loans us a flashlight and invites us to enter what is picturesquely termed the "dog house." As shown in Fig. 1–7, it is that portion of the boiler located above the roof of the furnace. We can understand why it is sometimes described as a maze of steel spaghetti as we view supports for furnace walls, interconnecting piping for many hundreds of circuits of boiler tubing and numerous instrument connections for measuring flow and tem-

Fig. 1–7. This has been described as a boiler "dog house"

perature conditions. We can also see a number of headers, cylindrical heavy-walled sections, of which the one in the foreground of Fig. 1–7 is typical. Their function is to collect and distribute fluid from a series of parallel tubes, which reminds us that there is more to a boiler than the furnace in which combustion of fuel takes place.

Leaving the confined space of the dog house, we descend one flight of stairs and our guide shows us the outside of what he describes as the convection section of the boiler. This extends from the furnace outlet downward about 50 ft, cooling the products of combustion primarily by convection heat transfer and passing them through the economizer and on to the four regenerative air heaters with which the boiler is equipped.

But our mind is still fascinated by the size of the furnace which we had viewed from the bottom a few minutes previously, and we ask, "How does it look from the top down?" Our guide decides he has built up enough suspense and points to an observation door located just below the furnace roof. On looking down

Fig. 1–6. An elevator is a decided convenience when a boiler reaches skyscraper height

Fig. 1—8. Looking down — a photographic study of tubes and burners and ash pit

through this opening we find ourselves literally poised on the top of a steel cliff, Fig. 1–8. The superheater tube assemblies that seemed so distant and tiny when observed from the furnace bottom, Fig. 1–5, suddenly become enormous and obscure part of our view. Yet as we continue our gaze downward, these assemblies provide welcome physical support and assurance. Quite to our surprise, the furnace seems to enlarge perceptibly when our eyes become accustomed to the low level of lighting. Faint sounds and a partially hidden light indicate that someone is working in the ashpit, the horizontal area toward which the sloping lower furnace walls appear to converge in the center of Fig. 1–8. Next we become aware of the two burners which are barely visible in the left and right corners, but they give the impression of having become miniaturized. The view gradually becomes a sort of intoxicant, and our sense of logic and geometry is befogged. Finally we too succumb to the striking optical illusion of a huge furnace and agree with our guide's inference that down appears to be farther than up.

It is difficult to give up the fascination of this vista and even more difficult to envision the amount of fuel and flame to fill such a tremendous steel cavity. Our guide feels it imperative to remind us that this boiler has two furnaces of the same size and that every hour they consume 100 tons of coal in performing their basic function of steam generation. We become more conscious of this as we walk over the steel grating commonly used in power plants and come upon the array of piping shown in Fig. 1–9. Not only does the boiler supply primary steam to the turbine, as shown by the pipe which begins at the far left and slopes downward below part of the railing, but it is also called upon to reheat a portion of the steam after it has partially expanded in the turbine. Part of the reheat piping is shown in the center and right hand side of Fig. 1–9.

Fig. 1–9. Main steam and reheat piping

Fig. 1–10.   View of turbine, feedwater heaters and piping

To gain a better understanding of the piping layout, we take the elevator to Elevation 51, about 100 ft below, where we can see one of the turbines and some of the vertical leads from the boiler, Fig. 1–10. Thus we observe how steam, the end product of the boiler, reaches the turbine, and if we look closely at Fig. 1–11 we can see that it is at the supercritical pressure of 5000 psig.

Fig. 1–11.   Steam pressure gage reads 5000 psig — boiler stop valves in background

We are now back near our starting point, and so it is appropriate to determine if the original boiler cross section, Fig. 1–1, is more understandable when the parts we have just seen are identified, as in Fig. 1–12. Before completing our

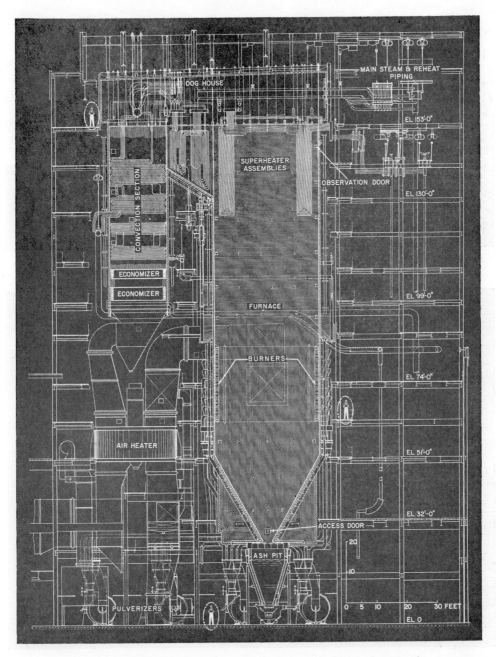

Fig. 1—12. Boiler cross section, same as Fig. 1–1 but keyed to photographic sequence

Fig. 1–13. Central control room with two operators on duty

Fig. 1–14. Dramatic view of exterior of Eddystone Station

tour of Eddystone, however, our guide invites us to visit the control room. What impresses us there, Fig. 1–13, is not the size but the fact that the operating requirement of the entire station normally can be handled by but two men. Finally we journey outside to look at the station from the vantage of the coal storage pile.

The two stacks, as shown in Fig. 1–14, serve to frame in the conveyor structures of the coal handling system on the left and the ash handling system on the right. We accompany our guide back to the station lobby, thanking him for showing us in so much detail what a boiler is and does.[2]

What Is a Nuclear Reactor?

A boiler is the oldest device used to convert water to steam in a power plant, but it is not the only one. The nuclear reactor performs an analogous role and gives promise of having an increasingly wider use in power plants of the future. But the differences are more striking than the similarities, and it therefore seems appropriate to note some of them in this section.

The most obvious difference stems from the contrasting properties of nuclear and fossil fuels. When a molecule of carbon is combined with oxygen to form carbon dioxide, the energy released in this basic combustion reaction is on the order of four electron volts per molecule. By contrast, when the nucleus of uranium-235 captures a subatomic particle called a neutron, the energy released by this act of fission is approximately 200,000,000 electron volts. This increase in theoretical energy release by a factor of 50,000,000 distinctly affects both the engineering design and appearance of a nuclear reactor.

For the same thermal output, a device to burn a fuel so rich in energy is obviously much smaller than the furnace of a conventional boiler. Not only is the re-

actor smaller but it is also capable of storing within its fuel elements enough energy to supply the power plant for a period of two or three years or more. Thus the reactor differs from the boiler both in its size and self-sufficiency of fuel supply.

These advantages are gained at a price of other complications. Safety is a prime factor in the control of nuclear reactions. An operating reactor must be properly contained so as to prevent the escape of radioactive materials in case of malfunction; it must also be adequately shielded to confine radiation and maintain the exterior at a safe level for human tolerance. Refueling is a complicated process, much of which must be done by remote handling devices. The long-lived fuel supply gradually accumulates fission poisons which can only be removed by chemical processing, something generally accomplished at a location other than the reactor power plant.

Another difference between boilers and reactors may be understood by comparing the respective ways of controlling combustion and fission reactions. Both must be started from some external source of energy, the boiler from the flame of an

---

[2] The interested reader is referred to the more elementary but appealing approach used by Andrew W. Kramer in "A Power Plant Primer," Technical Publishing Company, Barrington, Illinois.

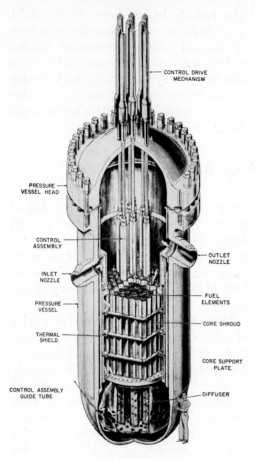

Fig. 1–15.   Cutaway view of nuclear reactor

ignition burner and the reactor by the application of a neutron source. The boiler requires continuous input of fuel and combustion air and continuous removal of waste products of combustion. The reactor, as previously noted, has its fuel supply in the form of self-contained fuel elements, and waste products are generally not removed until the fuel supply is replaced. For continuous regulation of the combustion process there is a combustion control system which adjusts the rate of fuel and air supply with respect to the power demand of the station. The analogous function in a nuclear power plant is performed by the reactor control rods which not only start up and shut down the nuclear reactions but also regulate the power level.

In terms of heat transfer surface, the nuclear reactor is a far more compact device than the conventional boiler. There is quite a difference between the tremendous open physical volume of one of the furnaces of the Eddystone boiler, Figs. 1–5 and 1–8, and the nearly completely filled interior of the reactor vessel, Fig. 1–15. As shown, assemblies of fuel elements and control rods are arranged vertically, and the heat transfer fluid is

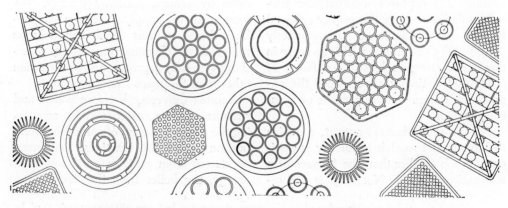

Fig. 1–16.   Geometric patterns symbolic of nuclear energy

circulated within the vessel, increasing in temperature as it moves from the inlet to the outlet. Distinctive geometries associated with the nuclear reactor are shown in Fig. 1–16 which is made up of cross sections of reactors and fuel elements.

Finally a nuclear reactor gives no outward demonstration of the release of fission energy. The observer must look to instruments to determine that the reactor is functioning properly, for there is nothing comparable to the visible flame of the combustion process. When in operation the nuclear reactor is a silent and inaccessible device that performs the same functions as the more familiar boiler.[3]

Mathematics and the Steam Power Plant

A power plant may be an impressive sight, but it reaches this stage by the use of the combined knowledge of mathematics, physical science and applied engineering. It is the purpose of this section to look at the power plant from the standpoint of mathematical relationships and physical phenomena.

Applied mathematics deals with a picture of a physical situation. This can be just a passing glance — an oversimplification of reality — or it may be a very comprehensive view requiring the most advanced levels of mathematical sophistication. The engineer must develop a balanced judgment of the significant factors in any physical situation, choosing his variables and making his assumptions in terms of mathematical considerations and desired end results. He must understand the strengths and limitations of both the physical assumptions and the mathematical methods.

In recent years the high speed computer has become an integral part of applied mathematics.[4] Modern computers can perform difficult operations rapidly and routinely. In the end, however, the calculations can be no better than the choice of variables and mathematical relationships involved in the particular physical situation. The engineer must be cautious of end results even though the computer is capable of expressing them to what appears to be many significant digits.

In engineering applications, physical measurements provide the numerical values that are used in computation. While the numbers may be exact and unambiguous when manipulated mathematically, the measurements are not. They are subject to error, and the answers can be no more precise than the original data used in the calculations.[5] Depending upon his needs, the engineer may use anything from a slide rule to a high speed computer to obtain his results. At times a value obtained from a single simple arithmetical calculation will be adequate,

---

[3] A visit to a nuclear power plant under construction is described in an editorial entitled "Shippingport Impressions," *Combustion*, Vol. 27, May 1956, p. 45.

[4] A very stimulating book with considerable historical information on computers and more than usual attention to engineering applications is *Mathematics and Computers* by G. R. Stibitz and J. A. Larrivee, McGraw-Hill Publishing Co., 1957.

[5] See Chapter 12, Power Plant Tests and Measurements, for a discussion of precision of measurements and sources of experimental error. This chapter also includes an example showing the use of a computer for the reduction of test data.

whereas on other occasions the machine solution of fifteen simultaneous differential equations may be insufficient.

The development of many types of high speed computers has greatly extended the ability of the engineer to use numerical methods to solve more complex mathematical relationships. For any given physical situation this may mean fewer assumptions and the ability to take into consideration more factors or to study more variables. Instead of defining a problem to computational limitations, the engineer — often in collaboration with the mathematician and computer technician — is able to approximate actual physical conditions more closely or to extend his results from a limited number of answers to a much wider range of cases. Computers also save much time and manpower if lengthy and repetitive calculation are required, such as in the reduction of test and experimental data.[6]

An understanding of differential equations is especially important for the engineer who may use them as a starting point in studying the behavior of a system or any of its parts. Differential equations are formulated by applying fundamental theorems (such as the law of conservation of energy or Newton's laws of motion) and known physical relationships (such as Fourier's heat conduction equation and Bernoulli's equation of fluid dynamics) to a differential element of the system. This provides a means to express a natural law in terms of small differences of time and space. After the equations have been set up, the next step is to find solutions, and this may be quite a task, particularly when partial derivatives occur. If exact solutions cannot be found, numerical methods may be used. It is at this point that the large high speed computer has an especially important role.

The Laplace transform is a mathematical technique for the algebraic solution of differential equations. Although it dates back to the eighteenth century, this approach has found increasing engineering use in the solution of control problems and certain aspects of nuclear reactor design. The method is applicable when a physical system can be described by a system of linear differential equations having time as the independent variable. Under certain circumstances the technique is also suitable for approximate solutions of systems of higher order differential equations.

Some Mathematical Examples

Beyond these general considerations of applied mathematics there are innumerable specific applications. The reader will encounter many of them in later chapters dealing with such subjects as heat transfer, fluid flow and stress analysis. Yet it seems appropriate to take another sweeping look at the steam power plant and see where mathematics fits into the picture.

Perhaps the most striking observation is the extent to which so many branches of mathematics are involved in the power plant. Geometry is indispensable in the layout of equipment, and techniques of orthographic projection and descriptive geometry find extensive use in the design of three-dimensional piping systems. Stresses in these piping systems, as well as those in reactor vessels and boiler pressure parts, require the formulation

---

[6] The use of a computer to extend a series of calculated values over a much wider range than was feasible with hand computations is illustrated in Chapter 21, Combustion and Boiler Calculations. A technical article of related interest is "Extending Engineering Skills with Large-Scale Digital Computers" by Allen Keller, *Mechanical Engineering*, Vol. 75, Nov. 1953, pp. 891–895.

and solution of many simultaneous algebraic and differential equations.

Moving into other areas of mathematics, statistical techniques are applied to fuel sampling, reactor core design and experimental correlations. Concepts of probability find use in determining sizes of new power plant units and predicting outages in existing equipment. The differential equation can be applied almost everywhere in the power plant and is an integral part of the mathematical treatment of heat transfer, fluid flow and control functions. Reactor physics design involves more advanced realms of mathematics, including perturbation theory and Monte Carlo techniques.

Simple arithmetic must not be overlooked in the power plant. There are many routine calculations in both design and operation for which there is no substitute for arithmetic. In other areas of the power plant, some processes are incompletely understood and cannot be expressed in exact analytical forms. The mathematical approach is then one of combining rational and empirical methods, as in curve fitting and power plant test correlations.

Rise of a Plume from a Power Plant Stack

One of the distinguishing characteristics of a steam power plant is the stack. It therefore seems appropriate to begin this series of mathematical examples by showing a semiempirical equation for the rise of a plume from a power plant stack. This represents a partially rational approach based on the combined effect of differences of temperature and relative velocities of the wind and stack gases. It is also an empirical approach in which

the coefficients shown in the equation were determined by experimental means.[7]

When the potential atmospheric gradient is positive, the plume reaches a maximum height when its density becomes equal to that of the surrounding atmosphere. The maximum height attained by the plume is given approximately by the following equation, the symbols for which are identified below.

$$H = H_s + \frac{4 \cdot 77}{1 + 0 \cdot 43 \frac{v}{u}} \times \frac{\sqrt{Qu}}{v}$$

$$+ 6 \cdot 37g \frac{Q\Delta}{v^3 T_1} \left(\log_e J^2 + \frac{2}{J} - 2 \right)$$

where

$$J = \frac{v^2}{\sqrt{Qu}} \left(0 \cdot 43 \sqrt{\frac{T_1}{gG}} - 0 \cdot 28 \frac{u}{g} \frac{T_1}{\Delta} \right) + 1$$

H_s is the stack height,

$$\frac{4 \cdot 77}{1 + 0 \cdot 43 \frac{v}{u}} \times \frac{\sqrt{Qu}}{v} \text{ gives the rise caused by the}$$

velocity of the stack gases,

and $6 \cdot 37g \dfrac{Q\Delta}{v^3 T_1} \left(\log_e J^2 + \dfrac{2}{J} - 2 \right)$ gives

the rise caused by the density difference and the temperature gradient effects.

g = acceleration due to gravity
G = gradient of potential atmospheric temperature, deg per ft
H = height of plume, ft
H_s = height of stack, ft
Q = gas rate measured at temperature T_1, cu ft per sec
T_1 = temperature at which density of flue gases is equal to that of the atmosphere, deg C abs
u = actual gas velocity in stack exit, ft per sec
v = wind velocity, ft per sec
Δ = temperature difference between actual flue gas temperature and T_1, deg C

---

[7] C. H. Bosanquet, W. F. Carey and E. M. Halton, "Dust Deposition from Chimney Stacks," *Proceedings,* Institution of Mechanical Engineers, Vol. 162, 1950, pp. 355–364.

Power Plant Efficiency

Looking at the power plant as a whole, the maximum possible thermal efficiency is expressed by this elementary relationship of the Carnot cycle.

$$\eta = \frac{T_2 - T_1}{T_2}$$

where T_2 is the maximum power plant fluid temperature and T_1 is the minimum fluid temperature, both expressed in absolute temperature units.

When it comes to evaluating power plant cycle refinements, such as the many variations of the Rankine cycle, the mathematical relationships become far more involved. An example is shown in the following expression for the fractional gain due to reheat in a reheat regenerative cycle. This equation was developed to assist in monitoring the effectiveness of steam power plant components, and the principal terms are illustrated in Fig. 1–17.[8]

$$G_r = [r_n(1 - G_r) - 1]$$
$$\left\{ \frac{H_2 - H_x}{H_1 - h_f} \left[\left(1 + \frac{\Delta h}{H_E - h_{bf}} \right) \right. \right.$$
$$\left. \left. \left(1 - \Delta h \frac{H_E - H_x}{(H_E - h_f)(H_2 - H_x)} \right) \right] \right\}$$

The following nomenclature applies to this equation:

G_r = fractional reduction in heat rate due to reheat

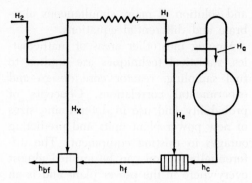

Fig. 1–17. Portion of reheat regenerative cycle showing nomenclature

r_n = dimensionless heat rate of nonreheat portion of cycle

Δh = rise in enthalpy through highest pressure heater

h = enthalpy of feedwater, as indicated

H = enthalpy of steam, as indicated

Steam Tables for Automatic Computation

Steam tables are used in many areas of power plant equipment design. Many engineers are accustomed to consulting these tables and picking out values for hand calculations. With the increased availability of high speed computers, a demand has arisen for expression of the physical properties of steam in forms convenient for automatic computation. This involves the mathematical process of curve fitting to cover the widest possible range of values. An example of an equation developed for this purpose is the following expression[9] for enthalpy in the superheated steam region, based on the tables of Keenan and Keyes.[10]

---

[8] J. K. Salisbury, "Power Plant Performance Monitoring," ASME *Trans.* Series A, *Journal of Engineering for Power*, Vol. 83, 1961, pp. 409–422.

[9] "Formulations for the Thermodynamic Properties of Steam and Water" by H. C. Schnackel, *Trans.* ASME, Vol. 80, 1958, pp. 959–966.

[10] *Thermodynamic Properties of Steam* by J. H. Keenan and F. G. Keyes, John Wiley & Sons, Inc., 1936.

$$h = F + 0.043557 \left[F_0 P + \frac{B_0}{2} \left(\frac{P}{T} \right)^2 \right.$$

$$\left. \left\{ -B_6 + B_0 \left[B_2 - B_3 + 2B_7 \frac{B_0}{2} \left(\frac{P}{T} \right)^2 \right] \right\} \right]$$

where h = enthalpy, P = pressure, T = temperature and the remaining terms are as noted.

$$B_0 = 1.89 - B_1$$

$$B_1 = \frac{2641.62}{T} 10^{80870/T^2}$$

$$B_2 = 82.546$$

$$B_3 = \frac{162460}{T}$$

$$B_4 = 0.21828T$$

$$B_5 = \frac{126970}{T}$$

$$B_6 = B_0 B_3 - 2F_0(B_2 - B_3)$$

$$B_7 = 2F_0(B_4 - B_5) - B_0 B_5$$

$$F_0 = 1.89 - B_1 \left(\frac{372420}{T^2} + 2 \right)$$

$$F = 775.596 + 0.63296T + 0.000162467T^2$$
$$+ 47.3635 \log_{10} T$$

Thermal Gradients in Pressure Vessels

In the design of thick-walled boiler and reactor components, such as boiler drums and reactor pressure vessels, it is sometimes necessary to know the exact temperature gradient through a section of material. This is particularly essential in the study of the effects of transient conditions, including startup, shutdown and load changes. Development of analytical methods to calculate temperature gradients requires a knowledge of stress analysis and differential equations, and these relationships become exceedingly complex for all but the most elementary

geometrical and heat transfer relationships. The following expression for temperature is based upon the solution of differential equations formulated with appropriate assumptions for one-dimensional heat flow through a thick slab which corresponds to the wall of a pressure vessel that might be designed and manufactured for a nuclear power plant.[11]

$$T_x = T_0 \pm \frac{m\tau}{N_{Fo}} \left[N_{Fo} - \xi \left(1 - \frac{\xi}{2} \right) \right.$$

$$\left. + \frac{2}{\pi^3} \sum_{n=0}^{\infty} \frac{e^{-(n+1/2)^2 \pi^2 N_{Fo}}}{(n + \frac{1}{2})^3} \sin (n + \tfrac{1}{2}) \pi \xi \right]$$

b = wall thickness, ft

m = linear transient rate, deg F per hr

T_0 = initial temperature of a point in vessel wall at a distance x ft from inner surface, deg F

T_x = temperature at a point in vessel wall at a distance x ft from inner surface, deg F

α = thermal diffusivity of material, sq ft per hr

ξ = dimensionless distance x/b

π = Pi

τ = time, hr

N_{Fo} = Fourier modulus, $\alpha\tau/b^2$

Analysis of a Natural Circulation System

Many types of boilers and nuclear reactors operate on the principle of circulation induced by differences in density of fluid. This is a very simple and readily understandable physical concept. Unfortunately this simplicity is quickly lost in even a very elementary natural circulation loop. The following analysis is based upon a boiling water reactor shown

---

[11] "An Analytical Method of Predicting Temperature Gradients in Thick-Walled Pressure Vessels" by J. S. Hucks and A. L. Gaines, ASME Paper No. 57–A–231.

schematically in Fig. 1–18.[12] Comparable complexity is found in analytical investigations of natural circulation boilers.

In a natural circulation system

$$\Sigma \Delta P = 0,$$

which states that the summation of the pressure drops, $\triangle P$, around the closed loop, consisting of riser and downcomer, must be equal to zero.

The systems of Fig. 1–18 is broken into various segments, and these can be added and simplified to give the following expression.

$$\frac{v_{sat}^2}{2g} [N_1 + N_2 + N_3 + N_4 + N_5 + N_6 + N_7 + N_8 + N_9 + \Sigma N_i + N_{11}]$$

$$- \rho_D(L_{DT} - L_{DB}) + \rho_D[L_{LPT} - L_{LPB}] + \rho_{NB}(L_{sat} - L_{HSB})$$

$$+ \bar{\rho}_B(L_{HSE} - L_{sat}) + \rho_R(L_{RT} - L_{RB}) = 0$$

By combining certain elements of system geometry, simplifying and taking into account risers of varying diameters, the following equation is obtained.

$$\frac{v_{sat}^2}{2g} = \frac{L_{NB}(\rho_D - \bar{\rho}_{NB}) + L_B(\rho_D - \bar{\rho}_B) + \Sigma L_{Ri}(\rho_D - \rho_{Ri})}{N_1 + N_2 + N_3 + N_4 + N_5 + N_6 + N_7 + N_8 + N_9 + \Sigma N_i + \Sigma N_{11}}$$

The individual N terms in the previous equation may be classified as follows:

$$N_1 = \rho_f \left(\frac{A_{HS}}{A_D}\right)^2 [1 + K_{cUP}]$$

= acceleration of the fluid from the upper plenum to downcomer and frictional resistance at contraction.

$$N_2 = f_D \left(\frac{L_D}{D_D}\right) \left(\frac{\rho_f^2}{\rho_D}\right) \left(\frac{A_{HS}}{A_D}\right)^2$$

= frictional resistance in downcomer.

$$N_3 = \frac{\rho_f^2}{\rho_D} \left(\frac{A_{HS}}{A_D}\right)^2 \left[\left(\frac{A_D}{A_{LP}}\right)^2 - 1 + K_{ELPB}\right]$$

= deceleration of fluid and frictional losses at the expansion from the downcomer to lower plenum.

$$N_4 = \frac{\rho_f^2}{\rho_D} \left[1 - \left(\frac{A_{HS}}{A_{LP}}\right)^2 + K_{cHSB}\right]$$

= acceleration of fluid and frictional losses at the contraction from lower plenum to the heated section.

$$N_5 = 2\rho_f \left[\frac{\rho_{HSB} - \rho_f}{\rho_{HSB}}\right]$$

= acceleration of fluid in nonboiling length due to density change with temperature.

$$N_6 = \frac{\rho_f^2}{\rho_{NB}} \left(\frac{f_{HS}}{D_{HS}}\right) (L_{NB})$$

= frictional resistance in the nonboiling segment of the heated section.

[12] "Lecture Notes on Heat Extraction from Boiling Water Power Reactors" by P. A. Lottes, M. Petrick and J. F. Marchaterre of Argonne National Laboratory, ANL–6063, October 1959, pp. 89–110.

$$N_7 = \frac{\rho_f^2}{\rho_{LB}} (\overline{R}_{LB}) \left(\frac{f_{HS}}{D_{HS}}\right) (L_{LB})$$

= frictional resistance in the local boiling segment of the heated section.

$$N_8 = 2(r)(\rho_f)^2$$

= acceleration of fluid due to formation of steam voids in the heated channel.

$$N_9 = \rho_f(\overline{R}) \left(\frac{f_{HS}}{D_{HS}}\right) (L_B)$$

= frictional resistance in the boiling segment.

$$N_{10} = 2\rho_f \left(\frac{A_{HS}}{A_{i+1}}\right) \left\{ x_{HSE}^2 \left(\frac{\rho_f}{\rho_g} \frac{1}{(\alpha_{i+1})}\right. \right.$$
$$\left. - \frac{A_{HS}}{A_i} \frac{1}{2_i}\right) + (1 - x_{HSE})^2$$

= total pressure drop due to an expansion or contraction.

$$\left[\left(\frac{A_{HS}}{A_{i+1}}\right) \frac{1}{(1 - \alpha_i)} - \frac{A_{HS}}{A_i \alpha_i} \right] \right\}$$

$$N_{11} = Rf_R \left(\frac{A_{HS}}{A_R}\right)^2 \frac{\rho_f}{D_R} L_R$$

= frictional loss in the adiabatic risers.

g = acceleration of gravity
K_c = contraction coefficient
K_E = expansion coefficient
L = length
P = pressure
q'' = heat flux
r = acceleration multiplier
V, v = velocity
x_e = quality at exit
α = volume fraction of vapor
ρ = density

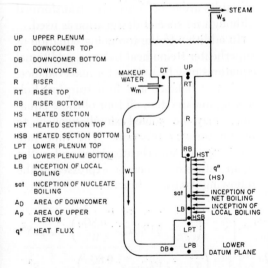

UP   UPPER PLENUM
DT   DOWNCOMER TOP
DB   DOWNCOMER BOTTOM
D   DOWNCOMER
R   RISER
RT   RISER TOP
RB   RISER BOTTOM
HS   HEATED SECTION
HST   HEATED SECTION TOP
HSB   HEATED SECTION BOTTOM
LPT   LOWER PLENUM TOP
LPB   LOWER PLENUM BOTTOM
LB   INCEPTION OF LOCAL BOILING
sat   INCEPTION OF NUCLEATE BOILING
A_D AREA OF DOWNCOMER
A_p AREA OF UPPER PLENUM
q'' HEAT FLUX

Fig. 1–18. Natural circulation system

Superheater Transfer Function

To work toward the goal of a completely automatic power plant it is necessary to know how the individual components might interact on a time basis. That is, knowledge must be obtained of the time behavior in order to design a control system integrating all of the power plant components. Accomplishment of this objective requires analysis of what goes on, for example, in the many separate heat transfer processes throughout the power plant and an understanding of the

The following nomenclature applies to the preceding equations.

A = area
D = equivalent diameter
f = friction factor

rate at which these processes can be varied and controlled. Among the most useful mathematical tools for this type of analysis are the linearization of ordinary differential equations and their conversion to algebraic form by use of the Laplace transform. The following example shows the application of these methods to the dynamic analysis of a superheater for a central station boiler.[13]

The heat balance equation for a superheater section may be written in the following form.

$$Q + W_i h_i - W_o h_o = V \frac{d}{dt}\left(\frac{\rho_i h_i + \rho_o h_o}{2}\right)$$

where Q is the rate of heat addition to the superheater, W_i and W_o are the weight rates of flow into and out of the superheater, h_i and h_o are the inlet and outlet enthalpies, V is the volume, and ρ_i and ρ_o are the specific weights of fluid entering and leaving the superheater.

The preceding equation can be linearized to appear as follows:

$$Q + W_i \Delta h_i + h_i \Delta W_i - W_o \Delta h_o - h_o \Delta W_o$$
$$= \tfrac{1}{2}V\left[\rho_i \frac{d}{dt}(\Delta h_i) + h_i \frac{d}{dt}(\Delta \rho_i)\right.$$
$$\left. + \rho_0 \frac{d}{dt}(\Delta h_0) + h_o \frac{d}{dt}(\Delta \rho_0)\right]$$

This is now a linear equation in the variables

$$\Delta Q, \Delta h_i, \Delta W_i, \Delta h_0, \Delta W_0, \Delta \rho_i, \text{ and } \Delta \rho_0.$$

All other symbols are now to be regarded as constants at their steady-state values.

The Laplace transform is taken to reduce the differential equation to an algebraic equation to facilitate solution. Since only perturbations about a steady-state operating point are considered, all initial values can be taken as zero. The transformed equation is

$$\Delta Q + W_i \Delta h_i + h_i \Delta W_i - W_0 \Delta h_0 - h_0 \Delta W_0$$
$$= \tfrac{1}{2}V[\rho_i S \Delta h_i + h_i S \Delta \rho_i + \rho_0 S \Delta h_0 + h_0 S \Delta \rho_0]$$

where S is the Laplace operator and all variables are to be considered transformed although no special designation is used.

In addition to the foregoing equation of superheater steam heat balance, additional equations may be written for mass balance, tube heat balance and heat transfer. Following linearization all four of these equations may be solved simultaneously to obtain transfer functions. The time rate of change of superheater inlet and outlet temperature may then be expressed as the following transfer function.[14]

$$F_t = \frac{\dfrac{Q_0}{\theta_0}W_0 c_{pi} - \left[\left(\dfrac{Q_0}{2\theta_0} - W_0 c_{pi}\right)m_w c_{pw} + \dfrac{Q_0}{\theta_0}\gamma_n\right]S - \left(\gamma_n + \tfrac{1}{2}Vh_0\mu_i \times \dfrac{0.8Q_0}{2W_0}\right)m_w c_{pw}S^2}{\dfrac{Q_0}{\theta_0}W_0 c_{pi} + \left[\left(\dfrac{Q_0}{2\theta_0} + W_0 c_{pi}\right)m_w c_{pw} + \dfrac{Q_0}{\theta_0}\gamma_d\right]S + \left(\gamma_d + \tfrac{1}{2}Vh_0\mu_0 \times \dfrac{0.8Q_0}{2W_0}\right)m_w c_{pw}S^2}$$

where $\gamma_n = \tfrac{1}{2}V[\rho_i c_{pi} - (h_0 - h_i)\mu_i]$ and $\gamma_d = \tfrac{1}{2}V\rho_0 c_{p0}$

[13] "Dynamic Representation of a Large Boiler-Turbine Unit" by J. H. Daniels, Mark Enns and R. D. Hottenstine, ASME Paper 61–SA–69.

[14] "Comparison of Dynamic Models of a Superheater" by Mark Enns, *Trans.* ASME, Series C, Vol. 84, 1963, pp. 375–382. See also Chapter 22, Controls and Instruments.

Men, Money and Materials

Thus far the reader has been conducted on a tour of Eddystone Station, has gotten a glimpse of a nuclear power plant and has been exposed to some of the applications of mathematics and physical science to power plant design. All of these are important and interrelated, but by the very nature of technological specialization they are apt to become isolated and separated. The engineer who is in charge of erecting power plant equipment, for example, may have little grasp of the problems of operation or the analytical techniques of design. The manufacturing engineer may have considerable knowledge of materials and production scheduling but fail to understand the crucial importance of quality control in the end product. The designer may become so preoccupied with the intricacies of a special investigation that he loses sight of the fact that his ideas must be turned into steel by a manufacturing plant before they can be incorporated in an operating boiler or reactor.

The power plant is a place where men, money and materials must unite in the optimization of design and the minimizing of capital charges and operating costs. *The dollar sign is important in the power plant,* for a modern central station may involve expenditures of the magnitude of $100,000,000. Many economic alternatives must be studied, and the ideal of what is theoretically attainable must sometimes be compromised in favor of the practicable accomplishment in economic and technical terms. Design problems, as engineers soon learn in practice,

seldom have but one "correct" answer, and the choice from among several alternates involves major elements of *engineering judgment.* This is one of the most challenging aspects of the power plant field, where decisions involve large sums of money as well as degrees of uncertainty.

One must also look at men, money and materials through the perspective of time.[15] There are many driving forces that impel men to contribute to power progress. One of them is prestige, the self-satisfaction and personal acclaim that accrue to the pioneer. Economic return is closely related to prestige, and an economy based on competitive free enterprise makes "firsts" rewarding. But progress in power, like progress in other areas of technology, is related to what is known as the state of the art. Man's imagination often outruns the available techniques and materials, and some of the boldest ideas must await the passage of time for successful application. Pulverized coal firing provides a typical example. Although the first patents date back to 1806, successful central station applications did not occur until the early 1920's. At this point the creative ideas of the engineer merged with other developments in materials and combustion of fuel to start a new era of boiler design. Furnaces as big as those of Eddystone, Figs. 1–5 and 1–8, were beyond the realm of practicality before the development of pulverized coal firing.

There is another aspect to looking at power plant progress through time per-

[15] This idea is further developed in an article by Glenn R. Fryling entitled "Patterns for Power Progress," *Mechanical Engineering,* Vol. 80, November 1958, pp. 62–65. It is much easier to duplicate an existing design than to move forward to something new, but the engineer who upsets established practice contributes most to power progress.

spective. In looking ahead to new developments much can be learned from the past. The bold idea that could not be applied a century or even a decade ago, or the project that failed for lack of suitable materials, may come within the realm of practical possibility as a result of technological developments during the intervening period. The interested engineer will find an occasional browsing trip through old technical publications a rewarding and sometimes humbling experience. For example, he might read with profit and inspiration the visionary ideas of the 1880's set forth by Robert H. Thurston,[16] first president of The American Society of Mechanical Engineers, and the penetrating observations of Dr. A. Stodola[17] in the 1920's on "The Prospects of the Thermal Prime Mover."

Visualizing the steam power plant in terms of men, money and materials is the first step toward *vision*, something the dictionary defines as unusual discernment or foresight. Philip Sporn, a distinguished leader of the electric utility industry, has captured its meaning in a way that should be grasped by all engineers who hope to contribute to power progress.[18]

". . . For unless the fog of the future is pierced by vision, neither size nor technical dimensions can be visualized. As a matter of fact, unless social-economic trends are visualized, the very foundation for future systems cannot be developed.

In short, sound development of power systems is not possible unless boldness and imagination — vision — in projection and conception are liberally intermingled with technical soundness and economic responsibility.

"Vision obviously isn't introduced merely by making engineering studies and evaluations, or economic projections — even though these activities help. The technical studies, as often as not, stop short just at the point where they need very much to advance. To paraphrase John Tyndall — we cannot stop abruptly where our slide rule value ceases to be of use. Here vision is needed; here special insight and intuition are required to supplement the purely technical judgment. Vision obviously cannot be confined to things physical in a field such as electric power where perception is needed in the social, social-economic and even political sphere. Like a good many chemical reactions which cannot occur except in a solution of a certain pH, it seems to me that vision is impossible except against a background of understanding of the life of the community, recognition of the aspirations of the various segments of the population and awareness of the basis of their economic well being and of their social habits.

"To some extent vision has the characteristics of being both swift and transient. In an instant one may see clearly and boldly a full development, a system,

---

[16] ASME *Transactions*, Vol. 1, 1880, pp. 1–15, and Vol. 2, 1881, pp. 415–442, and *Robert Henry Thurston — A Biography* by W. F. Durand, published by ASME, 1929.

[17] *Steam and Gas Turbines* by A. Stodola, two volumes, translated by L. C. Loewenstein, McGraw-Hill Book Co., 1927, pp. 1271–1330.

[18] "Vision in Power," an address presented to the American Power Conference, March 27, 1952 and published in the *Proceedings*, Vol. 14, pp. 52–57, and in *Mechanical Engineering*, Vol. 74, June 1952, pp. 465–466. An elaboration of this concept is found in his later book, *Foundations of Engineering*, Pergamon Press, 1964, 143 pages.

or the consequences of a policy, and in that instant he may get a clear basis for judging intrinsic worth, economic soundness, or basic wisdom of each of these respectively. An almost infinite amount of work may be necessary to fill in various phases of the picture before it can meet, in the light of cold judgment, the test of reason and analysis. It may even be necessary to invent new tools, devices and organizations not previously tried or known. But unless the end vision is clearly kept in mind these will never come into being, and the end so desirable and desired will never be brought about."

Vision is the human quality which has contributed much to the continuing series of advances by the power industry since the pioneering days of Thomas A. Edison and his contemporaries. *The progress has been spectacular.* Steam conditions have increased from about 100 psig and saturation temperature to superheat at supercritical pressures. Unit sizes have grown from around 100 kw to the 1,000,000 kw range. Fig. 1–19 provides graphic evidence of engineering success in improving power plant efficiency as represented by the best central stations.

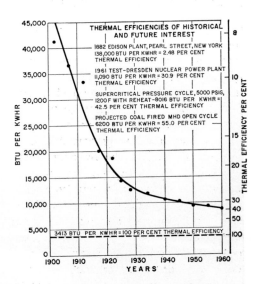

Fig. 1–19. Improvements in power plant heat rates, a measure of efficiency

As noted at the begining of this chapter, engineering is both an art and a science. Vision links the two. The engineer must not only visualize what takes place within the power plant but also envision future needs. This is the challenge and continuing attraction of power engineering.

Acknowledgment. A word of special appreciation is due to Mr. R. C. Cox of Philadelphia Electric Company for his cooperation and assistance in obtaining photographs of Eddystone Station. The interior views of the boiler were taken by Mr. H. R. Towse and several of the other special photos by Mr. T. Gawlicki. The basic idea for this chapter originated at a meeting of the engineering trainees of the Chattanooga Division of Combustion Engineering, Inc., arranged in December of 1959 by Messrs. A. C. Richardson and E. T. Sliger. During a subsequent visit to Eddystone Station, Mr. E. L. Kochey, one of the designers of the Eddystone boilers, pointed out the optical illusions in a large furnace and made other suggestions regarding the visual impact of large central station boilers.

Visualization — the reality of engineering hardware

2

Elements of Power Plant Design[1]

VISUALIZATION IS AN AID to the engineering designer. Through it he can gain a comprehension of the function of equipment and the interrelationships which exist in the systems which make up the steam power plant. The visual and verbal pictures of the preceding chapter must now be turned into the hardware of an actual power plant. This is the work of the engineer, either as an individual or in collaboration with other members of a design team.

Attention in this chapter will be focussed on the design of the power plant as a whole. Because of their comparative simplicity, the elements of design will be chosen from the field of industrial and institutional power plants. These ele-

ments are also involved in the more complex design problems of the central station, which is the subject of the next chapter. Later in the book there will be more specific discussions of the design of boilers and reactors, together with their various components and supporting systems.

The most elementary type of industrial or institutional power plant incorporates a boiler as a heat source and a heating system as a load to dissipate the thermal energy released by the fuel fired to the boiler. The thermal transport medium may be steam or hot water, but in either case it will be returned to the boiler at a lower temperature level. Figs. 2–1 and 2–2 show these elementary plants.

[1] Material contributed by Stuart W. Allen, consulting engineer.

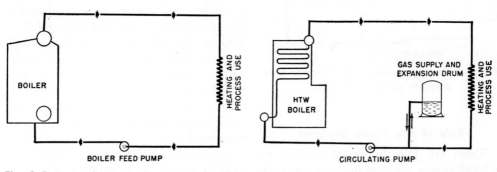

Fig. 2–1 Basic elements of a steam heating plant

Fig. 2–2 Basic elements of a high temperature water heating plant

From this point onward the industrial or institutional power plant may encompass various degrees of complexity. Power may be generated in a condensing plant, thus making the equivalent of a small central station. Steam may be supplied to process directly and not returned as condensed feedwater, or it may be passed through a turbine acting as a reducing valve, followed by use for heating and process as shown in Fig. 2–3. Cycles may range from the simplicity and low level of thermal efficiency exemplified by the noncondensing steam locomotive to the most complex and efficient thermodynamic arrangements proposed for central stations, including combinations of steam and gas turbines. Boiler size may range from the generation of a few thousand pounds of steam per hour to several million in large installations, and the same capacity spread is true of turbines for power generation. In so many words, the industrial or institutional power plant can be used to illustrate virtually every aspect of conventional thermal engineering.

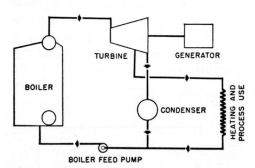

Fig. 2–3 Basic elements of a plant for back pressure power generation

Role of the Young Engineer

There are four important and interrelated groups involved in the design and construction of industrial or institutional power plants:

1. The organization for whom the plant is being built
2. The consulting engineer who is coordinating the design efforts
3. The manufacturers who are supplying equipment
4. The contractors who are constructing the plant

The young engineer may encounter these groups in a variety of ways. He may be attached to the engineering staff of an industrial plant that is in the midst of an expansion program. He may be working for a senior engineer in a consulting engineering firm engaged in the design of industrial and institutional power plants. Manufacturers may assign the young engineer to assist in selecting and pricing equipment to meet specifications of the purchaser, or he may be employed by contractors to supervise some phases of construction. In any one of these assignments the young engineer may be called upon to use his knowledge of thermodynamics, heat transfer and fluid flow, plus his skill in directing other individuals. He will quickly learn, however, that the design of industrial and institutional power plants is closely tied to economics. Compromises may have to be made that will rule out the ultimate in engineering perfection and substitute the practicable in terms of financial limitations. Yet the young engineer will observe that such decisions are made without sacrifice of basic safety of the installation and within the rules and regulations set forth by the various private and governmental agencies which may be concerned.

Engineering judgment is probably the most important single attribute of the designer of industrial and institutional power plants. Local conditions obviously differ from plant to plant, as do fuel and water supplies and quality of operating personnel. Each plant must be approached from an impartial basis and as a separate entity. Ideas suited to one situation should not be carried over to another power plant without careful evaluation. In particular, those whose design experience has been primarily with central stations must recognize that the industrial or institutional power plant has the same basic engineering elements but cannot justify as much engineering manpower and financial support for comprehensive studies of design details.[2]

Trends in Power Plant Design

Up to this point the term "industrial or institutional power plant" has been used without definition. In engineering terms there is no physical difference between the two types. Power generation was at one time a part of virtually every industrial and institutional power plant, but this is no longer the case. There are several reasons for this change, which accelerated during and after World War II:

1. The public utility systems are more securely and effectively interconnected electrically, and service is very reliable.

2. The cost of purchased electric power has resisted the effects of inflation better than almost any other commodity, thereby diminishing the percentage of total industrial or institutional expenditures for power.

3. The demands for additional electrical power have generally grown faster than the demands for heating, thereby

exceeding the capabilities of back-pressure generation.

4. It has been found that the same dollar investment brings a greater return when applied to production facilities or institutional expansion than when spent in the power plant.

The end result has been that the vast majority of industrial and institutional power plants built in the last decade or so have been primarily installations for space heating and process steam. The numerous exceptions have been based upon situations like the following:

1. Coordinated demands for steam and power, accompanied by the availability of waste fuels suitable for combustion in boilers. Examples are found in such industries as pulp and paper, chemicals, petroleum and steel, plus certain types of raw materials processing, such as bagasse and grain refuse.

2. A balanced growth of electrical and steam heating requirements. This is found in many institutional settings, such as universities, hospitals of various types, penal institutions and some district heating schemes in metropolitan areas. Here back pressure power generation has marked economic advantages.

From the foregoing it can be seen that industrial and institutional power plants have much in common. Either type may be built for space or process heating alone, or power generation facilities may be incorporated, depending upon specific industrial and institutional requirements. Most engineering considerations apply with equal validity to both types, and the equipment does not differ from one to the other.

[2] A short but informative article on this subject by S. E. Friedeberg, "Trends in the Small Industrial Steam Plant Offer Opportunities for Young Engineers," appeared in *Combustion* Vol. 21, April 1950, p. 71.

Power Plant Studies

The starting point of an industrial or institutional power plant is an engineering study. Power and steam loads must be ascertained and costs estimated before construction can be considered. In some instances the organization for whom the power plant is being built may have an engineering staff of sufficient size and experience to make preliminary studies, develop the detailed design, evaluate bids, award contracts and supervise construction. More often than not, however, a consulting engineer is called upon to perform one or more of these functions.

In any case a preliminary report must be written in order to obtain authorization of capital funds. This report must consider not only the total investment but outlays for such items as operation, maintenance, depreciation, insurance, interest and taxes. With its primary emphasis on economic factors, the preliminary report must be written so as to be intelligible to those whose background may be in finance or law rather than engineering. A form of report presentation which has been looked upon with favor over the years is one which first defines the problem being studied, then discusses all technical items having a bearing on the problem and finally offers conclusions and recommendations.

The preliminary report, whether it deals with a new power plant or an extension to an existing one, always includes a tabulation of steam and power requirements. This important task can only be accomplished by painstaking work of the "pick and shovel" variety, for all factors having a bearing on future operation must be considered. Young engineers may be assigned to collect such data, but final evaluation should be by an engineer with considerable experience in the design of industrial and institutional power plants.

An important part of the preliminary report is the charting of anticipated loads for different conditions, such as daily load curves for winter and summer, weekdays, Saturdays, Sundays and holidays. Special consideration must be given to any unusual operating conditions and to the time of peak loads. If a manufacturing operation is involved and if it incorporates some process equipment with marked swings in demand, a detailed study should be made of the nature and frequency of the operation and its steam and power demands. As a part of load studies of existing plants, the peaks and valleys should be investigated with the objective of determining whether corrective measures might be taken to level out the curves and to increase the output and efficiency.

Typical load curves, as shown in Figs. 2–4, 2–5 and 2–6, are used as an aid in

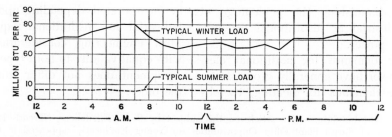

Fig. 2–4 Summer and winter heating loads in a high temperature water installation

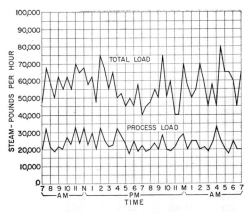

Fig. 2–5 Widely fluctuating process load curve

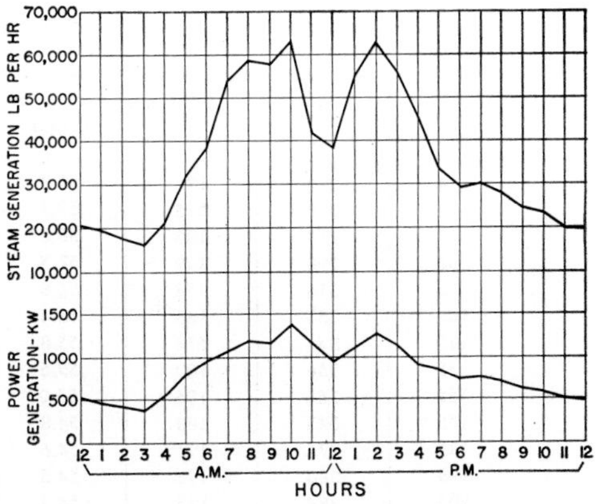

Fig. 2–6 Load curves for back pressure steam and power generation

sizing such equipment as boilers, turbines and auxiliaries. Studies must then be made of the capability of the equipment to meet not only the conditions plotted on the basis of past experience but also those forecast for a limited time in the future. Load curves should be made for both power and steam requirements, with due allowance for the relative growth of power and steam in the future.

The engineer to whom is assigned the task of studying the power and steam requirements must become thoroughly acquainted with the operating characteristics of the proposed installation or the extension to existing facilities. There may be wide variations in some of these requirements, and they will have a bearing on the reliability of the power plant. In the case of a mental hospital supplied by an isolated power plant, dependability of service is of paramount importance. The same may be true of an industrial process of a continuous nature, where an emergency may be very costly and possibly hazardous as well. On the other hand, some industrial and institutional power plants may have firm electrical connections to outside sources, and here the de-

sign emphasis might be on continuity of service despite outage of generating plant equipment. In other situations, power and heating interruptions may be inconvenient without causing severe problems and losses.

Based on the definition of the problem and the detailed technical analysis, the preliminary report should offer conclusions and recommendations. These should include estimates of the required capital investment along with operating costs and fixed charges. In most reports of this nature there will be a number of analyses of economic alternatives. These are intended to aid management in making decisions prior to authorization of power plant construction.

Design Investigations

Detailed design follows acceptance of the preliminary engineering study and authorization to proceed. Some of the topics discussed in the preliminary report are then investigated more thoroughly. These investigations are a part of the design process and are coordinated with the purchase of materials and equipment and the making of detailed construction drawings.

Table   2–1   Comparison of Heat Content — Water Versus Steam

Pressure Psia	Saturated Temperatures		Density — lb per cu ft		Total Heat — Btu per cu ft		Ratio Water to Steam
	F	C	Water	Steam	Water	Steam	
14.7	212	100	59.8	.0373	10,760	42.9	251.0
25	240	115	59.2	.0573	12,320	66.5	185.5
45	274	135	58.3	.1063	14,170	124.7	113.5
65	298	149	57.5	.1502	15,360	177.0	86.8
85	316	158	56.8	.1938	16,260	229.4	71.0
105	331	166	56.4	.2365	17,000	281.0	60.5
125	344	174	55.8	.2790	17,600	332.4	52.9
145	356	180	55.5	.3215	18,170	383.8	47.4
165	366	186	55.0	.3635	18,610	434.0	43.0
175	371	188	54.8	.3850	18,830	461.0	40.0
185	375	191	54.6	.4060	19,040	486.0	39.2
195	380	193	54.5	.4270	19,220	511.0	37.7
205	384	195	54.3	.4480	19,400	537.0	36.2
215	388	198	54.1	.4690	19,570	562.0	34.8
250	400	204	53.5	.5470	20,335	653.0	31.0
270	407	208	53.3	.5850	20,400	704.0	29.0
300	417	214	52.9	.6480	20,800	780.0	26.6
350	432	222	52.4	.7540	21,400	905.0	23.7
400	445	230	51.8	.8600	22,400	1035.0	21.6
450	456	235	51.3	.9700	22,500	1170.0	19.3
500	467	242	50.8	1.0800	22,800	1300.0	17.5

The number and scope of design investigations will vary from plant to plant. As a very minimum, decisions must be made as to choice of cycle, selection of fuel, number and types of auxiliaries, extent of instrumentation and automatic control, and plans for isolated or interconnected operation.

Choice of Cycle

In considering the design of a new industrial or institutional power plant, careful consideration must be given to the choice of thermal cycle. If an existing plant is to be enlarged, consideration might be given to "topping" the plant with a steam cycle operating at a higher pressure. Alternatively, the same cycle may be retained and expanded.

If electrical power generation is a factor, the choice of a steam cycle is obvious. Actual selection of steam conditions is more complicated and involves the study of alternatives. Although an almost infinite variety of steam conditions could be studied, the designer usually limits himself to choosing among a few widely used cycles for which standard equipment is available.

If space heating and process use constitute the entire load, then there can be a choice between a steam and a high temperature water cycle. Table 2-1 shows a comparison of heat content of water and steam at various pressure conditions.

In terms of usage, high temperature water installations have become quite common in the United States since the end of World War II. On the other hand, the use of steam has been widespread since the early development of central heating. Much equipment is on the market to use steam as a source of heat, although some of this can be adapted to high temperature water by the addition of a heat exchanger.[3]

[3] Additional background and design information may be found in *High Temperature Water Systems* by Owen S. Lieberg, The Industrial Press, 1958.

Because of its relatively great heat storage capacity, a high temperature water system provides a means of close temperature control. The heat storage capacity also forms a reserve so that large use demands may be met without affecting the temperature of individual heat consuming units. The distribution lines for a high temperature water system are much smaller than for a steam system of the same heating capacity, and no steam traps or condensate pumps are required. All of these factors must be evaluated in terms of the requirements of the proposed installation.

Power plants serving institutions may have to distribute steam or high temperature water over a large area with terrain varying sharply in elevation. In addition to space heating there may be limited requirements for low pressure steam for use in kitchens and laundries. Distribution and return lines must be designed, and heat exchangers may be required for local sources of steam or to reduce thermal losses. The choice of steam versus high temperature water cycle must take all of these factors into consideration, plus recognizing that institutional power plants may have to function with somewhat less than the highest quality of operating and maintenance personnel.

Large industrial power plants with substantial process and electric loads are likely to be well staffed and make use of more advanced cycles. Some of these plants may be owned by an electric utility company and operate under a sales contract in which the industry purchases both steam and electrical output. In certain instances the industry may supply byproduct fuels and retain ownership of portions of the power plant.[4]

Choice of Fuel

The choice of fuel is based on a combined investigation of availability, cost and operating requirements. Most industrial and institutional power plants use solid, liquid or gaseous fuels, either singly or in combination. Generally these are commercially available fuels, but sometimes they are byproducts of manufacturing and processing.

In considering the cost of fuel for comparison purposes, the following factors should be tabulated:

1. Base price of fuel
2. Cost of fuel delivery
3. Cost of handling and reclaiming
4. Cost of labor, including firing and disposition of refuse
5. Cost of plant services, including power
6. Fixed charges on fuel handling and burning equipment

Careful study of the above outlays, adjusted to an annual basis, will provide a basis for fuel choice. Other less tangible factors should also be evaluated, such as reliability of supply, individual fuel cost trends, ease of conversion from one fuel to another and extent of probable future power plant expansion.

There are other facts that must be taken into consideration with regard to fuel handling. Steam and electricity may be required for heating and pumping liquid fuels. Unless solid fuels are delivered directly to the bunker, which is rather uncommon, they must be rehandled from outside storage before firing. Gaseous fuels ordinarily do not require storage or rehandling but may be subject to varying charges at different times of the year.

Charges for byproduct fuels depend

---

[4] See such publications as *Combustion, Electric Light & Power, Electrical World, Power* and *Power Engineering* for articles on this subject.

upon the method of accounting for process and power plant costs. In some industries, such as steel and petroleum refining, byproduct fuels must either be burned in power plant boilers as fast as they are produced or consumed as atmospheric flares. Other byproduct fuels, such as some types of wood and plant refuse, may be stored for limited periods. The economics of such byproduct fuels can become very complex or be as simple as the necessity of disposing of them immediately by some form of combustion. In many instances it is necessary to supplement byproduct fuels with conventional solid, liquid or gaseous fuels.[5]

Choice of Auxiliaries

No steam power plant cycle is complete with merely a boiler and a turbine. Auxiliary equipment is required in the form of fans, pumps, heaters, tanks and piping. In some instances, heat recovery equipment is added to boilers, and generally some form of water conditioning equipment will be required. Both fuel and ash handling systems are required if solid fuel is fired. If all electrical requirements cannot be satisfied through back pressure operation, a condenser is a necessity.

The designer of an industrial or institutional power plant must make design investigations of some sort for all of these auxiliaries. In the case of tanks and piping, the investigation may be confined to the determination of optimum sizes and the selection from among alternative piping and equipment arrangements. In other cases the designer may have to decide merely whether or not to use the auxiliary equipment.

Motor or Turbine Drives. In most industrial and institutional power plants the designer has a choice of steam turbine or electric motor drive for rotating auxiliaries. Electric drives are commonly used for such items as forced and induced draft fans and pumps for boiler feed, condensate and fuel oil. Yet the possibilities and advantages of turbine drives should not be overlooked. The latter may contribute to improvement of plant heat balance as well as insure continuity of boiler plant operation in the event of power failure. Where more than one fan and pump is installed for each power plant auxiliary service, the combination of motor and turbine drives becomes attractive. Provision can be made for the automatic starting of the steam driven auxiliary in the event of power failure.

Continuity of service is absolutely essential for the boiler feed pump, and it is common practice to provide a steam-driven pump for use in the event of electric power failure. Provision may also be made to start this pump automatically if there is a marked drop of pressure in the boiler feed line.

The question of turbine drives for forced and induced draft fans does not have an answer quite as clear cut as in the case of the boiler feed pump. Consideration should be given to the probability of electric power outage and the necessity for maintaining full load output in the event of such outage. The economics of operation must be weighed against the requirements for service continuity.

Effect of Load Changes on Auxiliaries. Load swings in an industrial or institutional power plant can have a pronounced effect upon the design, selection and sizing of auxiliaries. For example, in an institutional power plant serving widely scattered buildings there might be a substantial

---

[5] See Chapter 27, Boilers and Recovery Units for Pulp and Paper Industry, and Chapter 23, Natural Circulation Boilers, for additional information.

time lag in the return of condensate from these buildings to the central power station. Should there be a sudden demand for steam, condensate or makeup water would be required. If the condensate system has insufficient storage capacity, the effect of such a load swing may be to add so much makeup that the delayed condensate returns would eventually flood the system. In this instance the sizing of condensate storage tanks can have a pronounced effect upon a system operation.

Boilers may be equipped with heat recovery equipment, and this should be evaluated in terms of both economy and adaptability to load changes. For the latter purpose an investigation should be made of anticipated maximum load, minimum load, normal load and the duration of each type of load. If heat recovery equipment is selected on the basis of estimated normal load and there are extended periods of operation at minimum load, then provision must be made for bypassing the equipment under the latter conditions. If this is not done, there is a strong probability that the exit gases from the boiler furnace will drop below the dew point and cause deterioration of the metal in the heat recovery equipment, duct work, induced draft fan and stack. This can be very costly in terms of maintenance expenditures and overcome savings which might otherwise result from installation of heat recovery equipment.

Instrumentation and Automatic Control

Industrial and institutional power plants vary widely in their use of instrumentation and automatic control. Instrumentation may be installed as an aid to operation or as a means of keeping records of use of fuel, steam and electricity or for both purposes. Automatic controls may be specified to reduce operating personnel to a minimum and to assist in maintaining operation at a high level of efficiency.

In applying controls and instruments to the industrial or institutional power plant, the designer must recognize the limitations of the individuals who operate and maintain these power plants. If elaborate control systems are installed but not kept in working order, the end result may be the creation of hazardous operating conditions, thereby defeating the safety objectives for which the control system was originally designed. Similarly, if the control systems are extremely complex and beyond the comprehension of the operators, serious errors may be made in times of emergency.[6]

Instruments assist in the operation of a power plant as well as providing information on the cost of steam and power consumption. The designer must keep in mind the type of information which must be available at all times to the operator and select the necessary instruments to provide this information. Some of these instruments will be of the indicating type, while others will record data over prolonged periods. Both types are essential, and there is likely to be some overlapping and duplication of readings. This can be justified because of the differing uses for operating and recorded information.

Every industrial and institutional power plant will incorporate instrumentation to indicate boiler and turbine loading. It is also common practice to provide instruments to show various steam and flue gas temperatures, air and steam flow, feedwater and steam pressures, and electrical outputs. The extent of this instrumentation will depend upon the type of power

---

[6] See Chapter 17, Fuel Burning Systems, and Chapter 22, Controls and Instruments.

plant and the amount of information required for accounting purposes. Where there are large heating or process loads serving many separate buildings or departments, flowmeters are essential for determining consumption and allocating costs.[7]

Plans and Specifications

In order that a power plant be built, plans and specifications must be prepared for the purposes of obtaining bids and exercising proper supervision over purchasing and construction. The objective of plans and specifications is to describe the work to be done, primarily from the point of view of the results to be achieved. The engineer must use extreme care to see that they are clear, concise and capable of but one interpretation. The plans or drawings describe the work graphically, while the specifications represent verbal descriptions.

It is well to consider the specifications as the rule book which governs the entire project. The drawings should indicate the location of equipment, including interconnecting piping and wiring. Between the two, the work to be done should be clearly set forth, with nothing essential omitted and with a determined effort to avoid inconsistencies. The specifications should set forth the functions and limits of each item shown on the plans or drawings. By their very nature specifications are intended to be very *specific* about what is to be done, even though they may include some general provisions which relate to the work as a whole.

As an example consider a piping system for an industrial or institutional power plant. The drawings will show a piping layout, including detailed dimensions, and will indicate the pressure characteristics of the system. The specifications should list all design requirements: design pressure and temperature; operating pressure and temperature; the grade designation, sometimes called the schedule, of piping, fittings and valves; the type and pressure characteristics of joints, including any special requirements. These piping specifications should also have provisions covering quality of materials and workmanship, including inspection and acceptance requirements.

Performance Specification

In the specifying of power plant equipment it is well to write a *performance specification* with only such descriptions or physical limitations as are necessary to provide for the desired quality of materials and workmanship. Within this framework it is desirable that the manufacturer be given as much freedom as possible to provide equipment which will best fulfill the functional requirements of the installation. By reason of his specialized experience, a manufacturer is in a much better position than the individual power plant designer or consultant to determine the detailed design of his particular equipment.

One of the legal requirements for bidding on practically all types of government projects is that the greatest possible freedom be allowed to bidders so as to encourage competition. Too much detailed description or the use of proprietary names in the specifications has the effect of limiting the number of suppliers qualified or willing to bid. Specifications should be worded so that the particular brand in mind will meet them, along with any others which may also be able to do so. In so doing care should be taken to be

---

[7] Allocation of steam and power costs has been the subject of many technical articles and papers in a wide variety of power plant publications.

certain that the specification emphasis is on major requirements rather than minor details.

The use of performance specifications provides another advantage to the purchaser. When physical requirements are specified, he is in a position to accept or reject an item or to obtain service from the supplier on the basis of performance tests. On the other hand, if performance requirements are subordinated to elaborate descriptive specifications, the purchased equipment may pass inspection as set forth in the specifications without necessarily being capable of performing the required duty. The specification writer must keep this in mind, placing emphasis on performance without being overly restrictive, on the one hand, or leaving too much to the discretion of the contractor or supplier, on the other.

Writing Specifications

Specification writing, as the foregoing implies, involves the careful weighing of many factors. The writer of specifications must not only have the ability to write in simple and concise terms, but he should also have a thorough understanding of power plant design. This is necessary to delineate responsibility in a precise manner and to prevent either overlapping or omission of work. The specifications must set forth the special conditions under which the contractor or supplier must carry out his work and his responsibility for its satisfactory completion. There must be provisions for inspection and for correcting of unsatisfactory conditions prior to final acceptance and payment.

Occasionally confusion arises between the written specification and the accompanying plans or drawings. It is preferable that important items be set forth in the specifications because in the event of a disagreement the specifications will generally be given greater legal weight than the drawings. By following this practice and by avoiding duplication in specifications and drawings, changes may be made in either without materially affecting the other.

A typical industrial or institutional power plant may require a dozen or more individual specifications plus various types of drawings accompanying these specifications. Changes will inevitably be required as the detailed power plant design progresses. With duplication of information between drawings and specifications, there is a high probability of making a correction in one place while overlooking it in others. This can be the cause of much misunderstanding and very serious disputes. The power plant designer must be aware of this possibility and make every effort to coordinate the preparation of drawings and the writing of specifications.

The foregoing again is a reminder of the *importance of engineering judgment and common sense*. The design of a power plant involves many individuals and many interests. The language of the drawing and of the specification is a most important factor in bringing all of these together in the form of a completed and operative power plant. Reports, specifications and drawings are among the most important *elements* for engineers engaged in power plant design.

Evolution of central station design

3

Design of Central Stations[1]

THE OBJECTIVE of this chapter is to show the steps that must be taken and the decisions that must be made in the *preliminary* design of a central station for the generation of electric power. These must precede the detailed final design which involves the efforts of large teams of engineers and draftsmen. Much the same kind of thinking and analysis is required in the first stages of the design of both conventional and nuclear central stations. The reader will rapidly become aware that the design of a central station is a far more involved process than the design of an industrial or institutional power plant such as outlined previously in Chapter 2.

The rate of growth of the electric utilities is such that they are continuously thinking about the generating facilities that must be in operation five, ten or even more years in the future. The final design and construction of new capacity will typically require not less than three years. For these reasons all basic decisions must be made at least that long before the capacity is needed.

Management must find the best practicable answers to four fundamental questions about the provision of additional capacity: *When? How big? Where? What*

kind? In more formal language, the following steps must be undertaken:

1. Forecast of loads to determine timing and size of additions
2. Selection of plant location
3. Selection of types of equipment

Each step is the subject of a subsequent section of this chapter and involves the careful weighing of both economic and technical alternatives.

Forecast of Loads

The answers to *When?* and *How big?* are approached by making a forecast of future electric demands. Such activity is a continuous function in a major utility and is, necessarily, a matter of *judgment* applied to the interpretation of company records, economic trends, population shifts, technological changes and related factors.

There are two significant characteristics of electric demand (usually called "load") in this connection: the *peak load*, which is the maximum demand on the generating plant for a relatively short period, as 15 minutes or one hour; and the *average demand* over a longer period, usually a month or a year. The ratio of the two is called the *load factor* and is typically in

---

[1] Material contributed by R. L. Anthony, consulting engineer.

the range 40 to 60 per cent.[2] A system with a relatively high load factor is fortunate in that it uses, on the average, more of its installed capacity profitably; it spreads its investment costs over a greater production than would be true of another system of the same size, having the same peak load, but with a lower load factor. The high-load-factor system can therefore afford to spend more money for more efficient equipment that will reduce operating costs. The chief of these is the cost of fuel, expenditures for which vary directly with station output. Improvements in station thermal efficiency are one way to reduce the total outlay for fuel.

The records of electric demands are usually kept in three major classifications: residential, commercial and industrial. Special records applying to unusually large users of power are also available.

The forecaster studies the history of each type of load but chiefly gathers all available data on the growth of the area with which he is concerned. He watches population shifts, growth of suburban shopping centers, trends toward air conditioning and electric heating, changing processes in industry, development programs to attract new employers, statistics on per capita use of electricity; in short, every factor that bears on the future use of electrical energy in his area.

The result of this process is to produce a graph showing the expected peak loads and load factors for a period of years into the future. An example of a peak load forecast is the line X–X in Fig. 3–1.

In order to be reasonably sure of carrying the peak load of any given year, the total generating capacity of the system must exceed the expected peak load by a margin for reserve. The necessary reserve is of two kinds:

a. *Spinning reserve* is excess generating capacity that is in operation and on the line at the time of peak load. It must be at least equal to the capacity of the largest single generating unit in use at that time on the system or its interconnections. It is necessary to provide spinning reserve to guard against the possibility of a mishap to the largest unit causing loss of its generating capacity, even if only for a few minutes.

b. *Reserve for scheduled outages* is generating capacity that is installed on the system but is not necessarily in operation at the time of peak load. Such reserve is needed because equipment must be inspected and overhauled at regular intervals. The amount of this reserve must be not less than the size of the largest unit that will be overhauled during the peak load season.[3]

A simplified example will illustrate the point. Assume a *system* composed of twelve identical generating units, each capable of generating a continuous output designated as M kw, where M is any number. The total installed capacity is 12 M kw. The spinning reserve is one unit, and the reserve for scheduled outages is another unit since an overhaul typically takes about a month. The system can therefore be expected to carry a peak load of 10 M kw, its firm capacity.

If the system consists of six units each

[2] For definitions see "Glossary of Electric Utility Terms" prepared by the Statistical Committee of the Edison Electric Institute, New York, 1961, portions of which are incorporated in Appendix B, Glossary of Boiler and Electric Utility Terms.

[3] For a more detailed discussion of reserve for outage, see "A Classification of Outages of Facilities in Electric Power Systems" by Arnold Rich, *Combustion*, Vol. 24, March 1953, pp. 43–47.

of 2 M kw capacity, the installed capacity is the same as before, but deduction of the spinning reserve will bring its capacity down to 10 M kw, and the further deduction of reserve for scheduled outages will leave a firm capacity of only 8 M kw. However, it may be possible to schedule the overhauls of six units wholly outside the peak load season, depending on the character of the system load variations through the year; this would make the firm capacity of the system 10 M kw as before.

Another example is indicated in Fig. 3–1. The system is assumed to consist of six identical units each of M kw capacity. The present installed capacity is indicated by line A. Deduction of spinning reserve gives line B, and further deduction of reserve for scheduled outages leaves the firm capacity, line C. Another unit must

be in operation before the peak load season of the fourth year. If this unit is of M kw capacity, the new situation is indicated by lines E, F and G. Similarly, other M kw units must be added, one before the seventh year, one before the ninth year, and so on.

If the seventh unit is twice the size of the earlier ones, the installed capacity in the fourth year is shown by line D. Spinning reserve must now be $2M$ kw, the size of the largest unit. Reserve for scheduled outages will, however, be M kw, making the firm capacity line G, the same as if unit seven were of the smaller size. It follows that the installation of a large unit increases the firm capacity of a system only by an amount equal to the capacity of some smaller unit.

When the second larger unit is installed, as is indicated for years seven to ten, the

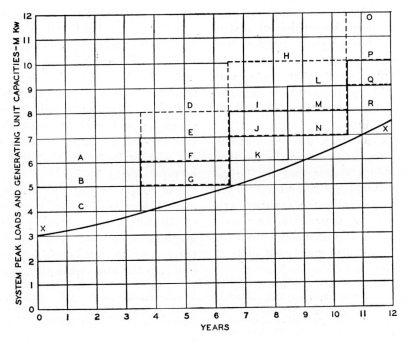

Fig. 3–1 Relationship between peak loads and installed capacity

firm capacity will increase by 2M kw if it is possible to schedule outages of the two larger units out of the peak load season (lines *H, I* and *J*). Otherwise line *K* will give the firm capacity.

Further additions of capacity are also indicated on Fig. 3–1. Solid lines apply to *M* kw units and dash lines to the larger 2M kw size.

The foregoing is known as the block system of generating capacity addition. The objective is to install the equivalent of two blocks more than the peak load, one to provide spinning reserve and the other to permit scheduled outages. This method of capacity addition has the virtue of simplicity and has been commonly used since the early days of the utility industry.

Several factors have led to modifications and deviations from this method of capacity addition. Not only has load grown but so has available unit generating size. At the same time knowledge of system operation has become more complete, and reliability of components is better understood. This means that entire systems may be simulated by mathematical models and that unit outages may be predicted by probability methods.[4]

Using this approach the required system reserve requirements may be less than under the block system, but the largest single unit should not exceed five to ten per cent of the total system capacity. As a matter of policy, many systems refrain from increasing unit size until predicted load growth requires successive units of the larger size.

In practice, these considerations for system capacity additions are far from clear cut for many reasons, among which are:

1. The units will be of different types, sizes, ages and vulnerability to accidental shutdown.

2. The actual capacity of a plant varies with condensing water temperature, and at times is subject to variations caused by changes in the fuel.

3. A system usually includes transmission lines, which are subject to interruption of service from causes quite different from those that affect generating units. Outages from such interruptions may be greater than the loss of a single unit.

4. There is the possibility that not only one unit, but two or more, may suffer unexpected interruptions simultaneously or following closely upon one another.

The question of the availability of generating plant equipment for service has been studied intensively, and records of experience are published regularly. Improvements in equipment, controls and methods of operation have contributed to increased reliability. Mathematical methods of treatment by calculating probabilities of interruptions to service have been developed and will be increasingly important, but will not displace the need for the engineering judgment that is developed by experience.

The graph of Fig. 3–1 is basically a plot of predicted annual peak loads for certain future years. Another informative graph is constructed by getting from system records the numbers of hours per year in which the load equalled or exceeded a

---

[4] Many technical papers on this subject have been sponsored by the AIEE Power Generation and System Engineering Committees and published in AIEE *Transactions*. A 63-item bibliography tracing the application of probability methods is included in AIEE Paper CP 60–37, "Application of Probability Methods to Generating Capacity Problems" by AIEE Probability Applications Working Group. A digital simulation approach using models of power systems and the steam generation process is explained in "Modern Scientific Tools Used in the Power Industry for Tomorrow's Problems" by C. J. Baldwin, *Proceedings* of the American Power Conference, Vol. 24, 1962, pp. 94–105.

given amount. The system minimum load will correspond to 8760 hours per year, and the maximum load will appear, in all probability, for only one hour. Such a graph is called a load duration curve. An idealized example is presented as Fig. 3–2. The areas are energy units expressed as kwhr, and the total area under the curve divided by the area of the rectangle enclosing it is the annual load factor.

The chief value of this curve is to emphasize the brief period during which peak loads must be generated in the typical system. Even though the curve is drawn for a past year, its shape will not change markedly in the future unless the character of the load changes materially. Load duration curves can therefore be drawn for future years, subject to the uncertainty of the predicted peak loads and load factors discussed earlier in this chapter.

If we look at such a series of curves on a single set of axes, Fig. 3–2, it is apparent that the system already has enough equipment to generate all but a relatively small part of the predicted loads, to wit, the peaks, lasting a short time and enclosing only a few kwhr, that extend above a horizontal line representing the system firm capacity. Assume for the moment that all equipment in the system is in good condition and can be expected to operate successfully throughout the period under study. On this assumption, the problem of meeting the future growth in peak load can be solved simply by providing the cheapest possible generating capacity large enough to take care of the growth in load; its fuel economy is not of prime importance because it will be used only a few hours per year, whereas investment costs go on continuously and must be kept to a minimum.

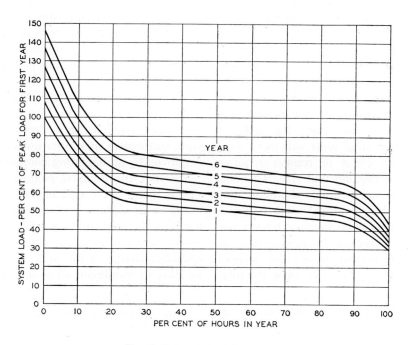

Fig. 3–2 Load duration curves

The solution just described might be a stripped down steam plant, a gas turbine or a diesel generating unit. A pumped storage hydro system, for example, may be the best under some conditions. However, the following line of reasoning also results in an economical method of caring for load growth.[5]

The typical system includes generating units that have been in operation for some years and have higher operating costs, coupled with lower investment costs, than would be true of a new unit. It may therefore be financially advantageous to install a modern high economy unit of suitable size and run it at full capacity for as many hours per year as is possible, thus allowing its operating cost economy to outweigh its greater investment costs. This decision results in providing a new base load unit for the system, pushing the older units in succession one step higher on the ladder of the load duration curve. The oldest becomes the peak load unit, being operated only when the load on the system requires it.

To return to the questions of *When?* and *How Big?* there will be a set of several possible answers based upon the predicted loads shown in Fig. 3–1 and the policies established for reserve capacity. In some instances, the reduced capital cost of large units will more than outweigh the effect of reserve requirements in determining unit size. The reasons for this are twofold: doubling unit size may reduce central station cost per unit of capacity by as much as twenty per cent, and increased interconnection of public utility systems means that reserve requirements may be based upon the total

firm capacity of the interconnection rather than of a single system. The trend has been toward the installation of larger generating units on a coordinated basis by companies strongly tied to interconnected systems.

Final decisions as to size and timing may well be tied in with the decisions as to location and type of equipment. However, the analysis and study described to this point will disclose a relatively small number of practical possibilities, each of which must be studied in some detail to set up comparative investment and operating costs over a period of years. At the same time it is important not to neglect the effect of each alternate possibility on the cost of operating the existing system.

It is at this point that a consulting engineering firm may supplement the resources of the utility company by taking over the detailed study of the several alternatives. There is no hard and fast procedure. Some utility systems are large enough to be continuously designing new installations and find it desirable to have their own staffs of engineers, designers and draftsmen quite equivalent to those of the consultants. In other instances, the utility feels that the consultant can provide more detailed experience, a broader view and expert specialists not ordinarily employed by an operating company.

Whether the detailed engineering design is done by the staff of the operating utility or an outside engineering consulting firm, the steps that must be taken are about the same. Someone must be in responsible charge of the project, and it is his duty to coordinate all of the individu-

[5] Many technical articles have been published on this subject, including a special section in *Power Engineering* entitled "Power for Peaking," Vol. 64, Oct. 1960, pp. 59–82.

als and organizations involved in the design and construction of the new installation.[6] In any case, the project manager will have the support of teams of engineers and draftsmen to create the designs that will result in the construction of a steam electric generating station that is safe and economical.

Selection of Plant Location

The *location* of an electric generating station is determined by analysis of many factors that influence the selection in diverse ways. During the study and forecasting of future loads, it will usually become apparent that only a few attractive sites are available. Each of these must be studied to determine the effect of individual factors on its desirability. The object of the study is to make an engineering economic analysis that will disclose the best choice, which in general is the location that will result in the lowest total cost to the owner in the long run.

The factors that are usually significant are discussed below for a typical problem of this kind. Relative importance of these factors will vary from one system to another, but they must always be the subject of engineering study.

Condensing Water Supply

As is well known, a steam turbine requires a relatively great quantity of condensing water for its economical operation. Under average conditions it is estimated that about 800 tons of water are required for each ton of coal burned. The supply of water should not vary through the year, its temperature should be as low as possible, the water should not be corrosive to the usual materials, and it should not contain suspended material that will interfere with the flow through pumps and tubes. These considerations suggest a river, a lake or an ocean, and central stations are located whenever possible on the bank of some such body of water.

The alternate to such a location is to provide cooling towers wherein the condensing water is cooled nearly to the prevailing wet bulb temperature by the forced or natural-draft circulation of air through the water. The investment in a cooling tower is high, but this higher cost would be somewhat offset by the need of smaller waterfront construction and tunnels.

The extent to which condensing water is available sets a limit on the amount of power that can be generated at the site. Advanced steam conditions not only achieve greater cycle efficiency but also result in less rejection of heat to the condenser. For example, for the same initial steam conditions and a limited amount of condensing water, selection of a reheat regenerative cycle permits greater power output than a nonreheat cycle, everything else being equal. This can be of considerable importance to central stations which are being redeveloped on sites having limited amounts of cooling water. Fig. 3–3 shows the reduction of heat rejection to condenser cooling water as cycles of increased thermal efficiency and decreased net plant heat rate are incorporated in power plants.[7]

---

[6] The functions of a project manager are explained in an editorial entitled "A Tribute to the Project Manager," *Combustion*, Vol. 21, November 1949, p. 31.

[7] This curve was suggested by and adapted from information in ASME Paper 61–WA–141 by Stanley Moyer, "Industry's Problems in Sharing Our Water Resources." This was published in abridged form in *Mechanical Engineering*, Vol. 84, March 1962, pp. 46–49.

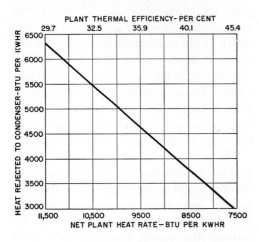

Fig. 3–3 Heat rejected versus net plant heat rate based on 1½ in. Hg back pressure

If a central station is located on what is in effect a pond, the ultimate rejection of heat from the cycle occurs largely by evaporation from the surface of the pond. Since many stations are actually so situated, attempts have been made to analyze the complex hydraulic and thermodynamic picture, but much more must be done before the capabilities of a site can be evaluated with confidence.

The influence of condensing water supply on site selection includes an early hydraulic study of the possible ways of getting the water into and out of the station. The study will cover construction costs, cost of pumping, avoiding recirculation from discharge to intake, flood protection and similar matters.

Fuel Supply

Although steam plants have been built at mine mouth to reduce the cost of shipping and handling coal, in general it is more economical to take the fuel to the plant. The choice of fuel in any given area is likely to be limited to one, two or, at most, three types. The fuel will be deliv-

ered by rail, water, pipe line or truck. The cost of getting fuel to the plant, and perhaps of handling it within the station, must be evaluated for each site and for each type of fuel under consideration. For solid fuels, the cost of disposing of refuse may also be significant in the study.

An associated factor is the availability of space for fuel storage. There must be enough area to store fuel to carry the plant through any reasonable interruption in supply, and, in the case of coal, this space must permit economical handling of the fuel to and from the storage area.

The same principles apply to a nuclear station, although to a different degree, because the bulk of the fuel and the frequency of handling are much less than in a conventional plant. There are, however, other complications in terms of precautions in handling both new and spent fuel. Criticality must be guarded against, and adequate shielding to confine highly radioactive products must be provided.[8]

It is generally desirable that the central station be located as close as possible to the point where its output will be needed.

[8] See "The Engineering Design of Power Reactors" by N. J. Palladino and H. L. Davis, *Nucleonics*, Vol. 18, June 1960, pp. 85–116.

The effect of this factor is evaluated by estimating the costs associated with the transmission system that will be required for each site being studied. The costs will include right of way, construction costs, maintenance costs, and an estimate of hazard or likelihood of interruption. Existing power plant sites in metropolitan areas are often redeveloped because of their proximity to load centers. On the other hand, lower fuel costs at so-called mine mouth plants may make such locations attractive. Availability of transmission facilities and desire to have power generation dispersed at several sites also have a bearing upon the choice of location.

Air Pollution

The products of combustion of a conventional station are obvious pollutants of the atmosphere, the solid particles and sulfur compounds being the most objectionable. A substantial amount is discharged hourly from every plant. The plant designer can hope merely to minimize the objectionable discharge. Means for reducing it include selection of fuel, proper furnace design, correct operation and provision of removal devices such as mechanical dust collectors, electrostatic precipitators and wet scrubbers. Removal devices are expensive in investment, maintenance and operating costs and contribute nothing to plant economy. Nevertheless, to provide them is a practical necessity at most sites as a matter of good neighbor policy and to comply with air pollution regulations.

The gases with the solids that escape the removal system will be discharged from the stack and will ultimately mix with and be diluted by the air. While the designer will have some freedom to select stack height and exit velocity, the influence of prevailing winds and surrounding terrain may be of utmost importance in affecting the desirability of an otherwise suitable site. This matter must be studied both by analysis and by wind tunnel model tests. The study should take into account large structures, as a cooling tower or nearby building, that may be erected in the future, and must include analyses of records of wind velocity and direction, humidity, fog, temperature inversions and the like. Similar studies are made in connection with locating nuclear stations.

Water Pollution

The possibility of water pollution arising from the plant is not likely to influence site selection, for such pollution is generally avoidable and certainly should be avoided. Pollution by sewage should never occur, of course. However, a central station may by accident release a quantity of oil into the water, which could have more serious consequences at one site than at another. The effect of the power plant in increasing the temperature of the water and its possible harm to aquatic life may be of some concern, particularly when the generating station is located on a small stream or where there may be a concentration of stations on a larger stream, lake or harbor.[9]

[9] An interesting article on this subject is, "Condensing Water — How Does It Affect the River?" by M. D. Engle, *Mechanical Engineering*, Vol. 83, January 1961, pp. 34–38; also the extended discussion of this article in the May 1961 issue of *Mechanical Engineering*, pp. 110–118. A more detailed study is found in "Forecasting Heat Loss in Ponds and Streams" by C. J. Velz and J. J. Gannon, *Journal* of the Water Pollution Control Federation, Vol. 32, April 1960, pp. 392–417.

Public Opinion

The effect of public opinion on the choice of a site can be profound. As long as much of the public thinks of a power plant as an ugly, noisy, dirty place, spreading smoke, dust and ash around the neighborhood, so long will it instantly object to admitting one to genteel surroundings. The remedy is to design and build central stations that have good architectural treatment, that are clean and as quiet as possible, meanwhile educating the public to the reality that a power plant can be a good neighbor. This has been done quite successfully by many public utilities. It is, however, essential to respect public opinion and to treat it as a real factor in the problem.

There is an additional public reaction to be expected if the proposed station is nuclear, that of potential hazard to the community and surrounding territory. It may be expected that this reaction will become less severe as nuclear installations become more common and their safe operation continues to be demonstrated.

Other Considerations

The usual considerations for selecting an industrial plant site will need to be considered. These include availability of municipal services and suitable labor, appropriate zoning, convenient access, climate, tax situation and the like. Room for growth and freedom from undue risk of flood and earthquake are ordinarily essential.

The nature of surrounding installations may play a part in the selection. For example, the height of stacks will be subject to Civil Aeronautics Authority regulations and would be restricted near an airport.

In many site selection problems, one possibility is that of adding to an existing station. To do so has obvious economies in making use of existing facilities, no matter how much new construction may have to be provided. If the existing station site is large enough and has enough condensing water, and especially if it was designed for expansion, it is unlikely that a new site can compete successfully. Each case must be studied on its merits; the danger is in assuming that the "obvious" answer is the best.

Finally, in all studies and analyses, it is essential to remember that future conditions determine the best solution. All available data apply to past years, or at best to the present, and must be reviewed critically to ensure that the most likely future conditions have been derived or projected from them. This statement applies, of course, to every engineering economic study.

Selection of Types of Equipment

Having determined fairly definitely the size, timing and location of the installation by the steps previously described, we must tackle the question, *What kind?* In practice, the steps are not taken separately and in succession; they overlap considerably but may follow the sequence of this chapter.

The primary choice is among the several plant fuel cycles; that is, conventional fuel, nuclear energy, and internal combustion (diesel or gas turbine). The possible consideration of hydro or purchased power would take place before site selection and is outside the scope of this book. Strictly on the basis of total economy, steam with conventional fuel will be preferred in larger sizes, with internal combustion having an advantage for smaller units. Nuclear energy must be considered seriously by a public utility for all energy cost areas where it may be competitive with fossil fuels. The ranges of size within which each type of plant fits best are reasonably well defined by experience and will not be the subject of intensive study in the typical instance. Capacity installed for peaking purposes may be subject to very different economic evaluation than is the case for base load generating equipment. Heat rate economies dominate the latter, while availability of peak shaving capacity for short periods is of most importance in the former.

Assuming that a conventional steam cycle has been selected, studies will be made to find the best conditions as to steam and reheat pressures and temperatures, number and location of extraction stages, condenser pressure, and a host of similar cycle characteristics.[10] Only with experience and judgment as a guide is it possible to keep the combinations of variables within practical bounds. Even with the help of advanced methods of analysis and computation, the basic method of solution is to assume a reasonable set of conditions and calculate the required investment in the central station and the resulting cost of operation under future load conditions. In some instances, the influence of a variable can be isolated and analyzed by itself, but all too often a change in assumed design conditions will be reflected through the cycle, resulting in an unexpected and perhaps undesired change at another point.[11]

If there is a choice in the fuel to be used, it comes logically at this point. Again, it is the overall influence on the station and the system that must be sought, not simply the effect on the cost of generating steam. Because uncertain future economic conditions are fundamental to the analysis, management is inclined to buy future flexibility by designing for more than one fuel, even though only one is contemplated for the years immediately ahead.

The sizes of the units will have been fairly well determined by the studies of load growth and estimated capital cost. The unit system, under which a single boiler serves a single turbine, each with its own auxiliaries, is rather generally accepted, but there may well be exceptions, especially when a central station has a process steam load in addition to an electric load.

At this point, a number of subsidiary economic studies will be required; for example, heater and condenser surface, turbine versus motor-driven auxiliaries, voltage of electric auxiliary drives and extent of building enclosure. The object is always to reduce the initial investment without increasing maintenance and operating costs unduly.

Investment costs are initially determined by making a preliminary design of the feature in question and estimating from quotations and past experience the cost of its purchase and installation, keeping in mind the fact that such matters as building volume, foundations, steel work, piping, wiring, and controls cannot be ignored.

Operating costs are estimated by calculating plant performance over the necessary range of loads under the assumed conditions and applying load duration data

---

[10] See Chapter 5, Thermodynamic Cycles for Power Plants, for additional information on factors affecting choice of cycle.

[11] See "An Analytic Procedure for Optimizing the Selection of Power Plant Components," by W. A. Wilson, *Trans.* ASME, Vol. 79, 1957, pp. 1120–1128.

to find annual costs. It is generally necessary to include maintenance costs for a
complete comparison.

The several assumed combinations are
compared by standard methods of engineering economy to find the one that
promises the lowest overall cost over the
life of the station, giving due regard to
the time value of money.

Certain features of design will be
adopted to allow future expansion of the
central station, unless growth is clearly
impossible. How much to pay now to save
a future cost is always a difficult decision.

The result of this engineering process
will be to produce a set of preliminary
arrangement drawings showing the station as it has been conceived; a set of
abbreviated specifications covering the
important equipment, structures and systems; a reasonably reliable construction
cost estimate; and a report covering the
alternates considered, advantages and disadvantages of each, comparative investment and operating costs, and other data
individual to each case. Management will
be able to base its decision on this material if it is complete and well presented.
Then and only then does the *detailed* design of a central station begin.

4

Operation and Maintenance

POWER PLANT OPERATION is an interesting assignment which young engineers may encounter during summer jobs as undergraduates or as a part of postgraduate training and orientation programs by manufacturers and users of power equipment. Such an assignment represents a real opportunity to become directly acquainted with the physical size and arrangement of boilers and reactors as well as to learn some of their operating characteristics. This first hand knowledge of operation can become extremely valuable to those who may at some future time be concerned with designing new plants or equipment. Careful observation of operation will enable young engineers to appreciate some of the limitations of analytical approaches studied in engineering science courses and to understand some of the complexities for which assumptions must be made in the practical art of engineering design.[1]

One of the first lessons to be learned from operation is that equipment requires maintenance periodically. The subjects of maintenance and operation are inseparable in the sense that operation is a dynamic process in which such factors as friction, corrosion, erosion, fatigue, contamination, overstress and unbalance affect condition of equipment. Maintenance and operation are also interrelated with such external factors as process steam demand in an industrial plant and system load requirements in a central station. Likewise, scheduled and forced outages, including those due to system disturbances and natural calamities, have an effect upon maintenance and operation.

Another lesson to be gained from an assignment in operation is that a power plant is a sort of operating laboratory. The skills of observation developed in elementary physics and chemistry courses are basic tools in a power plant. Reading of instruments and compiling of data are vital in power plant operation. A keen sense of the sound of rotating machinery is an example of using the senses as an aid in the detection of malfunction of equipment. Sight of unusual flame patterns through a boiler peep hole or the smell of overheated metal in a fan bearing may foreshadow trouble which can be prevented or minimized by immediate corrective action. The feel and appearance of external deposits on a boiler tube may

---

[1] For an interesting article which greatly expands this viewpoint, see "An Engineering Career in the Power Field" by V. F. Estcourt, *Mechanical Engineering*, Vol. 80, November 1958, pp. 89–93; also, by the same engineer, "The Challenge of an Engineering Career in the Exploding Technology of Thermal Electric Power," *Combustion*, Vol. 33, April 1962, pp. 22–26, and *Proceedings* of the American Power Conference, Vol. 24, 1962, pp. 76–86.

give some clue to their nature and cause.

Relation of Operation to Design

Crawling through a boiler drum or looking into a distribution header may be a revelation to the young engineer who can formulate and solve differential equations for two phase flow and steam separation but who has not previously seen the results of extended periods of operation in physical equipment. The alert graduate who can relate these observations to the fundamental laws which explain their occurrence will find that knowledge of operation and maintenance problems is also of assistance in the design of new equipment.

In addition to learning the importance of power plant maintenance and benefiting from perceptive physical observations, the young engineer will find that power plant operation offers many lessons in human relations. Here is a chance to see the reactions of individuals to a crisis occasioned by the sudden loss of electrical load or the failure of a piece of auxiliary equipment. Depending upon the steps taken, the results may be just a passing incident or a serious event involving possible major damage to equipment and injury to fellow operators. It is an opportunity to become safety conscious: to know the hazards of fluids at high temperatures and pressures, of equipment rotating at high speeds, and of physical forces of considerable magnitude. Safety considerations, it will be learned, are of importance in design, operation and maintenance and must never be allowed to be totally obscured by other objectives.

Cutting across all branches of engineering as it does, safety may also serve as a reminder to the young engineer that power plant operation involves the merging of many engineering disciplines. The turbine-generator is a common meeting ground of electrical and mechanical engineering. Water conditioning apparatus and related instruments and controls are an integral part of all high pressure power plants and involve applications of chemistry and chemical engineering. Obviously there is a large amount of electrical engineering in station power supply, communication and control systems, and the dispatch of power over transmission lines. An operation such as coal handling involves modern earthmoving machinery developed by civil engineers. All of these and many others are linked together by the station superintendent who must have a thorough knowledge of industrial management as well as technical subjects. By being alert to what is going on around him the young engineer can gain a fuller appreciation of the interrelationship and interdependence of the major engineering fields.

Opportunities to Learn and Teach

Power plant operation also provides a good example of the merging of many vocational and professional skills: the craftsmanship and manual ability of the maintenance mechanic; the manipulative skill of the instrument technician; the operating skill and management understanding of the power plant superintendent; the specialized professional knowledge of the chemist or the metallurgist who may be called upon to diagnose and make recommendations to solve special problems. To the young engineer who has become accustomed to an academic atmosphere, the power plant represents a vastly different realm of engineering. It is a place to get hands dirty, work sometimes long and uncertain hours, meet practitioners of many skills, observe theory in practical application, and encounter the excitement of seeing a complex assembly of piping, ductwork, pumps, boilers, turbines, condensers and instruments perform the power generating functions for which the station was designed.

The young engineer who is assigned to a central station that is just being started may have an opportunity to assist in training operating personnel. He may be called upon to teach formal classes or to lead seminars dealing with the description and operation of specific power plant equipment. It is generally possible to accompany such classroom activity with inspection of the actual equipment, so that engineering theory and practice are closely linked. The young engineer must adapt his methods of instruction to the intellectual capabilities of men having less formal education than he. Yet the question and answer periods that are an integral part of training programs will quickly reveal that the operators are capable of raising fundamental and sometimes perplexing questions. The engineer must make every effort to answer these thoughtfully and completely.

Operation with Centralized Control

From the smallest industrial power plant to the largest central station the position of operator has been transformed from a primarily manual occupation to one of a skilled technician whose duties are much more closely related to those of the white collar worker. This transformation has been a gradual evolution, advancing more rapidly in some situations than others.[2]

The development of practical and economically justifiable instruments and controls has been a leading factor in changing the duties of the power plant operators. Alert management, in the face of demands for more power and steam, has found that

power plants can be run more efficiently with a minimum of operating personnel by integrating equipment operation through control loops.

The amount of instrumentation and extent of centralized control generally vary with the size and complexity of the power plant. However, it is somewhat of a paradox that some of the smallest industrial and institutional power plants and some of the largest central stations are the most nearly automatic and require the least amount of operator attention. Plants of intermediate size vary widely in the amount of centralized control installed.

As older central stations have been modernized or replaced by new installations, the capacity per operator has steadily increased. This is indicated graphically in Fig. 4–1 which shows a time plot of the sharp rise in the installed megawatt ca-

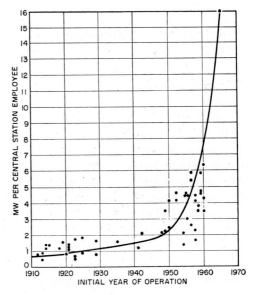

Fig. 4–1 Increase in megawatt capacity per central station employee, based upon reports to Federal Power Commission

[2] See Chapter 22, Controls and Instruments.

pacity per central station employee. There are three reasons for this manpower trend: decrease in amount of required manual work, increased capacity of equipment and installation of more instrumentation and control loops.

Centralized control affords an opportunity to design many safety features into the power plant. This is one of the greatest economic attractions of the fully automatic power plant in which the control loops are completed by means of a computer instead of a human operator. Complete automation for startup, shutdown and load changes envisions that the most reliable, safe and economic power plant operation can be achieved by incorporating the best operating experience into the control systems and power plant equipment. In other words, engineering is concentrated in the design stage, and operation is programmed for computer control, monitoring and calculation of results.

Preventive Maintenance

If power plant operation has a golden rule, it might be expressed in these terms: minimize the occurrence of foreseeable or preventable interruptions of service. As expressed by J. M. Totten,[3] this can be greatly aided by *preventive maintenance,* a means to anticipate trouble rather than to wait until it happens. To accomplish this someone must have enough knowledge and interest in power plant equipment to know what to look for, interpret what he sees, decide what should be done and how, and take the necessary steps to do it.

The young engineer on a power plant operating assignment may be surprised to learn how much planning goes into maintenance. Preventive maintenance involves record keeping, scheduling of downtime and equipment outages, purchase of spare parts and replacement materials, mobilization of manpower and careful coordination with all production requirements and other interested departments of an organization.

Maintenance is also related to power plant design. Saving building volume at the expense of space for access to machinery which must be dismantled for periodical maintenance can prove very costly over the life of a power plant. The same goes for use of outdoor construction in regions of severe climate without making provision to perform maintenance under the most adverse conditions. The cost of maintenance may be minimized by (1) installing equipment of demonstrated reliability, (2) selecting equipment that may be readily disassembled, repaired and reassembled, (3) designing facilities to permit rapid overhaul and (4) keeping equipment in good operating condition by periodic overhauls rather than waiting until an operational breakdown occurs.[4]

Nuclear Operation and Maintenance

Sufficient experience in operating and maintaining nuclear power reactors has been gained to interpret some of the similarities and differences with respect to conventional power plant operation and maintenance. The Shippingport Station of Duquesne Light Company has shown that a pressurized water reactor is capable of operating as a base or peak load plant

[3] "How Reliable Is Your Plant?" by J. M. Totten, *Power Engineering,* Vol. 64, November 1960, pp. 68–69.

[4] "Broom Closets or the Effect of Maintenance Upon Design of Steam Power Plants" by B. C. Mallory and F. W. Argue, ASME Paper 52–S–12. Anther informative paper on this subject is "Plant Management and Other Factors Affecting Maintenance Costs in Steam Generating Stations" by V. F. Estcourt, *Trans.* ASME, Vol. 79, 1957, pp. 161–172.

which is fully integrated into an electric utility system. In its first several years of service, Shippingport demonstrated unusual flexibility of operation and favorable load response characteristics, and this experience has been duplicated by other power reactors of markedly different design.[5]

Maintenance at Shippingport proved to be substantially greater than anticipated and therefore considerably more than experienced in a comparable period of operation of a conventional station. While some of this can be attributed to the extensive experimental and test programs carried on at Shippingport, it is evident that the necessity to keep radiation exposures to a safe minimum is a complicating factor in nuclear power plant maintenance.

Operation of a nuclear power plant resembles that of a conventional central station in many respects. Each installation has a central control room with instruments, controllers and scanning and recording devices. These provide the operator with detailed information on conditions throughout the power plant. Communications link the central control room to roving operators in other parts of the plant as well as to the system load dispatcher and station superintendent.

Unlike the conventional power plant where equipment is accessible during operation, some portions of a nuclear power plant are normally isolated and sealed off to prevent operator exposure to dangerous amounts of radiation. This means that certain functions, such as closing valves or starting auxiliary equipment, must be performed from the central control room or not at all. Failure of remotely operated equipment generally results in shutdown of the reactor power plant.

Reactor power plant operators and certain supervisors are licensed on the basis of examinations administered by the U. S. Atomic Energy Commission. In most localities, operators of conventional high pressure power plants are also licensed by state or municipal authorities. Qualifications for nuclear power plant operators are more stringent because of the requirements of knowledge of elementary reactor theory, health physics and radiation safeguards. This is in addition to the understanding of equipment and control functions, operating procedures and safety practices required for operators for both types of power plants.

Unusual alertness is required for nuclear reactor operators in order to prevent shutdowns due to malfunction of the many required auxiliary systems and to prevent damage to the physical components of the reactor plant. Because of the added function of health physics and the developmental nature of nuclear power plants, operating manpower per unit of installed generating capacity is greater than for conventional plants.

Experience has been gained in virtually every type of reactor maintenance from complete refueling to replacement of fluid temperature measuring devices. The necessity of keeping radiation exposure levels

[5] For additional information, see "Selected Operating Experience of Commission Power Reactors" by J. O. Roberts, presented at AIEE Summer General Meeting, Ithaca, N.Y., June 18, 1961; "Shippingport Operations from Startup to First Refueling, December 1957 to October 1959" by J. E. Gray, W. H. Hamilton and W. E. Wynne, available in AEC Depository Libraries as DLCS–364; and "Operation of the Shippingport Atomic Power Station" by F. C. Duvall, *Chemical Engineering Progress*, Vol. 57, March 1961, pp. 46–49. Operating information is presented at meetings of ASME, IEEE, AIChE, American Power Conference, American Nuclear Society and Atomic Industrial Forum. These sources should be consulted, along with AEC publications, for current operational status.

to a minimum has led to the development of methods and techniques to confine the spread of contamination, to increase the effectiveness of maintenance workers in highly radioactive areas and to decontaminate radioactive equipment.

The principal differences encountered in nuclear plants relate to the more extensive training of operators and maintenance personnel. While these requirements are greater than for a conventional central station, they have been successfully met at Shippingport and other nuclear power plants. In a related area there is the necessity for more detailed and rigorous operating and maintenance procedures. At Shippingport, for example, these procedures are contained in a manual consisting of four volumes and more than 100 chapters.

Boiler Operation

Boiler operation involves both fuel firing and steam generation. Both of these can be hazardous if inadequate attention is paid to safety conditions. Air, fuel and ignition energy are the principal ingredients for firing a furnace, but in improper combination and timing they can also cause an explosion. As fuel is fired, energy is stored in the water in the boiler as well as in the steam generated, and failure of the pressure parts can release this thermal energy of the fluid at a catastrophic rate. Back as far as 1871 some experimental waterside boiler explosions were conducted at Sandy Hook, New Jersey. Professor Robert H. Thurston, who subsequently was one of the founders as well as the first president of ASME, calculated that the theoretical amount of energy released was in excess of 2,000,000,000 ft lb,

or more than enough to lift a 35 ton boiler to a height of five miles. Fireside explosions may likewise release large quantities of energy and cause extensive physical damage.[6]

Safety considerations necessarily exert strong influence over the operation of boilers. The ideal relationship of safety devices to boiler operation is not only to shut off the unit safely when predetermined danger points are met but also to feed back information to correct conditions before the danger point is reached.

Boiler Maintenance

Outages for the repair or replacement of equipment parts that have failed in service can be, and often are, very costly. Through the application of proper operating procedures and careful inspection, it is possible to increase the length of time over which a boiler can be carried on the line before any repairs are required. This, in turn, will prolong the useful life of the equipment and minimize outage charges.

The principal causes of forced boiler outages and excessive maintenance are:
1. Sustained and frequent overloading of fuel burning equipment
2. Operating with improper air flow conditions
3. Fouling of external heating surfaces
4. Inadequate water conditioning
5. Improper lubrication

Where prolonged overloading is unavoidable, good operation and careful attention to maintenance are especially important.

Of prime importance to the operation of all equipment is the use of correct lubricants, at sufficiently frequent intervals, and at all points requiring lubrication.

---

[6] See Chapter 17, Fuel Burning Systems, for additional information on furnace protection and its relationship to burner design.

Adherence to a definite schedule for proper lubrication is of considerable assistance in this respect.

Internal maintenance of the boiler is concerned with the prevention of corrosion, scale or oil deposits. This is primarily a matter of proper treatment of feedwater. In its early stages of operation a boiler should be inspected internally at frequent intervals, until there is certainty that the feedwater treatment and methods of control are adequate to allow operation over longer periods.

The heating surfaces of the unit should be inspected and cleaned periodically. This is done during operation by means of mechanical soot blowers. It is important to prevent accumulation of slag on the superheater or on the boiler tubes between the furnace and superheater. Partially blocked gas passes in this section of the boiler will result in localized overheating and subsequent failure of superheater elements. If chronic slagging difficulties are experienced, hand lancing during operation can be used to aid in keeping the boiler in service over longer periods. Retractable or telescopic soot blowers may be used in high temperature gas zones where slagging may be troublesome.

Boiler tubes adjacent to soot blowers should be inspected to be sure they are not cut by jet impingement. Such attachments as superheater supports and spacers should be checked to see that no deterioration is taking place. Expansion spaces for boiler drums, waterwalls and headers should be ample for the hot condition and free from deposits of dirt or slag.

One of the largest preventable losses in efficiency is due to air leakage through the boiler casing or setting. Some of the principal sources of such leakage are various types of access doors and peepholes, air seals, expansion joints and ashpit connections. It is well to check casing tightness before and after each operating period.

There should be an established schedule of boiler maintenance in order to minimize forced outages. Scheduled maintenance work makes it possible to have other boilers available to carry the load or to perform the work when the boilers are not required. By planning maintenance in advance, the necessary spare parts, tools and maintenance personnel can be present to do the work most effectively and economically. This is in contrast to the disorganized and hectic efforts that too often characterize maintenance efforts following an unexpected forced outage.

While forced outages cannot be entirely prevented, they can be reduced to a minimum by a program of preventive maintenance. Attention to details, even the apparently insignificant ones, is of paramount importance in such a program. Steam sampling lines, for example, may become blocked. Although they do not affect the rate of steam generation, stoppage of such lines does prevent water analyses that might give some clue to changed conditions that might cause a boiler outage. Boilers are equipped with many warning alarm systems, but if these become inoperative because of inadequate checks of their functioning, then they are no longer serving their original purpose of giving advance warning of trouble. These examples could be multiplied many times, but each one will point to the same objective: preventive maintenance that is based on planned attention to details is the best way to minimize forced outages.[7]

[7] For an interesting account of the role of the engineer in operation and maintenance, see "Professional Integrity — The Engineer in Field Service" by James J. Ragusan, *Mechanical Engineering*, Vol. 84, May 1962, p. 44.

Closed loop for laboratory study of heat transfer in subcritical and
supercritical pressure thermodynamic cycles

5

Thermodynamic Cycles for Power Plants[1]

THERMODYNAMICS had its beginning in attempts to understand the potentialities of systems designed to produce work from various energy sources. The first practical power systems for continuously converting heat into work used steam as a working fluid.

A *thermodynamic cycle* is defined as a series of processes combined in such a way that the thermodynamic states at which the working fluid exists are repeated periodically. Customarily, in an electric generating station the fluid is cycled through a sequence of processes in a closed loop designed to produce the maximum generation of electric power from the fuel consumed consistent with plant economics.[2]

Laws of Thermodynamics

The thermodynamic analysis of such fluid cycles is conducted using the First and Second Laws of thermodynamics. In equation form these may be stated as follows.

First Law

$$\Delta E = Q - W + \sum_i (h_i + e_{xi}) m_i \qquad (5\text{--}1)$$

where ΔE is change in energy content of system, Q is heat transferred *to* system, W is work transferred *from* system and $(h_i + e_{xi}) m_i$ is energy convected into or out of system by mass, m_i, having enthalpy, h_i, and extrinsic energy, e_{xi}.

e_{xi} is extrinsic energy, i.e. energy dependent on frame of reference. For a fluid system e_{xi} = kinetic energy + potential energy. $e_{xi} = V^2/2 + z$ in which V is velocity and z is elevation above datum.

This equation applies equally to processes and cycles, steady and transient flow situations. For example, in a closed system where fluid streams do not cross the boundary, $m_i = O$, and if the process is cyclic, then $\Delta E = O$ and Eq. 5–1 becomes

$$\sum_{\text{cycle}} Q = \sum_{\text{cycle}} W \qquad (5\text{--}2)$$

---

[1] Material contributed by Warren E. Ibele, Department of Mechanical Engineering, University of Minnesota.

[2] The design of a specific power plant represents an optimization of thermodynamic and economic considerations, the latter including initial, producton, and distribution costs.

As another example, if the steady state, adiabatic expansion in a turbine is being analyzed, then $\Delta E = O$, $Q = O$, and Eq. 5–1 reduces to:

$$W = - \sum_i (h_i + e_{xi}) m_i$$

$$= m[(h + e_x)_{in} - (h + e_x)_{out}]$$

$$W = m\left[\left(h + \frac{V^2}{2} + z\right)_{in} - \left(h + \frac{V^2}{2} + z\right)_{out}\right] \quad (5\text{–}3)$$

When changes in kinetic energy and elevation of the fluid stream may be neglected Eq. 5–3 reduces to the familiar $W \simeq m(h_{in} - h_{out})$.

Second Law

$$\Delta S = \left(\frac{Q}{T}\right) + I + \sum_i S_i \quad (5\text{–}4)$$

where ΔS is change in entropy of system, $(Q/T) = \Sigma_i (Q_i/T_i)$, i.e. the sum over the system boundaries of the heat transferred, Q_i, at a position on the boundary where the local temperature is T_i, I is irreversibility (For consistency with other second law statements $I \geqq O$. For reversible processes or cycles, $I = O$; for irreversible processes or cycles, $I > O$) and $\Sigma_i S_i$ = entropy flow into and out of system associated with mass flow, m_i, into and

out of system. For a reversible cyclic process involving a closed system, $I = O$, $\Delta S = O$, $\Sigma_i S_i = O$ and Eq. 5–4 reduces to

$$\left(\frac{Q}{T}\right) = 0 \quad (5\text{–}5)$$

The steady flow, adiabatic expansion through a turbine is governed by the following equation.

$$I = - \sum_i m_i s_i = -m(s_{in} - s_{out})$$

$$= m(s_{out} - s_{in}) \quad (5\text{–}6)$$

For reversible, adiabatic expansion, $I = O$ and the process is characterized by the familiar isentropic property, $s_{out} = s_{in}$. The primary advantage of writing the Second Law in an equation (Eq. 5–4) rather than the usual inequality is its usefulness in analyzing processes and cycles in a direct, quantitative, manner, similar to the First Law analysis.[3]

Eqs. 5–1 and 5–4 thus provide quantitative means of examining all processes encountered in power plant analysis regardless of the fluids used or the specific cycle employed.

Carnot Cycle

In 1824, Sadi Carnot, a French engineer, published a small, moderately technical book, modestly entitled *Reflections on the*

---

[3] Second Law analysis is not used as commonly as First Law analysis in steam power engineering practice. However, the former can be a very helpful aid in studying losses and determining where future cycle improvements may be made. See *Available Energy and the Second Law Analysis* by Edward A. Bruges, Academic Press, 1959, 124 pages and the following articles and technical papers: "A Steam Chart for Second Law Analysis — A Study of Thermodynamic Availability in the Steam Power Plant" by J. H. Keenan, *Mechanical Engineering*, Vol. 54, March 1932, pp. 195–204; "The Virtue of Energy, Its Meaning and Practical Significance" by M. W. Thring, *Journal of The Institute of Fuel*, April 1944, pp. 116–123; "Evaluation and Location of the Losses in a 60,000 Kw Power Station" by C. Birnie and E. F. Obert, *Proceedings* of the American (Midwest) Power Conference, 1949, pp. 187–193; "The Evaluation of Steam Power Plant Losses by Means of the Entropy Balance Diagram" by Allen Keller, *Trans.* ASME, Vol. 72, 1950, pp. 949–953; and "Availability Balance of Steam Power Plants" by C. A. Meyer, G. J. Silvestri and J. A. Martin, *Trans.* ASME, Vol. 81, 1959, Series A, *Journal of Engineering for Power*, pp. 35–42.

Motive Power of Fire.[4] Carnot made here three important contributions: the concept of reversibility, the concept of a cycle, and the specification of the heat engine producing maximum work when operating cyclically between two fixed temperature reservoirs.

The Carnot cycle consists of alternate reversible, isothermal and isentropic processes which may be viewed as occurring either in the non-flow or flow device shown in Fig. 5–1. In the first instance, the heat source and sink are placed in contact with the device to accomplish the required isothermal heat addition (*a-b*) and rejection (*c-d*) respectively. The insulation shown replaces the heat reservoirs for executing the reversible adiabatic processes involving expansion (*b-c*) and compression (*d-a*). The process characteristics for good heat transfer and work transfer are not the same and are partially in conflict; Fig. 5–1(b) therefore shows a flow system for executing the Carnot cycle with the work and heat transfer processes assigned to separate devices. For both non-flow and flow systems the state changes experienced by the working fluid are shown in the temperature-entropy diagram of Fig. 5–1.

Practical attempts to attain the Carnot cycle encounter irreversibilities in the form of finite temperature differences during the heat transfer processes and fluid friction during work transfer processes. The compression process *d-a* moreover is difficult to perform on a two-phase mixture and requires an input of work ranging from a fifth to a third of the turbine output. When realistic irreversibilities are introduced, the Carnot cycle net work is reduced, the size and cost of equipment

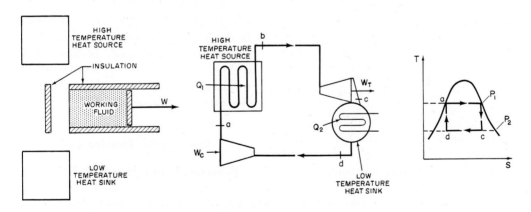

Fig. 5–1. Carnot cycle

(a) Non-flow device

(b) Flow device

(c) Temperature-entropy diagram

---

[4] This is available, together with other papers by E. Clapeyron and R. Clausius, as a paperback from Dover Publications, 1960, 152 pages; under the title, *Reflection on the Motive Power of Heat and on Machines Fitted to Develop This Power*, ASME in 1943 published a translation and commentary on the Carnot work made in 1890 by Robert H. Thurston, one of its founders and first president.

increase, and consequently other cycles appear more attractive as practical models.[5]

Rankine Cycle

The basis of the modern steam power plant is a modification of the Carnot cycle proposed by W. J. M. Rankine[6], a distinguished Scotch engineering professor of thermodynamics and applied mechanics. The elements comprising the Rankine cycle are the same as those appearing in Fig. 5–1(b) with one exception; since the condensation process accompanying the heat rejection process continues until the saturated liquid state is reached, a simple liquid pump replaces the two-phase compressor. The state changes for the Rankine cycle are shown in the temperature-entropy and enthalpy-entropy diagrams of Fig. 5–2. The cycle resembles a Carnot cycle compressing liquid except that compression terminates (state a) at boiling pressure rather than the boiling temperature (state a'). The triangle bounded by a-a' and the line connecting to the temperature entropy curve in Fig. 5–2(a) signifies the loss of cycle work due to the irreversible heating of the liquid from state a to saturated liquid. The lower pressure at state a, compared to a', makes possible a much smaller work of compression be-

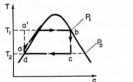 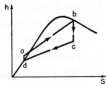

Fig. 5–2.   Rankine cycle
(a) Temperature-entropy diagram
(b) Enthalpy-entropy (Mollier) diagram

tween d-a. For operating plants it amounts to one percent or less of the turbine output. This modification eliminates the two-phase vapor compression process, reduces compression work to a negligible amount, and makes the Rankine cycle less sensitive than the Carnot cycle to the irreversibilities bound to occur in an actual plant. As a result, when compared with a Carnot cycle operating between the same temperature limits and with realistic component efficiencies, the Rankine cycle has a larger net work output per unit mass of fluid circulated, smaller size and lower cost of equipment and, because of its relative insensitivity to irreversibilities, will have operating plant thermal efficiencies exceeding those of the Carnot cycle.

Regenerative Rankine Cycle

Refinements in component design soon

---

[5] For a detailed comparison of Carnot and Rankine cycles on both a theoretical and practical basis, see *Thermodynamics* Chapter 15, Vapor Cycles and Processes, by Edward F. Obert and Richard A. Gaggioli, Second Edition, McGraw-Hill, 1963 and *Engineering Thermodynamics,* Chapter 18, Work Producing Systems, by Newman A. Hall and Warren E. Ibele, Prentice-Hall, 1960.

[6] Rankine established a sound theoretical thermodynamics base for steam power plant practice with the publication of *A Manual of the Steam Engine and Other Prime Movers* in 1859, about 150 years after Thomas Newcomen in Great Britain built the first practical steam engine. Though engineers designed and built engines which effectively operated on the Rankine cycle prior to Rankine's *Manual,* its appearance and the work of his contemporaries in thermodynamics greatly accelerated progress in power production. A modern thermodynamics textbook with many historical references to the background and development of this science is *Engineering Thermodynamics, An Introductory Textbook* by J. B. Jones and G. A. Hawkins, Wiley, 1960, 724 pages.

brought power plants based on the Rankine cycle to their peak thermal efficiencies and further increases were realized by modifying the basic cycle. This occurred through increasing the temperature of saturated steam supplied to the turbine, by increasing the turbine inlet temperature through constant pressure superheat, by reducing the sink temperature, and by reheating the working vapor after partial expansion followed by continued expansion to the final sink temperature.[7] In practice all of these are employed with yet another important modification. In the previous section the irreversibility associated with the heating of the compressed liquid to saturation by a finite temperature difference was cited as the primary thermodynamic cause of lower thermal efficiency for the Rankine cycle. The *regenerative cycle* attempts to eliminate this irreversibility by using other parts of the cycle as heat sources with temperatures always slightly above that of the compressed liquid being heated. An idealized form of such a procedure appears in Fig.

5–3. The condensed liquid at f is pumped to the pressure p_1, and passes through coils around the turbine, receiving heat from the fluid expanding in the turbine. The liquid and vapor flows are counter to one another and by reversible heat transfer over the infinitesimal temperature difference dT the liquid is brought to the saturated state at T_1 (process b-c) and rejecting heat at the constant temperature T_2 (process e-f). Such a system, by the Second Law, will have a thermal efficiency equal to a Carnot cycle operating between the same temperatures.

This procedure of transferring heat from one part of a cycle to another in order to eliminate or reduce external irreversibilities is called *regenerative heating* and is a basic element in all *regenerative cycles*. Though thermodynamically desirable, the idealized regenerative cycle just described has several features which preclude its use in practice. Locating the heat exchanger with the turbine increases design difficulties and cost. Even if these problems were solved, heat transfer could not

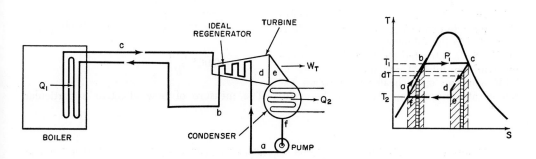

Fig. 5–3.   Regenerative Rankine cycle

(a) Flow diagram

(b) Temperature-entropy diagram

[7] For a quantitative discussion of the effect of these modifications on the basic Rankine cycle performance see *Engineering Thermodynamics*, Chapter 18, by Hall and Ibele.

be accomplished reversibly in the time available, and the cooling causes the vapor to reach excessive moisture content. For these reasons the scheme shown in Fig. 5–4 permits a practical approach to regeneration without encountering these problems. Extraction or "bleeding" of steam at state c for use in the "open" heater[8] avoids excessive cooling of the vapor during turbine expansion; in the heater, liquid from the condenser increases in temperature by ΔT. The extraction and heating substitutes the finite temperature difference ΔT for the infinitesimal dT used in the theoretical regeneration process, a substitution which while failing to realize the full potential of regeneration nevertheless halves the temperature difference through which the condensate must be heated in the basic Rankine cycle. Additional extractions and heaters permit a closer approximation to the maximum efficiency of the idealized regenerative cycle[9], and further improvement over the simple Rankine cycle shown in Fig. 5–2.

Example

The method of First and Second law analysis of a single extraction regenerative cycle is illustrated in the following example as shown in Fig. 5–4. Saturated steam at 500 psia enters turbine inlet. Condensation occurs at 70 F and one open heater uses steam extracted at a mean temperature for the cycle.

Determine thermal efficiency, internal irreversibility, and extraction pressure if all processes are taken as reversible except the regenerative heater.

The state points and associated properties[10] are summarized in Table 5–1.

By specification, the temperature at extraction (state c) is

$$T_c = \tfrac{1}{2}(T_b + T_d) = \tfrac{1}{2}(467 + 70) = 268.5\ F$$

and since state c is in the mixture region the corresponding vapor pressure is 41 psia. Other states and properties are determined in the customary way.

For the processes comprising the cycle pertinent quantities are recorded in Table 5–2.

The quantities in Table 5–2 are obtained by applying the First and Second Law statements as Eqs. 5–1 and 5–4 for the prevailing steady state conditions.

Thermal efficiency: $\eta = \dfrac{W_{net}}{Q_1} = \dfrac{379}{965} = 0.39$

For the basic Rankine cycle operating under the same conditions, $\eta_R = 0.37$, and for the Carnot cycle operating between same temperature extremes, $\eta_c = 0.43$. If heat is supplied the regenerative cycle from an external heat source at the saturation temperature of 729 R then the total irreversibility is:

$$I = (\eta_c - \eta)\frac{Q_1}{T_0} = (0.43 - 0.39)\frac{965}{530}$$

$$= 0.064\ \frac{Btu}{R}$$

The measure of how effective a particular

---

[8] Regenerative cycle heaters are called "open" or "closed" depending on whether hot and cold fluids are mixed directly to exchange energy or kept separate with energy exchange occurring by the use of metal coils.

[9] See "Optimization of Heater Enthalpy Rises in Feed-Heating Trains" by C. D. Weir, *Proceedings* of IME, Vol. 174, 1960, pp. 769–796 and particularly the relationships developed by R. W. Haywood in his discussion on pp. 784–787. An economic, as distinguished from a thermodynamic, optimization is presented in a paper by G. Chiantore, D. Borges, F. Baldo and J. H. Potter, "Optimizing a Regenerative Steam Turbine Cycle", *Trans.* ASME, Vol. 83, Series A, 1961, pp. 433–443.

[10] Calculated from *Thermodynamic Properties of Steam* by J. H. Keenan and F. G. Keyes, Wiley, 1936 or *Steam Tables*, Third Edition, Combustion Engineering Inc., 1940.

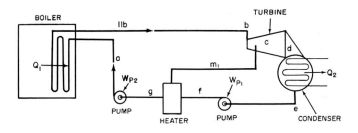

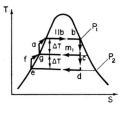

Fig. 5—4. Single extraction regenerative cycle

(a) Flow diagram

(b) Temperature-entropy diagram

Table 5—1 State Properties
(See Fig. 5—4)

State	T R	P Psia	h Btu/lb	s Btu/lb R	x Quality
a	720	500	239	0.394	—
b	927	500	1204	1.463	1.00
c	729	41	1016	1.463	0.84
d	530	0.36	774	1.463	0.70
e	530	0.36	38	0.074	0
f	530	41	38.1	0.074	—
g	729	41	238	0.394	0

Table 5—2

Process	Δh Btu/lb	ω	m Δh Btu	W Btu	Q Btu	Δs Btu/lb R	m Δs Btu/R	(Q/T) Btu/R	I Btu/R
a-b	965	1.0	965	0	965	1.069	1.069	1.069	0
b-c	−188	1.0	−188	188	0	0	0	0	0
c-d	−242	0.80	−193	193	0	0	0	0	0
d-e	−736	0.80	−586	0	−586	−1.389	−1.106	−1.106	0
e-f	0.1	0.80	0.1	−0.1	0	0	0	0	0
f-g	200	0.80	159 ⎫	0	0	0.320	0.254 ⎫	0	0.036
c-g	−778	0.20	−159 ⎭			−1.069	−0.218 ⎭		
g-a	1.5	1.0	1.5	−1.5	0	0	0	0	0
Net	. . .		. . .	0	379.4	379	. . .	0	−0.036	0.036

system is operating with respect to its cycle potentialities is given by the thermodynamic effectiveness, ϵ, for an ambient temperature T_0:

$$\epsilon = \frac{W}{W + T_0 I} = \frac{379}{379 + 0.064\,(530)} = 0.92$$

Reduction of the temperature difference between the liquid entering the boiler and that of the source increases the cycle thermal efficiency at the price of reducing the net work produced per pound of vapor entering the turbine and increasing the size,

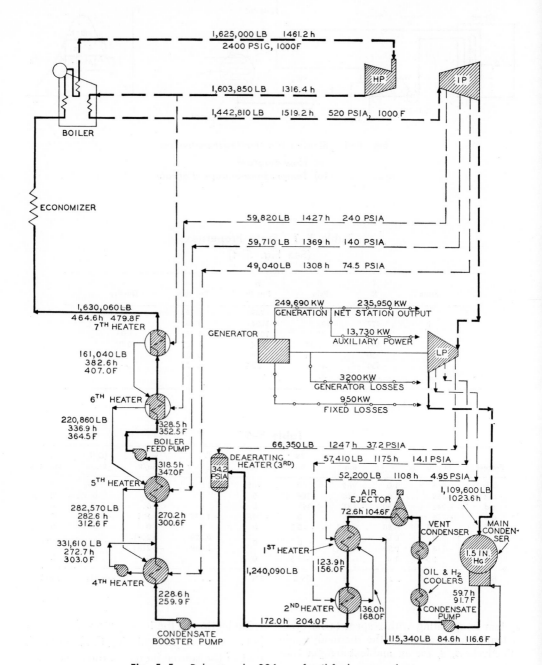

Fig. 5—5.   Reheat cycle, 236-mw fossil fuel power plant

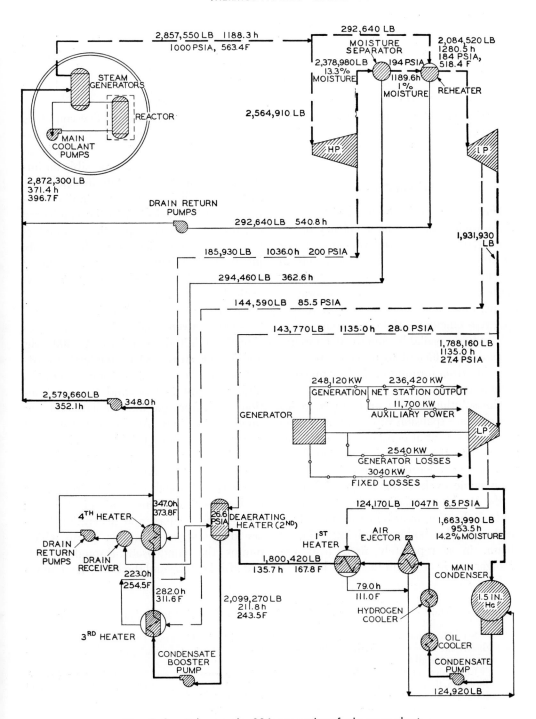

Fig. 5–6. Reheat cycle, 236-mw nuclear fuel power plant

complexity and initial cost of the plant. Further improvements in cycle performance may be realized by continuing to accept the consequences of increasing the number of feedwater heating stages. Balancing cycle thermal efficiency against plant size, complexity and cost for production of power at minimum cost determines the optimum number of heaters.[11]

Reheat Cycle

The use of superheat offers a simple way of improving the thermal efficiency of the basic Rankine cycle and reducing vapor moisture content to acceptable levels in the low pressure stages of the turbine. With continued increase of evaporation temperatures and pressures to achieve better cycle efficiency, there are some situations where available superheat temperatures are insufficient to prevent excessive moisture from forming in the low pressure turbine stages.

The solution to this problem is to interrupt the expansion process, remove the vapor for reheat at constant pressure, and return it to the turbine for continued expansion to condenser pressure.[12] The thermodynamic cycle using this modification of the Rankine cycle is called the *reheat cycle*. Reheating may be carried out in a section of the boiler supplying primary steam, in a separately fired heat exchanger, or in a steam-to-steam heat exchanger. Separately fired reheat-superheaters are found in some nuclear power plants, as shown in Fig. 5–6, but most central stations operating on the reheat cycle combine superheater and reheater in the same boiler.

Usual central station practice combines both regenerative and reheat modifications to the basic Rankine cycle. For large installations, reheat makes possible an improvement of approximately five per cent in thermal efficiency and substantially reduces the heat rejected to the condenser cooling water.[13] The operating characteristics and economics of modern plants justify the installation of only one stage of reheat except for units operating at supercritical pressure.

Fig. 5–5 shows the flow diagram for a 236-mw conventional reheat cycle designed for initial conditions of 2400 psig and 1000 F steam. Seven feedwater heaters are supplied by exhaust steam from the high pressure turbine and three extractions each from the intermediate and low pressure turbines. All heaters, save the deaerating heater (third), are shown as closed heaters. Three pumps are shown: the condensate pump which pumps the condensate through oil and hydrogen gas coolers, vent condenser, air ejector, first and second heaters, and deaerating heaters; the condensate booster pump which pumps the condensate through fourth and fifth heaters; and the boiler feed pump

---

[11] For details of such analyses see *Steam Turbines and Their Cycles,* Part 3, Cycle Analysis, by J. K. Salisbury, Wiley, 1950, 645 pages.

[12] See *Mechanical Engineering Thermodynamics,* D. A. Mooney, Prentice-Hall, 1953, for discussion of the relationship between utilization of reheat cycle and progress in high temperature metallurgy.

[13] Literature on the reheat cycle is extensive. For a summary see "The Reheat Cycle — A Re-evaluation" [by Glenn R. Fryling], *Combustion,* Vol. 21, June 1950, pp. 38–40. Detailed information is given in "Symposium on the Reheat Cycle," *Trans.* ASME, Vol. 71, 1949, pp. 673–749. See also two papers by J. K. Salisbury, "Analysis of the Steam Turbine Reheat Cycle," *Trans.* ASME, Vol. 80, 1958, pp. 1629–1642 and "Power Plant Performance Monitoring," *Trans.* ASME, Vol. 83, Series A, 1961, pp. 409–422.

which pumps the condensate through the sixth and seventh heaters to the economizer and boiler. The mass flows noted on the diagram are in pounds per hour at the prescribed conditions for full load operation.

Fig. 5–6 shows a flow diagram for a 236-mw pressurized water nuclear reactor reheat cycle designed for initial conditions of 1000 psia and 563 F steam. Here, four feedwater heaters are supplied with steam from the high pressure turbine exhaust (fourth) extraction from the intermediate pressure turbine for the deaerating heater (second), and extraction from the low pressure turbine (first). Three main pumps are also used but in addition there are two drain return pumps. Located between the high and intermediate pressure turbines is a steam-to-steam reheater. As in the previous figure, the mass flows noted are in pounds per hour and the steam conditions those holding for full load operation.

These two cycles of nearly identical station output (236-mw) show striking differences due to the lower turbine inlet temperature and pressure required for certain types of nuclear power reactors. Thus the nuclear reactor plant requires a main steam flow 75 per cent larger and achieves a thermodynamic cycle efficiency substantially less than a conventional reheat cycle in a fossil fuel fired central station.

Supercritical Pressure Cycle

There is a definite relationship between operating temperature of a cycle and optimum pressure of the cycle. Metallurgy has progressed to the point where temperatures can be utilized which make attractive the use of steam pressures above the critical pressure of water. At 1200 F steam temperature optimum cycle economy can be obtained with steam pressures of approximately 5000 psia. Operation of an actual plant at these extremes of temperature and pressure poses severe design difficulties for nearly all cycle components.[14]

A regenerative-reheat cycle is used with six to eight stages of feedwater heating and, because of the high inlet temperature and pressure, two stages of reheat are justified. Fig. 5–7 shows schematic flow and temperature-entropy diagrams of such a cycle. Seven feedwater heaters are shown with steam extractions from the various turbines supplying energy for the regenerative heating processes. Two stages of reheat are used to keep the moisture content of the vapor from becoming excessive[15] and to achieve higher thermal efficiency. For such supercritical pressure plants thermal efficiencies in excess of 40 per cent have been reached.

Process Steam Cycle

There are many instances where power and heating needs may be combined in a single power plant which will operate at a high annual load factor and thermal efficiency. For heating service, the steam may be generated at a pressure and temperature sufficiently high that exhaust from the turbine is at steam conditions suitable for delivery to the steam mains and distribution to users. The needs of industrial plants for process steam may be met by similar arrangements using either

[14] See Chapter 25, Combined Circulation Boilers, for an account of the evolution of boiler design to meet the challenges of supercritical pressure steam power plant cycles.
[15] For a discussion of the effects of moisture content see *Power Plant Engineering*, 3rd Edition, by F. T. Morse, D. Van Nostrand, 1953, pp. 384–390.

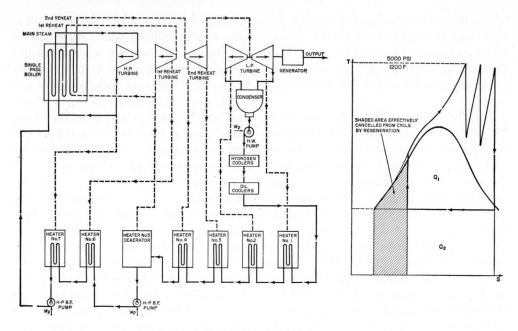

Fig. 5–7.   Supercritical pressure cycle

(a) Flow diagram

(b) Temperature-entropy diagram

turbine exhaust steam or extracted steam from an appropriate turbine stage. The selection of optimum exhaust or extraction conditions will depend on the proportions of power and process heat required of the particular plant. Process steam requirements are usually in the low pressure range with modest superheat required if at all; consequently initial steam pressure and temperature will generally be below the limits of current technology with a commensurate easing of boiler and turbine design requirements.

The great variety of power process steam requirements offer a continuing challenge to designers. Cycles have been developed and applied over a wide range of capacities extending from the small in-dustrial power plants to large central stations serving the heating needs of a metropolitan center or the power process needs of a major petro-chemical installation. The steel, chemical, and paper industries are three examples from among the many important industrial users of process steam cycles.[16]

Fig. 5–8 shows a schematic diagram of a power process cycle using a back pressure turbine. After steam generation at a suitable working pressure it is admitted to the turbine and emerges usually in the superheated state, c. Because temperature control is difficult to attain and heat transfer lower for superheated than saturated steam, a desuperheater is often used. Saturated steam d enters the heater and is en-

[16] A comprehensive treatment of this subject is to be found in *The Efficient Use of Steam* by Oliver Lyle, Her Majesty's Stationery Office, London, 1947, 912 pages. See especially Chapter 3, Combined Power and Heating, of this valuable reference work.

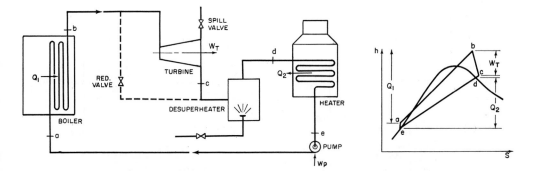

Fig. 5–8. Power process cycle using a back pressure turbine

(a) Flow diagram

(b) Enthalpy-entropy (Mollier) diagram

tirely condensed. The steam required for power generation will not equal at all times that required for process work and means of controlling the exhaust steam pressure must be employed if variations in the pressure (and therefore the steam saturation temperature) are to be avoided.

The control method depends on the circumstances. An ordinary centrifugal governor fitted to the back pressure turbine will cause the quantity of available exhaust steam to be controlled by the load on the turbine. Should the available exhaust be too small, live steam may be

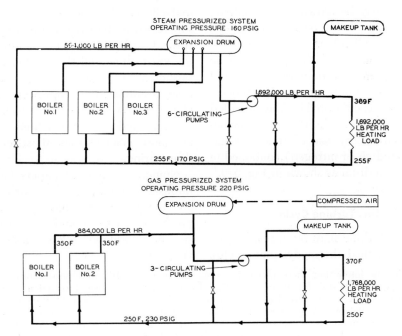

Fig. 5–9. Flow diagrams of heat process cycle using high temperature water

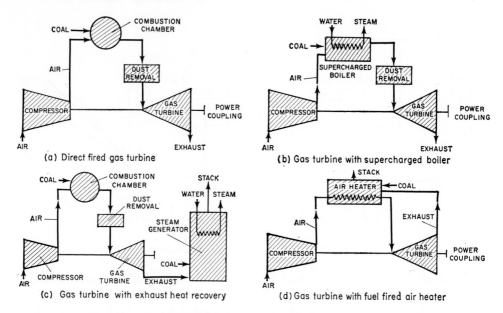

Fig. 5–10.   Gas turbine cycles

passed through a reducing valve into the desuperheater. If the quantity of exhaust steam exceeds requirements, then the excess steam may be blown to atmosphere, into an accumulator, or feed tank, etc. through the spill valve.

Another version of the process cycle uses high temperature water circulated by pumps to supply energy for process and heating. The thermal head is provided by a water "boiler," the entire system being pressurized by use of steam or gas (compressed air or nitrogen) contained in an expansion drum as shown in Fig. 5–9.[17]

Gas Turbine Cycle

The gas turbine may be applied many ways in practical thermodynamic cycles.

Four examples are shown in Fig. 5–10. While the direct fired unit has the advantage of simplicity, it ranks low in thermal efficiency. In the cycle employing a supercharged boiler, the furnace is pressurized with air from the compressor of the gas turbine and the products of combustion are expanded through the gas turbine, resulting in an improvement of efficiency. Likewise, cycles with exhaust heat recovery and with a fuel fired air heater are more efficient than those employing direct firing.

Numerous technical papers have been published on the various gas turbine cycles and the particular economics of their application. These should be consulted for specific information related to current developments.

[17] For an interesting thermodynamic approach offering substantial possibilities, see "High Temperature Water for Process Heating Combined with Power Production" by Paul L. Geiringer and Floyd Hasselriis, *Proceedings* of the American Power Conference, Vol. 26m 1954, pp. 580–590. A paper of related interest, linking central station practice to process and heating requirements, is "The Steam Generating Station as a Source and Sink for the Heat Pump" by J. A. Eibling and B. A. Landry, *Mechanical Engineering*, Vol. 73, July 1951, pp. 554–558, 564.

6

Heat Transfer[1]

HEAT TRANSFER undoubtedly ranks as the most important of the engineering sciences employed in the design of boilers and nuclear reactors. Although it has been of theoretical interest to scientists for several centuries, heat transfer has been developed more by empirically minded engineers faced with practical design requirements than by analytically minded scientists. Not until comparatively recent times have these interests converged to the point that heat transfer has truly become an engineering science.[2]

A necessary step in the design of boilers and reactors is a detailed engineering analysis of heat transfer in order to estimate the cost, practicability and size of equipment to interchange a specified amount of heat in a given time. A furnace wall or a reactor fuel element, for example, can be operated successfully over extended periods only if surface temperatures can be maintained within acceptable limits by removing heat continuously and at rapid rates. The size and geometry of a boiler furnace are de-

pendent not only upon the amount of heat to be transmitted but also on the rate at which it can be absorbed or transferred.

This chapter will be primarily concerned with heat transfer in boilers and steam generating units and will emphasize the complexity of the phenomena taking place in the boiler furnace. An introductory section is intended to give a sense of historical perspective to the laws of heat transfer. This is followed by consideration of elements of boiler heat transfer, an analytical approach to heat transfer in the boiler furnace and an account of experimental work relating the laws of heat transfer to actual boiler performance.

Historical Background[3]

Most textbooks on heat transfer define three modes of heat flow: *convection, conduction* and *radiation*. These three encompass much of the field of physics including mechanics, heat, acoustics, optics and electricity. For gases, conduction

---

[1] There are several sources of the information contained in this chapter, including the First Edition of *Combustion Engineering* and a paper prepared under the auspices of the ASME Furnace Performance Factors Committee. The late Martin Mayers was commissioned to write a major section entitled The Boiler Furnace — An Analytical Approach.
[2] Pioneering works in the English language include *Heat Transmission by Radiation, Conduction and Convection* by R. Royds, London, 1921, 238 pages and *Heat Transmission* by William H. McAdams, a book sponsored by the Committee on Heat Transmission of the National Research Council, the first edition of which was published in New York in 1933.
[3] Material contributed by Glenn R. Fryling.

takes place by elastic impact; for solid nonconductors, in longitudinal vibration; and for metals, in electronic movement. The laws of aerodynamics and hydrodynamics govern convection which involves the transportation and exchange of heat due to the mixing motion of different parts of a fluid. Radiation is a part of optics in its geometry as well as its dynamics.

In most practical situations heat is transferred simultaneously by several of these modes. However, the student must master the fundamentals of each process before he can hope to understand and analyze the most complex combinations met in engineering practice. Attaching dates and names to the three basic laws may help to put them in time perspective in relation to the development of steam power plants as well as the science of heat transfer.

Convection

Authorities differ as to whether Sir Isaac Newton formulated a definition of convection or a law of cooling when the following relationship was first expressed in 1701:

$$q = hA_s \Delta T \qquad (6\text{-}1)$$

where q denotes the time rate of heat flow, h is the surface or film coefficient of heat transfer, A_s is the heat transfer surface area and ΔT is a temperature difference between a surface and a fluid in contact with it.[4]

Three years before Newton presented this relationship to the Royal Society in London, Thomas Savery described the ar-

rangement and operation of his model steam "fire engine" to this same internationally known Society. According to the minutes of the meeting, "Mr. Savery entertained the Society with showing his engine to raise water by the force of fire. He was thanked for showing the experiment which succeeded according to expectation and was approved of." The device was capable of lifting water a maximum of 24 ft and was a forerunner of the pumping machines that led to the development of the steam engine in Great Britain.[5]

Conduction

More than a century later in 1828 the French physicist and mathematician, J. B. J. Fourier, formulated the basic law of heat conduction, which may be expressed as follows:

$$q = -kA_c \frac{dT}{dx} \qquad (6\text{-}2)$$

where k is the thermal conductivity, A_c is a constant cross-sectional area and dT/dx is the temperature gradient at the section. The minus sign signifies that the heat is flowing in the direction of decreasing temperature, in accordance with the second law of thermodynamics.[6]

In the little more than a century separating the formulation of these two laws, the steam power plant came into reality as a useful adjunct to industry. There were such important developments as the Newcomen engine and the invention of the condenser and the improvement of the steam engine by James Watt. Steam

---

[4] The original paper appeared in the *Philosophical Transactions* of the Royal Society of London, Vol. 22, 1701, p. 824.

[5] See the account in *A History of the Growth of the Steam Engine* by Robert H. Thurston, Centennial Edition, Cornell University Press, 1939, p. 33.

[6] An English translation of his classical work, *The Analytical Theory of Heat*, is available in paperback from Dover Publications.

power found application in marine, turn-pike and railroad service. Substantial advances were made during this period in the design of boilers and machine tools, thus contributing a dependable source of heat and more precise manufacturing techniques to the evolving steam power plant.

Radiation

The third fundamental law of heat transfer, the basic equation for total thermal radiation from an ideal radiator or black body, was discovered empirically by Josef Stefan in 1879 and was derived theoretically by Ludwig Boltzmann in 1884.

It may be expressed as follows:

$$q = \sigma A_s T^4 \qquad (6-3)$$

where σ is the Stefan-Boltzmann constant for total black radiation, A_s is the heat transfer surface area and T is the absolute temperature.

The Stefan-Boltzmann equation represents the total radiant energy emitted by a black body in all directions, but it does not reveal the distribution of energy in the spectrum. The distribution of emissive power among the different wave lengths was derived by Max Planck in 1900, using the quantum concept.[7]

The three laws of heat transfer may now be seen to have spanned the period from Newton to Planck, or in other words to have covered the period from the beginnings of classical physics in the early eighteenth century to the beginnings of modern physics at the start of the twentieth century. By a strange coincidence this interval also practically marks the origin,

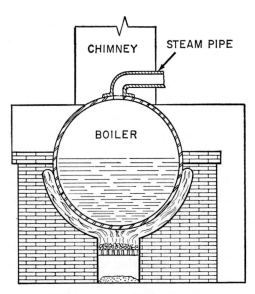

Fig. 6–1. Early globular boiler

rise and decline of the steam engine which had its most intensive development during the early part of the eighteenth century and reached its position of almost universal use as a thermal prime mover during the latter part of the nineteenth century. The beginning of modern physics took place about the same time as the technical developments that led to the challenge of the internal combustion engine and the steam turbine and their subsequent eclipse of the steam engine.

Over the years the boiler has evolved from a simple fuel burning device that generated steam a few pounds above atmospheric pressure to an extremely large equipment complex operating at supercritical pressure conditions and producing several million pounds of steam per hour. The two ends of this spectrum may be represented by the globular boiler, Fig. 6–1, invented by the Marquis of Worces-

[7] See "Uber die Beziehung Zwischen der Warmestrahlung und der Temperatur" by J. Stefan, *Wiener Berichte*, Vol. 79, 1879, pp. 391–428, and "Deduction of Stefan's Formula for Radiation from Maxwell's Electromagnetic Theory of Light" by L. Boltzmann, *Wiedendorf Annalen*, Vol. 22, 1884, p. 291. The work of Max Planck is available in paperback form, *The Theory of Heat Radiation*, Dover Publications, 1959, 224 pages.

ter in 1663 to provide steam for lifting water, and the modern central station boiler at Eddystone.[8]

This historical interlude gives some clue to the relationship between the power plant designer and the science of heat transfer. Countless trillions of tons of steam were generated successfully in boilers before the basic laws of heat radiation were formulated. In a sense this is evidence that a fire can be built without understanding the phenomena of combustion, and water may be boiled without an understanding of thermal conductivity and thermodynamic properties of fluids and gases. Engineering science has demonstrated its capability of increasing man's understanding of these phenomena, thereby contributing to the design and construction of large modern boilers operating at advanced steam conditions.[9]

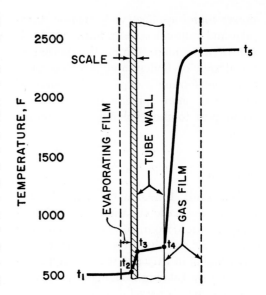

Fig. 6–2. Temperature gradient for bare furnace tubes exposed to radiant heat

[8] See Chapter 1, section entitled, What Is a Boiler? Fig. 6–1 originally appeared in *A Practical Treatise on Boilers and Boiler-Making* by N. P. Burgh, London, 1873, 390 pages, one of two major works dealing with boiler history. The other is *Steam Boilers — Their History and Development* by H. P. Powles, London, 1905, 336 pages. The former places major emphasis on fire tube boilers and the latter on water tube boilers, but both regrettably are out of print.
[9] The literature of boiler heat transfer is very extensive. A most comprehensive survey up to the early 1900's was made by W. E. Dalby who compiled a chronological and annotated list of 406 technical papers published between 1760 and 1909. This list which appeared under the title "Heat Transmission" in the *Proceedings* of the Institution of Mechanical Engineers, Parts 3–4, 1909, pp. 921–1071, was divided into thirteen subject matter categories dealing with such topics as heat transmission, boiler circulation, combustion and temperature distribution. Many of the most significant papers were abstracted in a manner that presents a revealing picture of the evolution of understanding of heat transmission in boilers.

In 1935 an 80-item bibliography was published as a part of a paper entitled "An Experimental Investigation of Heat Absorption in Boiler Furnaces" by W. J. Wohlenberg, H. F. Mullikin, W. H. Armacost and C. W. Gordon, *Trans.* ASME, Vol. 57, 1935, pp. 541–554.

A pioneering paper by Osborne Reynolds is entitled "On the Extent and Action of the Heating Surface for Steam Boilers" and originally appeared in the *Proceedings* of the Manchester Literary and Philosophical Society, Vol. 14, 1874, pp. 7–12. It is linked to more recent work in heat transfer by a paper entitled "Remarks on the Analogy Between Heat Transfer and Momentum Transfer" by L. M. K. Boelter, R. C. Martinelli and F. Jonassen, *Trans.* ASME, Vol. 63, 1941, pp. 447–455.

A frequently quoted paper is "Studies of Heat Transmission Through Boiler Tubing at Pressures from 500 to 3300 Pounds" by W. F. Davidson, P. H. Hardie, C. G. R. Humphreys, A. A. Markson, A. R. Mumford and T. Ravese, *Trans.* ASME, Vol. 65, 1943, pp. 553–591. An informative discussion of this paper is found in Vol. II of *Heat Transfer* by Max Jakob, New York, 1957, pp. 373–381.

An inclusive Russian work available in English translation is *Fundamentals of Heat Transfer* by S. S. Kutateladze, Academic Press, New York, 1963, 485 pages. See especially Chapter XIX, Thermal Radiation.

However, recognition must also be given to the reality that mere additions to scientific knowledge encounter a law of diminishing technical returns insofar as their contribution to the art of boiler design is concerned.

Elements of Boiler Heat Transfer[10]

The basic problem in the design of a boiler is to proportion and arrange the heating surface so as to secure the maximum economical and trouble-free transfer of available heat from the fuel fired into the steam generated. As previously noted, heat is transferred from the gas to the water and steam in three ways: radiation, convection and conduction. All are present in varying degrees in each part of the steam generating unit. For example, the heat which is given up by the furnace gas, and which results in the generation of steam within the tube exposed to that gas, must pass through the series resistances interposed by the following: the gas film adjacent to the tube, slag on the tube surface, tube wall, internal scale deposited by the water evaporated; the water and steam film. Furthermore, if the slag and scale are not intimately bonded to the tube surface, two additional resistances may be added: gas film between the slag and tube, and steam film between the internal scale and the tube wall. The temperature gradient resulting from the flow of heat through some of these series resistances is illustrated in Fig. 6–2.

Heat transfer through the gas film and the evaporating film does not follow the simple equation for conduction. The temperature gradient through the other resistances, however, is inversely proportional to the thermal conductivity. For conductance through a body having flat parallel plane surfaces, the following equation may be used:

$$\Delta t = \frac{(q/A_s)x}{k} \qquad (6\text{--}4)$$

where Δt is the temperature drop across any single resistance and x is the thickness of resistances.

The surfaces of a tube are curved, and thus the heat transfer area decreases as the center is approached. For radial heat flow, the above equation must therefore be modified to allow for the difference between the inside and the outside radius of the surfaces as follows:

$$\Delta t = \frac{q/A_s}{k} r_2 \left[\log_e \frac{r_2}{r_1} \right] \qquad (6\text{--}5)$$

where r_2 is the outside radius, r_1 is the inside radius and q/A_s is the heat flux at the outside tube surface.

The temperature gradient shown in Fig. 6–2 is typical of furnace tubes exposed to radiant heat with no ash or slag accumulation on the outside surface. It should be apparent from inspection that the resistance having the dominating influence on the rate of heat transfer is that through the gas film. Furthermore, for all practical purposes the temperature of the receiving surface may be taken as equal to that of the water and steam within the tube. This approximation is closer to fact

---

[10] This section has been adapted from a portion of Chapter 25 of the First Edition of *Combustion Engineering*.

when studying heat transfer in convection zones, such as superheaters, boiler tube banks and economizers. Accumulations of slag or flyash on the outside surface, or scale on the inside, may easily become the controlling resistance to heat transfer if allowed to continue unchecked. The result would be loss in efficiency in all cases, or overheating of the tube metal and subsequent tube failure in the case of scale. In most studies of convection heat transfer in steam generating units, clean heating surfaces inside and outside are assumed, and the temperature of water and steam within the tube is used as the receiving temperature.

Effect of Fluid Flow

How the gas flows, whether parallel or transverse to the axis of the tubes, has a profound effect on the rate of heat transfer. The most direct applications of parallel flow are:

1. Gas flowing through tubes of firetube boilers

2. Gas flowing through tubes of tubular air heaters

3. Gas flowing outside, but parallel to axis, of tube bundles, such as, superheater, boiler tube banks and air heater tubes

When gas flows through tubes, the flow is parallel to the axis for their entire length. When flowing outside the tubes in tube banks, however, there is cross flow at the entrance to and exit from the bank. Therefore, the parallel flow passes of steam boilers must be figured as a combination of parallel flow convection, cross flow convection, and nonluminous radiation.

Equations for heat transfer with parallel flow contain a factor for inside tube diameter, but the actual tube diameter can be used only when the gas actually

flows through the tubes. For flow outside the tubes, an *equivalent diameter* may be used:

$$d_e = \frac{4A_c}{P} \tag{6-6}$$

where d_e is the equivalent diameter, A_c is the free gas passage area and P is the gas touched perimeter of tubes.

When calculating the heat transfer in a parallel flow pass of a boiler, coefficients for flow parallel to the axis of the tubes should be applied only to those portions where the gas is confined between parallel baffles and forced to travel without much turbulence along the axis of the tubes. For the portions at the ends of such passes, cross flow transfer rates may be used for the effective surface opposite the entrance and exit openings. Proper consideration should be given to the variation of mass velocities in those portions, if any.

When flow is generally parallel to the axis of the tubes, but not confined to the tube bank, baffles may be used to direct the gas into the tube bank. In this case flow will be neither parallel to nor across the tubes, and proper allowance must be made in determining the corresponding heat transfer rate.

There are many direct applications of cross flow in the design and construction of steam generating units, such as flow over boiler banks, superheaters, economizers and tubular air heaters.

In general, the convective heat transfer coefficient with flow across tube banks is considerable higher than with parallel flow. Under some conditions it is twice as much for comparable velocities. The approximate variation is shown in Fig. 6–3. The upper limit represents flow across small diameter tubes, and the lower limit,

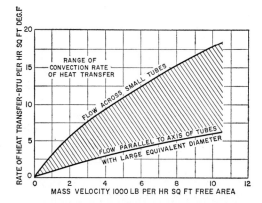

RATE OF HEAT TRANSFER-BTU PER HR SQ FT DEG.F

RANGE OF CONVECTION RATE OF HEAT TRANSFER

FLOW ACROSS SMALL TUBES

FLOW PARALLEL TO AXIS OF TUBES WITH LARGE EQUIVALENT DIAMETER

MASS VELOCITY 1000 LB PER HR SQ FT FREE AREA

Fig. 6–3. Chart showing limits of heat transfer rate between conditions of parallel and cross flow of gas

flow parallel to tubes on relatively wide centers.

Pure cross flow is seldom found in boilers. Rarely is there sufficient space at the ends of baffles to allow the gas to turn outside the tube bank. Turning within the bank means that some of the gas is not flowing at right angles to the tubes. This fact, along with the ever present stratification of gas and ineffective heating surfaces due to structural shapes and requirements, makes a background of practical or actual operating experience most important.

A screen of boiler tubes is usually interposed between the furnace and the superheater so as to reduce slag accumulation in the latter. Owing to the uncertainty of the actual direction and uniformity of gas flow over surface of this type of tube bank, it must be considered as a special case in the calculation of heat transfer, and the empirical approach may be more desirable than the theoretical.

The equation used for the convection heat-transfer coefficient in this case is:

$$h_c = N c_p G^a / D^b \qquad (6\text{–}7)$$

where h_c is pure convection heat transfer

coefficient, gas to metal, in Btu per hr sq ft deg F; N is a constant; c_p is specific heat of gas at constant pressure; G is core mass velocity (1000 lb gas per hr sq ft free area); D is tube diameter, in.; a, b are exponents.

The constant and exponents must be determined experimentally, and will depend on the type of gas flow, tube arrangement, spacing and other factors.

It is difficult to learn from tests on large commercial boilers or other heat recovery equipment the precise effect on heat transfer of variations in velocity, tube diameter, tube spacing, or gas temperature. However, the constant of the laboratory or text book equation must be modified by results obtained through practice.

Effect of Nonluminous Radiation

Carbon dioxide and water vapor are capable of absorbing heat by radiation and of radiating heat to colder surfaces which are encountered in boilers, superheaters and economizers. The amount of this so-called *nonluminous* radiation depends on the following factors: temperature of the gas and the surface, quantity of carbon dioxide and water vapor present, arrangement of the tubes.

In all cases where the flue gas temperature is high and the tube spacing relatively great, the nonluminous radiation will be of considerable magnitude and should be added to the pure convection rate.

In waterwalls or economizer surface the temperature difference between cold fluid and clean heating surface will be very small compared to the temperature difference between the clean surface and the mean gas temperature because the thermal conductance of the water film is high. In an air heater or a superheater, on the other hand, the temperature gradient across the cold film will be higher because the thermal conductance of these films is lower.

In the design and proportioning of waterwall and economizer surface, interest is primarily in the overall thermal conductance or heat transfer rate, and the intermediate rates or temperatures are of secondary concern because the metal temperature will be close to that of the cold fluid. Design of superheaters, furnace waterwalls and air heaters must also take into consideration the metal temperatures. In the case of superheaters, knowledge of metal temperature is necessary for the most economical use of alloy material. The air heater designer, on the other hand, needs to know the temperature of the metal separating the two fluids in order to combat condensation of moisture and acid vapors, or to minimize the effect by selection of noncorrosive materials.

Effect of Variation in Temperature Difference

The essential difference in the performance of the parts of the steam generating unit results from the variation of temperature difference. In the steam generating section of drum-type, subcritical pressure boilers, the cold temperature will be constant and equal to the temperature of saturated steam. In other parts of the unit, the temperature of both fluids will vary, and the difference which produces the flow of heat will depend on the relative direction of the two fluids passing through or over the heating surface, i.e., whether they flow counter to, parallel to, across one another, or some combination thereof. In the case of parallel or counter flow, the logarithmic mean temperature difference will equal

$$\text{LMTD} = \frac{\text{greatest difference} - \text{least difference}}{\log_e\left(\dfrac{\text{greatest difference}}{\text{least difference}}\right)} \quad (6\text{–}8)$$

or,

$$\text{LMTD} = \frac{\Delta T_1 - \Delta T_2}{\log_e\left(\dfrac{\Delta T_1}{\Delta T_2}\right)} \quad (6\text{–}9)$$

where ΔT_1 and ΔT_2 are given in Fig. 6–4.

Examination of these figures will reveal that the greatest temperature difference will be obtained, and the least heating surface required, for a given heat recovery when the two fluids flow counter to each other. Furthermore, with parallel flow, the highest temperature of the heated fluid can only approach but not equal the lowest temperature of the heating fluid.

Economizers and air heaters are almost always designed for counter flow, because of the low temperature differences involved and the desire for high efficiencies. Superheaters, on the other hand, are frequently designed for a combination of parallel and counter flow, with gas flow along the tubes. This may prove economical from a construction viewpoint when large temperature differences exist. When steam temperatures of 900 F or higher are desired, however, counter flow is usually desirable.

Application of Heat Transfer Rates to Boiler Calculations

Heat transfer takes place at constant temperature on the steam side of the tubes, because in the drum type recirculation boiler the feedwater is fed to the steam drums and allowed to reach saturation temperature before entering the boiler tubes.

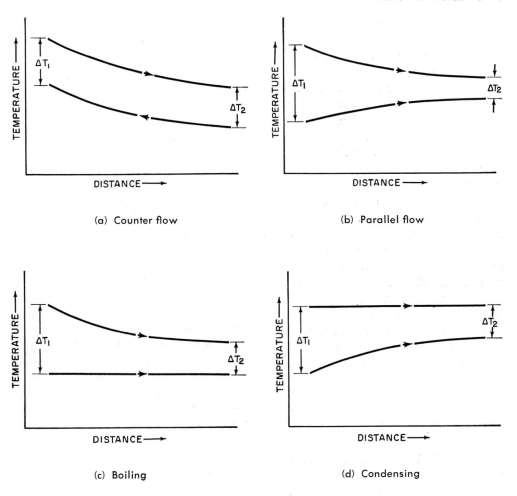

Fig. 6–4.   Fluid temperatures in heat exchangers

It is apparent from Fig. 6–5 that the gas cannot be cooled to the steam temperature, T_s, unless the gas is kept in contact with an infinite amount of surface for an infinite length of time. The amount of heat that a given surface will absorb is proportional to the temperature difference and the heat transfer rate. This follows merely from the definition. Therefore:

$$\frac{q}{A_s} = (U)\,(\text{LMTD}) \qquad (6\text{–}10)$$

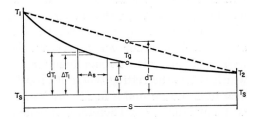

Fig. 6–5.   Temperature gradients between inlet and outlet of the convection section of a boiler

where U is the overall rate, fluid to fluid, in Btu per hr sq ft deg F, and LMTD is the logarithmic mean temperature difference, fluid to fluid, in deg F.

The logarithmic mean temperature difference must be used in the above equation, because the reduction in temperature between T_1 and T_2 is not directly proportional to the amount of surface passed over. However, when a small portion of surface, such as A_s in Fig. 6–5 is considered, there will be no appreciable error in using the arithmetic mean, T_m, instead of the logarithmic mean, LMTD.

For a closed system in which the weight of gas entering the boiler is equal to the weight leaving, and one in which there are no heat losses from the setting, the quantity of heat absorbed by the boiler surface will equal the heat given up by the gas, or in equation form:

$$q = (W)(c_p)(T_1 - T_2) \qquad (6\text{--}11)$$

where W is the weight flow rate, $C_p =$ specific heat at constant pressure, and $(T_1 - T_2)$ is the gas temperature drop, deg F.

Examination of this equation will show that care must be used in collecting test data on commercial apparatus if these data are to be used for heat transfer rate determinations. For example, every boiler setting has air inflation, so that the gas weight is greater at the boiler outlet, where it is generally measured, than at the inlet. The difference represents the weight of cold air at room temperature which enters the setting where it absorbs heat from the gas and is finally discharged at temperature T_2. Therefore, if calculated results on commercial equipment are to be compared with accurate laboratory data, corrections for infiltration and

heat losses from the setting should be made.

When heat transfer in commercial apparatus is calculated from changes in fluid temperature determined by test measurements on similar apparatus, several additional errors may be introduced. In taking the temperature readings, the gas stream is large, and simultaneous readings at many points are necessary. If there is stratification or nonuniform flow, the arithmetic average of these readings may introduce an error which may be much larger than any error in the temperature readings themselves. An incorrect specific heat value will introduce another error which can be eliminated in the research laboratory by supplying the heat in some way which can be measured with a high degree of accuracy.

In order to convert the heat quantity to the rate per square foot or, vice versa, to calculate the quantity from the rate per square foot, the effective heating surface must be known. Surface which is covered with deposits or by baffles, or which is out of the path of the gas stream, is not as effective as clean gas swept heating surface. Therefore, if heat transfer rates are to be used which were determined from tests on clean, uniformly gas swept surface, and applied to commercial apparatus which will not duplicate these conditions either the installed heating surface or the transfer rate per square foot must be adjusted to allow for deposits and surface which may be ineffective due to baffle or tube arrangement.

The formula for the calculation of gas temperatures leaving a boiler or section thereof is obtained by equating the right hand side of Eqs. 6–10 and 6–11 and then substituting for LMTD from Eq. 6–9. Then, simplifying and transposing, the following may be written:

$$(T_2 - T_s) = (T_1 - T_s)/e^{-\left(\frac{UA_s}{Wc_p}\right)} \qquad (6\text{--}12)$$

From the above discussion, it can be understood that care and judgment must be exercised in determining the correct values of U, A_s, W and c_p for substitution in this equation.

The Boiler Furnace—An Analytical Approach[11]

The boiler furnace is a primary member of a major heat transfer device, but *heat transfer is only one of the functions it performs*. It is also the most common industrial form of a *chemical reactor* and, moreover, has a major part in the *disposal of the refuse* produced by the combustion of fuels. Analysis of the operations of the boiler furnace is complicated and made more difficult because of this multiplicity of functions.

This section examines the availability of methods and information which will permit detailed analytical prediction of the performance of a given boiler furnace. It is not concerned with the empirical relationships but with the anticipated future realization of a rigorous and rational design approach.

Heat transfer might be considered, in one sense, the "payoff" operation of a boiler furnace. In reality, however, it occupies a middle position in the overall scheme of furnace performance: (1) heat released in the furnace by the combustion process, (2) transfer of the heat input to the working fluid and (3) removal of combustion products from the furnace.

The boiler furnace performs as a chemical reactor in providing for controlled and complete combustion. In a sense, the furnace is the limiting factor in combustion, for if the reaction is not completed there it is most unlikely that it will be finished elsewhere.

A large fraction of the heat released in the furnace is transmitted directly to the water or steam contained within the metallic tubing that forms its geometrical arrangement and boundaries. More is involved than radiant heat transmission, for the products of combustion and incombustible residue must be cooled to the point that the latter can be collected or removed, either as solid particles or as a stream of molten slag.

As indicated earlier the heat exchange process in the boiler furnace is very complex. All three modes of heat transfer are involved; *radiation* plays a dominant part in the overall transfer and *conduction*, an important role in the processes of heating and ignition of the incoming fuel. Finally, *convection* occurs in both its forced and natural convection phases. It is a major factor in providing a source of ignition energy and contributes significantly to the overall heat transfer process.

Boiler Furnace Processes

Before proceeding to a detailed consideration of each of these heat transfer mechanisms, it is desirable to outline briefly

[11] Contributed by the late Martin Mayers. This section represents the personal views of one who for some years was engaged in basic research in solid fuel technology and subsequently served as chief mechanical engineer for consulting engineering firms engaged in the design of large central stations. It is written at an advanced level in the hope of showing that the field of heat transfer in boiler furnaces offers many challenges of high intellectual worth.

the processes which occur in the boiler furnace and to mention its parts. The furnace is considered to comprise the chamber or cavity into which fuel and air are injected and in which the process of release of the chemical energy of the fuel occurs. It is bounded by impermeable walls except for the burners or stoker through which the fuel and air are injected and the furnace outlet through which the more or less completely burned out gases pass to the convection passes of the rest of the steam generator. The walls of the furnace may be of refractory, wholly or in part, in which case they approximate an adiabatic boundry. More commonly, however, especially in large boilers, the furnace walls consist of boiler tubes, containing steam or water or both under boiler pressure. Such a wall is said to be "cold" by comparison with the hot gases within the furnace. Cold walls are the principal recipients of the heat transferred by radiation and convection in the furnace.

Fuel and air enter the furnace, either together as in the stream of primary air and fuel in the pulverized coal furnace, or through intersecting channels or streams, as in stokers or certain types of burners. The entering fuel is subjected to rapid heating by processes (which will form the subject of further consideration) until its temperature rises to the point where the rate of combustion becomes rapid enough to sustain itself and further increase the temperature, at which time the temperature dependence of the reactions becomes relatively unimportant. From this point on, combustion proceeds rapidly either within the fuel bed, if one exists, or in the free flame. The instantaneous rate of combustion at any point depends on the concentration of fuel and oxygen in the air or furnace gas at that point; in a fuel

bed the concentration decreases from the point of entrance to the top of the bed. In the pulverized coal flame, in which fuel and air flow concurrently, both fuel surface and oxygen concentration decrease with their progress through the furnace, so that the combustion rate may drop below that required to maintain a temperature-independent reaction and ultimately may be practically quenched, resulting in the discharge of unburned fuel through the furnace outlet.

When, as indicated above, the combustion reactions become self-sustaining, heat is released extremely rapidly as a result of their strongly exothermic nature. When this occurs in an open flame as in gas, oil or pulverized fuel fired furnaces, the regions in which the rapid heat release occurs can be "seen" by the cold boundary surfaces. Accordingly, the heat, while appearing initially in temperature rise of the fuel and gases of combustion, is transmitted extremely rapidly to the cold surfaces by a series of radiation processes which thus limit the maximum temperature attained in the furnace. In fuel beds, on the other hand, the maximum heat release rates usually occur in regions shielded by other parts of the bed, itself, and the theoretical combustion temperatures may be more nearly attained. These extremely high temperatures are the primary cause of the fusion of the ash that occurs in fuel beds and which makes them so liable to clinker trouble.

Heat continues to be transmitted from the flame throughout the combustion process and from the remaining flue gases even afterward, during their flow through the furnace. The principal process continues to be radiation, although a significant fraction of convective heat transfer occurs where the furnace gases flow over cold surface in their path toward the furnace outlet. Cooling of the gases is accompanied by cooling of particles of fuel or of incombustible residue suspended in them. It is a major object of furnace design to ensure that these particles are cooled to a point below which they will not adhere to solid surfaces with which they come in contact in their flow through convection passes. This is the primary function of the furnace as a refuse disposal unit, since only by such treatment of the refuse can it be kept from fouling, and ultimately, blocking the furnace outlet and possibly also such heat transfer components as superheaters, reheaters, economizers and air heaters.

Modes of Heat Transfer in the Furnace Cavity

It is of interest to note in which of these processes the different modes of heat transfer make their contributions.

Conduction

Conduction is most significant, from the present point of view, in its contribution to the heating of incoming fuel particles toward their ignition. It continues to be effective, however, throughout the time that particles of fuel or of residue remain in contact with the gas stream, in keeping the temperature throughout the particle close to that of its surface. Generally, the dimensions of suspended particles are so small that the temperatures of their interiors can lag those of their surfaces by only small amounts, while the very small scale convection process between the particles and the suspending gas keeps the particle surface temperature close to that of the gas. In this way conduction helps to assure that the heat capacity of the suspended particles is additive to that of the gas stream in which they are suspended, so that the entire suspension may be considered from a thermal point of view to have an average specific heat.

Conduction also is responsible for cooling ash that may be deposited on the cold walls bounding the furnace cavity. Such deposits receive heat on their surfaces exposed to the furnace, and conduct it to the cold surfaces to which they adhere. They approximate the behavior of insulation applied to the cold walls, reducing the flow of heat into them. The thicker the layer of deposit, the more closely the hot surface temperature approaches that of the furnace and the less the heat flow to the covered portion of the cold wall.

Convection

As mentioned above, forced convection heat transfer plays a part in the overall heat transfer from the furnace gases to cold surface, although it is secondary in importance to radiation in the furnace. This action of the convection mode is also of secondary significance when compared to the importance of this mode of heat transfer in maintaining continuous ignition of a free flame. Convection processes act at two very different levels of turbulence in carrying out this function.

In a free flame issuing from burners of the size used in industrial furnaces, the flow is highly turbulent, as distinguished from the laminar flow that occurs, for instance, in the jet from a Bunsen burner. Even in such a stream, heat transport across a surface parallel to stream lines may be expressed by a change in the conduction equation in which gaseous thermal conductivity K must be replaced by an eddy thermal conductivity κ, which is very much greater than the molecular thermal conductivity. The eddy conductivity is due to the mixing of portions of gases of different temperatures by the small scale eddies produced by the random velocity perturbations which occur in turbulent flow. This kind of convection heat transfer through the body of the entering jet is of great importance in igniting the entering stream and in maintaining a degree of uniformity of temperature within the body of the flame throughout its passage through the furnace, as are here considered. This is a gross recirculation of a portion of the gases of the partly or completely burned out flame back to the entering jet. This recirculation brings a source of heat at a high temperature to assure rapid heating of at least a portion of the entering jet, and may also introduce active centers of combustion, in the case of a coal or oil flame, or active species for chain reaction initiation into the outer boundary layers of the jet issuing from the burner.

Radiation

Finally, radiation plays an important role in the heat transfer process in a furnace. It enters into several of the constituent processes that occur in the furnace; furthermore, it manifests itself in several different forms including that arising from solid surfaces having black or gray characteristics and that arising from bodies of high temperature gas. The most important areas in which radiation is significant are those between the gas mass and the boundary wall and between the suspended particles in the gas and the boundary. As indicated earlier in this section, this is the pay-off operation, considering the furnace as a heat exchanger; it is the effectiveness of these processes that justifies the large size of water walls in modern furnace structures. It must be noted, however, that there is an appreciable interchange of radiant heat between the suspended particles and the gas mass itself; this is usually accounted for in terms of absorption coefficients of the gas for radiation originating at particle surfaces.

Radiant heat transfer, moreover, assists the process of ignition by transferring heat back from the active flame to the incoming fuel-air mixture. This was formerly thought to be the dominant process in the heating and ignition of the incoming fuel in free flames. Experimental work on flames in the last decade or two has shown that the recirculation phenomenon, mentioned in the discussion of convection above, is of major importance in most flames, but it is likely that a portion, at least, of the load is carried by back radiation.

The variety of the processes occurring within the furnace and the relatively independent behavior of the elements entering these processes make it difficult to define any single furnace temperature. While such "radiant mean" temperatures have been used in the past in analysis of heat transfer by radiation, in the light of present knowledge they may be more of an obstacle than a help to an understanding of significant details of the heat transfer process. Knowledge of the constituent processes has progressed to the point where the spatial and temporal variations of the temperatures of fuel and refuse particles and of incoming air and gases may be taken into account, both in relation to their traverse through the furnace and in respect to radial distances outward from the suspended particles.

The importance of radiation processes as well as the simultaneous occurrence of heat release and heat transfer make it difficult to calculate heat transfer by the use of such shortcuts as "mean temperature difference" which are applicable to simpler types of heat exchangers. In the present state of knowledge, there appears to be no way to avoid the separate calculation of heat transmitted by the separate analysis of each of the constituent processes; as noted above, an improvement will result from taking account of the local values of the variables which affect each of these processes.

Considerations for Radiant Heat Transfer. Heat transfer in a boiler furnace is predominantly by radiation supplemented by conduction and convection. The radiant heat absorption in watercooled furnaces may be approximately calculated in accordance with the following adaptation of the Stefan-Boltzmann law shown earlier in Eq. 6–3.

$$q = 0.173 A_s \mathrm{E} \left(\left[\frac{T_g}{100} \right]^4 - \left[\frac{T_w}{100} \right]^4 \right) \quad (6\text{–}13)$$

where E is the combined emissivity of cold surface and flame, T_g is the absolute flame temperature and T_w is the absolute cold surface temperature.

The area of the flame will vary substantially, depending on the furnace design and fuel fired. The type of firing employed affects the rate at which gas sweeps over heating surface, and the area of the flame varies with the rate of firing, other things being constant. Flame emissivity depends on many factors, such as flame luminosity due to burning particles, the concentration of water vapor and carbon dioxide in the flame, the volume of flame and its temperature. The temperature of the flame envelope will not be constant or uniform in a watercooled furnace of a steam generating unit. Combustion characteristics of the different types of firing equipment vary widely. Some produce a short, intense and highly turbulent flame, while combustion with others is relatively slow, thereby producing a comparatively long, lazy flame of greater volume.

For any one furnace, the area of cold surface is fixed, but its effectiveness may be affected by slag accumulation. The effective portion will depend on the nature and amount of watercooling surface installed. The emissivity of the cold surface depends on the material used, and its condition. For an oxidized steel furnace, however, the emissivity will approach unity at high temperatures, and may be assumed to be 0.95 for a boiler surface. Examination of the temperature gradient discussed above and shown earlier in Fig. 6–2 will make clear that generally the temperature of the cold surface may be taken as that of the water and steam inside the tube, without introducing an appreciable error. Slag accumulation, however, depending on its area, thickness and density, will not only affect the area but the temperature of the cold or receiving surface.

Basis for an Analytical Description

Even a brief review of the literature on the boiler furnace is sufficient to show that there does not now exist a complete analysis of this complex system involving large mechanical components and the interaction of thermodynamic, fluid flow and heat transfer considerations. Many individuals have examined one aspect of it or another, but, until the present time, there has not been available sufficiently advanced treatment of even the most important component processes to permit a treatment of the entire system. There have been sufficient advances, however, to allow us to outline the nature of this broad picture; it is now possible to state the nature of certain portions of the general solution we seek.

Free Flames

Consider, first, a furnace in which a free flame exists. In effect, this embraces substantially all furnaces whether fired by fuel in suspension in the air, as oil or pulverized fuel; by fuel in solution in the air, as in gas or vaporized oil firing; or by solid fuel in a fixed fuel bed, since some mixture of combustible components with fresh or partially consumed air always rises from such a bed and is burned out in the furnace space above it.

The combustion process is initiated by means which can be described qualitatively even though they have not been reduced to analytical form for such turbulent flames as are here considered. The nature of the qualitative description is suggested by the relatively successful work in describing gaseous flames in laminar viscous flow systems.[12] In a one dimensional system in which the rate of the reaction is explicitly dependent on the temperature of the gaseous mixture, the flow is laminar, and there is no loss of heat, the energy equation may be stated as

$$\frac{d}{dx}\left[k\frac{dT}{dx}\right] + Q\frac{d}{dx}\left[D_A\rho\frac{dm_A}{dx}\right]$$

$$+ \frac{d}{dx}\left[T\sum_j C_{\rho j}D_{j\rho}\frac{dm_j}{dx}\right]$$

$$- G\frac{d}{dx}\left[T\sum_j C_{\rho j}m_j + m_A Q\right] = 0$$

$$(6\text{--}14)$$

and the concentrations of the gaseous components A and B are given by

$$\frac{d}{dx}\left(D_A\rho\frac{dm_A}{dx}\right) - G\frac{dm_A}{dx} = \dot{m}_A''' \tag{6--15}$$

$$\frac{d}{dx}\left(D_B\rho\frac{dm_B}{dx}\right) - G\frac{dm_B}{dx} = r\dot{m}_A''' \tag{6--16}$$

with boundary conditions

$$\left.\begin{aligned} x &= -\infty\,; \\ &\quad T = T_u,\ m_A = m_{A_u},\ m_B = m_{B_u} \\ x &= +\infty\,; \\ &\quad T = T_b,\ m_A = m_{A_b},\ m_B = m_{B_b} \end{aligned}\right\} (6\text{--}17)$$

where D is the diffusion coefficient; G is mass flow rate per unit area; m is mass of component j per unit mass of mixture; $\dot{m}_A'''$ is mass of A consumed by chemical reaction per unit volume per unit time; Q is standard heat of reaction of main reactant A; r is mass of B reacting with unit mass of A; subscripts u and b refer to the unburned and burned states.

By assuming the Lewis number to be unity, i.e.,

$$\frac{D\rho C_p}{k} = 1$$

and making suitable transformations of the variables, these equations can be reduced to forms equivalent to

$$\frac{d^2\tau}{dy^2} - \frac{d\tau}{dy} = -\lambda\Phi(\tau) \tag{6--18}$$

with the boundary conditions

$$\left.\begin{aligned} \tau &= 0; & \frac{d\tau}{dy} &= 0 \\ \tau &= 1; & \frac{d\tau}{dy} &= 0 \end{aligned}\right\} (6\text{--}19)$$

---

[12] "Predicting the Laminar Flame Speed in Gases with Temperature Explicit Reaction Rates" and "One Dimensional Laminar Flame Theory for Temperature Explicit Reaction Rates," by D. B. Spalding, *Combustion and Flame*, Vol. 1, 1957, pp. 287–295 and 296–307.

where

$$\tau = \left(\frac{T - T_u}{T_b - T_u}\right)$$

and

$$dy = \frac{C_p G}{k}\, dx$$

and in which λ contains a kind of mean reaction rate for complete combustion and becomes an eigen or characteristic value which permits a solution of Eq. 6–18 meeting the boundary conditions of Eq. 6–19.

There is no point to reviewing the nature of the solutions that are obtained for this case, since it is not of immediate interest for the conditions of concern. It is, however, instructive to examine the basic differential equations for the information they may provide on the probable nature of the solutions that will, some day, be obtained for the case of the turbulent flame. The first term in Eq. 6–14 represents the conduction of heat, the second that of heat of combustion, and the third that of sensible heat along the direction of flow, while the last term represents the convection of heat of combustion and sensible heat through transport of the flue gas by the fluid flow itself.

For turbulent flow, it is probable that at least two dimensions will have to be considered, taking account of eddy diffusion, rather than the molecular type, at right angles to the flow. This effect will probably override diffusion terms parallel to the flow direction, so that they may no longer have to be considered. In addition, a model of the gross recirculation that is known to be responsible for ignition in turbulent flames will have to be established and represented analytically, perhaps as a boundary condition in the direction at right angles to the flow direction. Presumably, the reaction rate will then appear in the direction normal to the flow and may be expected to be dependent on the eddy diffusivity, fluctuations in the concentrations of the combustible components and similar quantities, as well as the local temperature. This description of the ignition process in turbulent flames is yet to be accomplished but it is essential to a complete description of the furnace process.[13]

Once combustion has been initiated and the temperature of the fuel-air mixture has risen to the point where the reaction rates are only slightly affected by temperature, the combustion process is again susceptible to fairly exact description at least for flames of particulate fuel suspensions, such as oil and pulverized coal. Perhaps the most general of these descriptions is that of Spalding[14] which assumes only that the particles have a property ζ which contact with the fluid causes to vary, and that the variation of ζ is controlled by an expression such as

$$\frac{D\zeta}{Dt} = -FZ \qquad (6\text{–}20)$$

in which F is a function only of the local fluid properties, such as temperature, viscosity, diffusivity, and concentrations of gas components while Z is a function only of ζ. In the case of pulverized coal or oil

---

[13] For a discussion by Walter Olson, see the *Sixth Symposium (International) on Combustion*, Reinhold, New York, 1957, p. 936. See also *Thermal Regimes of Combustion* by Lev Ambramovich Vulis, McGraw-Hill, New York, 1961, particularly Section 7–2, Turbulent Motion and Gas Combustion, and Section 3–2, Thermal Region of Coal Combustion.
[14] "Transport Processes between Fluids and Clouds of Suspended Particles: Some Exact Solutions" by D. B. Spalding, *Proceedings* of the Royal Society of London, Vol. A242, 1957, pp. 430–443.

flames, the property ζ might be the radius of the particle. When, as in the usual case, the initial size of the fuel particles is not uniform, solutions for the different size consists may be superimposed for the final solution.

Spalding points out that since differences in velocity and composition are present in practical cases "a description in Lagrangian terms . . . leads into probability theory. The present paper avoids this difficulty by a discussion in Eulerian terms," which implies that the total derivative of a property at point x, y, z is given by

$$\frac{D}{Dt} = u\frac{\partial}{\partial x} + v\frac{\partial}{\partial y} + w\frac{\partial}{\partial z} + \frac{\partial}{\partial t}$$

where u, v, w, are the local velocity components parallel to the x, y, and z axes respectively, at the point and time, t. Then, for an element of furnace volume, δV, which is small enough for the statistical properties of fluid to be uniform, but large enough for them to be invariant with time in a steadily operating furnace, the number of particles, n, having ζ values within the range of ζ to $\zeta + \delta\zeta$ (of those starting with a particular initial value ζ_0, 0), will be given by

$$F\rho\,\frac{\partial nZ}{\partial \zeta} = \nabla \cdot (\epsilon\rho\nabla n) - \nabla \cdot (n\mathbf{G}) \qquad (6\text{--}21)$$

By substituting $nZ = \phi$; $\dfrac{d\zeta}{z} = -d\theta$, this becomes

$$F\rho\,\frac{\partial \phi}{\partial \theta} = \nabla \cdot (\epsilon\rho\nabla\phi) - \nabla \cdot (\phi\mathbf{G}) \qquad (6\text{--}22)$$

which is the form of the transient state heat conduction equation, for which many solutions are known.

In principle, this equation is general enough so that it may also represent the ignition process, provided that F can be made to represent the strong dependence on temperature characteristic of that regime, that a suitable expression for the temperature in terms of the same coordinates can be obtained, and that $\mathbf{G}$ can be appropriately expressed in terms of the same coordinates. It is an important characteristic of this expression for the combustion process that it does not demand that the process be adiabatic, and explicit solutions for the temperature throughout the process are required only to the extent necessary to permit correct characterization of F and $\mathbf{G}$. It might be possible to obtain a solution for Eq. 6–22 by numerical methods, although the likelihood of analytical solutions becomes very small. In practice, however, this would present almost insurmountable difficulties, and solutions can probably be obtained practically only when F, or some combination of that function with other quantities, remains constant, or varies only slightly with temperature, as is the case for extremely rapid combustion.

Along this line, a one dimensional solution has been obtained by Spalding for a simplified representation of combustion in turbulent flow in a long pipe for a fuel consisting of a single class of particles. This might represent, for instance, the combustion of a closely sized pulverized fuel fraction in such an experimental furnace as that used by Sherman at Battelle Memorial Institute, at least for the region beyond the expanding flow from the burner proper.[15] For this case, Eq. 6–22

[15] "Burning Characteristics of Pulverized Coals and Radiation from their Flames" by R. A. Sherman, *Trans.* ASME, Vol. 56, 1934, pp. 401–409.

becomes

$$F\rho \frac{\partial \phi}{\partial \theta} = \frac{\partial}{\partial x}\left(\epsilon\rho \frac{\partial \phi}{\partial x}\right) - G\frac{\partial \phi}{\partial x}$$

Taking $F\epsilon\rho^2 = \dfrac{1}{\alpha}$ to be constant, and

substituting

$$\epsilon\rho\, dy = dx, \quad \phi = \omega \exp\left(\tfrac{1}{2}Gy\right)\exp\left(-\tfrac{1}{4}\alpha\theta G^2\right)$$

this becomes

$$\frac{\partial \omega}{\partial \theta} = \alpha \frac{\partial^2 \omega}{\partial y^2} \qquad (6\text{-}23)$$

with the boundary conditions

$$\left.\begin{array}{l} \theta = 0,\ y > 0;\ \omega = 0 \\[2ex] \theta = 0;\ \displaystyle\int_0^y \omega\, dy = \alpha\dot{N}'' \\[2ex] \theta > 0,\ y = 0;\ \dfrac{\partial \omega}{\partial y} - \tfrac{1}{2}G\omega = 0 \end{array}\right\} \qquad (6\text{-}24)$$

The solution for Eq. 6–23 and the boundary conditions of Eq. 6–24, shown in Fig. 6–6, represents the variation of the characteristic ϕ, with y, which is related to distance along the path of the flame, for different values of the state of the particle represented by θ. The interpretation is that ϕ is to be considered a transform of the concentration of particles of a particular state defined by the value of its transform θ. The larger the value of θ, the further the reaction involving the particles has gone toward its completion. Thus the representation in terms of ϕ and θ is equivalent to and can be represented in terms of the concentration n of Eq. 6–21 and the particle property ζ of the

same equation. Hence, to the extent that the assumptions made in the definition of α and the constancy of the fluid properties are legitimate, this result represents the course of combustion of a cloud of pulverized fuel particles of a specific size.

As there are not now data which meet these very stringent conditions, no detailed check of this result with observations can be made. Either a more extended solution, for a fuel covering a range of particle sizes equivalent to those for which observations have been made, will have to be worked out, or experimental data must be secured on essentially a single fuel particle size, before such a comparison can be made. If this were done, it would become possible to note whether the solution were qualitatively correct; and, if it were, to establish experimental values of the function F. This would represent a beginning, at least, of a rational understanding of the process in a flame of suspended particles. It can hardly be doubted that such a beginning would lead to more critical experimental work which, in turn, would further stimulate analytical attack.

The considerations of the last few paragraphs have applied to flames containing fuels in suspension. Flames of gaseous or vapor fuels in high rate combustors such as those of aircraft gas turbines or ramjets can be represented by the behavior of one or a combination of more than one "well-stirred reactor". This term arose from an attempt[16] to develop a device that would measure the minimum reaction time, characteristic of a particular fuel, by eliminating the lags due to transport processes. The analysis of the performance

[16] J. P. Longwell and M. A. Weiss, *Industrial and Engineering Chemistry*, Vol. 27, 1955, pp. 1634–43.

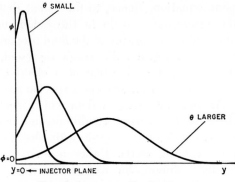

Fig. 6–6. $\phi - y$ distribution at successive θ values

of this reactor was broadened[17] to permit the estimation of the behavior of real devices by the assumption of their being composed of more than one such device differing in characteristics. On the other hand, it was suggested that low rate combustion chambers, such as those of industrial furnaces, in which transport lags were certainly significant, might be represented by a combination of the well-stirred reactor with a chamber typified by plug flow. That this concept might serve for estimates of radiation heat transfer has been established as at least a fair approximation.[18]

Heat Transfer From Free Flames

In order to examine the heat transfer characteristics of a flame described as above, it is necessary to apply the energy equation to the element of volume, δV, within which heat is being released at a rate $F\rho\eta ZH = F\rho\phi H$, where FZ is defined by Eq. 6–20. Heat also enters the element of volume by conduction and convection, introducing terms similar to those of Eq. 6–14, except that the relevant conductivities and diffusivities are the eddy induced terms of turbulent flow. In addition there will be a set of radiation terms whose effects will greatly outweigh those just mentioned except in the immediate vicinity of the furnace boundaries.

The result of this treatment will be a solution for the temperatures of the gas and of fuel and refuse particles or of some transform of those temperatures as a function of the coordinates of the particle state, ζ or θ. If it is possible to perform the inverse transformation back to furnace coordinates, this result may be the equivalent of a field of radiation intensity, the evaluation of whose boundary transmissions will give a detailed picture of the variation of radiant heat transfer with position in the furnace walls.

Whether or not this inverse transformation is possible, the solution for temperature (or its transform) will permit a better evaluation of the coefficients of Eq. 6–21 and Eq. 6–22 so that a better approximation to their complete solution may be obtained. Since these coefficients will now be functions of the coordinates it is likely that numerical, perhaps machine, methods of solution will be required.

A method of treating radiation heat exchange for such elementary volumes has not yet been developed, but there are ample formulations of the effect of the agents responsible for individual components of the radiant transmission on which to draw. These include the data on gas radiation and absorption coefficients as well as the essentially black radiation of fuel and refuse particles and of furnace

[17] "Application of Well-Stirred Reactor Theory to the Prediction of Combustor Performance" by H. C. Hottell, G. C. Williams and A. H. Bonnell, *Combustion and Flame*, Vol. 2, 1958, pp. 13–34.
[18] "Radiative Transfer in Combustion Chambers" by H. C. Hottell, *Journal* of the Institute of Fuel, Vol. 34, 1961, pp. 220–234.

walls. This will be discussed in a subsequent section.

Fuel Beds

The relatively slight importance of stoker or grate firing in large modern boilers makes it unnecessary to dwell on this topic except for completeness. It may be noted, however, that an analytical description of the variation of both gas components and of temperature through a fuel bed has already been given.[19] A solution for a simple special case was obtained and qualitative agreement with experimental determinations for that case was demonstrated. With the facilities available at the time only a one-dimensional case could be solved; with current computer facilities and methods it might be possible to solve the differential equations for multi-dimensional coordinate systems that might approach the behavior of real fuel beds.

Flow Description and Refuse Disposal

It has been implicit in all the discussions of this section so far that a suitable description of the flow through the furnace is available. This description is embodied in the statement of the vector **G** which enters the equations of this section as well as certain of the boundary conditions. While it is improbable that a detailed correspondence with the complex flows of practical furnaces can ever be managed analytically, it is essential for any successful treatment of turbulent flames that a model having certain of the features of real flows be explicitly set forth.

The study of the pattern of gas flow in furnaces, moreover, has additional objectives. This pattern influences strongly the effectiveness and stability of the recirculation flow which is responsible for ignition of the incoming fuel-air mixture; it may also be responsible for the deposit of refuse on heating surfaces or its failure to be deposited or to remain in ashpits or other spaces designed to receive it.

Accordingly, there are several different, but related, objectives for the study of furnace gas flow, only some of which are required for the analytical expression of combustion and heat transfer processes. Correspondingly, a number of different methods for their study must be followed. Among these are the visualization of the flows in real furnaces, perhaps by motion picture studies of injected inert particles or of fuel particle traces themselves; model studies, both isothermal and non-isothermal, to permit the study of the factors that control flow patterns in detail;[20] and the establishment of the minimum of characteristics required analytically to describe the essential flow properties of a turbulent flame.

With respect to the last topic, a start has been made in other fields of combustion research. A considerable amount of experimental work has been done on the stabilization of flames in simplified systems simulating ramjet and gas turbine combustors. It seems likely that these data may be reduced to some sort of quasi-analytic statement.

To represent boiler furnace conditions, the following characteristics will probably have to be taken into account: divergent

---

[19] See Chapter 18, section on Stokers and the Combustion Process, for a discussion of and excerpts from "Temperature and Combustion Rates in Fuel Beds" by Martin A. Mayers, *Trans.* ASME, Vol. 59, 1937, pp. 279–288.
[20] See Chapter 7, Fluid Flow, section on Flow Modeling of Furnaces and Ducts.

flow in the jet issuing from the burner; variability, perhaps to be represented as a statistical distribution, in the concentration of fuel in that stream; the presence of a parallel or opposing stream along a boundary of the jet in which combustion is well advanced or complete to serve as a source of ignition energy; and the presence of other sources and sinks of energy.

More generally, the flow model should be capable of representing various levels of small scale turbulence and should incorporate the gravitational field since natural convection effects may be of considerable importance at the low average velocities that normally prevail in such enclosures. The resulting differences in stream tube pattern will be great enough so that separate solutions for the combustion equations may have to be sought for each, with the overall furnace characteristic developing from their superposition.

Furnace Heat Transfer— An Earlier Approach

The foregoing sections have shown the interdependence of the flow pattern, the combustion reactions and heat transfer. They have also indicated the present understanding of the combustion reactions, with some references to current literature in this field. The subject of furnace heat transfer, however, was extensively treated some years ago on a different basis than has been here proposed, and it yielded overall average results that were sufficient to facilitate design at that time. As a matter of fact, the treatment of radiation heat transfer from the point of view of the boiler furnace reached a peak during the 1920's and 1930's as a result of the great change in boiler design that accompanied the introduction and great success of pul-

verized coal firing. By showing the effectiveness of radiation as a heat transfer mechanism these studies helped to guide the development toward the use of large amounts of cold surface in furnace walls. Finally they contributed to the development of high temperature superheated steam by providing a basic understanding of the conditions that controlled the temperature of flue gas leaving the furnace, even though the detailed methods of computation that were developed were not and are not now commonly used in design.

From the early 1940's until quite recently there has been comparatively little work reported in the American engineering literature on the treatment of furnace radiation from an analytical or computational point of view. There has, however, been a significant amount of experimental work abroad, notably in the program at Ijmuiden, whose progress is reported from time to time by the Joint Committee of the International Flame Research Foundation. In addition research and analysis of thermal radiation have recently been spurred by the current emphasis on space flight and the necessity of controlling the environment to which space travellers are exposed. While this work does not bear directly on furnace problems, it is likely that it may produce methods which are applicable to the kind of analysis outlined in the preceding sections.

Early in 1940, a series of lectures was delivered by Prof. W. J. Wohlenberg at Purdue University which serves to some extent as a resume of the work of the preceding decades.[21] While it is based primarily on his own papers, starting with Wohlenberg and Morrow in 1925, and

[21] "Heat Transfer by Radiation" published by the Purdue University Engineering Experiment Station as Research Series No. 75, Vol. 24, August 1940, 72 pp.

continuing through the next fifteen years, it also includes the most significant results obtained by other workers in the field, including Hottel, Schmidt, Jakob and Eckert. This bulletin therefore provides a review of the status of knowledge of boiler furnace radiation at that time and is worth restudying in terms of present understanding. Much of the following has been adapted from the Bulletin.

The approach to radiation calculations was through the assumption that the entire furnace could be treated as an entity for practical purposes, having certain "radiant mean" temperatures; that is, temperatures which, if they were uniform throughout the furnace volume, would yield the same flux of radiant energy integrated over the boundaries, as does the actual variable furnace temperature. While the earliest treatments[22] based their calculations on a single such temperature, the Purdue lectures used three, one for burning particles (or flame), another for ash particles, and the third for gaseous products in the furnace.

Radiation flux is calculated separately between each pair of the components to which a radiant mean temperature is assigned. Accordingly, the flux of radiant energy from, say, the burning particles of fuel to cold surface is given by an expression of the form

$$q_{R_{bc}} = \sigma_{bc} \Upsilon_{bc} A'_b \overline{\overline{F}}_{bc} (T_{bc}^4 - T_c^4) \qquad (6\text{-}25)$$

where $q_{R_{bc}}$ represents the net rate of interchange of radiant energy between the components indicated by the subscripts per pound of fuel fired. In Wohlenberg's notation, the subscript b represents the burning fuel component, while the subscript c represents cold surface. In the

same way, subscript r refers to refractory furnace surface, g refers to the radiating gas mass, and a refers to the cloud of burned-out refuse particles.

σ_{bc} is the coefficient of black-body radiation multiplied by the effective combined absorptivity of the surfaces involved. It depends on the nature of the surfaces, their extent and their relative orientation.

Υ_{bc} is the transmissivity of the radiant gas mass to radiation from the burning particles. It is averaged over the zone of interchange, the burning particles being taken at their radiant mean positions. The quantity depends on the gas and particle temperatures, the gas composition, gas mass thickness, and may also depend on the density of the fuel cloud suspension.

A'_b is the extent of fuel surface per pound of fuel fired, averaged over the time of burning.

$\overline{\overline{F}}_{bc}$ is the angle factor over which the radiation extends averaged over the burning time and taken with the particles at their radiant mean position.

There are four such expressions involving the subscript b, representing energy interchange with the cold walls, the refractory, the gas mass and the cloud of burned out particles. In the same way, there are four involving the subscript a and three more defining interchange between refractory and cold surfaces, between gas mass and cold surfaces. In addition, expressions are developed for the conduction heat transfer between burning particles and the gas, $q_{c_{bg}}$ and between the gas and refuse particles $q_{c_{ag}}$.

In solving a problem, the unknowns are initially, the four temperatures T_b, T_a, T_g and T_r, representing the radiant mean temperatures of the burning fuel, the

---

[22] See "Radiation in the Pulverized Fuel Furnace" by W. J. Wohlenberg and D. G. Morrow, *Trans. ASME*, Vol. 47, 1925, pp. 127–176; also "Combustion and Heat Transfer" by R. T. Haslam and H. C. Hottel, Trans. ASME, Vol. 50, 1927–28, FSP-50-3, pp. 9–19.

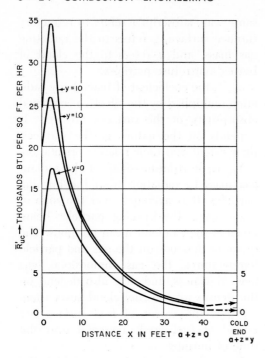

Fig. 6–7. Net radiant energy interchange between burning particles and cold walls ($T_u = 3460mR$, $T_c = 1000$ R)

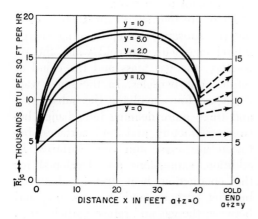

Fig. 6–8. Net radiant energy interchange between ash particles and cold walls ($T_j = 2453$ R, $T_c = 1000$ R)

refuse particles, the gas mass and the refractory surfaces, respectively. The val-

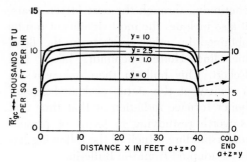

Fig. 6–9. Net radiant energy interchange between gas and cold walls ($T_g = 2465$ R, $T_c = 1000$ R)

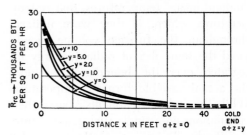

Fig. 6–10. Net radiant energy interchange between refractory wall surface and cold walls ($T_r = 2450$ R, $T_c = 1000$ C)

ues of these quantities which yield the desired solution are those which satisfy a set of four energy equations which represent the mean rate of heat interchange between the contents of the furnace cavity and its walls, and the steady states that exist at the surfaces of the burning particles and the refuse particles and at the refractory walls.[23] The solution was obtained by a method of successive approximations, assuming values of T_b and T_g, and improving the assumptions by going through the balance calculations. At the time, this method of solution was one of the major handicaps to the general use of this analytical procedure since it was tedious and time-consuming. Such repeti-

[23] See Wohlenberg Purdue Lectures, p. 51, Eq. 95.

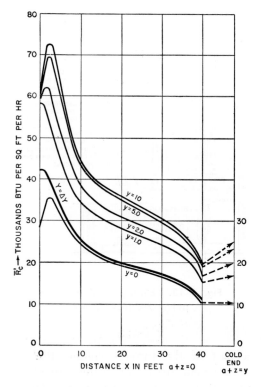

Fig. 6–11.   Overall net radiant energy transfer to cold walls

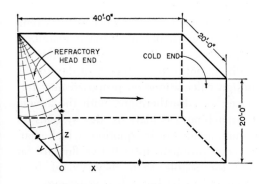

Fig. 6–12.   Model furnace cavity (arrow represents direction of flow of air or gas mass carrying fuel and refuse particles)

tive calculations are, however made to order for modern machine computation; it is possible that an appreciable improvement in furnace radiation calculations could be made by setting up a program for the application of this method to design problems.

The type of results obtained is represented by Figs. 6–7 to 6–11 taken from the Purdue Bulletin. These represent the energy interchanges between the four radiating sources, fuel and refuse particles, gas and refractory; and the cold walls; as well as the sum of these four in Fig. 6–11. In all the figures, the quantity plotted on the ordinate is the heat transmission rate by the mechanism under consideration to one square foot of cold surface in a model furnace cavity represented by Fig. 6–12. This quantity is plotted against distance along the path of travel of the fuel or refuse-air mixture, which for this model is proportional to the residue time within the cavity since the mass velocity is taken to be uniform. The curves are plotted for different values of the parameter, y, which represents the distance along the wall, at right angles to the length of the furnace, away from the corner of the furnace. Thus, even though only single radiant mean temperatures are calculated for each of the radiating components, some account is taken of the variability of heat received at each point of the cold walls because of the varying geometrical relationships arising from the differences in radiant mean position associated with each component and from the variation in point of view of different positions in the wall surface.

The integration of these results over the entire furnace yields the overall energy distribution shown in Fig. 6–13. This figure summarizes a number of important conclusions as follows:

1. A large fraction of the heat released from the fuel, in this case about 50 per cent is transferred to the cold walls primarily by radiation processes within the confines of the furnace itself.

2. A highly significant proportion of this transfer, in this case over ⅓ of the total, is by radiation from the gas mass.

3. Convective processes (or, in Wohlenberg's terminology, thermal conduction) between the fuel and refuse particles, and the gas in which they are suspended, "act as a powerful binding property which holds the energy distribution in the configuration which it assumes". In particular, the figure shows that about 70 per cent of the energy released at the surface of fuel particles is transferred directly to the gas; while the temperature data show that the radiant mean temperature of the refuse particles is substantially the same as that of the gas mass, since T_g minus T_a is only 12 deg F.

A comparatively recent paper by Hottel, however, shows that a fair approximation to furnace performance can be calculated on assumptions that the furnace gas is at a single uniform temperature, that the escaping gas is at a temperature somewhat below this value, and that the walls are at some temperature between that of the cold surface and the temperature that refractory surface would assume.[24] In the same paper, he describes a procedure that would permit taking account of variations in temperature through the furnace but even here he does not propose to take detailed account of the details of the combustion reactions on the ground that the reaction occupies so small

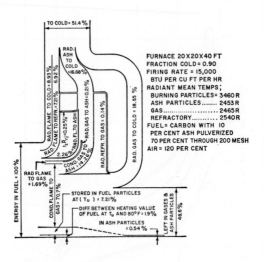

Fig. 6–13. Energy distribution in a pulverized fuel furnace

a part of the furnace volume that an approximate treatment of this part of the phenomenon would be sufficient. Hottel closes his discussion with a statement which may be taken to justify the more extensive analytical treatment proposed above:

"It is clear that allowance for gas temperature gradients in furnace chambers introduces complications which take the problem out of the category of day-to-day design calculations on proposed new furnaces. . . . Furthermore, with the advent of machine calculations the systems of simultaneous linear equations which characterize problems in radiative flux are far less formidable than they would have appeared to be but a few years ago. . . . The development of sound methods of

[24] "Radiative Transfer in Combustion Chambers," *Journal* of The Institute of Fuel, Vol. 34, 1961, pp. 220–234.

simple and quick approximation is dependent on the availability of a rigorous method against which to check the shortcut."

Some indication of the complexity of temperature gradients in a pulverized coal fired furnace is found in the following equation from the Russian literature:[25]

$$\frac{T}{T_0} = \varphi_T \left(\frac{x_{2_0}}{x_{1_0}}, \frac{x_{3_0}}{x_{1_0}}, \frac{\omega_{2_0}}{\omega_{1_0}}, \frac{\omega_{3_0}}{\omega_{1_0}}, Fr_0, Re_0, \right.$$

$$Pr_{g0}, Pr_0, \frac{\sigma_0 T_0^3 x_{1_0}}{C_{v_0}\mu_0}, Bu_0, Ar_0,$$

$$\frac{E_{v0}}{E_{S_0}}, \frac{K_{S_0}}{\omega_{1_0}}, \frac{K_{v_0} dm_0}{K_{S_0}}, \frac{q_{v_0}}{q_{s_0}},$$

$$\frac{q_{S_0}}{c_{v_0}T_0}, A_{cr_0} E_{S_0}, \frac{d_{m_0}}{x_{1_0}}, \frac{\rho_0^{0_2}}{\rho_0^C}, \frac{\rho_0^{0_2}}{\rho_0}$$

$$\left. \frac{\rho_0^r}{\rho_0}, \frac{\rho_0'}{\rho_0}, \frac{x_a}{x_{a_0}} \right)$$

$$(6–26)$$

$$\alpha = 1, 2, 3$$

Eq. 6–26 shows that the temperature field depends upon a large number of criteria which are related to the geometrical arrangement of the boiler furnace (x_{2_0}/x_{1_0} and x_{3_0}/x_{1_0}) and to the characteristics of the burners (w_{2_0}/w_{1_0} and w_{3_0}/w_{1_0}) as well as to the working processes involved. The criteria Ar_0, E_{v_0}/E_{s_0}, K_{s_0}/w_{1_0}, $K_{v_0}d_{m_0}/K_{s_0}$, q_{v_0}/q_{s_0}, $q_{s_0}/c_{v_0}T_0$ reflect the chemical kinetics of the combustion process of the fuel; the criteria Fr_0, Re_0, Pr_{g0}, Pr_0, $\sigma_0 T_0 x_{1_0}/C_{v_0}\mu_0$ characterize the mass and energy transfer processes; the optical properties of the dust-air mixture and the fineness of the pulverized fuel are deter-

mined by the criteria Bu_0 and dm_0/x_{1_0}; the concentration ratios $\rho_0^{0_2}/\rho_0^C$, $\rho_0/\rho_0^{0_2}/\rho_0$, ρ_0^r/ρ_0, ρ_0'/ρ_0 determine the composition of the working mixture; the absorption properties of the dust particles of the fuel and of the heat absorbing surfaces of the furnace are represented by the magnitudes E_{s_0} and A_{cr_0}.

Since some of these factors have much more influence than others, some simplification of Eq. 6–26 can be made. For a truly rigorous analytical approach, however, all of the terms have some degree of importance.

Simplified Design Approach

From the foregoing discussion of the variables affecting the temperature field and radiant heat transfer in the boiler furnace, the reasons why the designer does not usually approach the problem in a purely theoretical manner should be apparent. In commercial engineering practice, he resorts to the use and interpretation of empirical data collected from boilers of similar design operating under similar conditions. Known theories of heat transfer are applied to the empirical data so that they may be used for conditions differing from those tested. This is necessary in order to improve and advance the art of designing boiler furnaces. Furthermore, to predict the temperature of flue gas leaving a given furnace in advance of actual operation requires a background of accumulated data, experience and judgment such as is generally only possessed by manufacturers of the equipment involved.

In the simplified empirical design ap-

---

[25] "Temperature Field in Combustion Chambers" by B. A. Khrustalev and S. S. Filimonov, *Teploenergetika*, 1959, translated in December 1961 as "Heat Engineering. Part 1" and designated as AEC-tr-4496.

proach, traverses are made of the gas stream leaving the furnace so as to determine the weighted average temperature.[26] This temperature, in conjunction with the weight of the products of combustion and the mean specific heat above an arbitrary datum, will give the heat content of the gas leaving the furnace above the datum. This may be done according to the following equation:

$$q = Wc_p(T_2 - 70) \qquad (6\text{--}27)$$

where c_p is the mean specific heat at constant pressure from 70 F to the leaving temperature, T_2 is the gas temperature leaving the furnace, and W is the weight flow rate of gas.

The heat absorbed by the radiant heating surface exposed to the furnace gas is the difference between the net heat liberated in the furnace available for absorption and the heat content of the gas leaving the furnace. This, of course, is subject to error in the amount of heat lost to the boiler room by radiation from the outside of the furnace setting. In the case of a watercooled furnace, however, this item is so small that it may be neglected in calculations of furnace performance.

The net heat released in a furnace differs from the gross heat input with the fuel, because allowance must be made for the following: the additional heat supplied to the furnace with preheated combustion air; the heat unavailable for absorption due to incomplete combustion; and the latent heat of vaporization of the water vapor in the products of combustion.

Experimental Determination of Furnace Heat Transfer[27]

Much theoretical and experimental work has been done to elucidate the fundamental problems related to the design of boiler furnaces. This work, however, has been hampered by the great difficulty in isolating the individual processes that are related to combustion and heat transfer. To those familiar with the problems of furnace design it is apparent that the predic- tion of furnace heat absorption has not yet been resolved to a fundamental basis nor to clearly rational methods of calculation. The practical need for proceeding in advance of rational treatment calls for the use of empirical design factors. In the past these have been very inadequate in some cases, although there is much evidence that the work of the ASME Furnace

[26] Elsewhere in this chapter the concept of using a single average temperature is subject to question, despite its practical use in empirical design. The work of the ASME Furnace Performance Factors Committee is also significant in this respect and is discussed in the following section of this chapter.

[27] Much of this section is based directly on a paper summarizing the work of the ASME Furnace Performance Factors Committee over a period of approximately 15 years. "Evaluation of Factors Affecting Heat Transfer in Furnaces" by Murray Greyson, G. P. Mazie, J. W. Myers, R. C. Corey and E. G. Graf appeared in *Trans.* ASME, Vol. 78, 1956, pp. 1741–46 and in *Combustion*, Vol. 27, February 1956, pp. 34–39. Much of the same material is covered in differing interpretations by British and Russian investigators: "Heat Transfer in the Furnaces of Water Tube Boilers" by G. G. Thurlow, *Bulletin* of the British Coal Utilization Research Association, May 1953, pp. 173–199 and "Correlation of New American Studies on Heat Transfer in Boiler Furnaces" by A. M. Gurvich and A. G. Blokh, *Teploenergetika*, May 1957, pp. 18–24.

Performance Factors Committee has increased the knowledge available to boiler designers.

The Special Research Committee on Furnace Performance Factors was initiated by ASME in 1943. Its purpose was to gain more factual and fundamental knowledge of the various factors which affect the performance of large central station furnaces. Procurement of this experimental information required the use of special instrumentation and procedures not commonly available and the development of new techniques. The experimental procedures for measuring physical and chemical properties of flames and hot gases are difficult and subject to errors of unknown origin.

Data from full scale furnaces are of immediate practical value if they are sufficiently precise and comprehensive, and they may be used to develop empirical relationships between the operating variables and the furnace heat absorption efficiency. Such relationships, however, are necessarily limited in scope and do not achieve the ultimate objective in this field of research, that of relating flame radiation to heat absorption by a general equation. Moreover, experiments on full-scale equipment are limited in the range of operating variables that can be studied, the number and location of points where observations and measurements can be made and the constancy of operating conditions within a given time interval.

Several different methods for determining heat absorption in a water cooled furnace are available. These methods may be classified under two general categories: calculations from formulas using empirical factors and actual measurements using a sampling technique.

Between 1948 and 1953 the U.S. Bureau of Mines, in cooperation with the ASME Furnace Performance Factors Committee, published a series of papers covering details of experimental work involving five large boiler furnaces.[28] These studies included work on three boilers fired by pulverized coal (Tidd, Paddy's Run and Willow Island stations), one boiler fired by a spreader stoker (Whiting refinery) and one gas fired boiler (Sterlington station).

Empirical Relationships

One of the earliest attempts to relate the heat transmission in a furnace to the radiant surface area, the rate at which fuel was consumed and the air-fuel ratio was made in England by Hudson in 1890.[29] He proposed the following empirical equation for the heat absorption efficiency of the furnace:

---

[28] The results of this work were reported in the following papers in ASME *Transactions:*
"An Investigation of the Variations in Heat Absorption in a Pulverized Coal Fired Water Cooled Steam Boiler Furnace" by W. T. Reid, Paul Cohen and R. C. Corey, Vol. 70, 1948, pp. 569–586.
"Furnace Heat Absorption in Paddy's Run Pulverized Coal Fired Steam Generators Using Turbulent Burners" by R. C. Corey and Paul Cohen, Vol. 71, 1949, pp. 925–936.
"Furnace Heat Absorption in a Pulverized Coal Fired Steam Generator" by J. W. Myers and R. C. Corey, Vol. 73, 1951, pp. 419–432.
"Variations in Heat Absorption in a Natural Gas Fired, Water Cooled Steam Boiler Furnace" by A. R. Mumford and R. C. Corey, Vol. 74, 1952, pp. 1191–1215.
"Furnace Heat Absorption Efficiency in a Spreader Stoker Fired Steam Generator" by J. W. Myers and R. C. Corey, Vol. 75, 1953, pp. 909–924.
[29] "Heat Transmission in Boilers" by J. G. Hudson, *The Engineer,* Vol. 70, 1890, pp. 449–450, 483–484, 523–525.

$$\eta = \frac{(q/A_s)(A_s/W_f)}{Q}$$

$$= 1 - \frac{(W_f/W_a)}{(W_f/W_a) - 45A_s}$$

$$(6\text{--}28)$$

where η is the heat absorption efficiency, q/A_s is the rate of heat transmission per hour per square foot of radiant wall surface, Q is the available heat per pound of coal fired, A_s/W_f is the number of square feet of radiant wall surface per pound of coal fired per hour and W_f/W_a is the fuel-air weight ratio.

This equation was not universally applicable, and in 1925 was modified by Orrok[30] as follows"

$$\eta = \frac{(q/A_s)}{\left(\dfrac{1}{A_s}\right)Q} = \frac{1}{1 + \left(\dfrac{W_f}{W_a}\right)\sqrt{\dfrac{1}{A_s}}\dfrac{1}{27}}$$

$$(6\text{--}29)$$

At the same time that Orrok suggested his empirical modification of Hudson's equation, Broido presented an empirical curve that was obtained from the average data of six boiler stations, and which related available heat per unit area of radiant surface to the heat-absorption efficiency of the furnace. Broido claimed that most existing data could be fitted to the curve with a precision of ±10 per cent.[31]

Empirical correlations such as the Hudson, Hudson-Orrok and Broido techniques supplied information about the overall performance of a furnace, but gave no information about operating variables such as flame emissivities, flame temperatures, cold wall temperatures, flame volumes and specific burning rates of fuel. Moreover, the effects of ash and slag on the emissivity and temperatures of the cold wall of the furnace were not considered.

One of the first attempts to place furnace data on a fundamental basis was made by Wohlenberg and his associates at Yale University.[32] Beginning in 1925, they published a series of papers that relate various effects within a furnace to the operating parameters of the furnace. The approach used by these investigators was to apply certain heat-transfer equations to furnaces having specific assumed characteristics, and to calculate the theoretical heat-absorption efficiencies for these assumed furnaces. Experimentally determined furnace heat-absorption efficiencies were then compared with the calculated efficiencies when individual operating parameters were varied. The corrections to the theoretical efficiencies were then plotted as functions of the level of the operating parameters, and a series of factor-curves was developed. By applying the proper set of factors to the calculated efficiency, it was then possible to calculate the heat-absorption efficiency of a real furnace. The equation used by Wohlenberg for the application of correction factor was

---

[30] See discussion by George A. Orrok of a paper by B. N. Broido, "Radiation in Boiler Furnaces", *Trans.* ASME, Vol. 47, 1925, pp. 1148–1155. The modified Hudson-Orrok equation appears on page 1152.

[31] See "Radiation in Boiler Furnaces", *Trans.* ASME, Vol. 47, 1925, pp. 1123–1177.

[32] For an interpretation of this work, see Furnace Heat Transfer—An Earlier Approach, in the preceding section entitled The Boiler Furnace—An Analytical Approach. The results of practically all of the Wohlenberg studies were published in the *Transactions* of ASME.

$$\eta = \eta_0 \prod_{i=1}^{8} F_i + \phi \qquad (6\text{-}30)$$

where η_o is the efficiency of the assumed furnace, F_i are corrective factors related to furnace volume, fraction of total furnace wall that is cold, heat-liberation rate, per cent excess air, heating value of fuel, size of fuel particle, effective radiant-heating surface, and combinations thereof; and ϕ is a factor related to preheated air temperature.

Other fundamental approaches have also been tried.

By a dimensional analysis of the furnace system, Gurvich developed the following equation:[33]

$$B_o = \frac{W_f Q \eta}{A_s \mathcal{E}_o T_f^4 \left(1 - \dfrac{T_o}{T_f}\right)} \qquad (6\text{-}31)$$

where B_o is a modified Boltzmann number, W_f is the fuel-consumption rate, A_s is the radiant-wall area, $\mathcal{E}_o$ is the overall emissivity of the combustion chamber, T_f is the adiabatic flame temperature, and $\dfrac{T_o}{T_f}$ is the dimensionless ratio of the flue-gas temperature at the furnace outlet to the adiabatic flame temperature.

Gurvich showed by experiment that $\dfrac{T_o}{T_f}$ and B_o were related by an equation of the form

$$\frac{T_o}{T_f} = \frac{B_o}{1 + B_o} \qquad (6\text{-}32)$$

where α is a constant equal to 0.6 for coal-fired furnaces. Konokov[34] improved upon Gurvich's equation by suggesting the heat-balance equation

$$\left[\frac{T_o}{T_1}\right]^4 \epsilon \frac{C_o\left[\dfrac{T_f}{100}\right]^3}{100 W_f v C_p}\left[\frac{T_o}{T_f}\right]^4 + \frac{T_o}{T_f} - 1 = 0 \qquad (6\text{-}33)$$

where T_1 is the temperature of the flame surface, T_o is the flue-gas temperature at the furnace outlet, W_f is the fuel consumption rate, v is the volume of flue gas per unit weight of fuel, C_p is the average specific heat of the flue gas, C_o is the Stefan-Boltzmann constant, and ϵ is the emissivity of the firebox.

The equations cited above are just a few examples of the many attempts that have been made to correlate furnace performance data and operating parameters and have been selected to illustrate the variety of approaches that have been used in this work. It is sufficient to state here that the lack of precision of data collected in the past has prevented a comprehensive evaluation of the applicability of most of these correlations.

Procedures for Data Analysis

The analyses made by the Bureau of Mines of the data from the five boiler stations were divided into three separate steps; the first analysis was concerned with the general correlation of all of the data as a group with any one or all of five cor-

[33] "Analogy of Heat Transfer Phenomena in Boiler Houses" by A. M. Gurvich, *Bulletin* of the Academy of Sciences, USSR, Nos. 1–2, 1943, p. 23. For a more recent Russian treatment of this subject, see *Fundamentals of Heat Transfer* by S. S. Kutateladze, New York, 1963, especially the sections of Chapter XIX dealing with radiation from dust filled gases and balance equations of heat transfer in furnaces, pp. 426–434.

[34] "Heat Emission in Boiler Fireboxes" by P. K. Konokov, *Bulletin* of the Academy of Sciences, USSR, Technical Scientific Section, March 1952, pp. 367–373.

relations; the Broido, the Hudson-Orrok, a modified Hudson-Orrok, the Wohlenberg, and the Gurvich equations. In this phase, limited statistical techniques were used to compare heat-absorption efficiencies that were determined experimentally and those that were calculated or predicted from the proposed correlations. Accordingly, it was possible to determine whether or not the differences that were observed were statistically significant.

The second analysis was concerned with individual correlations and consisted of fitting the experimental data from individual stations to these proposed equations, and determining the significance of any differences that were observed between experimental efficiencies and those calculated from the equations. This phase was found to be necessary because in some instances the overall data were very adequately described by an equation, whereas data from individual stations differed appreciably from those calculated by the equation.

The third analysis was an attempt to find a generalized correlation that would describe the furnace data both as a group and individually by station. This phase of the work, of course, depended upon the results of the previous phases.

To date, most of the data correlation has been completed. The data from all five stations have been compared with the Broido, Hudson-Orrok, modified Hudson-Orrok, and Wohlenberg relationships. In addition, the data from the gas-fired furnace have been plotted, by means of estimated adiabatic flame temperatures, in the manner suggested by Gurvich and Konokov.

Correlation of Results

Fig. 6–14 shows the 96 furnace tests from the five stations plotted according to Broido's curve, which is shown on the figure. To show better the relationship between the predicted and experimental efficiencies, the same data have been re-plotted around a "check line" in Fig. 6–15.

The spread of points around the line is characterized by an average of difference of -0.0028 and a standard deviation of 0.03455. If the average difference between the predicted and experimental heat-absorption efficiencies is assumed to be due to a random distribution of experimental errors, and this average is compared with zero by means of the Student t-test, no significant difference is found between the predicted and experimentally-determined efficiencies. The calculated t value is equal to 0.9099, and compares favorably with values from a double-sided t-table of 2.635 and 1.988 per the 1-and 5-per cent probability levels, respectively.

The experimentally determined heat-absorption efficiencies are plotted in Fig. 6–16 according to the Hudson-Orrok equation, together with the curve obtained from the equation. In Fig. 6–17 the same data are plotted according to a modified Hudson-Orrok equation in which fuel consumption is expressed as thousands of Btu of available heat per square foot of radiant heating surface, and the air-fuel ratio as pounds of air per thousand Btu of available heat.

The difference between the predicted efficiencies calculated from the Hudson-Orrok equation and experimental results are shown in Fig. 6–18 in which the check line technique was used. The plot is characterized by a mean difference of 0.00494, and a standard deviation of 0.0441. The calculated value of t of 1.097, when compared with table values of 2.635 and 1.988 for the 1-and 5-per cent probability levels, respectively, indicate that there is no significant difference between the calculated and the experimentally determined efficiencies.

Fig. 6–19 shows the experimental data plotted against the efficiencies calculated by the Wohlenberg equation. In this plot, the mean difference of -0.02984 and the standard deviation of 0.04150, and the t value for 69 test points (gas-fired furnace data could not be used) of 5.964 indicate that the Wohlenberg equation cannot be used to describe these furnace data. The table values of t for the 1- and 5-per cent probability levels are 2.657 and 1.998, respectively.

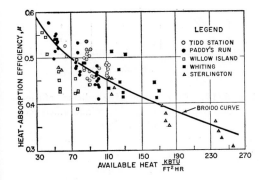

Fig. 6–14. Correlations of experimental heat absorption efficiencies by a Broido curve

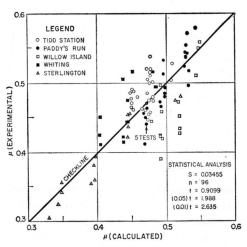

Fig. 6–15. Correlation of predicted efficiencies and experimentally determined efficiencies (Broido)

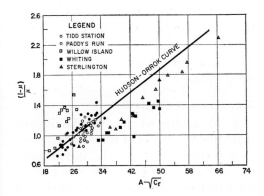

Fig. 6–16. Correlation of experimental heat absorption efficiencies by a Hudson-Orrok equation

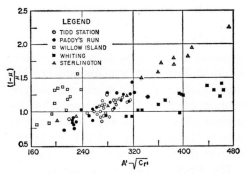

Fig. 6–17. Correlation of experimental heat absorption efficiencies by a modified Hudson-Orrok equation

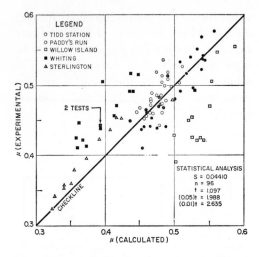

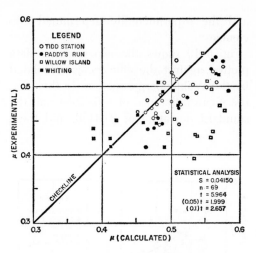

Fig. 6–18. Correlation of predicted efficiencies and experimentally determined efficiencies (Hudson-Orrok)

Fig. 6–19. Correlation of predicted efficiencies and experimentally determined efficiencies (Wohlenberg)

Similar analyses of data from individual stations were also made. Experimental data were compared with predicted data from each of the three equations. The results are shown in Table 6–1. No significant differences were observed between Paddy's Run data, and the data calculated from the Broido and Hudson-Orrok equations. These two techniques could also be used to describe the data from the gas-fired unit at Sterlington. The Wohlenberg equation, however, was only satisfactory for describing the spreader-stoker data from Whiting. On the whole, no one correlation described the data from all of the stations taken individually, and in two instances, Tidd Station and Willow Island, none of the correlations were adequate.

The Gurvich and the Konokov equations, both involving adiabatic flame temperatures, were used to correlate the data from the gas-fired unit at Sterlington. These data are plotted by a Gurvich equation (Eq. 6–31) in Fig. 6–20. The param-

eters of the plot are $\dfrac{T_0}{T_f}$ and $\dfrac{W_f\,\eta}{T_f{}^4\left[1-\dfrac{T_0}{T_f}\right]}\times$ 10^{-6} which have been defined in a previous section of the paper. The parameter β in Fig. 6–20 is equal to $\left[\dfrac{T_0}{T_f}\right]\dfrac{1}{A_s\varepsilon o}$ which is a constant for the furnace. In both instances, very satisfactory correlations of the data were obtained, despite the estimated flame temperatures that were used.

Discussion and Conclusions

As demonstrated by the Sterlington data, the correlation of furnace data from clean-walled combustion chambers may be obtained in many ways. The small variations that are observed can be attributed to a number of factors such as changes in flame shapes and volumes with load, excess air, and burner arrangement. As soon as the furnace walls become covered by ash and slag, however, the differences be-

Table 6–1—Statistical Tests of Furnace Data

Station	Type of Firing	Type of Correlation	No. of (1)	Average Difference between Efficiencies	Standard Deviation	$t =$	t at 95%	Significant Variation
Tidd	Pulverized fuel	Broido	26	+0.016115	0.023090	3.621	2.060	Yes
		Hudson-Orrok	26	+0.010884	0.019443	2.918	2.060	Yes
		Wohlenberg	26	− 0.015000	0.025456	2.999	2.060	Yes
Paddy's Run	Pulverized fuel	Broido	28	− 0.006714	0.024244	1.4654	2.052	No
		Hudson-Orrok	28	− 0.005110	0.020780	1.3010	2.052	No
		Wohlenberg	15	− 0.031800	0.019139	6.4350	2.145	Yes
Willow Island	Pulverized fuel	Broido	13	− 0.049770	0.036255	4.9400	2.180	Yes
		Hudson-Orrok	13	− 0.071600	0.035160	7.3430	2.180	Yes
		Wohlenberg	13	− 0.084920	0.042450	7.2140	2.180	Yes
Whiting	Spreader stoker	Broido	15	0.022067	0.031721	2.6942	2.145	Yes
		Hudson-Orrok	15	0.067466	0.017869	16.1822	2.145	Yes
		Wohlenberg	15	− 0.005867	0.038118	0.5961	2.145	No
Sterlington	Gas	Broido	14	− 0.015857	0.017974	1.0439	2.160	No
		Hudson-Orrok	14	0.018071	0.015340	1.3940	2.160	No
		Wohlenberg		This type of correlation not applied to gas-fired furnaces.					

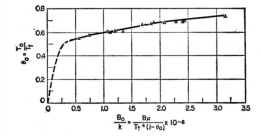

Fig. 6–20. Correlation of a Sterlington heat absorption efficiency by a Gurvich equation

tween predicted and experimental values for heat transfer become larger, and the whole problem becomes extremely complex. Factors that are present and influence the operation of coal-fired equipment, and which are not present in gas-fired equipment include the heat conductivity, and the temperature and emissivity of the flame and the ash and slag coating the furnace-wall tubes.

Although an attempt to correlate furnace data from coal-fired equipment by means of one or more of the fundamental flame-temperature relationships will be attempted, it is doubtful that improved correlations will be obtained. This conclusion is suggested by the fact that most fundamental relationships involve a radiation variable related to the temperature of the furnace wall.

In most fundamental furnace expressions the radiation from the furnace wall back to the flame is considered to be negligible and is neglected. For clean-walled furnaces, such as Sterlington, this assumption is valid since the temperature of the walls and boiler tubes are in the range 700–800 F, as compared to the flame temperature of approximately 3000 F. When, however, the wall is covered by a coating of ash and slag, which may vary in temperature from 700 to 2000 F, the assumption is not valid, and may not be made. Some attempts have been made to allow for this slag-ash factor. Mullikin[35], as well as Mumford and Bice[36], have suggested methods that can be used to correct radiant heat-absorbing surface. These techniques, however, involve very many assumptions, and do not allow for the temperature of the slag coating.

Further Experimental Work

To evaluate properly the heat transfer in a furnace, it is necessary to know flame temperature and flame emissivities, and the effects on these factors of such variables as flame shape, flame length, type of fuel, degree of mixing of fuel and air, and per cent excess air. It is possible that such information can be obtained by designing experimental furnaces as sectionalized calorimeters, such is being done at the International Flame-Radiation Trials at Ijmuiden, Holland. However, the experimental problems are numerous and complex and will only be solved by the application of experimental experience.

In addition to information on flames, future experimental work should be directed at obtaining the radiation and conductivity characteristics of the slag and ash coatings of furnace walls, as well as the fraction of wall area covered by ash and slag. In large scale industrial experimentation, some indications of these characteristics may be obtained by measuring slag and ash temperatures as well as tube metal temperatures. These temperatures are necessary if the reradiation from the wall back to the flame and the heat transfer to the boiler tubes is to be evaluated.

Experimental work should be planned so that all data can be interpreted statistically and so that an estimate of the precision of measurements can be made in advance.[37] This approach would probably require a factorially designed program to facilitate the gathering of the most meaningful data with the least amount of effort.

A Look to the Future

Measurement of boiler furnace performance is simple in principle but difficult to attain in practice. There are problems in taking measurements at high temperature in a complex equipment configuration of large size. Large quantities must be sampled, and this may introduce errors. Many diverse and intangible factors can affect overall performance, and because of their interacting nature it is not always possible to isolate individual factors and subject them to independent variation. This fre-

[35] "Determining Furnace Heat Transfer by Gas Temperature Measurement" by H. F. Mullikin, *Power Generation* (now *Power Engineering*), Vol. 54, August 1948, pp. 68–71, 116–122; also, "Evaluation of Effective Radiant Heat Surface and Application of the Stefan-Boltzmann Law to Heat Absorption in Boiler Furnaces" by H. F. Mullikin, *Trans.* ASME, Vol. 57, 1935, pp. 517–529.

[36] "An Investigation of the Variation of Heat Absorption in a Pulverized Coal Fired, Water Cooled Steam Boiler Furnace—Part IV, Comparison and Correlation of the Results of Furnace Heat Absorption Investigations" by A. R. Mumford and G. W. Bice, *Trans.* ASME, Vol. 70, 1948, pp. 601–614.

[37] See the beginning sections of Chapter 12, Power Plant Tests and Measurements, for related information.

quently calls for a statistical approach and indirect evaluation.

The future offers hopeful prospects for both improvement in experimental accuracy and greater facility in data reduction. Instruments of greater sensitivity developed for other research purposes have found a place in boiler testing and evaluation. High speed computers are coming into much wider use in the recording and calculation of large quantities of experimental data.

The availability of more precise experimental information acts as a challenge to devise improved analytical methods and to develop more sophisticated theoretical understanding of what transpires in the boiler furnace. The link between the empirical and the theoretical, between research and engineering practice has been recognized by two distinguished investigators in the fields of fuels and combustion. M. W. Thring observed that combustion shows in a very fascinating way the possibilities for the fusion of pure scientific research and the practical design of industrial appliances.[38]

Ralph Sherman summarized his beliefs as follows: "The crying need in all research is for an improved understanding between the engineers who have the task of applying research results and those who have the task of doing the research. The engineer must tell the research worker what it is that he needs to know to design improved equipment and processes. The research worker must then attempt to interpret the data that he is obtaining. If he is not working along needed lines, he could well change his line."[39]

[38] *The Science of Flames and Furnaces,* Second Edition, John Wiley, 1962, p. 133.
[39] "An Appraisal of Combustion Research", *Proceedings,* 1955 Joint Conference on Combustion sponsored by IME and ASME, p. 31.

Laboratory apparatus for studying steam and water separation in boiler drums

7

Fluid Flow[1]

In the art of boiler and reactor design, fluid mechanics, the engineering science which deals with *fluid flow*, plays a most important role. As with heat transfer, to which it is very closely related both in theory and application, fluid flow and its related physical phenomena were imperfectly understood in the early days of boiler design. Likewise, there arose in engineering circles a sort of entrenched empiricism based upon the successful operation of many thousands of boilers. Extrapolation of successful experience became the watchword of boiler designers, supplemented by field investigation when troubles were encountered. Both the experimental laboratory and the idealized theoretical approach to fluid flow were viewed with suspicion by many boiler designers until comparatively recent times.

The scope and importance of fluid mechanics to boiler and reactor designers can be understood by reference to a selected list of topics that are of direct concern. These include flow of feedwater in pipes, two-phase flow in boilers and nuclear reactors, superheated steam flow, forced flow of air and flue gas by mechanical fans, aerodynamic design of boilers and ductwork, flow through headers, flow of fuels through pipes and fittings, flow of liquid metals and dispersion of finely divided particles from stack discharges.

Designers and users of power equipment are nominally familiar with some of the great names responsible for the evolutionary development of hydraulics and fluid mechanics. Without being aware of their origin, engineers may use the so-called Bernoulli equation in flow calculations, obtain experimental data from Venturi meters (largely a late nineteenth century development of an American, Clemens Herschel), utilize Pitot tubes in a variety of laboratory and field investigations and carry out analytical studies with the aid of dimensionless parameters bearing the names of Reynolds and Prandtl. Yet knowledge of the origin and development of these fluid flow concepts and measuring instruments together with some background on the lives of their originators from many scientific and engineer-

[1] Material for this chapter was obtained from several individuals who are recognized at the place of their contribution.

ing disciplines can be of considerable aid in appreciating the nature and solution of fluid flow problems.[2]

The life of Osborne Reynolds has great significance for boiler designers because of his work in heat transmission.[3] Accompanying his many accomplishments in theoretical and analytical areas of fluid mechanics was an unusually keen interest in applied engineering subjects.[4] The work of Ludwig Prandtl also reflects concern with problems of boiler design.[5]

Boiler Circulation

Boiler circulation provides an appropriate link between the history of fluid flow and the contemporary problems of the boiler designer. The use of model techniques to obtain quantitative and qualitative data is now commonplace in boiler testing laboratories and is discussed later in this chapter. However, evidence of the skepticism with which this approach was originally greeted is provided by the following quotation from an ASME paper which was virtually ignored by the boiler industry for a period of nearly forty years following its presentation.[6]

"In reply to the members who have questioned the value of experiments on models, the author wishes to point out that in the solution of problems involving the flow of fluids, that is in hydrodynamics and aerodynamics — the use of models is invaluable.

"The fundamental data of the subject of aerodynamics have been derived very largely from experiments on models. Langley's figures for model planes, modified by Lilienthal's experiments, provided the information from which the earliest flying machines were

[2] For an interesting exposition of this viewpoint, see *History of Hydraulics* by Hunter Rouse and Simon Ince, originally published in 1957 by the Iowa Institute of Hydraulic Research of the State University of Iowa and now available as a paperback from Dover Publications.

[3] His classical paper is entitled "On the Extent and Action of Heating Surface for Steam Boilers" and appeared in the *Proceedings* of the Manchester Literary and Philosophical Society, Vol. 14, 1874, pp. 7–12, and in his *Collected Papers*, Vol. 1, pp. 81–85. A. H. Gibson has written a brief but fascinating biography entitled *Osborne Reynolds and His Work in Hydraulics and Hydrodynamics*. Longmans Green, London, 1946.

[4] The diversity of interests shown by Reynolds is shown by the titles and place of presentation of the following three papers: "On the Use of High Pressure Steam," a paper read before the Manchester Association of Employers, Foremen Engineers and Draughtsmen and published in *Engineering*, Feb. 7, 1873, p. 104; "The Prevention of Smoke," presidential address before the Manchester Scientific and Mechanical Society and published in *The Engineer*, Oct. 19, 1877, pp. 278–279; and "An Experimental Investigation of the Circumstances Which Determine Whether the Motion of Water Shall be Direct or Sinuous and of the Law of Resistance in Parallel Channels," *Philosophical Transactions* of the Royal Society of London, Vol. 174, 1883, pp. 935–982.

[5] See the English translation of *"Essentials of Fluid Dynamics With Applications to Hydraulics, Aeronautics, Meteorology and Other Subjects,"* Blackie & Son, London, 1952, discussion of heat transfer in moving fluids and cases of flow due to heat, pp. 396–411.

[6] "Circulation in Horizontal Water Tube Boilers" by Paul A. Bancel, *Trans.* ASME, Vol. 37, 1915, pp. 1011–1042.

constructed. The work of Lancaster, Bryan and Eiffel was based largely on experiments with models. As to ship propulsion, the testing of models of ships has been carried on for years.

"The circulation in a water tube boiler is a highly complex problem, involving not only a complicated circuit with tubes working at different loads, discharging into a common header, but also the movement of two fluids, steam and water, at dissimilar and varying velocities. In quoting results of researches with a model, the writer made no attempt to predict or state the circulation or the pressures influencing circulation on the various types of actual boilers, confining his remarks to the model. His knowledge of the laws of similitude connecting a model water tube boiler and its prototype when circulating non-homogeneous mixtures of steam bubbles and water, is not sufficient to permit of such predictions, but he sees no reason why the results obtained should not be similar in kind, at least, to those to be obtained in an actual boiler. . . ."

Innovations of Goldsworthy Gurney[7]

A clue to the importance of *circulation* in boiler design is found in the literal meanings of the words "boiler" and "steam generator." Intuitively one can grasp the basic principle by observing what happens when heat is applied to a tea kettle partially filled with water. The formation and escape of bubbles are indications of differences in density of the heated fluid and of the effect of transfer of heat from an outside source.

In a sense the tea kettle represents a batch process in which the water must be intermittently replenished after the original contents are converted to steam. If the process is to become continuous, then there must be available an ample supply of water in the liquid state, appropriately known as *feedwater*, and a closed vessel

having an inlet for admitting water and an outlet for discharging steam as soon as it is generated, all of this taking place at a controlled rate. A simplified version of such a device is shown in Fig. 7–1, which is a representation of the first known study of boiler circulation. The experimental work was conducted in England about the year 1825 by a self-taught engineer, Goldsworthy Gurney, who had been educated as a chemist and as a physician. He used a glass tube bent in the form of a loop and added some light flocculent matter to the water within the tube to aid in visualization and qualitative evaluation. As heat was applied near the bottom of the loop the heated water ascended and the colder water followed, establishing the indicated circulation as steam was discharged and feedwater added.

At a Hearing of a Select Committee of the British House of Commons on July 17, 1834, Mr. Gurney recalled these experiments and testified as follows regarding

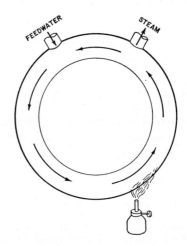

Fig. 7–1. Apparatus used in first known boiler circulation experiment performed by Goldsworthy Gurney, 1825

---

[7] Material in this section contributed by Glenn R. Fryling.

his attempts to design a boiler that would generate more steam per unit of heating surface than any previously built:

". . . I made a series of experiments to ascertain the peculiar changes that took place in water under certain increase of temperature, increase of pressure, formation of steam, and the compressing of it; and also when escaping from the vessel. . . . The result of those experiments was, first, the observation that a circulation in the vessel took place in virtue of the change of specific gravity occasioned by the heat passing to the fluid, in a rapidity proportional to the intensity of heat."

Mr. Gurney then described what he meant by boiler circulation:

"The particles of water which are in contact with the heated surface become lighter and ascend; they are succeeded by cooler portions that descend in virtue of greater specific gravity. I beg further to observe that when particles of water are converted into steam they rise so very rapidly that they carry a large portion of water with them, which, in a vessel sufficiently large, are returned through a current setting down in some portion of the same vessel: there is an exceedingly rapid circulation of ascending steam and descending water when under strong heat. The steam remains on the upper surface, and the water falls to the bottom. The reason why water is driven out of the tubes is that the particles of water being mixed and mechanically driven with the steam become part of the current and invariably pass off with it when allowed to escape."[8]

The genius of Gurney was to transform these perceptive experimental observations and fruitful deductions into several practicable designs of water tube boilers. Regrettably, his work was far in advance of the thinking of most of his engineering contemporaries who were unwilling to accept these novel ideas concerning boiler circulation and to continue development. Although there was some revival of interest in the Gurney concepts by British marine boiler designers who were faced with severe circulation problems in the latter portion of the nineteenth century, in a very real sense his work fell into oblivion despite the very substantial amount of published technical literature in the decade between 1825 and 1835.[9]

Evolution of Boiler Design

To comprehend this neglect one must be aware of the historical evolution of boiler design as well as the traditional resistance to innovations which might upset established boiler practice. Starting from the time of Thomas Newcomen's first operable steam pumping engine in 1712, British boilers were of two general but related types. The earliest ones were composed of pressure vessels supported above a fire and became known as *haystack* boilers. The second type was the fire tube boiler in which the products of combustion passed through comparatively long tubes surrounded by the water from which steam was generated. An early example of this type was the *wagon* boiler introduced by James Watt in 1788, and it

---

[8] These are excerpts from the "Report from the Select Committee on Mr. Goldsworthy Gurney's Case, with the Minutes of Evidence." The complete testimony may be found in the Parliamentary Report, British House of Commons, Session of 1834, Vol. 11, pp. 223–312.

[9] For example, an 1831 British House of Commons report on steam carriages, in which the work of Gurney featured prominently, was ordered to be reprinted in the United States by the House of Representatives. Numerous articles appeared in the *Franklin Institute Journal* and the British *Mechanics' Magazine,* and French engineers were able to learn of the developments in *Annales des Ponts et Chausées* from an illustrated article in 1833. An extensive bibliography by Rhys Jenkins was published in London about 1900 under the title, *Power Locomotion on the Highway.*

was followed in the next several decades by the *Cornish* and *Lancashire* boilers. These firetube boilers have an inherent simplicity of arrangement and construction which probably accounts for their popularity over the span of nearly two centuries in which their designs have been perpetuated.

Goldsworthy Gurney grew up in Cornwall, a portion of southwestern England distinguished for its many contributions to steam power engineering. He was a personal acquaintance and boyhood admirer of Richard Trevithick, pioneer in applications of high pressure steam and a major contributor to the development of the Cornish boiler. Perhaps because of his educational background and experience in chemistry and medicine, Gurney was not rigidly bound to conventional engineering practice, and his circulation experiments served as a basis for a major departure in boiler design. He first conceived, Fig. 7–2, the now familiar arrangement of an external vessel or drum for steam separation in conjunction with unheated downcomers (large vertical tubes removed from the combustion zone) to insure positive circulation in a furnace whose interior surfaces were composed largely of tubes, now commonly called waterwalls.

This geometrical arrangement, in combination with a rational understanding of circulation as determined by physical experimentation, marked a crucial point in the history of boiler design. Gurney's awareness of this is demonstrated by this additional testimony in 1834 to the Select Committee of the British House of Commons. When asked about the prevention of burnout or metal failure in water-starved tubes of boilers of his design, Gurney replied:

"The plan I adopted to overcome the difficulty was to pass the water back again through a separate vessel, which made a distinct descending curve away from the heating surface. Previous to entering . . . it was also carried into a separate or distinct vessel provided for the purpose of separation. . . . The steam being separated from the water remains on the surface and out of the influence of heat; the water being separated descends through the separate current and supplies the place of the ascending portion of the current that was driven along by the steam. By these means the difficulty of keeping water when it was under any pressure, or submitted to any extent of heat in tubes, was overcome; the separate vessel which I call a separator was highly essential, inasmuch as it effects a complete separation of steam and water. . . . The circulation and separation, in distinct vessels, are the great points. I was obliged to make two distinct vessels [referring to the system of tubing as one and the separator as the other]; I was obliged to employ tubes in consequence of their being necessary to reduce the size or weight of the generator for the purposes of effecting locomotion."

In principle the flow of water and steam in the largest natural circulation boilers ever built does not differ from the Gurney design shown on page 7–6 in Fig. 7–2. The old and the new, spanning more than a century of time, are characterized by an elevated drum to provide a circulation head and a combustion chamber made up of waterwall tubing. The original Gurney boilers were intended for use in steam carriages, but contemporary records indicate they were also applied to railway locomotives and marine vessels.

A glance through the boiler patent literature of the century between 1825 and 1925 will serve as reminder of the wide departure from the inherent simplicity and basic physical rationale of the Gurney concepts. Notwithstanding a trend toward complexity sometimes involving as many as eight or nine boiler drums and tubing bent in incredibly complex shapes, the introduction of pulverized coal firing to central station practice following World War I forced an *empirical rediscovery* of the circulation principles and boiler designs originally proposed by Gurney. The use of large amounts of refractory material in boiler furnaces proved impractical with this new form of firing. For this reason, tubing in the form of watercooled surface was introduced to improve heat transfer and to overcome slagging problems which caused deterioration of refractory. These metallic surfaces were rather cautiously integrated into the boiler circulating system, first as bottom screens and later as furnace sidewalls.[10]

The ultimate end of this evolution of boiler design bears a striking resemblance to the early Gurney boilers. By way of example, Fig. 7–3 shows the first fully watercooled C-E steam generating unit. Designed for pulverized coal firing and placed in operation in 1926 at the Atlas Portland Cement Company plant at Northampton, Penna., this was the progenitor

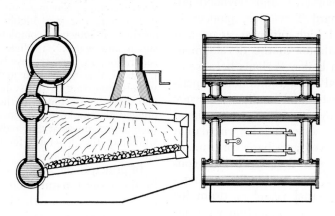

Fig. 7–2. Water tube boiler designed by Goldsworthy Gurney, about 1827

of a whole family of boiler designs now in widespread use. All incorporate principles of circulation and arrangements of surface foreshadowed by the laboratory tests which Gurney conducted more than a century earlier.

Lessons from Gurney

In view of the extreme importance of circulation in boiler design, it may be well to consider some of the human and technical factors that underlay the innovations of Gurney.[11] Three stand out: (1) his education and training in chemistry rather than engineering; (2) his strong motivation growing out of seeing the first steam carriage built by Richard Trevithick; and (3) his scientific objectivity and personal detachment from the mainstream of boiler design.

---

[10] This evolution is traced in an article by Otto de Lorenzi, "Water Cooled Furnace Bottoms," *Combustion*, Vol. 3, August 1931, pp. 16–19. See also, "Development of a Major Principle of Pulverized Coal Firing" by Fred L. Dornbrook, *Trans.* ASME, Vol. 63, 1941, pp. 261–266.
[11] For a counterpart applying to more recent boiler design practices, see Chapter 25, Combined Circulation Boilers.

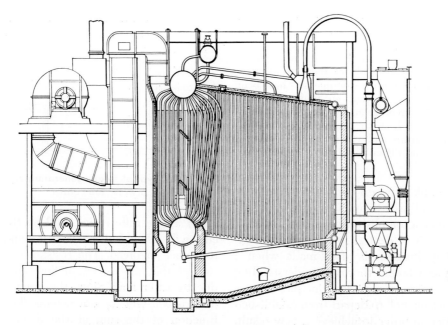

Fig. 7–3. First fully watercooled C-E steam generating unit

The attitude of Gurney toward learning is well expressed by these excerpts from a remarkable series of lectures which were delivered in 1822 and demonstrated his comprehensive understanding of the science of his time:

"As it is the primary object of these lectures to teach the elements of chemical science, I consider that the most effectual mode of preparing my audience for the reception of the knowledge will be an endeavour to impress them with a sense of its beauty and utility, and thus necessarily engender in them that desire to learn, which is the first and most important step towards all acquirement, and in the absence of which no acquirement can be made to any permanent or valuable effect. . . ."[12]

As a boy of eleven Mr. Gurney saw Trevithick's first steam carriage in operation and subsequently learned of the opposition and ridicule that contemporary engineers showered upon the theories of locomotion and high pressure steam espoused by that pioneering genius. Several decades later Gurney himself, experiencing comparable opposition to his own unorthodox ideas of boiler and steam carriage design, was prompted to write these words:

". . . had the members of that profession to which enquiries of this nature are particularly fitted — I mean the practical engineers of the day — done what may be looked upon as their duty in this matter; nay, had they not, with a degree of opposition that was scarcely to be looked for in a profession ranking among the most enlightened of the day, thrown obstacles in my way almost insurmountable, I should long ago have left the subject in that state in which my early experiments placed it . . . But (incredible as it may at first sight seem) at the commencement of my experiments I was, for the want

---

[12] *Course of Lectures in Chemical Science* delivered at the Surrey Institution by Goldsworthy Gurney and published by G. and U. B. Whittaker, London, 1823, pp. 14–15.

of a practical engineer to second or assist my views and objects, compelled to *turn engineer myself*. This, in point of fact, I did; and every experiment that has since been made, and every mechanical or other arrangement necessary to those experiments, has been conducted and carried on under my own immediate direction and observation. I mention this solely with the view of illustrating the nature and extent of the *practical* and personal difficulties I have had to overcome. . . ."[13]

The link between the practical and the theoretical, as exemplified by the experience and accomplishments of Goldsworthy Gurney, is of central importance in engineering. Progress is often made when a designer who has thorough understanding of underlying scientific principles is courageous enough to depart from established practice in order to achieve a new result. In the case of Gurney, the engineering profession of his day was unwilling to accept his ideas on boiler circulation, and it took nearly a century of pursuing many blind alleys before empirical rediscovery took place. This resistance to technical innovation can also be found among more sophisticated designers who are well grounded in engineering science. The way in which Goldsworthy Gurney linked the interpretation of scientific observations to practical boiler design is a timeless lesson that all engineers would do well to master.

Circulation in a Water Tube Circuit[14]

Before proceeding to analytical and quantitative approaches to the theory of boiler circulation, it may be well to take a qualitative look at what happens in a water tube circuit of a modern boiler. Such a steam generating circuit, illustrated in Fig. 7–4, will circulate as much

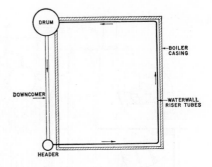

Fig. 7–4.   Typical steam generating circuit in a water tube boiler

water as the differential head on the circuit will allow for the velocity and the resistance involved. The resistance is the sum of that due to steam flow and that due to water flow. Since the downcomer head is constant the downcomer flow is a function of the sum of the downcomer head and the riser circuit losses. Steam flow is a function of the firing rate, and the water to steam ratio in the riser circuit will vary for each steaming condition. At the high steaming rates the water to steam ratio is reduced since the downcomer water flow is essentially constant. At low steam rates the water to steam ratio is high because the downcomer water flow is essentially maintained.

The water in the mixture does not necessarily flow uniformly and at the same velocity as the steam, since most riser circuits are more or less vertical, and the flow is against gravity. As the water is heavier, it tends to separate and recirculate. The degree of such steam-water slippage and recirculation depends upon the relative densities of steam and water, the relative amounts of steam and water in the mixture, the chemical and physical condition of the water, the steam flow velocity and the internal area of the riser

[13] *Mr. Gurney's Observations on Steam Carriages on Turnpike Roads* published by Baldwin and Cradock, London, 1832, p. 5.
[14] Adapted from a report by P. B. Place.

tube. Maximum slippage, as might be expected, is found in boilers having large diameter tubes, high ratios of water to steam, low flow velocities and water which has little tendency to foam. Minimum slippage occurs in boilers having small diameter tubes, high flow velocities, controlled and low circulation ratios and foamy boiler waters.[15]

Unified Theory of Boiler Circulation

There are two distinct but related ways of considering boiler circulation. One relates to the use of a circulating fluid to transmit heat from an external source to a machine whereby thermal energy may be converted into mechanical energy. In this view the boiler is looked upon as a sort of thermal transformer in which heat transfer functions are of primary importance and depend upon fluid circulation.

A second viewpoint of circulation is that it is a means of protecting the structure of the boiler by moving fluid through its drums, tubes and headers rapidly enough to prevent overheating and thereby guarantee safety of operation. This places circulation in the role of a structural protective mechanism.

Ideally these viewpoints are combined in a design in which safety and efficiency of heat transfer are maximized while cost is minimized.

From a physical standpoint, there are three principles involved in the study of natural circulation of fluid in a circuit.

1. Circulation is caused by the pressure created by expansion of the fluid due to the application of heat to some portion of the circuit.

2. When equilibrium has been established, the work available from expansion balances the work done against resistances to flow in the circuit.

3. The mass flow of fluid in a closed circuit is constant throughout the circuit and unaffected by change of volume by expansion under steady state heat input.

A unified theory of boiler circulation proposed by R. W. Haywood in 1951 incorporated revisions of the hydraulic theory proposed by W. Y. Lewis and S. A. Robertson in 1940, the thermodynamic theory proposed by R. S. Silver in 1943 and the expansion theory set forth by R. F. Davis in 1947. The following is a presentation of the Haywood theory with but minor changes in wording and terminology.[16] Subsequently, experimental work to supplement this theoretical study was carried out in the Engineering Department of Cambridge University un-

---

[15] An academic research approach to this subject by G. A. Nothmann and R. C. Binder, adapted from a master's degree thesis of the former, is the subject of an article published in *Combustion*, Vol. 14, June 1943, pp. 40–43, under title, "Slip Velocity in Boiler Tube Circuits." Experimental work is reported, and there are references to the important studies in boiler circulation conducted in Germany in the period between World War I and World War II.

[16] The pertinent references are as follows:

"Research into Fundamentals of Boiler Circulation Theory" published in the *General Discussion on Heat Transfer*, pp. 63–65, jointly sponsored by ASME-IME, 1951. Permission to reprint granted by Institution of Mechanical Engineers.

"The Circulation of Water and Steam in Water Tube Boilers and the Rational Simplification of Boiler Design," *Proceedings* IME, Vol. 143, 1940, pp. 147–178 plus discussion, Proceedings IME, Vol. 144, 1940, pp. 184–190.

"A Thermodynamic Theory of Circulation in Water Tube Boilers" by R. S. Silver, *Proceedings* IME, Vol. 153, 1945, pp. 261–281.

"Expansion Theory of Circulation in Water Tube Boilers" by R. F. Davis, *Engineering*, Vol. 163, 1947 pp. 145–148.

der the sponsorship of the Water Tube Boilermakers' Association.[17]

The Frictional Flow of a Homogeneous Fluid Along a Heated Pipe

The fundamental theory of frictional flow of a homogeneous fluid along a heated pipe must be understood before it can be applied to the special case of circulation, without bubble slip, in a boiler U-tube circuit.

The general energy equation relating to a unit mass of a homogeneous fluid in steady flow in a heated pipe is:

$$Jdq = Jdh + d\left(\frac{V^2}{2g_0}\right) + \frac{g}{g_0} dZ \qquad (7\text{--}1)$$

$$= JdE + pdv + vdp + \frac{VdV}{g_0} + \frac{g}{g_0} dZ$$
$$(7\text{--}2)$$

where q is heat flow into the unit; h is enthalpy of the unit; V is velocity of the unit; Z is height above a datum level; J is mechanical equivalent of heat; g_0 is standard gravitational acceleration; g is acceleration; E is internal energy; p is pressure and v is specific volume.

This equation applies whether the flow is frictional or frictionless. To develop from it the equation for frictional flow the equation of state for the fluid is needed, namely,

$$dE + \frac{pdv}{J} = TdS \qquad (7\text{--}3)$$

and the fact that for frictional flow

$$TdS = dq + \frac{dW_f}{J} \qquad (7\text{--}4)$$

where S is entropy of the unit, and W_f is the mechanical work dissipated by friction per unit mass of fluid.

The substitution of Eq. 7–3 and Eq. 7–4 in Eq. 7–2 gives

$$dW_f + vdp + \frac{VdV}{g_0} + \frac{g}{g_0} dZ = 0 \qquad (7\text{--}5)$$

All the terms in Eq. 7–5 represent energy quantities per unit mass of fluid, and dW_f is that part of the available mechanical energy which is dissipated by friction. In the simple case of skin friction in a straight pipe

$$dW_f = \frac{4f}{d} \frac{V^2}{2g_0} dl \qquad (7\text{--}6)$$

where f is a dimensionless friction coefficient; d is the inside diameter of the pipe and l is length of pipe.

The substitution of this in Eq. 7–5 would give the momentum equation for frictional flow in a straight pipe, but this is only a special case of the more general equation. For other "losses", such as in bends, etc., dW_f may usually be expressed as some function of the kinetic energy at the point, namely,

$$dW_f = K \frac{V^2}{2g_0} \qquad (7\text{--}7)$$

where K is friction loss coefficient for a particular point.

It is important to note that the units of

---

[17] For results of this research, see "Experimental Study of the Flow Conditions and Pressure Drop of Steam-Water Mixtures at High Pressures in Heated and Unheated Tubes" by R. W. Haywood, G. A. Knights, G. E. Middleton and J. R. S. Thom, *Proceedings* IME, Vol. 175, 1961, pp. 669–747. A later paper related to the same research is "Prediction of Pressure Drop During Forced Circulation Boiling of Water" by J. R. S. Thom, *International Journal of Heat and Mass Transfer*, Vol. 7, 1964, pp. 709–724.

dW_f are ft-lb-weight of energy per lb mass of fluid.

The Simple U-Circuit

In order not to obscure the main theme with unnecessary side issues, and to show as readily as possible, the equivalence of the different theories of circulation, the idealized simple U-circuit shown in Fig. 7–5 is considered. In these circumstances the following simplifying assumptions are justified where in other circumstances they might be questionable:

(1) The pressures at points A and F, just outside the tubes, are assumed to be the same, and equal to p_s, and the kinetic energy of the fluid is assumed to be negligible at A and F.

(2) D–E is a heated riser, in which the steam and water are assumed to move together as a homogeneous mixture, and in which there is a uniform increase in specific volume of the mixture with distance along the tube from D to E. Hence, in DE, $dZ = dl = a\,dv$, where $a = l/[v_1\,(v_2/v_1 - 1)]$.

(3) Frictional effects in the portion of the circuit from C to D are neglected.

The Hydrodynamic Theory of Circulation

The hydrodynamic theory of circulation is concerned with the variation of *pressure* (not "head"), the condition to be fulfilled being that

$$\int_A^F dp = 0$$

around the circuit. Hence Eq. 7–5 is applied in the form

$$-\int dp = \int \frac{g}{g_0}\frac{dz}{v} + \int \frac{V\,dV}{g_0 v} + \int \frac{dW_f}{v}$$

$$\tag{7-8}$$

whence

$$\int_C^B \frac{g}{g_0}\frac{dz}{v} - \int_D^E \frac{g}{g_0}\frac{dz}{v}$$

$$= \int_A^F \frac{dW_f}{v} + \int_A^F \frac{V\,dV}{g_0 v} \tag{7-9}$$

All the terms in Eq. 7–9 represent pressures (e.g. lb weight per sq ft), so that the hydrodynamic theory of circulation may be given formal expression in the following words:

"The rate of circulation adjusts itself until a state of equilibrium has been reached such that the difference between the 'hydrostatic' pressures at the feet of the downcomer and riser legs is equal to the sum of the total pressure drops due to friction and acceleration in the circuit.

"Hydrostatic pressure is the pressure which would exist at the point if there were a stationary column of liquid above the point, whose density varied in the same way as it would under the actual dynamic conditions of circulation. Pressure rise due to deceleration is included within the meaning of the term 'pressure drop due to acceleration'."

By carrying out these integrations for the circuit of Fig. 7–5, the respective terms of Eq. 7–9 are readily shown to be

$$\int_B^C \frac{g}{g_0}\frac{dz}{v} - \int_D^E \frac{g}{g_0}\frac{dz}{v}$$

$$= \frac{g}{g_0}\frac{l}{v_1}\left[1 - \frac{1}{v_2/v_1 - 1}\log_e v_2/v_1\right]$$

$$\tag{7-10}$$

$$\int_A^F \frac{dW_f}{v} = \frac{V_1^2}{2g_0 v_1}$$

$$\times\,[K_A + (v_2/v_1)K_F + (2f\,l/d)(v_2/v_1 + 3)] \tag{7-11}$$

$$\int_A^F \frac{V\,dV}{g_0 v} = \frac{V_1^2}{2g_0 v_1}\,(v_2/v_1 - 1) \tag{7-12}$$

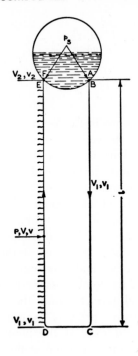

Fig. 7–5. Simple U-circuit

whence the velocity of circulation is given non-dimensionally by the expression

$$\frac{V_1^2}{2gl} = \frac{1 - \dfrac{1}{v_2/v_1 - 1} \log_e v_2/v_1}{C} \tag{7-13}$$

where

$$C = [(K_A + \{v_2/v_1\} K_F)$$
$$+ (2fl/d)(v_2/v_1 + 3) + (v_2/v_1 - 1)] \tag{7-14}$$

The Thermodynamic (or Expansion) Theory of Circulation

There is no real difference between the thermodynamic theory of Silver and the expansion theory of Davis, for the case when the fluid is assumed to flow as a homogeneous mixture, basically the same answer being arrived at by a slightly different reasoning and the work of both being subject to certain errors.

The corrected theory presented here is consequently termed the thermodynamic (or expansion) theory of circulation. It results from an essentially thermodynamic approach to the problem; at the same time it is very expressive of the physical nature of the process to describe it as an expansion theory. Its development is dependent on an understanding of the significance of the expansion work term, pdv, in the frictional, steady flow process. This may be found by substituting in Eq. 7–5 the relation

$$vdp = d(pv) - pdv \tag{7-15}$$

giving

$$pdv = dW_f + d(pv) + d\left(\frac{V^2}{2g_0}\right) + \frac{g}{g_0} dz \tag{7-16}$$

All the terms in Eq. 7–16 represent energy quantities (e.g. ft lb weight of energy per lb mass of fluid).

For integration round the circuit, Eq. 7–16 may be written

$$\int pdv = \int dW_f + \Delta FE + \Delta KE + \Delta PE \tag{7-17}$$

where ΔFE is increase in flow energy pv; ΔKE is increase in kinetic energy and ΔPE is increase in potential energy.

Applying this to the simple circuit of Fig. 7–5

$$\Delta FE = p_s(v_2 - v_1), \quad \Delta KE = 0, \quad \Delta PE = 0$$

Also, $p = p_s + p'$, where p' is the local excess of pressure at any point above the drum pressure. Substitution of these relations in Eq. 7–17 gives

$$\int_A^F p'dv = \int_A^F dW_f \qquad (7\text{--}18)$$

The thermodynamic (or expansion) theory of circulation may thus be given the following formal expression:

"When unit mass of fluid flowing round the circuit expands by an amount dv at a point where the pressure is $(p_s + p')$, it does an amount of work $(p_s + p')dv$ against the surrounding fluid, but the work done at the boundaries of the system in consequence of this expansion is only $p_s dv$.

"Hence there is an excess of mechanical work equal to $p'dv$ which is available for overcoming friction (or which, in the more general case, would also be available for imparting increased kinetic and potential energy to the fluid). This excess of mechanical work may thus be termed the 'work available for circulation', and the rate of circulation adjusts itself until a state of equilibrium is established between the work available for circulation and the mechanical energy dissipated by friction in the circuit."

It is evident that the thermodynamic (or expansion) theory will give the same answer for the rate of circulation as that given by the hydrodynamic theory from the fact that both are derived from the same basic equation. The hydrodynamic theory is simpler to apply because the thermodynamic (or expansion) theory requires a knowledge of the pressure at all points in the circuit where expansion is taking place, and this pressure must first be calculated by the procedure used in the hydrodynamic theory. The steps involved are outlined as follows:

In evaluating $\int_A^F p'dv$ it is necessary to integrate only over that part of the circuit where there is a change in volume, namely, in the heated riser. Thus

$$\int_A^F p'dv = \int_D^E p''dv + (p_E - p_s)(v_2 - v_1) \qquad (7\text{--}19)$$

where $p'' = (p - p_E)$, and is evaluated from Eq. 7–8 to give

$$p'' = \frac{g}{g_0} a \log_e \frac{v_2}{v} + \frac{G^2}{g_0}(v_2 - v)$$
$$+ \frac{aB}{2}(v_2^2 - v^2) \qquad (7\text{--}20)$$

where $B = 2fG^2/g_o d$ and G is mass velocity, V/v.

Also

$$(p_E - p_s) = -v_2/v_1(1 - K_F)\frac{V_1^2}{2g_0 v_1} \qquad (7\text{--}21)$$

Substituting Eqs. 7–20 and 7–21 in Eq. 7–19 and integrating,

$$\text{"work available"} = \int_A^F p'dv = \frac{g}{g_0} l$$
$$\times \left[1 - \frac{1}{v_2/v_1 - 1} \log_e v_2/v_1 \right] + \frac{V_1^2}{2g_0}$$
$$\times \left[(v_2/v_1 - 1)^2 + \frac{2fl/d}{3}(2\{v_2/v_1\} + 1) \right.$$
$$\times (v_2/v_1 - 1) - v_2/v_1$$
$$\left. \times (v_2/v_1 - 1)(1 - K_F) \right] \qquad (7\text{--}22)$$

The mechanical energy dissipated in friction in the whole circuit is given by

$$\int_A^F dW_f = K_A \frac{V_1^2}{2g_0} + 4fl/d \frac{V_1^2}{2g_0}$$
$$+ aB \int_{v_1}^{v_2} v^2 dv + K_F \frac{V_2^2}{2g_0}$$

where $a = \dfrac{l}{(v_2 - v_1)}$.

Hence

$$W_f = \frac{V_1^2}{2g_0}\left[K_A + (v_2/v_1)^2 K_F + \frac{4fl/d}{3}\right.$$
$$\left. \times \left((v_2/v_1)^2 + (v_2/v_1) + 4\right)\right]$$

$$(7\text{--}23)$$

Equating Eqs. 7–22 and 7–23 results again in Eqs. 7–13 and 7–14, thus giving the same answer for the rate of circulation as was given by the hydrodynamic theory. Nevertheless, although the thermodynamic (or expansion) theory may add to the better understanding of the physical processes involved in circulation, the evaluation of the rate of circulation by this means is seen to be considerably more complicated than by the hydrodynamic theory, and the latter is therefore much preferred for practical use.

Two Phase Flow[18]

The design of boiler furnaces in the subcritical pressure range has moved into areas that require closer consideration of the adequacy of coolant flow required to keep the evaporative process in waterwall tubes within the nucleate boiling range. The growing importance of this aspect of two phase flow has been brought about by the elevated steam pressures and increased steam qualities for which boilers are being designed. Conditions are aggravated by the increased and varying absorption rates to which some furnaces are subjected.[19]

In simplest terms, the design problem centers on the choice of a physical arrangement that provides for the coolest waterwall with minimum pump power expenditure. To accomplish this the designer must have knowledge of the conditions under which the evaporative process passes from nucleate to transitional and finally to film boiling, plus information on the manner in which waterwall metal temperature can be expected to change as these phases occur.

An understanding of what is involved in two phase flow under these conditions can be gained by observing the changes that are produced in the film conductance. This is indicated most directly by the inside tube metal temperature when the principal variables of heat flux, coolant mass flow, enthalpy and pressure are changed.

If a tube were to be heated uniformly along its length while water at a sufficiently high mass flow were passed through it at a given pressure level, the

[18] Material contributed by H. J. Blaskowski.
[19] The analytical and experimental literature relating to two phase flow is extremely voluminous, quite frequently repetitive and occasionally contradictory. General summaries of this work may be found in *Heat, Mass and Momentum Transfer* by Warren M. Rohsenow and Harry Y. Choi, Prentice-Hall, 1961, Chapter 9, Heat Transfer with Boiling, and in *Fundamentals of Heat Transfer* by S. S. Kutateladze, Academic Press, 1963, Chapter XVII, Heat Transfer in Boiling, and Chapter XVIII, Critical Heat Fluxes in Boiling. An unusually fine Ph.D. thesis by Novak Zuber, "Hydrodynamic Aspects of Boiling Heat Transfer," has been published by the U. S. Atomic Energy Commission as AECU 4439, 1959, 210 pp. A Russian translation available from the same source is "Hydrodynamics and Heat Transfer During Boiling in High Pressure Boilers" edited by M. A. Styrikovich, AEC-tr-4490, 1955, 272 pp.

inside metal temperature would follow a plot as described by the solid line in Fig. 7–6. If the flow rate were reduced, a point would be reached along the mixed or quality phase section of the plot where the metal temperature rises as indicated by the dashed line in the same illustration.

The point of departure from the horizontal is known as *DNB* or the point of departure from nucleate boiling. The maximum point on the dotted curve is variously referred to as the point of film boiling, the minimum conductance point of the burnout (*BO*) point. The section between *DNB* and *BO* is the region of transitional boiling.

Fig. 7–7 illustrates how both the *BO* point and the *DNB* point for the same mass flow and heat flux rates are affected by changes in pressure. Fig. 7–8 illustrates the effect of change in flow rate for values of pressure and heat flux. Fig. 7–9 illustrates the effect produced by change of heat flux for pressure and flow rate.

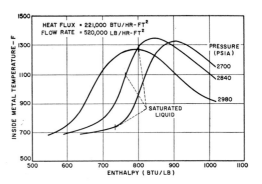

Fig. 7–7. Effect or change in pressure on BO and DNB points

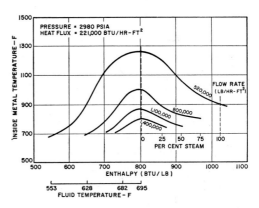

Fig. 7–8. Effect or change in flow on BO and DNB points

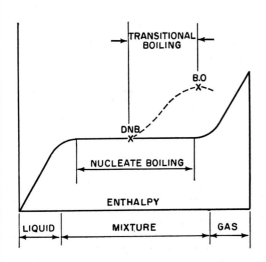

Fig. 7–6. Inside tube metal temperature as a function of two phase flow conditions

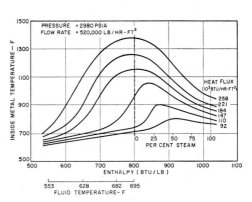

Fig. 7–9. Effect of change in heat flux on BO and DNB points

Header Flow Distribution[20]

A header is a pipe or manifold for collecting a fluid from or distributing a fluid to a number of smaller size pipes or tubes. Many such headers are used in the design of boilers for the distribution and collection of steam from the various heat absorbing surfaces. For example, in a reheater, spent steam from the turbine is returned to the boiler for reheating through one or more large size pipes, 18 to 36 in. in diameter. Heat is most efficiently transferred to the steam through a great number of small diameter tubes usually around 2 in. in diameter. The steam is transferred from the turbine leads to the reheater tubes through a header or headers. Likewise, the reheated steam is returned to the turbine through a collecting or outlet header.

The question arises: What size should a header be? That is, to supply a given number and size of tubes with a given quantity of steam, what diameter header should be utilized? If the header is too small, pressure gradients will take place in the header resulting in greater than average flow taking place in some tubes while other tubes are starved of flow. This is a disastrous condition which could result in overheating or burnout of the tubes which are starved. On the other hand, headers could be built so large that they would approach plenum chambers which have little or no pressure gradient within, but this would be prohibitively expensive. Typical headers in large boilers are from 25 to 100 ft long, supply 50 to 2000 tubes and are designed for 100 to 5000 psig and temperatures to 1200 F. Therefore, header design represents an economic compromise between tubing cost and header cost. As the size of a header is increased, the resulting imbalance in tube flows decreases, but the cost of the header increases. Conversely, as the size and cost of the header decrease, a resulting imbalance in tube flows increases. This can be designed for, but the tube tolerances, tube metal temperatures, tube wall thickness and possibly the grade of tube alloy will increase, resulting in increased tubing cost. The situation is illustrated graphically in Fig. 7–10.

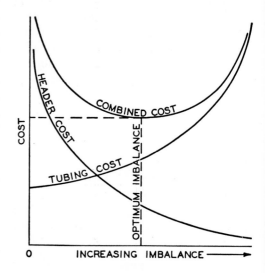

Fig. 7–10.   Economic effect of imbalance in tube flows

Nature of Header Flow

To resolve the problem, something must be known about the nature of flow in

---

[20] Material in this section contributed by W. J. Deane.

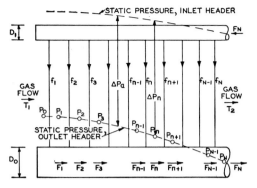

Fig. 7–11. Header system

headers and how it is distributed to each tube. Consider the header system shown schematically in Fig. 7–11.

Steam enters the inlet header at the right end, is distributed to a total of N parallel tubes in a hot gas path which heats the steam to a higher temperature and is discharged into an outlet header where the steam combines and again leaves the outlet header at the right end. Actually, there are a great number of header arrangements possible, but for illustrative purposes the simplest one has been chosen. The steam may enter through both ends, through a tee in the center, through an arbitrary number of tees distributed along the length of the inlet header, and each in combination with as many possible outlet arrangements. In general, there will be a separate solution for each arrangement.

Superimposed on the schematic diagram of Fig. 7–11 are characteristic header pressure gradient curves. In the inlet header the pressure rises in the direction of flow due to the deceleration of the steam as it approaches the dead end. In the outlet header the pressure falls in the direction of flow due to the acceleration of the steam as it approaches the outlet and also due to the interference or turbulence loss created by the jet issuing from each tube

outlet, piercing or obstructing the bulk flow in the header.

In general, there are three distinct components of the pressure gradient in an outlet header. These are, in order of importance, (1) the loss created by the acceleration of the fluid as it combines with fluid from a tube opening, which loss would be predicted by Bernoulli's equation, (2) the interference or turbulence loss referred to above which cannot very accurately be predicted from theoretical fluid mechanics but must be determined by experiment and (3) the loss due to pipe friction on the wall of the header. The third and last item is of least significance and is here neglected for simplicity.

Analysis of Outlet Header

Consider the enlarged detail of section n of the outlet header shown in Fig. 7–12.

The flow in the header at section $n-1$ is M_{n-1} and the velocity is V_{n-1}. This combines with the flow m_n from the tube n, resulting in a net flow M_n at section n and corresponding velocity, V_n.

Thus,

$$M_n = M_{n-1} + m_n \qquad (7\text{–}24)$$

Considering the flow which crosses both sections $n-1$ and n in the header, applica-

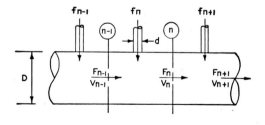

Fig. 7–12. Outlet header

tion of the steady flow energy equation yields

$$P_{n-1}v + \frac{V_{n-1}^2}{2g} = P_nv + \frac{V_n^2}{2g} + H$$

where H represents the head lost due to turbulence, interference and friction and v is the specific volume of the fluid. Since the pressure drop and velocities are very small compared with the absolute pressure it is justified to assume constant density throughout the header and thus incompressible flow phenomena may be employed. The steady flow energy equation, therefore, reduces to Bernoulli's formula with a term included to represent head loss.

Converting velocity to mass flow and eliminating M_{n-1} by use of Eq. 7–24, the energy or Bernoulli equation becomes

$$P_{n-1} - P_n = \frac{M_n^2 v}{2gA^2} [1 - (1 - m_n/M_n)^2] + H/v$$

Various investigators, experimenting with many sizes of tubes and pipes, have furnished test data on the head loss.[21] From graphs of these data plotted on suitable coordinates, an excellent fit may be found with curves of the form

$$H/v = (C_0 - 1) \frac{M_n^2 v}{2gA^2} [1 - (1 - m_n/M_n)^2]$$

where C_o is a constant loss coefficient, the value of which depends on the diameter ratio, d/D, and the number of rows of tubes at a section. For simplicity only one row of tubes is being considered, but in actual systems there may be two, six, or more rows per section and C_o may vary from 1.5 to 3.5. That is, the turbulence loss may be from 50 per cent less to 250 per cent more than the conversion of static pressure to velocity head.

Including the expression above for the head loss, the actual static pressure drop across a tube opening becomes

$$P_{n-1} - P_n = C_0 \frac{M_n^2 v}{2gA^2} [1 - (1 - m_n/M_n)^2]$$

$$(7\text{--}25)$$

Analysis of Inlet Header

Next, attention is focused on the inlet header as shown in Fig. 7–13. In the case of the inlet header there is less turbulence loss because the flow is dividing rather than combining. Therefore, the equation for pressure rise along the inlet header in the vicinity of a tube opening takes the same form as Eq. 7–25 but is distinguished by a different loss coefficient.

$$P_{n-1} - P_n = C_i \frac{M_n^2 v}{2gA^2} [1 - (1 - m_n/M_n)^2]$$

$$(7\text{--}26)$$

This is identical to Eq. 7–25 although it must be remembered that P, v and A in Eq. 7–25 refer to conditions in the outlet header only and in Eq. 7–26 to conditions in the inlet header only.

Simplifying Assumptions

Now, the assumption is made that the header-to-header pressure drop across any

[21] The following references may be cited as being especially valuable and helpful: "Mechanics of Manifold Flow," by John S. McNown, Paper No. 2714, Trans. ASCE, Vol. 119, 1954, pp. 1103–1142; "The Manifold Problem," by J. D. Keller, Trans. ASME, Journal of Applied Mechanics, Vol. 16, 1949, pp. 77–85; and "Guide to the Calculations of Head Losses in Piping Systems," by S. T. Bonnington, Publication TN445, The British Hydromechanics Research Association, January 1953.

tube is proportional to some power of the flow and it is further assumed that the factor of proportionality is the same for each tube.

Thus

$$\left. \begin{array}{c} P_{ni} - P_{n0} = K m_n^S \\ \text{and} \\ P_{(n-1)i} - P_{(n-1)0} = K m_{n-1}^S \end{array} \right\} \quad (7\text{-}27)$$

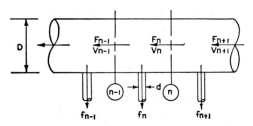

Fig. 7–13. Inlet header

where K includes the sum of all loss coefficients including tube friction, entrance and exit losses, bends, etc. It should be noted that S is not necessarily equal to two as classical pressure drop formulas would indicate, because the tubes are subject to heat absorption, and the specific volume varies along the tube length and also from one tube to another.

Eqs. 7–25 and 7–26, including the appropriate subscripts in accordance with Eq. 7–27, may be rewritten as

$$(P_{n-1} - P_n)_0 = C_0 \frac{M_n^2 v_0}{2g A_0^2}$$
$$\times [1 - (1 - m_n/M_n)^2] \quad (7\text{-}28)$$

$$(P_{n-1} - P_n)_i = C_i \frac{M_n^2 v_i}{2g A_i^2}$$
$$\times [1 - (1 - m_n/M_n)^2] \quad (7\text{-}29)$$

Four basic equations for the solution of the problem are presented in Eqs. 7–27 through 7–29. There are N unknown tube flows, $N+1$ unknown inlet header pressures from $(P_o$ to $P_n)_i$ and assuming the outlet pressure, P_{No}, is known there are N unknown outlet header pressures from $(P_o$ to $P_{n-1})$. Then, there are $3N+1$ unknowns associated with the problem. To obtain a solution, Eq. 7–27 may be written N times as n varies from 1 to N. Eq. 7–28 may be written N times as n varies from 1 to N and Eq. 7–29 may be written N times as N varies from 1 to N. The final

equation necessary to a solution comes from the fact that the total flow entering the system equals the sum of all the tube flows or

$$M_n = m_1 + m_2 + m_3 + \cdots + m_n + \cdots + m_N$$

There is now a system of $3N+1$ equations in $3N+1$ unknowns where N is the total number of parallel tubes. Therefore, with 1000 tubes or more the problem could not be solved by hand but would have to be programmed on a digital computer. In this type of applied header problem, intermediate pressures along the header are of no particular interest. However, individual tube flows are of major concern. Pressure may be eliminated completely from Eqs. 7–27 through 7–29 by reduction to one equation in terms of flow only. Physically, this is equivalent to saying that the sum of the pressure drops around a loop bounded by two adjacent tubes equals zero, analogous to Kirchoff's law in electric circuitry. The problem would then be reduced to N simultaneous second-order equations in N unknown tube flows, which still would be a monumental task to solve by hand for all but the most trivial cases of two, three or four tubes. In general, boiler header design does not warrant so precise, rigorous or expensive a solution. Actually, the absolute value of all the tube flows need not be known, but rather, some index of the distribution, such as the deviation from the average of the *minimum* tube flow. Such an index will tell the extent of overheating of the tube which is starved the most. This is the most important consideration in header design.

Practical Simplified Solution

In practice, the variation of flow from one tube to another due to header effects is very slight. In fact, no more than about five per cent deviation of the minimum from the average can be tolerated, and in general it is less than that. To economize any more than this on the headers would drive the tubing costs too high. Therefore, with the qualification of small deviations from the average in mind, it can be seen that,

$$m_1 \cong m_2 \cong m_3 \cong m_n \cong m_{n-1} \cong m_a \cong M_N/N$$

and

$$M_n \cong n m_a \cong (n/N) M_N$$

Making the indicated substitution in Eq. 7–28 this becomes,

$$(P_{n-1} - P_n)_0 = C_0 \frac{M_{Nv0}^2}{2g A_0^2} \left(\frac{2n-1}{N^2} \right)$$

Therefore a close approximation of the pressure drop across each section may be obtained by substituting $n = 1, 2, 3, \ldots$, recognizing that the term $\dfrac{M_{Nv0}^2}{2g A_0^2}$ is the velocity head at the outlet section of the outlet header.

Thus,

$$(P_0 - P_1)_0 = C_0 \frac{M_{Nv0}^2}{2g A_0^2} \left(\frac{1}{N^2} \right)$$

$$(P_1 - P_2)_0 = C_0 \frac{M_{Nv0}^2}{2g A_0^2} \left(\frac{3}{N^2} \right)$$

$$(P_2 - P_3)_0 = C_0 \frac{M_{Nv0}^2}{2g A_0^2} \left(\frac{5}{N^2} \right)$$

and so on.

To determine the pressure from P_o to P_n it is necessary to add up each section differential.

$$
\begin{aligned}
(P_0 - P_n)_0 &= (P_0 - P_1)_0 + (P_1 - P_2)_0 \\
&\quad + (P_2 - P_3)_0 + \cdots \\
&\quad + (P_{n-1} - P_n)_0 \\
&= C_0 \frac{M_{Nv0}^2}{2g A_0^2} \frac{1}{N^2} \\
&\quad \times (1 + 3 + 5 + \cdots + 2n - 1)
\end{aligned}
$$

It can be shown that the sum of the first $2n$–1 integers is

$$1 + 3 + 5 + \cdots + 2n - 1 = \sum_{n=1}^{n} (2n - 1)$$

$$= n^2$$

Then

$$(P_0 - P_n)_0 = C_0 \frac{M_{Nv0}^2}{2g A_0^2} \left(\frac{n}{N} \right)^2 \qquad (7\text{--}30)$$

and

$$(P_0 - P_N)_0 = C_0 \frac{M_{Nv0}^2}{2g A_0^2}$$

and

$$(P_n - P_N)_0 = C_0 \frac{M_{Nv0}^2}{2g A_0^2} [1 - (n/N)^2]$$

Similarly for the inlet header, from Eq. 7–29

$$(P_{n-1} - P_n)_i = C_i \frac{M_{Nvi}^2}{2g A_i^2} \left(\frac{2n-1}{N^2} \right)$$

and

$$
\begin{aligned}
(P_0 - P_n)_i &= (P_0 - P_1)_i + (P_1 - P_2)_i \\
&\quad + (P_2 - P_3)_i + \cdots + (P_{n-1} - P_n)_i
\end{aligned}
$$

$$= C_i \frac{M_{NV_i}^2}{2g A_i^2} \frac{1}{N^2}$$

$$\times (1 + 3 + 5 + \cdots + 2n - 1)$$

$$= C_i \frac{M_{NV_i}^2}{2g A_i^2} \left(\frac{n}{N}\right)^2 \qquad (7\text{-}31)$$

and

$$(P_0 - P_N)_i = C_i \frac{M_{NV_i}^2}{2g A_i^2}$$

and

$$(P_n - P_N)_i = C_i \frac{M_{NV_i}^2}{2g A_i^2} [1 - (n/N)^2]$$

The pressure drop across the nth tube is then,

$$P_{ni} - P_{n0} = (P_0 - P_n)_0$$
$$\quad - (P_0 - P_n)_i + P_{0i} - P_{00}$$

where P_{oi} and P_{oo} are the static pressures at the dead end of the inlet header and outlet header, respectively. Substituting from Eqs. 7–30 and 7–31, this becomes

$$P_{ni} - P_{n0} = C_0 \frac{M_{NV0}^2}{2g A_0^2} \left(\frac{n}{N}\right)^2$$

$$\quad - C_i \frac{M_{NV_i}^2}{2g A_i^2} \left(\frac{n}{N}\right)^2 + P_{0i} - P_{00}$$

$$(7\text{-}32)$$

Denoting tube friction drop by ΔP, Eq. 7–32 becomes

$$P_{ni} - P_{n0} = \Delta P_n - Z/v_n$$

$$= C_0 \frac{M_{NV0}^2}{2g A_0^2} \left(\frac{n}{N}\right)^2$$

$$\quad - C_i \frac{M_{NV_i}^2}{2g A_i^2} \left(\frac{n}{N}\right)^2 + \Delta P_0 - Z/v_n$$

and

$$\Delta P_n = \Delta P_0 + C_0 \frac{M_{NV0}^2}{2g A_0^2} \left(\frac{n}{N}\right)^2$$

$$\quad - C_i \frac{M_{NV_i}^2}{2g A_i^2} \left(\frac{n}{N}\right)^2 + Z\left(\frac{1}{v_n} - \frac{1}{v_0}\right)$$

$$(7\text{-}33)$$

where v_n and v_o are the mean fluid volumes of the nth and first tube, respectively. The last term on the right represents elevation head effects but for steam flow is usually very small compared with the friction drop ΔP_o and so may be neglected. However, there are cases where the elevation head differences do need to be accounted for but this is a separate problem outside the scope of this presentation.

In Eq. 7–27 the elevation terms have already been neglected. Now, the average pressure drop or the pressure drop produced by the average tube flow is equal to the integral of ΔP_n across the panel. Thus,

$$\Delta P_a = \frac{\int_0^1 \Delta P_n \, d(n/N)}{\int_0^1 d(n/N)}$$

Substituting from Eq. 7–33 and performing the indicated integration,

$$\Delta P_a = \int_0^1 \left[\Delta P_0 + C_0 \frac{M_{NV0}^2}{2g A_0^2} \left(\frac{n}{N}\right)^2\right.$$

$$\left. - C_i \frac{M_{NV_i}^2}{2g A_i^2} \left(\frac{n}{N}\right)^2\right] d(n/N)$$

$$= \Delta P_0 + 1/3 \left(C_0 \frac{M_{NV0}^2}{2g A_0^2} - C_i \frac{M_{NV_i}^2}{2g A_i^2}\right)$$

or

$$\Delta P_0 = \Delta P_a - 1/3 \left(C_0 \frac{M_{NV0}^2}{2g A_0^2} - C_i \frac{M_{NV_i}^2}{2g A_i^2}\right)$$

$$(7\text{-}34)$$

Including this value of ΔP_o in Eq. 7–33

$$\Delta P_n = \Delta P_a - 1/3\left(C_0 \frac{M_{NV0}^2}{2gA_0^2} - C_i \frac{M_{NVi}^2}{2gA_i^2}\right)$$

$$+ (n/N)^2\left(C_0 \frac{M_{NV0}^2}{2gA_0^2} - C_i \frac{M_{NVi}^2}{2gA_i^2}\right)$$

$$\Delta P_n = \Delta P_a - \left[C_0 \frac{M_{NV0}^2}{2gA_0^2} - C_i \frac{M_{NVi}^2}{2gA_i^2}\right]$$

$$\times [1/3 - (n/N)^2] \qquad (7\text{-}35)$$

From Eq. 7–27,

$$m_n = (\Delta P_n/K)^{1/S}$$
$$m_a = (\Delta P_a/K)^{1/S}$$

or

$$m_n/m_a = (\Delta P_n/\Delta P_a)^{1/S}$$

Substituting from Eq. 7–35,

$$m_n/m_a = \frac{\Delta P_a - \left[C_0 \dfrac{M_{NV0}^2}{2gA_0^2} - C_i \dfrac{M_{NVi}^2}{2gA_i^2}\right] \times [1/3 - (n/N)^2]^{1/S}}{\Delta P_a}$$

Dividing numerator and denominator by ΔP_a, replacing $\dfrac{M_{NV}^2}{2gA^2}$ by VH (velocity head) and factoring out VH_i, the following relationship is obtained:

$$m_n/m_a = \left\{1 - \frac{VH_i}{\Delta P_a}\left[C_0 \frac{VH_0}{VH_i} - C_i\right]\right.$$
$$\left. \times [1/3 - (n/N)^2]\right\}^{1/S}$$

$$(7\text{-}36)$$

Eq. 7–36 gives the variation of tube flow across the whole system as a percentage of the average flow, both as a function of axial position, n/N and also as a function of header size (VH_i, VH_0). It can be seen that the tube flow equals the average flow when

$$1/3 - (n/N)^2 = 0$$

or when

$$n/N = \frac{\sqrt{3}}{3} = 0.577$$

for all header selections. It can also be seen that all tube flows equal the average flow when

$$C_0 \frac{VH_0}{VH_i} - C_i = 0$$

This condition exists when the pressure rise in the inlet header just equals the pressure drop in the outlet header. It is also seen that when

$$C_0 \frac{VH_0}{VH_i} - C_i > 0$$

m_n/m_a is a minimum at $n/N = 0$ and when $C_0 \dfrac{VH_0}{VH_i} - C_i < 0$ m_n/m_a is a minimum at $n/N = 1$.

To illustrate these conditions, Eq. 7–36 is plotted on Fig. 7–14 with $S = 1.85$ and for various values of

$$X = \frac{VH_i}{\Delta P_a}\left(C_0 \frac{VH_0}{VH_i} - C_i\right)$$

In order to make practical utilization of Eq. 7–36 or Fig. 7–10, one must first determine the values of C_o and C_i by experiment. This is accomplished by the construction of a header-tubing system in which equal diameter, equal coefficient orifices are installed in each tube to measure the flow and simulate pressure drop. Then with the measured values of flow, pressure drop and velocity head, the coefficients are calculated from Eq. 7–36. Great care must be exercised in the construction of the equipment in order to isolate the header effects only.

If the orifices have slightly dissimilar co-efficients or if the tubes have slightly different diameters or lengths, then these effects also will contribute to the unbalance in tube flows making it very difficult to separate the effects.

As mentioned previously, the values of C_o and C_i depend on the tubing to header diameter ratio and also on the number of tube rows per section, or,

$$C_0 = \phi_0(d_0/D_0, R_0)$$
$$C_i = \phi_i(d_i/D_i, R_i)$$

Eq. 7–36 has been derived for the simple arrangement with one end inlet and one end outlet both on the same side of the tubing system. There are some twenty-five other header arrangements in common use, and each will have a distinct

solution, similar to Eq. 7–36 but with different combinations of the coefficients.

As stated previously, interest is not primarily in the magnitude of all tube flows but more particularly in the maximum deviations from the average. Recalling that the whole derivation is based on small deviations from the average, then expanding Eq. 7–36 by the binomial theorem and dropping second order terms and higher,

$$m_n/m_a = 1 - \frac{1}{S}\frac{VH_i}{\Delta P_a}\left[C_0\frac{VH_0}{VH_i} - C_i\right]$$
$$\times [1/3 - (n/N)^2]$$

Since the location of the maximum and minimum flows is known from Fig. 7–10, the following relationships may be expressed

$$\left.\begin{array}{l}\dfrac{m_{\max}}{m_a} = 1 + 2/3\,\dfrac{1}{S}\dfrac{VH_i}{\Delta P_a}\left(C_0\dfrac{VH_0}{VH_i} - C_i\right)\\[4mm]\dfrac{m_{\min}}{m_a} = 1 - 1/3\,\dfrac{1}{S}\dfrac{VH_i}{\Delta P_a}\left(C_0\dfrac{VH_0}{VH_i} - C_i\right)\end{array}\right\}\text{when } C_0\dfrac{VH_0}{VH_i} > C_i \qquad (7\text{–}37)$$

and

$$\left.\begin{array}{l}\dfrac{m_{\max}}{m_a} = 1 + 1/3\,\dfrac{1}{S}\dfrac{VH_i}{\Delta P_a}\left(C_i - C_0\dfrac{VH_0}{VH_i}\right)\\[4mm]\dfrac{m_{\min}}{m_a} = 1 - 2/3\,\dfrac{1}{S}\dfrac{VH_i}{\Delta P_a}\left(C_i - C_0\dfrac{VH_0}{VH_i}\right)\end{array}\right\}\text{when } C_0\dfrac{VH_0}{VH_i} < C_i \qquad (7\text{–}38)$$

The index of distribution, U, may be defined as the percentage deviation of the minimum flow from the average, or,

$$U \equiv \frac{m_a - m_{\min}}{m_a} = 1 - \frac{m_{\min}}{m_a}$$

Substituting in Eqs. 7–37 and 7–38,

$$\left.\begin{array}{l}U = \dfrac{1}{3S}\dfrac{VH_i}{\Delta P_a}\left(C_0\dfrac{VH_0}{VH_i} - C_i\right) \quad \text{when } C_0\dfrac{VH_0}{VH_i} > C_i\\[4mm]U = \dfrac{2}{3S}\dfrac{VH_i}{\Delta P_a}\left(C_i - C_0\dfrac{VH_0}{VH_i}\right) \quad \text{when } C_0\dfrac{VH_0}{VH_i} < C_i\end{array}\right\} \qquad (7\text{–}39)$$

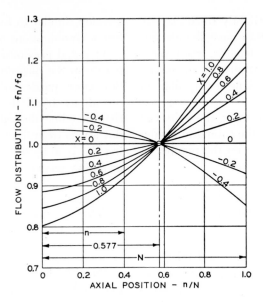

Fig. 7—14. Distribution of flow across header system

Thus, with limits on U set up from experience, header sizes and corresponding velocity heads are selected to yield a value of U within allowable limits.

Flow Modeling of Furnaces and Ducts[22]

Cold flow modeling is a useful adjunct to the design of furnaces. When properly applied, cold flow models may avoid pitfalls of extrapolation of experience from smaller to larger units. As physical size and the required quantities of fuel and combustion products increase, defects or inadequacy of design that might be tolerable in smaller boilers may become intolerable from the standpoint of fluid flow, heat transfer, pressure loss, corrosion, selection of materials or overall performance.

Techniques of flow modeling must meet one fundamental requirement before they are useful as an aid to design. They must obey the *principle of similarity*[23] so that model results may be directly compared or translated to conditions in full scale installations. To one degree or another, the following types of similarity should be taken into consideration: geometrical, mechanical, thermal and chemical. At this point a great deal of judgment enters in, for the effects in some cases may be negligible, while in others they may involve

[22] Material in this section contributed by R. C. Patterson and R. F. Abrahamsen.
[23] See *Pilot Plants, Models and Scaleup Methods in Chemical Engineering* by R. E. Johnstone and M. W. Thring, McGraw-Hill, 1957. Chapter 3 of this basic reference deals with the principle of similarity and Chapter 4, with dimensional analysis.

scale effects for which corrections must be provided. *Dimensional analysis* is a technique for minimizing the number of independent variables that must be taken into account in modeling and other experimental approaches. One of the most significant generalizations useful in dimensional analysis is known as Buckingham's Pi Theorem, a derivation of which is found on pages 289–292 of *ASME Transactions*, Vol 37, 1915.[24] An expression of this theorem, as applied to flow modeling, is as follows:

$$\frac{p}{\rho v^2} = f\left(\frac{\lambda}{l}, \frac{\eta}{l}, \frac{\rho v l}{\mu}, \frac{\rho v^2 l}{\sigma}, \frac{\rho v^2}{e}, \frac{v^2}{gl}\right)$$

$$(7\text{--}40)$$

This functional equation shows that the relation of pressure and velocity in a flow system is a function of at least six ratios of the various physical characteristics which affect the systems. The first two ratios on the right hand side of the equation define the geometrical similarity of shape and cross section. Next is the Reynolds number which incorporates the effects of fluid density and viscosity. Surface tension, which can be related to conditions at the boundary layer, is considered in the fourth term, known as the Weber number. The last two terms are the Cauchy and Froude numbers which take into account, respectively, the relationships of fluid velocity to that of sound and the acceleration of gravity.

In flow modeling of furnaces and ducts,

decisions must be reached as to which of these physical characteristics must be faithfully reproduced and which can be approximated or neglected. Ideally, the models should be fuel fired, and this was one of the very early approaches used in the iron and steel industry.[25] This method of attack has not gained widespread acceptance in the boiler industry because of the complexities of modeling the combustion process.

Among the techniques used in cold flow modeling are two dimensional smoke tables, three dimensional water models and three dimensional air models. Despite their isothermal nature, these three techniques can be applied to almost any significant flow distribution problem in furnaces or connecting ductwork. Visual impact of flow phenomena, as shown by direct observation or by motion picture or still photography, constitutes one of the most important factors in cold flow model work.

Obviously, complete similarity in flow modeling of furnaces and ducts would be difficult and extremely costly. The major decisions in flow modeling are decisions as to which of the physical characteristics must be faithfully reproduced or simulated.

Present day furnaces of all types tend to be substantially larger even than their predecessors of the recent past. Recent growth in physical size of commercial equipment is dictated largely by economics and is a part of the continual at-

---

[24] In the light of emphasis on engineering science, the reader will find of interest not only the paper entitled "Model Experiments and the Forms of Empirical Equations," pp. 263–296, but also the discussion on heat transmission on pp. 72–78 of the same volume by Edgar Buckingham, then a physicist at the U. S. Bureau of Standards.

[25] A book covering these applications as well as some in the boiler industry is *The Science of Flames and Furnaces* by M. W. Thring, Second Edition, John Wiley, 1962. An early paper dealing with model boilers fired with fuel is "Circulation in Horizontal Water Tube Boilers" by Paul A. Bancel, *Trans.* ASME, Vol. 37, 1915, pp. 1011–1042.

tempt to reduce capital investment per unit of output and to reduce costs of operation. The substantial increase in physical size of commercial furnaces and auxiliary equipment, together with increasing emphasis on high availability and minimum cost of operation, puts a distinct premium on effective design. Simple extrapolation of previous designs often is not enough, since tolerable flow maldistributions of earlier designs may become intolerable from the standpoint of heat transfer, pressure loss, corrosion, wear, material selection or overall performance. Properly applied cold flow models are a useful and necessary tool for identifying all of the major pitfalls and many of the minor pitfalls which should be avoided in duct and furnace design.

Flow modeling techniques must meet one fundamental requirement before they are useful as an aid to design. The requirement is that model results must be directly comparable or translatable to the prototype. Areas of doubt immediately arise as to the adequacy of a model for truly representing the flow phenomena which will exist in the prototype. It is possible to circumvent these areas of doubt by use of all the similarity criteria of Eq. 7–40 with hot gas or fuel fired models. Such an approach is expensive, time consuming, and probably unnecessary.

In flow modeling work related to boilers and boiler furnaces, one area of considerable interest is the simulation or representation of the flow of products of combustion in boiler furnaces and gas passages so that heat transfer surfaces can be selected and located in the most effective manner. In general, the best use of heat transfer surface is accomplished with uniform flow distribution of the heat transfer fluids.

Experience has shown that there is no single modeling technique that is superior to all others as a guide for obtaining uniform flow distribution in the gas passages of a boiler. On the other hand, utilization of a variety of modeling and test techniques often leads to the quickest and most accurate solution of gas flow distribution problems.

Two dimensional smoke table models, three dimensional water models, and three dimensional air models can be adapted to virtually any significant flow distribution problem in furnaces or ductwork, despite the isothermal nature of each of the three modeling techniques. None of the methods result in so-called true models, but they can be called "adequate" models for lack of a better term. All that is necessary for successful utilization of each of the methods is recognition of the similarity criteria which need to or need *not* be maintained for each method. The similarity criteria, which are essential to the successful use of each type of model, will be discussed, and the degree of correlation with prototype performance will be cited.

Smoke Table Testing

Smoke table modeling provides a quick method of making a visual assessment of the aerodynamic characteristics of fluid flow systems. This technique lends itself to rapid screening of a series of proposed design features. The models are simple, inexpensive, easily set up and readily modified. Modeling is limited to two dimensional flow studies. This technique provides pertinent information as to areas in which further study, using more refined methods, should be carried out. In many cases smoke table tests of themselves are sufficient to provide a suitable answer as to the effectiveness of a design.[26]

Qualitative data is obtained from smoke table models. Records of the model flow characteristics may be made by tracing the flow streamlines on the glass top of the table, making freehand sketches of flow patterns, and making still photographs or motion pictures of the operating model. Relative values may be arrived at by scaling the size of the indicated eddies, stagnant areas or the portion of a flow channel that is being effectively used.

The model is simply a mockup of a section or a slice model of the three dimensional flow envelope to be studied. A typical example would be a duct configuration or furnace elevation. The model is sandwiched between two pieces of glass that are backlighted to make flow conditions, as traced by the smoke, visible. The models are cut from soft insulation board. Where necessary, sheet metal is used for vanes or baffles. Small internal components may be made from plastic, wood or rubber. A typical smoke table setup is shown in Fig. 7–15.

Exact geometrical similarity with the prototype is used in smoke table slice models. In some instances, a component upstream or downstream of the model is not scale modeled. An example of this would be a regenerative type air heater in which the draft loss is ten or more times greater than the loss in the ductwork ahead of it. The air heater in this case tends to improve flow distribution upstream, due to the flow resistance. When modeling the ductwork, a screen or perforated plate is used to simulate the air heater resistance in the system. The screen approximates the effect of a complicated air heater section.

Flow velocities in the areas under study are maintained in the laminar flow range. If the flow velocities are increased to the turbulent range, the smoke streamers dissipate in the air, making interpretation of results much more difficult. The operation of the smoke table is quite simple, for the adjustments in general are made by visual inspection. A nearly constant mass flow is used for all models to maintain the same relative smoke density in the unit while photographing. This is done to insure uniform lighting conditions in a sequence of photographs.

These models are quite effective for demonstration purposes. Areas where flow separation from the boundaries occurs may be readily seen. Stagnant areas and eddies are apparent to the observer. Flow disturbances may be traced to their source and their magnitude assessed. The investigator can readily illustrate the flow streamlines, trace effects of flow separation and point out good and bad design features. The fluid motion can be clearly seen and judged without resorting to vectors, contours or other conventional graphical methods of presenting flow information. A series of models can be demonstrated quickly to show a sequence in development of an acceptable design. A typical "before" and "after" sequence is shown in Fig. 7–16 which illustrates the boundary flow separation which can occur and the correction that can be made in the flue gas ductwork between the economizer and the air heater of a large boiler.

---

[26] A pioneering paper by M. J. Archbold deals with the smoke table approach to the design of power plant ductwork. It is entitled "A Visual Qualitative Approach to Duct Design for Power Plants" and appeared in *Combustion*, Vol. 29, April 1958, pp. 34–40.

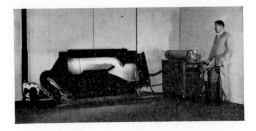

Fig. 7–15.   Smoke table apparatus

Three Dimensional Water Models

Many flow problems are inherently three dimensional and cannot be handled satisfactorily with two dimensional smoke table models. Three dimensional water modeling requires a geometrically accurate transparent plastic model of the furnace or duct envelope. Exact reproduction of heat transfer surface in the form of tubes or rods spaced as they would be spaced in the prototype is unnecessary; in fact, it is undesirable for cost and operational reasons. Simulation of tube bundles by a convenient spacing of several thin plastic sheets cut to the overall outline of the prototype surface is completely adequate for the purposes of this type testing. If prototype tube arrangement is such that lateral or cross flow can occur, the thin plastic sheet may be perforated so that the same lateral free cross flow area exists in model and prototype.

In addition to maintenance of exact geometric similarity between model furnaces and prototypes, it is necessary to base model burner dimensions on the jet momentum principle outlined by Johnstone and Thring.[27] This results in geometric distortion of the model burners

with respect to the furnace. The type flame being modeled determines the direction such distortion will take, but in general the result for a cold water model is that free flow area in the burners is slightly greater than geometric similarity with the prototype would dictate. There should be no distortion of physical location of burners with respect to other major features of furnace geometry.

Maintenance of Reynolds number similarity in cold water furnace models is optional with the investigator if his principal interest is the study of flow distribution. Most commercial furnaces operate with Reynolds numbers well into the turbulent range. No significant variations in flow contours have been noted when Reynolds number was intentionally varied over a wide range in the turbulent region.

One of the principal advantages of cold water models is the relatively small scale to which they can be built. A scale of 30:1 or 36:1 results in a furnace model of convenient "table top" size which gives accurate representations of flow patterns in a typical boiler prototype which may be 30 feet square and 120 feet high or larger.

Various flow pattern tracers have been used, but the most satisfactory have been thermoplastic resin pellets of specific gravity 1.00 to 1.02. Such pellets or chips are available in various sizes, shapes and colors, and they faithfully follow the water flow paths in the model because their density is essentially the same as water. Fig. 7–17 shows a typical furnace flow pattern traced by such beads in a water model.

For best results, three dimensional water model work requires close attention to details of construction and operation of the models and the attendant water sys-

---

[27] See *Pilot Plants, Models and Scaleup Methods in Chemical Engineering,* op. cit., pp. 202–212.

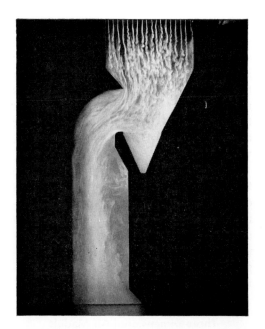

Fig. 7—16. Smoke table hot duct model

(a) Showing separation from flow boundary, left
(b) Showing improved flow pattern due to redesign of duct, right

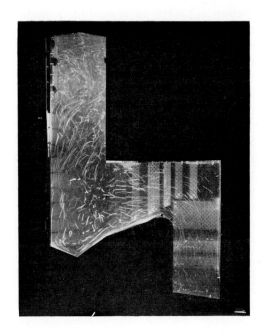

Fig. 7—17. Typical water model flow pattern, side elevation of a top fired furnace

Fig. 7—18. Apparatus for making color movies of flow patterns in water models

tem. Up to 300,000 lb per hr of water may be circulated continuously through a table top model. It should be clean water and must remain clean if maximum clarity is to be obtained.

Visual impact best describes the reaction created by three dimensional water models. Three dimensional flow patterns that have been measured quantitatively in air models or prototypes often are difficult to explain in words or to represent with clarity in two dimensional plots. In most cases, observation of a three dimensional water model leads to a more nearly complete understanding of flow phenomena which may have been measured but misunderstood in other work.

Three dimensional water models have been primarily qualitative tools for demonstrating significant variations in flow patterns. They are an aid in studying basic furnace and duct designs for significant flow maldistribution and in suggesting design corrections to improve flow distribution. The design features deemed worthy of precise evaluation then can be checked quantitatively in a suitable cold air model. The degree of agreement between these two types of model testing has been excellent. Design features that are visually good in a water model always have proved to be good and geometrically accurate when subjected to quantitative study in air models and full scale units.

Special lighting and photographic techniques have been developed to enable investigators to observe and record on film the flow patterns which exist in the interior portions of a three dimensional water model. In many cases, interior flow patterns away from the flow boundaries (walls) of the model are of greater interest than the flow patterns at the walls which are easily observed. Suitable masking of the model with black paper, coupled with high intensity slits of light aligned with the masking, makes it possible to "slice" the model in virtually any plane of interest. The flow patterns within the "light slice" are the only patterns readily visible with illumination of this type. Fig. 7–18 shows a typical setup for taking a color movie of flow patterns in a water model.

Further refinement of photographic techniques may make it possible to obtain quantitative data from water models. Direction of flow is well defined in such models, and the length of light streaks made by individual beads on a photograph is a measure of velocity when correlated with shutter speed.

Three Dimensional Air Models

Engineers ultimately must have numbers to work with in any design. Cold air flow scale models provide a reliable laboratory approach to obtaining quantitative data. In addition, they can be used for some visual studies of complex three dimension flow. The distribution, magnitude and direction of velocities at any point in a flow system may be measured and recorded by means of directional pitot tubes or hot wire anemometer type probes. Smoke, yarn streamers, or particle tracers may be used to visually explore the system. Fig. 7–19 shows the use of yarn streamers to illustrate the existence and method of correction of a severe eddy found in an air foil used for combustion air measurement.

Very good correlation has been experienced between model work and actual boiler operation. Laboratory and test personnel have measured practically identical gas flow velocity distributions in air models and their prototype operating boilers.

The recorded velocity data from air models must be translated into usable forms such as contour and distribution plots and graphs. In studies requiring analysis of flow in a large number of reference planes, manual data reduction rapidly becomes cumbersome and time consuming. The use of standard computer programs to process data helps reduce the time and cost of data reduction. Preliminary work can be carried out in the other types of models previously described reserving the cold air flow model technique for obtaining quantitative data.

Much air modeling work has been done at a scale of 12:1 or 16:1. Such models are of a convenient size, both from the fabrication and operating standpoint. Exact scale is adhered to in making the flow envelope. Some features, such as burners, are geometrically distorted to produce conditions dictated by model similitude criteria. This is done in accordance with the concepts set forth by Johnstone and Thring.[28] The net result for cold air models is that burners should have roughly three times the free flow area that would be predicted from exact geometric scaling of the prototype.

The required air flow through the models, as dictated by Reynolds number model criteria, is determined in the same manner. Exact duplication of dimensionless criteria is not necessary. It has been determined that Reynolds number may vary considerably as long as the flow remains in the turbulent range. In the case where the effect of changes of the model configuration on pressure losses is studied, the velocity of a full scale duct is maintained. Data may be obtained that can be used to assess the relative improvement in pressure losses due to improvement in existing flow conditions.

The models are built from any convenient combinations of materials. Plastic or glass windows or sides may be built into the models so that the path of a particle, smoke, yarn streamer or other form of flow tracer may be observed. Burners and internal components are made of plywood or sheet metal. In some cases, liberal use of epoxy resin filled with metal powder has been employed to obtain the necessary smooth contours and buildup to obtain required model dimensions. In the case of tube panels with free projected areas, perforated plate or smooth expanded metal has been used. This provides a simple model representation without resorting to exact modeling, that is, representing all of these intricate shapes with small diameter tubes or wires. Fig. 7–20 shows the details of construction of a cold air model of a furnace.

A directional pitot tube shown in Fig. 7–21, is used to measure air flow.[29] This provides an indication of both velocity and direction. The plane to be explored is divided into a grid of constant area increments. Probe inserts are then provided to transverse the plane with the pitot tube. The recorded data present a history of the flow through the plane. In the case where pressure losses are established between two planes, total pressure readings are recorded using an impact tube. The instrumentation for a cold air model test is shown in Fig. 7–22.

The pitot tube is used as a primary

[28] See discussion of jet momentum principle in *Pilot Plants, Models and Scaleup Methods in Chemical Engineering*, op. cit., pp. 202–212.
[29] See paper entitled "Measurement of Static Pressures" by C. J. Fechheimer, *Trans. ASME*, 1926, Vol. 48, pp. 965–977.

Fig. 7–19.   Use of yarn streamers to study flow patterns in air model of
air foil meter section
(a) Indicating eddies, upper
(b) Indicating smoothed flow, lower

Fig. 7–20. View of air model of furnace
showing construction details

element whenever the air flow angle must be determined, and with it the angle of attack can be established within ± 5 deg. A hot wire anemometer type probe has an angle of attack sensitivity of ± 15 deg. This probe is useful in making quick checks of velocity distribution, and for traversing sections in which flow is normal to the traverse plane. It also has the advantage of direct reading and is a convenient method for measuring velocities under 10 fps.

In order to utilize fully the quantitative data obtained from air model tests, the information must be reduced to a form that is meaningful. This dictates that in some cases data from planes of differing area, number of readings and mean velocity must be compared on a common basis. The contour, vector and strip average plots are used to represent flow distribution in a given plane. These provide

Fig. 7–21. Directional Pitot tube

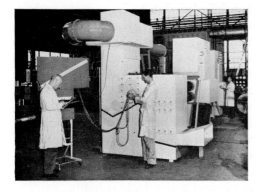

Fig. 7–22. View showing three air models connected to air duct

information as to the specific or average velocity at points or areas in the plane.

Comparison of data from different tests or planes requires that numerical results be utilized to eliminate the necessity of making eye averages and relying upon human judgment. In this case an empirical equation is employed to calculate index numbers representative of velocity uniformity in a plane. The equation is arranged such that velocity deviations above the average plane value contribute to the index in an exponential manner. Thus large velocity deviations tend to produce large index numbers, and the effect of small deviations is minimized. Improvement trends from test to test become apparent, and direct comparison of a number of designs is possible by this technique.

The cold air flow model data may also be used as a basis for calculating heat transfer coefficients on an incremental area basis in a plane. Such information must be used cautiously since the model data does not predict hot gas temperature variations that may exist.

Diffusion of Stack Gases[30]

The diffusion of stack effluents in the atmosphere is a problem of considerable importance, and a great deal of effort, both theoretical and experimental, has been devoted to it. In this section several of the mathematical approaches to the problem are examined, and some of the difficulties associated with the various theories are indicated.

Fickian Diffusion

The first meteorological theory of diffusion was formulated independently by G. I. Taylor and W. Schmidt.[31] These

---

[30] Material in this section contributed by J. D. Sensenbaugh.
[31] "Diffusion by Continuous Movements" by G. I. Taylor, *Proceedings* of London Mathematical Society, Vol. 20, 1921, pp. 196–212; "Der Massen austausch in freien Luft" by W. Schmidt, Hamburg, 1925.

authors stated the problem in terms of the following differential equation:

$$\frac{dX}{dt} = \frac{\partial}{\partial x}\left(K_x \frac{\partial X}{\partial x}\right) + \frac{\partial}{\partial y}\left(K_y \frac{\partial X}{\partial y}\right)$$
$$+ \frac{\partial}{\partial z}\left(K_z \frac{\partial X}{\partial z}\right) \qquad (7\text{–}41)$$

where X is the concentration of material in units of weight per unit volume and K_x, K_y, and K_z are coefficients of diffusion (also called "eddy diffusivities") in the x, y, and z directions.

This theory of diffusion is based on Fick's Law, which itself is derived by analogy from Fourier's development of the law of heat conduction. Fourier's theory was first applied to diffusion by the physiologist Fick whose law of molecular diffusion may be stated as follows:[32]

Diffusion of material is in the direction of decreasing concentration and is proportional to the concentration gradient.

The equation for Fick's law is

$$\nabla^2 X = \frac{1}{d}\frac{\partial X}{\partial t} \qquad (7\text{–}42)$$

where the constant of proportionality d is the molecular diffusivity. The mathematical problem is to solve Eq. 7–41 in relation to appropriate boundary conditions. In practice, realistic meteorological conditions produce rather formidable mathematical complications, which limit the utility of this sort of theory. Nevertheless, a number of workers have used this approach and have developed a generalized Fickian theory which is also known as the K theory of atmospheric diffusion.

Limitations of the K theory have led other workers to develop statistical theories of turbulent diffusion. The K theory

and the statistical theories are not fundamentally in opposition. On the contrary, each has its place depending on the scale of events under consideration.

The basic difficulty with the K theory is its inability to deal with the wide variation in K values that may successively apply to the same smoke puff or plume. If the eddy diffusivity K is evaluated by fitting experimental observations to Eq. 7–41, it is found that the K values may vary from about 0.2 sq cm per sec for molecular diffusion to 10^{11} sq cm per sec for diffusion due to large scale cyclonic storms in the atmosphere. Such a range may apply successively to a single stack cloud. Immediately after emission, when the cloud is concentrated, diffusion on a molecular scale may be controlling. When the cloud enlarges to a few meters in size, it may be affected by small scale turbulent wind gusts. Eventually, as the cloud becomes dispersed throughout the whole atmosphere, it is subject to large scale cyclonic and anticyclonic currents.

In dealing with the problem of atmospheric diffusion, it may be said that essentially one is concerned with diffusion on three different scales. The first scale, extending to about a kilometer from the focal point, is involved, for example, in certain chemical warfare problems. In this case, one requires precise information on concentrations close to sources near ground level. The second scale, extending to the order of tens of kilometers, is involved in cases of air pollution from stacks. The third scale includes distances of continental or global magnitude. This scale is involved in dealing with the diffusion of radioactive material produced by the detonation of nuclear devices. For the first and third cases, appropriate Fickian

[32] The original reference is "Ueber Diffusion" by Adolf Fick, *Annalen der Physik und Chemie,* Vol. 94, 1855, pp. 59–86.

theories have proved applicable. For the intermediate scale, statistical diffusion theories have been found more satisfactory.

Statistical Theories of Diffusion

In another paper, G. I. Taylor developed equations for the time history of individual parcels of air in a region where the statistical properties of the turbulence are homogeneous and isotropic. He proved that in this case the rate of diffusion depends on the variance of the wind velocity fluctuation distributions. However, Taylor's equations cannot be used directly, as they involve mathematical functions that are difficult for practical evaluation.[33]

Following Taylor, other workers developed theories based on the assumption that the mean concentrations of material in a diffusion cloud follow a three dimensional Gaussian distribution. Reasoning along these lines and invoking some dimensional arguments, O. G. Sutton developed the following equation for diffusion from an instantaneous point source in the anisotropic case:[34]

$$X(x, y, z, t) = \frac{Q}{\pi^{3/2} C_x C_y C_z (\bar{\mu} t)^{3(2-n)/2}}$$
$$\times \exp\left[-(\bar{\mu} t)^{n-2} \left(\frac{x^2}{C_x^2} + \frac{y^2}{C_y^2} + \frac{z^2}{C_z^2}\right)\right]$$

(7–43)

where Q is pollutant emission rate at atmospheric temperature, C_x, C_y, C_z are eddy diffusion coefficients in the x, y, and z directions, n is the turbulence parameter (also called velocity gradient factor), $\bar{\mu}$ is the mean wind speed and t time.

Sutton assumed that the ground acted as a perfect reflector of diffusing particles and accounted for this by using the "method of images." This doubles the right side of Eq. 7-43 for a source located at the ground. Integrating with respect to x and t, the Sutton equation for the anisotropic case becomes

$$X = \frac{2Q}{\pi C_y C_z \bar{\mu} x^{2-n}} \exp\left[-x^{n-2} \left(\frac{y^2}{C_y^2} + \frac{H_e^2}{C_z^2}\right)\right]$$

(7–44)

where H_e is the effective stack height which will be discussed later. Eq. 7–44 gives the ground level concentration X downwind a distance x and crosswind a distance y from an elevated source of effective height H_e emitting pollutant at a constant rate Q.

By somewhat similar statistical reasoning and again employing some dimensional arguments, Bosanquet and Pearson[35] derived the following equation, analogous to Eq. 7–44, for ground level concentration due to a continuous elevated point source:

$$X = \frac{Q}{(2\pi)^{1/2} pq\bar{\mu} x^2} \exp\left(-\frac{H_e}{px} - \frac{y^2}{2q^2 x^2}\right)$$

(7–45)

where p and q are turbulence parameters or, more specifically, vertical and lateral diffusion coefficients.

[33] "Eddy Motion in the Atmosphere" by G. I. Taylor, *Philosophical Trans.*, Royal Society of London, Series A, Vol. 215, 1915, pp. 1–26.
[34] "A Theory of Eddy Diffusion in the Atmosphere" by O. G. Sutton, *Proceedings*, Royal Society of London, Series A, Vol. 135, 1932, pp. 143–165.
[35] "The Spread of Smoke and Gases from Chimneys" by C. H. Bosanquet and J. L. Pearson, *Trans.* Faraday Society, Vol. 32, 1936, pp. 1249–1264.

It will be noted that in order to apply Eq. 7–44 to a practical case values are required for the diffusion coefficients C_y and C_z and for the turbulence parameter n. Similarly, Eq. 7–45 requires values for p and q. Values proposed by the original authors for these parameters are given in more extensive works on the subject.[36] These proposed values have been the subject of considerable experimental work; as might be expected, the agreement between the experimental values and those proposed by the authors varies under different circumstances. Ideally, suitable values of the parameters should be determined by diffusion tests made in the field in the particular locality under study. In the absence of such determinations, one has no choice but to make the most judicious selection from the values in the literature.

Limitations of the Sutton and Bosanquet-Pearson Equations

It is important to mention briefly some of the limitations of the equations most commonly used to calculate ground-level concentrations of stack effluents. First of all, Eqs. 7–44 and 7–45 apply to a single elevated source with a constant stack emission rate.

Atmospheric Temperature Profile

With respect to the vertical temperature profile in the atmosphere, two conditions are recognized: the *lapse* condition in which temperature decreases with height and the *inversion* condition in which temperature increases with height. While there are many gradations of these conditions, the important point with regard to the Sutton and Bosanquet-Pearson equations is that these equations may be applied successfully to lapse conditions, but they are not suitable for inversions. The reason for this is that both vertical and horizontal diffusion are assumed in these equations, while in actual fact the vertical dispersion is practically nonexistent during inversions.

Influence of Terrain

The equations were derived on the assumption that the earth's surface is aerodynamically smooth; almost always the surface of the earth is aerodynamically rough. As a result, the equations tend to overestimate the contaminant concentration downwind from a source. In the case of tall stacks, it is believed that the diffusion parameters appropriate in this situation are closely related to long period convective eddies and, as such, are not strongly influenced by minor surface variations.[37]

Particular terrain features in certain areas, such as long, parallel ridges and valleys, may produce wind patterns that tend to be repeated frequently. High concentrations, not predicted by the equations, may be found in such areas.

Time Factors

Concentrations calculated by the diffusion equations represent mean concentrations over a certain time period and do not necessarily apply to other time periods.

---

[36] See the following publications: *Air Pollution Handbook* edited by P. L. Magill, F. R. Holden and C. Ackley, McGraw-Hill, New York, 1956, Chapter 5; *Air Pollution Abatement Manual*, Manufacturing Chemists' Association, Washington, 1952, Chapter 8; *Meteorology and Atomic Energy*, AECU-3066, U. S. Government Printing Office, Washington, 1955, Chapters 4 and 5.

[37] See "Atmospheric Diffusion Formulae and Practical Pollution Problems" by M. E. Smith, *Journal* of the Air Pollution Control Association, Vol. 6, 1956, p. 11.

Values obtained from the Sutton equation apply fairly well to "averaging time" periods of about three minutes, but the concentrations predicted are too high for hourly average values. Experimental studies have shown that the ratio between peak (10 sec) and test average (30 min to 1 hr) concentrations is about 20:1.

On the other hand, the Bosanquet-Pearson equation yields values that apply to about thirty minute periods. Instantaneous concentrations may be fifty times this value, while one minute average concentrations may be ten to twenty times the thirty minute value.

Space Factors

In addition to the time factors mentioned above, it is obvious from the form of the diffusion equations that a single calculation applies only to a specific distance from the source. In practice, it has been found that the peak-to-mean concentration ratio varies with the distance from the source, decreasing with increasing distance. The 20:1 ratio quoted above holds up to about 1.2 miles from the source; at greater distances, the ratio has been found to be about 6:1. Thus, calculations based on point source diffusion equations give better agreement with observed concentrations with increasing distance from the source, because such factors as local aerodynamics, errors in estimating the effective stack height, and complications due to multiple sources become less important at greater distances.

Particulate Emissions

The diffusion equations apply only to gaseous effluents or to particulates smaller than about 10 microns in diameter. Use of these equations with relation to particu-

late deposition serves only to set limiting theoretical values. The deposition of large particles (greater than about 20 microns) can be estimated using other techniques, such as that of Bosanquet, Carey and Halton[38] which will not be discussed here.

Effective Stack Height

The term effective stack height, mentioned previously, should be explained. If stack gases are emitted at an elevated temperature or with an appreciable exit velocity, the effective stack height is greater than the actual stack height due to buoyancy and jet effects. The effective stack height is given by

$$H_e = h_s + h_v + h_t \qquad (7\text{–}46)$$

where H_e is effective stack height, h_s is actual stack height, h_v is velocity rise and h_t is thermal rise.

The velocity rise at distance x downwind of the stack (h_{vx}) is given by Bosanquet, Carey and Halton in terms of the maximum velocity rise $(h_{v\ max})$ as follows:

$$h_{vx} = h_{v\ max} \left(1 - 0.8\, \frac{h_{v\ max}}{x} \right) \qquad (7\text{–}47)$$

where x is greater than about $2h_{v\ max}$, and

$$h_{v\ max} = \frac{4.77}{1 + 0.43\, \dfrac{\bar{\mu}}{v_s}} \left(\frac{\sqrt{Q_{T_1} v_s}}{\bar{\mu}} \right) \qquad (7\text{–}48)$$

where $\bar{\mu}$ is mean wind speed, v_s is stack exit velocity, Q_{T_1} is total (gas + pollutant) emission rate of effluent at temperature T_1, T is atmospheric temperature, and T_1 is temperature at which stack gas density equals that of the atmosphere.

The maximum thermal rise is given by Bosanquet, Carey and Halton as follows:

[38] "Dust Deposition from Chimney Stacks" by C. H. Bosanquet, W. F. Carey and E. M. Halton, *Proceedings*, Institution of Mechanical Engineers, Vol. 162, 1950, pp. 355–364.

$$h_{t\;max} = 6.37g \frac{Q_{T_1}\Delta}{\bar{\mu}^3 T_1} Z \qquad (7\text{-}49)$$

where
$$Z = \ln J^2 + \frac{2}{J} - 2 \qquad (7\text{-}50)$$

and

$$J = \frac{\bar{\mu}^2}{\sqrt{Q_{T_1}v_s}} \left(0.43 \sqrt{\frac{T_1}{gG}} - 0.28 \frac{v_s}{g} \frac{T_1}{\Delta} \right) + 1$$
$$(7\text{-}51)$$

where g is acceleration due to gravity, T_s is stack gas temperature, $\Delta = T_s - T_1$ and G is gradient of potential atmospheric temperature.

It may be seen that the meteorological parameters of wind speed and atmospheric temperature gradient are taken into consideration in the above equations for the maximum thermal rise, as well as stack emission parameters. Eq. 7–49 indicates that thermal rise is strongly dependent on wind speed. Increasing the wind speed by a factor of two produces an eightfold reduction in thermal rise. The effect of vertical temperature gradient is taken into account by the factor G. The potential temperature of dry air is defined as the temperature the air would assume if brought adiabatically from its actual pressure to a standard pressure of 1000 mb. The gradient of potential temperature, G, varies according to the degree of lapse or inversion conditions in such a way that the effect of a temperature inversion is to reduce the thermal rise. This is in agreement with qualitative considerations by which one might expect that a temperature inversion would suppress vertical movement in the atmosphere.

Concluding Remark

In this discussion, the aim has been to give a brief picture of the problems involved in calculating ground-level concentrations of emissions from an elevated source, indicating the basis for the equations used and the limitations involved. For further details, the interested reader is referred to more extended discussions in the literature of stack gas diffusion.

8

Water Technology[1]

WATER IS A BASIC *engineering material* used in the production of steam for power generation and process use. Effective *treatment* or *conditioning* of water has made possible the use of more efficient steam cycles in the subcritical and supercritical pressure ranges. The practical application of nuclear energy to generation of steam also requires stringent controls of water to prevent general corrosion, stress corrosion cracking and the formation of solids which may increase the level of radioactivity in the reactor or in the turbine. Many industrial processes have special requirements for high quality water free from objectionable contaminants.

All of these are indicative of the significant role of *water technology* as an interdisciplinary professional field which comprises elements of basic chemistry and chemical and mechanical engineering. Attention in this chapter is to be focussed upon specific boiler and nuclear reactor applications of water technology, but many of the same considerations hold for various types of process operations. In practically every instance a careful review of sources of water and its con-

ditioning is required if economic losses due to slowdown in production, damage to equipment and increased costs of operation are to be averted.

The sources of water supply to an industrial site vary and can originate from a polluted river or stream, mountain runoff, wells or a lake. The composition of impurities in water varies over a wide range. Water may be polluted with sewage, chemical or organic wastes, bacteria, dissolved gases, suspended mineral matter and dissolved solids of both scaling and nonscaling composition. If water were pure "H_2O" and nothing else, or were of a constant solids composition, the conditioning of water for industrial use would be uniform and simple. This is not the case, however, and the conditioning of water contains elements of both a specialized science and an engineering art.

The extent of water conditioning or treatment depends both on the original supply source and the ultimate end use of the product. Table 8–1 lists common impurities found in water, sets forth some of the resulting problems and indicates widely used treatment methods.

[1] Material contributed by H. A. Grabowski and P. B. Place.

Table 8–1 Common Impurities Found in Water*

Constituent	Chemical Formula	Difficulties Caused	Means of Treatment
Turbidity	None — expressed in analysis as units.	Imparts unsightly appearance to water. Deposits in water lines, process equipment, boilers, etc. Interferes with most process uses.	Coagulation, settling and filtration.
Color	None — expressed in analysis as "units" of color on arbitrary scale.	May cause foaming in boilers. Hinders precipitation methods such as iron removal, hot phosphate softening. Can stain product in process use.	Coagulation and filtration. Chlorination. Adsorption by activated carbon.
Hardness	Calcium and magnesium salts expressed as $CaCO_3$.	Chief source of scale in heat exchange equipment, boilers, pipe lines, etc. Forms curds with soap, interferes with dyeing, etc.	Softening, Distillation. Internal boiler water treatment. Surface active agents.
Alkalinity	Bicarbonate (HCO_3), carbonate (CO_3), and hydrate (OH), expressed as $CaCO_3$.	Foaming and carryover of solids with steam. Embrittlement of boiler steel. Bicarbonate and carbonate produce CO_2 in steam, a source of corrosion.	Lime and lime-soda softening. Acid treatment. Hydrogen zeolite softening. Demineralization. Dealkalization by anion exchange. Distillation.
Free Mineral Acid	H_2SO_4, HCl, etc. expressed as $CaCO_3$.	Corrosion	Neutralization with alkalies.
Carbon Dioxide	CO_2	Corrosion in water lines and particularly steam and condensate lines.	Aeration. Deaeration. Neutralization with alkalies. Filming and neutralizing amines.
pH	Hydrogen ion concentration defined as: $pH = \log \dfrac{1}{(H^+)}$	pH varies according to acidic or alkaline solids in water. Most natural waters have a pH of 6–8.	pH can be increased by alkalies and decreased by acids.
Sulfate	$(SO_4)^{--}$	Adds to solids content of water, but, in itself, is not usually significant. Combines with calcium to form calcium sulfate scale.	Demineralization. Distillation.
Chloride	Cl^-	Adds to solids content and increases corrosive character of water.	Demineralization. Distillation.
Nitrate	$(NO_3)^-$	Adds to solids content, but is not usually significant industrially. Useful for control of boiler metal embrittlement.	Demineralization. Distillation.
Fluoride	F^-	Cause of mottled enamel in teeth. Also used for control of dental decay. Not usually significant industrially.	Adsorption with magnesium hydroxide, calcium phosphate, or bone black. Alum coagulation.
Silica	SiO_2	Scale in boilers and cooling water systems. Insoluble turbine blade deposits due to silica vaporization.	Hot process removal with magnesium salts. Adsorption by highly basic anion exchange resins, in conjunction with demineralization. Distillation.

Table 8—1 Common Impurities Found in Water* (Continued)

Iron	F++ (ferrous) Fe+++ (ferric)	Discolors water on precipitation. Source of deposits in water lines, boilers, etc. Interferes with dyeing, tanning, paper manufacturing, etc.	Aeration. Coagulation and filtration. Lime softening. Cation exchange. Contact filtration. Surface active agents for iron retention.
Manganese	Mn++	Same as iron.	Same as iron.
Oil	Expressed as oil or chloroform extractible matter.	Scale, sludge and foaming in boilers. Impedes heat exchange. Undesirable in most processes.	Baffle separators. Strainers. Coagulation and filtration. Diatomaceous earth filtration.
Oxygen	O_2	Corrosion of water lines, heat exchange equipment, boilers, return lines, etc.	Deaeration, Sodium sulfite. Corrosion inhibitors.
Hydrogen Sulfide	H_2S	Cause of "rotten egg" odor. Corrosion.	Aeration. Chlorination. Highly basic anion exchange.
Ammonia	NH_3	Corrosion of copper and zinc alloys by formation of complex soluble ion.	Cation exchange with hydrogen zeolite. Chlorination. Deaeration.
Conductivity	Expressed as micromhos, specific conductance.	Conductivity is the result of ionizable solids in solution. High conductivity can increase the corrosive characteristics of a water.	Any process which decreases dissolved solids content will decrease conductivity. Examples are demineralization, lime softening.
Dissolved Solids	None	"Dissolved solids" is measure of total amount of dissolved matter, determined by evaporation. High concentrations of dissolved solids are objectionable because of process interference and as a cause of foaming in boilers.	Various softening process, such as lime softening and cation exchange by hydrogen zeolite, will reduce dissolved solids. Demineralization. Distillation.
Suspended Solids	None	"Suspended Solids" is the measure of undissolved matter, determined gravimetrically. Suspended solids plug lines, cause deposits in heat exchange equipment, boilers, etc.	Subsidence. Filtration, usually preceded by coagulation and settling.
Total Solids	None	"Total Solids" is the sum of dissolved and suspended solids, determined gravimetrically.	See "Dissolved Solids" and "Suspended Solids."

* Adapted from *Betz Handbook of Industrial Water Conditioning*, 6th Edition, 1963, Betz Laboratories, Inc., Philadelphia, Pa.

In an industrial application of water for generation of steam for process or electric power, consideration must be given towards treatment of water to prevent corrosion, scaling and contamination of steam. This attention must entail the treatment of the raw water introduced into the cycle and in many cases also the conditioning of the water present in the preboiler cycle and in the boiler itself. The degree of attention given to the contaminants present in water depends largely upon the end use of the water. From an operating standpoint, boiler pressure and boiler water temperature are the chief factors which determine limits of water quality necessary to prevent scaling and corrosion.

The formation of deposits and the corrosion of metals in contact with water are influenced by an increase in temperature. A specified treatment must be suited for the operating pressure since chemical reactions and corrosion processes increase in activity and become more critical as the cycle advances from the comparatively low levels found in industrial and institutional power plants to the supercritical pressures for large central stations.

Techniques of Water Treatment

The techniques of water treatment cover a wide variety of raw water preparation schemes. This art is covered in detail in established references.[2] Some of the basic chemical reactions involved in the treatment of raw water to produce suitable makeup for boilers and nuclear reactors will be discussed in a general manner in this chapter.

Any evaluation of water conditioning must consider the impurities present in power station raw water makeup in relation to tendencies toward scaling, corrosion and deposits. Raw water contains a variety of contaminating elements. Among those present in various water sources are (1) mud, clay and silt; (2) oxygen, carbon dioxide and hydrogen sulfide; (3) sewage, bacteria and algae;

(4) scale forming compounds of calcium, magnesium and silica; (5) oil; (6) iron compounds; (7) organic wastes; (8) sulfuric, hydrochloric and other acids; (9) normally soluble compounds, such as sodium bicarbonate, sodium carbonate, sodium hydroxide and sodium chloride.

Typical analyses of water supplies of the United States are given in Table 8–2. The analyses of river waters are of filtered water, and for the most part represent yearly averages. River waters vary considerably with the seasons, and the maximum and minimum concentrations may be 50 per cent above and 50 per cent below the average. Spring and well waters and waters from large lakes have a fairly constant composition.[3]

The usual unit for reporting dissolved

[2] See especially three basic American reference books: *Water Treatment for Industrial and Other Uses* by Eskel Nordell, Reinhold Publishing Co., Second Edition, 1961; *Water Conditioning for Industry* by S. T. Powell, McGraw-Hill Publishing Co., 1954; and *Betz Handbook of Industrial Water Conditioning*, Betz Laboratories, Inc., Philadelphia 24, Penna., Sixth Edition, 1963. A British work worthy of consideration is *Industrial Water Treatment Practice*, edited by P. Hamer, J. Jackson and E. F. Thurston, Butterworths Scientific Publications, London, 1961. This contains an extremely valuable appendix of 88 pages of physico-chemical data and an international bibliography of 521 items keyed to discussion in the text.

[3] The analyses in Table 8–2 are adapted from *The Industrial Utility of Public Water Supplies in the United States, 1952* by E. W. Lohr and S. K. Love. Published in two parts by the U.S. Government Printing Office in 1954, each volume includes an identical 49-page section dealing with the sources of analyses, composition and properties of water, treatment of water and a list of publications and references. Part 1 deals with states east of the Mississippi River and Part 2 with states west of the Mississippi River. They are designated respectively as Geological Survey Water Supply Papers 1299 and 1300 and comprise over 1100 pages of text.

Table 8–2   Analyses of Typical Surface and Ground Waters in the United States

Analysis Number[a]	1	2	3	4	5	6	7	8	9	10	11	12	13
Silica (SiO_2)	2.5	0.4	2.3	8.2	13	8.0	8.4	9.6	16	23	34	12	39
Iron (Fe)	0.03	0.05	.09	.12	0.04		0.15	0.04	0.0			2.1	.09
Calcium (Ca)	5.3	27	32	1.7	72	79	40	3.4	7.2	70	26	72	7.2
Magnesium (Mg)	1.7	7	10	0.4	6.4	28	16	1.5	2.5	24	10	33	4.2
Sodium (Na)	1.4 }	3[b] }	3.5	1.9	41	99 }	94 }	5.6 }	147 }	12[b] }	138 }	358[b] }	7.5
Potassium (K)	0.6 }		1.0	0.7	4.7	4 }			0.4 }		1.6 }		
Carbonate (CO_3)	0	1	0	0	0	4	0	0	0		0		
Bicarbonate (HCO_3)	10	99	138	3	174	137	46	21	328	179	170	293	50
Sulfate (SO_4)	11	13	17	4.4	138	290	298	3.3	2.6	135	70	560	0.8
Chloride (Cl)	2.6	7	6.5	2.6	9.5	79	14	3.6	51	8	139	195	6.8
Fluoride (F)	0.1		0.1	0.6	0.4	0.4	0.1	0.2	0.8			2.5	0.0
Nitrate (NO_3)	0.3	0.2		0.2	4.0	0.2	3.6	0.7	0.0		0.0	1.1	0.0
Dissolved solids	34	130	171	23	386	661	554	42	392	392	503	1380	90[c]
Total hardness as $CaCO_3$	20	98	121	6	206	315	166	15	28	276	106	316	35
Noncarbonate hardness	6	16	8	3	64	197	128	0	0	126	0	76	0
Specific conductance (micromhos at 25 C)	53.4		263	29.5	575	1040	822	55.5	651		867		
Color	1		3	15	5		6	4	10			0	2.5
pH	6.9	8.1	8.2	5.8	7.7	8.4	7.6	7.0	8.0	7.6	7.9		7.5

[a] Analyses numbers are identified as follows:

1 = New York City, Catskill supply (reservoir — finished).
2 = Detroit, Michigan, Detroit River (raw).
3 = Chicago, Illinois, Lake Michigan (raw).
4 = Fitchburg, Massachusetts, Pond (finished).
5 = Omaha, Nebraska, Missouri River (raw).
6 = Los Angeles, California, Colorado River (raw).
7 = Pittsburgh, Pennsylvania, Monongahela River (finished).
8 = Macon, Georgia, Ocmulgee River (raw).
9 = Houston, Texas, Well 1932 ft deep.
10 = Jacksonville, Florida, Well 1064 ft deep.
11 = El Paso, Texas, Well 703 ft deep.
12 = Galesburg, Illinois, Well 2450 ft deep.
13 = Bremerton, Washington, Anderson Creek.

[b] Computed by difference in epm and reported as sodium.
[c] Sum of determined constituents.

Values are in parts per million where this unit is appropriate.

and also suspended solids in feedwater and boiler water is parts per million (*ppm*). This is a rational unit which is easily understood and which admits of little chance of misunderstanding. In other words, one million pounds of water will contain so many pounds of solids. With the advent of supercritical pressure boilers requiring very pure water, the term parts per billion (*ppb*) is coming into use. One ppb equals 0.001 ppm.

Raw Water Processes

Raw water contains a variety of gaseous and solid impurities which must be reduced before it can be supplied as makeup to a boiler. This is particularly true if the water is taken from a river which may be contaminated with mine washings, gases, organic and chemical wastes as well as silt and other mineral impurities. The processes commonly used to reduce these substances are aeration, settling, coagulation and filtering. A brief description of these processes follows.

Aeration

This process aims to remove such undesirable gases as carbon dioxide and hydrogen sulfide from water by admixing water and air in a manner so as to reduce the solubility of the objectionable gas in water. The removal of gas follows Henry's Law which indicates that the solubility of a gas in water is directly proportional to its partial pressure in the surrounding atmosphere. The partial pressure of a gas such as carbon dioxide is low in a normal atmosphere. Establishing an equilibrium between water and air by aeration results in saturation of the water with oxygen and nitrogen and results in the practical elimination of such gases as carbon dioxide and hydrogen sulfide. Increasing the temperature, the aeration time and the surface area of water improves the removal of gases.

Coagulation

Contamination in surface waters in the form of coarse suspended solids, silt, turbidity, color and colloids is reduced by clarification of the water by the addition of chemical coagulating materials. A *floc* is formed by the chemicals and assists in agglomerating the impurities. Settlement of the particles permits a clear effluent from the coagulating chamber. Removal of colloids requires a careful analysis of the impurity to establish the nature of their electrical charge which is one of the principal factors that contribute to their remaining in the suspended state. Some of the chemicals used for coagulation are filter alum, sodium aluminate, copperas, ferrisul, activated silica and various proprietary organic compounds. Temperature, pH and mixing affect the efficiency of coagulation. Some of the reactions involved are:

Filter alum (formation of aluminum hydroxide)

$$Al_2(SO_4)_3 + 3Ca(HCO_3)_2 \longrightarrow$$
$$3CaSO_4 + 2Al(OH)_3 + 6CO_2$$

Sodium aluminate

$$6NaAlO_2 + Al_2(SO_4)_3 \cdot 18H_2O \longrightarrow$$
$$8Al(OH)_3 + 3Na_2SO_4 + 6H_2O$$

Copperas (formation of ferrous hydroxide)

$$FeSO_4 + Ca(HCO_3)_2 \longrightarrow$$
$$CaSO_4 + Fe(HCO_3)_2$$

$$Fe(HCO_3)_2 + 2Ca(OH)_2 \longrightarrow$$
$$Fe(OH)_2 + 2CaCO_3 + 2H_2O$$

Ferrisul

$$Fe_2(SO_4)_3 + 3Ca(HCO_3)_2 \rightleftarrows$$
$$2Fe(OH)_3 + 3CaSO_4 + 6CO_2$$

Filtration

Filters are used to separate coarse suspended matter from raw water or to remove floc or sludge components from coagulation or process softening systems. Gravity and pressure type of filters are in general used for this purpose. Beds of graded stone gravel or coarse anthracite are the common materials used in the filter bed. Diatomaceous earth and special precoat filters are in common use to remove oil and reduce color in feedwater makeup.

Chemical Softening Processes

Nonscaling feedwater can be obtained by utilizing a proper pretreatment of raw water. The chemical softening processes developed in the industry are described in succeeding paragraphs.

Various chemical combinations can be utilized to remove hardness, silica and silt from makeup water. The technique selected for the application will be determined by considerations of economics and operating pressure.

Lime-Soda Softening

To soften water by this process, lime (calcium hydroxide) is added to precipitate the calcium bicarbonate as calcium carbonate and magnesium salts as magnesium hydroxide. Soda ash (sodium carbonate) is added to react with calcium chloride and calcium sulfate to form calcium carbonate. The general reactions are as follows:

$$Ca(HCO_3)_2 + Ca(OH)_2 \longrightarrow$$
$$2CaCO_3 \downarrow + 2H_2O$$

$$CaSO_4 + Na_2CO_3 \longrightarrow CaCO_3 \downarrow + Na_2SO_4$$

$$Mg(HCO_3)_2 + 2Ca(OH)_2 \longrightarrow$$
$$Mg(OH)_2 \downarrow + 2CaCO_3 \downarrow + 2H_2O$$

$$MgSO_4 + Ca(OH)_2 \longrightarrow$$
$$Mg(OH)_2 \downarrow + CaSO_4$$

This process is more efficient at hot temperatures due to the increase in reaction rate and the decrease in solubility of calcium carbonate. The hardness in the effluent of a cold lime-soda process is dependent upon the excess of soda ash and is generally above 33 ppm. Alkalinity reduction depends on the removal of magnesium and calcium bicarbonates. In the hot lime-soda process, the hardness residual in the effluent is in the range 17–25 ppm.

Hot Process Phosphate Softening

In this process calcium and magnesium salts are chemically precipitated by the addition of phosphate. The calcium hardness is precipitated in the form of tricalcium phosphate and the magnesium as magnesium hydroxide. Chemical reactions are completed at a temperature of 212 F or above. The reactions can be controlled to reduce the hardness to nearly zero.

Normal low hardness, below 60 ppm, can be eliminated in a single stage. Higher hardness water is generally handled in a two stage softener arrangement. The hot process phosphate softener is particularly suited for turbid waters low in hardness and alkalinity. Softening, turbidity control, deaeration and silica reduction can be combined in a single unit. Usually, surface acting organic agents are added to stabilize the precipitates formed in the softener. Anthracite coal filters are most suited for removal of turbidity from the effluent. Some of the chemical reactions in the softener to reduce calcium and magnesium hardness are:

$$3Ca(HCO_3)_2 + 6NaOH \longrightarrow$$
$$3CaCO_3 \downarrow + 3Na_2CO_3 + 6H_2O$$

$$3CaCO_3 + 2Na_3PO_4 \longrightarrow$$
$$Ca_3(PO_4)_2 \downarrow + 3Na_2CO_3$$

$$Mg(HCO_3) + 4NaOH \longrightarrow$$
$$Mg(OH)_2 \downarrow + 2Na_2CO_3 + 2H_2O$$

Addition of magnesium sulfate, magnesium hydroxide, dolomitic lime and magnesium oxide aids in the reduction of silica. Removal of silica from solution is accomplished by adsorption by the presence of magnesium hydroxide formed in the softener.

Zeolite Softening

The name *zeolite* refers to a group of water softening chemicals capable of exchanging ions with which they come in contact. These materials may be natural compounds (green sand) or synthetic compounds such as sulfonated coal, phenolic and polystyrene resins. Hard water is passed downward through a bed of sodium regenerated zeolite contained in a steel pressure vessel. As the water passes through the ion exchange material, the calcium and magnesium ions are exchanged for sodium in the zeolite (Z). The reactions are:

$$Ca(HCO_3)_2 + Na_2Z \longrightarrow CaZ \downarrow + 2NaHCO_3$$

$$Mg(HCO_3)_2 + Na_2Z \longrightarrow MgZ \downarrow + 2NaHCO_3$$

Regeneration of the zeolite bed is accomplished by passing a salt solution through the softener.

$$CaZ + 2NaCl \longrightarrow CaCl_2 + Na_2Z$$

The calcium chloride is passed to waste and the zeolite bed is ready for further softening.

Synthetic zeolites can be regenerated by the use of salt (sodium chloride) or acid. Acid and salt regenerated zeolites can be used in combination to reduce alkalinity in waters having a high bicarbonate hardness. The reaction in the hydrogen zeolite may be written as follows:

$$Ca(HCO_3)_2 + H_2Z \longrightarrow CaZ \downarrow + 2H_2CO_3$$

$$Mg(HCO_3)_2 + H_2Z \longrightarrow MgZ \downarrow + 2H_2CO_3$$

The mixed effluent from the hydrogen and sodium zeolites is deaerated to remove the carbon dioxide. The exhausted acid zeolite is regenerated generally with sulfuric acid.

Zeolite softening of makeup is the most common method of preparing water for use in industrial boilers. It is simple to operate and control. While sodium zeolite softening is very attractive, it must be applied with understanding of its limitations. Turbid waters are unsuited, total solids are not reduced and with high bicarbonate water, high quantities of carbon dioxide can be expected in the steam. Silica is not reduced by zeolite softening.

While there is a reduction in solids by the use of the hydrogen zeolite, there are a number of disadvantages which must be recognized by the operator of this equipment. As in the sodium zeolite, turbidity must be low. The cost of the chemicals, acid and salt, may be considerable. Handling of acids introduces a hazard to operators, and corrosion resistant pipe must be used to handle the water to the degasifier.

Synthetic zeolites are used in conjunction with other water softening equipment in preparation of water makeup. The hot lime zeolite softener is a widely used technique in preparing water for intermediate pressure industrial boilers. Reduction of hardness, alkalinity and silica is facilitated by the use of chemicals at temperatures about 250 F. The hot lime softening reduces the carbonate and magnesium hardness as well as the total solids in the raw water. If the magnesium content in the raw water is below the level to reduce silica, activated magnesium oxide or dolomitic lime is added for reaction.

Use of the hot lime zeolite produces a water of 0–2 ppm hardness, 20–30 ppm alkalinity and 0.5–1.0 ppm of silica.

Demineralization

Demineralization is a process in which ionized mineral salts are removed by ion exchange. Cations as calcium, magnesium and sodium are removed in the hydrogen cation exchanger and anions as bicarbonates, sulfates, chloride and soluble silica are removed in the anion exchanger.

Synthetic cation and anion exchange resins are used in demineralization of water. Sulfonic, carboxylic and phenolic hydroxyl compounds are used for cation exchange; amino or quartenary nitrogen, for anion exchange. The cation exchanger is regenerated with acid while the anion exchange material is regenerated with caustic. If the cation resin is designated as Z and the anion material as R, the simple reactions in a two stage demineralizer may be expressed as:

Cation: $H_2Z + CaSO_4 \longrightarrow CaZ + H_2SO_4$

Anion: $H_2SO_4 + 2R \cdot OH \longrightarrow$
$$R \cdot SO_4 + H_2O$$

A pure water equal to or superior to the best evaporated vapor can be achieved by demineralization. The anion and cation resins can be arranged in a variety of combinations to produce the best water most economically. Two, three or four bed units or a single mixed bed demineralizer can be used to accomplish the required result.

Strong base exchangers are temperature sensitive and should not be used at above 120 F. Cation exchange resins can tolerate temperatures of 250 F.

Use of finely sized resins in demineralizers requires a water source low in turbidity and organic matter. Clarification, filtration and chlorination are generally required to reduce organic matter to a low level. Failure to reduce the organic level in the water results in a marked reduction in capacity of the exchangers due to the coating of the resins.

The advance of demineralization as a means of providing a high purity makeup water may be partly attributed to the development of highly basic anion exchange resins which allow the removal of soluble silica from raw water. Mixed bed demineralizers, in which the cation and anion resins are intimately interspersed, have been used successfully in providing a high quality makeup water as well as for polishing purposes in cleaning up impurities in condensates of utility and nuclear applications.

Water Technology for Boilers

In the field of high boiler pressures, there cannot be a compromise in water treatment. The most efficient combination of techniques must be utilized to assure a delivery of pure water, nearly free of soluble and insoluble solids, to the boiler feedwater system. Evaporation or demineralization of makeup must be used to assure the reduction of solids such as silica in the water supply to the boiler. Normally, silica vaporization is the principal control item for solids content in the boiler water. The makeup to high pressure central station boilers is generally less than one per cent of the feedwater supply. For this application, the more costly methods for solids removal can be economically justified since operation with low blowdown of water from the boiler can be assured. Also, the purity of the steam is of a magnitude which results in less deposition of solids in the turbine, thus assuring sustained high efficiency. Quite similar requirements for water purity are necessary in high pressure industrial boilers where makeup requirements are high, ranging from 30 to 100 per cent of the feedwater supply.

At lower steam pressures, below 600 psig, there is a greater latitude in the selection of methods for the preparation of boiler makeup. Turbine problems relating to vaporized solids are minor, and the requirements for feedwater are primarily concerned with the prevention of scale and sludge formation in the boilers. Most industrial boilers operate with high makeup, and the raw water to these units is treated to remove hardness, insoluble residues like silt, excess silica and alkalinity.

The capital and operating costs for the treatment of water to these boilers is substantially less than for higher pressure industrial and central station units. Higher solids and turbidities are tolerated in the boiler water of these low pressure units. The problems of steam contamination and deposits increase under these circumstances. Addition of foam depressers, dispersing chemical substances and the employment of higher quantities of boiler water blowdown are often necessary to permit sustained operation. The cleaning of boiler water surfaces of deposits must be followed at more frequent intervals to prevent tube ruptures in operation.

The greatest incidence of problems in

steam generating equipment is related to (1) scale or deposits, (2) corrosion and (3) carryover of solids with the steam to the superheater. A brief discussion of these items follows.

Scale and Deposits

The principal items contributing to the formation of a heat deterrent scale or deposit are (1) contaminating elements present in the makeup water, (2) corrosion products formed outside the boiler and introduced into the unit with the feedwater, (3) contaminants from process industries introduced into condensate returned to the boiler and (4) the solids which are present in condenser leakage.

Scale and sludge deposits form on heated surfaces of a boiler tube in the process of evaporation of water to steam. The chemical substances in water concentrate in a film at the evaporation surface. Soluble constituents are readily redissolved by the water displacing the bubble of steam at the point of evaporation. Insoluble substances tend to form on the metal surface, gradually raising the metal temperature until creep and failure occur. Most scale forming substances have a decreasing solubility in water with an increase in temperature. Hence, the higher the temperature, the more rapidly a heat deterrent scale will form on the metal surface. Scale formation is influenced by operating temperature, the rate of heat release at the evaporation surface and the nature of the chemical substance.

Substances such as calcium bicarbonate decompose in the boiler water to form calcium carbonate, carbon dioxide and water as follows:

$$Ca(HCO_3)_2 \longrightarrow CaCO_3 + CO_2 + H_2O$$

Calcium carbonate has a limited solubility and will agglomerate at the heated surface to form a scale. At lower pressures and steaming rates, this reaction can be tolerated and the bulk of the deposit can be removed by blowdown.

Calcium sulfate (permanent hardness) is more soluble than calcium carbonate and will deposit as a heat deterrent scale in place on the tube. At lower pressures, and during the early history of steam generation, calcium sulfate scaling was controlled by the addition of soda ash.

$$CaSO_4 + Na_2CO_3 \longrightarrow CaCO_3 + Na_2SO_4$$

The presence of alumina, iron and copper oxides, and silica with calcium and magnesium compounds in raw water aggravates the scale problem in low and medium pressure boilers where a limited amount of external softening is used in preparing boiler feed water. Chemical reactions in boilers at heated surfaces, in these cases, leads to the formation of undesirable scale as calcium silicate ($CaSiO_3$), quartz (SiO_2), analcite ($Na_2O \cdot Al_2O_3 \cdot 4SiO_2 \cdot 2H_2O$), acmite ($Na_2O \cdot Fe_2O_3 \cdot 4SiO_2$) and magnesium silicate ($MgSiO_3$). Formation of these compounds on heated surfaces occurs in evaporation of boiler water due to limited solubility or by interaction with other chemical components present at the point of steam formation. These substances have a low thermal conductivity, and a paper thin scale layer will overheat the boiler tube metal.

Use of Phosphates for Internal Treatment

The work of R. E. Hall and associates led to the use of phosphates for the conversion of calcium and magnesium salts to phosphates which are readily dispersed and removed by blow down. Trisodium phosphate, disodium hydrogen phosphate and sodium metaphosphate or sodium pyrophosphate are used to condition water in an alkaline condition. Some of the reactions are:[4]

$$2Na_3PO_4 + 3CaSO_4 \longrightarrow$$
$$Ca_3(PO_4)_2 + 3Na_2SO_4$$

$$3MgCO_3 + 2Na_3PO_4 \longrightarrow$$
$$Mg_3(PO_4)_2 + 3Na_2CO_3$$

$$Mg(HCO_3)_2 + 4NaOH \longrightarrow$$
$$Mg(OH)_2 + 2Na_2CO_3 + H_2O$$

$$MgCl_2 + 2NaOH + SiO_2 \longrightarrow$$
$$MgSiO_3 + 2NaCl + H_2O$$

The preferred form of magnesium salts in boiler water is magnesium hydroxide. Silica is generally reduced in industrial boiler water by magnesium. The preferred form of calcium phosphate is the apatite form which is formed in a higher alkalinity water. This reaction may be written as:

$$10CaCO_3 + 6Na_3PO_4 + 2NaOH \longrightarrow$$
$$3Ca_3(PO_4)_2 \cdot Ca(OH)_2 + 10Na_2CO_3$$

The degree of internal treatment varies with the quality of makeup water. Deposit formation is minor where the hardness is below two ppm in the feedwater. Best results are obtained when the calcium and magnesium salts are zero. The latter condition is mandatory at higher boiler pressures. The quantity of silica and hardness which can be tolerated in boilers depends largely on the pressure, rate of steam generation and the operating factors involved. Better quality water is required where efficiency and economy at high ratings receive prime consideration. Where internal treatment is used in industrial boilers to control deposits, a boiler water pH value of 10.5 to 11.5 and a phosphate residual of 20 to 50 ppm is generally maintained in solution.

Increasing the schedule of internal treatment results in a boiler water with a high solids content. To operate boilers in this manner it is generally necessary to add organic substances like tannins, starches, lignin sulfonates and seaweed derivatives to condition sludge in boiler water. Increasing the solids content in the boiler water in the presence of organic impurities, oil or process contaminants leads to the formation of foam. In this condition, antifoam chemicals must be added to prevent contamination of steam by carryover. Clearly, excessive treatment, or a lack of external treatment, leads to severe problems in the generation of steam. These can and should be avoided.

Significance of Iron — Water Reaction

The reaction of boiler steel and water is affected by the chemical constituents present in solution, the quantity of dissolved gases, the structural characteristics of the steel and the rate of heat input to the boiler metal. While the reaction is understood in a general sense, there is insufficient information to explain the mechanism in exact detail. Many theories have been forwarded to clarify this problem. However, in spite of the lack of fundamental data, experience and experimental evidence have permitted the development of controls which satisfactorily contain the corrosive activity. This section will deal with existing techniques developed to understand and control reactions in boilers.

The fundamental reaction of iron and water is to produce iron hydroxide and hydrogen as follows:

$$Fe + 2H_2O \longrightarrow Fe(OH)_2 + H_2$$

---

[4] See "Phosphate in Boiler Water Conditioning" by R. E. Hall and associates, *Journal* of the American Water Works Association, Vol. 21, 1929, pp. 79–100.

It is an established fact that the end product of reaction in boilers is magnetic oxide of iron. The control of corrosion, therefore, is based on the knowledge of the rate controlling step in the overall reaction. Schikorr established a mechanism which accounted for the production of magnetic oxide of iron. In simplest form, the reactions would be:[5]

$$Fe + 2H_2O \longrightarrow Fe(OH)_2 + H_2$$
$$3Fe(OH)_2 \longrightarrow Fe_3O_4 + 2H_2O + H_2$$

From a consideration of physical chemical relationships it can be shown that the formation of iron hydroxide is the rate controlling step in the Schikorr hypothesis. Therefore, the rate of the overall reaction is based on the solubility and stability of this product.

The initial reaction above is pH or alkalinity controlled since, by the laws of chemical equilibrium, addition of alkalinity would reverse the reaction to the left. Corey and Finnegan found that iron placed in contact with deaerated and chemically pure water will produce an equilibrium pH of approximately 8.3. Increasing the alkalinity reduces the solubility of the iron corrosion product and inhibits reactivity. The control of this reaction has been well established in the protection of metal surfaces existing upstream of the boiler.[6]

A boiler is sometimes described as a film of magnetic iron oxide supported by metallic iron. It is the preservation of this film which leads to successful operation. The use of sodium hydroxide to provide a protective pH has the longest history of application in the control of the iron water reaction. It is largely based on research published by Berl and van Taack in Germany in 1930.[7] This control, shown in Fig. 8–1, indicates that corrosion cannot be entirely eliminated but is a minimum at a pH of 11.5.

There have been many variations in the manner of control of the iron-water reaction. Recent investigations, and the results drawn from operation in the field, indicate a new mechanism of iron and water reaction at higher temperatures. The stability or existence of the intermediate product, iron hydroxide, is high at lower temperatures. Thus, it is possible to protect steel in the preboiler cycle by pH control. At temperatures above 400 to 450 F, this compound is extremely unstable and its presence is difficult to detect. This observation leads to the belief that another mechanism controls corrosion at higher temperatures.

The current theory regarding the reaction of iron and water in a boiler at temperatures above 450 F is shown in Fig. 8–2. It may be referred to as the diffusion controlled reaction. Iron atoms in the body of the steel, activated by temperature, diffuse to the iron—iron oxide interface. At this point, iron ions are formed. The iron ions diffuse through the lattice openings of the iron oxide crystals to the iron oxide—water interface. At this point, the reaction of the iron ions and

---

[5] See "Uber das System Eisen-Wasser" by G. Schikorr, *Zeitschrift fur Elektrochemie*, Vol. 35, 1929, pp. 62–65.

[6] See "The pH, Dissolved Iron Concentration and Solid Product Resulting from the Reaction Between Iron and Pure Water at Room Temperature" by R. C. Corey and T. J. Finnegan, *Proceedings* ASTM, Vol. 39, 1939, pp. 1242–1260.

[7] See "Über die Einwirkung von Laugen und Salzen auf Flusseisen unter Hochdruckbedingungen und über die Schutzwirkung von Natriumsulfat gegen den Angriff von Ätznatron und von Chlormagensium" by E. Berl and F. van Taack, *Forschungsarbeiten*, No. 330, VDI, Berlin, 1930.

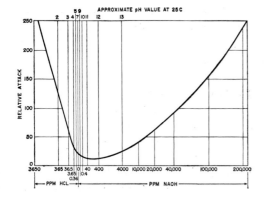

Fig. 8–1. Attack on steel by water of varying degrees of acidity and alkalinity

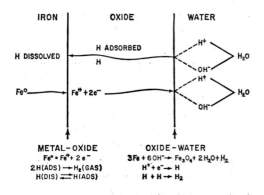

Fig. 8–2. Reaction of iron and water in a boiler

the hydroxyl component of water results in the formation of magnetic oxide of iron, water and hydrogen.

To complete the electrical neutrality of the reaction, hydrogen ions from the body of the water react at the water—iron oxide interface to form atomic hydrogen. The atomic hydrogen diffuses through the oxide to the oxide—metal interface and molecular hydrogen is discharged. At each side of this interface, there is a balance of the hydrogen dissolved in the steel and the hydrogen

absorbed by the oxide. Conditions leading to an unbalance, as by additional temperature rise or local corrosion, can lead to accelerate the solution of hydrogen in the steel and its reaction with carbon in the steel.

Deposition of metal oxides from boiler water at the tube surface can increase the local concentration of chemicals between the protective metal oxide and deposit. Presence of chemicals such as sodium hydroxide can lead to the solution of the protective oxide permitting the reaction described to proceed until the metal is reduced to a point of failure. The presence of a compact oxide, or a corrosion cell set up by oxygen or oxides of iron and copper, can lead to an accelerated reaction due to the rise in temperature. In this condition, hydrogen dissolves rapidly into the steel, as described previously, to result in a brittle failure with little loss of tube metal.

Experience indicates that alkalinity is not a basic requirement for establishing a film of magnetic oxide of iron at steam pressures above 900 psig. This is at variance with the concept that a boiler water pH of about 10.5 to 11.0 is necessary to establish a stable film of magnetic oxide of iron. Such conflicting opinions will continue to exist until the mechanism of the iron-water reaction is clearly determined by experimental results obtained under controlled test conditions.

Coordinated Phosphate Control

Boiler water pH can be established without the use of caustic soda. Sodium phosphate can be utilized to acquire a suitable alkalinity in boiler water without the negative reaction associated with caustic soda. Whirl and Purcell[8] developed the method of pH control termed the *coordinated phosphate pH control*. This method is illustrated by the relationship of pH and the phosphate concentration in boiler water shown in Fig. 8–3. Values noted on the curve represent pH values obtained by dissolving stoichiometrically pure trisodium phosphate (Na_3PO_4). Conditions below the curve represent solutions of trisodium phosphate and disodium hydrogen phosphate (Na_2HPO_4). The area above the curve, which represents solutions of trisodium phosphate and caustic, is to be avoided.

In the coordinated phosphate pH control, specifications can be maintained by the addition of sodium hydroxide in conjunction with disodium phosphate (Na_2HPO_4), sodium metaphosphate ($NaPO_3$) or phosphoric acid (H_3PO_4). Normally, combinations of trisodium

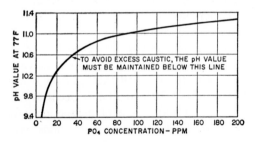

Fig. 8–3. Coordinated phosphate pH control

phosphate and disodium phosphate are preferred since difficulties from erroneous chemical feed are less serious.

Alkalinity control is attained by the addition of phosphate ions to water to produce a captive quantity for hydroxide (OH) by the reversed hydrolysis reaction as follows:

$$PO_4 \equiv + H_2O \rightleftarrows OH^- + HPO_4 \equiv$$

This reaction is complete at pH levels below 11.0. The hydrolysis reaction of dibasic phosphate also proceeds in water as follows:

$$HPO_4 = + H_2O \rightleftarrows OH^- + H_2PO_4^-$$

The latter reaction is complete at low pH levels 5 to 7 but is less than 0.1 per cent at a pH level of 10. Thus, dibasic phosphate neither hydrolyzes nor dissociates in the normal boiler water pH range. Additions of disodium phosphate has little effect on pH in the range 10 to 11.0.

Monobasic phosphate dissociates to the dibasic form and the addition of one mole of monosodium phosphate (NaH_2PO_4) is capable of neutralizing one mole of sodium hydroxide. pH control can be assured by trisodium phosphate since one mole of this compound will increase boiler water pH equivalent to the addition of one mole of sodium hydroxide. Reduction of excess caustic can be accomplished by the addition of monosodium phosphate.

Role of Oxygen

The reaction of iron and water is accelerated by the presence of oxygen. Oxygen can react with iron hydroxide to form a hydrated ferric oxide or magnetite. This action is generally localized and forms a pit in the metal. Severe attack can occur if the pit becomes progressively anodic in operation. Oxygen reacts with hydrogen at the cathodic surface and depolarizes the surface locally. This permits more iron to dissolve gradually creating a pit.

---

[8] See "Protection Against Caustic Embrittlement by Coordinated Phosphate pH Control" by T. E. Purcell and S. F. Whirl, *Proceedings* of Third Annual Water Conference, Engineers' Society of Western Pennsylvania, 1942, pp. 45–60.

The most severe corrosion action occurs when a small area is covered by a deposit. The creation of a differential aeration cell about the deposit can lead to a severe local action. The metal beneath the deposit is lower in oxygen than areas surrounding it, becomes anodic and is attacked. Pitting is most prevalent in stressed sections of boiler tubing, such as at welds and cold worked sections, and at surface discontinuities in the metal. Pits formed when boilers are in standby condition or during low load operation lead to severe localized metal attack when the metal temperature is increased at higher heat transfer rates.

Power plants employing tight cycles to prevent oxygen infiltration and condenser leakage are generally free from corrosion problems. Unfortunately, many cycles are vulnerable to oxygen leakage into the feedwater as a result of design or operation. Too often, oxygen enters the system undetected during periods of operation which are poorly monitored.

Some typical operating conditions in which considerable oxygen is introduced into the feedwater are low load operation and startup operation of boilers. In either case, deaeration in the cycle is poor or completely absent, leading to a corrosive condition. Oxygen enters the feedwater in normal operation if poorly vented evaporated makeup water is introduced into the cycle, if air laden heater drips are pumped into the condensate, or if undeaerated condensate is added to the feedwater as makeup to the system.

Efficient operation of boilers requires the exclusion of oxygen from the feedwater. The normal guaranteed value of oxygen leaving the deaerating heater or a deaerating condenser is less than 0.005 ppm. To achieve this low residual, it is necessary to exclude air leakage into the condenser, to prevent the addition of undeaerated water to the condensate or feedwater, to prevent the addition of aerated heater drips into the condensate and to assure the exclusion of air into the feedwater cycle during short outages of the boiler.[9]

One of the major problems in curtailing corrosion due to oxygen is the exclusion of air upon startup of a boiler. Normally, pressure in a deaerator is not attained until steam is admitted to the turbine and bleed steam is available for heating. It is possible to introduce more oxygen into the boiler at this time than in several months of normal operation. Much of this problem can be prevented by admitting auxiliary steam to a deaerator to pressurize the unit to 3–5 psig. In this condition, air is excluded and the feedwater delivered to the boiler is low in oxygen during startup operation. Use of a small deaerator, to remove oxygen from the condensate during the vacuum raising period in the condenser, is another method of excluding oxygen from the condensate of systems which employ only a deaerating condenser.

Removal of Residual Oxygen

Chemical agents are generally added to the feedwater or boiler water to remove small residual quantities of oxygen. The most frequently used chemicals are *hydrazine* (N_2H_4) and *sodium sulfite* (Na_2SO_3). Sulfite reacts with oxygen to form a soluble sodium sulfate as follows:

$$Na_2SO_3 + \frac{1}{2} O_2 \longrightarrow Na_2SO_4$$

[9] See "Problems in Deaeration of Boiler Feedwater" by H. A. Grabowski, H. D. Ongman, W. B. Willsey and W. Nelson, *Combustion,* Vol. 26, March 1955, pp. 43–48.

This chemical action increases the concentration of solids in boiler water. Hydrazine reacts with oxygen to form nitrogen and water.

$$N_2H_4 + O_2 \longrightarrow N_2 + 2H_2O$$

Temperature affects the reactivity and stability of sulfite and hydrazine. The reaction of sulfite with oxygen proceeds at room temperature. A cobalt catalyst is generally added to speed up the reaction at lower temperatures. Sulfite decomposition increases with temperature and local concentration in boiler water. Sodium sulfite decomposes in boiler water as follows:

$$Na_2SO_3 + 2H_2O \longrightarrow 2NaOH + H_2SO_3$$
$$H_2SO_3 \longrightarrow H_2O + SO_2$$

Sulfur dioxide (SO_2) is an acidic anhydride and increases corrosion of metals when it is dissolved in condensate films formed on wetted surface of a turbine or condenser.

Concentration of sulfite must be controlled to minimize decomposition at elevated pressures. Recommended limits are shown in Table 8–3.

Sulfite decomposition is accelerated above 2100 psig and should not be used for reducing oxygen in very high pressure boilers.

Sodium sulfite is an effective reducing agent on boiler water. Besides its reaction with oxygen, the chemical reduces oxides of iron and copper as follows:

$$2CuO + Na_2SO_3 \longrightarrow Cu_2O + Na_2SO_4$$
$$3Fe_2O_3 + Na_2SO_3 \longrightarrow 2Fe_3O_4 + Na_2SO_4$$

Its consumption in boiler water is a measure of oxygen and oxidized substances added with the feedwater into a boiler. The reduction of cupric oxide begins at about 280 F and is complete at about 400 F. Reduction of ferric oxide

Table 8–3   Limits of Sulfite

Boiler Pressure, psig	Concentration, ppm
Below 700	20–30
700–1000	10–20
1000–1500	5–10
1500–1800	2–5
1800–2100	< 2

begins at about 440 F and is complete at 540 F.

Hydrazine reacts with oxygen very slowly at temperatures below 350 F. Above 450 F, hydrazine is decomposed rapidly to nitrogen, hydrogen and ammonia. The principal benefit of hydrazine is its ability to reduce the oxidized forms of copper and iron. In this state the general corrosion of the metal surfaces is reduced in the preboiler cycle. Copper oxide is reduced with hydrazine at temperatures as low as 150 F. Iron oxide (Fe_2O_3) can be reduced at a temperature of 250 F.

Normally, hydrazine is added to the cycle at the outlet of the condensate pump at a rate to assure a residual of 10–20 ppb (parts per billion) at the inlet of the economizer.

Some of the reactions of hydrazine in the feedwater cycle and boiler are:

Decomposition

$$3N_2H_4 \longrightarrow N_2 + 4NH_3$$
$$2N_2H_4 \longrightarrow N_2 + H_2 + 2NH_3$$

Reduction

$$6Fe_2O_3 + N_2H_4 \longrightarrow 4Fe_3O_4 + N_2 + 2H_2O$$
$$2\,CuO + N_2H_4 \longrightarrow Cu_2O + N_2 + 2H_2O$$

The use of reducing agents aids in curbing corrosion but will not prevent metal attack when oxygen is present in the boiler feedwater. The action of oxygen with steel exceeds that of the reducing agents at higher temperatures.

Thus, the principal emphasis should be placed on reducing oxygen. One theory considers the higher oxidized forms of copper and iron as effective reducing agents of the normal protective boiler tube surface. Hence, maintenance of reducing condition of a boiler is imperative.

Boiler Water Controls — High Pressure Boilers

Boiler water controls commonly used in high pressure boilers maintain pH by (1) caustic (2) coordinated phosphate or (3) volatile treatment. The use of caustic has the longest history and is the least preferred manner of control. The negative effects of caustic concentration under deposits increase the incidence of tube metal failures.

Treatment of boiler water is used to control contamination. The preferred control of pH in a higher pressure boiler where contamination is a factor is the coordinated phosphate pH control. As is shown previously in Fig. 8–3 the control of pH is adjusted by the addition of sodium phosphate. Controlling concentrations of phosphate at or below the curve insures an absence of caustic in the boiler water. The coordinated phosphate method, as mentioned earlier, was developed in the 1940's by Whirl and Purcell to offset the negative effects of caustic in the prevention of caustic embrittlement and caustic bonded soluble type turbine blade deposits. This treatment has an excellent record of protection in boilers up to 2600 psig. Table 8–4 lists the recommended controls.

The development of the diffusion concept of reaction of boiler surfaces above 450 F aids in justifying the application of the volatile treatment type of control. The fundamental aim in the control is the maintenance of a pH by the use of a volatile alkaline chemical and to insure the proper state of reduction by the application of hydrazine. Table 8–5 illustrates the controls inherent in this method.

Separation of metal oxides on heated or unheated surfaces is a function of the pH and conductance of boiler water. Higher pH boiler waters have contributed to the metal oxide deposition problem. In controlled circulation boilers the proper application of controls has minimized the deposition of metal oxides on

Table 8–4 Coordinated Phosphate pH Control

Feedwater Controls	
pH	8.8 to 9.2
Total Solids	< 0.5 ppm
Silica	< 0.02 ppm
Iron	< 0.01 ppm
Copper	< 0.01 ppm
Hydrazine	0.01 to 0.02 ppm
Boiler Water	
pH	10.0 to 10.2
Phosphate (PO_4)	10 to 15 ppm
Free Caustic (NaOH)	0 & < 2.0 ppm
Silica	Based on Fig. 8–22
Sulfite *	< 2.0 ppm
Total Sulfite Solids	< 100 ppm

* Recommended only for drum pressures below 2100 psig

Table 8–5 Volatile Treatment Control

Feedwater Controls	
pH	8.8 to 9.2
Total Solids	< 0.25 ppm
Silica	< 0.02 ppm
Iron	< 0.01 ppm
Copper	< 0.01 ppm
Hydrazine	0.01 to 0.02 ppm
Boiler Water	
pH	8.5 to 9.0
Total Solids	< 2.0 ppm

orifices leading to waterwall circuits. Fig. 8–4 illustrates the reduction in deposition, as measured by pressure drop increase across the pump, by the application of the volatile treatment. As shown,

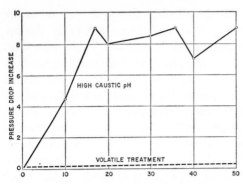

Fig. 8–4. Effect of volatile treatment in reducing deposits

deposition was not apparent in a period of one year with the volatile treatment as compared to the caustic based treatment used previously in the boiler water of a 2000 psig boiler.

Boiler Water Controls–Supercritical Pressure Boilers

The trend to more efficient central station cycles and the installation of once through boilers have required the development of new concepts to increase water purity supplied to units operating near or above the critical pressure of 3206 psia. Experience has shown that water of exceptionally high quality is necessary if large boiler-turbine units are to perform without interruption and with high availability.

The application of *filters* for the removal of suspended corrosion products has assisted measurably to advance water technology at high pressures. Tubular type filters, consisting of fine stainless steel wire mesh or plate type filters, have been used successfully to remove iron and copper oxides. These filters are supplied with precoat and a filter aid of a cellulose base material which trap the oxides. The filter aid is recirculated in the unit. Reaching a set pressure drop increase, the filter cake is removed by

backwashing, normally by the application of air. After backwashing the filter is precoated and returned to service. Filtering equipment has been installed at the outlet of the condensate pump to handle from 10 to 100 per cent of the total flow in many high pressure steam plants.

Tight condensers are a requirement at high pressures. The need to guard against sudden tube leaks in the condenser or to aid in cleaning up water upon a startup of a boiler has brought about the development of *polishing demineralizers*. These units are normally mixed bed units located at the outlet of the condenser or downstream of a filter if one is used. They are usually in continuous service during normal power plant operation, reprocessing all or a major portion of the feedwater flow.

While conventional water flow rates are generally used in most polishing demineralizer systems, there is a trend to the application of high flow units. Polishing units capable of handling up to 100 gallons per square foot of bed have been successfully utilized in nuclear applications. Some of these units are used as filters and demineralizers. Regeneration is achieved by physically separating the resins and chemically treating them in separate compartments. This scheme is not commonly used in conventional filter-demineralizer combinations.

The advent of subcritical pressure once through boilers required the availability of a tight cycle with a pure makeup. This has been possible with evaporators and demineralizers. An example of the water limits set for this operation is shown in Table 8–6. These boilers operate with a separator and it has not been necessary to use filters or condensate polishing units.[10]

[10] See Chapter 25, Combined Circulation Boilers.

Improvement in condenser and water makeup technology has permitted the application of the supercritical pressure cycle. Filters and condensate polishing units are necessary since any contaminant can pass directly from the boiler to the turbine. The water controls are more stringent as evidenced by the limits shown in Table 8–7.

Table 8–6   Water Conditions Subcritical Pressure Once Through Units

Total Solids	0.5 ppm maximum
pH	8.8 to 9.2
Hydrazine	Slight excess
Dissolved Oxygen	0.007 ppm

Table 8–7   Water Conditions Supercritical Pressure Once Through Units

Total Solids	0.25 ppm (0.5 ppm for short periods)
pH	9.0 to 9.5 (by N_2H_4 and NH_3)
Total Iron	0.01 ppm
Total Copper	0.01 ppm
Silica	0.02 ppm
Dissolved Oxygen	0.007 ppm

Preboiler Corrosion

Elimination of corrosion in the feedwater heaters and piping aids materially in decreasing the problem of deposition of oxides on heat transfer surfaces of boilers. This is accomplished by reducing the level of dissolved gases, as oxygen and carbon dioxide, in feedwater and by adjusting the pH of the water. Initially, this was accomplished by adding compounds such as caustic to the feedwater or by adding a part of the boiler blowdown to the condensate.

Desuperheating of steam, by spraying feedwater into the inlet of the superheater or reheater, does not permit the addition of solid chemicals, such as caustic or phosphate, to the feedwater. To assure protection to preboiler equipment, volatile alkaline chemicals have been developed which raise the pH of the water but do not form solid residues in the boiler. The choice of chemical used is based on its temperature stability in the superheater and reheater.

Controlled quantities of ammonia (NH_3), morpholine (C_4H_9NO) or cyclohexylamine ($C_6H_{11}NH_2$) will elevate the pH of the feedwater. These compounds volatilize with the steam from boilerwater and react with gases like carbon dioxide to neutralize the acidity of the condensate. These compounds are classed as neutralizing amines and are commonly used to protect metallic surfaces from corrosion in the equipment upstream of the boiler.

Amines such as morpholine and cyclohexylamine are preferred to ammonia for pH control in situations where excessive decomposition of these chemicals does not occur in the boiler. Ammonia, if present in high concentrations, will attack the copper alloys in feedwater heaters. A copper ammonium complex is formed when the pH of the condensate is above 9.7. Also, the copper activity with ammonia is accelerated in the presence of oxygen. Typical reactions of copper and excessive ammonia are:

$$2Cu + 4NH_3 + 2H_2O \longrightarrow$$
$$2Cu(NH_3)_2{}^{++} + H_2 + 2OH-$$

$$Cu + 4NH_3 + 2H_2O \longrightarrow$$
$$Cu(NH_3)_4{}^{++} + H_2 + 2OH-$$

Amines do not exhibit similar reaction tendencies. It has also been established that ammonia, in controlled quantities of 0.2 to 0.3 ppm in a condensate low in carbon dioxide, will assure a protective pH in the cycle (9.0) and will not attack copper surfaces.

The stability characteristics of volatile amines are shown in Table 8–8. Both

Table 8-8   Stability of Volatile Water Treating Materials

Chemical	Formula	Press psig	Temp. F	Per cent Decom- posed
Ammonia	NH_3	4270	1202	0
Cyclohexylamine	$C_6H_{11}NH_2$	4270	1202	88
Morpholine	$O(C_2H_4)_2NH$	4270	1202	100
Hydrazine	N_2H_4	4270	1202	100

morpholine and cyclohexylamine have temperature stability limits. Ammonia, hydrogen and carbon decomposition products are formed in the dissociation of these amines at high temperatures. Ammonia is stable and has been used at steam temperatures as high as 1200 F. As a result, ammonia is the recommended compound for use in controlling pH of condensate in high pressure, high temperature boiler systems. The other amines are not recommended where metal temperatures in the boiler are above 1050 F.

Another method used to protect feed-water heaters and piping is by the addition of filming amines. Their function is to form an impervious nonwettable film that acts as a barrier to reaction between the metal and water. Octadecylamine ($C_{18}H_{37}NH_2$) is the most commonly used filming amine. These compounds have practical value in industrial plants where the area of surfaces to be protected are large and the makeup is high. Best results are obtained when the pH level of the water is below 8.0.

Control of iron and copper corrosion in the feedwater system should be regulated to assure less than 10 ppb of these compounds in the feedwater. This is obtained in systems using neutralizing amines at a pH level of 8.8 to 9.2 and where the oxygen content is low.

Minimum corrosion of metals in feed-water heaters and piping occurs when a protective pH is maintained and the content of dissolved gases such as oxygen, carbon dioxide, sulfur dioxide and hydrogen sulfide is at a minimum. The chemical control for pH by ammonia or neutralizing amines must be established to ascertain that the rise in alkalinity is due to the chemical itself. As noted in the laboratory studies of Corey and Finnegan previously cited, pure condensate (neutral pH) will dissolve iron and copper so as to elevate the pH of the feedwater to a value approaching 8.5 at the inlet to the economizer. Thus, in this case the pH rise is at the expense of metals, and the boiler feedwater will contain excessive quantities of corrosion products.

Oxygen will increase the overall corrosion problem in the feedwater system. Ferric hydroxide ($Fe[OH]_3$) is highly insoluble and precipitates readily on heated surfaces. Changes in flow characteristics dislodge the oxides and they are eventually introduced into the boiler. Analysis of feedwater will, in most cases, not disclose the presence of corrosion where oxygen is high. The reaction in forming the insoluble residue is:

$$Fe + 2H_2O \longrightarrow Fe(OH)_2 + H_2$$
$$4Fe(OH)_2 + O_2 + 2H_2O \longrightarrow 4Fe(OH)_3$$

While a pH value of about 9.0 will reduce the solution of copper, the principal influence in the attack of copper is the presence of oxygen. In the reactions:

$$2Cu + 2H_2O \longrightarrow 2Cu^+ + H_2 + 2e^-$$
$$Cu + 2H_2O \longrightarrow Cu^{++} + H_2 + 2OH$$

it is apparent that presence of oxygen reduces the hydrogen overvoltage of the copper and accelerates corrosion.[11]

[11] An informative article on this subject is "Overvoltage and Its Significance in Corrosion" by Samuel Glasstone, *Journal of Corrosion*, June–July 1946, pp. 15–18.

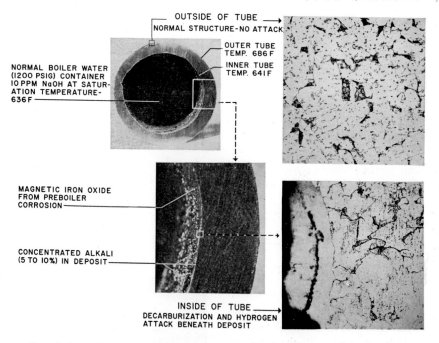

NORMAL BOILER WATER
(1200 PSIG) CONTAINER
10 PPM NaOH AT SATUR-
ATION TEMPERATURE-
636 F

OUTSIDE OF TUBE
NORMAL STRUCTURE-NO ATTACK

OUTER TUBE
TEMP. 686 F

INNER TUBE
TEMP. 641 F

MAGNETIC IRON OXIDE
FROM PREBOILER
CORROSION

CONCENTRATED ALKALI
(5 TO 10%) IN DEPOSIT

INSIDE OF TUBE
DECARBURIZATION AND HYDROGEN
ATTACK BENEATH DEPOSIT

Fig. 8–5. Effect of attack upon metal lying beneath an oxide deposit

Corrosion Problems in Boiler Tubing

Corrosion problems in boiler tubing occur with an increasing frequency as the temperature and pressure increases in boiler design. Failures are characterized as being of the ductile or brittle type. In either case, the failures result in costly outages. For the most part it is difficult to locate areas which may be damaged by corrosive action, which is generally localized and provides no visible signs of distress when tubing is viewed from the furnace side.

The reaction of steel and boiler water is influenced significantly by the quantity of metal oxides introduced into the boiler with the feedwater. Corrosion products formed in the preboiler circuit separate on the heat transfer surfaces of the boiler to raise the temperatures of the local

film and tube metal. This condition permits boiler water to concentrate between the deposit and the tube metal and to dissolve the protective film of metal oxide of the tube. The thinning of the tube metal can proceed without any external evidence of overheating until a failure due to a pinhole causes the boiler to be removed from service. Unscheduled outages result, and it is difficult to estimate the degree of damage existing in the boiler without the use of special techniques.

An example of the concentration of boiler water salts between the tube metal and on oxide deposited on the metal is shown in Fig. 8–5. As can be seen, boiler water salts are trapped between the metal and deposit. These salts concentrate during evaporation and can lead to a serious tube corrosion. Salts like sodium hydroxide increase in strength with a few degrees of superheat. In a concentrated form, the caustic can dissolve the protective metal oxide and promote the iron water reaction:

$$Fe_3O_4 + 6NaOH \longrightarrow$$
$$3Na_2FeO_2 + 3H_2O + \tfrac{1}{2} O_2$$

$$3Fe + 4H_2O \longrightarrow Fe_3O_4 + 4H_2$$

The sodium ferroate decomposes by two possible mechanisms to release magnetite:

$$3Na_2FeO_2 + 4H_2O \longrightarrow$$
$$Fe_3O_4 + 6NaOH + H_2$$
$$3Na_2FeO_2 + 4H_2O + \tfrac{1}{2}O \longrightarrow$$
$$Fe_3O_4 + 6NaOH + H_2O$$

The decomposition increases the quantity of deposit at a point away from the initial reaction. The chemical activity can proceed until the metal is reduced in thickness to a point of failure.

Brittle type of boiler tube failures can also occur due to the increased rate of reaction of steel and water caused by a local deposition of corrosion products. Decarburization at the grain boundaries of the water contacted surfaces leads to a gradual embrittling of the steel. Hydrogen diffusing into the steel, as the result of the iron-water reaction, reacts with the carbon to weaken the structure of the steel. Zapffe's hypothesis indicates this action to be due to hydrogen which diffuses into the steel along the grain boundaries and reacts with iron carbides to form methane.[12] The partial pressure of the methane gas is sufficient to promote penetration into the steel. The decarbu-

rization causes a local brittle structure which leads to a catastrophic failure. This reaction would be:

$$FeC + H_2 \longrightarrow CH_4 + 3Fe$$

Some authorities on corrosion do not agree with the methane gas theory, and additional investigation of the mechanism is required.[13] Generally, the brittleness is found only in the vicinity of the local corrosive activity. The oxide formation is hard and dense in the immediate vicinity of corrosion and does not resemble the porous, granular type of deposit associated with corrosion where chemicals

Fig. 8–6.   Corrosion of oxy-acetylene field weld with backing ring

concentrate between the metal and the oxide layer previously described.

The brittle type of failure occurs most generally in stressed areas such as those at welds and bent or machined sections of tubing. It has also been found in straight sections of tubing away from welded areas where welding reinforce-

---

[12] See "Boiler Embrittlement" by C. A. Zapffe, *Trans.* ASME, Vol. 66, 1944, pp. 81–126.
[13] For additional information see "The Mechanism of the Formation of Films on Metals" by U. R. Evans, *Journal of Corrosion*, July–August 1948, pp. 15–19.

There are many theories for the initiation and propagation of corrosion on heated surfaces of boiler tubing. This is to be expected since there is a significant difference in the water treatment schedules established in the operation of boilers. The effect of copper, surface flaws of tubing and pits formed during standby or outage periods has been widely discussed as the basic cause of corrosion in operation.

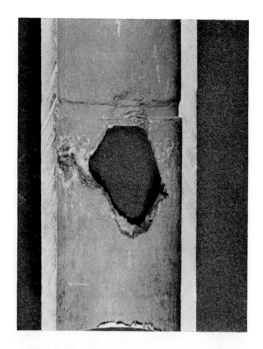

Fig. 8–7. Corrosion of shop flash weld

ments may contribute to the problem. Examples of this serious type of attack are shown in Figs. 8–6, 8–7 and 8–8. The corrosion proceeds along the grain boundaries from the water contacted surface to the fireside of the tube. The decarburization and intercrystalline cracking is noted in Figs. 8–9 and 8–10. As noted in Fig. 8–10, the outer structure of the tube is normal (fireside) lamellar pearlite in a ferrite matrix with no evidence of carbon loss or cracking. This is in marked contrast to the inside or waterside surface. There is no evidence of the classical overheating of the metal where decarburization would be noted on the fireside of the tube with a tendency for the pearlite to spheroidize.[14]

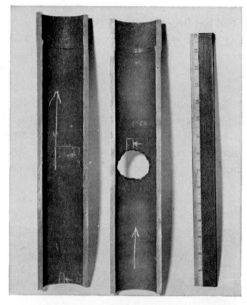

Fig. 8–8. Corroded area away from shop weld

Pits formed in furnace wall tubes are potential foci of accelerated attack. The oxide with which they are filled is essentially a semipermeable matrix in

[14] Metallurgical terms are defined and discussed in Chapter 9, Materials and Metallurgy. An interesting account of their origin is found in A History of Metallography by Cyril Stanley Smith, University of Chicago Press, 1960, pp. 225–228.

which boiler water salts can concentrate and lead to attack in a manner similar to that which occurs in crevices; that is, by direct chemical attack and by complex concentration cell processes. Further, the presence of a discontinuity in the surface of a tube, as is presented by an oxide filled pit, might conceivably cause a type of nucleate boiling. The specific rate of release of steam bubbles would be high under this condition and might therefore have an effect of intensifying attack at such a point.

The role of copper in the corrosion of steel has been discussed widely with varying opinions over many years. A common conception is that copper and its oxides are generally found in the vicinity of corrosion but do not initiate the attack.

Many chemists have attributed copper as a cause of corrosion by observing that a couple forms between copper and steel with which it is in contact, the steel being anodic. The corrosive activity due

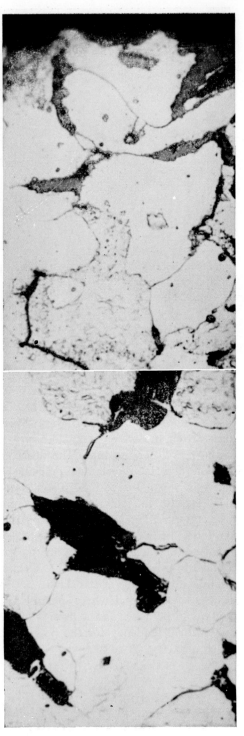

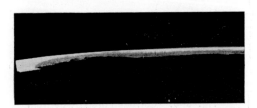

Fig. 8–9.   Cross section in an embrittled tube wall

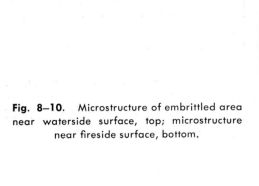

Fig. 8–10.   Microstructure of embrittled area near waterside surface, top; microstructure near fireside surface, bottom.

to the galvanic action is attractive but it has not been proven to exist in high pressure boilers.

The fact that corrosion takes place while a boiler is not operating often is disregarded. In fact, serious corrosion can take place during and immediately after the draining period. Corrosion initiated in this way may provide foci for further corrosion during operation, and a roughened surface is more likely to gather deposits than a smooth one.

Serious corrosion also can take place while the boiler is standing idle filled with water, as is the case before start of operation and during outage periods. Filling the units completely with water containing about 100 ppm hydrazine and applying a slight pressure with an inert gas such as nitrogen has been found to eliminate this problem.

Caustic Embrittlement

Intercrystalline cracking or *caustic embrittlement,* although seldom found in present day operation, occurs generally along riveted seams or crevices at tube ends. There is little chance of this occurring in welded joints, but the possibility of embrittlement still exists in some older boilers.

There are three factors necessary for intercrystalline cracking of boiler metal: (1) leakage of the boiler water must take place so as to permit escape of steam and concentration of the boiler water at the point of leakage, (2) the boiler metal must be subjected to high stress and (3) the boiler water must possess embrittling characteristics. The first two are dif-ficult to evaluate; the third is the basis of a test (ASTM D 807–52) used to determine whether preventive means should be taken.

Cleaning of Boilers

The internal surfaces of a boiler in contact with water or steam must be kept clean to assure an efficient transfer of heat in the generation of steam. Several cleaning procedures are available to assure a removal of foreign matter introduced into the boiler during the manufacturing process, erection of the equipment and in operation. The general cleaning processes are classified under alkaline boilout and acid washing.

An *alkaline boilout* of a unit is normally conducted to remove contaminants generally found in a boiler following its shop assembly or field erection. Materials such as lubricants, oil, rust, sand, metal fragments and assorted debris are removed during the alkaline boilout of a steam generator.

Acid cleaning of boilers is used to remove scales and deposits formed on internal heat transfer surfaces which are in contact with water. This procedure is used to dissolve compounds formed in the boiler as a result of contaminants in the feedwater delivered to the boiler. Acid cleaning can also be used to remove mill scale and corrosion products.[15]

Alkaline Boilout

The basic reason for an alkaline boilout of a boiler is to remove water- and alkali-soluble and saponifiable compounds from the water side surfaces of

---

[15] The first application of acid cleaning to a water tube boiler is believed to have been carried out by Goldsworthy Gurney in 1828. For iron tubes he made use of one part of hydrochloric acid to one hundred parts of water. To expedite the cleaning he proposed making a small fire in the boiler so that the steam could be used to blow the dissolved incrustations from the tubes. He also advocated the use of distilled water to avoid formation of deposits.

the unit. These materials consist primarily of lubricants used in the erection of the boiler, such as tube rolling into the headers and drums, and protective coatings applied to prevent atmospheric rusting following shop fabrication.

A majority of the lubricants used in boiler erection are of the water soluble type, and these do not offer any difficulty to removal during boilout. Nonwater soluble oils and greases are introduced in small quantities into the boiler from oil lubricated equipment and workmen's clothes. Every effort should be made to minimize the introduction of oil and grease into the boiler since the quantity of these materials determines the length of cleaning and the degree of difficulty in obtaining clean surfaces.

Sand, loose mill scale and corrosion products formed on the tube surfaces during erection and following the hydrostatic test are removed by blowdown during the boilout procedure.

The chemicals used for boiling out a steam generator vary in composition. Generally, some combination of the following chemical compounds is used during an alkaline boilout: caustic soda, soda ash, sodium phosphate, sodium sulfite and sodium nitrate. Sodium sulfite is used to reduce oxygen corrosion and sodium nitrate is added to prevent the possibility of caustic embrittlement. Soda ash and sodium phosphate are most commonly used because of the ease of handling. Potassium salts can be substituted for the sodium form.

Organic detergents are frequently added to improve the effectiveness of the alkaline boilout. These materials must be used with care and according to the supplier's recommendation. Their indiscriminate use may lead to foaming and carryover of chemical to the superheater. The temperature stability of the organic detergent should be ascertained prior to use within a boiler.

The use of sulfite, nitrate and organic detergents are refinements in the boilout procedure. Their utility has not been shown to be of a prime necessity. The principal chemical action is the reaction of the alkaline chemicals with nonwater soluble oils and greases. Experience has shown that an effective boilout can be attained by any of the following combinations:

1. Soda ash — 4000 ppm
   Sodium phosphate — 4000 ppm
2. Sodium hydroxide — 2000 ppm
   Sodium carbonate or
   Sodium phosphate — 2000 ppm
3. Sodium phosphate — 5000 ppm
   Caustic soda — 500 ppm
4. Sodium carbonate — 2000 ppm
   Sodium phosphate — 4000 ppm
   Caustic soda — 2000 ppm

The first combination shown above is the most commonly recommended for boilout of higher pressure boilers. In some instances, a chemical such as sodium silicate is included in the boilout formula. Although this is an effective additive, it is not recommended for use in high pressure boilers. High silica concentrations in the boiler water have been observed during initial operation when metasilicate was used in the boilout formula.

Boilout Procedure. Preparatory to boiling out, the boiler should be filled with water to about the normal operating level in the steam drum. Chemicals to be added to the boiler should be completely dissolved before introducing them into the unit. In natural circulation units, these chemicals are most suitably introduced into the boiler by pumping them through the existing chemical feed line in the boiler drum. They also may be added by draining the chemical solution into the steam drum through an open manhole. In controlled circulation boilers, the boilout chemicals may be pumped into the lower distribution drums and circulator pump header. The boiler is then filled with water to the operating level by use of the boiler feed pump.

Steam pressure is raised in the boiler slowly by the use of pilot torches and warmup burners. The slow heating assures an even distribution of the surfaces in the boiler. Steam pressure is increased in a unit to assure a circulation of water and a good mixing of chemicals in the boiler circuits. In natural circulation boilers, this has been achieved by raising the boiler pressure to about ⅓ of the operating pressure or 300 psig, which ever is lower. A pressure of not less than 100 psig is recommended for lower pressure boilers.

Controlled circulation boilers are equipped with pumps and positive circulation can be assumed at all pressures. In these units, excellent results have been obtained in boiling out at a pressure of 100 psig.

Once through boilers do not contain a storage drum as found in conventional recirculating type units. As a result, cleaning is accomplished by circulating an alkaline solution through the boiler parts to a deaerating heater which acts as a storage tank in the system. The pressure and temperature are controlled at a level at which boiling does not occur.

The length of boilout is determined by the quantity of oil and grease found in a boiler. Boilers of recent design have been cleaned effectively in a period of 8 to 24 hours at the assigned pressure. During the pressure holding period, boiler water solids are purged by blowdown at about four hour intervals. A chemical balance is re-established at the end of each purging of boiler water. At the completion of boilout, the boiler is cooled slowly, drained, flushed free of residues and inspected for cleanliness.

Acid Cleaning

The removal of mill scale and operational scale and deposits can be best realized by acid washing. Mechanical cleaning of equipment is time consuming and nearly impossible to accomplish in modern units where boiler tubes may be a 100 ft or more in length. Acid washing will remove scales which cannot be removed by mechanical means. Cleaning by acid assures a removal of deposits in all parts of the boilers and is less time consuming and expensive than mechanical cleaning.

New boilers are frequently acid cleaned prior to initial operation. This cleaning assures the removal of accumulated oxides and mill scale.

The type of operational scale found in steam generators is related to the quality of makeup supplied to the boiler. In industrial boilers, the principal deposits are calcium and magnesium phosphates, calcium and magnesium silicate, complex silicates as acmite or analcite, quartz, oxides of iron and copper and organic matter. In central station boilers, the principal deposits are corrosion products, iron and copper oxides.

Acid washing should be carried out under qualified supervision. Experience has shown that best results and economy can be obtained by use of the services of a reputable acid cleaning concern. Such an organization is equipped with the necessary staff, apparatus and laboratory facilities for analysis and research purposes.

The principal items for consideration in acid washing are temperature, acid concentration, inhibitor efficiency, time, composition of deposits and metal composition. A proper evaluation of these items assures a successful removal of deposits without incidental attack due to acid.

Acids. Hydrochloric acid is the principal solvent used in chemical cleaning. Its wide use has been largely related to its lower cost, availability and ease of inhibition. Other acids used in cleaning boilers include phosphoric acid and organic acids such as sulfamic and citric. The use of phosphoric acid and the organic acids is especially suited to applications where solutions free of chlorides are required. There is a trend toward a greater utilization of organic acids in cleaning superheaters, reheaters and once through boilers.

Temperature. Temperature of the metal is closely controlled to assure maximum activity in the dissolution of deposits and remain within the effective range of inhibitor protection. The temperature at which a boiler is cleaned varies with the solvent under consideration. Hydrochloric acid and sulfamic acid are normally used at metal temperatures of 150 to 165 F. Citric acid is effective at temperatures at and above 200 F. Phosphoric acid can be safely inhibited at temperatures of 212 to 220 F. Both phosphoric and citric acids can be boiled without incurring metal loss.

Inhibitors. The successful use of any acid depends upon the protection afforded by the inhibitor to the boiler steel. The improvements in cleaning techniques have been directly related to development of new inhibitors. The development of polyethanolamine inhibitors has markedly reduced the attack of steel by hydrochloric acid by comparison to that previously experienced with coal tar derivatives. Equally effective inhibitors are available for other mineral and organic acids. The prime consideration in the selection of the acid is the cost and special application features.

Composition. To be effective, an acid wash should be related to the composition of the deposits in the boiler. Special compounds are used in dissolving complex scales. Ammonium bifluoride is added to the acid solution when silica deposits are known to be present. Other solvents may be necessary if the deposit contains an excess of organic matter or is high in copper. A complete analysis of the scale is necessary for cleaning processes other than normal mill scale removal.

Precautions. Safety precautions must be exercised in cleaning a boiler with acid. Care should be taken to provide adequate signs and wearing apparel to acquaint and protect operating personnel from a spill of chemicals.

Hydrogen is evolved in cleaning a boiler with acid. Adequate vents should be provided to prevent an accumulation of gas pockets. The acid must be neutralized, upon draining a boiler, if there is a risk of polluting water streams in the vicinity of the boiler plant.

Acid Cleaning Procedures. The precautions relative to acid cleaning are common to all solvents currently used in practice. The metal temperature of the boiler is raised either by heating water by direct use of auxiliary burners or by circulating water which has been increased in temperature by the addition of live steam. The addition of heat by the use of burners is prohibited when the boiler is filled with inhibited hydrochloric acid. This is to prevent a destruction of an inhibitor due to localized application of heat. A similar precaution may be required when organic acids are used for cleaning purposes.

In natural circulation boilers, thermal circulation is depended upon to assure solvent movement. There is reason to doubt the effectiveness of solvent movement at the low temperatures of 150–165 F. The distribution of acid strength and temperature is obtained readily in a controlled circulation boiler where the boiler circulating pumps can be used intermittently for this purpose.

Inhibited acid, at the correct temperature, is pumped into the boiler by the use of equipment supplied by the cleaning firm. Superheaters are flooded with condensate prior to the addition of acid to prevent the spillage of the solvent to this section. Boilers are generally cleaned by the soaking process. Samples are taken periodically to check the degree of reaction in the boiler.

The deposits usually found in boilers consist of iron oxides, silicates, phosphate sludges and metallic copper. The first three materials are soluble in inhibited hydrochloric acid and thus can be removed. Copper is not soluble but may be dissolved by ferric chloride which is formed by the reaction of iron oxide and acid. Whenever this happens, the copper will deposit on the boiler surfaces in the form of sheets. In order to remove the copper from the boiler, it is necessary to use an additional ammoniacal oxidizing solution. Such a solution will oxidize the copper into a soluble form which can be converted to a copper complex that prevents the deposition of copper. The use of a copper complexing agent in an acid solution has also been developed, com-bining both dissolving actions in one procedure. The method promises a more positive removal of copper with less time and cost required than for the two stage wash.

Boilers are soaked for a period of four to six hours. The acid is drained by pressurizing with nitrogen. This step is taken to prevent the oxidation of cleaned surfaces during this time. Water is used to displace nitrogen in rinsing the metal surfaces of acid. The rinse water is subsequently displaced with nitrogen or equivalent gas. Two rinses are usually sufficient to attain a pH of between five and six.

The boiler is then filled with water containing soda ash, 0.5 to 1.0 per cent solution, to the spill line. The water is dropped to the operating level and the temperature is raised to correspond to a pressure of about 50 psi. About two to four hours are required to effect neutralization of the acid and passivation of the metal. The boiler is drained and inspected at the conclusion of the wash period.

Controlled circulation boilers can be cleaned efficiently since the circulation pumps can be used to equalize acid temperatures and concentrations throughout the boiler. The acid is circulated with one pump for five minutes of each hour of cleaning, normally a total of five or six hours.

Once through boilers are acid cleaned by circulating the acid solution continuously. This is done to prevent the buildup of gas pockets in the unit. Organic type acids are preferred for this application and also for cleaning pendant type superheater surfaces. Adequate pumping facilities must be provided to assure a flow of acid to all of the circuits. At the conclusion of the acid wash, the solvent is displaced by pumping water through the circuits. When the system has been purged of acid, condensate containing ammonia and hydrazine is pumped through the system to effect neutralization.

Water Technology for Nuclear Power Plants

Certain marked similarities as well as distinctive differences are found in comparing water technology for conventional steam and nuclear power plants. Some of the reactor systems used for power generation are operated in a range of saturated steam temperatures from 400 to 600 F. These conditions of temperature and their related pressures are in regions where conventional fossil fuel fired boilers have operated safely and efficiently for many years. Unfortunately, all of this experience cannot be used since the analogy between a steam plant and a nuclear reactor cannot be based on steam temperature and pressure alone. The problem of handling radioactivity and the exposure of metals and water to a high neutron source in the reactor core requires a re-evaluation in the approach to water technology and corrosion.

The accumulation, transport and disposal of radioactivity is a matter of paramount concern. Radiation promotes chemical reactions which may be classed under (1) corrosion, (2) water dissociation, (3) radiation synthesis and (4) nuclear reactions. Radioactive products are not removable by blowdown as in conventional boilers. These materials are removed from the circulating water stream by application of ion exchange apparatus.

Corrosion products and other impurities in a water passing through a reactor core become radioactive. Some of the radioactivity is long lived and remains in the system even after the reactor is shut down. The disposal of these waste products creates an engineering and health hazard. One way to minimize this problem is to select materials which have a high resistance to corrosion. While the approach is an expensive one, it has been the method followed in the development of nuclear operated steam plants. Stainless steel and special alloys have been used extensively in the boiling water and pressurized water reactors designed to date. These materials are excellent in their resistance to corrosion. However, stainless steel is susceptible to stress corrosion cracking which can result in catastrophic failures. Carbon steel has not been evaluated sufficiently to be used extensively in a service exposed to high levels of radioactivity.

Corrosion and Its Control

Control of the corrosion process is a basic requirement in a nuclear power plant. General corrosion can be effectively controlled by providing a pure source of water, low in oxygen and matched to appropriate properties of metals in a reactor and its associated steam generator. Austenitic stainless steels, Inconel, Zircaloy and other commercial alloys are commonly used in nuclear installations. Due to cost and heat transfer considerations, it is necessary to use thin tube wall construction and clad pressure vessels. Corrosion and fouling limits must be set at a minimum to achieve anticipated economic benefits from the use of nuclear reactors.

Stress corrosion cracking of stainless steels is a prime source of concern to the nuclear engineer. Chloride stress corrosion cracking of austenitic stainless steels has been studied extensively to overcome the catastrophic effects of failure. Stainless steel equipment, which contains a residual stress as a result of fabrication, is susceptible to cracking in high temperature water containing chloride and oxygen. It has been observed that the absence of either oxygen, an oxidizing agent or chloride will prevent cracking.

Stress corrosion is the acceleration of corrosion by static stress. Transgranular cracking, generally associated with chloride stress corrosion of austenitic stainless steels, is believed to occur as a result of the concurrent action of chemical attack and mechanical forces. With Type 18–8 stainless steels, the evidence favors an almost completely electrochemical mechanism. There has been no indication that a threshold applied stress exists below which cracking will not occur.

During the initial stage of stress corrosion activity, reactions occur which lead to corrosion but not to mechanical damage. It is a period of film repair, breakdown and pitting corrosion, the duration of which is not influenced by applied stress or their magnitude. Local chemical activity becomes established and eventually leads to film breakdown. High temperature and high chlorides hasten film breakdown. Cracking starts at anodically active metal surfaces which are exposed during the electrochemical attack.

Oxygen and chloride will produce stress corrosion cracking in stainless steels. The absence of one component increases the tolerance of the second to corrosion activity. In the absence of oxygen, it is possible to tolerate higher chloride concentrations without experiencing cracking. It is not always possible to assure the absence of chloride due to uncontrolled leakage as in a condenser of a sea going vessel. Fortunately, several methods, chemical and mechanical, can be utilized to reduce oxygen in water. The use of chemical agents, hydrazine and sodium sulfite, can reduce the oxygen concentration in the reactor water of a pressurized water reactor. Mechanical deaeration is used to remove oxygen from feedwater in the pressurized and boiling water reactor systems. Where possible, hydrogen gas should be added to suppress dissociation and remove oxygen. This is generally applicable to the primary loop of a pressurized water reactor.

Water Treatment for Nuclear Steam Generators

Nuclear steam generators require a "boiler feedwater" containing a minimum of corroding agents. Great care is taken to reduce the level of oxygen, chloride, iron, copper and cobalt to a trace level. Condensate and reactor water of a boiling water reactor and the primary coolant of a pressurized reactor must be scavenged by the use of bypass or total flow demineralizers to reduce the level of corrosion products to a minimum. This corresponds to a "blowdown" in a conventional boiler and is aimed to prevent the deposition of solids on the heat transfer surfaces of a reactor core. This action prevents the formation of hot spots which could be the cause of a premature replacement or result in a failure of fuel elements. The rate of fuel element replacement is a major cost of operation, and failure of these elements is a potential source of considerable trouble. High quality reactor water is an important contribution to economical trouble free operation. Impurities present in the water become radioactive and create maintenance problems when they deposit in the reactor or in equipment outside the reactor.

Makeup water supplied to a reactor system is either demineralized or evaporated water. The highest purity specifications are applied to assure a freedom from chloride and other impurities capable of forming deposits or promoting corrosion.

The feedwater supplied to the steam generator consists of deaerated condensate. The manner in which the feedwater and boiler water is treated in the various reactors depends largely on the characteristics of the system. In the boiling water reactor, water acts in a dual capacity in the reactor pressure vessel as coolant and moderator. Steam is generated in the reactor vessel and goes directly to a turbine generator. This system requires pure feedwater and solid chemicals like caustic, sulfite and phosphate cannot be added to the reactor water to minimize corrosive activity. A greater latitude of chemical control is permitted in a pressurized water reactor where steam is not generated in the reactor core.

In a pressurized water reactor, water is supplied as makeup to the primary coolant circuit and to the boiling section. The primary water acts as a neutron moderator and the reactor coolant. It is contained in a loop and is pumped at a high pressure (above the boiling point of the coolant) through the core and through a tube bank in the boiling section. The solids in this water are subject to induced radiation in passing through the core. The primary water, and the feedwater supplied to the boiling section, can be chemically treated to curb corrosion.

The principal considerations in the treatment of water in the two systems are summarized in the following sections.

Pressurized Water Reactor

Primary coolant. Makeup to the primary coolant must be deaerated demineralized water. Hydrogen is maintained in the coolant (25 cc per kg) to react with air and to repress the dissociation of water. Lithium hydroxide is fed to the coolant to maintain a pH between 9.5 and 10.5. This chemical serves to reduce the corrosion in the primary loop. A portion of the coolant is continuously cycled through demineralizers to reduce the radioactive corrosion products in the loop. The resins are initially regenerated with lithium hydroxide and delivered to waste when exhausted.

The heat exchanger is supplied with a deaerated feedwater. The addition of solid chemicals can be used to protect against oxygen and general corrosion. In general, the coordinated phosphate pH control is used to control alkalinity in the boiler water. Sodium sulfite is added to protect the system against oxygen. Every effort is made to exclude chloride from the feed and "boiler" water. A general range of solids in water for a pressurized water reactor is shown in Table 8–9.

Boiling Water Reactor

Total solids in the reactor water result from corrosion products in the reactor circulating system and solids which enter the feedwater. Corrosion products from the turbine and condensate system and leakage of the cooling water contribute to the impurity content. High flow demineralizers have been developed to remove these impurities in the reactor feedwater. Solids of more than a quarter of a part per million can be reduced to the few parts per billion range. The materials removed are not generally radioactive and the resins in the demineralizers can be

Table 8–9 Water Limits —
Pressurized Water Reactor

Boiler Water				
Sulfite	—	SO$_3$	25	— 100 ppm
Phosphate	—	PO$_4$	100	— 300 ppm
pH			10.6	— 11.0
Chloride	—	Cl	0.3	ppm Max
Total Solids			1000	ppm Max
Free caustic	—	OH	0.0	ppm
Feedwater				
Oxygen				< 0.01 ppm
Chloride				< 0.1 ppm
Total Solids				< 0.5 ppm

Table 8–10 Water Limits —
Boiling Water Reactor

Reactor Water Limits	
Total Solids	< 600 ppb
Chloride	< 100 ppb
Specific Conductance	< 1 mmho
Reactor Feedwater Limits	
Copper	2 ppb
Iron	2 ppb
Cobalt	< 1 ppb
Specific Conductance	0.1 mmho
Plant Makeup Limits	
Chloride	10 ppb
Fluoride	1 ppb
Sodium	10 ppb
Silica	10 ppb
Conductivity	1 mmho

readily regenerated. Should they become radioactive, provisions are available to wash the resins to a radioactive resin storage vault.

The reactor water is contaminated with radioactive corrosion products. A portion of this water is passed through a demineralizer to remove soluble and insoluble solids and reduce the radioactivity level in the water. The solids content in the reactor water is kept low, and it is necessary to purify the steam leaving the reactor to prevent the buildup of radioactive deposits in the turbine. Typical controls of water for the boiling water reactor system are shown in Table 8–10.

Steam and Water Separation

Water technology for boilers and reactors is not limited to conditioning or treatment of makeup and feedwater. It is also concerned with the phase transformation of water to steam and the separation of liquid and gaseous constituents. The study of these phenomena involves considerations of physical chemistry, fluid flow and mechanical design.

Over the years many theoretical analyses of steam and water separation have been made, and a great number of hypotheses have been proposed to explain these phenomena. Nevertheless, steam and water separation in both boilers and nuclear reactors retains many aspects of an engineering art and has thus far defied completely rational understanding.

Experimental work on both model and full scale apparatus continues to provide useful information. To provide engineering criteria for the design of steam and water separators these laboratory results must be correlated with widely varied experience as evidenced by the successful operation for many years of effective and efficient separation devices. A challenge remains, however, to develop a verifiable theoretical structure that provides an analytically rigorous explanation of the phenomena of steam and water separation in terms of the mass flows and physical equipment size found in large boilers and nuclear reactors.

Steam generated in a boiler is intimately mixed with relatively large and variable amounts of circulating boiler water. Before the steam leaves the boiler and enters the superheater, practically all of this associated boiler water must be separated from the steam. This separation must be done within a limited space in the drum, within a matter of seconds and under a variety of velocity, pressure and other operating conditions. The pressure drop across the steam and water separators must not be sufficient to affect boiler circulation or water level control. The equipment should be reasonable in cost, resistant to corrosion and sufficiently removable to allow access to the drum for inspection and cleaning.

Practically all of the liquid and solid impurities in the steam and water mixture must be separated from the steam before it is suitable for use. Any unseparated liquid in the steam contains dissolved and suspended boiler water salts which appear as a solids impurity in the steam when the moisture is evaporated in the superheater or directed to a turbine or other steam driven apparatus.

The moisture content in a saturated steam is defined by its *quality*, which is a measure of the per cent by weight of dry steam or moisture in the mixture. The solids content in a saturated steam is defined by its *purity*, which is a measure of the parts per million of solids impurity in the steam. Solids content in steam from high pressure or supercritical boilers is measured in parts per billion of solids impurity.

The relationship between moisture carryover, solids carryover and boiler water concentration is best illustrated by an example. For a 0.01 per cent moisture carryover of boiler water having 1000 ppm concentration, the solids in the steam would be 1000×0.0001 or 0.1 ppm. Conversely, the per cent moisture carryover can be calculated if the boiler water concentration and the steam impurity content is known.

The weight of water in the mixture delivered to the drum for separation depends on the circulation and may range from less than four to over 25 times the weight of steam. To reduce this water to the small fraction found in the steam requires a high efficiency of water separation. With a circulation ration of 10 pounds of water per pound of steam, and with a boiler water of 1000 ppm concentration, the contamination to be separated from the steam amounts to 10,000 ppm. To reduce this contamination to one ppm in the outlet steam, 99.99 per cent of the circulating water must be separated from the steam in the drum. The equation indicating the per cent of water separation necessary to give a steam impurity may be expressed as:

$$\text{Per cent of water separation} = 100 - \frac{100\,P_s}{N\,C_b}$$

where

P_s = ppm of impurity in steam

N = circulation ratio, lb of water per lb of steam

C_b = boiler water concentration

Drum Internals

Drum internals are devices used to separate water from steam and to direct the flow of water and steam in a manner so as to obtain an optimum distribution of drum metal temperature in boiler operation. Such apparatus may consist of baffle arrangements, devices which change the direction of flow of a steam and water mixture, separators which employ a spinning action for removing water from steam, or steam purifiers as washers and screen driers. These devices are used singly or in consort with others to remove impurities from the steam leaving the boiler drum.

A basic design criterion is that an arrangement of drum internals must normally consist of two or more integrated devices, each of which may be quite different in design and operate on totally different principles. Each stage must have a high separation efficiency. The greater the number of stages of separation, the lower the required efficiency for each stage. Thus, two stages at 99 per cent efficiency, three stages at 90 per cent and six stages at 70 per cent will give similar results in reducing 10 pounds of water to 0.01 pound. There are, of course, strict limitations to the number of stages that can be installed in a boiler drum, but such a basic criterion can be used to advantage to design within existing limits.

There are a number of factors which affect the separation of water from steam in a boiler. Among the more important items are density of water with respect to the steam, the available pressure drop for drum internal design, the relative quantity of water to steam in the mixture delivered to the steam drum, the quantity or total throughput of water and steam to be separated, factors such as viscosity and surface tension which are affected by an increase in pressure, boiler water level and the concentration of boiler water solids.

There is a considerable difference in the density of water and steam as the pressure increases toward the critical point. This relationship is shown in Fig. 8–11 which is a plot of the ratio of the density of water to the density of steam with pressure. The density of water at 1200 psia is approximately 16 times that of steam. At 2600 psia, the density of water is about four times that of steam. Thus, with an increase in pressure, the

separation of water from steam by simple devices becomes increasingly difficult, and it is necessary to use more efficient apparatus if primary separation is to be achieved in a confined area.

The force necessary for disengaging the water particle from steam is necessarily related to the circulating head that is available. In natural circulation boilers, the available head is created by the difference in density of the circulating fluid in the downcomer and riser circuits. The factors affecting that head are first, the height of the furnace; secondly, the ratio of the quantity of water entering the evaporative circuit to the steam generated in that circuit, and thirdly, the steam pressure. Thus, in designing steam drum internals, it is necessary to maintain a low pressure drop across the separators so as not to reduce the circulation in the boiler and cause overheating and tube failures.

In controlled circulation boilers the water in the boiler is circulated by a pump. The pressure drop made available by the circulating pump can be effectively utilized to supply energy to disengage

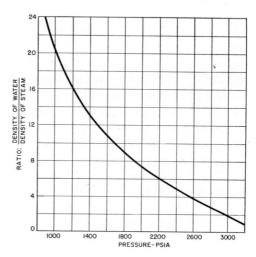

Fig. 8–11.   Steam water density relationship

water from steam. It is possible to use a higher pressure drop through the drum internals to obtain a more efficient separation of water from steam thereby assuring a better steam quality.[16]

Stages of Water Separation

The stages of water separation are designated as *primary separation, secondary separation* and *drying*, and the devices used are termed primary separators, secondary separators and dryers. The term "dryer" was established during the course of development of water tube boilers on the basis that the final stage of separation delivered a "dry" and saturated steam.

Primary and Secondary Separators

The function of primary and secondary separation is to reduce the water content from the boiler tube circuits entering the drum to a moisture content which may be handled by a final stage dryer. The design of equipment for the primary and secondary separation is frequently governed as much by boiler design as by the basic function of separating water from steam.

Practically all drum internals are made up of plate baffles, banks of screens, arrangements of corrugated or bent plate and devices employing radial acceleration of water from steam.

Baffle plates are generally used to change or reverse a flow pattern to assist gravity separation in open drum space. Examples of simple baffle arrangements are illustrated in Fig. 8–12. Baffle plates change flow direction of water and steam and act as impact plates. Water separating on such plates will normally drain off through or adjacent to the steam flow,

and a controlling factor in design and operation is the steam flow velocity through such drainage. Areas under and around baffles must be sufficient to prevent excessive re-entrainment of spray. Plate baffles have limited impact separating capacity and their chief purpose is to direct flow to make maximum use of the gravity separating capacity of low velocity steam space in the drum.

Screens of wire mesh woven screen material are generally satisfactory for secondary separators or dryers. The limiting factor for screen separators is the steam flow velocity through the free area of the screen and the water drainage capacity of the screen. Screens are effective in separating spray. Riser mixtures normally have too much water in them for screens to handle as primary separators. Other factors which affect the performance of screens as primary separators are circulation ratio, size of the screen, the rating and the steam flow velocity through the screen. Examples of screen arrangements as primary or secondary separators in boiler drums are shown in Fig. 8–13.

Bent and corrugated plates are commonly used for all three stages of separation. Their continued use is evidence of satisfactory performance even though other designs may be better in some respects. One example of a corrugated plate assembly is shown in Fig. 8–14. One advantage of the corrugated plate design is that it has a higher ratio of free area to projected area than screens, and equipment can be smaller for the same steam flow velocity.

Bulk separators, Fig. 8–15, are used to deflect larger quantities of water directed into the drum from active risers. The apparatus reduces the bulk water en-

[16] See Chapter 7, Fluid Flow, section on boiler circulation, and Chapter 24, Controlled Circulation Boilers.

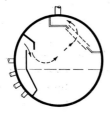

Fig. 8–12. Use of baffle plates

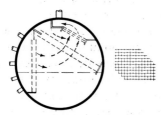

Fig. 8–13. Use of screens

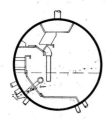

Fig. 8–14. Use of corrugated plates

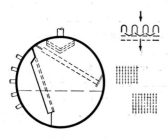

Fig. 8–15. Bulk separators

trained with the steam and directs it to below the water level. This design has enabled the use of higher evaporation rates per foot of furnace width since it has satisfactorily removed the bulk of the spray water from the steam. The bulk separator reduces moisture by providing impact surface, a change of direction for the mixture, a drain trough and a screen layer for reduction of fine spray.

Reversing hoods, shown in Fig. 8–16, have a classical and practical interest in that the internals combine all the desirable design features of baffle and change of direction principles. As indicated, steam and water from the active generating tubes are directed behind a baffle into the slotted reversing hoods. These primary separators are simply an arrangement of baffle plates to guide steam and water in a manner to give maximum utilization of gravity separation in open drum space. By accelerating gravity flow of water and reversing steam flow, normal gravity potential is increased and separation is promoted.

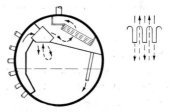

Fig. 8–16. Reversing hoods

At higher pressures, the separation of water and steam is accomplished most efficiently in a drum internal which utilizes radial acceleration to disengage the entrained particle from the steam. A spinning action can be imparted to the turbulent mixture by means of guide vanes. The circular motion imparted to the mixture causes the heavier water particles to move radially outward through the steam and to impinge upon the outer wall of the separator where they can be collected. The efficiency of separation is related to pressure in that the relative densities of water and steam determine the resistance to particle motion due to buoyant effects. As operating pressure is increased, and as the density of saturated steam approaches that of water, relative motion is more difficult to achieve and collection efficiency is decreased.

The *turbo separator*, shown in Fig. 8–17, is a device employing the radial acceleration principle. Equipped with a corrugated plate assembly at the outlet of the separator, it provides a highly efficient primary and secondary separation of water from steam in boilers operating at pressures up to the critical point.

The water and steam mixture circulated from the water walls is introduced into the drum in a manner so as to sweep the drum shell on its path to the bottom. Effective velocities and rapid heat transfer are created by the confining baffle concentric with the drum shell. The mixture enters the separators arranged along the length of the drum. A separating force is created by vanes which give the mixture a spinning action as it travels upward through the separators. The concentrated layer of water, flowing upward along the surface of the primary tube, is skimmed off and directed downward through an outer concentric tube. It is discharged below the waterline with a minimum disturbance to the water level.

The steam and the remaining entrained water continue upward through a steam collector nozzle and turn horizontally

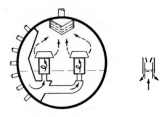

Fig. 8–17. Turbo separator

into the secondary separator. The velocity at this point is low and water cannot be re-entrained from wetted surfaces and runs off the plates. The steam leaves the separator and flows upward into the final dryer. This separator facilitates handling of spray and dehydration of foam. The turbo separator has no inherent capacity limit because there is no water seal under a high differential pressure. The efficiency is not affected by changes in water level.[17]

Dryers

Dryers are a component of internals and function to remove residual moisture from steam after most of the circulating water has been eliminated by primary and secondary separators. They are designed to have a large surface area on which moisture can deposit and from which it can drain back into the drum by gravity. Flow velocity through the free area of a dryer must be kept below limits above which deposition or drainage may be inhibited.

Closely spaced corrugated or bent plates, screens or matts of woven wire mesh can be utilized as dryer surface materials. The screen dryers are a practical compromise of performance and

[17] See "The Application and Development of the Turbo Steam Separator" by T. Ravese, *Combustion*, Vol. 26, July 1954, pp. 45–47. This subject is also discussed in more generality in ASME Paper 54-A-242, "Drum Internals and High Pressure Boiler Design" by E. M. Powell and H. A. Grabowski.

drainability that have given satisfactory service for years.

The design of dryers requires consideration of a number of factors. Space limitation in the drum sets limits on the dryer size which can be installed. Such factors as sturdiness, leak proof installation, drainage facilities and provision for cleaning due to possible plugging of dryer free areas must be considered in selection of a steam dryer. The pressure drop across a dryer is normally low because of the low flow velocities and relatively small amounts of water involved.

Dryers operate on a low velocity deposition principle and not on a velocity separation principle. Formation of insoluble residues on the dryers from boiler water entrained with the steam, decreases the free area and increases the local velocity and promotes carryover. Similar results are noted by the filming action of foamy boiler water in the dryer. The free surface areas are reduced significantly, increasing the local velocity and facilitating re-entrainment of boiler water and carryover. Dryers in boilers operating with foamy boiler water or high suspended matter in the boiler water should be inspected periodically and cleaned as necessary. An illustration of a screen dryer is shown in Fig. 8–18.

Auxiliary Drum Internals

Feedwater lines, blowdown lines and chemical feed lines are also installed in the boiler drum. In some marine boilers, desuperheaters may also be installed. Feedwater, blowdown and chemical feed lines do not normally take up much drum space but their location can be a minor complication in the overall internals arrangement. To give satisfactory distribution of flow, these lines are usually run to

Fig. 8–18. Screen dryer

the center of the drum and fed to perforated branch lines.

Feedwater lines are submerged in the drum boiler water. Care must be used to avoid discharge of a cold feedwater against the drum shell as severe thermal stresses can be set up in the thick drum shells by cycles of temperature variation. In some cases, it is desirable to concentrate the colder feedwater flow into the downcomer tubes to condense steam entrained in the downcomer flow and improve boiler circulation. In general, it is better to mix the feedwater with drum boiler water ahead of the downcomer circuits to accelerate precipitation of sludge products in the drum. Care must be taken to prevent *water hammer* in the feed lines. This can occur readily if steam leaks back into the feedwater system. The steam accumulation may be suddenly condensed by the inflow of cold water and create a vacuum. Water hammer results when the water rushing into the vacuum is stopped by some barrier.

Chemical feed lines are used to introduce chemicals into the boiler for control of scale, sludge and corrosion. The chemicals are introduced into the drum in a manner so as to insure rapid mixing with the feedwater. They are generally added in a concentrated form, and it is necessary to flush the lines periodically with clean water to prevent plugging due to reaction and deposition in the lines.

Blowdown lines are used to remove periodically or continuously a portion of water from the boiler. Sufficient concentrated boiler water is removed and replaced by low concentration feedwater to maintain a desired concentration limit in the boiler water. These lines are located in such a way as to minimize the occlusion of feedwater and chemical feed and are designed to prevent entrainment of steam.

Distribution of steam flow can be achieved by the use of perforated plates or tapered plate restriction located at the top of the drum. This dry box arrangement does not act as a steam dryer but as a means to distribute the flow to enable the use of minimum steam outlets or to assure a satisfactory velocity distribution to a steam dryer. An illustration of dry box construction is shown in Fig. 8–19.

Fig. 8–19.   Dry box construction

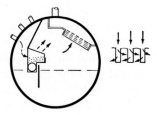

Fig. 8–20.   Bubble type washer

Steam Washers

Steam washers are a special type of drum internals. The original concept of steam washing in the mid 1930's involved rinsing wet steam with low concentration feedwater to dilute the solids content in the moisture carryover to the steam dryer. One of the first concepts was to spray feedwater into the drum steam space. An alternate design used spray water directed on screens through which steam passed to the dryer. A more efficient scheme, Fig. 8–20, used a bubble or hood type washer. Steam with a small amount of entrained boiler water was intimately mixed with feedwater in the washer. These applications were designed for multiple drum boilers at pressures from 600 to 1200 psig.

Increase in pressure and boiler efficiency in the years preceding and following World War II reduced the number of drums in a boiler. At the same time significant improvement in the water supplied to the boiler resulted in operation with lower boiler water solids in the boiler water. Development of the turbo separator previously described assured a steam purity which exceeded that obtained with the steam washer. This work permitted simplification in design of the steam drum and improved the distribution of water and steam flows and the temperature in the drum. Drums with smaller diameters could be used to obtain pure steam and uniform temperature distribution during transient operation. In view of this development, the use of the steam washer was generally discontinued in high pressure boilers.

A principal reason for renewed interest of steam washers in high pressure boilers is the possibility of reducing the amount of silica vaporized with the steam from the boiler water. Chemicals vaporized or becoming solubilized in the steam cannot be reduced with mechanical devices used to separate water from steam.

Vaporization of silica increases with pressure. Fig. 8–21 illustrates the distribution of silica in steam and in boiler water at various steam pressures. The ratio increases rapidly from 0.0065 at 1500 psia to 0.024 at 2000 psia and 0.06 at 2500 psia. At 2500 psia the silica in the steam is about ten times the quantity at 1500 psia, for the same concentration in the boiler water.[18]

The revival of interest in steam washers in the 1950's was brought about by the desire to reduce silica in the steam. Laboratory results and field data conclusively indicate that silica reduction by steam washing in boilers above 1800 psig is ineffective. The physical limitations in

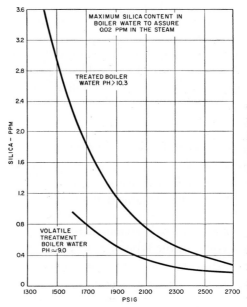

Fig. 8–22. Silica in boiler water — relationship with pressure

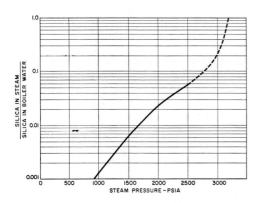

Fig. 8–21. Distribution of silica in steam and water

Boiler water pH affects the vaporization of silica and the data in Fig. 8–22 show the recommended limitations on silica in boiler water for the two ranges of pH normally carried in high pressure boilers. Controlling silica at the recommended values will assure less than 20 ppb of silica in the steam. The latter content will not form objectionable deposits on turbine blades.

the drum and the short time of contact obviate the removal of silica at pressures where the distribution ratio is high and the controlling action is the silica in the water draining from the washer. The washer complicates drum design and impedes the proper distribution of water in the drum. Improving the quality of the makeup water is the most effective means of controlling the silica problem.[19]

[18] See "Silica Deposition in Steam Turbines" by F. G. Straub and H. A. Grabowski, *Trans.* ASME, Vol. 67, 1945, pp. 309–316.

[19] See "Evaluation of Steam Washers in Power Plant Boilers" by H. A. Klein, *Trans.* ASME; Series A, *Journal of Engineering for Power*, Vol. 83, 1961, pp. 343–353.

Carryover and Steam Sampling [20]

This concluding section deals with the phenomenon of carryover and methods of steam sampling and steam purity determination. Once again these subjects cannot be understood solely by rigorous theoretical analysis. Knowledge of laboratory testing procedures and ability to interpret field operating experience are required. Despite intensive research efforts, there is incomplete understanding and much empiricism remains in the techniques for correcting problems resulting from incomplete separation of steam and water in boiler and nuclear reactor equipment.

Classification of Carryover

Carryover is a general term applied to any and all contamination carried out of the boiler by the delivered steam. It may be in the gaseous, liquid or solid phase. Gaseous contamination is independent of the type of mechanical steam separation apparatus and is dependent on the chemical properties of the volatilized substance. Normally, carryover may be classified under four types: priming, spray, leakage and foam carryover. Each of these problems results in troublesome deposits in the superheater or on the turbine blades.

Priming is the development of excessive moisture in the steam due to spouting or surging of boiler water into the steam outlet. This is a rare and easily identified type of carryover. It is usually promoted by the maintenance of too high a water level in the drum, spouting of a submerged riser or sudden swelling of the water in the boiler on a drop in pressure or sudden increase in rating. Priming is rarely if ever associated with boiler water concentration.

Spray carryover, mist or *fog* are degrees of atomization of the boiler water. Steam is borne from the drum by the steam in the same manner as dust is carried by air currents. This carryover is present to a degree in all boilers, and it is the function of drum internals to separate and filter out such spray before the steam leaves the drum. Development of spray carryover indicates failure of the drum internals due to exceeding the velocity limitations of the purification equipment. It is characterized by initial development below the full rating of the boiler and by a consistent increase with an increase in rating. Spray carryover is not sensitive to boiler water concentration below the foaming range. Improved drum internals are capable of reducing the steam borne mist to a value as low as a few parts per billion of solids.

Leakage is a general term applied to bypassing of impure steam or boiler water through the drum internals. This form of carryover is normally localized and is directly related to poor design or installation of drum internals. At times, the local contamination may not be sufficient to be reflected in steam purity measurements of total steam flow. A careful inspection of drum internals will usually reveal this source of carryover. Where the leakage is sufficient to register impurity tests of steam, it will be found that the impurity increases slowly with rating and is relatively insensitive to changes in water level and boiler water concentration.

Foam carryover is the development of

---

[20] Much of the information in this section is based on the extensive laboratory and field experience of P. B. Place.

excessive moisture in the steam due to carryover of foam from the drum. It is the most common, most troublesome and most erratic type of carryover. Foam forms in the steam generating sections of the boiler when the water films around the generated steam bubbles are stabilized by the impurities in boiler water. Boiler circulation carries this foam up to the boiler drum where it tends to accumulate on the water level. The foam produced may entirely fill the steam space of the boiler drum or it may be of a relatively minor depth. Foaming in boilers has been recognized for many years but its causes are not clearly defined and are worthy of further investigation.

The bulk water in the circulating mixture entering the drum is readily separated, but the wet emulsion of very small foam bubbles collects on the water level to a depth largely dependent on the rate of drainage of excess water out of the foamy mass. A considerable amount of moisture is trapped in the foam. When foam carryover occurs, it is frequently sudden and excessive, and the steam sample registers a solids content characteristic of boiler water.

Identification of Carryover

Identification of carryover can be accomplished by a systematic field investigation. The development of sources of carryover and the carryover itself are affected to different degrees by variety of factors which may be classified as mechanical conditions, water conditions and operating conditions. Of the basic types of carryover, that due to foaming in the boiler is most common, the most troublesome and erratic. Special test methods have been devised to demonstrate the presence of foam blankets and for obtaining boiler performance without danger of serious carryover to the superheater and turbine.[21]

Steam flow, water level and boiler water concentration are the three major factors that can create carryover. By varying these three factors, one at a time, test results can usually be interpreted to determine the specific source of a carryover condition. Steam flow establishes the velocity distribution in the boiler drum. Increasing the steam flow excessively can increase the steam velocity to a point that moisture can be entrained to a degree where the dryer can be overloaded. High water level can create spouting and excessive carryover. This can occur with low steaming rates and boiler water concentrations. Foaming is a characteristic of boiler water concentration. Any carryover which can be precipitated or eliminated by a change in boiler water concentration, water level and steaming rate being at recommended values, can be attributed to foaming.

The development of foaming in a drum is illustrated in Fig. 8–23. The plot indicates purity values of steam samples taken ahead of the steam drier and at the outlet of the boiler drum for a constant level of water in the drum and a typical steam load. The principal

---

[21] For more detailed information the reader is referred to the published works of P. B. Place. See "Carryover Problems and Identification of Carryover Types," *Combustion*, Vol. 18, March 1947, pp. 29–47, and the informative discussion generated by this paper which is included in the *Proceedings* of the Seventh Annual Water Conference, Engineers' Society of Western Pennsylvania, 1947, pp. 43–62. See also "Steam Purity Determination," *Combustion*, Vol. 25, in three parts: "Evaluation of Test Results," April 1954, pp. 62–65; "Methods of Sampling and Testing," May 1954, pp. 41–44; "Interpretation of Test Results," June 1954, pp. 43–46.

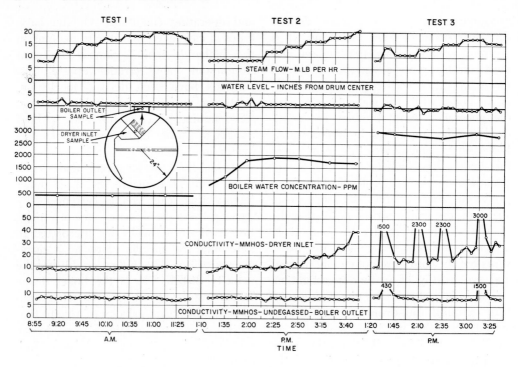

Fig. 8–23. Development of foaming in a boiler drum

change is in the boiler water concentration.[22]

At a boiler water concentration of about 550 ppm, the sample ahead of the dryer was about 5 mmhos (1 mmho is approximately 0.5 ppm of solids) and the sample at the boiler outlet was about 7 mmhos. Increasing the boiler water concentration to about 1800 to 2000 ppm did not alter the purity of the steam leaving the boiler drum. However, the sample ahead of the steam dryer increased gradually to a value of about 40 mmhos. Thus, with an established steam flow, and a similar water level, there was a marked increase in solids content of the steam entering the dryer. This is indicative of the presence of a mildly foamy condition

in the boiler drum as the only change was in the concentration of boiler water solids.

Increase of boiler water solids to about 2800 to 3000 ppm in the boiler water, at the same steam load and water level in the prior two tests, produced severe foaming in the boiler. The space between the water level and the dryer was practically filled with a foam blanket on the water. This is evident in the high solids content of the sample entering the dryer. Severe foam carryover occurred when the water level in the drum was at or above drum center. This was not a factor in the prior tests. Thus, a small change in water level was sufficient to push the foam blanket into the drum internals

---

[22] This example is adapted from "Steam Purity Determination, Part III, Interpretation of Test Results" by P. B. Place, *Combustion*, Vol. 25, June 1954, pp. 43–46.

creating a severe case of foam carryover.

Causes of Foaming

Foaming is basically a result of chemical conditions, and boiler water concentration and composition are important factors involved. High total solids and high suspended solids aggravate the formation of foam. High caustic alkalinity, oil, organic contamination and excess phosphate also increase the foaming tendency in boiler water. While the general effect of a component upon foaming may be anticipated, it is impossible to predict whether foam formation will occur by a cursory examination of boiler water. Extreme cases are on record where excessive foamover occurred with less than 650 ppm in one boiler and, in another case, no carryover troubles developed with concentrations as high as 15,000 ppm. While these inconsistencies exist, it is necessary to maintain a lower value of foam producing chemicals in boiler water or add foam dispersing chemicals to the water.

Organic antifoam agents have been developed which have the capacity of dispelling certain foams at higher steam pressures. Ordinary tannin and starch compounds are only effective at low pressures. Lignin sulfonates, alkaline polyamides, polymerized esters and alcohols have been effective foam dispersing agents. The action of an efficient antifoam agent is to reduce the number of small bubbles and to confine steam bubble formation to a small number of large bubbles which will exhibit the tendency to coalesce and grow larger. Under these conditions, the bubbles are unstable and tend to break easily. Antifoam agents are not equally effective with all boiler waters. It is necessary to select an antifoam compatible with the chemical characteristics of the boiler water, and trial of several compounds may be necessary before the foam can be neutralized satisfactorily.

Foam will fill the free surface area of a separating device increasing local velocities and promoting a serious carryover of boiler water. Foam carryover may be stopped by a quick reduction in boiler water concentration or lowering the drum level. Centrifugal devices have shown a greater ability to handle foamy waters than simple internals. The basic function of a centrifugal device is to dehydrate the foamy emulsion. The dehydrated foam bubbles can be easily broken up by screens or other simple devices. Foam in this type of separator will decrease the water separating efficiency of the device.

In general, foam carryover from a boiler can be avoided by keeping boiler water concentrations within the range set by the American Boiler Manufacturers Association. These specifications, however, are no guarantee against foaming from the boiler. As indicated previously, this is primarily a chemical problem rather than one of physical boiler design. The specifications were established in 1932 as typical of average experience. They have not been changed because of the inability to determine the exact cause of foam production in boiler waters. Concentration limits as a function of pressure are shown in Table 8–11.

Adherence to the specifications set by ABMA has produced satisfactory operation because of marked improvements in water technology and boiler design. They serve as an effective guide for industrial pressure operation. Normally, the steam purity specification limit for low pressure boilers is less than 0.5 per cent moisture in the steam. With the use of superheaters and higher pressures, the boilers

Table   8–11   ABMA Allowable Boiler Water Concentrations

Pressure at Outlet of Steam Generating Unit — psig	Total Solids ppm	Total Alkalinity ppm	Suspended Solids — ppm
0– 300	3500	700	300
301– 450	3000	600	250
451– 600	2500	500	150
601– 750	2000	400	100
751– 900	1500	300	60
901–1000	1250	250	40
1001–1500	1000	200	20
1501–2000	750	150	10
2001 and higher	500	100	5

must deliver a steam product containing less than one ppm of solids entrained in the steam. Steam purity of high pressure boilers has been improved at high pressures and values of less than 0.1 ppm of impurity have been recorded from test data. This has been possible due to improved water technology and the performance of such improved devices as turbo separators.

Steam Sampling Methods

Samples of steam for measurement of purity may be taken before or after a superheater. As fouling of superheater elements is a matter of concern, the sample is usually taken ahead of the superheater. Samples taken for determination of purity are condensed and cooled. Where moisture in the steam is to be determined, use of a throttling calorimeter is a common method in establishing the steam quality. The latter sample flow is fixed by a calorimeter orifice and steam line pressure.

Collection of a true sample that is representative of a large mass of material always presents a difficult problem. The size of the sample, particle size distribution and density relationship are some factors which must be considered where

there is a question of lack of homogeneity. In a homogeneous sample of fine particle size, sampling is a relatively easy operation.[23]

In sampling steam, the impurities may be solid, liquid and gaseous. The solid may be in the form of a finely divided sludge particle. Liquid impurity may be in the form of fog or mist in minute droplets, possibly having a solid particle as a nucleus. More adversely, it may be in a form of a film on the surface of a pipe wall. Moisture itself is not involved in the concept of steam purity except that it may carry solids in solution or suspension.

Sampling impurities in steam is analogous to the difficulty of locating a needle in a haystack. At a sampling rate of 100 pounds per hour, the impurity content of 1 ppm is represented by the withdrawal of 0.7 grains of solid per hour. Steam lines contain bends, elbows, valves and other fittings which can disturb the flow and segregate the impurities.

B. J. Cross has outlined the assumptions reached in the design of the steam sampling nozzle described in ASTM D 1066. The velocity front must be reasonably flat, and the density difference of steam and mist or fog carried along

---

[23] See previously mentioned series of articles by P. B. Place entitled "Steam Purity Determination," *Combustion,* Vol. 25, April, May and June 1954.

with it must be in the same order of magnitude as that of water and steam at the pressure and temperature of the steam in the line. Basic prerequisites for use of the ASTM nozzle design are that the velocity of the steam entering the ports is the same as the line velocity of the steam. Also, that each port of the sampling nozzle shall represent an equal area of the sampling section.[24]

Distribution of solid and liquid impurities is affected by turns and other irregularities of the steam line. The point of sampling should be as remote as possible from a source of disturbance. It is suggested that the sample point be located where there is a run of at least ten diameters of straight pipes. Preferred sample location with respect to position, in order of *decreasing* preference is as follows:

(a) vertical pipe, downward flow
(b) vertical pipe, upward flow
(c) horizontal pipe — vertical insertion
(d) horizontal pipe, horizontal insertion

The principal difficulty in establishing a sampling nozzle which is acceptable to the industry is in the inconsistency in purity readings due to the presence of film of moisture carried along the wall of pipe. Cross, in the paper just noted, suggested a design to circumvent this problem by providing a modified nozzle set in a pipe which would re-entrain the film into the bulk stream and a sampling tube at the expanding portion of the steam

after the nozzle. This has been verified in laboratory investigations, and suggested methods for sampling steam have been described in the international technical literature.[25]

Determination of Steam Purity

Steam purity is normally determined by measuring the conductivity of the condensed steam sample. This method is described in ASTM method D 1125–64. Methods of Test for Electrical Conductivity of Industrial Water and Industrial Waste Water. Gases dissolved in the condensed sample affect the conductance and indicate an erroneous level of solid impurity. These gases may be removed by degasification of the sample. Methods suggested for establishing the content of solids impurity in the steam are described in ASTM D 2186–65T, Tentative Methods of Test for Deposit-Forming Impurities in Steam, providing four alternative techniques for these measurements. The referee method for establishing the total solids in the steam is by evaporation as specified in ASTM method D 1069–62T.

Determination of solids in steam by conductance lacks the required degree of sensitivity of analysis when impurity in terms of parts per billion is required. Analysis of the steam sample to determine the sodium content in the impurity, by flame spectrophotometric technique, is the most accurate method developed in establishing the solids content. This technique

---

[24] The original source of this information is "The Sampling of Steam for the Determination of Purity" by B. J. Cross, *Proceedings of the Eleventh Annual Water Conference, Engineers' Society of Western Pennsylvania*, 1950, pp. 71–82. See also ASTM D 1066–59T, Method of Sampling Steam.

[25] Two British articles which include references to work in steam sampling in Russia, Germany, New Zealand and Great Britain are "Recent Developments in Steam Sampling and Purity Measurement" by J. Jackson, *The Engineer*, Vol. 208, Nov. 27, 1959, pp. 683–687, and "Steam Sampling in Russia" by J. Jackson, *Engineering*, Vol. 190, No. 4, 1960, p. 627.

is described in ASTM method D 1428–64.

Vaporization and solubility of salts in steam at pressures approaching the critical point has been described in the literature.[26] The complexity of steam purification is increased at pressures above 2400 psig. Investigations conducted by Klein indicate that the vaporous carry-over from boilers operating at steam drum pressures at 2600 psig and below will not present a serious problem as long as the total salt content is maintained below 25 ppm.[27] This is in accordance with recommendations made to operate high pressure boilers by the volatile treatment of water control or with a low solids control at or below 25 ppm.

[26] Examples are "Working Process of Super High Pressure Once Through Boilers" by M. A. Styrikovich, *Combustion*, Vol. 28, September 1956, pp. 49–53, including a bibliography of additional Russian papers on related subjects; "Die Löslichkeit von Sulzen in Hochgespanntem Wasserdampf in Hinsicht auf die Turbineversalzung" by V. Sastry, *Chemiker Zeitung*, Vol. 82, July 10, 1958, pp. 456–457; "The Solubility of Quartz and Some Other Substances in Superheated Steam at High Pressures" by G. W. Morey and J. M. Hesselgesser, *Trans.* ASME, Vol. 73, 1951, pp. 865–875; and "Solubility of Salts in Steam at High Pressure" by F. G. Straub, *Proceedings* of the Third Annual Water Conference, Engineers' Society of Western Pennsylvania, 1942, pp. 31–42.

[27] See "Impurities in Steam from High Pressure Boilers" by R. C. Ulmer and H. A. Klein, *Proceedings* ASTM, Vol. 61, 1961, pp. 1396–1423.

9

Materials and Metallurgy [1]

THE AIM of the designer of boilers and nuclear reactors is to choose materials and design the overall part such that the most economical material and the most economical fabrication will result in a part which will fulfill its desired performance for the design life. In well-established products, most design criteria are sufficiently well-known to permit reaching this goal. In newer services, overdesign may lead to successful performance but at an excessive cost. Conversely, there is always the possibility that some important design factor may be overlooked with a resulting unsatisfactory product.

The engineering designer must know the strength and ductility of the various materials at the various temperatures encountered in service and during fabrication. He must know their corrosion resistance to the expected environment and their rate of deterioration in mechanical properties with time. In addition to knowing the properties of materials under static loading, the designer frequently needs to know material behavior under cyclic loading and mechnical or thermal shock. He must know the effect of number of cycles of stress loading in damaging the material. Besides being able to calculate the stresses imposed by various loadings, he must eliminate design or

fabrication notches which concentrate stresses to unacceptably high values, some of which are difficult or impossible to calculate. He must know the effects of various types of stresses such as residual stresses in the materials from fabrication working, thermal stresses from differences in temperature in service, and stresses from mechanical loadings of internal or external pressures or other superimposed loadings. Since all of the variables of the types mentioned may interact with other variables, the designer must utilize all the data evolved through past experience and research in order to properly select materials and to specify fabrication procedures, destructive and non-destructive tests, and operating limits and controls which will assure satisfactory service.

It is the purpose of this chapter to discuss some of the metallurgical aspects pertinent to selection of materials and operation in service and to point out typical service difficulties which are important for the designer to know, anticipate and control.

Operating Temperatures and Pressures

Conventional boiler equipment, designed for a life of twenty years or more, is operating as high as 5000 psig at 1200 F steam temperature (maximum metal tem-

[1] Material contributed by R. E. Lorentz, Jr., and W. L. Harding.

perature of approximately 1300 F). Pressurized water nuclear reactor vessel equipment is operating up to 2500 psig at 650 F metal temperature. Nuclear reactor vessels in which liquid metal is the heat transfer medium are operating at metal temperatures up to approximately 1000 F. These do not represent absolute limits of pressure or temperature for such equipment, because such practical limits are affected also by the size of the equipment. Equipment of relatively small diameter and heavy wall thickness, for instance, has been in use for many years at internal pressures up to 30,000 psig.

Specifications and Codes

In the selection and application of materials the designer of boilers and pressure vessels is aided by a number of codes and specifications. In the United States the most comprehensive code in this field is the ASME Boiler and Pressure Vessel Code. This Code was developed basically as a safety code to prevent boiler explosions, and by assisting standardization of safety rules it promotes acceptance of properly designed equipment on a national and international basis.

The first boiler explosion probably took place around 1700 in a British mine in which a primitive steam-operated pumping device had been installed. There was increased use of boilers in stationary installations over the next hundred years, but it was the loss of life resulting from marine boiler explosions in the early 1800's that led to a pioneering American investigation by the Franklin Institute of Pennsylvania in 1830. Many state laws subsequently were enacted to regulate boiler construction and operation, but it was not until the period 1911–1914 that the ASME Boiler Code was developed.[2] As formally adopted in 1915 and since administered by the Society, the Code embodied many of the earlier regulations and resolved many of the conflicts in the rules. Since that time a majority of the states, as well as the provinces of Canada, have adopted boiler laws which make the ASME Boiler and Pressure Vessel Code the basis of their legal requirements. The technical rules of the ASME Code are kept up to date by continuing review of the Boiler and Pressure Vessel Committee, a group which contains a balanced representation of material suppliers, fabricators, users, insurors and enforcement jurisdictions. This group sponsors regular revisions of the Code to keep up with technical changes and develops answers to questions of interpretation of the rules. Administration of Code requirements is the responsibility of the individual state in which the boiler is to be installed, and this effort is coordinated by the National Board of Boiler and Pressure Vessel Inspectors.

Another technical group, the American Society for Testing and Materials(ASTM), incorporated in 1902, prepares and publishes specifications for the purchase and testing of a wide variety of materials. This activity, which is directly related to the Society objective of promoting knowledge of engineering materials, is carried on through committees which include representatives of producers, fabricators

[2] For a fascinating account of the development of the ASME Boiler Code and the events which preceded its adoption, see "History of the ASME Boiler Code" by Arthur M. Greene, Jr., published by The American Society of Mechanical Engineers, 1955. It is interesting to note from this very detailed historical work that the first Federal government grant for private research was awarded by the House of Representatives in 1831 to the Franklin Institute of Philadelphia to conduct tests on the causes of and means for preventing explosions of steam boilers.

Fig. 9–1. Typical central station boiler drum fabricated from plates up to 6½ in. thickness.

and consumers.[3] Such specifications form a widely useful basis for procurement of materials to meet defined levels of quality, acceptance tests and the like, thus promoting both safety and economy. These materials specifications are also used, either as written or with modifications, by groups such as the ASME Boiler and Pressure Vessel Committee to establish recognized grades of materials to which their Codes rules for design, allowable stresses, fabrication methods and inspection are applicable.

The American Standards Association (ASA) publishes a variety of standards, a number of which apply to boiler and pressure vessel construction or related uses. Standards such as ASA B31.1 (Code for Pressure Piping) and ASA B16.5 (Steel Pipe Flanges and Flanged Fittings) are frequently used.

The United States Government also publishes codes and specifications for some equipment used in its facilities.

A basic limitation of all codes is that their rules must be expressed in sufficiently general terms to cover a wide range of applications. They can therefore only define reasonable minimum standards, and there are sure to arise cases in which the engineering designer must make further investigation and exercise additional effort. A great variety of supplementary information is available from publications of the various engineering societies and from technical bulletins of equipment suppliers.

Raw Material Forms

The metallic materials available to the designer consist of plates and sheets, forgings, castings, tubing and piping, and rolled and extruded shapes of various other types. All of these are limited in size by the facilities and capabilities of the various material suppliers. Table 9–1, on the next page, lists a number of materials presently in wide use for both fossil fueled boilers and nuclear reactor vessels.

Plates

Boiler drums and pressurized water reactor vessels presently use the largest size *plates* made. For boiler drums of diameters of five or six feet, of which Fig. 9–1 is a typical example, these plates are up to 6½ in. thick and are used for shells and heads of these units. For larger diameter

---

[3] For additional information see *ASTM Year Book* published by the Society at 1916 Race Street, Philadelphia 3, Penna.

Table 9-1 Typical Materials Used in Boilers and Nuclear Reactor Vessels*

Product form	ASME Spec. No.	Grade	Minimum Tensile Strength TS PSI	Minimum Yield Strength YS PSI	Chemical Requirements, Per Cent								
					Carbon C min–max	Manganese Mn min–max	Phosphorus P max	Sulfur S max	Silicon Si min–max	Nickel Ni min–max	Chromium Cr min–max	Molybdenum Mo min–max	Other
Carbon Steel													
Low Strength Carbon													
Tubes	SA–192	–	(47,000)	(26,000)	0.06–0.18	0.27–0.63	0.048	0.058	0.25	–	–	–	–
Tubes (ERW)	SA–178	A	–	–	0.06–0.18	0.27–0.63	0.050	0.060	–	–	–	–	–
Tubes (ERW)	SA–226	–	(47,000)	(26,000)	0.06–0.18	0.27–0.63	0.050	0.060	0.25	–	–	–	–
Intermediate Strength Carbon													
Tubes	SA–210	C	60,000	37,000	0.27	0.93	0.048	0.058	0.10	–	–	–	–
Tubes (ERW)	SA–178	C	60,000	37,000	0.35	0.80	0.050	0.060	–	–	–	–	–
Pipe	SA–106	B	60,000	35,000	0.30	0.29–1.06	0.048	0.058	0.10	–	–	–	–
Plate	SA–201	B	60,000	32,000	0.35	0.80	0.035	0.04	0.15–0.30	–	–	–	–
Forging	SA–105	I	60,000	30,000	0.35	0.90	0.05	0.05	0.35	–	–	–	–
Casting	SA–216	WCA	60,000	30,000	0.25	0.70	0.05	0.06	0.60	–	–	–	–
High Strength Carbon													
Pipe	SA–106	C	70,000	40,000	0.35	0.29–1.06	0.048	0.058	0.10	–	–	–	–
Plate	SA–212	B	70,000	38,000	0.35	0.90	0.035	0.04	0.15–0.30	–	–	–	–
Forging	SA–105	II	70,000	36,000	0.35	0.90	0.05	0.05	0.35	–	–	–	–
Casting	SA–216	WCB	70,000	36,000	0.30	1.00	0.05	0.06	0.60	–	–	–	–
Ferritic Alloy													
Mn – 1/2 Mo													
Plate	SA–302	B	80,000	50,000	0.25	1.15–1.50	0.035	0.040	0.15–0.30	–	–	0.45–0.60	–
C – 1/2 Mo													
Tubes	SA–209	T1	55,000	30,000	0.10–0.20	0.30–0.80	0.045	0.045	0.10–0.50	–	–	0.44–0.65	–
1 Cr – 1/2 Mo													
Tubes	SA–213	T12	60,000	30,000	0.15	0.30–0.61	0.045	0.045	0.50	–	0.80–1.25	0.44–0.65	–
Pipe	SA–335	P12	60,000	30,000	0.15	0.30–0.61	0.045	0.045	0.50	–	0.80–1.25	0.44–0.65	–
Plate	SA–387	B	60,000	35,000	0.17	0.40–0.65	0.035	0.040	0.15–0.30	–	0.80–1.15	0.45–0.65	–
Forging	SA–182	F12	70,000	40,000	0.10–0.20	0.30–0.80	0.040	0.040	0.10–0.60	–	0.80–1.25	0.44–0.65	–
1 1/4 Cr – 1/2 Mo													
Tubes	SA–213	T11	60,000	30,000	0.15	0.30–0.60	0.030	0.030	0.50–1.00	–	1.00–1.50	0.44–0.65	–
Pipe	SA–335	P11	60,000	30,000	0.15	0.30–0.60	0.030	0.030	0.50–1.00	–	1.00–1.50	0.44–0.65	–
Plate	SA–387	C	60,000	35,000	0.17	0.40–0.65	0.035	0.040	0.50–1.00	–	1.00–1.50	0.45–0.65	–
Forging	SA–182	F11	70,000	40,000	0.10–0.20	0.30–0.80	0.040	0.040	0.50–1.00	–	1.00–1.50	0.45–0.65	–
Casting	SA–217	WC6	70,000	40,000	0.20	0.50–0.80	0.05	0.06	0.60	–	1.00–1.50	0.45–0.65	–

*Data from ASME Boiler and Pressure Vessel Code, Section II, Material Specifications (1965 Edition and Addenda).

Product form	Spec. No.	Grade	TS PSI	YS PSI	C min-max	Mn min-max	P max	S max	Si min-max	Ni min-max	Cr min-max	Mo min-max	Other
2¼ Cr – 1 Mo													
Tubes	SA-213	T22	60,000	30,000	0.15	0.30-0.60	0.030	0.030	0.50	—	1.90- 2.60	0.87-1.13	
Pipe	SA-335	P22	60,000	30,000	0.15	0.30-0.60	0.030	0.030	0.50	—	1.90- 2.60	0.87-1.13	
Plate	SA-387	D	60,000	30,000	0.15	0.30-0.60	0.035	0.035	0.50	—	2.00- 2.50	0.90-1.10	
Forging	SA-182	F22	70,000	40,000	0.15	0.30-0.60	0.040	0.040	0.50	—	2.00- 2.50	0.87-1.13	
Casting	SA-217	WC9	70,000	40,000	0.18	0.40-0.70	0.05	0.06	0.60	—	2.00- 2.75	0.90-1.20	
5 Cr – ½ Mo													
Tubes	SA-213	T5	60,000	30,000	0.15	0.30-0.60	0.03	0.03	0.50	—	4.00- 6.00	0.45-0.65	
Pipe	SA-335	P5	60,000	30,000	0.15	0.30-0.60	0.030	0.030	0.50	—	4.00- 6.00	0.45-0.65	
Plate	SA-357	–		30,000	0.15	0.30-0.60	0.04	0.03	0.50	—	4.00- 6.00	0.45-0.65	
Forging	SA-182	F5	60,000	30,000	0.15	0.30-0.60	0.030	0.030	0.50	0.50	4.0 – 6.0	0.44-0.65	
Casting	SA-217	C5	90,000	60,000	0.20	0.40-0.70	0.05	0.06	0.75	—	4.00- 6.50	0.45-0.65	
9 Cr – 1 Mo													
Tubes	SA-213	T9	60,000	30,000	0.15	0.30-0.60	0.03	0.03	0.25-1.00	—	8.00-10.00	0.90-1.10	
Pipe	SA-335	P9	60,000	30,000	0.15	0.30-0.60	0.030	0.030	0.25-1.00	—	8.00-10.00	0.90-1.10	
Forging	SA-182	F9	100,000	70,000	0.15	0.30-0.60	0.030	0.030	0.50-1.00	—	8.0 –10.0	0.90-1.10	
Casting	SA-217	C12	90,000	60,000	0.20	0.35-0.65	0.05	0.06	1.00	—	8.00-10.00	0.90-1.20	
Austenitic Stainless Alloy													
18 Cr – 8 Ni													
Tubes	SA-213	TP304H	75,000	30,000	0.04-0.10	2.00	0.040	0.030	0.75	8.00-11.0	18.0 –20.0	—	
Pipe	SA-376	TP304H	75,000	30,000	0.04-0.10	2.00	0.030	0.030	0.75	8.0 –11.0	18.0 –20.0	—	
Plate	SA-240	304	75,000	30,000	0.08	2.00	0.045	0.030	1.00	8.00-12.00	18.00-20.00	—	
Forging	SA-182	F304H	75,000	30,000	0.04-0.10	2.00	0.040	0.030	1.00	8.00-11.00	18.00-20.00	—	
Casting	SA-351	CF8	70,000	30,000	0.08	1.50	0.040	0.040	2.00	8.0 –11.0	18.0 –21.0	—	
18 Cr – 10 Ni – Ti													
Tubes	SA-213	TP321H	75,000	30,000	0.04-0.10	2.00	0.030	0.030	0.75	9.00-13.0	17.0 –20.0	—	a
Pipe	SA-376	TP321H	75,000	30,000	0.04-0.10	2.00	0.030	0.030	0.75	9.0 –13.0	17.0 –20.0	—	a
Plate	SA-240	321	75,000	30,000	0.08	2.00	0.045	0.030	1.00	9.00-12.00	17.00-19.00	—	b
Forging	SA-182	F321H	75,000	30,000	0.04-0.10	2.50	0.035	0.030	0.85	9.00	17.00	—	a
18 Cr – 10 Ni – Cb													
Tubes	SA-213	TP347H	75,000	30,000	0.04-0.10	2.00	0.030	0.030	1.00	9.00-13.0	17.0 –20.0	—	c
Pipe	SA-376	TP347H	75,000	30,000	0.04-0.10	2.00	0.030	0.030	0.75	9.0 –13.0	17.0 –20.0	—	c
Plate	SA-240	347	75,000	30,000	0.08	2.00	0.045	0.030	1.00	9.00-13.00	17.00-19.00	—	d
Forging	SA-182	F347H	75,000	30,000	0.04-0.10	2.00	0.030	0.030	1.00	9.00-13.00	17.00-20.00	—	c
Casting	SA-351	CF8C	70,000	30,000	0.08	1.50	0.040	0.040	2.00	9.0 –12.0	18.0 –21.0	—	c
16 Cr – 13 Ni – 3 Mo													
Tubes	SA-213	TP316H	75,000	30,000	0.04-0.10	2.00	0.030	0.030	0.75	11.0 –14.0	16.0 –18.0	2.00-3.00	
Pipe	SA-376	TP316H	75,000	30,000	0.04-0.10	2.00	0.030	0.030	0.75	11.0 –14.0	16.0 –18.0	2.0 –3.0	
Plate	SA-240	316	75,000	30,000	0.08	2.00	0.045	0.030	1.00	10.00-14.00	16.00-18.00	2.00-3.00	
Forging	SA-182	F316H	75,000	30,000	0.04-0.10	2.00	0.040	0.030	1.00	10.00-14.00	16.00-18.00	2.00-3.00	
Casting	SA-351	CF8M	70,000	30,000	0.08	1.50	0.040	0.040	1.50	9.0 –12.0	18.0 –21.0	2.0 –3.0	

a Titanium content of not less than four times the carbon content and not more than 0.60 per cent.

b Titanium content of not less than five times the carbon content and not more than 0.70 per cent.

c Columbium plus tantalum content of not less than eight times the carbon content and not more than 1.00 per cent.

d Columbium plus tantalum content of not less than ten times the carbon content and not more than 1.10 per cent.

Fig. 9–2. Shell of nuclear reactor vessel utilizing plates up to ten inches thickness.

shells, these plates may be up to ten inches thick, as shown in Fig. 9–2. This thickness approaches the capacity of the plate mills to produce reasonably large-size plates. These generally represent a reduction from the ingot thickness to the plate thickness of at least four to one.

Pressurized water nuclear reactor vessels and chemical process vessels may also require plates with a corrosion-resisting cladding. In this construction a thin layer of high-alloy material is bonded to a heavier thickness of low alloy or carbon steel backing material. Plates are available with such cladding applied as a roll-bonded or braze-bonded product, or the cladding may be applied by welding.

Plates may exhibit *directional* or *anisotropic* properties, being weaker when tested across the thickness. This results from discontinuities and heterogeneities in the ingot being oriented in the rolling process so as to have their greatest dimension parallel to the direction of rolling, their lesser dimension transverse to the direction of rolling, and their least dimension perpendicular to the plate surfaces. These types of discontinuities are generally not harmful except when they are large enough in size to affect heat transfer or excessive in quantity so as to affect weldability. The general practice

for heavy plates used in nuclear applications is to apply ultrasonic tests to determine that the material is free of excessive discontinuities and heterogeneities.

Forgings

Boiler drums and similar non-nuclear vessels may use *forgings* for reinforcing rings around openings, and some moderate size high pressure vessels are made entirely by forging. In most cases the largest opening required for a boiler drum is a manway of about 16 in. size. Nuclear reactor vessels introduced the need in many cases for much larger diameter openings, usually with removable heads or covers to facilitate inserting or changing fuel elements or control rods.

Pressurized water nuclear reactor vessels have required a removable head consisting of a flanged and bolted head-to-shells connection. The heads of some design have required very heavy thickness because of numerous penetrations and complex patterns. Fig. 9–3 shows a typical forged flange welded to a shell. Such a flange of approximately two feet by two feet cross section and nine feet inside diameter uses 42 bolts, six inches in diameter by six feet long, weighing about 575 lb each. Fig. 9–4 shows a head fabricated from a flange forging and a dome

Fig. 9–3. Forge flange for welded to shell of nuclear reactor vessel.

Fig. 9–4. Head of nuclear reactor vessel fabricated by welding a flange forging and a builtup dome.

Fig. 9–5. Builtup dome for head of nuclear reactor vessel.

section; the latter is made from segmented formed plates as shown in Fig. 9–5.

These large forgings are presently made from ingots cast by a vacuum-pouring technique which keeps hydrogen to a minimum in the ingot and eliminates troublesome "hydrogen flaking" problems present with air pouring. Prior to the development of this technique, a forging of this type would require several months of carefully controlled heating and cooling in the attempt to eliminate hydrogen flaking, which might even then be found on final ultrasonic examination.

Tubing

Steam is generated and superheated primarily in *tubing*.[4] The tubing is de-

[4] From the standpoint of geometrical shape and physical construction, there is no essential difference between *pipe* and *tubing*. Pipe sizes are generally designated by their nominal inside diameter for a particular type of service. Tubes, by contrast, are usually specified in terms of outside diameter and minimum wall thickness.

Pipe is made in a relatively few standard sizes and manufactured in large quantities. Tubing, on the other hand, is generally made in smaller quantities to relatively strict specifications as to tolerances, finish, chemical composition and physical properties.

Pipe sizes and wall thickness are standardized with due consideration to threading ends for joining together lengths with such fittings as flanges, nipples, valves, tees and the like. Such fittings are generally not installed with tubing. Where pressure tight connections must be made, tubes are welded together, or their ends are expanded into tube sheets.

Fig. 9—6. Looking up into furnace of large central station boiler showing waterwall enclosure and superheater elements hanging from top.

signed to last the life of the unit (up to 20 or more years) even though, in the case of superheated steam tubing or power plant piping, it is operated at a visibly "red-hot" temperature up to 1200 to 1300 F.

Selection of the material used depends upon the actual metal temperature to be sustained. The steam generation tubes are primarily of carbon-steel material. The superheater and reheater tubing is also of carbon-steel analysis in low-temperature regions, but progresses, depending upon the design metal temperatures in the various areas, to carbon-molybdenum steel, low chromium-molybdenum

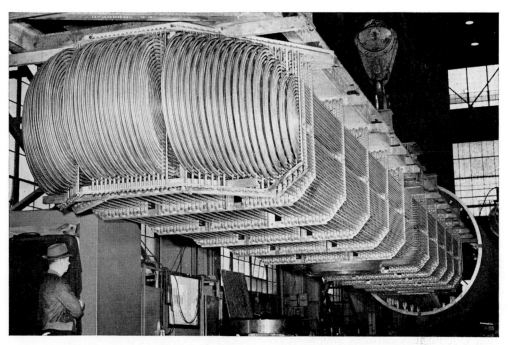

Fig. 9–7. Tube bundle and shell for nuclear steam generator.

steel, intermediate chromium-molybdenum steel, and finally *austenitic stainless steel*.[5] Type 321 austenitic stainless steel has been used for the high-temperature passes for several years. Types 347, 304 and 316 austenitic stainless steel have also been in use. At present the H-grades of Types 321, 347, 304 and 316 are specified for high temperature service. Specifications for typical tubing materials are listed in Table 9–1. Fig. 9–6 is a view of the furnace of a central station boiler showing a portion of the steam generation and superheater tubing. Large units of this type may require as much as 300 miles of such tubing.

Steam generator tubing and a heat exchanger shell for a large nuclear reactor are shown in Fig. 9–7. Tube assemblies

and half of the steam collection manifold for the same heat exchanger are shown in Fig. 9–8.

Castings

Castings have not been used to a great extent in boilers or pressure vessels except

Fig. 9–8. Close-up view of manifold and tube assemblies.

[5] This is a type of steel containing sufficient amounts of such alloying elements as nickel and chromium to retain austenite, a solid solution of carbon in gamma iron, at atmospheric temperature.

in special applications such as valve or pump bodies, where the relative ease in forming special shapes has been an advantage. Techniques in casting steel have improved, supported by developments in nondestructive tests such as radiography and ultrasonic examination. With the availability of welding to repair defects so found, steel castings may find a wider range of use in future vessel applications.

Castings are also used to advantage in such boiler auxiliaries as stokers and pulverizers. Cast iron finds application in stoker keys which can be cast to the desired shape with little or no machining. Composition of the iron or low alloy steel may be varied to match the severity of the high temperature service. Bases for bowl mills use gray cast iron because of its excellent vibration damping characteristics. Ductile iron castings and steel castings are used in other parts of pulverizing mills. Special alloy iron castings and forgings of hard, abrasion resistant materials are available for liners, grinding rings, rolls and other parts where wear resistance is a major requirement.

Metallurgical Fundamentals[6]

For purpose of classification, the science of metallurgy is generally divided into two fields. These consist of *process metallurgy* which is defined as the science of obtaining metals from their ores and *physical metallurgy* which is defined as the science concerned with the physical and mechanical characteristics of metal and alloys. These fields, in turn, are portions of the basic sciences of chemistry and physics involving the study of the structures of atoms — their sizes and forces of attraction and the arrangements of these atoms in forming molecular structures, grain structures, and grain boundaries of multicrystalline materials.

Phase Diagrams

Some metals used for engineering purposes are commercially pure. This is true of copper for electrical wiring. Enhanced mechanical or physical properties may be obtained by deliberately combining elements so as to form an alloy. Some combinations result in a *single-phase, solid-solution* alloy. It is called single phase because the atoms are dissolved in the structure such that visual, microscopic and X-ray observations reveal a single crystal structure. Such a solid solution most readily forms when the two components are similar in atomic size and in electronic structure. The distribution of the atoms may be *random* as shown in Fig. 9–9 or *ordered* as shown in Fig. 9–10 or *interstitial* as shown in Fig. 9–11.

Element combinations may result, however, in a mixture of two or more phases. Fig. 9–12 shows a two-phase structure of *sigma phase*[7] in austenite (Type 321 material). Fig. 9–13 shows a two-phase structure of *pearlite* (which consists of alternate lamellae of cementite[8] and ferrite[9]) and *ferrite* (carbon steel SA–192 of Table 9–1).

The phase relationships are dependent

---

[6] Much of this section is adapted from *Elements of Materials Science — An Introductory Text for Engineering Students* by Lawrence H. Van Vlack, Addison-Wesley Publishing Co., Reading, Mass., 1964. Each chapter of this book contains an annotated bibliography which suggests additional references.

[7] This is a hard and brittle intermetallic compound of variable composition that adversely affects the ductility and corrosion resistance of stainless steel.

[8] A compound of iron and carbon known as iron carbide which has the approximate chemical formula, Fe_3C, and is characterized by an orthorhombic crystal structure.

[9] A solid solution in which alpha iron is a solvent, and which is characterized by a body-centered cubic crystal structure.

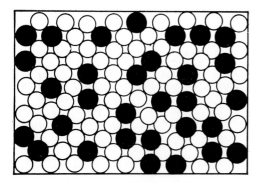

Fig. 9–9. Random substitutional solid solution (zinc in copper). No alteration of crystal pattern. (From *Introductory Physical Metallurgy* by Clyde Mason, American Society for Metals, 1947.)

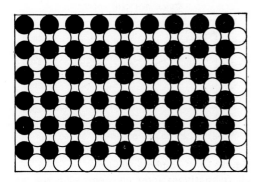

Fig. 9–10. Ordered substitutional solid solution. (From *Introductory Physical Metallurgy* by Clyde Mason, American Society for Metals, 1947.)

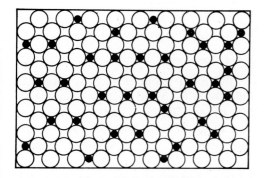

Fig. 9–11. Interstitial solid solution (carbon in iron having a face-centered cubic structure). (From *Introductory Physical Metallurgy* by Clyde Mason, American Society for Metals, 1947.)

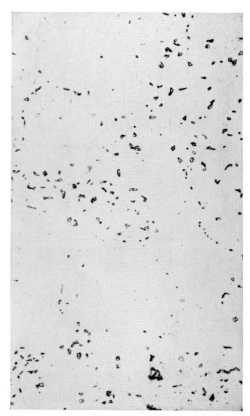

Fig. 9–12. Two-phase structure of sigma phase in austenite (Type 321 material). 500 magnification. Ten per cent potassium hydroxide etch, one half second.

upon temperature. Fig. 9–14 shows a *phase diagram* for a simple system of lead and tin at equilibrium conditions. This diagram can be used as a "map" from which the phases present at any particular temperature and composition can be read. For example, at 50 per cent tin and 212 F (100 C), the phase diagram indicates two solid phases. Alpha is a solid solution of lead with some dissolved tin; beta is almost pure tin with very little dissolved lead. At 392 F (200 C) an alloy of 10 per cent tin and 90 per cent lead lies in an area which is entirely in the alpha phase. It is a solid solution of lead with some tin dissolved in it. At the same

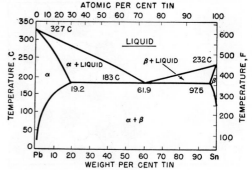

Fig. 9–13. Two-phase structure of pearlite and ferrite in low carbon steel. 500 magnification. Two per cent nital etch.

Fig. 9–14. Phase diagram for a simple system of lead and tin at equilibrium conditions. (From *ASM Handbook of Metals,* American Society for Metals, 1948.)

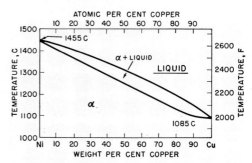

Fig. 9–15. Two-phase diagram. In lower part all compositions form only one solid solution and therefore only one crystal structure. (From *ASM Handbook of Metals,* American Society for Metals, 1948.)

temperature, but for 30 per cent tin and 70 per cent lead, the phase diagram indicates a mixture of liquid and a solid solution. If this latter composition were heated to a temperature of 572 F (300 C), it would become all liquid.

The phase fields in equilibrium diagrams, of course, depend on the particular alloy systems depicted. When copper and nickel are mixed, the phase diagram is as shown in Fig. 9–15. This phase diagram is comparatively simple, since only two phases are present. In the lower part of the diagram, all compositions form only one solid solution and therefore only one crystal structure.

The phase relations for a ternary alloy become more complex as shown for an iron-carbon-chromium alloy in Fig. 9–16. Such phase relationships are used in regulating heat treatments in alloys.

T–T–T Curves

The phase relations such as shown in Figs. 9–14, 9–15 and 9–16 are representative of equilibrium conditions obtained as a result of slow heating, slow cooling and long time at temperature. Time is required for change from one phase to another. Energy change is involved. Reaction rates are usually faster at higher temperatures except near the temperature of transformation from one phase to an-

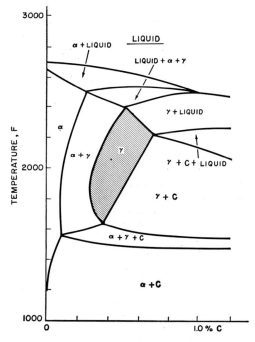

Fig. 9–16. Phase diagram for a ternary iron-chromium-carbon alloy. (From *Elements of Materials Science* by L. H. Van Vlack, Addison-Wesley Publishing Co., Reading, Mass., 1964.)

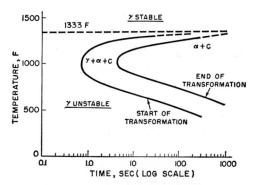

Fig. 9–17. Temperature-Time-Transformation curves for a eutectoid steel. (From *Elements of Materials Science* by L. H. Van Vlack, Addison-Wesley Publishing Co., Reading, Mass., 1964.)

other where extra energy is required to nucleate a new phase. Reaction rates for phase changes are exemplified by *Temperature—Time—Transformation Curves* (*T–T–T*) such as that shown in Fig. 9–17

which is for steel of 0.8 per cent carbon content shown in the equilibrium diagram, Fig. 9–16, 15 per cent chromium. It can be seen that rapidly cooling this steel to low temperature allows the *gamma phase* (austenitic material) to be present down to low temperature for a considerable time element before transformation occurs. The transformation product at this low temperature is different from what it would be if transformation occurred at a higher temperature and is of higher hardness and strength with sufficiently high carbon content. This transformation product is a hard material called *martensite*. Such a phenomenon is one of the basic methods of varying properties of steel by heat treatment. Each alloy subject to phase changes with temperature change exhibits a characteristic T–T–T curve.

Grain Structure

A *grain* is a single crystal which usually does not have a regular external crystalline shape. The shape of a grain in a solid is usually controlled by the presence of surrounding grains. Within any particular grain, all the atoms are arranged with one pattern, characterized by the unit cell. However, at the grain boundary between two adjacent grains there is a transition zone which is not directly aligned with either grain. This is depicted in Fig. 9–18.

When a metal is observed under a microscope, although the individual atoms cannot be seen, the grain boundaries can be readily located if the metal has been smoothly polished to a mirror-like surface and etched with an acid. The grain boundaries will be attacked differently from the body of the grain and become visible. Different phases will also become visible. Note the grain boundaries of the single-phase austenitic alloy of Fig. 9–19

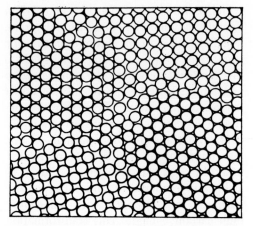

Fig. 9–18. Transition zone at grain boundary between two adjacent grains. (From *Introductory Physical Metallurgy* by Clyde Mason, American Society for Metals, 1947.)

showing fine and coarse-grained material (ASTM A–213–TP321).

The grain size can be regulated by thermal treatment. An increase in temperature causes increased thermal vibration of the atoms which facilitates transfer of atoms across the grain boundary from small to large grains. A subsequent decrease in temperature slows or stops the process but does not reverse it. Grains may grow through mechanical working, by the use of heat treatment, through phase changes, or a combination of these methods. The only way to refine the grain size is to distort, break or remove the grains which have grown and start new grains. The process is dependent upon the characteristics of the particular alloy involved. Grain growth will occur only above certain temperatures and is dependent upon time at temperature. This temperature may be quite low with some materials which have been critically cold worked.

The American Society for Testing and Materials has standardized a grain size index in which the grain size number, n, is obtained as follows: $N = 2^{n-1}$

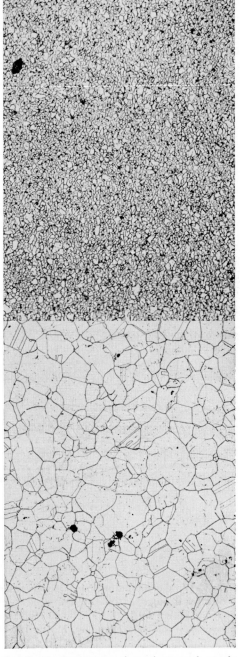

Fig. 9–19. Grain size boundaries of single-phase austenitic alloy showing fine and coarse grained material (ASTM A–213–TP321) Grain size number eight and smaller, top, and four to seven, bottom. 100 magnification. Sixty per cent nitric acid etch.

where N is the number of grains observed per square inch at a linear magnification of 100X. For most metals, the grain size ranges from number one to number eight, number one being a large grain and number eight a small grain.

Since the properties of metals vary greatly depending upon grain size, proper control must be exercised.

Hardenability

A plain carbon steel, as discussed previously in the section on T–T–T curves, is hardened by quenching in water so as to cool the piece rapidly so that it does not have time to transform at the fastest reaction rate temperature of 1000 F. This is possible if the thickness of material is light enough to cool completely at the required rate. A heavy thickness piece, however, cannot be cooled sufficiently rapidly at the center of the thickness and transformation will take place more rapidly and at a higher temperature at the center. This results in a softer transformation product. Further alloy additions to this steel retard the transformation rate (shift the curve of Fig. 9–17 to the right) and allow hardening to greater depths. This also allows less severe quenching and results in lower thermal stress and less possibility of cracking. Highly alloyed steels may be hardened by air cooling. Since steels hardened to high values are also brittle as hardened, a reduction of hardness is generally accomplished by heating back to an intermediate temperature. This markedly improves toughness. This process is called *tempering*.

Heat Treatments

Table 9–2[10] aids in understanding some of the processes whereby metallic structure can be changed through heat treatments to meet the needs of specific industrial applications.

High Temperature Service Considerations

At elevated temperature many metals are subject to metallurgical phase changes which may drastically alter the material characteristics. Even below the temperature for metallurgical phase changes there is a range of temperature in which the mechanical properties and corrosion resistance may vary markedly with temperature and time of exposure or stress at this temperature.

Properties

Above about 650 F most steels suffer a gradual decrease in tensile and yield strength. At still higher temperatures it is found that the strain in a material is a function not only of the applied stress but of the time under stress at temperature. In this high temperature range the metal will deform (*creep*) continuously even at stresses much lower than the short-time yield strength. If held for sufficient time under these conditions the material will rupture. Since no way has been found to predict this behavior quantitatively from short-time tests, it is necessary to run tests of creep and stress rupture at several stress levels, temperatures and periods of time as long as possible. From such tests, extrapolated as necessary, values of creep strength and stress-rupture strength are established. The creep strength of a metal at a certain temperature is the steady stress to produce a specified low rate of elongation. For long-time service, such as ASME Boiler Code applications, a creep rate of 0.01 per cent

---

[10] This has been adapted from Table 11–1, Common Heat Treating Processes, which originally appeared in *Elements of Materials Science* by Lawrence H. Van Vlack, Addison-Wesley Publishing Co., Reading, Mass., Second Edition, 445 pages, 1964.

Table 9-2   Heat Treating Processes

Process	Example	Purpose	Procedure
Annealing	Cold-worked metals	To remove strain hardening[1] and increase ductility	Heat above recrystallization[2] temperature
Annealing	Steel	To soften	Heat into austenitic[3] range and slow cool
Normalizing	Steel	Homogenization and strain relief[1]	Heat into austentic range and air cool
Process annealing and stress relieving	Steel	To soften and toughen	Heat close to, but below, the eutectoid[4] temperature
Spheroidizing	Steel	To soften and toughen	Heat for a sufficiently long time close to, but below, the eutectoid[4] temperature
Quenching	Steel	To harden	Quench from austenite to martensite[5]. (This is followed by tempering.)
Tempering	Quenched steel	To toughen	Heat briefly at low temperature
Austempering	Steel	To harden without developing brittle martensite	Quench from austenite to a low temperature below the "knee"[6] of the transformation curve, but above the martensite transforma-temperature. Hold until transformation is complete.
Marquenching	Steel	To harden without quench cracking	Quench from austenite to a temperature below the knee of the transformation curve, but above the martensite transforming temperature. Hold until temperature has equalized. Cool slowly to martensite. (This is followed by tempering).
Solution treating	Stainless steel	To produce a single phase alloy	Heat above the solubility curve into a single phase area and quench to room temperature.
Age hardening	Various ferrous and non-ferrous alloys	To harden	Solution treat. Cool to provide supersaturation. Reheat to an intermediate temperature until the initial precipitation starts. Cool to surrounding temperatures.

[1] When a sufficient stress is applied to a metal such that the piece does not return to its original dimensions, the yield strength has been exceeded. Since most metals are weaker in shear than in pure tension, they yield by plastic shear or slip of one plane of atoms over another. This slip occurs most readily along planes containing the greatest number of atoms per unit of area. These parallel planes are more widely separated than other planes. Plastic movement along these planes causes distortion of the planes due to restraint of surrounding metal and allows added amount of slip to occur less readily. This resultant increase in strength is called **strain hardening**.

[2] Since plastic deformation at low temperatures cause distorted crystal patterns, the tendency is for the atoms to return to a more perfect unrestrained condition. Heating to a higher temperature increases thermal vibration of the atoms which allows readjustment to take place. Since such re-adjustment also results in decreased hardness, the temperature of marked softening is called the **recrystallization temperature**. Recrystallization temperature is dependent upon degree of plastic deformation (cold work), time at temperature, material, and material purity. Generally, it is between

in 1000 hours is used. The stress-rupture strength is the steady stress required at a particular temperature to cause rupture in a specified long period of time.

Fig. 9–20 illustrates the use of test data to establish creep rupture strengths for a 2¼ Cr — 1 Mo steel. Creep rate data for 1000, 1100 and 1200 F are plotted versus stress, and the intersection of the data lines with that for 0.01 per cent in 1000 hours sets the respective creep strengths of 7800 psi, 5000 psi and 2400 psi. The

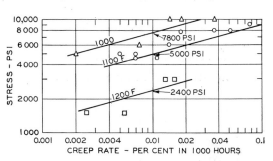

Fig. 9–20. Creep rate (right) and rupture strength (below) for a 2¼–1 Mo steel.

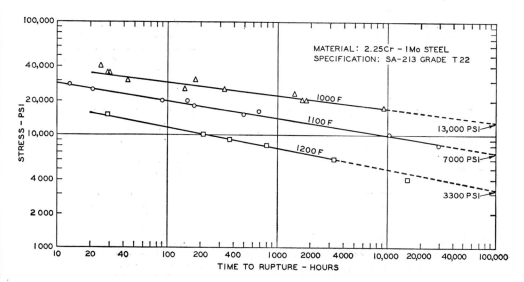

¹⁄₃ and ¹⁄₂ of the melting temperature (degrees absolute). Plastic deformation at temperature below the recrystallization temperature is called **cold working.** Plastic deformation above the recrystallization temperature is called **hot working.**

[3] A solid solution in which gamma iron is the solvent; characterized by a face-centered cubic crystal structure.

[4] See Fig. 9–16. Eutectoid temperature for 0 per cent Cr is 1330 F. Eutectoid carbon content for zero per cent Cr is 0.8 per cent.

[5] An unstable constituent in quenched steel, formed without diffusion and only during cooling below a certain temperature known as the M_s (or A_r) temperature. The structure is characterized by its acicular or needle-like appearance on the surface of a polished and etched specimen. Martensite is the hardest of the transformation products of austenite. **Tetragonality** of the crystal structure is observed when the carbon content is greater than about 0.5 per cent.

[6] See Fig 9–17. "Knee" of curve is at approximately 1000 F. Martensite transformation temperature on cooling for this steel is approximately 250 F.

other curves show rupture life versus stress for the same three temperatures. Lines through these data are extrapolated to 100,000 hours to establish rupture strengths of 13,000 psi, 7000 psi and 3300 psi respectively.

For design purposes the ASME Boiler and Pressure Vessel Code establishes minimum allowable stresses not to exceed any of these five criteria:

1. Twenty-five per cent of the specified minimum tensile strength at room temperature.
2. Twenty-five per cent of the minimum expected tensile strength at temperature.
3. Sixty-two and one half per cent of the minimum expected yield strength for 0.2 per cent offset at temperature.
4. One hundred per cent of the stress to produce a creep rate of 0.01 per cent per 1000 hours.
5. Either 60 per cent of the average stress to produce rupture in 100,000 hours or 80 per cent of the minimum stress for rupture in 100,000 hours, whichever is lower. (This applies to Section I, Power Boilers; Section VIII, Unfired Pressure Vessels, uses 100 per cent of the stress for rupture in 100,000 hours.)

Fig. 9–21 shows the application of these criteria to establish the allowable stress for a 2¼ Cr — 1 Mo steel. For this material the first criterion mentioned above controls up to 800 F. At 950 F and above the creep strength and rupture strength, the fourth and fifth criteria require a rather sharp decrease in the allowable stress.

Relative influence of the different criteria varies with materials as well as with temperature. Fig. 9–22 shows the effect of temperature on ASME Boiler Code al-

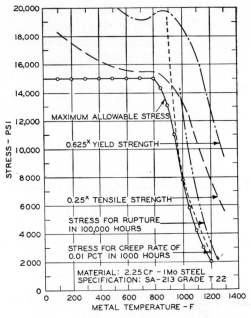

Fig. 9–21. Use of ASME Boiler Code criteria to establish allowable stress for a 2¼ Cr–1 Mo steel.

Fig. 9–22. Effect of temperature on ASME Boiler Code allowable stresses for various steels.

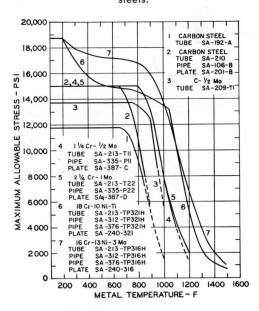

lowable stresses for a number of alloys used for high temperature service. The carbon steels begin to lose strength above 700 F, and by 850 F are down to about one-half their room temperature values. The low chromium ferritic alloys start to lose strength above 800 F and are down to half strength about 1000 F. The austenitic stainless steels decline somewhat from room temperature to 1000 F because of reduction in yield strength; above 1000 F, creep and rupture strength cause a rapid decrease to half strength or less by 1200 F.

The high temperature strength and ductility of tubing are strongly affected by grain size, cold working, heat treatment and other variables. Tubing and equipment manufacturers must give due consideration to these factors in their design and fabrication requirements for specific applications.

Phase Changes

Above 785 F, carbon steel is subject to *graphitization*, while above 850 F, carbon-molybdenum steel is similarly affected.[11] The carbon normally present in the steel in the form of carbides transforms to graphite over a long-time period. If it does this preferentially along heat affected zones of welds or along stress lines, it may be concentrated sufficiently and oriented such that the strength of the part will be drastically reduced and result in failure. If it forms in well dispersed globules, little or no damage results. Use of steels containing ½ per cent or more chromium eliminates the danger of graphitization. Fig. 9–23 shows the macrostructure and microstructure of a tube which

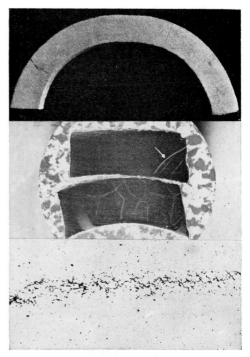

Fig. 9–23. Macrostructure and microstructure of a tube which failed due to graphitization along stress planes. Two to three magnification, upper left and right; 100 magnification, bottom. Unetched.

failed due to graphitization along stress planes.

Above about 900 F, carbon steel and low-alloy steels are subject to spheroidization. The carbides coalesce gradually at about 900 F, requiring several thousand hours to completely spheroidize at this temperature, but only a few hours at a temperature of 1300 F. The metallurgist uses this phenomenon in determining whether a failed part has overheated in service. Above 1300 F, other phase changes occur which can be recognized

---

[11] The subject of graphitization, with particular reference to steel piping, has been investigated and discussed with great thoroughness in three special pamphlets bound at the end of *ASME Transactions*. The 1944 report, Vol. 66, contains 34 pages; the 1945 report in Vol. 67, 89 pages; and the 1947 report in Vol. 69, 51 pages.

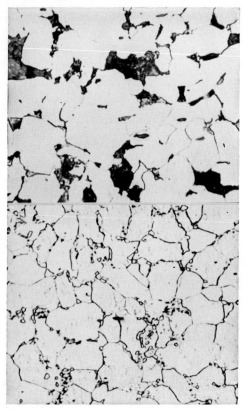

Fig. 9–24. Photomicrographs showing an annealed structure at top and a spheroidized structure at bottom. 500 magnification. Nital etch.

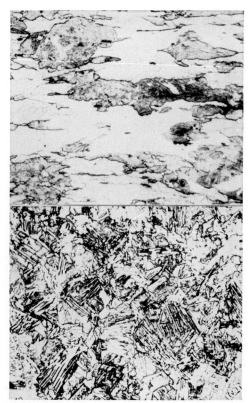

Fig. 9–25. Microstructure resulting from over heating to between the lower and upper critical temperatures (1330 to 1600 F) for carbon steel tube material, at the top, and to above the upper critical temperature, at the bottom, both followed by rapid cooling due to rupture. 500 magnification. Nital etch.

in metallographic examination. Fig. 9–24 shows an annealed structure at top and a spheroidized structure at the bottom. Fig. 9–25 shows the structure resulting from overheating to between the lower and upper critical temperature (1300 to 1600 F) for carbon-steel tube material at the top and to above the upper critical temperature at the bottom, followed by rapid quenching due to rupture.

Fig. 9–26 shows a carbon-steel tube stress-rupture failure due to overheating over a long time period at a low spheroidizing temperature and a stress-rupture failure due to overheating for only a few minutes to a temperature close to the

upper critical temperature. Many cracks, generally parallel to the main fracture, are present in the long-time failure, whereas the short-time failure exhibits no such cracking and the metal at the failure has stretched to a "knife edge." The low ducility of the long-time overheating failure and the high ductility of the short-time overheating failure are characteristic of these types of failures. Fig. 9–27 shows the macrostructure and microstructure of a heavy wall carbon-molybdenum steel pipe which has failed due to stress rupture over a long period

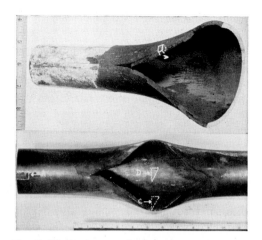

Fig. 9–26. Carbon steel tube stress rupture failure due to overheating over a long time period at a low spheroidizing temperature, top, and a stress rupture failure due to overheating for only a few minutes to a temperature close to the upper critical temperature, bottom.

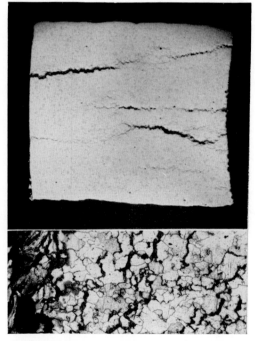

Fig. 9–27. Macrostructure and microstructure of a heavy wall carbon-molybdenum steel pipe which has failed due to stress rupture over a long period of time at a temperature near 1100 F. Two magnification, top; 100 magnification, bottom. Nital etch.

of time at temperature near 1100 F. Note the intergranular oxidation shown by the presence of oxides at the grain boundaries.

The austenitic high-alloy steels, such as Type 321 material of Table 9–1 and Fig. 9–19, are subject to a phase change at operating temperature consisting of formation of particles of *sigma phase*. This phase in this material is a non-magnetic complex iron-chromium intermetallic compound of tetragonal structure. Its appearance in the microstructure of a Type 321 material is shown in Fig. 9–28. Excessive quantity of this phase, which forms slowly at temperatures of 1000 F and more rapidly up to about 1700 F (above which this phase goes back into

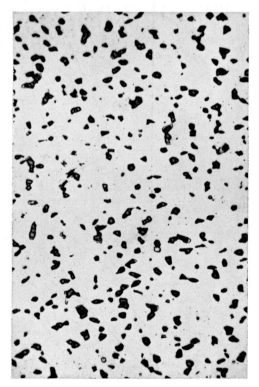

Fig. 9–28. Microstructure showing excessive quantity of sigma phase in Type 321 material. 500 magnification. Ten per cent potassium hydroxide etch.

solution), results in some room-tempera-
ture embrittlement of the material.

Oxidation Resistance

Oxidation in the broad sense is one of
the principal mechanisms of corrosion
and is discussed in greater detail later in
this chapter. Some aspects are considered
here in this section on high temperature
because of the direct effects which temperature has on the selection and behavior
of steels for boiler use.

Oxygen is present in the products of
combustion outside the tubes and in the
steam inside superheater and reheater
tubes. Above certain limiting temperatures
which depend on the alloy content of the
material, the oxygen combines with the
iron to cause significant wastage and deterioration. Oxidation occurs first at the
surface of a metal and the resulting scale
may form a barrier restricting further
oxidation. For scaling to continue, either
the metal must diffuse through the scale
toward the surface or the oxygen must
diffuse through the scale toward the

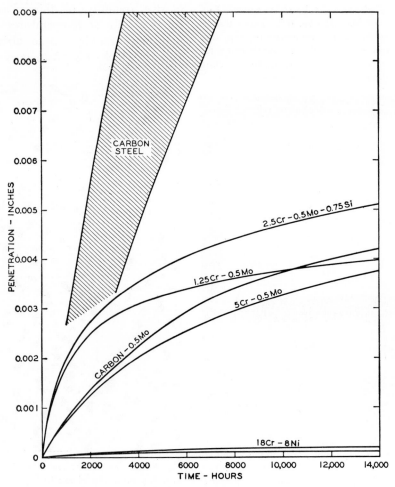

Fig. 9–29. Penetration (a measure of wastage) versus time
for several steels in steam at 1100 F.

metal; both may occur. In the case of iron, because the iron ion is smaller than the oxygen ion, the iron diffuses outward more readily and the iron-oxygen combination takes place near the surface of the scale. If the volume of the oxide is slightly greater than the metal volume, the scale may be protective. If the oxide volume is less, as it is with such metals as magnesium, lithium, potassium and sodium, the oxide will shrink and be porous; then oxidation will not decrease with time. If the oxide is not adherent because of too large a change in volume or too widely different structure orientation, again no protection will result. Fortunately many of the steels used in boilers develop reasonably adherent scales.

Fig. 9–29 shows data on total wastage penetration versus time for several steels tested in steam at 1100 F.[12] While the carbon steels are clearly above their limit for suitable application, the low chromium alloy steels show penetration rates which decrease with long time service and the austenitic steels show practically

[12] Adapted from "High Temperature Steam Corrosion Studies at Detroit" by I. A. Rohrig, R. M. Van Duzer, Jr. and C. H. Fellows, *Trans. ASME*, Vol. 66, 1944, pp. 270–290.

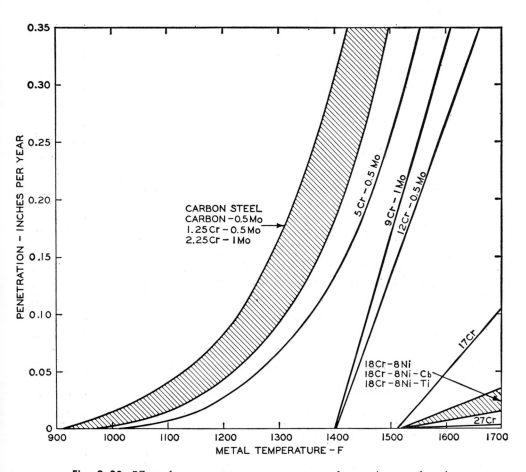

Fig. 9–30. Effect of temperature on wastage rates of several types of steel.

no attack under these conditions. These long time effects are fortunate from the standpoint of extended service but complicate the collection of laboratory data, since short time tests can be quite misleading as to actual rates.

Chromium is one of the most useful alloying elements for imparting corrosion resistance to steel. Selective oxidation of chromium in steel, as well as silicon in cast iron or steel, produces a tightly adhering and protective scale. Fig. 9–30 shows the effect of temperature on the wastage rates of a number of boiler and reactor vessel materials.[13] It will be noted that at this temperature the addition of small amounts of chromium does not increase the oxidation resistance as markedly as it does the high temperature strength, but use of five per cent chromium or more produces significantly higher oxidation resistance.

In the final selection of materials for high temperature service the corrosion resistance and the creep-rupture strength must be balanced against the higher cost of the alloys required to provide it. The economic solution is to use each material up to the limit for acceptable life before specifying a higher and more costly alloy.

Furnace Atmosphere Attack

Metals operating above 1200 F are subject to attack by furnace gases containing vanadium, sulfur and other corrosive media. Certain oils containing vanadium are particularly destructive to metals such as support and alignment lugs and baffles which are not cooled by the water or steam tubes and therefore reach these high temperatures. Coatings of various types have been partially protective but have limited service life. Design so as to keep metal temperatures below 1200 F eliminates attack. Additives to fuels and furnace gases have also shown promise.[14]

Molten slag or deposit has also caused excessive attack even at metal temperatures below 1200 F. Ash particles in the furnace atmosphere from the combustion of coal may form corrosive deposits on boiler surfaces. Because of the high temperatures, reactions take place between various constituents of the deposit and gases passing nearby, particularly sulfur trioxide and sulfur dioxide. The resulting compounds may then react with metal surfaces to cause corrosion. Compounds such as alkali pyrosulfates and alkali metal trisulfates have been found in deposits taken from high temperature boiler tubes. These compounds are strongly oxidizing and are molten at metal surface temperatures above 1000 F and therefore cause metal wastage. Other compounds sometimes found in deposits that may react with the metals are acid sulfates and sulfide compounds.

Deposit type corrosion can be eliminated by prevention of deposits, by the use of shields or by operating at tube metal temperatures below or above the critical temperature range (about 1000 to 1300 F) at which accelerated corrosion occurs. These factors are related to unit design,

---

[13] Adapted from "Oxidation of Superheater Metals by High Temperature Steam" by J. Hoke and F. Eberle, ASME Paper 57–A–175 and "Creep Strength, Stability of Microstructure and Oxidation Resistance of Cr–Mo and 18 Cr–8 Ni Steels" by R. F. Miller, W. G. Benz and M. J. Day, American Society for Metals, 1943 Reprint.

[14] The interested reader is referred to the critical evaluation of past literature and the need for future research contained in *A Review of Available Information on Corrosion and Deposits in Coal and Oil Fired Boilers and Gas Turbines* prepared by members of the staff of Battelle Memorial Institute for the ASME Research Committee on Corrosion and Deposits from Combustion Gases, published by ASME, 1959, 234 pages.

fuel composition and operation procedures.[15]

In operation at low temperatures, below the dew point of corrosive constituents such as sulfuric acid in the gas, chemical attack may occur. A small change in material analysis may impart greatly improved resistance to attack or a small change in temperature may greatly alter attack.

Low Temperature Service Considerations

This section will discuss some considerations of service for portions of boilers and reactor vessels which operate at low or moderate temperatures. This temperature range begins at the lowest the equipment may experience during fabrication, erection or service. The upper limit is that above which creep-rupture behavior and oxidation resistance are significant. The intervening range is one in which design is based on an elastic material whose properties are essentially independent of service hours.

Impact Properties

Metals of a body-centered cubic crystal such as alpha iron (ferritic material) shown in Fig. 9–16 are subject to a change in the mode of failure from ductile (shear) to brittle (cleavage) as the temperature is lowered. The temperature at which this occurs is called the *transition temperature*. Material below its transition temperature may crack extensively if subjected to an impact load, or even if a low nominal stress is increased at some point by a stress-concentrating notch. Material above its transition temperature can deform plastically under impact or at points of stress concentration without having a crack propagate to give a catastrophic brittle fracture.

The transition temperature is dependent upon the particular metal composition and melting practice as well as the subsequent working and heat treatment. For many types of carbon or low alloy steels the transition temperature may be as high as room temperature or above. The possibility of brittle fracture must be considered in the fabrication of materials (bending and forming in various manners), in testing the finished structure, and in any service involving operation below the transition temperature. Care in design, fabrication and inspection is called for to eliminate all possible stress-concentrating notches such as sharp corners, sharp nicks or notches from mishandling, weld-metal and base-metal defects, and metallurgical notches of abrupt differences of hardness.

This characteristic of materials is receiving much study. The Charpy V-notch impact test is a laboratory test which has been used with some success to relate the basic susceptibility to brittle fracture to the results on larger test specimens which simulate structures in service. Other types of impact and bend tests are being investigated. One product of such studies has been the knowledge of how comparatively minor changes in melting practice and composition can produce substantial gain in resistance to brittle fractures. Such changes have already been made in some steels.

[15] See "Corrosion of Superheaters and Reheaters of Pulverized Coal Fired Boilers" by Wharton Nelson and Carl Cain, Jr., *Trans. ASME, Journal of Engineering for Power*. Part I appeared in Vol. 82, Series A, 1960, pp. 194-204 and Part II, in Vol. 83, Series A, 1961, pp. 468-474. A related reference is "External Corrosion of Superheaters in Boilers Firing High Alkali Coals" by P. Sedor, E. K. Diehl and D. H. Barnhart, *Trans. ASME*, Vol. 82, Series A, 1960, pp. 181-193.

Fig. 9–31 shows the impact strength versus temperature for a material having a high transition temperature. Also shown are the broken surfaces of the impact specimens in which the ductility variation with temperature of testing is obvious. The material tested at the lower temperature has broken in a cleavage fracture

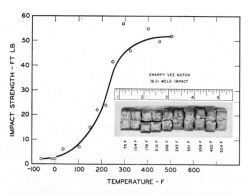

Fig. 9–31. Relationship of impact strength to temperature for a material having a high transition temperature. (16 Cr weld impact)

along crystallographic planes and shows a shiny-grain appearance which at one time led to the mistaken impression the material had "crystallized." Actually, what appears in the figure is the progression from a brittle-cleavage fracture to a ductile-shear fracture as the temperature of testing is increased. This material is fabricated into corrosion-resisting pressure vessels and used successfully provided due consideration is given to this property. The importance of degree of stress-concentrating mechanical notch in this type material is shown in Fig. 9–32.

The examples given above are for chromium-iron materials having a particularly high-transition temperature. Steels used in boilers and nuclear reactor vessels have transition temperatures considerably below that shown in the example. Metals to

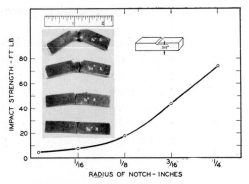

Fig. 9–32. Effect of radius of notch (shown by stress concentration) on impact values of 18 per cent chromium weld metal.

be stressed in operation at low temperatures are selected based upon these considerations and purchased to specified impact requirements.

Heat-treatable steels in the quenched and tempered condition may have considerably improved transition-temperature properties. High nickel steels exhibit low-transition temperatures. Austenitic stainless steels and metals such as copper and aluminum, in general, do not change abruptly in toughness as a function of temperature and may be used to liquid air temperatures.

Irradiation Effects

Materials near the core of a nuclear reactor are subject to several forms of radiation, including gamma radiation and particles such as alpha particles (helium nuclei), beta particles (electrons), neutrons, protons and fission fragments. This radiation supplies energy which may assist in the breaking of bonds and rearrangement of the atoms in new structures. The collision of the nuclear particle with atoms of the base material can displace a considerable number of these from their normal or equilibrium position in the lattice. Some of the atoms so displaced will remain in an interstitial position, and a sufficient number of such metallurgical dislocations can cause significant changes in the mechanical properties of the material. Absorption of the high energy of fission fragments or fast neutrons within a very small volume sets up small regions which for very short periods of time reach high temperature. Local distortion of the lattice will occur under this high temperature, and the rapid cooling by the mass of surrounding material will prevent some of the atoms from returning to equilibrium positions.

Irradiation of steels such as used in nuclear reactor vessels distorts the lattice structure in the ways just described. In general, this decreases ease of slip and results in increasing the material tensile strength, yield strength and hardness, and decreasing the ductility and toughness. It may markedly increase the transition temperature of low-alloy steels. As a consequence, materials subject to this bombardment are selected and heat treated so as to have a low transition temperature before placing in service so that the damage may be kept below excessive amounts. The damage which occurs, of course, is dependent upon intensity of irradiation, temperature of the materials, time of irradiation and several other factors. Damage may be removed by subsequent heat treatment in much the same manner that cold-working effects may be removed by the same kind of heat treatment. Annealing temperatures required are generally lower than those required for annealing of cold-worked materials and, in some cases, operation temperatures are sufficiently high to repair the damage as fast as it occurs.

Fatigue

The stress a material can withstand under repeated application and removal of load is less than that it can withstand under static conditions. The *yield strength,* which is a measure of static stress a material can stand without appreciable permanent deformation, can be used as a guide in design only for material subjected to static loading. Dynamic, cyclic loading causes slip and cold working in minute areas localized at grain boundaries and at stress-concentrating notches of various types. As sufficient work hardening develops, microscopic cracking develops and grows until complete fracture results. *Fatigue strength* is the magnitude of a cyclic stress which a material can withstand for a specified number of cycles before failure. At sufficiently low stress levels, however, an almost infinite number of cycles can be withstood by many materials. An example of the *endurance limit* for one material is shown in Fig. 9–33.

Fig. 9–33. Endurance limit for a hot-worked bar stock at low stress levels. (From *Interpretation of Tests and Correlation with Service* by M. F. Garwood, H. H. Zurburg and M. A. Erickson, American Society for Metals, 1951.)

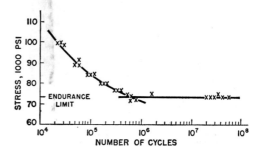

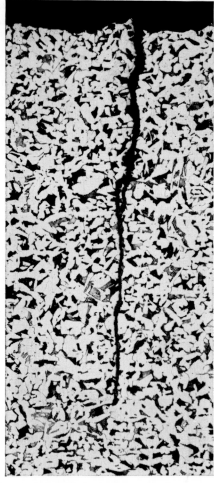

Fig. 9–34. Photomacrograph and photomicrograph of a carbon steel pressure vessel, 10 ft OD, 45 ft long and $1\frac{1}{2}$ in. thick, which failed through the shell thickness due to cyclic thermal stress in which electric heating elements close to the inside diameter surface caused cyclic heating and cooling of a localized area which, over a period of several years of cycling, resulted in cracking penetrating the wall thickness. Bottom, 100 magnification. Nital etch.

The endurance limit is markedly decreased by stress-concentrating notches, as previously described in connection with impact properties, and by corrosion, which either causes formation of such notches or accentuates their effect.

Fatigue may be caused by thermal gradients, and generally service failures may result due to a combination of these factors.

Fig. 9–34 shows a photomacrograph and photomicrograph of a carbon-steel pressure vessel, ten feet outside diameter by forty-five feet long by one and a half inches shell thickness, which failed through the shell thickness due to cyclic thermal stress. Electric-heating elements close to the inside surface of the shell caused cyclic heating and cooling of a localized area which, over a period of several years of cycling, resulted in cracking penetrating the wall thickness.

Corrosion[16]

Corrosion is deterioration and loss of material due to chemical attack. It generally occurs through the interaction of processes of solution and oxidation.

Small molecules and ions dissolve most readily. Solution occurs more readily

[16] This section is based upon Chapter 12, section on Corrosion, from *Elements of Materials Science* by Lawrence H. Van Vlack, Addison-Wesley Publishing Co., Reading, Mass., 1964.

when the solvent and solute are structurally similar. For instance, metals are more soluble in liquid zinc than in liquid lead. The rate of solution increases with temperature.

Oxidation of iron (rusting) will not occur if the iron is submerged in oxygen-free water or is kept in moisture-free oxygen. Air with only a very small amount of moisture, however, will be corrosive to iron. *Oxidation* is the removal of electrons from an atom. The electrons are more readily removed in some environments than in others. *Oxidation potential,* therefore, varies depending upon environment and also varies from one metal to another.

As iron goes into solution as ions, excessive electrons are produced. This builds up an *electrode potential* which also varies depending upon environment and the metal. In addition, in any one metal, the atoms along a grain boundary, being less stable than those in the body of the crystal, ionize more readily. Since different electrode potentials can exist between dissimilar materials in contact or between different areas in one material, these can set up an electrical cell which will cause reactions to occur spontaneously. This is called *galvanic corrosion.* The electrode supplying the electrons to the circuit is called the anode and the electrode receiving the electrons from the circuit is called the cathode. The corrosion occurs at the anode.

A *composition cell* may be established between two dissimilar materials, such as steel in contact with copper or steel in contact with zinc. In the case of steel in contact with copper, the steel would be the anode. In the case of steel in contact with zinc, the zinc would be the anode. In this case, the zinc would give galvanic protection to the iron. This type protection is widely used. These relationships for

many metals are evident in Table 9–3. Since there is no size limit for galvanic cells, a two-phase alloy might be subject to galvanic corrosion. Generally, however, the potential difference between the two phases is small.

A *stress cell* may be established because of residual stresses or because of cold

Table 9–3   Electromotive Series of Common Alloys*

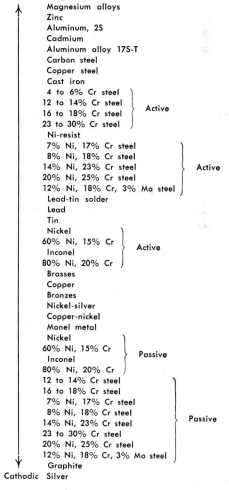

* From C. A. Zapffe, **Stainless Steels,** American Society for Metals, Metals Park, Ohio, 1949.

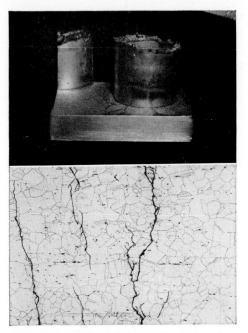

Fig. 9–35. Very rapid failure of Type 316 austenitic steel through stress corrosion on exposure to water containing excessive halogen and oxygen content.

Fig. 9–36. Oxygen pitting of a carbon steel boiler tube.

working and even between grain boundaries and the body of the crystal. The presence of stress in an engineering structure exposed to certain corrosive environments can result in very rapid failure through stress corrosion as shown in Fig. 9–35.

A *concentration cell* may be established because of differences of concentration in the corroding environment. The concentration cell accentuates corrosion, but it accentuates it where the concentration of electrolyte is lower. Similarly, the oxidation cell accentuates corrosion but it accentuates it where the oxygen concentration is lower. These conditions are illustrated in Fig. 9–36. Accumulation of corrosion products may further accelerate these conditions and result in localized

pitting. Fig. 9–36 shows what is often called oxygen pitting resulting from inadequate water treatment procedure in a boiler circuit in which excessive oxygen content was allowed to build up in the water.

Other examples are shown in Figs. 9–35 through 9–38. Fig. 9–37 shows a type of corrosion which occurs only in high pressure boilers in which a heavy, dense, magnetic iron oxide scale is formed in localized areas under which the carbon steel metal is decarburized and oxidized intergranularly. This process gradually penetrates the thickness of the metal and the portions affected have little or no ductility or strength. This is called *hydrogen embrittlement* and can be eliminated by proper water treatment.

Fig. 9–38 shows a type of corrosion,

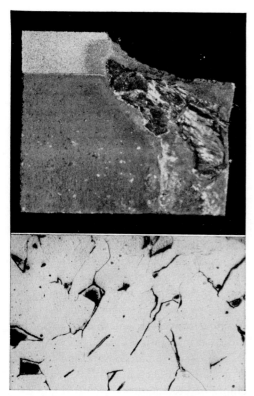

Fig. 9–37. Hydrogen embrittlement, a type of corrosion occurring in high pressure boilers. It is characterized by a heavy and dense magnetic iron oxide scale in localized areas in which the carbon steel metal is decarburized and oxidized intergranularly.

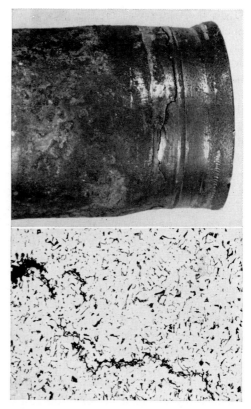

Fig. 9–38. Caustic embrittlement, a type of corrosion occurring at low or high pressures and associated with crevices in which caustic can concentrate. It is generally an intergranular attack, although it can also proceed transgranularly.

caustic embrittlement,[17] which occurs at low pressures or high pressures associated with crevices in which caustic can concentrate. It is generally an intergranular attack, although it can also proceed transgranularly. In the days when boilers were riveted and crevices were the rule, it was much more commonly found than in the welded construction of today. It is also eliminated by proper water treatment.

Fig. 9–35 shows a typical type of stress corrosion of austenitic stainless steel, in this case Type 316. In this type of corrosion the attack is generally transgranular. It occurs in the presence of halides such as chloride ions or fluoride ions in water which must also contain a small amount of oxygen. If water treatment is sufficiently controlled at all times to keep the halides and oxygen low, no such cracking will occur. If, however, oxygen content is allowed to build up and crevices are present in which halides can concentrate to harmful amounts, cracking may occur very quickly. In this particular case, in

[17] See "Symposium on Embrittlement", *Trans.* ASME, Vol. 64, 1942, pp. 397–444, for a more complete explanation.

which the water was on the outside diameter of the tubing, operation for five days within water having 18 ppm chloride content resulted in *catastrophic cracking.* Since this type attack also occurs only in the presence of tensile stress above a certain threshold value, certain precautions should be taken. The materials which are subject to this type corrosion are stress relieved by heat treatment, insofar as practical. Crevices on the water side are minimized by careful controlling of rolling of tubes into tube sheets to close the crevice and to maintain the cold-worked metal within the tube-sheet thickness such that the water does not contact it. Since this is not always feasible, the success of this type design is reliant primarily upon precise control of water impurities.

Single-phase alloys are generally more corrosion resistant than two-phase alloys. Each metal is corrosion resistant to limited environments. Each metal may be considerably changed in corrosion resistance by heat treatment or cold working or small changes in analysis.

Fabrication

With knowledge of the above type in mind, the fabricator must purchase the raw materials to proper requirements of strength, ductility, toughness and soundness and then shape them by machining, flame cutting, and hot and cold working. The materials must then be heat treated properly and separate portions joined together, generally by means of welding, or in some cases mechanically. The parts must be tested at various stages of fabrication both with test pieces destructively examined and the actual production parts non-destructively examined by such means as radiography, magnetic particle or dye penetrant, ultrasonic, eddy current, mass spectrometer and hydrostatic tests. Welds must be as sound and have mechanical properties equal to or exceeding the base material.

A study of the various joining methods is a large subject in itself. Special machines and techniques developed and used in the fabrication of boiler and reactor components are described in Chapter 11, Manufacture and Machine Design.

10

Stress Analysis and Structural Design[1]

As is emphasized throughout this book, safety is an important consideration in the design and operation of boilers and nuclear reactors. If an engineer had complete knowledge of materials and the exact values of forces to which they may be subjected, then design could proceed with absolute assurance of safety. In practice, of course, this is not true. Laboratory test conditions differ from field operating environment; loads may not be applied as originally assumed or may turn out to be larger or of a character different from that predicted; such factors as wear, erosion and corrosion may affect composition and cross section of materials subject to stress. Yet all of these uncertainties must be taken into consideration.

The principal topics covered in this chapter include stresses and nuclear reactor vessel design, photoelasticity, strength of furnace walls and structural design of boilers. The subject matter encompasses mathematical analysis, experimental techniques, application of safety code rules,

many design suggestions and a few typical calculations. The chapter is based upon techniques found useful in the commercial design of boilers and nuclear reactor pressure vessels.

The designer frequently makes use of the concept of *factor of safety* to account for the uncertainties in design. Where there are many, the value of the factor of safety is high, but it approaches unity in cases where there is extensive knowledge of material properties and few uncertainties in loading. In all cases the designer attempts to reduce the probability of failure to a suitable level which is dependent upon knowledge of and experience with specific applications.

The present knowledge of properties of materials, experimental techniques and analytical methods has evolved over several centuries of effort. This is well documented in several outstanding histories of the theory of elasticity, strength of materials, structural design and testing machines.[2] It is not so well known, however,

---

[1] Material for this chapter was obtained from several individuals whose contributions are indicated in appropriate places.

[2] See *A History of the Theory of Elasticity and of the Strength of Materials* by Isaac Todhunter and Karl Pearson, reprinted by Dover Publications, New York, 1960; *A Historical Appraisal of Mechanics* by Harvey F. Girvin, Scranton, Penna., 1948; *History of Strength of Materials* by Stephen P. Timoshenko, New York, 1953; "Materials Testing Machines" by C. H. Gibbons, a series of four historical articles published in *Baldwin Locomotives:* April and October, 1934, and January and April, 1935; and a more recent "philosophical history" of mechanical testing and experimental mechanics, *Tatnall on Testing* by F. G. Tatnall, American Society for Metals, 1966, 234 pages.

that some of these experimental and theoretical developments were directly influenced by the needs and demands of boiler designers, manufacturers and operators of stationary and marine units.

For example, it was an extensive investigation into the cause of boiler explosions that prompted the Franklin Institute of Philadelphia to install the first materials testing machine in the United States in 1832 and continue its use until 1837 to determine strength properties of boiler materials.[3] Over the years the mathematical theory of elasticity has attracted many brilliant scientific and engineering minds, one of the best known of which was Gabriel Lamé. In 1850 he read a paper before the French Academy in which he showed how this theory could be used to establish rules for the determination of the required thickness and curvature of the shell of a fire tube boiler.[4]

A few years later William Fairbairn began extensive experimental work on the strength of internal tubes of fire tube boilers. He reported to the British Royal Society in 1858 on the dangerous weakness of these tubes in comparison to the strength of the outer shell of the boiler and made recommendations to equalize the strength of tubes and shell.[5]

W. J. M. Rankine, better known to mechanical engineers for his formulation of the Second Law of thermodynamics and for the power plant cycle that bears his name, was among the first to bring the theory of elasticity to the attention of engineering students in an understandable scientific form. His *Manual of Applied Mechanics* was published in London in 1858 and presented the first systematic treatment in English of the concepts of stress and strain. The work incorporates an extensive treatment of the mathematical theory of elasticity and was praised by a contemporary reviewer as the most valuable and complete contribution to the science of engineering published to that time. In developing his ideas on factors of safety it is interesting to note that Rankine recommends a value of eight for designing shells of fire tube boilers.[6]

Figure 10–1. Lifting reactor pressure vessel head.

[3] See *History of the ASME Boiler Code* by Athur M. Greene, Jr., published by The American Society of Mechanical Engineers, 1955, pp. 2–4.
[4] The paper was entitled "Note sur les Épaisseurs et les Courbures des Appareils à Vapeur" and appeared in *Comptes Rendus*, Vol. 30, 1850, pp. 157–161.
[5] See his classical paper entitled "Resistance of Tubes to Collapse," *Philosophical Transactions* of the Royal Society, Vol. 148, Part II, 1858, pp. 389–413.
[6] Introductory and historical material contributed by Glenn R. Fryling.

It seems appropriate to conclude the introductory portion of this chapter with a simple example of one application of stress analysis in connection with the manufacture of boilers and reactors. Cranes are frequently used in handling heavy components and pose many interesting design problems. Figure 10–1 shows the head of a nuclear reactor pressure vessel being lifted by a single hook. In Figure 10–2 which provides details of the crane hook, the irregular shape is shown in Section AA'. This section, as shown in Figure 10–3, is divided into 16 increments so that Simpson's rule for numerical integration may be applied. With a load of 150,000 lb assumed to pass through the center of curvature of the hook, the maximum tensile stress is calculated to be 23,200 lb, which is well within the allowable stress for materials typically used for crane hooks.[7]

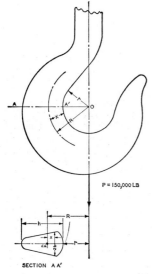

Figure 10–2. Crane hook with irregular section.

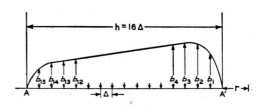

Figure 10–3. Division of half section of crane hook.

Stresses and Nuclear Reactor Vessel Design[8]

The structural reliability required of reactor vessels exceeds that required of conventional pressure vessels. Consequently, the engineering effort expended in design and design evaluation becomes substantially greater than is normally applied to the design of conventional vessels. Similarly, the criteria for limitation of stresses, qual-

---

[7] The procedure for this calculation may be found in "Calculations of Stress in Crane Hooks" by A. M. Wahl, *Trans.* ASME, *Journal of Applied Mechanics*, vol. 68, 1946, pp. A239–A242.
[8] Material for this major section contributed by L. W. Smith.

ity of design details and the degree of control of material and fabrication quality must be superior to practices normally used in the pressure vessel industry. Among other things, this means that design details specified on drawings must be adhered to in fabrication in order that the precautions taken by the designer are not lost by unwarranted changes during manufacture. Vessel integrity may be far more important than any such savings.

Some of the problems associated with reactor pressure vessel design are readily recognized because of their close association with the fission process. Most likely to be neglected are the old problems about which engineers have become complacent because these problems do not require comprehensive treatment in the design of conventional apparatus. Among the most important of these are thermal stresses.

Since a more detailed analysis is required for calculating stresses in nuclear vessels, additional consideration is given to the evaluation of a maximum allowable stress in these components. Calculated stresses are combined according to the maximum shear theory of failure. Consideration is given as to whether the type of stress can cause gross deformation or whether it is a secondary stress or a highly localized stress. The purpose of this section is to acquaint the reader with some of the design procedures required in solving problems in the design of nuclear vessels, and it highlights some of the important considerations the designer must factor into his design criteria. Details for performing the necessary analyses are contained in Section III of the ASME Boiler and Pressure Vessel Code.[9]

Factors in Reactor Vessel Design

The following is a summary of the most important new factors which must be considered in establishing design practices for nuclear reactor vessels:

1. Reliability has a higher value in the first unit of a prototype of a basically new type power plant because the operation of this unit provides a check on the quality of design and fabrication.

2. The difficulty of decontamination and the repair or replacement of a reactor pressure vessel might cause plant shutdown for a longer time than would a similar repair or replacement in a conventional power system.

3. The potential hazard to operating personnel, the public and property are greater than in a conventional power plant.

4. Radiation damage to structural material may impair desirable mechanical properties.

5. Dissociation of coolants may aggravate corrosion and hydrogen embrittlement problems.

6. Unusually severe thermal transients can occur, particularly in reactor systems employing a large temperature rise of coolant through the reactor.

7. Thermal stresses during normal startup and shutdown often require particular attention because the vessel configurations

---

[9] See the latest edition of *Rules for Construction of Nuclear Vessels*, ASME Boiler and Pressure Vessel Code, Section III. The first edition was published by ASME in 1963, 134 pages, plus a separate explanatory section entitled "Criteria of Section III of the ASME Boiler and Pressure Vessel Code for Nuclear Vessels," 22 pages. Additional information may be found in a book by John F. Harvey, *Pressure Vessel Design, Nuclear and Chemical Application,* Van Nostrand, 1963, 274 pages,

employed often have regions of slow thermal response.

8. Internal heat generation in the pressure vessel wall is a new problem. Heat generation may produce high thermal stresses which will be particularly significant in systems subject to frequent load cycling. This problem is of most concern in the heavy walls of vessels for gas or water-cooled reactors.

In view of these items, it is essential to have a comprehensive basis for control of stresses. There must be adequate consideration of corrosion of materials, and an extremely high quality of fabrication must be employed.

$$T = \frac{PR}{2S}$$

on an elastic shell basis.

The correct thickness for thin walled shells is given in the previous equation, but when the thickness of the shell is greater than about $0.36\,R$, the elastic theory requires that the thickness be calculated on a thick wall basis. The formula for thickness is:

$$T = R\left[3\sqrt{\frac{2(S + P)}{2S - P}} - 1\right]$$

Mechanical Stresses in Reactor Pressure Vessels

In a nuclear reactor container, thermal stresses and cyclic stresses due to pressure and temperature variation may be of primary significance, and, as a consequence, the minimum thickness for mechanical strength is frequently the optimum thickness for the overall stress condition.

Industrial safety codes, such as the ASME Boiler and Pressure Vessel Code, provide the designer with acceptable formulas for sizing various components of a pressure vessel. However, in this section typical formulas for specific shells of revolution are presented for the convenience of the reader by making use of equations from the basic theory of elasticity.

Cylindrical Shell

The minimum thickness for a thin wall cylindrical shell is

$$T = \frac{PR}{S}$$

if the thickness is calculated by the theory of elasticity.

For thick wall cylinders, the elastic theory requires that the shell wall thickness be determined from:

$$T = R\left(\sqrt{\frac{S + P}{S - P}} - 1\right)$$

Spherical Shell

The minimum thickness, T, of a spherical shell of inside radius, R, an internal pressure, P, and an allowable membrane stress, S, is

Hemispherical Head

The formulas for a hemispherical head are identical to those for a spherical shell. Required thicknesses for these shells can be determined by industrial code rules or by the theory of elasticity.[10] If a pressure vessel is made up of a cylindrical shell capped with a hemispherical head, the component sizes can be determined by industrial codes, or by the theory of elasticity using the simple membrane formulas.

Ellipsoidal Head

The standard ellipsoidal head, as recognized by the ASME Boiler and Pressure Vessel Code, has a major axis equal to twice the minor axis. By elastic theory this head requires a thickness of:

$$T = \frac{PR}{S}$$

which is identical with the thickness of a matching cylindrical shell. The R in the above equation is the length of the major axis, or the diameter of the mating cylinder.

Torispherical Head

A torispherical head is a shell which combines part of a torus with a spherical cap. In the ASME Boiler and Pressure Vessel Code the knuckle, or torus, radius is required to be 0.06 times the radius of the crown, or spherical cap, and the crown radius may not exceed the diameter of the pressure vessel. There are no directly applicable formulas based on elastic theory but any given head shape can readily be calculated from basic equations. The ASME Boiler and Pressure Vessel Code specifies the thickness to be:

$$T = \frac{5PL}{4.8SE}$$

where L is equal to the crown radius, and E is the weld efficiency for the welded construction. Another formula suggested by the ASME Code requires that the thickness of the shell be equal to:

$$T = \frac{0.855PL}{SE - 0.1P}$$

Formulas for variations from standard code ellipsoidal and torispherical heads are also given in an appendix of Section VIII of the ASME Code.[11]

Flat Head

A flat head can be considered as a circular plate which is uniformly loaded by pressure. The amount of end fixity depends on the method of mounting and the stiffness of the cylindrical shell to which the flat head is attached. If the plate is assumed to be simply supported, then no moments are transferred to the shell, and the maximum plate stress occurs at the center of the plate. The stress is:

$$S_{max} = \frac{3(3 + \nu)PR^2}{8t^2}$$

The degree of end fixity is determined by applied edge moments,

$$M_0 = C_1 PR^2$$

and superposed stresses,

$$S_s = \frac{6MO}{t^2}$$

By substituting allowable stresses in

---

[10] A basic reference is *Theory of Plates and Shells* by S. Timoshenko and S. Woinowsky-Krieger, Second Edition, McGraw-Hill, 1959, 580 pages.

[11] The latest edition of the ASME Boiler and Pressure Vessel Code should be consulted for modification of these formulas and those in the following section.

Table 10–1 Values of C_2

	ASME Code	Elastic Theory
Simply Supported	0.162	0.094
Fixed Ended	0.500	0.310

these equations, the required thickness of the plate can be expressed as:

$$T = 2R \sqrt{\frac{C_2 P}{S}}$$

The thickness of a flat head as required by the ASME Boiler and Pressure Vessel Code is given by the preceding equation. The constant C in the Equation must be found from appropriate tables in the ASME Code, and these tables usually specify the end fixity of the flat plate. In the industrial code, the constant is usually greater than that required by elastic theory, thereby adding another factor of safety to the code design. Table 10–1 shows typical values of C_2 from the ASME Boiler and Pressure Vessel Code as compared to the value of C_2 required from elastic theory.

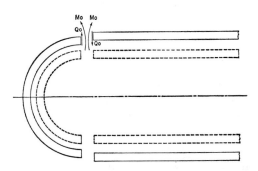

Figure 10–4. Discontinuity forces at a head-cylinder junction under internal pressure.

Discontinuity Stresses

When a pressure vessel is subjected to internal pressure, redundant forces and moments are induced in areas of structural discontinuity. An area of discontinuity would be, for example, the intersection of a cylindrical shell and a hemispherical head. This can best be visualized, Fig. 10–4, by assuming that the shell and head act as separate units with internal pressure applied to the individual, simply supported parts. Because the deflections of

the components differ, shear forces and moments must be applied at the edges to rejoin the components for a compatible structure. The resulting stresses, which are usually bending stresses, induced by these shear forces and moments, are called discontinuity stresses. The bending stresses reach a maximum at, or near, the discontinuity, but they attenuate with distance from the joint.[12] A commonly accepted approach to the derivation of these discontinuity stresses is the theory of beams on an elastic foundation.[13]

If a pressure vessel with a hemispherical head is designed for minimum thickness of the mating components, then the maximum stress in the pressure vessel will be 27 per cent higher than the circumferential stress in the cylindrical shell

---

[12] An extensive treatment of the discontinuity stresses in pressure vessels is found in a paper by G. W. Watts and W. R. Burrows, "Basic Elastic Theory of Vessel Heads Under Internal Pressure," *Trans.* ASME, *Journal of Applied Mechanics,* Vol. 71, 1949, pp. 55–73.

[13] See Timoshenko, op. cit., *Theory of Plates and Shells,* and M. Hetenyi, *Beams on Elastic Foundation,* University of Michigan Press, 1946.

away from all discontinuities. For a vessel of uniform thickness, however, the maximum stress is only 3 per cent higher than in the same size cylindrical shell.

A pressure vessel with a standard ellipsoidal head of the same thickness as a mating cylindrical shell exhibits a maximum stress 13 per cent higher than the circumferential membrane stress in the cylinder.[14] Unfortunately, however, membrane stresses and discontinuity stresses are very sensitive to changes in curvature. In a reference reporting research work for the Pressure Vessel Research Committee of the American Welding Society, the maximum stress in the pressure vessel with an approximately ellipsoidal head was calculated to be 95 per cent higher than the hoop stress in a cylindrical shell. The experimental verification indicated that the stress was actually increased about 41 per cent.

Reinforced Openings

For very small unreinforced circular holes, the theory of elasticity shows that a stress concentration factor of three will exist around the hole under an uniaxial tension. The stress concentration is reduced to two for the state of biaxial tension. In a cylindrical shell under pressure, the state of stress is such that the circumferential stress is twice the longitudinal stress. Under this condition the stress concentration at an unreinforced penetration would reach a peak of 2.5. The stress concentration effect would be localized at the edge of the hole and could cause a small amount of plastic deformation with an inherent redistribution of stresses.

The ASME Boiler and Pressure Vessel Code requires that for holes over a certain diameter, reinforcement to the opening should be added by the nozzle attachment, increased shell thickness, or the pad for a cover plate if the opening is for future servicing operations.

The rules of the ASME Code require that the area removed for the penetration in a given cross section be replaced in the form of reinforcing within specified boundaries. At best this is a crude method; however, experience has shown that the stresses do not cause failure at nozzles providing the level of stress in the shell is at a reasonable limit.[15] The best type of reinforcement is one in which the reinforcement is equally distributed on each side of the shell, that is, equal amounts of reinforcement extend inside and outside the shell.[16] This method of reinforcement is not always practical because the structure within the reactor vessel must often be removable for future servicing. This restriction means that all of the reinforcement must be on the outside of the shell, and with this method, the reduction of stress concentration for a code designed reinforcement is not as effective as would be expected if "proper reinforcement" were applied. If the stress concentration of 2.5 exists in an unreinforced hole, then proper reinforcement should reduce the stress concentration to unity.

[14] These results are discussed by G. K. Cooper and L. W. Smith, Final Report of PVRC Project, Purdue University, August 1952. This report can be obtained from Pressure Vessel Research Council, United Engineering Center, New York 17, N.Y.

[15] See J. Dubuc and G. Welter, "Investigation of Static and Fatigue Resistance of Model Pressure Vessels," The Welding Journal, Vol. 35, July 1956, Research Supplement, pp. 329s–337s.

[16] See G. J. Schoessow and E. A. Brooks, "Analysis of Experimental Data Regarding Certain Design Features with Pressure Vessels," Trans. ASME, Vol. 72, 1950, pp. 567–577.

Experimental data shows that the peak stress exists on the inner surface of the vessel at the intersection of the shell and the nozzle penetration, and the stress concentration is not appreciably decreased by the added reinforcement on the outside surface. When the added reinforcement exceeds that required by the code, experiments show that the stress concentration factor is still greater than 2.0. It is apparent from the limited experimental work that it is almost impossible to reduce the stress concentration factor to a level of unity.

One way to decrease the stress at an opening is to thicken the shell, and, therefore, decrease the membrane stress upon which the concentration is applied. This is not a practical solution, however, because added thickness brings about other complications caused by thermal loadings in pressure vessels, and in particular, nuclear reactor vessels.

Experimental data has shown that a stress concentration greater than 2.0 in a pressure vessel at a nozzle intersection can be sustained for thousands of cycles of pressure loading even though the stress calculated on a membrane basis may exceed the yield point of the material. Tests performed for the Pressure Vessel Research Committee of the Welding Research Council have shown that even when model vessels were pressurized to values which created membrane stress in the unpenetrated shell equal to or above the yield point of the material, the vessels were able to withstand thousands of pressure cycles of loading before failure occurred at the nozzle.[17] A significant item in the test reported by Professor Welter is that notches and other cracks in the vessel were not points of failure, even for the extremely high ranges of cyclic loadings. In vessels with notches, similar to that of a charpy V-notch specimen, weld pits, and other marks scribed into the vessel, failure of the models occurred either at a nozzle intersection or at a head-to-shell discontinuity junction. This shows that the additional bending stresses caused by the discontinuity plays an important role in the failure of the material. Here is an example where attention to details of discontinuities is an important factor in the design of pressure vessels.

Section III of the ASME Boiler and Pressure Vessel Code provides, in addition to the rule for stress analysis, certain welding design configurations as a guide to the designer. Other details of fabrication are outlined in the Code which the reader should consult for a more complete study of acceptable designs.

General Problem of a Head Design

A typical head design for a pressurized water reactor might consist of a flange ring, a torus section and a flat disc, as shown in Fig. 10–5. In order to calculate areas of critical stresses in this structure,

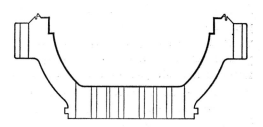

Figure 10–5. Reactor vessel head penetrations.

the analyst must divide the section into three basic elements, Fig. 10–6, a flange ring, a torus section, and a flat disc, each

---

[17] These tests are reported by Dubuc and Welter, op. cit.

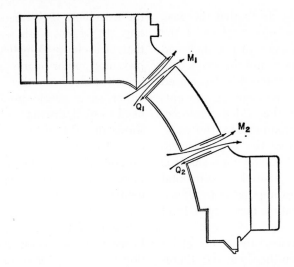

Figure 10–6.   Redundant forces and moments for a typical reactor vessel head.

with the proper edge forces and moments required for equilibrium. The influence coefficients for all these structures can be determined from appropriate references.[18]

The influence coefficients for a perforated plate, if the flat disc is assumed to contain penetrations for the control rod elements and instrument tubes, can be determined from papers by G. Horvay.[19] The results of Horvay's analysis have been favorably verified in Great Britain and reported in a paper by Duncan.[20] In this work, Duncan subjected tube sheets to pressure loadings and measured the deflections and stresses in the plates, and

from these tests he was able to verify, quite closely, the work of Horvay.

The analyst must solve the required system of unknown forces and moments in order to calculate the stresses in the structure. Photoelastic tests have been performed to substantiate structures designed in this manner.[21]

Thermal Stresses in Reactor Pressure Vessels

One important difference between vessels for reactor application and other industrial pressure vessels is the radial tem-

[18] See R. J. Roark, *Formulas for Stress and Strain*, Fourth Edition, McGraw-Hill, 1965, and Timoshenko, op. cit., *Theory of Plates and Shells.*
[19] See "Bending of Honeycombs and of Perforated Plates," *Trans.* ASME, *Journal of Applied Mechanics*, Vol. 74, 1952, pp. 122–123 and discussion on pp. 405–407; "The Plain Stress Problem of Perforated Plates," ibid., pp. 355–360; "Thermal Stresses in Perforated Plates," *Proceedings* of the First U.S. National Congress of Applied Mechanics, published by ASME, 1951, pp. 247–257.
[20] See J. P. Duncan, "The Structural Efficiency of Tube Plates for Heat Exchangers," *Proceedings* of the Institution of Mechanical Engineers, Vol. 169, 1955, pp. 789–810.
[21] For further information, see the following section of this chapter dealing with photoelasticity.

perature gradient generated in the shell wall of a nuclear reactor vessel by gamma ray attenuation of the steel. Usually, the wall is insulated on the external surface, and the inner surface is exposed to the primary coolant. The gamma ray attenuation in the steel wall causes heat generation in accordance with the general form,

$$I_x = I_0 e^{-ux}$$

where I_x is the heat generation per unit volume surface of the vessel, u is the material attenuation factor, and x is a lineal coordinate measured outward from the inner surface of the vessel.

If the external surface is insulated and heat is generated within the wall, the heat flow must be directed toward the inner surface of the vessel. Therefore, the inner surface will be at a lower temperature than the back, insulated surface. This particular temperature variation can be shown by solving the one dimensional steady-state heat transfer equation

$$\frac{d^2\theta}{dx^2} = \frac{-1}{k} I_0 e^{-ux}$$

where θ is the difference between the temperature at any point in the wall and the inner surface temperature. A typical temperature distribution through a shell wall for two arbitrary values of I_0 is shown in Fig. 10–7.

Temperature changes in a structure usually produce dimensional changes. Thermal stresses develop in a body if the expansion or contraction that would normally result from heating or cooling is prevented by external or internal constraint. In general thermal stresses can be divided into two categories:

1. The form of the body and the temperature distribution within the body are such that the stresses are produced due to

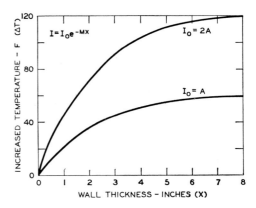

Figure 10–7. Typical temperature distributions in a shell wall for two levels of heat generation.

an incompatible set of thermal expansions in the absence of external restraint.

2. The stresses in the body are brought about by the constraining action of external forces.

A typical example of the self-constraint category is the spherical, or cylindrical, shell with a radial temperature distribution through the wall thickness. An example of thermal stresses caused by external constraint is a straight rod secured at each end by rigid supports and heated, or cooled, to a temperature different than that at installation.

If the design is such that thick structural material is required near the reactor core where the gamma ray heating is greatest, high temperature gradients and stresses are possible because of the thickness. The temperature gradients are also developed because changes in reactor power level over short periods of time will cause large and sudden coolant temperature variations. These power variations produce rapid changes of metal temperature, and significant stress may be induced because of the coolant temperature fluctuations and the corresponding changes of internal heat generation within the irradiated structure. In a reactor vessel, it is possible to have a maximum thermal stress existing locally for steady state reactor operating conditions, and to have maximum stresses at other points for transient reactor operation.

In general, thermal stresses are calculated by first determining the linear and rotational strains that the body would assume if free to move, and then determining the stresses required to maintain the body in its final equilibrium form. To calculate stresses, the redundant forces and moments must be determined by the appropriate equations of mechanics.

The numerical evaluation of stresses and strains caused by thermal loading and their significance to the life of the structure requires knowledge of the behavior of construction materials in design. The theory of elasticity, based primarily on Hooke's law (that stress is proportional to strain), provides a satisfactory approximation to the laws governing the behavior of most materials under applied load. The discussion of thermal stresses in this section will be based on elasticity conditions only. If, however, the material is ductile, and if the temperature and temperature differences are large enough to cause strains above the elastic limit, inelastic yielding and stress relaxation can account for a large portion of the stress induced deformation. Stresses caused by a sustained mechanical load satisfy the equilibrium criteria that the resulting forces and moments must be balanced by definite stresses in the material regardless of the strain that occurs. However, thermal stresses above the elastic limit must be calculated according to a reasonable realistic theory of plasticity, even though the mathematical difficulties encountered in such calculations make it necessary to use a greatly simplified and approximate idealization of plastic behavior.

Steady State Thermal Conditions

The temperature differences within a body produce strain differences and associated stress differences which keep the elementary parts of the body in compatibility. Temperatures which vary linearly with respect to a rectangular set of coordinants do not produce any stress in a body which is free to expand, because the associated expansions constitute a compatible system. Temperature differences do not give rise to boundary surface loads; therefore, in an unrestrained body, thermal stresses must be so distributed that the resulting forces and moments acting over any complete cross-section of the body are zero.

As a specific example of steady heat flow, the radial temperature distribution for a cylinder conducting heat from the inner (radius a) to the outer (radius b) surface is:

$$\theta = (T_a - T_b) = Q \frac{\ln b/a}{2\pi K}$$

where Q is the heat transmitted per unit length. The maximum circumferential and axial stresses are equal in such a temperature distribution and these maximum stresses occur at the inner surface of the cylinder. If $T_b = 0$, the elastic equations for the maximum stresses are:

$$S_i = \frac{E\alpha Q}{4\pi K(1 - \nu)} \left[1 - \frac{2}{1 - (a/b)^2} \ln b/a \right]$$

$$S_0 = \frac{E\alpha Q}{4\pi K(1 - \nu)} \left[1 - \frac{2}{(b/a)^2 - 1} \ln b/a \right]$$

Temperature due to internal heat generation, as stated previously, also causes thermal stresses in shells of revolution. Since the mathematical expressions for heat generation and for boundary conditions are numerous, specific solutions for thermal stress would be equally numerous. The solution to some specific boundary conditions have been prepared by Carter, including the following one for the case of a cylinder.[22]

Cylinder. The general equation for the temperature distribution in a cylinder with uniform internal heat generation is:

$$\frac{\partial^2 \theta}{\partial r^2} + \frac{1}{r}\frac{\partial \theta}{\partial r} + \frac{q}{k} = 0$$

The general equations for the thermal stresses (neglecting the end effects of any closure on the cylinder) are given by the following three expressions for the radial, circumferential and axial stresses:

$$S_r = \frac{E\alpha}{(1-\nu)r^2}$$
$$\times \left[\frac{r^2 - a^2}{b^2 - a^2}\int_a^b Tr\, dr - \int_a^r Tr\, dr\right]$$

$$S_t = \frac{E\alpha}{(1-\nu)r^2}\left[\frac{r^2 + a^2}{b^2 - a^2}\int_a^b Tr\, dr\right.$$
$$\left. + \int_a^r Tr\, dr - Tr^2\right]$$

$$S_z = -\frac{E\alpha}{1-\nu}\left[T - \frac{2}{b^2 - a^2}\int_a^b Tr\, dr\right]$$

where T is temperature and r is radius.

Obviously, there are a number of boundary value conditions if heat is removed from the inner or outer surface, and the temperature function for a particular condition must be determined to establish stresses from the general stress equation.

For the common case of heat generation in the wall, coolant on the inside face, and an insulated back surface, the general temperature difference equation is:

$$\theta = \frac{q}{2k}\left[b^2 \ln\left(\frac{r}{a}\right) - \frac{(r-a)}{2}\right]$$

and the radial, circumferential and axial stresses can be determined from the specific equations:

$$S_r = \frac{E\alpha q}{16K(1-\nu)r^2}\left[\frac{r^2 - a^2}{b^2 - a^2}\right.$$
$$\times \left(4b^4 \ln\frac{b}{a} - 3b^4 + 4a^2 b^2 - a^4\right) + 2b^2 r^2$$
$$\left. \times \left(1 - 2\ln\frac{r}{a}\right) - 2a^2(b^2 + r^2) + r^4 + a^4\right]$$

$$S_t = \frac{E\alpha q}{16K(1-\nu)r^2}\left[\frac{r^2 + a^2}{b^2 - a^2}\right.$$
$$\times \left(4b^4 \ln\frac{b}{a} - 3b^4 - 4a^2 b^2 - a^4\right) - 2b^2 r^2$$
$$\left. \times \left(1 + 2\ln\frac{r}{a}\right) + 2a^2(b^2 - r^2) + 3r^4 - a^4\right]$$

$$S_z = -\frac{E\alpha q}{16K(1-\nu)}$$
$$\times \left[8b^2 \ln\frac{r}{a} - 4r^2 + 4a^2 - \frac{2}{b^2 - a^2}\right.$$
$$\left. \times \left(4b^4 \ln\frac{b}{a} - 3b^4 + 4a^2 b^2 - a^4\right)\right]$$

Transient Thermal Conditions

The previous discussion has dealt with the determination of thermal stresses produced by steady state conditions. When fluids inside a container change temperature, the walls of the container are subjected to thermal stress. The magnitude of the thermal stress depends upon the rate of the temperature change, the total

---

[22] See J. C. Carter, "Temperature and Stress Distribution in Spheres, Rods, Tubes and Plates in which the Heat Source is within the Boundaries of the Solids," Argonne National Laboratory Report, ANL–4690, September 7, 1951, 13 pp.

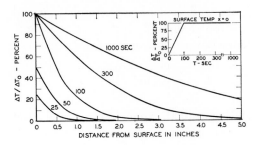

Figure 10–8. Temperature response of a semi-infinite slab of austenitic stainless steel to the indicated surface transient.

temperature excursion, the thickness of the material in the container wall and the film coefficient between the wall and the fluid. For an increase in temperature, a compressive stress will be induced on the inside surface and a tensile stress will be induced on the outside surface. For a decrease in temperature, the signs of the stresses will be reversed. The relative severity of a given temperature transient is judged by the magnitude of the stresses produced by the transient. Since the stress depends on both the rate of change and the total temperature excursion, the question arises as to which of several expected transients is the most serious.

A transient which looks "fast" to a thick wall may be "slow" for a thinner wall, and the only safe way to evaluate transients is to calculate the stresses they produce. The statement that a "fast" transient for a thick wall may be "slow" for a thin wall justifies the protective shielding often included in areas around discontinuities in a pressure vessel. In areas such as nozzles or other penetrations, thin, flexible non-structural material is used to protect the base metal from sudden temperature changes. "Fast" transients do not cause excessive stresses in the protective shielding,

if the shielding is not too thick. For the infrequent cases when the transient stresses are high, justification of the stress magnitude may be made on the basis that these stresses occur in non-structural members without loss of integrity to the main load carrying structure.

Fig. 10–8 shows the effect of a transient and the damping effect of the material. The curves indicate that the thermal transients are damped out with distance away from the disturbed surface. This shows that to protect vital structural elements a thermal shield should be used to protect the structure from "thermal shock." The shield material is essentially a barrier to heat flow. If it is assumed that the shield is constructed of the same material as the structure, then the temperature distribution in the shield-structure combination may be determined from a chart similar to that of Fig. 10–8. Temperature curves determined from such a chart would be pessimistic since any contact drop between shields would be neglected, and such an analytical approach would give a larger temperature variation across the structure than would exist in the actual case. A chart, such as Fig. 10–8, is an aid for quick analysis in designing thermal shield shock barriers.

A change in the rate of heat generation inside the metal wall of a container will also produce a temperature transient. These transients occur when the power level of the core is changed. If the power level is suddenly increased, the thermal stress rises to a higher value, but at a slower rate than the rate of power increase.

At no time during the transient from one steady state condition to the other does the stress exceed the final value attained at the higher power level. When the power change is accompanied by a change in coolant temperature, the analyst must know the rate at which the stress due to power generation approaches its final value in order to ascertain whether or not the stresses due to this condition must be added to the stresses produced by the coolant temperature change.

Mathematical solutions are available for the temperature distribution in a slab with linearly varying temperatures on one surface.[23] Substitution into the formulas presented by Anthony results in tedious calculations, but through the use of dimensionless parameters, charts have been prepared from which solutions of the most common problems can be obtained quite readily. In the dimensionless parameters, time can be expressed as a function of the thermal diffusivity, time, and thickness.

A common reactor design problem is a vessel in which the coolant temperature changes at a known, constant rate for a specific period of time. If it is assumed that the ratio of the vessel diameter to the wall thickness is large (greater than 10), the wall curvature may be ignored, and a one dimensional solution for the slab, free to expand but restrained against rotation, may be used. For the purpose of illustration, it will be assumed that the heat transfer from the primary coolant to the inner surface of the wall is very good, and the heat transfer from the outer surface to the surrounding atmosphere is poor. In other words, the outer boundary is well insulated. For analytical purposes, the temperature of the primary coolant at the beginning of the transient can be considered zero since the stress is a function

of temperature differences. The temperature distribution through the wall at any time throughout the transient can be found from the appropriate charts which establish the temperature as a function of non-dimensional distance for various periods of non-dimensional time. The stress at any point is proportional to the differences between the temperature at that point and the mean temperature.

The stresses which are usually of most interest are those at the inner and outer surfaces. Charts have been prepared which show that the stresses at any time, expressed non-dimensionally, after the start of the transient can be expressed as a function of the term

$$\frac{E\alpha\,\Delta T}{1 - \nu}$$

as modified by the factors presented.[24]

A finite film coefficient between the reactor coolant and the inner wall can be very effective in reducing the thermal stresses. The effect of film coefficient can be expressed as a dimensionless parameter,

$$\frac{k}{hL}.$$

The chart prepared by Fritz shows the variation of the stress as a function of the non-dimensionless time for various values of

$$\frac{k}{hL}.$$

If the wall is initially in a stress free

[23] See M. Anthony, "Temperature Distributions in Slabs with a Linear Temperature Rise at One Surface," Section III of *General Discussion on Heat Transfer* jointly published in 1951 by the Institution of Mechanical Engineers and The American Society of Mechanical Engineers, pp. 250–261.

[24] See R. J. Fritz, "Evaluation of Transient Temperatures and Stresses," *Trans.* ASME, Vol. 76, 1954, pp. 913–921.

condition, the maximum stress will always occur at the end of a linear transient, when the full value of the temperature change has been accomplished.

As an example of thermal stresses in a vessel structure, consider a vessel wall seven inches thick with a thermal diffusivity of 67 sq in. per hr. The stress for a 42 deg F change in 140 seconds, with an infinite film coefficient, would be 10,600 psi. This stress could be reduced if the film coefficient were some nominal figure in accordance with practice. Another part of the system, which is subjected to the same transient, would exhibit a different stress if the thickness were different. Consider a one inch thick pipe entering the vessel. The stress for the 42 deg F transient in 140 seconds, again considering an infinite film coefficient, would be only 1500 psi. Thus, in the thick wall cylinder the large "slow" transient is a serious one, but in a thinner wall section the stress is relatively small.

The comparison of transient effect can be carried further for the same vessel parameters but with the coolant transient acting on both units changed 26 deg F in 35 seconds. Again, an infinite film coefficient is assumed. In this case, the stress in the vessel wall would be 7260 psi while the stress in the pipe would be 3200 psi. This comparison shows that the "slow" transient is less severe on the thin wall structure than is the "fast" transient on that same structure, although the temperature excursion for the "slow" transient is greater than that for the "fast" transient.

Structural Significance of Applied Loadings

In general, the industrial codes do not consider operational loading in design calculations. It is a basic principle that the code rules are intended to provide minimum safety requirements for new construction, and not to cover deterioration which may occur in service as a result of corrosion, instability of the material, or unusual operating conditions such as fatigue or shock loading.

Significance of Thermal Stresses

Thermal stresses are generally less damaging than mechanically applied stresses because thermal yielding produces relaxation of the stresses. In general the industrial codes do not mention thermal loads except to list them as one of the loadings to be considered in designing pressure vessels. Section III of the ASME Boiler and Pressure Vessel Code considers thermal stresses which are generated by various types of thermal loading. Acceptable and required methods of evaluating these stresses are defined in this section of the Code.

Dimensional Changes. Objectionable dimensional changes can occur in a structure even when the thermal stresses are well within the elastic range of the material. A linear temperature gradient through the thickness of an unrestrained flat plate produces no stress, but the plate will assume a spherical shape and may not perform its intended function because of the change in curvature.

Temperatures Which Harm Metallurgical Structure. Peak metal temperatures must be calculated and evaluated with regard to their effect on metallurgical structure and mechanical properties. This evaluation is particularly important in a pressure vessel made of a material whose yield stress is affected by temperature. A vessel may be capable of containing the required pressure at the temperatures of its contents, but if radiation heating is sufficient to lower the yield point in a large percentage of the thickness, progressive yielding may occur.

Strains Beyond Ductile Limit. Ductile materials can withstand single applications of strain up to 50 to 60 per cent (as measured by the reduction of area) without failure as evidenced by tensile tests, although lateral restraint reduces this capacity. For such materials, the thermal stress as calculated by elastic analysis has little significance. Brittle materials can be expected to fail when the calculated stress reaches the ultimate stress as determined by tensile tests. As a rough approximation 10 per cent elongation in a 2-inch gage length in the standard ASTM tensile test is often used as a dividing line between metals which can and cannot be counted on to absorb single applications of thermal strains without damage.

Strain Concentration. A large percentage of the service failures produced by thermal stress involve some form of strain concentration.

Strain concentration in the plastic range can be even more insidious than the familiar stress concentration in the elastic range. Stress concentration can usually be avoided, or at least predicted, and it is common practice to ignore the effect for static loads on ductile materials. When an irregular member such as a tension bar with a reduced section is subjected to a fixed strain, the stretching will occur almost entirely in the reduced section as soon as the region passes the yield stress of the material. Thus, the length over which the strain is distributed is not the entire length of the bar, and the length of reduced section is subjected to much higher unit strains. The same phenomena could occur in a structure if some small region has a reduced yield strength because of local annealing, or if a low strength inclusion is in the metal.

Thermal Cycling. Repeated loading and unloading is almost always a factor in any failure of ductile material that is attributable to thermal stress. Thus this type of loading must be analyzed on a fatigue basis. All of the various cycles which will cause damage to the part should be investigated and the total damage created by each type of cycle must be summed. Procedures and allowable design values can be found in Section III of the ASME Boiler and Pressure Vessel Code, and the interested reader should consult this for detailed instructions.

Photoelasticity[25]

Rational design, concerned as it is with the causes and methods of prevention of failure of mechanisms and structural members, is directly related to accurate stress evaluation. Designs based on nominal stresses and specified allowables continue to fail because the use of average or linear stresses, ignoring the exact stress distribution, avoids the significant effect of stress concentrations. Those which originate at sharp discontinuities such as holes, grooves, slots, keyways, fillets and welds result in cracks which cause failure. Fatigue in connection with stress intensifiers

[25] Material for this major section contributed by E. Richardson.

may be the deciding factor in determining strength.

The mathematical theories of elasticity and plasticity provide methods for the exact determination of stress concentrations, but for complicated boundaries the analytical solution becomes too unwieldy for practical use and in addition needs corroboration of experiment. This can be provided by techniques of *photoelasticity* which is often the best method for the complete exploration of principal stresses and stresses on free boundaries when accuracy, speed and cost are considered. Recent simplifications in technique have made routine checks on complex designs both feasible and desirable, and new photoelastic materials have been developed which improve the accuracy. Photoelasticity has grown to full stature as an effective instrument for quantitative stress analysis.

Sequence of Developments

Like many another technique used in engineering design, photoelasticity had its origin in the physics laboratory and was extensively used and developed there before finding technical application. The earliest investigator was David Brewster who in 1812 discovered that the forced deformation of clear glass alters its optical properties. In the course of extended experiments he observed that glass under physical stress exhibits colored patterns when viewed under polarized light.[26]

Over the next forty years investigators developed the underlying theory and formulated the concept that the optical retardation producing the color effects is proportional to the difference of the principal stresses existing in the glass. Among the contributors to this development were F. E. Neumann in Germany and M. G. Wertheim in France. Brewster himself continued his study of the properties of light and was still living when James Clerk Maxwell related findings obtained by the use of polarized light to theoretical stress studies in classical mechanics.[27]

The first application of photoelasticity to a study of stresses in a bridge structure was performed in 1904 shortly after the development of celluloid. But it was not until 1915, more than a century after Brewster's first work, that Edgar Buckingham formulated the Pi theorem by which the method of dimensional analysis could be used to relate model and prototype.[28] In the years that followed engineers made increasing use of photoelastic techniques to analyze structures and engines. This growth was spurred on by necessity of obtaining more elaborate and accurate analyses in the rapidly expanding automotive and aircraft industries.

The frozen stress or fixation method is made possible by using a model of resin

---

[26] This work is reported in a number of communications to the Royal Society of London. The following titles from the *Philosophical Transactions* of the Society, Vol. 105, 1815, are particularly relevant: "Experiments on the Depolarization of Light," pp. 29–53, and "On the Effects of Simple Pressure in Producing that Species of Crystallization Which Forms Two Oppositely Polarized Images," pp. 60–64.

[27] "On the Equilibrium of Elastic Solids," *Transactions* of the Royal Society of Edinburgh, Vol. 20, 1853, pp. 87–120.

[28] See "Model Experiments and the Forms of Empirical Equations" by Edgar Buckingham, *Trans.* ASME, Vol. 37, 1915, pp. 263–296.

which has a strong structural lattice of polymers permeated by a fusible phase which will become viscous when heated to about 300 F. When a load is applied, the lattice deforms and the softened portion flows under stress to conform to the shape of the strained lattice. If the load is held constant while the model is slowly cooled, the fusible portion will solidify and offer resistance to the recovery of the strained lattice. Thus the deformed lattice is fixed or frozen and the stress remains in the model. This allows the model to be sliced into thin slices in any orientation for analysis.

Although the frozen stress technique was originally discovered in 1835, G. Oppel of Germany performed the first three-dimensional stress analysis more than a century later in 1936. This greatly broadened the field of usefulness of experimental stress analysis.[29]

Dynamic problems, in which a steady state of stress is produced by rotation of the part, may be solved by rotating the plastic model during the heat treatment cycle, thus freezing in the stress pattern. This method has been used frequently to determine the stress concentrations due to holes or slots in rotating members, and to learn the stress distribution resulting from centrifugal forces in impellers.

The quenching stresses that are developed in a complicated shape when the part is cooled rapidly from a high temperature may be studied to obtain a fairly accurate indication of the stress distribution. Also, the redistribution of residual stresses when quenched parts are machined may be investigated by machining the model after quenching.

The flow of fluids has been studied by using *photoviscous* fluids which become doubly refractive due to stresses of viscous shear. The flow patterns may be analyzed from the retardations measured in a polariscope.

Gravity stresses may be analyzed in models in which it is not necessary to reproduce the gravity forces. This is determined from the stresses produced by loading a small model with boundary forces varying linearly with the depth.

Steady state thermal stresses due to thermal gradients may be determined by displacing the boundary of the model in such a way as to simulate the thermally induced stresses. In addition to the dislocation, boundary loadings may be applied to simulate stress conditions for transient conditions of thermal stress.

The photoelastic method of stress analysis offers the following advantages:

1. An overall visual picture is obtained of the distribution of shearing stress throughout the body.

2. The actual peak values of stress may be determined since the stress is measured point by point.

3. Stresses may be determined in bodies that cannot be solved analytically.

4. The stresses in irregular members may be determined with accuracy comparable to that obtained with precise strain-gage techniques.

5. The design of a complex member may be developed or improved by changing the shape of the model to shift the maximum stresses away from critical areas.

Application to Reactor Vessel Design

It was mentioned earlier in this chapter

---

[29] See "The Photoelastic Investigation of Three-Dimensional Stress and Strain Conditions" by G. Oppel, NACA Technical Memorandum No. 824, April 1937.

that photoelastic tests may be used in the design of heads for nuclear reactor pressure vessels. These vessels may be very large and have very thick walls, as already indicated. The heads generally have many penetrations, resulting in complicated shapes. To determine the stress levels by analytical techniques requires the introduction of many simplifications which may yield conflicting or inconclusive answers. On the other hand, the vessel head may be analyzed by photoelastic methods, using a model which may be sliced in such a way as to permit the investigation of stresses at any particular point in question.

An illustration of a model of a nuclear reactor closure head is shown in Fig. 10–9. Loading of tightened bolts is simulated by means of flange bolts which hold the head against the vessel. Compression springs on the bolts provide a means of achieving a known bolt load at the upper temperature level of the heating cycle used in fixating the stresses. At the same time the vessel can be internally pressurized with an inert gas to simulate the operating pressure in the prototype.[30]

Figure 10—9.   Nuclear reactor pressure vessel closure head.

Strength of Furnace Walls[31]

Welded furnace walls are one of the most important components of boilers. They may be incorporated into the design of small shop assembled boilers as well as in the largest station units. *Furnace walls*, also frequently referred to as *water walls*, provide the enclosure around the major parts of a boiler and are integrally

---

[30] For additional information see the two volumes of *Photoelasticity* by M. M. Frocht, published by John Wiley in 1941, 411 pages, and 1948, 505 pages. Other useful references include *Handbook of Experimental Stress Analysis* edited by M. Hetenyi, John Wiley, 1950, 1077 pages and Introduction to the *Theoretical and Experimental Analysis of Stress and Strain* by A. J. Durelli, E. A. Phillips and C. H. Tsao, McGraw-Hill, 1958, 498 pages. Information on experimental techniques may be found in the *Manual on Experimental Stress Analysis Techniques* published by the Society for Experimental Stress Analysis, Cambridge, Mass., and in the *Proceedings* of that Society, publication of which began in 1943.

[31] Material for this major section contributed by C. W. Lawton.

concerned with all of its essential functions. As a link in the steam generating cycle, they are components of the pressure parts system. The support of the furnace wall system is linked to that of other components and will be discussed in the final section of this chapter dealing with structural design of boilers.

A wide range of operating conditions is encountered for which the welded furnace walls must be safe and reliable. The furnace tubes making up the furnace walls have the highest heat flux rates in the boiler and are subjected to the most extreme fluctuations in temperature and pressure. During boiler startup the walls are subjected to considerable overfiring. A wide range of pressure conditions is encountered as the unit is brought up to its normal operating level. The furnace wall enclosure must be designed so that it can withstand both positive and negative inside pressures. In addition, special conditions sometimes occur in which the enclosure must withstand wind and earthquake loadings.

The furnace walls of large central station boilers, which will be the principal type discussed in this section, are made up of panels with parallel tube circuits as shown in Fig. 10–10. Considerable design flexibility is required in the layout of the panels, for they must enclose, with equal reliability and safety, furnaces of many different sizes and shapes and burn many fuels. Since economical production of steam is the primary function of the furnace wall, the thermal performance of the wall is given careful consideration in wall design.

The most important feature in the protection of a furnace wall tube against failure is the assurance of adequate circulation of fluid within the tube under all operating conditions. For this reason the

Figure 10–10. Furnace wall panels.

internal diameter of the wall tube is determined by the thermodynamic requirement for that particular type of furnace. Thus for some furnaces the wall will contain small diameter tubing with thick walls while for other furnaces the tubing will be large diameter and relatively thin walls. For this reason the mechanical behavior of furnace walls will vary greatly for the different type of furnaces.

Mechanical Loading of Furnace Walls

The development of analytical and experimental techniques has made it possible to determine the stresses in the furnace wall in considerable detail. With this knowledge and the realization that different type stresses have different degrees of significance, the furnace walls are designed to give the desired thermal behavior and to be safe and reliable.

As a starting point, the tube thickness is determined which will give the required internal diameter for proper thermal performance of the furnace. Since the tubes are a part of the pressure system of the steam generator, the determination of wall thickness is within the jurisdiction of Section I of the ASME Boiler and Pressure Vessel Code.[32] Thus the following equation, issued with the Winter 1963 Addenda to the Code, is used for tube thickness:

$$t = \frac{PD}{2S + P} + 0.005D$$

where t is thickness, P is fluid pressure, D is outside tube diameter and S is the allowable stress (according to Table P–7 of Section I, ASME Boiler and Pressure Vessel Code).

This procedure will satisfy the ASME Code requirements and will give a wall panel with the required flexibility to keep the thermal stresses within reasonable limits on severe thermal transients. Except under special conditions, a thicker wall tube will not improve the overall stress condition. As the pressure stress becomes smaller because of thicker tube, the thermal stress increases rather rapidly with increased wall thickness. A change to a better material is the most satisfactory method of gaining improvement in strength requirements.

There are other mechanical loads which act on the furnace wall and must be analyzed to insure a reliable furnace wall. Some of these additional loads are furnace firing pressure, dead weight loads, wind loads, earthquake loads and reactive loads between furnace wall and the rigid buckstay system.

Determination of Furnace Stresses

The straight analytical determination of the stresses in the furnace walls is difficult because of the complex geometry of the panel. In order to start the solution it is necessary to assume a fin size. For a furnace panel with normal heat absorption rates the fin width will be in the neighborhood of one half inch. With this close spacing of the tubes the wall can be considered as a stiffened orthogonal plate. Using the notation of Timoshenko,[33] the differential equation of equilibrium for small displacements of an orthotropic plate is:

$$D_x \frac{\partial^4 W}{\partial x^4} + 2(D_1 + 2D_{xy}) \frac{\partial^4 W}{\partial x^2 \partial y^2}$$
$$+ D_y \frac{\partial^4 W}{\partial y^4} = q$$

where W is the lateral displacement,

$$D_x = \frac{E_x' h^3}{12}, \qquad D_y = \frac{E_y' h^3}{12},$$

$$D_1 = \frac{E'' h^3}{12}, \qquad D_{xy} = \frac{G h^3}{12},$$

q is uniform lateral load, E is the modulus of elasticity and h is wall thickness.

After the appropriate elastic constants have been determined the solution of this equation can be determined by the methods proposed by Timoshenko and Woinowsky-Krieger in the preceding reference for the imposed boundary conditions. An experimental procedure for determining the elastic constants has been developed by Beckett and others for this type of plate.[34]

---

[32] See Section I, *Rules for Construction of Power Boilers*, published by ASME.

[33] For further information, see *Theory of Plates and Shells* by S. Timoshenko and S. Woinowsky-Krieger, Second Edition, McGraw-Hill, 1959, Chapter 11, Bending of Anisotropic Plates.

[34] See "An Experimental Method for Determining the Elastic Constants of Orthogonally Stiffened Plates" by R. E. Beckett, R. J. Dohrmann and K. D. Ives, *Proceedings of the First International Congress on Experimental Mechanics*, edited by B. E. Rossi, Pergamon Press.

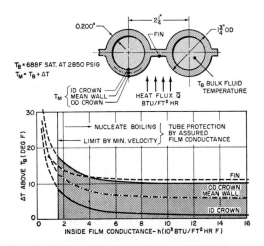

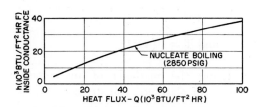

Figure 10–11. Furnace temperature plot.

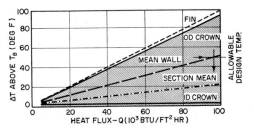

Figure 10–13. Temperatures above saturation.

Figure 10–12. Correlation between heat flux and nucleate boiling.

In many cases the buckstay system is carried on the furnace wall tubing. The additional stresses can be calculated with conventional structural analysis. It will be necessary to distribute the heavy concentrated loads over a sufficient area so that large local distortions do not occur in the wall.

Balanced Thermal Loading

Balanced thermal loading is defined as that condition of balanced heat absorption from one side of the wall which will result in local variation of temperature across the tube and fin which give rise to thermal stresses. The local metal temperatures existing in a tube and fin depend on the panel geometry, the heat flux, inside film coefficient and the type of boiler. An example of the performance of the four critical temperatures, at the outside, mean and inside diameter on the crown of the tube and at the fin tip, as a function of inside film coefficient, is shown in Fig. 10–11 for a typical controlled circulation boiler. The curves illustrate the importance of maintaining a minimum inside film coefficient to keep the tube cool. Using the relationship between heat flux and nucleate boiling coefficient (as correlated by recent literature) shown in Fig. 10–12, the actual maximum temperatures in the tube and fin above the saturation temperature are plotted against flux rate in Fig. 10–13. This relationship is essentially proportional and demonstrates the wide range of absorption to which the tubing and fin material may be exposed.

Temperature Distribution

The first step in determining the thermal stress in the fin and tube is to obtain a temperature distribution, T. The tube and fin respond with sufficient speed so that, at any given condition, this relationship can be approximated by the steady state.

Thus $\nabla^2 T = 0$

where $\nabla^2 T = \dfrac{\partial T^2}{\partial x^2} + \dfrac{\partial T^2}{\partial y^2}$

Solution for this equation can be built with Fourier Series or the equation can be readily solved by numerical relaxation methods as given by Southwell.[35] For the numerical solutions a digital computer will greatly reduce the required computation time. Another method of solution is the use of an analog computer, of which the electric sheet analog cut from a special conducting paper is a rather well known method.[36]

Thermal Stresses

Thermal stresses occur in the tube and fin because the elements cannot deform freely as shown in Fig. 10–14. Some of the thermal stress is because of differences between the mean temperature of the section and the local temperature. The remaining thermal stress is from the restraints imposed on the tube and fin by the comparatively stiff buckstay system. The tube and fin are separated into separate elements and the thermal stress in each element is calculated by solving the general thermoelastic differential equation in terms of stress function.

$$\nabla^4\varphi + \frac{E\alpha}{1 - \nu} \cdot \nabla^2 T = 0$$

where

$$\nabla^4\varphi = \frac{\partial^4\varphi}{\partial x^4} + 2\frac{\partial^4\varphi}{\partial x^2\,\partial y^2} + \frac{\partial^4\varphi}{\partial y^4}$$

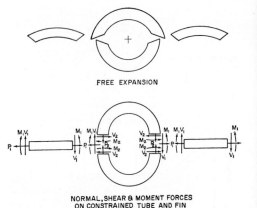

FREE EXPANSION

NORMAL, SHEAR & MOMENT FORCES
ON CONSTRAINED TUBE AND FIN

Figure 10–14.   Free body diagram of forces.

The stress functions are defined as

$$\sigma_x = \frac{\partial^2\varphi}{\partial y^2}, \quad \sigma_y = \frac{\partial^2\varphi}{\partial x^2}, \quad \tau_{xy} = -\frac{\partial^2\varphi}{\partial x\,\partial y}$$

and $T = f\,(x,y,t)$

Using the methods of mathematical theory of elasticity, the stresses, displacements and rotations for the various elements can be calculated for the tube and fin. In general, the displacements and rotation of the elements will not match at the points of attachment to give a continuous composite member. The additional normal, and shear forces and moments must be calculated to make the center lines match as shown in Fig. 10–14. This is accomplished by equating the calculated displacements and rotations of each element in terms of the redundant forces and moments to each other at each joint. Once the redundant forces and moments are known the additional stresses can be calculated. In addition, the mean

---

[35] See *Relaxation Methods in Engineering Science* by R. V. Southwell, Oxford, 1940, 252 pages.
[36] For further information, see *Conduction Heat Transfer* by P. J. Schneider, Chapter 13, Experimental Analogic Method, pp. 318–361, Addison-Wesley, 1955.

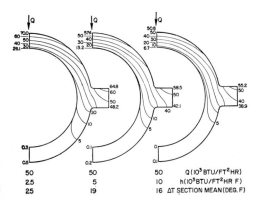

50	50	50	Q (10³ BTU/FT²HR)
2.5	5	10	h (10³ BTU/FT²HR F)
25	19	16	ΔT SECTION MEAN (DEG. F)

Figure 10–15. Temperature distribution.

temperature of the tube will not match that of the fin so an additional stress must be calculated to make the longitudinal growth of the tube match that of the fin. The total stress for the balanced thermal loading is the sum of the individual stresses.

Unbalanced Thermal Loading

Unbalanced thermal loading is defined as temperature distribution which varies in either direction along the furnace wall. The variation in heat absorption rates longitudinally and transversely across the wall is one reason for unbalanced temperature distribution. Fig. 10–13 shows how the metal temperatures vary with different heat absorption rates. Unbalances in the flow rate either in neighboring tubes or in different areas of the wall will give unbalanced temperatures. Flow rates in some boilers are very dependent on the heat absorption for a given tube. Further investigation will reveal a very complex interplay between heat absorption and flow rates for some types of furnaces with conditions that can lead to large tem-

perature unbalances. Fig. 10–15 shows temperature distributions for three different inside film coefficients which are very dependent upon flow rates. A third condition that will result in temperature variations in a furnace wall is that of varying fluid temperatures. In boilers of the once through type the fluid temperature continually varies as the fluid progresses from inlet to outlet. In each case there is a very complex interaction between these conditions, and it is the responsibility of the boiler designer to select a suitable set of parameters so that the temperature unbalances will be within reasonable limits.

An experimental technique has been used to determine the stresses from the unbalanced thermal loadings. As an example, Fig. 10–16 shows a furnace wall panel under test at the Kreisinger Devel-

Figure 10–16. Furnace wall test at Kreisinger Development Laboratory.

Figure 10–17. Photoelastic pattern.

center of the panel, at the top bend and at the soot blower opening to determine the influence of each type of discontinuity.[37] To complete the investigation, photoelastic tests were made to determine the stresses inside the tube. Fig. 10–17 shows the photoelastic pattern of a section of one of the panels that was investigated by mechanical loading to simulate the thermal action.

Significance of Calculated Stresses

The accurate and detailed determination of the mechanical and thermal stresses in the furnace wall are of little value until the designer knows the significance of these stresses in relation to failure of the wall to perform its function. Furthermore, a calculated or a measured value of stress or strain has little meaning until it is associated with its location and distribution in the panel and with the type of loading which produced it. As an example the average hoop stress in the tube from internal pressure has a different influence on the life of the panel than that of the peak stress at the intersection of the fin and tube from a redundant moment. An excessive hoop stress produces an instability in the tube which continues to grow and get thinner and thinner until rupture. However, the peak stress at the notch will relieve itself by yielding and only has a bearing on fatigue life or stress rupture life.

In order to help evaluate the different types of stresses that may act on the wall, the stresses are classified into categories

opment Laboratory of Combustion Engineering, Inc. In this test controlled temperature distributions were imposed on the panel, and the resulting strains were determined by electric strain gages on the outside surface of the panel. Strain gages were placed at the end of the panel, at

[37] For further information on strain gages, see *Strain Gage Primer* by C. C. Perry and H. R. Lisner, Second Edition, McGraw-Hill, 1962, 332 pages. An interesting and personal account of engineering innovations related to the development of bonded wire strain gages may be found in *Tatnall on Testing* by F. G. Tatnall, American Society for Metals, 1966, 234 pages.

as primary stresses, secondary stresses and local or peak stresses.

Primary Stress

A *primary stress* is a normal or shear stress developed by the imposed mechanical loading which is necessary to satisfy the laws of equilibrium of external and internal forces and moments. The basic characteristic of a primary stress is that it is not self-limiting. Primary stresses which exceed the yield strength will result in failure or gross distortion.

Secondary Stress

A *secondary stress* is a normal or shear stress developed by the constraint of an adjacent part or by self-constraint of a structure. The basic characteristic of a secondary stress is that it is self-limiting. Local yielding and minor distortion can satisfy the conditions which cause the stress to occur. Thermal stresses which produce gross distortions are considered as secondary stresses.

Local or Peak Stress

Local or *peak stress* is a normal or shear stress which is the highest in the region under consideration and is developed by changes in geometry such as a notch. Thermal stresses which are caused by self-constraint are treated as local stresses. The basic characteristic of a local or peak stress is that it causes no significant distortion and is objectionable only as a possible source of either a fatigue failure, brittle fracture, stress corrosion cracking or stress rupture failure. Within these categories a differentiation is made between a membrane stress (average value across a section) and the bending stress (linearly variable across a section).

Combination of Stresses

The characteristic material values on which strength calculations are based are determined under uniaxial tension. Usually this is the common tension test. The furnace walls are subjected to multiaxial stress, and a direct comparison of the stress in the wall with the characteristic strength value of the material is not directly admissible. Only with the aid of a strength hypothesis is it possible to calculate an equivalent stress for comparison with the characteristic strength value as determined by the conventional tension test.

Maximum Shear Theory

The maximum shear stress theory is used as the failure criterion for the furnace walls. The selection of the maximum shear stress theory is based on the use of a good ductile steel for the furnace walls. According to the maximum shear theory, if the principal stresses are σ_1, σ_2, σ_3 and further if $\sigma_1 > \sigma_2 > \sigma_3$, the maximum shear stress is

$$\tau_{\max} = \frac{\sigma_1 - \sigma_3}{2}$$

The equivalent stress to that of a simple tension or compression test would be

$$S = \sigma_1 - \sigma_3 = 2\sigma_{\max}$$

This equivalent stress is called *stress intensity*. This is not a single stress quantity but the combined stress as represented by the three principal stresses or their equivalent. The addition of stresses from different categories must be performed at the component level, not after translating the stress components into stress intensities. Similarly the calculation of membrane stress intensity involves the averaging of stresses across a section and this averaging must be performed at the component level.

The allowable stresses except for the membrane stress have been derived from the same considerations that were used in writing Section III, *Rules for Construction of Nuclear Vessels*, of the ASME Boiler and Pressure Vessel Code. It is an application of limit design theory tempered by engineering judgment and some conservative simplifications.

Allowable Membrane Stress

The first stress limit to consider is *primary membrane stress*. In this case the value is limited to the values as given in Table P–7 of the Section I, *Rules for Construction of Power Boilers*, of the ASME Boiler and Pressure Vessel Code since the tubing is part of the pressure system. In this case stress intensities are not determined because this section of the Code is based on maximum stress theory.

Allowable Local Membrane or Bending Stress

In the remaining evaluation the stress intensities are determined for comparison with the stress limits. The next limit is the sum of the primary membrane stress plus the primary bending stress plus any local membrane stress. These stresses are combined at the component level and then the stress intensity determined. This limit is set at 1.5 times the stress limits as given in Table P–7 of Section I of ASME Boiler and Pressure Vessel Code. Further, if the temperatures are at the level where stress rupture is the mode of failure, the combined value is limited to those values given in Table P–7.

Allowable Secondary Stress

In the next consideration, the primary stresses (membrane and bending) are combined with the secondary stresses at the component level and the stress intensities determined. These values are limited to three times the values from Table P–7 for temperatures below 700 F. If the temperature is about 700 F, the lower value of either three times the value from Table P–7 or the allowable alternating stress intensity for one million cycles at the highest operating temperature is used.

Allowable Peak Stress

For the next evaluation all the stresses, primary, secondary and local are combined for both the maximum and minimum conditions of an operational cycle. From these values the maximum and minimum stress intensities can be determined. Using these stress intensities the alternating stress is calculated. These stresses are usually evaluated on a fatigue basis which will be discussed in the next section.

In cases where the loads are at steady state or of very low cycle frequency and the temperatures are in the realm of stress rupture, the total stresses can be limited by yield stresses. In this region each material has a different behavior as influenced by notches and metallurgical changes. Therefore, a survey of the literature on the material should be made as an aid in the final evaluation. The stress limits for the various stress categories are summarized in Fig. 10–18.

Fatigue Analysis

The first step in the fatigue analysis is to estimate a stress history for the expected life of the unit. From this stress history, the different type of operating cycles, such as startups, shutdowns, load changes and other changes which cause

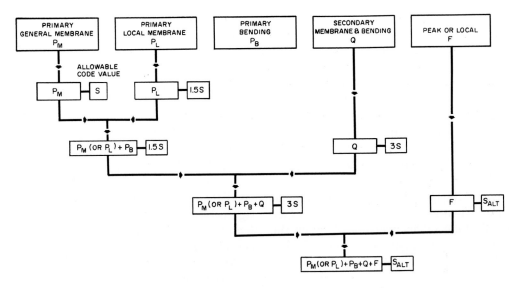

Figure 10–18.   Stress limits.

the stress level in the wall to vary, can be determined. In each of these cases, the maximum and minimum stress intensities are determined. Alternating stress intensities can then be calculated by

$$S_{alt} = \frac{S_{max} - S_{min}}{2}$$

If these stresses are significant, they will use up part of the life of the unit. The number of times the significant alternating stresses can be repeated is determined from a design fatigue curve as shown in Fig. 10–19. In these curves the alternating stress is plotted as a function of the cycles to failure with suitable safety factors. Because safety factors vary considerably and are dependent upon the mechanical behavior of the material, the

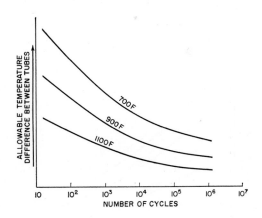

Figure 10–19.   Design fatigue curve.

uncertainty of the assumed loads and the uncertainty in the material (scatter of data), specific values of the ordinate of typical curves are not given. Curves such as these are determined by experimental methods and may be found in the literature. Some fatigue curves for materials normally used in furnace design can be found in Section III of the ASME Boiler and Pressure Vessel Code. These are believed to reflect a conservative design.

In the furnace wall the stresses on both sides of the wall must be determined. The trend of the decrease in fatigue life as the temperature increases is shown in Fig. 10–20. Thus, because of the temperature influence on fatigue life, the hot face of the tube or fin may fail although the higher stresses may be calculated elsewhere.

Cumulative Damage

The furnace wall is subjected to a wide variety of operating conditions, some of which produce no significant stresses and some of which will produce stresses worthy of consideration. When a design is for either static loads or for a large number of cycles, it is sufficient to design for the condition which produces the highest stresses and ignore all others. In this case, design is for infinite life, and all stress must be below the level which produces damage.

Usually the number of operational stress cycles which the furnace wall must withstand is not large, but the value of the operational stress is large unless severe restrictions are imposed on the unit.

As soon as the existence of strains beyond the elastic limit is accepted, the design is based on finite life and the damaging effect of all significant strains must be considered. The relationship between the alternating stress and cycles to failure can be determined from the design fatigue curves, and the number of required cycles can be estimated from the anticipated stress history. With these relationships established, the expected life can be estimated with fair accuracy by adding together the "cycle ratios" produced by each operating condition.

$$\text{Cumulative Damage Index} = \sum_{i=1}^{i=n} \frac{P_i}{N_i}$$

where P_i is the number of times operating cycle will occur and N_i is the number of times alternating stress can be withstood, based on the fatigue design curve.

Fatigue tests have shown that the cumulative damage index can vary over a range of 0.6 to 5. If the most damaging stresses are applied first, the cycles ratio may be as low as 0.6. If the lower stress values are applied first and followed by progressively higher stresses, the cycles ratio can be as high as five. These are extreme conditions. For the case with random distribution of cycle ratio as for a furnace wall, the cumulative sum will be close to unity. Thus the imposed limiting condition is

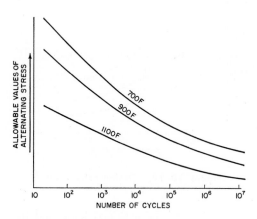

Figure 10–20. Decrease in fatigue life.

$$\sum_{i=1}^{i=n} \frac{P_i}{N_i} = 1$$

Welded furnace walls must be safe and reliable for a wide range of boiler operating conditions. The analytical techniques and experimental procedures discussed in this section give the boiler designer the necessary tools to make an evaluation of the strength of furnace walls and to assess the suitability of furnace wall design to withstand any of the various operating conditions.

Structural Design of Boilers[38]

Since the combustion process must be confined within a complex structure capable of supporting a wide variety of static and dynamic loads, *structural design* is an important sector of overall boiler design. It is unfortunately true, however, that the fundamental importance of heat transfer and fluid flow tends to obscure the role of the boiler structural designer. His task is to analyze the many internal and external loads and to select suitable structural members.

Structural design of boilers shares much in common with bridge and building design. There is a long history of progressive advancement in this engineering art.[39] Yet there is little evidence of a specialized literature of boiler structural design, and almost no consideration is given to structural problems in the most widely used works on power plant design.[40]

This section represents an attempt to fill this literature gap at an introductory level. The first of its two parts outlines the major considerations in boiler structural design and incorporates a series of drawings showing the structural arrangements of a central station reheat boiler. The second part presents an analysis and calculations for a small portion of a hypothetical boiler structure. Despite many simplifications and omission of expansion forces, transient conditions and vibration considerations, these calculations are found to be voluminous. Detailed structural calculations for a large central station boiler are extremely numerous and beyond the scope of this book.

General Structural Design Conditions

Structural design of boilers involves the consideration of many factors. The type

---

[38] Material for this major section contributed by Paul R. Walter and F. H. Engelhardt.

[39] This is exemplified in *Theory of Modern Steel Structures* by L. E. Grinter, Revised Edition, two volumes, Macmillan, 1949. See also "One Hundred Fifty Years Advance in Structural Analysis" by H. M. Westergaard, *Trans.* American Society of Civil Engineers, Vol. 94, 1930, pp. 220–246 and "The Historical Development of Structural Theory" by Stanley B. Hamilton, *Proceedings* of Institution of Civil Engineers, Part III, 1952, pp. 374–419.

[40] A notable exception is the Power Division of the American Society of Civil Engineers. For a computer program used in designing the major portion of the structural steel for a steam power plant, see "Integrated Structural Steel Design Program" by A. H. Palmer, K. Balkus, C. A. Veldon and H. T. Blomquist, *Journal* of the Power Division, American Society of Civil Engineers, Vol. 89, No. PO-1, Sept. 1963, pp. 67–82.

of boiler, its location and its method of construction all have a bearing, as do such things as design specifications, codes and ordinances, protective coatings and types of structure, including choice of members and connections.

Supports for boilers vary greatly, depending upon size and function. Central station boilers and the larger units for industrial service, including recovery units for pulp and paper mills, are top supported. On the other hand, shop assembled boilers of various types, including those for waste heat recovery and high temperature water, are bottom supported, as are those for marine service. This section, however, will be specifically concerned with the structural design of a top supported central station boiler.

Location of Installation

Boiler location has many effects upon structural design. It may determine whether indoor or outdoor construction is used. It has a bearing on the specification of domestic or foreign steel. It may require special consideration for climatic conditions, including both natural occurrences and those artificially induced, as in a chemical plant or oil refinery. It will establish wind loads, seismic conditions and soil bearing capabilities for foundations. Local ordinances and regulations may impose special requirements, including restrictions on materials and limitations of structural size.

Indoor boilers for central station service are a part of the power plant structure, using the building columns for vertical support. Lateral support is provided by the bracing system of the building, which is completely enclosed and roofed. Boiler platforms which are necessary for access and maintenance are coordinated with the elevations of power plant floors.

Outdoor units may have the boiler completely exposed to wind and weather. However, many are built with a full or partial roof and a protective enclosure around the burners. Special consideration must be given to the design of casings and insulation for outdoor units.

Sources of Design Information

Before calculations for structural design are started, many other decisions must be made. The first and most obvious ones are related to the capacity, system conditions and methods of firing the boiler. These decisions are an outcome of the preliminary studies leading to the design of a central station.[41]

With respect to the structure itself, an early decision must be made on the use of indoor or outdoor construction. The type of frame must also be decided upon, whether rigid, simple or semirigid. Related to this is the choice from among several alternative types of connections: riveted, bolted or welded. Bolted connections may use high strength materials. Likewise, it must be decided whether built-up structural members should be riveted or welded. It is also well at this time to give consideration to protective coatings and procedures for their application to structural steel.

There are many codes, standards and specifications which are pertinent to and helpful in making these decisions which must precede detailed structural design. One very useful publication is "Minimum Design Loads in Buildings and Other Structures"[42] which lists design loads for

---

[41] See Chapter 3, Design of Central Stations.
[42] "American Standard Building Code Requirements for Minimum Design Loads in Buildings and Other Structures" sponsored by the National Bureau of Standards and published by American Standards Association, A58.1–1955.

hundreds of materials, gives estimated weights of snowfall and wind loads for practically all geographical areas of the United States, and includes seismic factors relating to the most common occurrences of earthquakes. Detailed information on protective coatings for steel may be found in the "Steel Structures Painting Manual" which is published in two volumes.[43]

The American Institute of Steel Construction has published a *Manual of Steel Construction* which provides useful information that covers most routine design work.[44] There are seven parts to the *Manual* which includes the "AISC Specification for the Design, Fabrication and Erection of Structural Steel for Buildings" plus an extended commentary.[45]

Structural design of a large boiler involves the solution of many complex problems as well as the performance of many repetitive calculations. Such structures, it should be noted and remembered, are very large, in some cases exceeding 200 feet in height and involving the design and erection of several thousand tons of structural steel. The foregoing sources of design information are an aid in carrying out these steps, while the following sections include a description and representative drawings for the structure of a central station boiler plus calculations for a small portion of a hypothetical boiler structure.

Design of Structural Steel Framing

The steel framing for a boiler is de-signed as a fixed structure made up of rolled and built-up structural steel members. This structure must be adequate to withstand the weight of the boiler and other equipment that is to be supported, plus seismic and wind loads.

Winds and earthquakes produce dynamic lateral forces which must be resisted by the boiler supporting structure. It is standard practice to resolve these loads into equivalent static design forces. The most adverse loading condition due either to wind or earthquake is used as the design load, since maximum wind and earthquake loads are never considered to occur simultaneously.

The design wind load on the vertical surface of a boiler is usually 25 to 30 lb per sq ft unless a greater value is required either by a local building code or by local site conditions. Areas along the shoreline in zones which may experience hurricanes may require as much as 50 lb per sq ft design wind load.

The design equivalent static lateral seismic force is given by the relationship

$$F = CW$$

where F is the horizontal force, C is a coefficient and W is the total dead load at or above the elevation under consideration.

The size of the coefficient, C, is governed by the flexibility of the structure, the zone of seismic probability in which the structure is located, and the type of structure and risks involved. For boiler structures in earthquake zones of the United States the value of this coefficient ranges from 0.10 to 0.20. The point of ap-

---

[43] Volume 1 covers methods of surface preparation and paint systems. Volume 2 lists all types of important paint systems used in various industries; it also includes a guide with indexes for selection of suitable systems for various types of structures and exposure conditions, plus specifications for surface preparation and pretreatment, paint application and paints. These volumes may be obtained from the Steel Structures Painting Council, Pittsburgh 13, Penna.
[44] The Sixth Edition, 1963, is published by AISC, 101 Park Avenue, New York 17, N.Y.
[45] The latest edition of the Specification should be consulted for knowledge of current practice.

plication of the seismic forces is assumed to be at the center of gravity of the part of the boiler under consideration. The seismic loads due to the dead load of the boiler are transferred to the buckstays which support the boiler waterwalls horizontally through what is known as a seismic stop and then on to the vertical bracing of the structural steel framing and the boiler foundation.

If the boiler is located in areas where the building code or other considerations require added protection against the possibility of earthquake, it may be desirable to design an independent boiler support with its own bracing system. This avoids the objection of interconnecting two structures of different natural frequencies and offers additional protection against potential earthquake damage.

Design of Boiler Support Structure

Most large boilers are top supported by means of many hangers which carry the loads of the various component parts to the structural steel framing. The boiler is allowed to expand downward from the main supports at the top of the structure. Many types of supports are used, including structural steel and alloy members and hanger rods. In high temperature areas the hangers may be water cooled or steam cooled.

Materials for boiler supports must be selected for the maximum temperature which each member encounters, and the stress must be limited to that permissible for the particular material at the temperature involved. Typical values of allowable stresses for structural members at various temperatures are shown in Fig. 10–21, but these should be verified by checking the appropriate ASTM specification for specific grades.

In using the higher temperatures, it must be remembered that elongation and deflection increase with reduction in the modulus of elasticity as environmental temperature increases. The latter relationship is shown in Fig. 10–22. Allowable stresses for water cooled and steam cooled tube hangers can be obtained from Table P–7, Section I, *Rules for Construction of Power Boilers*, ASME Boiler and Pressure Vessel Code, for various materials used in boiler construction.

From the foregoing it should be apparent that boiler supports must function at differing temperatures and may be fabricated from a variety of materials. This makes it extremely important that the design of all boiler support hangers be coordinated so that each will perform its assigned function satisfactorily at all times. Under certain conditions of expansion, shifting of loads is unavoidable.

Spring supports, either of the constant load or coil type, are used in some cases. The constant load type, if properly designed and installed, will support the same load even when movement has occurred, but the coil spring load will change when

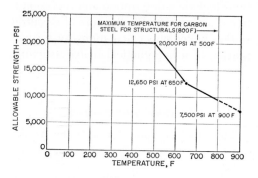

Figure 10–21. Recommended values of allowable strength for structural members of carbon steel.

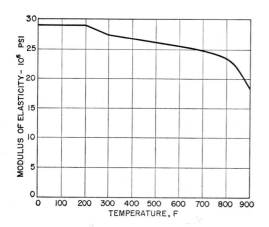

Figure 10–22. Recommended values of modulus of elasticity versus temperature for carbon steel.

the spring compression is increased or decreased. The support from which the coil spring is suspended must be designed for the maximum load the spring can pick up. Likewise, care should be taken so that other beams or supports are designed to take up loads released by coil springs. For boiler pressure part supports, the springs must be designed so that spring compression for expansion movement will not impose a load high enough to overstress the pressure parts.

Boiler and Equipment Loads

One of the most important tasks of the structural designer is to calculate the boiler weight as accurately as possible. In many cases preliminary load information is needed for foundation design before component parts are completely designed or located. Knowledge of similar boilers enables the designer to estimate these loads and to produce a suitable preliminary loading diagram.

Weights of each waterwall are calculated individually. The procedure is to determine the unit weight of the tubing (plus 100 per cent water load), insulation and casing and then to calculate the total weight of the wall area. Depending upon the location and construction, additional amounts must be added for the weight of the supporting buckstays, burners, ductwork, fuel and crossover piping, soot blowers and dust hoppers.

For superheaters and reheaters the weights are calculated on the basis of the surface exposed to the furnace plus an allowance for headers, part of the boiler roof and all tubing above the roof. A somewhat similar procedure is followed in calculating the weight of an economizer.

Depending upon the circumstances, air heaters may have an independent structure or be supported by special framing to boiler support columns. In addition to the calculated load of the air heater, allowance must be made for shifting of loads, expansion joint forces, and weight of insulation and ductwork.

Weights of ducts are determined by their actual makeup. This can vary quite widely, particularly with ducts which are lined inside. Details to be considered are duct plate, stiffeners, internal pipe trusses, insulation, dampers and any special internal equipment. Movements of ducts between startup and operating temperature can be quite complex, depending upon the rigidity of certain equipment.

Ducts are generally allowed to expand due to thermal conditions, but they are held against such external forces as caused by wind and seismic disturbances. Vertical movements are generally taken care of by hanger rods with coil springs. Rods with constant load springs are used to provide for larger movements. Horizontal loads are taken into the frame by stops located at points of zero expansion.

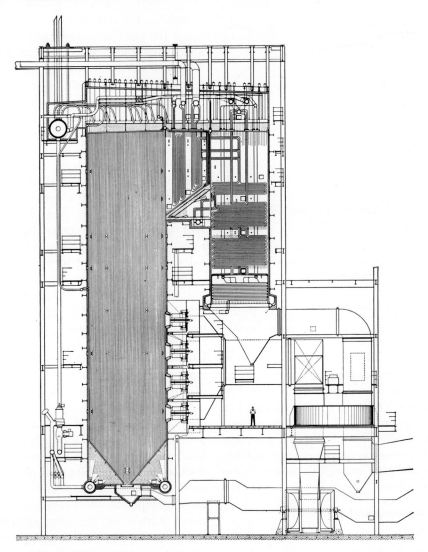

Figure 10–23.   Cross section of reheat boiler showing pressure parts and fuel burning equipment in detail.

Structural Design Procedure

When the preliminary power plant design is completed, including equipment selection, and when loads have been determined and boiler columns located, the structural engineer is in a position to begin the final design of the members of the structure. To aid in visualizing this pro-cedure the following descriptive information and simplified structural drawings are presented. For this example a controlled circulation reheat boiler with a capacity of 1,500,000 lb of steam per hour is chosen. Fig. 10–23 is a typical cross section of this boiler which has superheater outlet conditions of 2075 psig and 1000 F with reheat

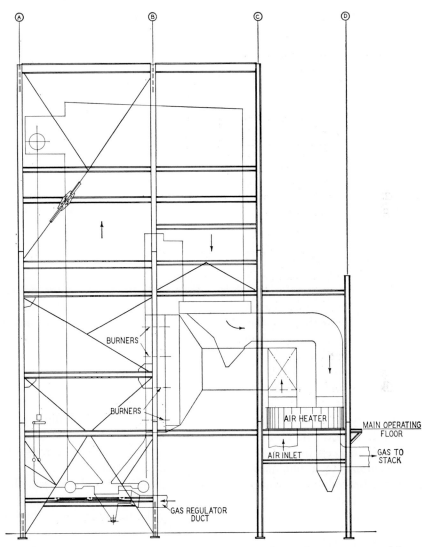

Figure 10–24.   Cross section of same reheat boiler with emphasis on vertical bracing and structural components.

to 1000 F. By contrast to the usual emphasis on pressure parts and firing equipment in Fig. 10–23, the structural elements of the reheat boiler are more conspicuous in Fig. 10–24.

First of all, platforms must be located. These are very important elements of a power plant because they provide means

of access for operation and maintenance. Certain platforms are assigned to receive horizontal trusses. The latter provide lateral support for all boiler columns that cannot be held in any other manner. These trusses provide a means of transferring the lateral forces due to wind and earthquake from the buckstay system of the boiler to

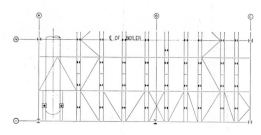

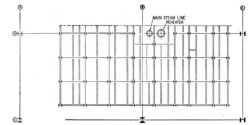

Figure 10–25. Structural arrangement at main boiler support level.

Figure 10–26. Structural arrangement at pressure parts support level.

the vertical bracing system for transmission to the boiler foundation. Encompassing the whole boiler as they do, the platform trusses provide effective safeguards against torsional rotation.

The vertical column bracing is selected to clear walkways and boiler equipment, such as soot blowers, and to allow maximum accessibility. The most important consideration in the design of vertical column bracing is to keep the net uplift of the boiler columns to a minimum. Fig. 10–24 shows a braced side elevation and the vertical bracing arrangement across the center columns.

Main Boiler Support Level

As noted earlier, the main boiler support level, Fig. 10–25, is the highest point of a top supported boiler structure. From this level the boiler is supported like a bell by many wide flange hangers. These hangers extend down to the pressure parts support level located below.

The main boiler support framing consists of longitudinal members which pick up the parallel channels carrying the wide flange hangers. The longitudinal girders

frame into the front, center and rear cross girders which transmit the weight of the boiler to the main columns and down to the foundation. The main steam drum is supported at this level, and in many installations the primary steam and reheat lines are also supported here. On some large boilers the weight of the drum and its component parts, including pumps and downtakes, may be on the order of 2,000,000 lb, requiring hanger rods $6\frac{1}{2}$ in. or more in diameter.

Longitudinal and lateral horizontal trusses secure the framing against wind or earthquake forces and give the boiler torsional stability.

Pressure Parts Support Level

Directly below the main boiler support level, and supported from it, is the pressure parts support level, Fig. 10–26. It consists of many double rows of channels which support the hangers holding up all waterwalls, superheater, reheater and economizer. In fact, as much as 95 per cent of the total boiler weight is collected and supported at the pressure parts support level.

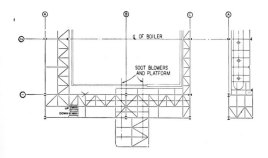

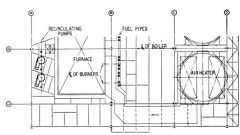

Figure 10–27. Horizontal bracing at boiler platform (left) and drum enclosure (right).

Figure 10–28. Horizontal bracing at main operating platform.

In order to design the framing for the pressure parts support level, the designer requires an arrangement drawing showing the pressure parts. With load and arrangement information, the designer can then proceed to locate the lines of supports. The steel is designed so that the hangers are perpendicular after expansion. The support members are designed for a reduced allowable maximum stress due to the elevated temperature.

Bracing System

The bracing system is chosen and designed with care since it must support the boiler structure rigidly against wind, earthquake and unbalanced internal or transient forces during startup. For example, excessive lateral movement could damage high pressure steam piping, auxiliary equipment or even the boiler proper. The bracing must be balanced so that there will be little if any torsion in the structure due to the differences in bracing deflection.

The conventional boiler bracing system consists of horizontal bracing at the main boiler support level and at each platform level. This bracing keeps the structure from twisting and also transfers the lateral loads from the boiler proper to the vertical bracing. Examples of horizontal bracing are shown in Figs. 10–27 and 10–28.

The vertical bracing, usually made of X or K frames, is located between as many main columns as possible. This transfers the tendency of uplift to the heavier loaded boiler columns. It should be obvious that no bracing can be allowed to pass through the boiler furnace. The type and location of the vertical bracing frequently has to be modified in order to avoid interference with soot blowers, air and gas ducts, various types of piping, stairs and walkway clearances. When seismic forces must be resisted, the bracing members become quite large, necessitating the use of wide flange beams rather than the usual angles. Examples of vertical bracing at four different column lines are shown in Fig. 10–29.

After the vertical bracing system is established, the designer calculates and assigns the proportional lateral loads to the respective platform elevations. From these loads the stresses in the bracing members

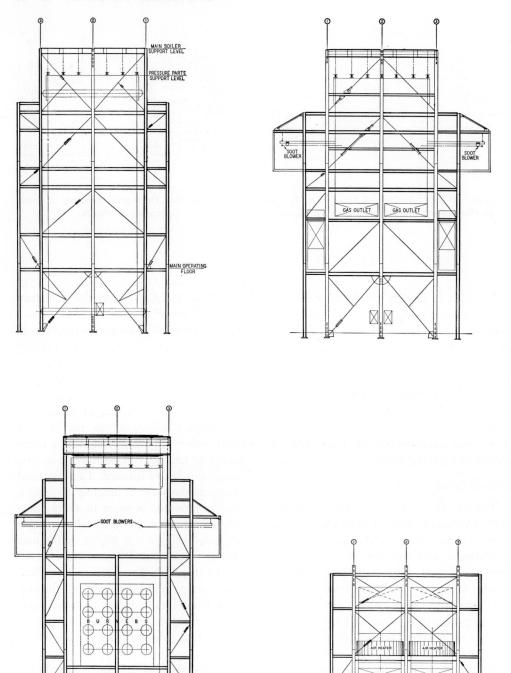

Figure 10–29. Vertical bracing through Column Line *A* (upper left), column line *B* (upper right), column line *C* (lower left) and column line *D* (lower right).

and columns are calculated and the member is sized.

The next step is to prepare sketches showing the framing arrangement for all platforms. This enables the designer to determine the amounts of platform live and dead loads to be assigned to the columns. Other equipment loads, such as the air heater, are also shown distributed to the columns.

With all loads known, a column schedule is prepared and the columns are sized. The designer is now in a position to design the column bases and locate the anchor bolts. A base plate and anchor bolt plan provides information for the design of the boiler foundation as shown in Fig. 10–30.

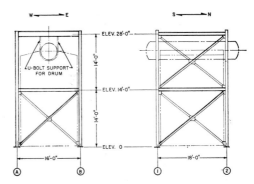

Figure 10–31.   Hypothetical boiler structure.

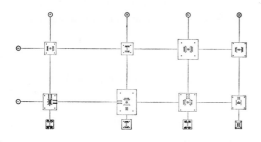

Figure 10–30.   Plan of anchor bolts and base plates for structural columns for reheat boiler.

Calculations for Hypothetical Boiler Structure[46]

Consideration of the number of structural elements in the boiler just illustrated discloses that the design of this structure requires very extensive calculations of many members with many different func-tions. Some repetitious calculations may be arranged for solution with high speed computers.

To illustrate the design procedure, however, it appears desirable to incorporate a simplified example, Fig. 10–31, of a hypothetical single drum boiler suspended by two U-bolts from an elementary structure comprising four columns, two support beams and necessary framing and bracing elements. The example illustrates a type of bracing commonly designated as conventional or simple framing. This assumes that the ends of beams and girders are connected for shear only and are free to rotate under load. Other types of framing might be selected, one example being continuous-rigid framing.

The structural designer can choose from a wide variety of standard structural steel shapes for use as beams, columns, braces and other members. Through experience he gains an ability to select the type of shape which will carry the required loads most economically.

An important aspect of design judgment is involved in knowing when more exact analysis will result in cost savings. There is a delicate balance between decreases in

[46] Calculation procedures in this section were developed by R. E. Kinney, consulting engineer.

weight of materials and increases in engineering costs. Conventional or simple framing may prove more economical than a continuous frame involving long and complex calculations.

In the simplified structure shown in Fig. 10–31 the location of the boiler drum and the principal structural members has been fixed. It is the task of the structural designer to determine the size of these members to support the boiler drum.

The following design data are known:

Boiler drum diameter	5'–0"
Boiler drum length	24'–0"
Weight of boiler drum and accessories	90 Kips[47]
Design wind pressure	30 lb per sq ft

Determination of Vertical and Wind Loads

The vertical loads due to the boiler drum and accessories are transmitted through two U-bolts. These loads are arranged so that the load is equal in each rod of each U-bolt. This means that the total load, W_b, must be divided in quarters.

$$W_b = 90,000/4 = 22.5 \text{ Kips per U-bolt rod}$$

The wind loads can act in any direction. For design, it is assumed that the wind first acts in a North-South direction. A second set of calculations is then based upon the wind acting in an East-West direction.

North-South Wind Loads. In separate calculations not shown here it is determined that the projected area exposed to winds acting in the North-South direction is 78.5 sq ft. The centroid of this area is found to be at an elevation of 22'–0" and symmetrically arranged within the structure. The N-S wind load, $W_{w(N-S)}$, is found by this simple relationship.

$$W_{w(N-S)} = 78.5 \times 30 = 2.36 \text{ Kips}$$

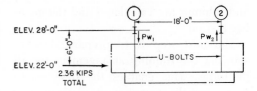

Figure 10–32. Couple produced by north-south wind loads.

Since the centroid is 6'–0" below the top framing members, a couple is produced causing a secondary up load on the far top beam as shown in Fig. 10–32.

Summing moments about beam 1 (near top beam) at elevation 28'–0":

$$\Sigma M = 2.36 \times 6.0 - P_{W2} \times 18.0 = 0$$

$$P_{W2} = 0.79 \text{ Kips or}$$

0.39 Kips per U-bolt rod (in compression)

Summing forces vertically:

$$\Sigma V = P_{W1} + P_{W2} = 0$$

$$P_{W1} = -0.79 \text{ Kips or}$$

−0.39 Kips per U-bolt rod (in tension)

East-West Wind Loads. In separate calculations not shown here it is determined that the projected area exposed to winds acting in the East-West direction is 240 sq ft. These calculations also indicate that the centroid of this area is at an elevation of 22'–0" and symmetrically arranged within the structure. The E-W wind load is then:

$$W_{w(E-W)} = 240 \times 30 = 7.20 \text{ Kips}$$

As in the case of the N-S wind load, the E-W wind load produces a couple as shown in Fig. 10–33.

Summing moments about the left connection at elevation 28'–0":

[47] Structural design practice is to use the expression *Kip* to represent 1000 lb.

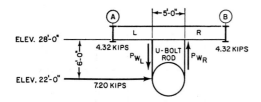

Figure 10–33. Couple produced by east-west wind loads.

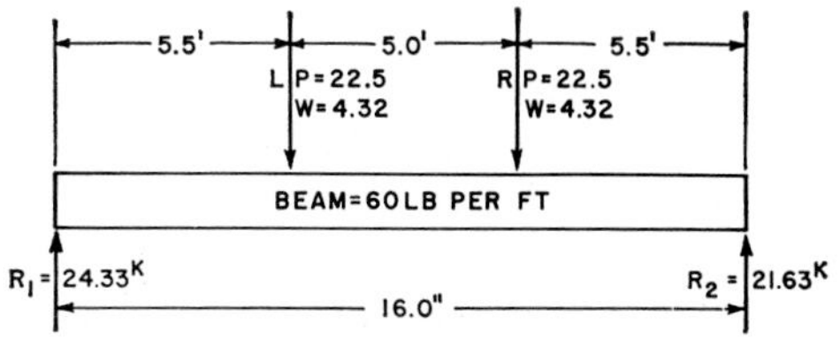

Figure 10–34. Beam A—1—B at Elevation 28'–0"

$$\Sigma M = 7.20 \times 6.0 - P_{WR} \times 5.0 = 0$$

$$P_{WR} = 8.64 \text{ Kips or}$$

4.32 Kips per U-bolt rod (in compression)

Summing forces vertically:

$$\Sigma V = P_{WR} + P_{WL} = 0$$

$$P_{WL} = -8.64 \text{ Kips or}$$

−4.32 Kips per U-bolt rod (in tension)

In this case the wind loads on individual structural members are small and will be neglected in the design of these individual members. However, after these members are selected the resultant wind loads will be included in the reactions due to that particular member.

Design of Beams at Elevation 28'–0"

In the design of main support beams, wind loads are combined with the drum loads. Section 1.5.6 of the 1963 AISC Structural Steel Specification mentioned earlier allows a 33⅓ per cent increase in allowable bending stresses for wind conditions, provided the required section computed on this basis is not less than that required for the design dead and live load. However, in this simplified design this will not be done, and the wind loads and drum loads will be combined without

increase in allowable stress values, thus providing more conservative results.

Referring to Fig. 10–34 and summing moments about R_1, the value of R_2 is calculated to be 21.63 Kips. Algebraic summation of vertical forces gives a value of R_1 of 24.33 Kips.

In order to size the main support beams, it is necessary to determine the maximum bending moment. The left, center line and right moments are calculated as follows:

$$M_L = 24.33 \times 5.5 - 0.060 \times 5.5 \times 5.5/2$$
$$= 132.9 \text{ Kip-ft}$$

$$M_{CL} = 24.33 \times 8.0 - (22.50 + 4.32)2.5$$
$$- 0.060 \times 8 \times 8/2$$
$$= 125.67 \text{ Kip-ft}$$

$$M_R = 21.63 \times 5.5 - 0.060 \times 5.5 \times 5.5/2$$
$$= 118.1 \text{ Kip-ft}$$

For a main support beam of 16 ft and a maximum bending moment of 132.9 Kip-ft, an 18WF60 beam is chosen. The unit bending stress f_b must be determined, using the section modulus S, the value of which may be obtained from the *Manual*, and the maximum bending moment M.

$$f_b = M/S = 132.9 \times 12 \times 1000/107.8$$
$$= 14,790 \text{ psi}$$

The allowable bending stresses depend

upon the proportions of the structural section. Sections with proportions resulting in thin wide flanges relative to beam depth and length are subject to local buckling under compressive stresses, and therefore the allowable bending stresses are reduced accordingly. The ratio ld/A_f, in which l is the length of the beam in inches and A_f is the area of the compression flange in square inches, expresses this proportion. When ld/A_f is equal to or less than 600, local buckling is not critical and the maximum allowable stress is 20,000 psi for steels with 33,000 psi specified yield point. If greater than 600, Section 1.5.1.4.5 of the 1963 AISC Specification provides the following method of determining values of allowable stress:

$$F_b = 12,000,000/(ld/A_f)$$

Substituting in this relationship the value of F_b for an 18WF60 beam is found to be 18,020 psi. The stress ratio of f_b to F_b has a value of 0.821.

The beam must also be checked for the stresses caused by the North-South wind loads. The stress ratios for lateral and vertical bending must be investigated to see that their sum is less than unity in accordance with AISC Specification requirements for combined stresses.

Wind Loads and Design of Bracing Members in A and B Vertical Planes

The members in the A and B vertical planes resisting North-South wind loads and the wind loads are shown in Fig. 10–35. Only the diagonal bracing members which act in tension are assumed to resist the wind loads. To require diagonal members to carry compressive loads would require that each be designed as a column, usually requiring heavier sections just to possess adequate stiffness to act as compressive load carrying members. The re-

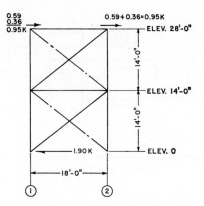

Figure 10–35. Bracing members in A and B vertical planes.

sult is generally a heavier structure than if it is assumed that only the members placed to carry tension loads are effective and that the other members are ineffective. The stresses shown in Fig. 10–35 are calculated by simple vector analysis of the joints.

Each of the horizontal members in these planes has an unbraced length of 18'-0", no bending load and an axial load of 0.95 Kips in compression. Since the structure is rather simple, this member may be considered to be a bracing compression member, in which case the value of the ratio of the length to radius of gyration, l/r, must be kept below 200. In this instance the minimum value of r is 1.08 in.

By reviewing available structural sections it can be seen that small WF sections offer the best r for the weakest axis for a given weight. The minimum value of r for a 6WF15.5 is 1.45 and for an 8WF17 is 1.16. If a beam of small depth to span ratio is chosen, some stiffness is sacrificed. Generally it is wise to keep the depth to span ratio to not less than 1/30. For this reason an 8WF17 member is chosen.

The basic allowable compressive stress is given by the following relationship in

Section 1.5.1.3.2 of the 1963 AISC Specification:

$$F_a = 149,000,000/(l/r)^2$$
$$= 4.27 \text{ Kips per sq in.}$$

From Section 1.5.1.3.3 the design allowable stress when l/r exceeds 120 is given by this relationship:

$$F_{as} = F_a/(1.6 - l/200r)$$
$$= 6.42 \text{ Kips per sq in.}$$

With an area of 5.00 sq in. an 8WF17 member has an allowable load capacity of 32.1 Kips. This same member is adequate in the central horizontal position where there is a load of 1.90 Kips in compression.

Although the members forming the X to the diagonal members acting in tension are assumed to carry no load, they do provide support at the midpoint of the tension diagonals in the vertical plane. The characteristics of the diagonals under consideration in Fig. 10–30 are as follows:

Unbraced length, lateral plane   22.8 ft
Unbraced length, vertical plane   11.4 ft
Axial load, tension   2.41 Kips

As indicated in Section 1.8.4 of the 1963 AISC Specification the maximum allowable l/r is 300. The required minimum values of r are as follows:

$$r_{min} = 22.8 \times 12/300 = 0.92 \text{ (one axis)}$$

$$r_{min} = 11.4 \times 12/300 = 0.46 \text{ (any axis)}$$

Structural angles have section properties adaptable to this condition. From the AISC *Manual* the following properties are found for a 3 × 2½ × ¼ angle:

Area	1.31 sq in.
r_{xx}	0.95 in.
r_{yy}	0.75 in.
r_{zz}	0.53 in.

With an allowable tension stress of 20.0

Kips per sq in. the allowable load is 26.2 Kips. For bracing members in the A and B planes 3 × 2½ × ¼ angles are chosen.

Wind Loads and Design of Bracing Members in 1 and 2 Vertical Planes

The wind loads in bracing members of *1* and *2* vertical planes, Fig. 10–36, are calculated and checked in the same manner as those in the A and B planes previously noted. Since the size of the bracing in the side planes is known, the wind loading of these members is added to the wind loading of the boiler proper. Upon selecting the size of the members in the end planes, the side bracing will be checked for these additional loads in the same manner.

The winds loads occurring at elevation 28.0, Fig. 10–36, must be transmitted to elevation 14.0 by resisting moments in the columns. These moments will be included and discussed in the section on column design and loadings.

The bracing members in the *1* and *2* vertical planes are designed and calculated in the same manner as previously set forth for the A and B vertical planes. The side bracing members should be rechecked with the wind loads due to end bracing included.

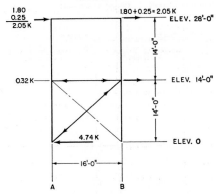

Figure 10–36. Bracing members in *1* and *2* vertical planes.

Tabulation of Bracing Reactions to Column Reactions

Table 10–2 indicates the resolution of the end reactions of each bracing member to the particular column which reacts the loading. These reactions are made up of the dead weight of the members and the vertical components of the loads in the members due to wind loading. The entire bracing is first resolved for North-South wind loads and then again resolved for East-West wind loads. The columns must be designed for the more severe wind condition. In some cases one wind condi-

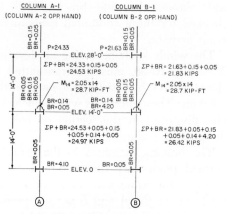

Figure 10–37.   Column   loadings — north-south wind loads.

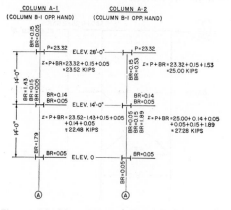

Figure 10–38.   Column   loadings — east-west wind loads.

tion will prove critical for some columns while another wind condition might be critical for others. Table 10–2 does not include the principal loads caused by the boiler drum and boiler support beams. All of these loads must be included in order to design columns.

Column Design and Loadings

The first step in column design is to determine the location and the magnitudes of the loads applied to the column. This is best visualized by making a sketch of each cross-section of the column where structural members attach. Starting at the top of the column, the vertical reactions of each member are shown beside that particular member. The elevations of the sections and the distances between are also shown together with amount and nature of the loads. Moments are indicated at the point of application.

The loadings on the columns are shown by a diagrammatic section through each column framing elevation. The lateral and diagonal members are shown as lines in the proper framing direction. If the structure is symmetrical, it is not necessary to show nor to calculate all columns. It is often found that certain columns are mirror images of other columns, and framing members fit these columns just opposite to the column being analyzed. In these cases the fact that a single analysis serves more than one column may be indicated as "Column B–1 opposite hand."

Fig. 10–37 indicates column loadings for North-South wind loads and Fig. 10–38, for East-West wind loads. In these figures values of BR, structural bracing loads, may be found in Table 10–2. The loads P in Fig. 10–38 are shown as reactions in Fig. 10–34 and are calculated in the section on design of beams at Eleva-

Table 10–2 Final Vertical Loads Due To Bracing To Be Applied To Columns

Wind Direction	Member		Load	Elev.	Reactions			
					A–1	A–2	B–1	B–2
North–South	Horizontal	1–2	Dead Wt.	28.0	0.15	0.15	0.15	0.15
	Upper Dia.	1–2	Dead Wt.	28.0	0.05	0.05	0.05	0.05
			Wind	28.0	0.00	1.48	0.00	1.48
			Total	28.0	0.05	1.53	0.05	1.53
	Upper Dia.	1–2	Dead Wt.	14.0	0.05	0.05	0.05	0.05
			Wind	14.0	−1.48	0.00	−1.48	0.00
			Total	14.0	−1.43	0.05	−1.43	0.05
	Horizontal	1–2	Dead Wt.	14.0	0.15	0.15	0.15	0.15
	Horizontal	A–B	Dead Wt.	14.0	0.14	0.14	0.14	0.14
	Lower Dia.	1–2	Dead Wt.	14.0	0.05	0.05	0.05	0.05
			Wind	14.0	0.00	1.84	0.00	1.84
			Total	14.0	0.05	1.89	0.05	1.89
	Lower Dia.	A–B	Dead Wt.	14.0	0.05	0.05	0.05	0.05
	Lower Dia.	1–2	Dead Wt.	0	0.05	0.05	0.05	0.05
			Wind	0	−1.84	0.00	−1.84	0.00
			Total	0	−1.79	0.05	−1.79	0.05
	Lower Dia.	A–B	Dead Wt.	0	0.05	0.05	0.05	0.05
East–West	Horizontal	1–2	Dead Wt.	28.0	0.15	0.15	0.15	0.15
	Upper Dia.	1–2	Dead Wt.	28.0	0.05	0.05	0.05	0.05
	Upper Dia.	1–2	Dead Wt.	14.0	0.05	0.05	0.05	0.05
	Horizontal	1–2	Dead Wt.	14.0	0.15	0.15	0.15	0.15
	Horizontal	A–B	Dead Wt.	14.0	0.14	0.14	0.14	0.14
	Lower Dia.	1–2	Dead Wt.	14.0	0.05	0.05	0.05	0.05
	Lower Dia.	A–B	Dead Wt.	14.0	0.05	0.05	0.05	0.05
			Wind	14.0	0.00	0.00	4.15	4.15
			Total	14.0	0.05	0.05	4.20	4.20
	Lower Dia.	1–2	Dead Wt.	0	0.05	0.05	0.05	0.05
	Lower Dia.	A–B	Dead Wt.	0	0.05	0.05	0.05	0.05
			Wind	0	−4.15	−4.15	0.00	0.00
			Total	0	−4.10	−4.10	0.05	0.05

tion 28′–0″. Calculation of the values of P in Fig. 10–37 has not been previously shown.

A study of the column loadings in Fig. 10–38 shows that one point of design consideration will be the loading at Elevation 14′–0″ with an East-West wind loading shown earlier in Fig. 10–36 and introducing a bending moment of 2.05 Kips acting over the 14 ft length of the column. The combination of the axial load and the bending load at this elevation appears more critical than other axial loadings without additional primary bending moments. The design conditions for Column A–1 at Elevation 14′–0″ are as follows:

Unbraced length
14′–0″
Axial load
24.53 Kips + column weight
Bending moment
28.7 Kip-ft

A 10WF33 member having the following section properties taken from the AISC *Manual* is selected as a column:

Area	9.71 sq in.
S_{xx}	35.0 in.³
S_{yy}	9.2 in.³
r_{xx}	4.20 in.
r_{yy}	1.94 in.
Depth	9.75 in.

In the 1963 AISC Specification the column slenderness ratio, C_c, is found to be 131.7 for steels with 33,000 psi specified yield point. The allowable bending stress, F_b, for the same steels is 20,000 psi.

From the preceding data the ratio of $1/r_{min}$ is found to be 87, and this is used to determine the axial compressive stress, F_a, which in Table 1–33 of the 1963 AISC Specifications has a value of 13.74 Kips per sq in.

The axial load, including the weight of the column is:

$$P = 24.53 + 0.033 \times 14 = 25.0 \text{ Kips}$$

The compressive stress is:

$$f_a = P/A = 2.58 \text{ Kips per sq in.}$$

$$f_a/F_a = 0.188$$

In addition to the bending moment caused by the wind load, a secondary bending moment is caused by the framing of the top support beams to the flange of the column. The entire beam reaction is placed into the inner flange of the column, so that the moment of this secondary bending moment is half of the column depth (9.75/2). The beam reaction, as shown in Fig. 10–34, is 24.33 Kips. The bending moment is as follows:

$$M = 24.33 \times 9.75/2 = 118 \text{ Kip-in.}$$

The total bending moment at Elevation 14′–0″ is 463 Kip-in., including the value just calculated and a primary bending moment due to wind load of 28.7 Kip-ft (345 Kip-in.) as indicated in Fig. 10–38. The bending stress, f_b, is then determined:

$$f_b = M/S = 463/35.0$$
$$= 13.2 \text{ Kips per sq in.}$$

According to the 1963 AISC Specification, Section 1.6.1, members subject to both axial compression and bending stresses must meet the following requirements:

$$\frac{f_a}{F_a} + \frac{C_m f_b}{\left(1 - \dfrac{f_a}{F'_e}\right) F_b} \leq 1.0$$

Substituting values previously determined and information from the 1963 AISC Specifications, using steels with 33,000 psi specified yield point, the value of this expression is found to be 0.837.

Another requirement for combined stresses is that at points in the plane of bending, $f_a/20{,}000 + f_b/F_b \leq 1.0$. For this case the value is found to be 0.789.

By observation it can be seen that the bending moments cause the greatest portion of the total stress in the column, and hence the other conditions of column loading are not critical for purposes of analysis.

Base Plates and Footings. The final concern with columns is to know the final column base reactions so that the base plates and concrete footings can be designed. Steel base plates are generally used under columns for distributing the column loads to the concrete foundations. There are two basic requirements for these base plates:

1. The plate must have sufficient area

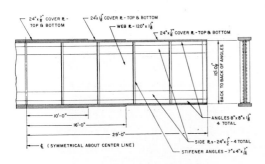

Figure 10–39. Basic arrangement of main support plate girder.

so as not to exceed allowable bearing pressures between the plate and the concrete.

2. The plate must have sufficient thickness to resist bending so that the column load may be distributed over the entire base plate area.

The structural designer usually provides the maximum and minimum column loadings so that the footings can be properly designed by others. Even though base plates and connections of structural members are generally standardized, it is important that the designer be aware of their importance and functions. While a great amount of consideration properly belongs to the major structural elements, structural details such as base plates must never be overlooked.

The total column loads can be obtained from the column loadings in Figs. 10–37 and 10–38 by adding the Elevation 0 reactions plus the column dead weights to the summation of column loadings given between Elevation 0 and 14'–0''. The maximum loading occurs with the North-South wind on Columns A–2 and B–2. The loads are:

$$P_T = 27.28 + 0.05 + 0.05 + 0.033 \times 28$$

$$= 28.31 \text{ Kips}$$

Since the minimum loads do not cause uplift, only the maximum loading is of interest to the designer of the footings. Although the analysis indicates that the maximum loads are found on Columns A–2 and B–2, reversal of the wind direction would cause a shift to Columns A–1 and B–1. For this reason the maximum load must be indicated at each of the four columns and be taken into consideration for design purposes.

Extent of Calculations

The preceding analysis of a hypothetical boiler structure represents but a small portion of the calculations required for a complete central station boiler. As experience in structural design is gained, many shortcuts become apparent. By choosing members whose strength has previously been checked, the structural designer is able to achieve cost economy in both design and erection. In actual practice he places just sufficient information on his calculation sheets to indicate loads, members and stresses. The preceding example contains more details of calculation than would normally be shown. In fact, too much exactness in calculations may result in many different sizes of structural members without commensurate savings in structural weight.

Some portions of a structure merit more detailed analysis. One example is the main support plate girder, Fig. 10–39, for the reheat boiler described earlier in this chapter. This girder or beam is itself quite complex and is required to carry heavy loads and to span a considerable distance. In a large central station in which the load to be carried is in excess of 10,000 tons at an elevation of 210 ft above the structural mat, five support girders spanning a width

Figure 10–40. Support girder in front of central station structure, left, and being hoisted into position, right.

of 116 ft and having a depth of about 15 ft are required.[48] Fig. 10–40 shows a main boiler support girder in the process of erection.

Some Special Considerations

In the span of about a decade boiler furnace sizes have more than quadrupled, and pressurized firing is more the rule than the exception in large central station boilers. Manufacturing techniques have been improved so that fusion and fin welded tube panels are shop assembled and field erected as large units. All of these factors have had a pronounced effect on structural design of boilers.

There are some structural considerations which relate directly to the thermal functions of the boiler. In once-through boilers with intermixed steam and water circuits, cubical expansion forces must be allowed for. These involve differential expansion movements which are more complex than those encountered in furnaces composed solely of waterwalls. Special provisions

must be made for anchoring parts subject to these forces and for sealing connections between components expanding by differing amounts.

A distinctive feature of boiler structural design is the buckstay system which protects the pressure parts against internal forces due to pressurized operation or furnace disturbances. The pressure parts, including waterwall tubing and wall radiant surface, are attached to and must therefore deflect with the buckstays. Spacing of buckstays is determined from furnace pressure, tube diameter, spacing and that part of the allowable stress in the tubing which can be allotted for bending. With furnaces being designed for internal pressures of 150 lb per sq ft and widths exceeding 70 ft in waterwall enclosures 200 ft or greater in height, the problems of designing buckstay systems have been greatly magnified.

A final consideration, transient forces encountered in the startup and shutdown of boilers, is beyond the scope of this treatment of boiler structural design.

---

[48] Plate girder design for such conditions becomes quite complex and is beyond the scope of the treatment in this section. The interested reader is referred to the Sixth Edition of the AISC *Manual of Steel Construction*, Sixth Edition, 1963, Part 2, Beam and Girder Design, pp. 2–55 through 2–65 and pp. 2–80 through 2–83, for a complete analysis.

11

Manufacture and Machine Design[1]

THE MANUFACTURE of boiler and reactor components requires many types of equipment and facilities. Tubing and plates are the two classes of material that are involved in most of these manufacturing operations. Welding of many types is used in the fabrication of tubing and plates. Heavy hydraulic presses are required to form segments of boiler drums and reactor pressure vessels, and machining likewise plays a part in boiler and reactor manufacture. Heat treatment, materials handling, inspection and quality control are important adjuncts of manufacturing operations.

The engineer must be continually aware of the interrelationship between product design and manufacture. A design that results in improved heat transfer efficiency may be useless if the component cannot be fabricated economically and within the tolerances proposed. On the other hand, savings in manufacturing costs that result in finished elements which do not meet design objectives cannot be justified. The lines of communication between design and manufacturing functions must be maintained if overall production economy and high quality products are to be the end results.[2]

New product design needs have significant effects upon manufacturing processes. Standardized production equipment may not be satisfactory, and new machines may have to be developed, as illustrated by the welding machines which are described later in this chapter. Machine design requires knowledge from many specialized fields, including production practices, component design, materials, metallurgy and controls.

This chapter is concerned with a selected group of *manufacturing operations* and with *machine design* as related to pulverizers. The first section deals with welding and its applications, including some of the steps involved in the design of automatic welding machines. This is followed by five manufacturing case studies and a discussion of optical tooling as applied to boiler and reactor manufacture.

---

[1] Material for this chapter was obtained from several individuals whose contributions are indicated in appropriate places.
[2] A textbook that elaborates this point of view is *Engineering Design — A Systematic Approach* by Robert Matousek, Interscience-Wiley, 1963, 264 pages. "The Art of the Practical Engineer" by Sir David Pye, *Proceedings* of the Institution of Mechanical Engineers, Vol. 167, 1953, pp. 265–271, presents a design philosophy that merits additional attention.

The final section on machine design of bowl mills treats many of the components of these intricate coal pulverizers and includes representative calculations.

Welding and Its Applications[3]

Welding is the basic tool for fabricating boiler and reactor components. While elements of a skilled art are retained in some aspects, welding is a recognized technical specialty and requires substantial background in the fields of metallurgy, electrical and mechanical engineering.[4]

In the application of welding process, skills in metallurgy are necessary in determining the effects of chemical composition and metal structure on the properties of the weld. Skills in electrical engineering are required in designing the welding power supply, welding controls and related equipment. Particularly in automatic

fusion welding, there must be precise control of the welding arc as well as the welding machine, and this usually involves electronics. Skills in mechanical engineering are essential to design automatic welding equipment, where the machine designer must have knowledge of mechanics, hydraulics, pneumatics and heat transfer.

Automatic welding, like other automatic manufacturing operations, is used only when it can produce a higher quality product at a lower cost than semiautomatic or manual operations. Numerous examples of the broad technical knowledge required in welding can be pointed out. There are applications in the space and aircraft industries so completely automatic

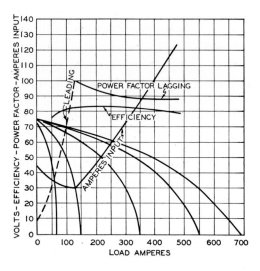

Fig. 11–1.   Volt ampere curve

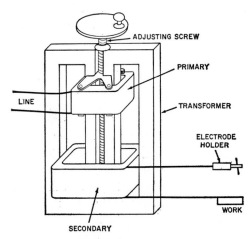

Fig. 11–2.   Method of changing power output of a-c supply

---

[3] Material contributed by R. W. Minga and reviewed by R. E. Lorentz, Jr.
[4] An authoritative work on this subject is the *Welding Handbook* issued in several volumes and revised periodically by the American Welding Society, United Engineering Center, New York.

that punched tape systems are used for indexing and control. In the boiler and nuclear power industries, however, it is uncommon to manufacture large numbers of duplicate units, and hence fully automatic techniques are less frequently utilized. Nonetheless, there are certain components which can be fabricated best by automatic methods, one example being the sheet metal used in boiler ducts and casings.

Welding Power Supplies

The most frequent encounter of the welding engineer with electrical engineering is in connection with welding power supplies which may be designed for either alternating or direct current. These supplies are commonly made in ratings which have been standardized by the National Electrical Manufacturers Association.

The alternating current power supply usually employs a special type of transformer with a means of varying the power output. The secondary side of the transformer is wound so that the voltage de-

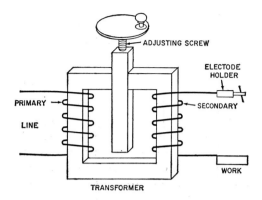

Fig. 11–3. Method of changing power output of a-c supply

creases as the current increases. This is known as a drooping characteristic and is shown in the volt-ampere curve of Fig. 11–1. Figs. 11–2 and 11–3 show two typical methods of changing the power output of alternating current welding power supplies.

Direct current welding power supplies are commonly used. There are two general types: the motor-generator type shown in Fig. 11–4 and the transformer-rectifier

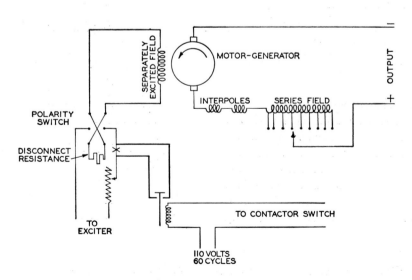

Fig. 11–4. Motor generator power supply

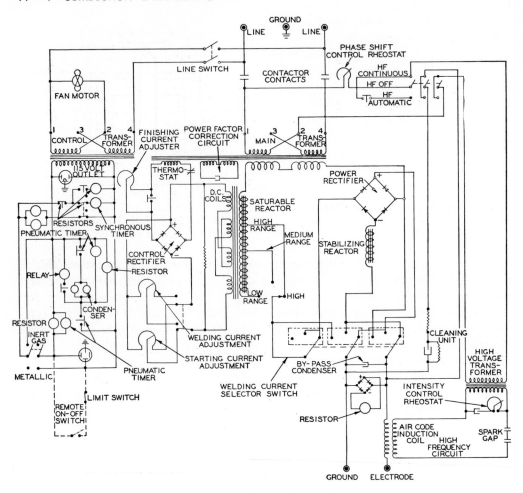

Fig. 11—5.   Transformer rectifier power supply

type shown in Fig. 11–5. The latter, which in this case is of the saturable reactor type, may be used on either alternating or direct current and is readily adapted to automatic welding. Depending upon the requirements, direct current power supplies may be produced with the constant current (or drooping characteristics) shown previously in Fig. 11–1 or with constant voltage characteristics. There are other direct current supplies having variable slope characteristics which lie between the con-

stant current and constant voltage types. Even with the constant current type, the slope of the volt-ampere curve can be varied as shown in Fig. 11–6.

Automatic Submerged Arc Welding

An interesting application of automatic submerged arc welding is found in the fabrication of boiler drums. The welding zone is completely covered and shielded by a blanket of granular fusible material that is referred to as flux, although the material performs functions in addition to those of a flux. There is no visible evidence of the passage of current between the welding electrode and the component being welded. The electrode is not in actual contact with the component. The welding current is carried across the gap through the molten flux which is supplied automatically along the seam to be welded. The entire welding action takes place beneath the flux without sparks, spatter, smoke or flash. No protective shields, helmets, smoke collectors or ventilating systems are needed, although gog-

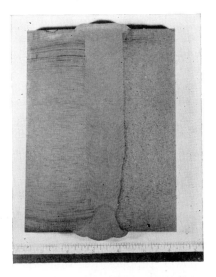

Fig. 11–7. Thick section submerged arc weld

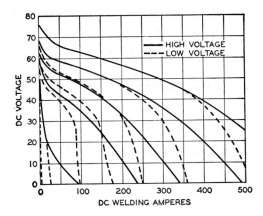

Fig. 11–6. Volt ampere curve

tween the two submerged electrodes. The intersection of the two electrodes is just high enough above the work piece to obtain good coalescence.

In the welding of boiler drums or reac-

gles may be worn as routine protection for the eyes. Fig. 11–7 shows a thick-section submerged arc weld.

Fig. 11–8 is a schematic diagram of a single electrode submerged arc circuit. This same basic circuit is frequently employed for series arc weld cladding of ferritic materials with a more corrosion-resistant material such as stainless steel. The series arc circuit is basically the same as that shown in Fig. 11–8 except that the ground lead is connected to a second welding head. The arc then occurs be-

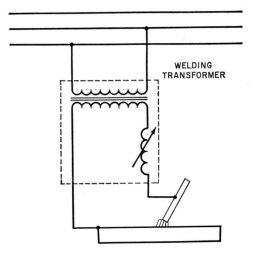

Fig. 11–8. Single electrode submerged arc circuit

tor vessels utilizing materials several inches in thickness, two submerged arc electrodes are frequently used to increase weld metal deposition rates. Fig. 11–9 is a schematic diagram of what is known as a closed delta system, which differs from a series arc circuit in that three power supplies are used to provide the greater electrical energy required for welding butt joints. A shop view of a Scott tandem setup for welding deep grooves in boiler drums is shown in Fig. 11–10. This is similar to the closed delta system except that only two power supplies are used.

As with most fusion welding processes, the power supplies for submerged arc welding can be either alternating or direct current. Each has its particular advantages, but alternating current is more widely used for this welding process because it is less susceptible to magnetic disturbances of the arc. This is a definite advantage in welding deep grooves in carbon and low alloy steels. Two or more alternating current arcs may be used in close proximity without causing magnetic disturbances which adversely affect the quality of the welds.

Another phenomenon that must be

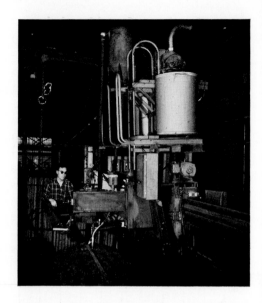

Fig. 11–10.   Welding boiler drum with submerged arc

taken into consideration in choosing between alternating and direct current for submerged arc welding is the ionization effects on the various elements in submerged arc wires and molten fluxes. Submerged arc welds are rarely of the same chemical composition as the material being welded, even with carbon steels. The alloying elements may be added through the flux, through wire or through both. Regardless of how the alloys are added, their recovery in the weld will be affected by the choice of welding power. As might be expected, the ionization effects on the chemical analysis of the weld are much greater with direct current welding power for any given wire or flux.

Automatic Gas Metal Arc Cladding

There are many applications in the chemical and nuclear fields in which homogeneous materials of the proper strength and corrosion resistance require-

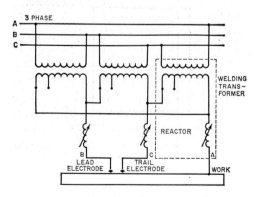

Fig. 11–9.   Closed delta connection

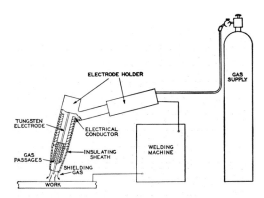

Fig. 11–11. Gas metal arc process

ments are not economically justified. One way to overcome this limitation is to use a low alloy for the base material and deposit upon it a thin section of high alloy material by weld *cladding*.

The gas metal arc process, a schematic diagram of which is shown in Fig. 11–11, is one of the processes used for cladding. In this process coalescence is produced by melting the electrode in an electric arc between the electrode and the work. Protective shielding is obtained from an inert gas such as helium or argon. Other gases or gas mixtures may also be used, including argon-oxygen and carbon dioxide. Direct current power supplies with reverse polarity are used.

In many reactor vessels, penetrations in the reactor head may be required for control rods, instrument connections and piping nozzles. Low alloy steel is usually the base metal for the reactor vessel and heads. The interior of the entire vessel, plus the head penetrations, may be clad with a material which has greater corrosion resistance.

Automatic gas metal arc welding is used for cladding the inside diameter of reactor head penetrations because of the good deposit quality and high deposition rates that may be obtained with this process. Reactor heads often weigh several

tons and cannot readily be positioned, but with an automatic machine the cladding may be performed with the axis of the penetration in the vertical position. Inside diameters of holes to be clad may be as small as four or five inches, with variable depth up to three feet.

A special machine was designed for this cladding application which could not be carried out satisfactorily by manual methods. The engineering skills required to design this welding machine are typical of those for other heavy industrial applications and will be described in some detail. The metallurgical problems differed but slightly from those worked out previously for less complex cladding operations.

The machine took the form of a specially designed gas metal arc torch that could be positioned in the penetrations of the reactor head to weld circumferentially around the inside surface of the penetrations as the torch was moved upward, thus producing a continuous deposit. Fig. 11–12 shows the machine for weld clad-

Fig. 11–12. Welding machine for cladding inside of nozzles

Fig. 11–13. Close-up of weld cladding

Fig. 11–14. Weld cladding after machining

ding, and Fig. 11–13 shows the inside of the reactor head penetrations after weld cladding and before machining. A finished machined sample of a clad penetration is shown in Fig. 11–14.

In the design of this welding machine there were electrical problems relating to the transmission of the welding current and control current to the rotating welding head. It was also necessary to control the filler wire feed and speed and to maintain constant rotation and vertical travel speeds. The wire extension from the welding torch nozzle likewise was critical, as the reactor head penetrations were made up of several steps or ledges. A control circuit also had to be worked out for this variable.

Slip rings and brushes were used for transmitting both the welding current and control current to the welding head. An electronic control was selected for the filler wire feed, and a constant voltage welding power supply was used. With this arrangement the proper welding current could be obtained by changing the wire feed speed.

The circuit for controlling rotational travel speed was simpler. The load on the vertical travel motor was constant so that an auto transformer was used to control the voltage across the armature through a full wave rectifier system.

The control of the distance of the torch from the wall of the head penetrations was difficult because of the presence of ledges. The solution was to utilize two photoelectric cells to sense the angle of arc light from the shielding gas nozzle of the torch. The two photoelectric cells were connected through an electronic amplifier and then to a servo motor. As the wire extension from the torch nozzle changed the angle of the light changed and in turn was relayed to the servo motor. The latter moved the welding head in or out as required by the changing contour of the reactor head penetration.

For this particular cladding machine there were no unusual mechanical design problems. Conventional gear type and ratios, jack screws, bearings and friction surfaces were used.

As a result of the application of metallurgical, electrical and mechanical engineering principles, a machine was designed and built to perform an automatic cladding operation that previously could not be done by manual or semiautomatic methods.

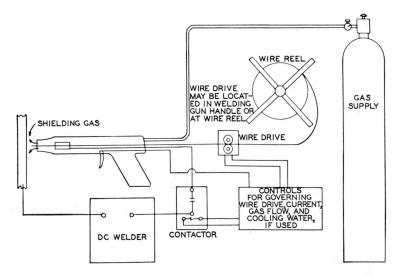

Fig. 11–15. Tungsten arc process

Tungsten Arc Welding of Tube Sheets

Steam generators for nuclear power plants differ in many respects from their boiler counterparts for conventional power plants. Some nuclear designs permit steam generation in the main reactor vessel, while others use a separate heat exchanger which bears some resemblance to the feedwater heaters used in large central stations. The diameter of the tubes is kept to a minimum in order to use as thin a tube section as possible and to increase the surface area, thereby improving heat transfer.

To obtain the strength and leak tightness required for nuclear steam generators the general practice is to strength weld the tubes to the tube sheets. This can be done manually for tubes which have sufficient wall thickness and spacing. However, to weld thin wall tubes of ½ and ⅝ in. outside diameter, with ¼ in. spacing between tubes, hand methods are not practicable. An automatic welding ma- chine had to be designed to meet these requirements.

The tungsten arc process, a schematic diagram of which is shown in Fig. 11–15, was chosen for this application because a small weld of extremely high quality was specified. Filler wire of a slightly different analysis from that of the tubes was selected for metallurgical reasons. This

Fig. 11–16. Automatic tube welding machine

process is generally similar to the gas metal arc method except for the substitution of a tungsten electrode for a consumable metal electrode.

Fig. 11–16 shows an automatic tube welding machine positioned above a test sample tube sheet. A close-up view of the panel for controlling the sequence of the welding gun is shown in Fig. 11–17, while Fig. 11–18 is a schematic diagram of the panel for controlling solenoid valves for cooling water and shielding gas, plus the Tesla coil for initiating the arc.

The comparatively low voltage supplied by the welding power supply is not sufficient to initiate the arc between the tungsten electrode and the work piece unless the electrode is made to come in contact with the work piece and then withdrawn to the proper arc length. It is essential in an automatic machine to establish the arc at the start of the weld without this "striking" technique. In the tube welding machine a Tesla high frequency induction coil, familiar to many through physics laboratory demonstrations, is used to transmit a very small current at extremely high voltage across the gap between the tungsten electrode and the work piece. This current, measured in milliamperes, ionizes a path through the shielding gas, and the welding current then establishes the welding arc. The arc starting current from the Tesla coil is needed for only about one half second and is controlled by a timer.

The operational sequence of the tube welding machine is quite simple. The operator places the mandrel of the welding gun in the tube hole and pushes the start button until the arc is established. Then after approximately fifteen seconds of weld cycle time the tube welding machine is moved to the next tube hole, and the process is repeated.

Fig. 11–17. Control panel for automatic tube welding machine

By referring to Figs. 11–17 and 11–18 it is possible to follow the actions that take place within the control panels. In sequence this consists of energizing the solenoids controlling the shielding gas and cooling water. Next the welding contactor is closed and the Tesla coil energized, firing a spark across the arc gap to establish the welding arc. The current relay then activates the weld cycle timer which starts the drive and wire feed motors. At the completion of the weld cycle a second timer is energized to keep the control solenoids engaged and to bring into action the slope controller, which allows the welding current to decay gradually before extinguishing the welding arc. By decaying the current in this manner crater defects at the weld overlap are eliminated. Finally the whole control circuit is de-energized, and another solenoid valve is opened to admit cooling air. This assists in removing heat from the mandrel, which serves the function of a weld chill as well as a machine support and positioner. A small diameter welded tube sheet is shown in Fig. 11–19.

Careful study of the circuit diagrams

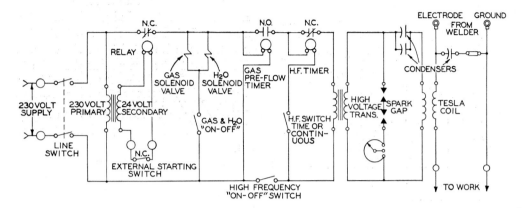

Fig. 11—18. Schematic diagram of control panel

Fig. 11—19. Welded tube sheet

and the assembly drawing of the tube welding machine will disclose that many basic elements of electrical and mechanical engineering must be understood and applied in designing and building the welding machine. It should be evident that the problem of developing a machine for welding tube sheets for a nuclear steam generator must be considered very broadly in the early stages. Questions like the following had to be formulated and answered.

Is it feasible to develop an automatic machine to perform a welding operation which cannot be done satisfactorily by hand? If so, what welding process should be used? With this process, will it be possible to make welds that will meet the rigid specifications for strength requirements and weld integrity?

An overall or systems approach was required to answer these questions. Then and only then could detailed design begin. It was necessary to make a preliminary appraisal of the principal components and determine which were available commercially and which would have to be built specifically for the welding machine. At the same time, consideration had to be given to many electrical details: size and type of power supply; selection of relays,

timers, solenoids and Tesla coil. Likewise, mechanical elements had to be designed and selected. These had to be
matched with the electrical components
and checked for size and ability to withstand anticipated stress. In addition, there
were considerations of heat flow in the
deposit of weld metal and in the removal
of heat during and following the completion of the weld cycle. The mandrel, for
example, not only centers the welding
machine in the tube but also absorbs heat
from the back side of the tube to prevent
the weld from burning through. Heat
transfer was also an important consideration in designing and setting the slope
controller which causes the welding current to decay at the end of the cycle in
a manner which eliminates weld defects.

There were other physical considerations in the design of this welding machine. As mentioned earlier, the Tesla coil

was put to practical engineering use in
initiating the arc. A solution to the problem of melting the tops of the steam generator tubes was found from physical
chemistry and knowledge of ionization
potential. It is known that the ionization
potential of helium is higher than argon.
The higher ionization potential results in
a smaller and more constricted arc plasma,
and hence helium was selected, greatly
minimizing what might have been a serious problem of melting off the tops of
tubes.

The foregoing description and explanation of an automatic tube welding machine have been presented in some detail
in order to illustrate the many physical
and engineering factors that enter into the
detailed design of such a machine. Similar
accounts could be written for many other
types of equipment used in the manufacture of boilers and nuclear reactors.

Manufacturing Case Studies[5]

As indicated earlier there is a close
relationship between product design and
manufacture. On some occasions, improvements in manufacturing techniques
may force reevaluation of boiler design
practices to take advantage of lower production costs and improvements in assembly.[6] Conversely, some manufacturing advances are a direct result of changes in
product design. That is, a production
machine must be developed or a process
improved in order to meet specific design
needs.

What follows are five manufacturing
case studies to describe and illustrate this
interplay of the requirements of product
design and machine design. Four of these
are chosen from the field of welding,
while the fifth involves a machining stage.
The reader should recognize that these
case studies were selected from among
several hundred possibilities in the broad
range of manufacturing activities involved
in the building of boilers and nuclear reactors. However, from the viewpoint of
engineering considerations that must be

[5] Material contributed by R. W. Fitzgerald, J. C. Campbell, W. Rupinski, and A. E. Klager.
[6] For additional information, see Chapter 26, Shop Assembled Boilers.

Fig. 11–20. Induction pressure welder

taken into account, the following are quite typical and representative.

Induction Pressure Welder

The *induction pressure welder* shown in Fig. 11–20 may be used to assemble tubes used in the economizer and superheater sections of a boiler, to make tube splices and to join tubes of different material compositions. The tube weld is made by clamping and aligning the tube ends, heating the joint with an electrical induction coil, and bringing the hot ends against each other with a precise and automatically controlled force. The resulting weld, Fig. 11–21, can be heat treated in the same machine to improve its strength and ductility. The resulting weld reinforcement, Fig. 11–22, is smooth and offers no restriction to flow or any irregularities to start corrosion on the inside of the tube. In this type of welding, the two essentials for a good joint are intimate surface contact and clean welding surfaces. Intimate contact of the weld surfaces is obtained by accurate machining of the abutting ends and by the upsetting force; clean weld surfaces are obtained by machining the tube ends, careful handling and the use of a protective atmosphere during the welding cycle to prevent oxidation.

The machine illustrated is capable of joining tubes from 1¼ to 3 in. diameter. The machine is loaded and controlled by an operator and a helper. The helper also prepares the tube ends for welding by facing on a scarfing machine and deburring.

Welding current is supplied to the machine by a totally enclosed, water cooled high frequency motor-generator unit. Two hydraulic systems are used: the first, for the weld upset pressure; the second, for clamping and aligning the tube. The upset pressure system has six selective circuits on which preset upset pressures may be selected by the operator for different tube diameters, tube wall thicknesses and materials or combinations of materials. These circuits are also interconnected with the welder controls to give the proper heats and time required. The tube clamping system is a dual pressure system using two tandem mounted, hydraulic pumps to supply the system with low and high hydraulic pressures. The low pressure is used to initially clamp and align the tubes

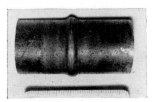

Fig. 11–21. Exterior view of induction pressure weld

Fig. 11–22. Interior view of induction pressure weld

to be joined; the high pressure is used to clamp and hold the tubes during the weld upset.

Continuous Fin Welder

To provide extended heat transfer surfaces in the low temperature sections of certain boiler types, lengths of flat bar stock or fin bars are attached to tubes as shown in Fig. 11–23. These finned tubes are submerged arc-welded on the machine shown in Fig. 11–24. This is a semiautomatic operation which requires an operator and helper to load and control the machine. Of versatile design, the *continuous fin welder* is capable of welding either a double or single finned tube on one or both sides using tubes up to 50 ft along with a 1½ to 4 in. outside diameter and fin bars ¼ to ½ in. thick. Its maximum overall fin and tube width capacity is 8½ in.

A centralized control station is used by the operator to run the machine. This station contains all the controls which are necessary to start, operate, and adjust the welding process.

The machine utilizes two fixed welding heads and a hydraulically powered tube-fin drive and alignment system to make the welds. Flux is deposited on the work ahead of the weld by a gate controlled, gravity feed hopper; after the weld, the excess flux is removed by a vacuum unit,

Fig. 11–24.   Continuous fin welding machine

Fig. 11–23.   Continuous
fin weld

filtered and returned to the hopper. To simplify design and as an economy measure, pneumatic cylinders are used in preference to hydraulic ones to position the weld ground shoes, tilt the welding heads and unload the finished tubes.

Two separate, individually controlled, welding circuits are used. Each supplies current at 900 amperes maximum, welding voltage at 26 volts maximum, and open circuit voltage at 40 volts maximum. Each circuit is supplied by a direct current motor-generator which has an adjustable open circuit voltage; the weld arc voltage is in turn adjusted by raising or lowering this open circuit. The welding current is controlled by the feed rate of the electrode wire which is varied by the operator using an electronic motor speed control. The welding system provides a stable arc voltage and gives more constant arc starting because of the high initial surge current.

The tube and fin bars are fed through

the machine by a series of drive and clamping idler wheels. These drive wheels are powered by an adjustable hydraulic motor which gives the machine a maximum speed of 78 in. per minute. The clamping idler wheels are actuated by limit switches during the passage of the tube and fins through the machine. Three sets of fin aligning wheels, two horizontal and one vertical, are used to position and hold the fin bars on the tube for welding.

Fig. 11–26. Peg fin welder

Peg Fin Welder

Peg finned tubes are used as filler and for tube spacing in extended side walls, steam cooled walls, and deflection arches, where, due to higher temperatures, it is not possible to use continuous finned tubes. A standard 1½ in. wide fin is spaced on tubes with an outside diameter of 1¼ in. or larger so that there is a $\frac{1}{16}$ to ⅛ in. gap between fins for expansion purposes. The peg fin finished height may be from ⅜ to 2¾ in. and the fin is either ¼ or $\frac{5}{16}$ in. thick, as shown in Fig. 11–25.

The pegs are attached to the tube by flash welding on a machine known as the *peg fin welder* shown in Fig. 11–26. These machines are capable of welding fins on one or both sides of a tube up to 35 ft long on a single pass or up to 65 ft long by repositioning the tube and making two passes. Approximately 13 fins may be

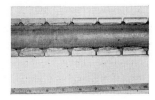

Fig. 11–25. Peg fins on tube

welded per minute on the machine. For the weld upset, $\frac{1}{16}$ in. is added to the finished height of the peg fin.

The peg fin welder illustrated is controlled and loaded by an operator and a helper. The weld power source is supplied from a central 12,000 volt, 500 kva, 60 cycle transformer where it is reduced to 230 volts required by the machine primary welding circuit. The tube drive motor and hydraulic pump motor are supplied with 440 volt, 60 cycle current from the plant lines. A transformer is used to reduce the main line 440 voltage to 110 volts for operating the machine control circuits.

The tube drive is an electrically powered rack and pinion type which pushes the tube through the machine. Operator controlled, this drive may be used either to index the tube automatically for fin spacing or to pass the tube by the welder for unfinned portions of the tube.

The operator and helper manually load the peg fins individually into peg clamps. After loading, the operator actuates the machine's sequencing mechanism to complete the welding process as follows: (1) the pneumatic peg clamps and hydraulic tube clamps close; (2) hydraulic rams or slides move the peg clamps toward the tube and position the pegs against the tube; (3) the weld heat timers are actuated causing the welding current to arc between the tube and peg for a preset length of time to melt the end of the peg and a small shallow area on the tube, (4) high hydraulic pressure is then applied to make the weld by forcing the molten end of the peg into the puddle of molten metal on the tube; (5) after the weld is made, it is cooled under high hydraulic presure; (6) the high pressure is shut off, the peg and tube clamps released and the hydraulic rams return under low pressure; and (7) the tube is advanced to the next position automatically.

Finished tubes are removed from the machine unloading rack by pneumatic actuated throwout arms.

Fusion Panel Welder

The *fusion panel welder*, otherwise known as the panel processing machine

Fig. 11–27.   Fusion panel welder

shown in Fig. 11–27, has the function of welding loose tubes into panel segments and then welding panel segments with additional loose tubes into panels which make up the waterwalls of high pressure boilers. Such panels are used in shop assembled boilers as well as in the largest central station boilers.[7]

Three welding arcs are used simultaneously to deposit molten metal which solidifies to form the web between the tubes. Optimum web widths are in the 3/8 to 1/2 in. range, and the welder can fabricate panels of 7/8 to 3 1/2 in. diameter tubes. The machine is capable of welding carbon and alloy tubing at rates up to about two feet per minute.

Basically, the fusion panel welder shown in the schematic diagram of Fig. 11–28 consists of a frame, three welding heads, tube drive, pressure rollers, copper chill bars, flux recovery and dispensing unit, filler wire feed, tube feed-in rack and conveyor, and feed-out and storage racks. One main and three secondary control stations are used to load and operate the machine.

In the welding cycle, tubes and panel segments are fed by means of the feed-in rack and conveyor against a gate which aligns the tube ends. The alignment gate is then lowered and the tube drive activated. Held in alignment by contoured pressure and drive rollers, the tubes and panel segments pass under the three welding electrodes where weld wire and filler wire are fed into each arc. A water cooled copper chill bar under each welding arc and between the tubes supports the individual weld puddles until they solidify to form the webs between the tube. One, two or all three welding heads may be stopped or started by the operator at any time during the welding cycle.

After the three webs are welded, the panel moves under automatic scaling hammers which remove the fused flux from the top of the weld. The panel is then discharged from the machine onto the feed-out racks where it is transferred to storage racks by a transfer mechanism.

The flux recovery unit is an electrically powered vacuum machine with a storage hopper, dispenser and pickup. A solenoid operated flux gate on each welding electrode dispenses flux for each weld. After welding, the unfused flux is picked up and returned to the flux hopper by vacuum operated pickups. The fused flux or slag which was broken up by the scaling hammers is removed by a vacuum operated slag removal unit.

The welding power for each electrode is furnished by a saturable reactor controlled alternating current welding transformer with electronic welding controls. The 1/4 in. steel weld wire for each arc is fed from a container mounted on a turntable above the machine, through the wire

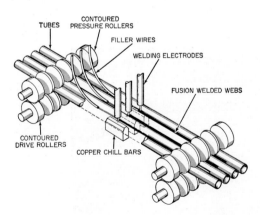

Fig. 11–28. Schematic arrangement of fusion panel welder

TUBES CONTOURED PRESSURE ROLLERS

FILLER WIRES

WELDING ELECTRODES

FUSION WELDED WEBS

CONTOURED DRIVE ROLLERS

COPPER CHILL BARS

[7] See Chapter 10, Section on Strength of Furnace Walls, p. 10–20, for additional information on the uses and physical properties of panel walls.

Fig. 11–29.   Plate edge milling machine

feeder, straightener and nozzle to the welding point where the power is supplied from the transformer. The ¼ in. steel filler wires are fed into the welding arcs by an adjustable speed drive from containers mounted on other turntables on the machine.

Plate Edge Milling Machine

The *plate edge milling machine* shown in Fig. 11–29 is used to mill weld grooves or to face header and drum half shell ends before the shell is formed. The weld groove, a combination of perpendicular,

sloping and radius surfaces, is machined by making multiple passes and using shaped milling cutters. Plates up to 12 in. thick and in any workable width, Fig. 11–30, are milled on this machine.

The milling head assembly, saddle drive, operator's station, hydraulic systems, and lubrication system are mounted as a self-contained unit on a moving saddle or carriage. This saddle moves along the hardened steel ways of the machine bed on bronze wear plates and is powered by a hydraulic motor driven rack and pinion. The saddle traverse speed range is from 0.5 to 36.5 in. per minute and is adjusted with hydraulic flow control valves. To prevent cutter shock loads, an anti-backlash device holds the drive pinion in contact with the rack teeth by hydraulically preloading the pinion.

The milling machine is equipped with a single spindle, horizontal milling head which is driven by a 25 hp electric motor through a heavy duty, automotive type, 10 speed, helical gear transmission. The spindle has a stroke or feed-in of 6⅝ in. and is manually positioned and locked. A hydraulic motor driven jackscrew is used

Fig. 11–30.   Heavy plate on milling machine

to move the milling head through a 12 in. vertical adjustment. For cutting bevels or sloping surfaces, the entire head and drive may be pivoted up to 45 degrees below the horizontal; the pivot is powered by a hydraulic cylinder. Two hydraulic clamping cylinders are used to lock the head in position. A 9 in. cutting head is used. Cutting oil is supplied by a remote pump connected to the sump under the machine bed. To remove chips, an oscillating conveyor is mounted under the cutter head over the entire length of the machine bed.

A 28 ft, 8 in. clamping beam equipped with 18 pneumatic cylinders on 17½ in. centers is used to position and clamp the work to be milled. The pneumatic cylinders are individually actuated by the operator and are supplied with 90 psig air from the plant lines.

Positive lubrication is supplied to the machine ways, transmission, spindle and other wear points by a pressurized, metered lubrication system. The lubricating unit is mechanically driven through a speed reducer by a hydraulic motor.

Optical Tooling[8]

Optical tooling principles have been used by some engineers to align machine tools and jigs as far back as the 1920's. Optical tooling, as known today, was perfected near the end of World War II because of the close tolerances required by the aircraft industry. Subsequently optical tooling found application by the ship building industry, machine tool builders and manufacturers of heavy equipment, including nuclear reactor vessels.

Optics provide essentially a line of sight that is absolutely straight, has no weight and from which measurements can be made with great accuracy. There are three basic instruments used in optical tooling. They are: the alignment telescope, the jig transit and the precise level. These optical instruments supplement and usually replace plumb bobs, straight edges, precise steel squares, surface plates, indicator

gauges and shop levels for various jigs, structures, component parts and assemblies.[9]

Optical tooling instruments are used where dimensions are needed accurate to thousandths of an inch and angles accurate to seconds of arc. All three basic instruments are self-checking. Therefore, their accuracy is independent of any master gauge.

There are some basic problems which optical tooling can solve easily, rapidly and very accurately. These include answers to such questions as the following:

1. Is the outboard support in line with the machine spindle?
2. Are the lathe bed ways parallel to the headstock spindle and the tailstock in line with the spindle?
3. How flat is a granite plate or machine bed?

[8] Material contributed by Edward Williams.
[9] For additional information, see *Optical Tooling for Precise Manufacture and Alignment* by Philip Kissam, McGraw-Hill, 1962 and "K&E Optical Tooling Manual" published by Keuffel & Esser Co. An early paper is "The Use of a Surveying Instrument in Machine Shop Practice" by Charles C. Tyler, *Trans.* ASME, Vol. 24, 1903, pp. 360–367.

4. How plumb are the ways of the machine, component part or column?
5. Is the mating surface of a vessel perpendicular to its centerline?
6. Are the internal and external keyways precisely located at the desired angles?

Instrument Applications

The following sections describe the principal instruments and how they are applied in actual manufacturing situations.

Alignment Telescope

The *alignment telescope* is equipped with built-in auto-reflection target, built-in auto-collimation illumination unit and built-in micrometer. This instrument can be focused from zero to infinity. The horizontal and vertical micrometers have a range of plus or minus 0.050 in. with direct reading to 0.001 in.

Optical scales (10, 20 and 40 in.) which are calibrated with graduations every 0.100 in. permit direct readings to 0.001 in. to reference surfaces up to 40 in. from the basic line of sight and distances from

Fig. 11-31. Application of alignment telescope

the telescope in excess of 100 ft. Optical targets for use in fixtures permit checking several inline bores to a basic line. Various types of targets include plastic bull's-eye type, glass target mounted in steel ring and open type target with nylon monofilament cross lines.

The built-in auto-reflection target and the auto-collimation illumination unit in the telescope, along with a reflection surface, permits checking the perpendicularity of flat surfaces to the instrument centerline. A specific application of auto-collimation is shown in Fig. 11–31. The alignment telescope is centered in a special fixture which centers the telescope to the centerline of the penetration housing. A mirror on an adjustable table is adjusted so its surface is parallel to the bottom face of the closure head. With the illumination unit turned on, the amount of displacement of the reflected image from the auto-reflection target is measured in thousandths of an inch on X and Y axes. The tilt or lean of the housing is calculated in thousandths of an inch per foot.

Optical Square

The *optical square* is an instrument mounted on the barrel of the telescope to establish a line of sight perpendicular to the basic line of sight with an accuracy of one second of arc. By rotating the telescope and optical square in the supporting bracket, a plane is established precisely perpendicular to the basic line of sight. The optical square is equipped with an opening "straight through" which permits reading targets or scales on the basic line of sight.

A specific application of the optical square is shown in Fig. 11–32. The alignment telescope with the optical square is adjusted so that the basic line of sight is perpendicular to the face of the closure

Fig. 11–32. Alignment of closure head to boring mill

head and centered to the reference bore inside the head. Next the horizontal boring mill with a target in the spindle is positioned so that the spindle centerline coincides with the line of sight. The vertical and horizontal mill scales are read and recorded as "zero" position. The machine operator relates various machining operations to this zero point.

The various components of a nuclear reactor pressure vessel, Fig. 11–33, are fabricated and inspected to assure proper relationships between the reactor closure head, *2*, main vessel, *1*, thermal shielding, *3*, and the core barrel assembly, *4*. These parts must fit together so that the components are concentric, parallel or perpendicular and in the correct plane location.

The following is an example of the use of an alignment telescope and a plumb aligner bracket in the final inspection of the nuclear reactor vessel shown in Fig. 11–33. The plumb aligner bracket is used to position the alignment telescope so that

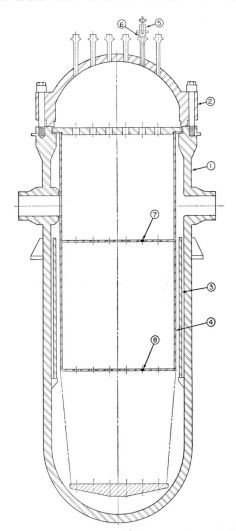

Fig. 11–33. Optical inspection of nuclear reactor pressure vessel

its line of sight is vertical within one second of arc (0.0015 in. at 25 ft). The instrument, *5*, is centered on a reference open nylon target in the control housing, *6*. Additional nylon targets are positioned in critical holes in the core barrel assembly, *4*, at locations 7 and 8.

The coordinate positions of the targets

Table 11–1   Optical Inspection
of Reactor Vessel

Target	Elevation 7		Elevation 8	
	X	Y	X	Y
A	+0.006″	+0.0335″	+0.030″	+0.021″
B	−0.005″	+0.0005″	+0.006″	+0.008″
C	−0.004″	+0.011″	+0.007″	+0.015″
D	+0.002″	+0.0065″	+0.011″	−0.003″
E	−0.002″	+0.017″	+0.011″	+0.021″
F	+0.018″	−0.0035″	+0.037″	−0.008″

in the core barrel assembly, referenced to a "plumb line" passing through targets in the control housing, had errors as shown in Table 11–1.

Tilting Level

The *tilting level* is equipped with a coincidence type bubble and a micrometer with a range of plus or minus 0.100 in. direct reading to 0.001 in. The coincidence reading bubble permits leveling the line of sight to one second of arc (approximately 0.001 in. per 17 ft). The level is used primarily to establish precise level planes.

Some typical uses of the level include leveling machine ways, leveling nuclear components for machining or inspection and checking sag in boring bars at various positions. A specific example is shown in Fig. 11–34. Here the level is used with the 10 in. optical scale to check the three horizontal machining ways of a 5 in. horizontal boring mill prior to doing a precision boring job.

Jig Transit

The *jig transit* is equipped with axle mirrors and an optical micrometer with a plus or minus 0.100 in. range, direct reading to 0.001 in. The transit can be focused from three feet to infinity. The removable micrometer can be rotated 90 deg to permit readings in a vertical or horizontal direction. The basic function is to establish precise vertical planes. However, it can be used to establish level planes to a less degree of accuracy than the tilting level.

The axle mirrors on the transit permit establishing perpendicular planes to the line of sight of the level or alignment telescope and at various distances from the instrument. A specific example is shown in Fig. 11–35. The transit and 10 in. optical scale are used to check the verticality of the 7 in. horizontal boring mill vertical ways.

Fig. 11–34.   Checking horizontal machining
ways

Fig. 11–35.   Checking verticality of boring
mill

Machine Design of Bowl Mills[10]

The C-E Raymond Bowl Mill for pulverizing coal and firing it directly into boilers was first placed in commercial service in 1935. Since that time there have been many refinements and improvements in both its overall design and that of individual components.[11]

The young engineer may expect to encounter assignments in which he is dealing with a well established design. As in the case of this example, this may well prove to be a challenge to find more satisfactory arrangements, to meet new operating requirements, to substitute newly developed materials for those previously used or to achieve cost reductions while improving reliability and performance.

This section goes into considerable detail on the many considerations involved in important areas of pulverizer design. Mention is made of the engineering reasoning involved in design decisions, and examples are provided showing how changes have been made to take advantage of advances in technology. Many of the routine calculations made in the course of commercial specification and production of pulverizers are closely related to those studied in undergraduate subject matter. Without becoming too involved in details, representative calculations are therefore included in this section.

To give the reader a better visual conception of the principal components of the C-E Raymond Bowl Mill, a cutaway view, Fig. 11–36, is included on page 11–24. In this type of pulverizer, coal is fed into a revolving bowl where size reduction takes place. The action of centrifugal force feeds the coal uniformly over the grinding ring to allow the rolls to exert the necessary pressure to pulverize the coal. The fines are then separated centrifugally from the larger particles and are entrained in hot air by which they are conveyed to the burners in the boiler.

Choice of Materials

The bowl mill base which houses the mill gearing is made of a sturdy multi-walled gray iron casting, meeting ASTM designation A-48, Class 30 specifications. Wall sections are designed for required strength.

The mill side, classifier body, classifier top, converter head, exhauster intake piping and the entire exhauster casing and side plates are all fabricated of heavy steel plate with all seams and joints welded. The mill side flanges and those of the mating classifier body and top are constructed of heavy steel bars rolled to suit, and lap welded to the cylindrical walls. Steel plate ASTM A-283, Grade C was selected for its strength, ease of fabrication and welding qualities.

The journal opening frames which are welded to the classifier body are steel castings, ASTM A-216, Grade WCA, which lends itself to welding to the fabricated classifier body. The mating covers are ductile iron castings ASTM A-339,

---

[10] Material contributed by L. J. Andresen.
[11] See Chapter 16, Pulverizers, for an extended discussion of the fuel and firing aspects of pulverizer design.

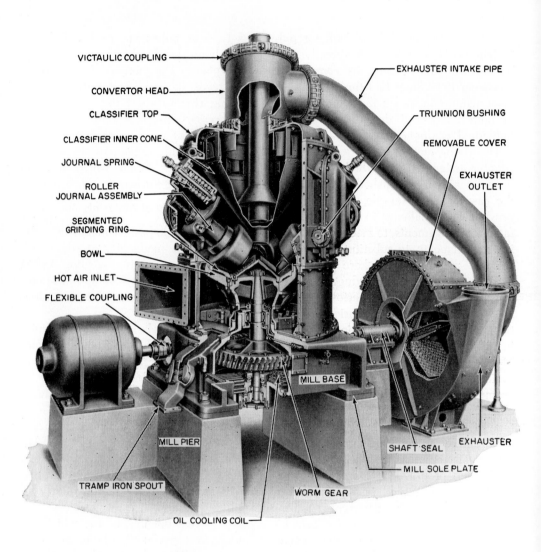

VICTAULIC COUPLING

CONVERTOR HEAD

CLASSIFIER TOP

CLASSIFIER INNER CONE

JOURNAL SPRING

ROLLER
JOURNAL ASSEMBLY

SEGMENTED
GRINDING RING

BOWL

HOT AIR INLET

FLEXIBLE COUPLING

MILL PIER

TRAMP IRON SPOUT

OIL COOLING COIL

WORM GEAR

MILL BASE

SHAFT SEAL

MILL SOLE PLATE

EXHAUSTER INTAKE PIPE

TRUNNION BUSHING

REMOVABLE COVER

EXHAUSTER
OUTLET

EXHAUSTER

Fig. 11–36.   Cutaway view of C-E Raymond Bowl Mill

Grade 60-45-10. Since there is considerable machining on this casting, ductile iron having about the same strength as a similar steel casting was selected because of its better machinability. Ductile iron is also used for the bowl, bowl hub and gear hub for similar reasons.

Lower mill side liners are made of steel plate and act as cover plates for the thermal insulation which provides greater comfort for operating personnel. The mill bottom liner plate is fabricated of thick abrasion resisting steel plate. Upper mill side liners are steel castings to which are welded hard faced air direction vanes.

The classifier body liners and bowl deflectors are Ni-Hard castings. This material having 4½ to 5 per cent nickel is well known for its excellent abrasion resistance. The grinding ring is cast of this same material, while the grinding rolls are usually centrifugally chill cast Raymix, which is a high grade white iron.

The exhauster periphery liners are sand cast of Raymix, while the side liners are steel plate.

Although it has been customary to use ordinary boiler plate for fan blades, longer wearing life is obtained by using four way pattern floor plate, with the raised tread beads at 45 degrees to the shaft axis. In order to obtain maximum life of the fan whizzer blades, the faces and leading edges are coated with a hard-weld material.

Design of Mill Base

The bowl mill base casting has two machined supporting feet which rest on machined steel sole plates as shown in Fig. 11–37. Because the worm drive shaft is offset from the mill centerline, it is desirable to keep the shaft centerline rather

than the mill centerline fixed, letting the mill centerline move horizontally as the mill warms up to operating temperature. To accomplish this, one of the sole plates is dowelled to the base with a large diameter pin pressed into both members on the shaft centerline. The opposite sole plate is provided with a slot on the shaft centerline which runs parallel to the shaft. The large dowel pin pressed into the base casting slides in the slot as the base expands. The mill worm shaft remains in preset alignment with the motor and exhauster regardless of temperature. The sole plates have a series of large diameter holes into which the grout is forced during setup, thereby keying or locking the sole plates to the mill foundation at the time of installation.

The height of the drive shaft above the mill base foot and that of the exhauster shaft above the bearing housing support foot is approximately the same as the height of the motor shaft above its feet, and since these three units all operate at about the same temperature, the shaft, once aligned horizontally, will tend to remain that way.

The exhauster bearing support base and casing feet also rest on separable sole plates. These are grouted in place after alignment is obtained. The mating parts

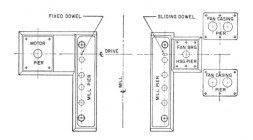

Fig. 11–37. Arrangement of bowl mill base

are then dowelled to the sole plates by means of suitable pins so that they can be readily realigned should it ever be necessary to remove these parts. Suitable shims are provided for the exhauster bearing assembly, the exhauster casing feet and the mill motor to take care of any future change in elevation of any of the components due to foundation settling. The sole plates of the exhauster casing have tapped holes in the corners for jack screws to facilitate alignment prior to grouting.

Stresses in Fabricated Components

All coal pulverizing equipment containing dust laden air is built in accordance with the Standards of the National Board of Fire Underwriters, Bulletin NBFU 60.[12] This states that such equipment is to be designed to withstand an internal pressure of 50 psig for containment of a possible internal explosion. If the parts are made of steel or other ductile material the allowable stress shall not exceed one fourth the ultimate strength of the material for cones, cylinders, tie rods, bolts, studs or other sections in tension, or one half the ultimate strength of the material for flat areas and sections subject to bending. If made of cast iron or other nonductile material the allowable stress shall not exceed one fourth the ultimate strength of the material for all parts.

To provide for wear, replaceable liner plates are used in all areas subjected to abrasion. Other areas, such as classifier bodies, tops, converter heads and piping have a wall thickness greater than would be needed for pressure alone as required by the Code.

By using high tensile bolts (100,000 psi) in the flanged joints of the separator body, separator top and mill side, the quantity of these bolts is about one half of those necessary were commercial bolts having 55,000 psi tensile strength to be used. This also shortens maintenance time when it is necessary to dismantle and reinstall any of these parts. The same is true of the bolts used in the large removable journal opening covers in the classifier body. Likewise, on the fan casing, weld studs having a tensile strength of 70,000 psi are used, cutting down the quantity somewhat over common studs having but 50,000 psi tensile strength. Here, again, maintenance time is shortened.

The Victaulic couplings provided for all coal-air piping meet the Underwriters Code. These require taking out but two bolts to dismantle any joint, as compared to the removal of many more, were conventional flanges to be used. This can be seen in Fig. 11–36.

The following calculations apply to the converter head cover, the classifier top and classifier body of a 20 ton per hour pulverizer.[13]

q = Internal explosion pressure = 50 psig

Moment along outer edge of circular flat plate, Fig. 11–38.

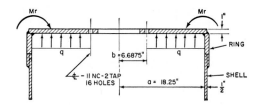

Fig. 11–38.   Converter head cover

---

[12] This Standard for the Installation and Operation of Pulverized Fuel Systems may be obtained from the National Board of Fire Underwriters, 85 John Street, New York 38, New York.
[13] A useful reference for such calculations is *Formulas for Stress and Strain* by Raymond J. Roark, Fourth Edition, McGraw-Hill, 1965, 432 pages.

$$M_r' = \frac{q}{8}(a^2 - 3b^2) + \frac{4b^4}{a^2 - b^2} \log\left(\frac{a}{b}\right)$$

$$= 1423 \text{ in. lb}$$

$$M_r'' = \frac{b^2 q}{4}\left[1 - \frac{2b^2}{a^2 - b^2} \log\left(\frac{a}{b}\right)\right] = 379 \text{ in. lb}$$

Total moment along outer edge of circular flat plate will be:

$$M_r = M_r' + M_r'' = 1423 + 379 = 1802 \text{ in. lb}$$

Stress in weld on Section A-A, Fig. 11–39.

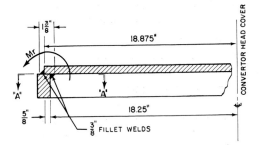

Fig. 11–39. Stress in converter head cover weld

$$I = (2)(1/12)(3/8)^3 + (3/8)(1/2)^2(2)$$

$$= 0.1963 \text{ in.}^4$$

$$Z = \frac{0.1963}{0.6875} = 0.2855 \text{ in.}^3 \text{ (Section Modulus)}$$

$$t = (2)(3/8) = 3/4 \text{ in.}$$

$$\therefore f_t = \frac{qa}{t} + \frac{M_r}{z} = 7529 \text{ psi}$$

Stress on throat area of weld

$$f_t = \frac{7529}{0.707} = 10,649 \text{ psi}$$

Stress in circular plate
Radial stress

$$f_r = \frac{6M_r}{t_h^2} = 10,812 \text{ psi}$$

Circumferential stress

$$f_c = Mf_r = 2811 \text{ psi}$$

Stress in the shell of head cover
Moment at end ring

$$M_0 = 0.304 \, qat_s = 138.7 \text{ in. lb}$$

$$V_0 = 0.78q\sqrt{at_s} = 117.81 \text{ lb}$$

Moment at any point x

$$M_x = \frac{1}{\lambda} V_0 e^{-\lambda x} \sin x$$
$$- M_0 e^{-\lambda x}(\cos \lambda x + \sin \lambda x)$$

In order to locate the maximum moment it is necessary to find $\dfrac{dM_x}{a_x} = 0$ and solve for X.

But in this case the maximum moment is found at $x = 0$. $\therefore M_{\max} = M_0$

Maximum longitudinal stress

$$f_l = \frac{qa}{2t_s} + \frac{6M_{\max}}{t_s^2} = 4241 \text{ psi}$$

Circumferential stress

$$f_c = \frac{qa}{t_s} + M\frac{6M_{\max}}{t_s^2} = 2690 \text{ psi}$$

Moment along the outer edge of flat classifier top, Fig. 11–40.

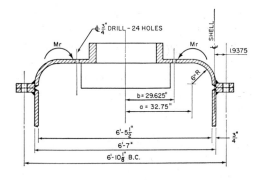

Fig. 11–40. Classifier body and top

$$M_r' = 1/8q(a^2 - 3b^2) + \frac{4b^4}{a^2 - b^2} \log\left(\frac{a}{b}\right)$$

$$= 156.39 \text{ in. lb}$$

$$M_r'' = \frac{W}{4\pi}\left[1 - \frac{2Xb^2}{a^2 - b^2} \log\left(\frac{a}{b}\right)\right]$$

$$= 1060.85 \text{ in. lb}$$

$M_r = M'_r + M''_r = 1217$ in. lb

Radial stress

$$f_r = \frac{6M_r}{t^2} = 12{,}981 \text{ psi}$$

Circumferential stress

$f_c = \mu f_r = 3376$ psi

Stress in weld of flange on Section A-A, Fig. 11–41.

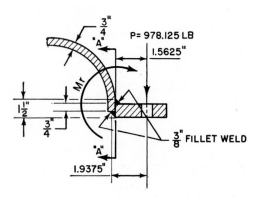

Fig. 11–41. Stress in weld of flange

$$P = \frac{qr}{z} = 978.125 \text{ lb}$$

$$M = M_r + P(1.5625)$$
$$= 2745 \text{ in. lb}$$

$$I = (2)(1/12)(3/8)^3 + (2)(3/8)(9/16)^2$$
$$= 0.2481 \text{ in.}^4$$

$$z = \frac{0.2481}{0.75} = 0.3281 \text{ in.}^3$$

$$f_s = \frac{P}{2t} = 1316 \text{ psi}$$

$$f_t = \frac{M}{z} = 8366 \text{ psi}$$

$$f_r = \sqrt{f_s^2 + f_t^2} = 8469 \text{ psi}$$

Stress in the shell and weld along longitudinal flange, Fig. 11–42.

$$r = 39.125'' \cos 11\tfrac{1}{4}° = 38.38 \text{ in.}$$

$P = qr = 1918.69$ lb

$P' = 1918.69 \cos 11\tfrac{1}{4}° = 1881.85$ lb

Stress in shell at Section A-A, Fig. 11–42.

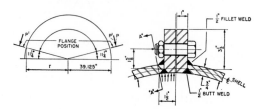

Fig. 11–42. Stress in shell and weld along longitudinal flange

$$M = 1881.85 \times 1.625 - 50 \left(\frac{3}{2}\right)^2 1/2$$
$$= 3002 \text{ in. lb}$$

$$f_t = \frac{1881.85}{3/4} + \frac{6(3002)}{(0.75)^2} = 34{,}530 \text{ psi}$$

Stress in weld, Fig. 11–43.

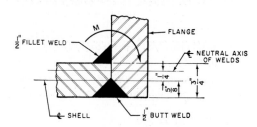

Fig. 11–43. Stress in butt and fillet welds

$$I_{zz} = (1/12)(1/2)^3(2) + (1/2)(3/8)^2(2)$$
$$= 0.1614 \text{ in.}^4$$

$$Z = \frac{0.1614}{0.625} = 0.2582 \text{ in.}^3$$

$M = 1881.85 \times (1.625 - .25) = 2588$ in. lb

Stress in butt weld

$$f_t = \frac{1882}{2 \times 1/2} + \frac{2588}{0.2582} = 11{,}905 \text{ psi}$$

Stress in fillet weld (throat area)

$$f_t = \frac{11{,}905}{0.707} = 16{,}839 \text{ psi}$$

Journal Spring

To give suitable roll pressure a spring having a rate of approximately 17,000 lb. per in. is required. In order to use existing parts, such as spring rod, spring housing, etc., an ID of 2¼ in. and an OD of 8¾ in. must be used. Free height is limited to 13 in., and to be able to accommodate large pieces of foreign material between the roll and ring, a spring movement or travel of about 2½ to 2¾ in. is required. A concentric multiple type was chosen because it provides for more load with equal travel in a given space. Fig. 11–44 shows the journal spring in relationship to the other principal parts of the bowl mill.

A double coil AISI C–1095 spring is de-

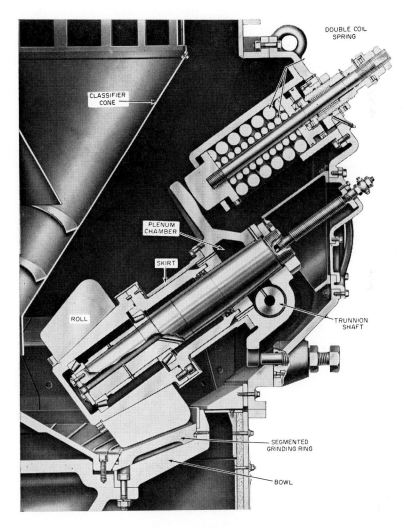

Fig. 11—44. Cutaway view of double coil spring, classifier cone, trunnion shaft, roll, segmented grinding ring and bowl

signed with ends squared and ground, using the following data.[14]

S = Allowable fiber stress in shear, 100,000 psi for carbon steel

C = Capacity of spring at 100,000 psi fiber stress, lb

d = Bar diameter

D = Mean coil diameter = $OD - d$

Δ = Deflection per coil at 100,000 psi

G = Torsional modulus of elasticity, 10,500,000 psi for carbon steel

H = Free height (spring not loaded)
  = Travel + Solid height

p = Pitch, free spring = $d\left(\dfrac{H - 1.5\,d}{h - 1.5\,d}\right)$

h = Solid height (coils in contact)
  = $\dfrac{d}{p}\,[H + 1.5(p - d)]$ (approximately)

R = Rate or load per inch of deflection

$C = \dfrac{\pi S d^3}{8 D}$

$\Delta = \dfrac{\pi S D^2}{G d}$

$R = \dfrac{C}{\text{Total deflection}}$

Solid capacity = $(H - h)R$

Solid stress = $\dfrac{\text{Solid capacity} \times 100,000}{C}$

Blunt bar length = $\dfrac{\pi D h}{d}$

W = Weight = Blunt bar length $\times$ 0.225 d^2

The stress limitation for carbon steel springs is usually in the range of 140,000 to 155,000 psi for applications such as the pulverizer journal. A K or stress concentration factor, commonly known as the Wahl correction factor, is applied. This is a function of the spring index, c, which is the ratio of the mean coil diameter to the bar diameter, or $c = D/d$.

$$K = \frac{4c - 1}{4c - 4} + \frac{0.615}{c}$$

The value of K is approximately 1.4 for the outer spring and 1.5 for the inner spring.

Dividing the above stress limitations by K results in an allowable stress of about 100,000 psi. The calculated values of solid stress are below this.

Outer Coil

Given:

$8\frac{3}{4}$ in. $OD \times 13$ in. $H \times 1\frac{7}{8}$ in. dia. wire size, $10\frac{1}{4}$ in. solid height

$$C = \frac{3.14 \times 100,000 \times (1.875)^3}{8 \times (8.75 - 1.875)} = 37,620 \text{ lb}$$

$$\Delta = \frac{3.14 \times 100,000 \times (6.875)^2}{10,500,000 \times 1.875} = 0.754 \text{ in.}$$

Number of coils:

$\dfrac{10.25}{1.875}$ = 5.48 coils–thickness in solid height
   + .50 (one half coil)
   5.98 total coils[15]

   −2.00 dead coils (one at each end)
   3.98 active coils

Total deflection = 3.98 × 0.754
       = 3.00 in. at 100,000 psi

Rate = $\dfrac{37,620}{3.00}$ = 12,540 lb per in.

---

[14] A basic reference is *Mechanical Springs* by A. M. Wahl, Second Edition, McGraw-Hill, 1963, 323 pages.

[15] One half coil is added because the bar actually twists and bends beyond the bearing surface and increases the deflection by this amount.

Solid capacity $= (13 - 10\frac{1}{4}) \times 12,540$
$\qquad = 34,490$ lb

Solid stress $= \dfrac{34,490 \times 100,000}{37,650}$
$\qquad = 91,680$ psi

$p = 1.87 \left[\dfrac{13 - (1.5 \times 1.87)}{10.25 - (1.5 \times 1.87)} \right] = 2.56$ in.

$h = $ (approx) $\dfrac{1.87}{2.56} [13 + 1.5(2.56 - 1.87)]$
$\qquad = 10.25$ in.

$ID = 8.75 - (1.875 \times 2) = 5$ in.

Blunt bar length $= \dfrac{3.14 \times 6.875 \times 10.25}{1.875}$
$\qquad = 118.0$ in.

$W = 118.0 \times 0.225 \times 1.875^2 = 93.4$ lb.

Inner Coil

Given:
$2\frac{1}{4}$ in. $ID \times 13$ in. $H \times 1$ in. dia. wire size, $10\frac{1}{4}$ in. solid height

$OD = 2\frac{1}{4} + (1 \times 2) = 4\frac{1}{4}$ in.,
$\qquad$ will fit inside 5 in. ID outer coil

$C = \dfrac{3.14 \times 100,000 \times (1)^3}{8 \times (4.25 - 1)} = 12,080$ lb

$\Delta = \dfrac{3.14 \times 100,000 \times (3.25)^2}{10,500,000 \times 1} = 0.332$ in.

No. coils $= \dfrac{10.25}{1}$
$\qquad = 10.25$ coils–thickness in solid height
$\qquad \underline{+.50}$ (one-half coil)
$\qquad 10.75$ total coils
$\qquad \underline{-2.0}$ dead coils
$\qquad 8.75$ active coils

Total deflection $= 8.75 \times 0.316$
$\qquad = 2.77$ in. at 100,000 psi

Rate $= \dfrac{12,080}{2.77} = 4360$ lb per in.

Solid capacity $= (13 - 10\frac{1}{4}) \times 4360$
$\qquad = 11,990$ lb.

Solid stress $= \dfrac{11,990 \times 100,000}{12080} = 99,250$ psi

$p = \dfrac{13 - (1.5 \times 1)}{10.25(1.5 \times 1)} = 1.31$ in.

$h = $ (approx) $\dfrac{13 + 1.5(1.31 - 1)}{1.31}$
$\qquad = 10.28$ in., say $10\frac{1}{4}$ in.

Blunt bar length $= \dfrac{3.14 \times 3.25 \times 10.28}{1}$
$\qquad = 105.0$ in.

$W = 105.0 \times 0.225 \times 1^2 = 23.6$ lb

Summary

	Outer Coil	Inner Coil	Double Coil
OD, in.	8¾	4¼	
Free height, in.	13	13	13
Bar dia., in.	1⅞	1	
Solid height, in.	10¼	10¼	10¼
Active coils	3.98	8.75	
Rate, lbs per in.	12,540	4360	16,900
Solid capacity, lbs.	34,490	11,990	46,480
Blunt bar length, in.	118.0	105.0	
Solid stress, psi	91,680	99,250	
Weight, lbs.	93.4	23.6	117

The inner coil carries approximately 25 per cent of the total load, while the outer coil carries about 75 per cent load. Where space permits, a double coil is usually designed so that the outer coil carries ⅔ of the total load and the inner coil supports the remainder. In this way, both springs would be stressed alike. However, if the next commercially available larger bar stock for the inner coil and the next smaller one for the outer coil had been selected, neither the spring rate nor the ideal conditions would have been met.

It is interesting to note that concentric multiple springs are always wound in opposite directions to prevent possible interlacing of the coils.

Trunnion Bushings

The trunnion shaft bushings of the roller journal in bowl mills, when made of metal, present a lubrication problem because the angular shaft movement is only a few degrees, is oscillating in nature and has its pressure concentrated in a small area. This all makes the establishment of a lubricating film very difficult.

It is known that either natural or synthetic rubber is capable of absorbing energy and producing a flexible bushing when subjected to radial pressure by confinement between metal sleeves. Such bushings can accommodate oscillating motion without wear or lubrication. They can also absorb limited amounts of vibration. As a consequence, these so-called torsion bushings have been adopted for trunnion shafts. The rubber is bonded to metal inner and outer sleeves, and is compounded to suit conditions of load and movement. The metal inner sleeve is pressed onto the shaft and the outer one is clamped in a housing. This construction obviates the need of a further seal between these units, when the mill is pressurized.

The hardness of the rubber is a factor in its behavior and is a consideration in the specification of a particular grade for this application.

Design and Selection of Bearings

In designing a pulverizer, the proper selection of bearings is important. There is a choice between journal type or sleeve bearings and the so-called antifriction bearings which include ball, tapered roller, cylindrical roller and spherical roller bearings. In certain cases rubber torsion bushings can be utilized.[16]

Specific application often determines which type to use. If loads are severe, and space is limited, an antifriction bearing is usually chosen. If close alignment of surfaces is a necessity, or if unbalanced loads at high speeds are present, then sleeve bearings with their inherent clearances are seldom used.

Antifriction bearings have attained their present state of near perfection after a lengthy period of research and development by various manufacturers, and standardized sizes and types are now available.

In ball bearings, the stress is very high since the contact area between balls and races is very small. In roller bearings, the stress is somewhat lower because of line contact. Consequently, a roller bearing having the same inside diameter, outside diameter and width as a ball bearing can carry a much greater load. However, the ball bearing can be operated at a higher speed with less heating and can tolerate more misalignment than can a roller bearing.

In selecting antifriction bearings, shaft dimensions will in some cases dictate bearing size, although in most cases bearings are chosen to carry a specific load for

---

[16] The literature of bearing design is very extensive. For one of many textbook introductions to the subject, see Chapter 9, Antifriction Bearings, in *Mechanical Engineering Design* by Joseph E. Shigley, McGraw-Hill, 1963. Publications of the Anti-Friction Bearing Manufacturers Association, New York, should be consulted for information on bearing definitions and standards. A book with an unusual amount of historical information on bearings and their design is *Anti-Friction Bearings* by Hudson T. Morton, Ann Arbor, Mich., 1954, 395 pages. Bearing manufacturers publish many catalogs and technical works with useful design data, an outstanding example being the *Timken Engineering Journal* published by Timken Roller Bearing Co., Canton, Ohio.

a given time period. The ratings shown in catalogs of most bearing manufacturers (except Timken) indicate the specific dynamic radial capacity which the bearing can endure for a minimum of one million revolutions. This is equivalent to 500 hours at 33⅓ rpm.

Base ratings of Timken tapered roller bearings are made upon a B–10 life expectancy of 3000 hours and upon a speed of rotation of the cone or inner raceway of 500 rpm. If the shaft and inner raceway are stationary and the outer race revolves, as is the case for the bearings in the grinding roller journal assemblies in the bowl mill, the calculated radial load must be multiplied by 1.25 to compensate for the increased number of stress applications. The resulting load is known as the *equivalent load*.

B–10 is defined as the life expectancy in hours, during which 90 per cent or more of a large group of similar bearings, under a specific loading and speed condition, will still be in service. The average life of all the above bearings would be about five times the B–10 life.

The life of a roller bearing varies inversely as the 10/3 power of the load; when the load is halved, the life is increased approximately 10 times. Conversely, if the load is doubled, the life will be about $\frac{1}{10}$ as long.

No bearing will give unlimited life because there are many unpredictable factors, such as environment (exposure to foreign material and moisture), lubrication, operating temperature, shaft and housing fits and other conditions. In addition to these factors there is the fatigue of the bearing material due to repeated stresses under rotation, and this is ultimately unavoidable. The number of revolutions a bearing can make before fatigue occurs is a function of bearing load and is a measure of a number of hours at a certain speed. Individual bearings of similar dimensions, operating under identical conditions, may have different lives. It is for this reason that a *nominal*, a *design* or a *rating life* is used as a basis for bearing selection. It is referred to herein as B–10 life. In order to insure trouble-free operation for machinery in continuous service, such as the components of a pulverizer or an exhauster, a nominal or B–10 life of 80,000 to 100,000 hours, or 10 to 13 years, is established as a goal.

The C-E Raymond Bowl Mill uses antifriction bearings on its vertical and horizontal shafts, the exhauster shaft, the roller journal assemblies, and the feeder shaft. For purposes of illustration, the most complex application, namely the vertical shaft, has been chosen.

Since the loading of the shaft is predominantly downward, a pure thrust bearing is selected for this application. Cylindrical roller bearings were chosen for absorbing radial load. In the case of the upper radial bearing, the large shaft diameter dictated the bearing size and hence its resultant phenomenal life expectancy.

There are a number of factors which must be given consideration, such as the eccentric loading of the shaft due to roll pressure, the loading of the radial bearings caused by the gear separation forces and the uplift of the worm gear because of the direction of rotation of the worm, all as shown in Fig. 11–45.

The upper radial bearing A is loaded at its maximum when one grinding roller assembly is located opposite the worm, and considered as doing all the grinding; the lower radial bearing B is usually loaded at maximum when one roller assembly is located above the worm with the same consideration as above. In this particular case, however, bearing B is loaded at its maximum when the roller assembly is located 90 deg clockwise from above the worm, because of the moments involved. The thrust bearing C absorbs the pressure due to all three grinding rollers acting on

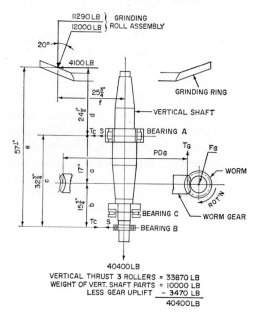

Fig. 11–45. Bearings on vertical shaft

the grinding ring, plus the weight of all rotating parts less the uplift of the worm gear.

The following calculations for a 20 ton per hour pulverizer include bearing selection and related shaft stresses.

Given:

Drive 200 hp, gear ratio 13.5:1

Gear

54 Teeth
RPM_G = 64.8
PD_G = 45.722″

Worm

4 Threads
RPM_W = 875
Pitch Dia., PD_W = 8.298″
Pressure Angle $P.A.$ = 25°
Lead Angle $L.A.$ = 22° 5′
Friction Angle $F.A.$ = 1° 4′
  (From *Timken Manual* for 1900 fpm rubbing speed)
$L.A. + F.A.$ = 23° 9′
Tan 25° = 0.466
Tan 23° 9′ = 0.427
Sin 23° 9′ = 0.393

Symbols for radial bearings:

T_G = Thrust force of gear
F_G = Tangential force of gear
S = Separating force of gear
$T.C.$ = Thrust couple
R_A = Radial load on Bearing A
R_B = Radial load on Bearing B
a, b, c, d, e, f, dimensions in inches
C = Basic dynamic radial capacity of bearing
$S.F.$ = Service factor = 1.3 for some shock
P = Equivalent load
L = Minimum life in millions of revolutions
$$= \left(\frac{C}{P}\right)^{10/3}$$
Spd = Speed of shaft and inner race
H = Hours of minimum life $(B\text{-}10)$
$$= \frac{L}{60\, Spd}$$

Symbols for thrust bearing:[17]

$Th.C$ = Thrust load on Bearing C
AF = Application factor = 1.33
SF = Speed factor
  = 1.846 (For 64.8 RPM)
SF = Speed factor
  = 1.995 (For 50 RPM)

$$T_G = \frac{126{,}000\ HP}{(PD_W)(RPM_W)} = \frac{(126{,}000)(200)}{(8.298)(875)}$$
$$= 3470\ \text{lb}$$

$$F_G = \frac{T_G}{\mathrm{Tan}(LA + FA)} = \frac{3470}{0.427} = 8130\ \text{lb}$$

[17] See *Timken Engineering Manual*, 1963, for definitions and values of application factor and speed factor.

$$\text{Brg } A = F_G \frac{b}{c} = \frac{(8130)(15.75)}{32.75}$$
$$= 3910 \text{ lb} = F_{G_A}$$

$$\text{Brg } B = F_G - F_{G_A} = 8130 - 3910$$
$$= 4220 \text{ lb} = F_{G_B}$$

$$S = \frac{T_G \text{ Tan } PA}{\text{Sin}(LA + FA)} = \frac{(3470)(0.466)}{0.393}$$
$$= 4110 \text{ lb}$$

$$\text{Bearing } A = S \frac{b}{c} = \frac{(4110)(15.75)}{32.75}$$
$$= 1980 \text{ lb} = S_A$$

$$\text{Bearing } B = S - S_A = 4110 - 1980$$
$$= 2130 \text{ lb} = S_B$$

$$\text{T.C.} = \frac{(T_G)(PD_G)}{c \times 2} = \frac{(3470)(45.7)}{(32.75)(2)}$$
$$= 2420 \text{ lb}$$

Load due to roll horizontal radial force, = DRR

$$\text{Bearing } A = \frac{4100e}{c} = \frac{(4100)(57.25)}{32.75}$$
$$= 7170 \text{ lb} = DRR_A$$

$$\text{Bearing } B = \frac{4100\,d}{c} = \frac{(4100)(24.5)}{32.75}$$
$$= 3070 \text{ lb} = DRR_B$$

Load due to roll vertical thrust force, = DRT

$$\text{Bearings } A \text{ and } B = \frac{11,290f}{c}$$
$$= \frac{(11,290)(25.75)}{32.75}$$
$$= 8880 \text{ lb}$$

With one roller loading, R_A

$$= \sqrt{3910^2 + (7170 + 8880 + 2420 + 1980)^2}$$
$$\quad\quad {}_{B_A} \quad\quad {}_{DRR_A} \quad {}_{DRT} \quad {}_{T.C.} \quad {}_{S_A}$$

$$= 20,820 \text{ lb, Roll assembly opposite worm}$$

and R_B

$$= \sqrt{(4220 + 3070 + 8880)^2 + (2420 - 2130)^2}$$
$$= 16,180 \text{ lb, Roll assembly } 90° \text{ from worm clockwise}$$

$$\text{T.C.} = 11,290 + 10,000 - 3470$$
$$= 17,820 \text{ lb}$$

With all three rollers loading,

$$R_A = \sqrt{3910^2 + (1980 + 2420)^2} = 5890 \text{ lb}$$
$$\quad\quad {}_{B_A} \quad\quad {}_{S_A} \quad {}_{T.C.}$$

$$R_B = \sqrt{4220^2 + (2130 - 2420)^2} = 4230 \text{ lb}$$

$$\text{T.C.} = 33,870 + 10,000 - 3470$$
$$= 40,400 \text{ lb}$$

Selection:

Radial bearing A, Rollway MUC–5240, See Rollway Bearing Catalog TR–854–DC revised Nov., 1959, Syracuse, N.Y. Maximum Loading (one roller)[18]

$$C = 297,700 \text{ lb (From catalog)}$$

$$P = 20,820 \times 1.3 = 27,100 \text{ lb}$$

$$L = \left(\frac{297,700}{27,100}\right)^{10/3}$$
$$= 2923 \times 10^6 \text{ revolutions}$$

$$H = \frac{(2923)(10^6)}{(60)(64.8)}$$
$$= 753,400 \text{ hours, } B\text{–}10$$

Average loading (all three rollers)

$$C = 297,700 \text{ lb}$$

$$P = 5890 \times 1.3 = 7660 \text{ lb}$$

$$L = \left(\frac{297,700}{7,660}\right)^{10/3}$$
$$= 196,400 \times 10^6 \text{ revolutions}$$

$$H = \frac{(196,400)(10^6)}{(60)(64.8)}$$
$$= 50,618,600 \text{ hours, } B\text{–}10$$

Radial bearing B, SKF N–320, See SKF Catalog #425, 1958, Philadelphia, Pa.

[18] The condition of one roller carrying all the load (maximum loading) rarely occurs, but when it does, it is only momentary. When all three rollers are acting simultaneously, their moments cancel each other insofar as radial bearing loads are concerned. The life of both bearings A and B is well in excess of requirements. Both radial bearing A and radial bearing B were selected by bore size, which was dictated by shaft diameter.

Maximum loading (one roller) [18]

$$C = 61,500 \text{ lb (From catalog)}$$

$$P = 16,180 \times 1.3 = 21,000 \text{ lb}$$

$$L = \left(\frac{61,500}{21,000}\right)^{10/3}$$

$$= 35.82 \times 10^6 \text{ revolutions}$$

$$H = \frac{(35.82)(10^6)}{(60)(64.8)} = 9200 \text{ hours, } B\text{-10}$$

Average loading (all three rollers)

$$C = 61,500 \text{ lb}$$

$$P = 4230 \times 1.3 = 5500 \text{ lb}$$

$$L = \left(\frac{61,500}{5500}\right)^{10/3}$$

$$= 3100 \times 10^6 \text{ revolutions}$$

$$H = \frac{(3100)(10^6)}{(60)(64.8)}$$

$$= 797,300 \text{ hours, } B\text{-10}$$

Equations for Timken bearings are based on a speed of 500 rpm. The thrust bearing capacity in the data table in the Timken Catalog is given at 50 rpm because these large thrust bearings are slow speed devices; it therefore becomes necessary to convert the catalog rating at 50 rpm to an equivalent rating at 500 rpm.

Selection:

Thrust bearing C, See catalog, Timken 611.

Catalog rating at 50 rpm = 220,000 lb
Equivalent rating at 500 rpm

$$= \frac{\text{Rating at 50 rpm}}{SF \text{ for 50 rpm}}$$

$$= \frac{220,000}{1.995} = 110,300 \text{ lb}$$

B-10 Life

$$= \left[\frac{\text{Equiv. Rating} \times SF \text{ for 64.8 rpm}}{\text{Thrust Load} \times A.F.}\right]^{10/3}$$

$$\times 3000 \text{ hours}$$

$$= \left[\frac{(110,300)(1.846)}{(40,400)(1.33)}\right]^{10/3} \times 3000$$

$$= 253,290 \text{ hours}$$

The above bearing was selected for its bore size which had to be large enough to accommodate the adapter fitted onto the shaft, which was necessary to distribute the thrust force from the narrow shaft shoulder to the wide upper bearing race plate. It has more than ample life.

Vertical shaft stresses

Given: 200 hp — 64.8 rpm

Material   AISI 4340 heat treated steel
Tensile strength — 130,000 psi minimum
Yield point — 120,000 psi minimum

Symbols:

M_b = Maximum bending moment, inch lb
D = Diameter of section subjected to stress
Z = Section modulus for bending
Z_p = Section modulus for torsion = $2Z$
S_b = Bending stress, psi
S_c = Combined stress due to bending and torsion, psi
S_t = Torsional stress, psi
T = Torque of shaft, inch lb
K_m = Combined shock and fatigue factor for bending = 1.75
K_t = Combined shock and fatigue factor for torsion = 1.25

K_m and K_t are factors for suddenly applied minor shocks.

As shown in Fig. 11–46, zone 1

$$M_b = (11,290)(25.75) + (4100)(22.25)$$

$$= 382,000 \text{ in. lb}$$

$$Z = 41.42 \text{ for 7.50 in. diameter}$$

$$S_b = \frac{382,000}{41.42} = 9220 \text{ psi}$$

$$T = \frac{(63,000)(200)}{64.8} = 194,400 \text{ in. lb}$$

$$Z_p = 82.84 \text{ for 7.50 in. diameter}$$

$$S_t = \frac{194,400}{82.84} = 2350 \text{ psi}$$

$$S_c = \frac{5.1\sqrt{(K_b \times M_b)^2 + (K_t \times T)^2}}{D^3}$$

$$= \frac{5.1\sqrt{(1.75 \times 382,000)^2 + (1.25 \times 194,400)^2}}{7.50^3}$$

$S_c = 8600$ psi

As shown in Fig. 11–46, zone 2

$$M_b = 16{,}180 \times 8.25 = 133{,}500 \text{ in. lb,}$$
max. condition, one roller loading

$Z = 10.52$ for 4.75″ dia.

$$S_b = \frac{133{,}500}{10.52} = 12{,}700 \text{ psi}$$

$$M_b = 4230 \times 8.25 = 34{,}900 \text{ in. lb,}$$
Avg. condition, 3 roller loading

$$S_b = \frac{34{,}900}{10.52} = 3320 \text{ psi}$$

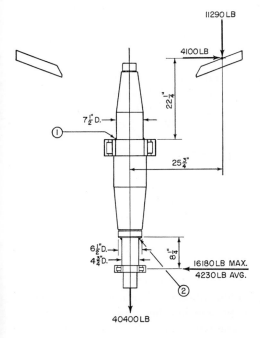

Fig. 11–46. Stresses on vertical shaft

Compressive stress, zone 2

To reduce stress concentration, add $\frac{1}{16}$ inch radius fillets. Smooth fillets are used at all points of change in shaft diameter in order to reduce this concentration. Such fillets change the effective inner diameter of the shaft shoulder.

Shaft diameter = 4.75 in.

Add fillets = $4.75 + (2 \times \frac{1}{16}) = 4.875$ in., effective inner diameter of shaft shoulder.

By simple arithmetic, for the geometry shown in Fig. 11–46, the effective area = $33.18 - 18.67 = 14.51$ sq in.

Compressive stress = $40{,}400/14.51 = 2790$ psi

Motor Characteristics

When both the mill and exhauster are driven by a single motor, the mill which uses the greater part of the motor output has, because of its slow speed, relatively low inertial forces to overcome even when the bowl is filled with coal. On the other hand, the exhauster, having lesser running power requirements, has a higher acceleration torque requirement. These forces tend to cancel each other; consequently a 135 per cent starting torque motor is adequate.

In the event of an emergency shutdown, after which it becomes necessary to start a number of motors almost simultaneously, low voltage is often encountered. Because the torque of the motor varies as the square of the percentage of design voltage, a 200 per cent starting torque motor would start the mill with a voltage reduction of

$$\sqrt{\frac{135}{200}}$$

or 82 per cent of design potential.

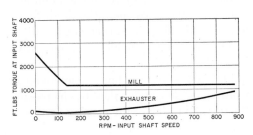

Fig. 11–47. Speed-torque curve of mill and exhauster

The WR^2 of a 20 ton per hour pulverizer and its exhauster is as follows:

Horizontal shaft	875 rpm
Vertical shaft	64.8 rpm
Ratio of speeds (horizontal to vertical shafts)	13.5:1
WR^2 mill worm	43 lb ft^2
WR^2 exhauster	3611 lb ft^2
WR^2, mill worm and exhauster	3654 lb ft^2
WR^2, vertical shaft and parts	34,500 lb ft^2
Equivalent WR^2 vertical shaft and parts = 34,500/(13.5)^2	190 lb ft^2
WR^2 of mill worm plus equivalent vertical shaft value	233 lb ft^2
Total WR^2 (mill and exhauster)	3844 lb ft^2

Where the mill and exhauster are driven by separate motors, 200 per cent starting torque units are usually supplied for reasons stated above.

A speed-torque curve covering mill and exhauster is shown in Fig. 11–47.

Worm Gear Drive

A worm gear drive has been selected for the bowl mill because it has a number of advantages over other types of drive. It requires small space and provides a large single speed reduction, thus permitting the use of a high speed motor on a slow speed mill. By extending the worm shaft through the gear housing, the mill exhauster can be driven from the same shaft, thus making an extremely compact installation.

The worm gear drive has a minimum number of parts. By mounting both shafts in antifriction bearings, correct gear alignment is accurately maintained. The drive is quiet in operation and its efficiency is quite high. Water cooling is employed in worm gear housings, thereby increasing the thermal rating of the gearing. By keeping the lubricant temperature below 140 F the oil life is substantially increased.

Since low pressure condensate is often used for cooling purposes, coolers are amply proportioned for use with this medium whose temperature is often in the range of 100 to 110 F. The calculations for the tube surface for a 20 ton per hour pulverizer follow:

Input — 154 kw
Gear ratio — 13.5:1
Gear efficiency — 95 per cent

$$\text{Kw loss per hr} = \frac{154 \times (100 - 5)}{100} = 7.7$$

$$\text{Btu loss per min} = \frac{7.7 \times 3413}{60} = 438$$

Btu transfer per sq ft per minute — assume 20 (empirical)

$$\text{Sq ft of tubing required} = \frac{438}{20} = 21.9$$

Length of tubes = 4 ft, 8$\frac{1}{2}$ in.
No. of $\frac{5}{8}$ in. OD tubes required

$$= \frac{21.9 \times 144}{56.5 \times 0.625 \times \pi} = 28.4$$

Since tubes are of the hairpin type, use 15 pairs or 30 tubes.

Worm gearing is selected in accordance with AGMA formula 440.03 which is based on 24 hour daily continuous moderate shock load service.[19] A worm drive is capable of shock load resistance because the teeth are under a crushing load rather than under cantilever loading, such as would be present in other forms of gearing.

The worm gear rim which has a center mounting flange and the worm, together with its bearing housings and usually the couplings, are so made as to be symmetrical about their respective center lines. The gear rim can be inverted on the hub casting, while the worm assembly can be turned end-for-end, thereby providing

---

[19] Further information may be obtained from the American Gear Manufacturers Association, One Thomas Circle, Washington 5, D.C.

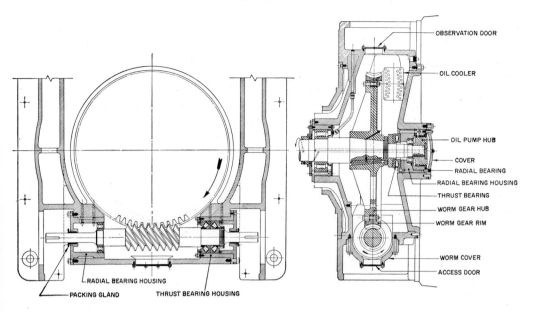

Fig. 11–48. Worm gear drive

new contact faces for each member. This is illustrated in Fig. 11–48.

Flexible Couplings

There are two positions in which the mill motor can be connected to the mill and exhauster. In one of these, the motor drives the mill worm shaft which is extended opposite the motor end to drive the exhauster, and in the other the motor is located between the mill and exhauster and is provided with a double ended shaft extension, driving the mill from one side and the exhauster from the other.

For a 20 ton per hour pulverizer when the exhauster is driven from the mill, the single motor coupling transmits the full 350 hp for both mill and exhauster. In the second position with the double ended motor, one coupling transmits the 200 hp mill power and the other the 150 hp exhauster power.

Fast's flexible coupling is used on the C-E Raymond Bowl Mill. This is a gear type, self-aligning coupling which compensates automatically for angular, offset and angular-offset misalignment. It has no fragile or perishable composition seals nor any seal parts subject to repeated bending, tension or compression; no flexible materials of any kind are used. The bearing rings at the ends of the hubs and shells keep out foreign material and prevent loss of lubricant, which can be either mineral oil or grease. Flexibility is obtained through mating splines which are covered by a lubricating film which prevents metal-to-metal wear.

Because these couplings have high power transmitting capabilities, the shaft diameter rather than the coupling rating determines coupling sizes. For example, when the above mill is driven by a 350 hp, 900 rpm motor, the mill shaft is 3½ in. in diameter, while the motor shaft is usually 3⅝ in. or 3⅞ in. dia., (depending on make and type). If the motor shaft were 3⅜ in. in diameter, the 3½ in. diameter mill shaft would dictate use of a No. 3½ Fast's coupling which has a capacity of 120 hp per 100 rpm. Using an application factor of 2.0 for a pulverizer drive, the coupling could transmit $\dfrac{120 \times 900}{2.0 \times 100} = 540$ hp. The coupling therefore has ample capacity. If the motor shaft were 3⅞ in. a No. 4 coupling (180 hp per 100 rpm) would be required with a much higher excess capacity. The mill shaft size governs the exhauster coupling size (No. 3½ in this case) which, of course, is amply large.

Mill motor type or extended coupling hubs are often used because they have a greater inner hub separation to permit removal of the exhauster bearing assembly in the short space between shaft ends. On other occasions, floating shaft coupling arrangements (which consist of two flexible hubs, two rigid hubs and a length of shafting) are installed to permit locating the exhauster at a distance from the mill. The maximum length of the shaft permitted for this arrangement is governed by the critical speed of the shaft, expressed by the relationship $\dfrac{4{,}760{,}000 \times D}{L^2}$, where $D =$ shaft diameter in inches and $L =$ shaft length in inches. On other occasions where shaft separations are too long for mill motor type hubs and too short for the floating shaft arrangement, coupling shell spacers are employed to separate the coupling halves and shaft ends.

Shrink Fits

Shrink or press fits are used on all inner races of antifriction bearings, on the tapered roller bearing cups in the roller assemblies and on the bronze worm gear ring to its hub. Flexible coupling hubs are also shrunk onto shaft extensions.

The degree of interference fit of bearings is determined by bearing size and service conditions and is found in published data supplied by bearing manufacturers. Since the bronze worm gear rim and its ductile iron hub have differing coefficients of expansion, sufficient interference must exist at room temperature so that the mating surfaces will remain in contact at operating temperatures. It has been found that a mean interference of 0.0005 in. per inch of mating face diameter suffices. For shaft couplings a mean interference of approximately 0.00035 in. per inch of shaft diameter is used.

Inner races of tapered and cylindrical roller bearings and entire ball bearings are usually heated in an infrared oven in the shop or in hot oil in the field to 250 F and are handled by men wearing asbestos gloves. The bearing bores are easily slid onto the shaft seats when heated to this temperature. The worm gear rim is immersed in water heated to 200 F. A torch is never used since localized heating would draw the tin from the bronze and would also cause distortion of the rim. The heated rim is transferred from the water bath to the hub by means of hoists attached to lifting eyebolts threaded into the gear rim.

Gear type coupling hubs have threaded puller holes into which threaded rods can be inserted for handling the heated hub in assembling it onto the shaft extension. The driving key must be fitted to both shaft and hub prior to mounting of the hub to the shaft. A temperature of 250 F is ample to expand the coupling hub for mounting.

The bearing cups of the tapered roller bearings in the roller assemblies are coated with grease to prevent later rusting due to frosting and are chilled (and shrunk) in a deep-freeze unit in the shop to −60 F. They are handled with asbestos gloves, being carefully dropped into the upstanding lower or upper journal housings. The cups can be chilled between slabs of dry ice large enough to cover the rings and suitably packed and insulated for field installation.

The gear hub, bowl hub, journal head and rolls are fitted onto tapered seats. The parts are driven tight by their respective lock nuts. Since the bowl hub taper is a nonbinding one, it being greater than 16 deg, included angle, it is readily removable from the shaft. The roll is driven from the housing taper as described later in the section on provisions for maintenance. A drive cap for threading onto the top of the journal shaft is provided with the mill tools for removal of the shaft from the head. For gear hub removal, which is usually a 10 to 12 deg taper, a partial circumferential groove is provided in the hub at the center of the tapered seat which is connected to a grease gun type fitting. Pumping oil into the groove breaks the tapered seat apart.

Lubrication

In pulverizing machinery where bearings and gears are in motion, good lubrication is a necessity. The lubricant serves to reduce friction of the bearings and the sliding surface of the worm gearing to diminish wear and to reduce heat in the gear housing.

In the C-E Raymond Bowl Mill, only two different oils are used in the mill, roller assemblies, exhauster bearings and the vari-stroke feeder drive unit. The feeder clutches require a small quantity of a different oil and the feeder mechanism uses grease.

Lubricating oils are identified by viscosity and compounding; greases by their consistency and soap bases. Viscosity is a measure of the ability of a lubricant to resist shearing stress or internal resistance to motion. In the laboratory it is often measured in poises or stokes. In commercial work, however, the most common means of determining the viscosity is with a device called a Viscosimeter. The Saybolt method is widely used and viscosities are given in Saybolt Universal Viscosity (SUV) in seconds at a given temperature such as 100 F, 210 F or both.

The Saybolt viscosity is the time in seconds required for 60 cc of the oil to flow through a standardized capillary tube, at a certain temperature; thus, a particular heavy oil may have a viscosity of, say, 1500 SUV at 100 F and 100 SUV at 210 F. A lighter grade of the same type oil would have a viscosity of about 150 SUV at 100 F and 42 SUV at 210 F. To show temperature viscosity relationships the American Society for Testing and Materials has devised a special chart similar to logarithmic paper in which the coordinates are viscosity and temperature. Viscosities plotted on this paper fall on a straight line and viscosities for intermediate temperatures can readily be determined. This is illustrated in Fig. 11–49.

Viscosity Index, VI, is an arbitrary number used to determine the quality of a lubricant. It is a measure of the amount of change of viscosity with temperature. The higher the VI number, the less change of viscosity for a given temperature differential. Multi-graded automotive motor oils have a VI of about 130; other oils have a much lower VI.[20] An example of the

---

[20] For additional information, see ASTM D 567–53, Methods for Calculating Viscosity Index.

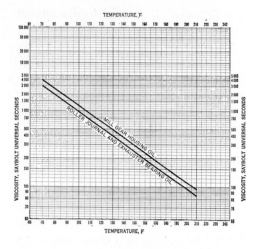

Fig. 11—49. Viscosity plot of oils used in C-E Raymond Bowl Mills

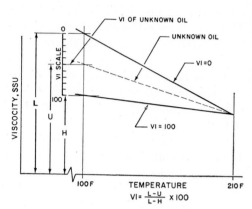

$$VI = \frac{L-U}{L-H} \times 100$$

Fig. 11—50. Plot of viscosity index, VI

plotting of VI is shown in Fig. 11–50.

In determining the viscosity of oil to be used, both the starting and running temperatures must be given consideration. In cold locations, pour point is important to prevent "channeling" of the cold lubricant. Conversely, if the oil is to be used for high temperature its flash point and firing temperatures must be considered.

Lubricating oils contain many additives, the choice of which is dependent upon conditions of use. Some of these affect lubricity or oiliness, rust prevention, oxidation inhibition, viscosity improvement, detergency, stability at high temperatures, film strength, defoaming, demulsibility and pour point depressions.

As previously stated, only two main lubricants are used in the C-E Raymond Bowl Mill. These are a lead naphthenate and a straight mineral oil. In 1935 when this type of mill was first built, the standard worm gear lubricant of that day was used, namely, steam refined cylinder oil. This lubricant contained five to ten per cent acidless tallow and had an approximate viscosity of 2000 SUV at 100 F and

150 SUV at 210 F. The tallow provided excellent lubricity for the sliding gear surfaces. Some years later noncorrosive EP type lead naphthenate soap oils having a viscosity similar to the cylinder oil were adopted but they caused a temperature rise over the oil previously used. It was found possible to use an oil two grades lighter with a temperature drop sufficient to give practically the same viscosity at the lowered operating temperature as the heavier oil had. Both EP oils had a Timken load rating of 45–50 lb. This lighter leaded oil is standard today. The high Timken rating of this oil provides a tough film that withstands shock loads when they occur.

The gear housing oil also has good resistance to thickening and foaming and its oxidation stability gives it long life. The VI is high, making for dependable circulation when starting a cold mill. The low pour point makes it well suited for outdoor units. Leaded oils have excellent adhesive properties, which cause the oil to adhere to shaft, worm teeth, upper radial bearing and exposed portions of the worm and its bearings above the oil level. This adhering oil film prevents rusting of the oil coated parts following shop assembly and test and during the intermittent operation that may occur when a unit is initially started.

The lubrication of the worm gearing and both the worm shaft and vertical shaft radial and thrust bearings is shown in an earlier illustration, Fig. 11–48. The oil level in the gear housing is carried just below the centerline of the worm gear drive. The lower thrust and radial bearings are immersed in oil and are flood lubricated. The upper radial bearing is lubricated by oil supplied by an integral spiral groove oil pump attached to the bottom of the vertical shaft. As the pump revolves, oil is forced downward between the hub and its bushing into the cavity at the bottom of the vertical shaft, from where it travels upward through a drilled hole in the shaft to the upper bearing. Here the upper bearing is flooded and the overflow with the bearing oil returns to the gear housing through suitable piping and through an oil sight glass where flow can be observed. A check valve at the bottom of the vertical shaft keeps the shaft hole filled and provides for quick lubrication of the upper bearing after shutdown.

The horizontal or worm shaft bearings are flood oiled from the bath of oil in the gear case which is just below the shaft centerline. The pumping action of the worm thrust bearing circulates oil through it; the worm radial bearing oil circulation is provided by the action of the worm gearing. The worm shaft is provided with packing ring seals. Oil can be added while the mill is in operation. A dial type thermometer mounted in a separable socket is provided in the housing wall to indicate oil bath temperature.

The roller journal assembly is lubricated by means of a self contained circulating system. The oil level in the hollow shaft is maintained at a point just below the shaft top. Due to the pumping action of the tapered roller bearings, oil is circulated from the reservoir in the lower journal housing to the annular chamber between the bearings and into the shaft bore where the cycle is completed. A straight mineral oil with optional rust and oxidation inhibiting additives is used for the roller assemblies. The viscosity is approximately 900 SUV at 100 F and about 90 SUV at 210 F. The oil level is checked by means of a dip stick and oil can be replenished while the mill is in operation.

Both exhauster bearings are mounted in a single cast iron bearing housing. Oil is carried to the center of the lowest rolling element in the housings, thereby eliminating the need of shaft seals. The same lubricating oil is used as is employed for the roller journal assemblies.

Design Considerations for Maintenance and Repairs

The C-E Raymond Bowl Mill is a rugged machine designed and built for continuous operation over an extended period with but little wear of the working parts. Iron pyrites and other abrasive substances in coal tend to shorten the life of such parts as rolls, grinding ring, mill side and classifier body liners, bowl deflectors, scraper blades, exhauster liners and exhauster blades and whizzer blades. Ready access to these parts is a design feature of bowl mills, as shown earlier in Fig. 11–36.

The classifier body is constructed in such a manner that part of its lower section can be removed, without disturbing such items as the converter head, exhauster intake pipe, center feed pipe or integral feeder. By removing this section the entire upper part of the mill is accessible for replacement of such parts as the grinding ring, classifier body liners, bowl deflectors and upper mill side liners.

The grinding ring is generally made of a number of segments or blocks which can be readily replaced in the bowl, either through an access door in the classifier body or through the openings provided by removing the roller journal assemblies. Another method is to install the segments when the mill has been opened by dismantling the removable classifier section.

Tapped holes are provided in the horizontal flange of the classifier top, adjacent to the split line, and similar holes are provided at the top and bottom of the vertical flanges of the large classifier body section for jack screws to facilitate disassembly of the removable section.

By removing the converter head cover which can be done by taking out two bolts from the Victaulic coupling, access to the inner cone of the classifier is provided.

The journals or roller assemblies are removed from the mill for roll renewal and also for ring renewal. Journals are removed with chain falls, cable slings and snubbing lines. Spring adjustment is not disturbed when the journal opening cover is removed, since the spring mechanism is a self-contained unit.

The roll is held to the tapered end of the lower journal housing by means of a lock nut which is removed prior to roll removal. The journal is suspended in a vertical position, with the bottom of the lower housing just off the floor, after which the roll can be heated slightly near its top center with a torch, or can be tapped off its taper seat with a lead or bronze hammer.

The bowl hub skirt is made with a removable section to provide for inspection and access to the upper vertical shaft seal and to the shaft air seal (when used) so that the bowl need not be removed for this purpose. The exhauster casing is provided with two removable periphery covers for access to the top liners which rest on a shelf (having no holding bolts which could wear, causing the liner plates to fall into the fan), and with a side door for access to the lower bolted-in liners (they can not drop if the bolt heads wear) and to the whizzer blades and main fan blades. Inspection ports are provided for examining the casing throat liner and the exhauster blades to determine the degree of wear. Both sides of the exhauster casing are protected with steel plate liners having tapped holes for anchorage. In this way maximum holding ability is maintained even though these parts may become worn.

The fan blades are bolted to the spider and whizzer plate. To replace the fan blades it is only necessary to remove the exhauster housing access door. After bolting new blades in place, the flexible coupling is opened, the shell is wedged centrally to the hub and the antifriction equipped bearing and shaft assembly is used as a balancing arbor.

If it is found desirable to remove the entire fan wheel, this can be accomplished by removing the lower exhauster inlet elbow and the casing inlet side plate. After the wheel is removed, the bearing housing assembly can also be removed.

The feeder is provided with renewable roll blades, end liners and hinged gate blade, all of which can be readily replaced when worn.

Victaulic couplings, Fig. 11–51, with inwardly inclined lips, consisting of a moulded high temperature "C"-shaped rubber gasket mounted on a circumferential band seat and surrounded by a sectional cast housing, are used on all coal and air piping joints. This results in a flexible arrangement to accommodate mis-

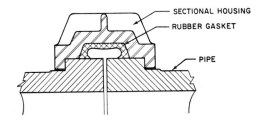

Fig. 11–51. Section through Victaulic coupling

alignment and differential expansion due to temperature changes. It is necessary to remove only two bolts to dismantle any such coupling.

Special Designs and Seals for Balanced and Pressurized Firing

With balanced draft firing, the entire pulverizing system from hot air inlet to exhauster discharge operates under suction.[21] This makes for easy sealing and dust free operation. Pyrites and tramp iron are discharged continuously into a suitable hopper adjacent to the mill. In the bottom of the mill an annular space is provided between the lower extremity of the revolving bowl hub skirt and the fixed collar on the top of the mill base cover plate. Suction in the space below the bowl draws atmospheric air through vent ports in the mill base wall and through the annular space to prevent any dust getting into the upper mill bearing or into the room. This inwardly moving air current also tends to cool the upper bearing, and the ribs on the inside of the bowl hub increase air circulation, as shown earlier in Fig. 11–36. Similarly, an annular space is provided between the revolving upper roller journal housing and the fixed skirt attached to the journal head. The trunnion shaft is hollow; in the central portion of its

length, cross holes are drilled which open into a plenum in the head casting. The plenum is connected to the skirt by a series of drilled holes. Mill suction aspirates room air through the parts described; dust cannot enter the bearings in the roller journal assemblies. An annular space is provided around the fan shaft also. Atmospheric air is drawn through the opening. It is interesting to note that the adjustable seal ring around the fan shaft is set low during initial installation, so that it will assume a higher setting when the exhauster casing comes up to operating temperature. This is shown in Fig. 11–52.

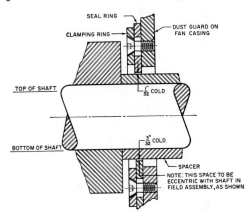

Fig. 11–52. Fan shaft seal — balanced firing

The exhauster bearing assembly has no lip seals or packing glands. The oil level is carried to approximately the center of the bottom rolling element in the bearings. The end caps are grooved; in register with the cap grooves are a pair of grooves in the fan end bearing spacer while on the coupling end, a step in the shaft diameter serves the purpose of tangentially discharging into the cap grooves any oil that might creep along the spacer or shaft. Attached to the fan end spacer and to the shaft at the coupling end and revolving

[21] See Chapter 16, Pulverizers, for a discussion of balanced and pressurized firing.

with the shaft are circular discs or slingers which operate in a recessed portion of the cap to prevent the infiltration of dust into the housing assembly.

Tempering of the hot air supply to the mill is accomplished by a balanced damper in an atmospheric air connection at the mill inlet. The feeder bearings being under suction require no seals.

When the mill system is arranged for pressurized firing, the mill and mill exhauster are under positive pressure, this pressure being supplied by the forced draft fan. Tempering air is provided from a connection between this fan and the air heater, and tempering takes place by a set of interconnected dampers in the hot air and cold air ducts adjacent to the mill. The pyrites hopper is totally enclosed with a valve or water seal at the bottom and the spout between the mill base and the hopper is provided with a valve also. When the hopper becomes filled, the valve in the upper spout is closed temporarily so the hopper contents can be sluiced away. Then the lower valve is reclosed and the upper one reopened to permit mill rejects to again fill the hopper.

To prevent coal dust from being blown out of the mill, a labyrinth type air seal is mounted around the vertical shaft between the top of the mill base and the underside of the bowl hub. The air seal housing has two sealing lips. The one on the bowl hub side has a smooth face since the pressure differential between housing and mill is quite small and ease of air flow is required. On the mill base side of the housing, the sealing lip is provided with a sawtoothed serrated surface since the pressure differential here is much greater than on the opposite side. The serrations impede air flow, thus reducing air leakage and assuring enough pressure to provide air flow through the smooth face above.

Clearance between the sealing lips and shaft is determined by the internal clearances in the upper and lower radial bearings on the vertical shaft, that between outer bearing races and housings and that between housings and mating parts. Since the bowl may not always be equally loaded beneath each roller, angular displacement of the shaft has to be consid-

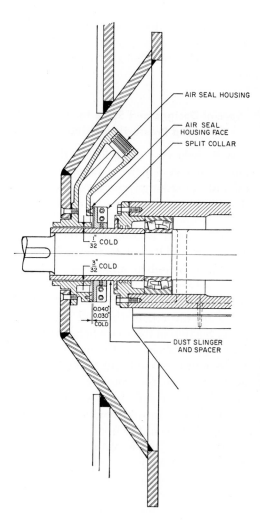

Fig. 11–53. Fan shaft seal — pressurized firing

ered in the clearance calculations. Numerous tests have been conducted in selecting the most efficient sealing surfaces.

Seal air is supplied to one end of each roller journal trunnion shaft, usually from a header surrounding the mill base. Seal air discharges into the plenum in the journal head for distribution to the skirt around the upper journal housing. The trunnion shaft bushings, being of rubber and pressed on the shaft and clamped in the housing casting, require no further sealing.

The exhauster shaft cannot be sealed in the same manner as the vertical mill shaft, since the air seal housing must be connected to the exhauster casing side plate, and with the amount of vertical movement of the casing relative to the shaft, as the casing comes up to operating temperature, much space between housing and shaft would be required, resulting in the use of a large volume of sealing air.

Instead, a horizontal face type seal was adopted, with relatively close mating sealing surfaces resulting in a small quantity of sealing air being required. This is shown in Fig. 11–53.

The feeder is provided with a double lipped seal around each end of the feed roll shaft, similar to the one used on the vertical mill shaft. Since the shaft is supported in needle bearings, seal clearances can be very small, with minimum seal air requirements. The hinged gate shaft, which oscillates in needle bearings, has a grease packed lip seal arrangement.

The adjustable classifier vane shaft supports have an "O" ring seal between the support casting and the separator top and a grease packed lip seal around each shaft.

With a full pressure mill system the mill exhauster is dispensed with. A seal air blower is then required to provide air under sufficient pressure to all sealing points described above.

Acknowledgment. Many of the illustrations of welding methods shown in the section on welding and its applications are from Vol. 2 of the *Welding Handbook* published by the American Welding Society. Most of the illustrations in this section were prepared by L. Bonadies; those in the section on machine design of bowl mills were drawn by John Wyszneweckyj. Both of these illustrators contributed many special drawings used throughout the book to aid the reader in visualizing the written subject matter. In addition, Harold N. Fonda merits a note of appreciation for his help in obtaining illustrative material and for his care in checking drawings.

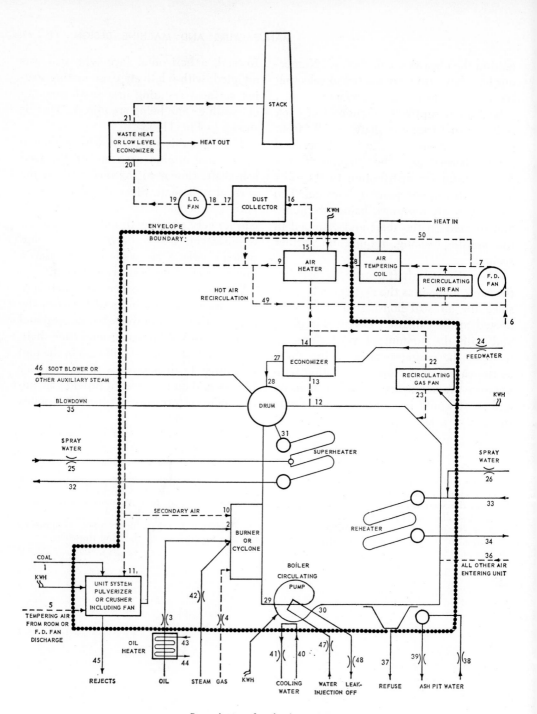

Boundaries for boiler testing

This diagram for boiler tests serves as a key to the numerical subscripts used throughout ASME Power Test Code 4.1, Steam Generating Units. A heat balance diagram showing the significance of such tests is found on page 12–23, Fig. 12–10. Typical forms used for recording and calculating the ASME Abbreviated Efficiency Test of boilers are found on pages 12–24 and 12–25.

12

Power Plant Tests and Measurements[1]

MEASUREMENTS in the modern power plant are made for two distinctly different reasons: to monitor various phases of power plant operation[2] and to test individual equipment or systems for purposes of initial acceptance or as a check of performance following a period of operation. This chapter is concerned with the latter type of measurements, many of which are governed by the comprehensive series of ASME Power Test Codes. Supplemented by additional tests of special character, the ASME Power Test Codes are of considerable interest to manufacturers and users of power equipment, and their results aid in the evaluation and improvement of designs.

It is very likely that most young engineers entering the power field will find a part of their early experience in testing equipment for various purposes. Although it is important to learn how to make physical measurements and to follow ordered procedures, this is only the beginning. The engineer must understand that testing is a part of the overall objective of equipment design. He must become aware of the nature of experimental errors, learn how a single error may influence the results calculated from multiple measure-

ments, and gain some knowledge of the effect of instrument selection in minimizing measurement uncertainty. For best results the engineer must be willing to question why certain procedures or instruments are used, changing them only if he can find better methods. Most important of all, the engineer must become skillful in interpreting test results and in drawing appropriate conclusions, all of which should be incorporated in clearly written reports.

Characteristics of Power Plant Testing

Power plant testing differs in one important respect from product quality control, to which it is sometimes compared. That is, most tests fall into the single-sample category. Unlike the repetitive tests made of product dimensions, for example, most power plant tests consist of individual readings taken over a period of time, during which some unwanted variations may be introduced. With the exception of a few unusually well equipped laboratories,[3] large scale power plant tests cannot be repeated a sufficient number of times to gain the type of statistical reliability expected for quality control.

---

[1] Material contributed by F. C. Lisevick, R. W. Robinson and R. C. Sherrill.
[2] See Chapter 22, Controls and Instruments, for additional information and related references.
[3] Outstanding examples are the Kreisinger Development Laboratory, Windsor, Conn., and the U.S. Naval Boiler and Turbine Laboratory at the Philadelphia Naval Base.

A single-sample experiment may be defined as one in which most or all of the uncertainties cannot be found from statistics and must be "guesstimated."[4] The result, R, for a single variable may be expressed in terms of the mean of the readings and an uncertainty interval based on specified odds.

$$R = V_m \pm w \ (b \text{ to } 1)$$

where V_m is the arithmetic mean; w, the uncertainty interval; and b, the odds.

For example the results of a series of temperature readings might be written

$$T = 1000 \ F \pm 10 \deg F \ (20 \text{ to } 1)$$

This means, in effect, that the experimenter would be willing to wager 20 to 1 that the true value of the temperature lies between 990 and 1010 F.

When tests are costly in terms of manpower, time and equipment, the uncertainty analyses made in advance can be very helpful in establishing procedures and assigning manpower. They can also be of assistance in determining how uncertainties propagate into the results. In their pioneering article on this subject, "Describing Uncertainties in Single-Sample Experiments,"[5] S. J. Kline and F. A. McClintock show that a given reduction in a large uncertainty is far more important than the same numerical reduction in a small uncertainty. This technique is also of assistance in choice of appropriate measuring instruments prior to the start of experimental work, but consideration must also be given to adequate cross checks while the experiment is being conducted.[6]

Errors and Experimental Planning

Advance planning of experiments is becoming increasingly important. Under some circumstances it is possible to set forth a fixed objective for overall accuracy and plan instrumentation accordingly. An example of this is found in Figs. 12–1 and 12–2 which show the accuracy of feedwater and steam temperature and steam pressure measurements necessary to determine marine boiler performance with less than one tenth of one per cent error.[7] More often, however, field tests are performed under less than ideal laboratory conditions, and the engineer has to be

Fig. 12–1. Accuracy of steam and water temperature measurements for 1/10 of 1% heat balance error

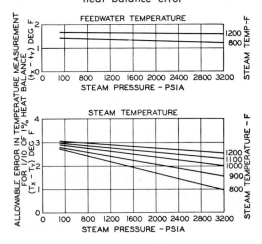

---

[4] See discussion by S. J. Kline of paper entitled "Design of Power Plant Tests to Insure Reliability of Results" by William A. Wilson, *Trans.* ASME, Vol. 77, 1955, p. 408.

[5] This article originally appeared in *Mechanical Engineering*, Vol. 75, January 1953, pp. 3–8.

[6] For additional information, see "Design of Power Plant Tests to Insure Reliability of Results" by William A. Wilson, *Trans.* ASME, Vol. 77, 1955, pp. 405–408; "A Practical Application of Uncertainty Calculations to Measured Data" by L. W. Thrasher and R. C. Binder, *Trans.* ASME, Vol. 79, 1957, pp. 373–376; and "The Effect of Measurement Errors on Plant Performance Tests" by S. Baron, *Combustion*, Vol. 25, February 1954, pp. 49–54.

[7] An interesting study of accuracy requirements is found in the paper from which these curves are taken, "Measurement Accuracy Requirements for Boiler Testing" by J. W. Murdock, *Journal* of the American Society of Naval Engineers, Vol. 62, 1950, pp. 823–833.

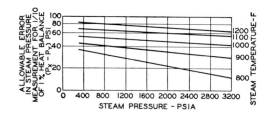

Fig. 12–2. Accuracy of steam pressure measurement for 1/10 of 1% heat balance error

capable of making a judicious selection of existing and special measuring instruments. If the objectives and desired end results are well defined, it may be found that some of the control panel instrumentation may be used, possibly with the aid of some special calibration or by checking against standard sources.

Large sums of money may be spent in devising special measuring equipment for a particular part of a test, but these expenditures may be largely wasted if supporting measurements are of a substantially lesser degree of precision. At the very least, the engineer should be familiar with the principal sources of error and their effect upon test results. Physicists have long been concerned with precision of measurements and their relationship to calculated values, and these considerations are of increasing importance to the engineer.[8] The following useful classification of errors was proposed by a physicist:[9]

   I. Systematic errors
     A. Errors of instrument calibration
     B. Personal errors
     C. Errors due to variation in experimental conditions
     D. Errors caused by imperfect technique
   II. Random errors
     A. Errors of judgment, particularly in reading instruments
     B. Fluctuating conditions, such as temperature or line voltage
     C. Small disturbances, including vibrations or pickup of spurious signals
     D. Lack of precise definitions of quantities
   III. Illegitimate errors
     A. Blunders caused by mistakes in reading instruments
     B. Errors of computation
     C. Chaotic errors due to effects of disturbances

Systematic errors are responsible for bias, a constant deviation between true and measured quantities. Random errors are the cause of lack of precision and lack of ability to duplicate results. Illegitimate errors are often termed extraneous errors.

By making an error analysis in advance of conducting tests, the engineer can determine crucial points of measurement and select his instruments accordingly.[10] He can also predict effects of propagation of errors on calculated results and obtain a much greater overall consistency in testing activities. In test reports the combination of an error analysis with interpretation of results adds to the usefulness of tests as a design tool.

Tests and measurements, as has been implied earlier, require a great deal of engineering thought. Their value is greatly

---

[8] A classic work in this area is *Theory of Errors of Observation* by George B. Airy, Macmillan, London, 1879. An American text widely used for many years is *Elements of the Precision of Measurements and Graphical Methods* by H. M. Goodwin, McGraw-Hill, 1913.
[9] *Introduction to the Theory of Error* by Yardley Beers, Addison-Wesley Publishing Co., Second Edition, 1957, pp. 5–6. The knowledge contained in this 72-page paperback book will be useful to anyone engaged in engineering testing activity.
[10] This viewpoint is expanded by John H. Born, Jr. in ASME Paper 60–WA–301, "The Effect of Measurement Errors on the Accuracy of Steam Generator Efficiency Calculation."

enhanced if the engineer is willing to ask searching questions and make all possible analyses before testing is begun. Finally, skill in reporting test results is of very great importance, particularly in the interpretation of what was observed. Important advances in engineering and science have resulted from skepticism of "obvious" results and perception of new factors that had previously been overlooked.[11]

Boiler Tests

When applied to the study of boilers, testing embraces activities ranging from daily performance observations using station supervisory instruments to unusual conditions with specialized measuring apparatus. In this latitude the scope of any single test and the measurement techniques used depend upon the kind of testing information being sought. Boiler tests may be conducted to obtain design information, to determine acceptance of units and to investigate operational aspects.

Since individual phases of a design problem may range from a completely scientific solution with exact relationships between variables to empirical approaches with variables only generally related, test work for design information is intended either to determine magnitudes and limits of these variables or to establish their cause and effect relationships. While a research laboratory can supply experimental information for basic investigations and observe behavior in many types of models,[12] testing on full scale units is vitally necessary to verify data thus obtained. In the case of small industrial boilers, tests may actually be carried out in a development laboratory as shown in Fig. 12–3, but for large central station boilers the power plant itself becomes the testing laboratory. In some cases where unusual fuels are being studied, large quantities may be shipped long distances in order to have tests conducted in a boiler having the desired firing equipment and design characteristics.

Emphasis from this point onward is on the testing of large central station boilers, but many of the measuring techniques are equally applicable to smaller units installed in marine, industrial and institutional power plants. The last sections of the chapter are concerned with the collection of data by automatic loggers and with the use of computers to calculate test results from the data.

Operational Testing

After a design has been completed and a boiler erected, the initial operating period provides the first opportunity to determine whether or not it meets performance guarantees. This acceptance work is handled as a normal function of the service organization and may include such items as determination of unit capacity, steam temperature control range, draft losses and pressure drops, and overall efficiency. If deficiencies exist, some additional testing may be necessary to

---

[11] These ideas are developed further in the introductory chapters of two undergraduate laboratory textbooks: *Mechanical Measurements* by T. G. Beckwith and N. L. Buck, Addison-Wesley Publishing Co., 1961 and *Theories of Engineering Experimentation* by Hilbert Schenck, Jr., McGraw-Hill Book Co., 1961.

[12] See Chapter 7, Fluid Flow, for further information on laboratory model testing.

Fig. 12–3. Kreisinger Development Laboratory

guide corrective action to meet contractual performance.

When a unit in a central station goes into commercial operation, it becomes an integrated part of a system. It is normal utility practice to determine the unit heat rate characteristics at this time and periodically later. In these days of high economic costs, optimum system efficiency is important, and information from these incremental load cost studies on each unit provides the basis for determining daily load distribution among system plants.

In some central stations, control room data logging equipment is designed to incorporate a computer which calculates heat rate information almost instantaneously. Such rapid information availability permits more detailed analysis of performance and aids in making decisions for optimizing unit operation under such conditions as extreme low loads or loss of a feedwater heater.

In addition to evaluating performance

end results, operational testing covers the more detailed aspects of routine operation such as startup procedures, adjustment and maintenance of unit control systems, and safe-limit monitoring of operating variables.

Test Conditions — Operating Concepts

The test condition desired is governed by the test objective and can be either at constant or transient load.

Historically the role of the newer, larger units in utility system steam plants has been one of base loading at design rating, with system load fluctuations being taken care of by the older and smaller equipment. Consequently, in the past the primary emphasis in new unit design was on steady state operating characteristics. However, the relationship between required short term peak capability and off-peak capacity has changed in many areas in recent years. Because peak load has outdistanced offpeak load growth, there is

increasing interest in transient characteristics of the largest and most modern units.
Many of these will be required to operate
at reduced load at times and even to be
shut down for weekends and other periods
of low electrical demands.

Constant load testing is required for
evaluation of unit heat absorption, heat
transfer parameters, unit efficiency and
heat rates. Transient testing is required
for unit and controls response study and
adjustment, and in connection with quick
startup and shutdown procedures.

Testing Measurements

Steam generator design and operation
revolves about three basic premises, any
one or all of which may be involved in a
test program:
1. Heat liberation
2. Heat absorption
3. Mechanical means to accomplish heat
   liberation and absorption

Heat liberation in the conventional unit
results from combustion of a fuel with
oxygen in the air. Any material is a potential fuel if its oxidation reaction releases
heat at a usable temperature level. Thus,
the first premise implies testing to obtain
knowledge of fuel properties and combustion characteristics. In general this means
theoretical fuel-air-products relationships
from fuel analysis and combining equations, and the actual combustion requirements in an operating furnace. Together
with the combustion efficiency, such things
as pulverizer (or other fuel burning equipment) power and capacity requirements,
ignition stability and ash deposits must be
evaluated. Testing for heat liberation requires considerable attention to fuel and
flue gas sampling to obtain representative
data.

Absorption of heat by unit components
is accompanied by reduction of heat level

of the flue gas and can be determined
from gas temperature measurements and
specific heat data. Similarly, the unrecovered heat quantity entering the stack is a
loss and must be determined. Also, both
solid and gaseous stack emissions are factors receiving considerable attention because of fly ash disposal problems and air
pollution aspects. System resistance appearing as pressure and draft losses must
be known in order to size fans and exhausters adequately. The foregoing are the
most common areas of test work in the
fuel-air cycle.

For a successful design, heating surface
must be properly allocated between furnace, superheater, reheater, economizer
and air heater so that the desired heat
absorption will be achieved and yield the
expected relationships of capacity and
steam temperature. Since in modern boilers the furnace represents the most important part of the evaporative surface, its
performance is a key factor. The furnace
must be sized to be capable of maximum
design evaporation yet provide flue gas at
a precise temperature level to superheat
and reheat the steam to a constant level
over the operating range. Miscalculation
at any one point will upset performance
in all the other sections because of the
series type processes involved.

Heat absorption values determined from
test steam temperature and flow measurements, together with gas temperatures
and flows, are used in developing the surface heat transfer relationships. Additional
performance items in the water-steam
cycle are pressure and pressure drops, and
quality-purity determinations. Circulation
studies in furnace waterwalls and flow distribution between circuits are other examples of water-steam cycle testing.

High availability and low maintenance
costs are prime requirements for steam

generating equipment. Therefore, selection of materials for long life operation of pressure parts at elevated temperatures and pressures is essential. Pressure parts and structural-mechanical equipment are subjected to erosion, abrasion, expansion and vibration in service, and their design requires knowledge of the magnitudes and character of these factors. This information is obtained only through field and laboratory experience.

Measurements Related to Heat Liberation

Fuel Flow

Measurement of fuel flow depends upon the fuel state and accuracy desired. Solid fuels such as coke and coal can be measured by scales. Many plants have automatic batch weighing-dumping equipment incorporated in the fuel handling system. Typical accuracy for these scales when properly adjusted and maintained is within three to four per cent of true total for 10 to 15 dumps. When greater accuracy is desired, as in efficiency tests, it is necessary to manually operate the scales as balances.

When greater accuracy is desired or where no scales are available, fuel rate is determined from a unit heat balance and fuel heating value. With certain solid fuels such as wood, bark, cellulose materials and other waste fuels, the heat balance method of fuel rate determination is the only practical way because of the extreme difficulty of accurately measuring the large bulk volumes of fuel involved.

For general test purposes, fuel oils are metered with volumetric instruments of the displacement rotating disc type. Heavy grades of oil must be heated for proper atomization in burners, and the viscosities resulting permit use of such meters even with these oils where moderate accuracy is satisfactory. If flow error of less than four per cent is required, however, meter calibration is necessary using the intended oil at operating temperature and with a similar piping arrangement. The foaming tendency and volatilization of some oils may prevent their accurate metering by this method.

The use of level change in large uncalibrated storage tanks as a flow index is at best an approximate method. For efficiency tests weigh tanks are the most accurate means of direct measurement, but their use is generally regarded as impractical with large flow rates. Their additional cost also prohibits widespread use.

Orifice flow measurement is most commonly used for gaseous fuels with high accuracy results, providing the actual installation has sufficient approach straight lengths and conforms to design locations of pressure taps and orifice-pipe size relationships.[13]

Fuel Sampling

The inhomogeneity of most fuels requires careful attention to sampling techniques in arriving at a representative sample. Much work has been done on this subject, especially for coal in which stratification of ash and moisture is pro-

---

[13] Detailed information on installation details and flow coefficients is available in the American Gas Association bulletin, Orifice Metering of Natural Gas, Gas Measurement Committee, Report No. 3, April, 1955 and in American Petroleum Institute Code 1105 on displacement meters. Similarly, coal and oil fuel rate measurement is covered in detail in the ASME Power Test Codes, Supplements on Instruments and Apparatus, PTC–19.5. These publications should be reviewed carefully for work requiring high accuracy as in heat input for efficiency measurements.

nounced, and is reported periodically by investigators. Accepted standard practices may be found in the ASTM Standard D271–64, "Methods of Laboratory Sampling and Analysis of Coal and Coke."

In general, solid fuels sampling procedures involve collection of small increments at regular intervals over the test period, and reduction of their aggregate to obtain laboratory size samples by successive quartering or riffling. For some coals, intermediate steps include crushing to definite screen sizes and mixing.[14]

Surface moisture of coal may vary considerably, and for tests requiring high accuracy separate samples are taken and sealed immediately for moisture-only determinations. This practice is mandatory for efficiency tests and desirable for any high-moisture fuel tests because the normal handling in aggregate reduction can produce significant moisture loss of the sample. Aggregate analysis is then adjusted for the average special moisture value to arrive at the as-fired analysis. The need for such care is readily apparent in weighed coal tests when the heat input is directly affected by such moisture loss.

Sampling of other solid fuels such as wood and bark should be made with similar care to avoid moisture loss.

With most pumped liquid and gaseous fuels the problem is one of possible overall change during the test period rather than inhomogeneity at any instant. Thus, sampling at a single point with fixed extraction rate for the entire test period should be adequate. The exceptions are where known stratification exists as in waste fuel ducts or in residual fuel lines.

Fuel Analysis

In its broadest sense, fuel analysis refers to determination of all physical and chemical properties of a fuel.[15]

The basic type of chemical analysis for coal is the proximate, which describes the fuel in weight per cent of fixed carbon, volatile material, ash, and moisture contents. To some extent, it is an index to ignition and burning ease, volatilization being the first phase of combustion. Moisture content is an important factor in pulverizer capacity and general ignition-combustion behavior in both suspension and fuel bed burning. Ash content is involved in formation of fireside deposits as well as in the wear and capacity of pulverizers and fuel handling equipment.

In the ultimate analysis, the fixed carbon and volatile material contents are reported in terms of total carbon, hydrogen, oxygen, nitrogen, and sulfur, this form being required for calculation of fuel-air quantities.

With both types of analysis, it is customary to report the coal heating value determined by oxygen bomb calorimeter. In this country, standard engineering practice is to use the higher or gross heating value.[16] For the lower heating value the latent heat of vaporization of all the moisture resulting in products is subtracted from the gross value. This differ-

---

[14] A symposium on coal sampling sponsored by ASTM and published in 1955 as Special Technical Publication 162 includes nine papers and extensive discussion on this subject.

[15] See Chapters 13 and 14 on solid, liquid and gaseous fuels for additional information and references. This section includes only basic information which is presented in more detail elsewhere in the book.

[16] A very clear explanation of the significance of heating values is found in "Uses of High and Low Heat Values" by A. G. Christie, Trans. ASME, Vol. 70, 1948, pp. 819–820.

ence represents a previously unrecovered heat quantity.

Some physical properties of coal are described by ash fusion range, sizing and fineness. The ash fusion range is determined by observing changes in shape of a cone of ground ash upon heating in a laboratory furnace under oxidizing and reducing atmospheres.[17] Actual furnace conditions depend upon zones or location and vary between the laboratory oxidizing and reducing extremes.

Fuel sizing generally refers to crusher-prepared coal sizing measured with screens of ⅛ inch opening and larger, and is of importance mainly for fuel bed distribution problems in stoker firing. Coal fineness usually means suspension burning sizes and for pulverized coal involves sieving of 50 to 200 mesh (openings per inch) particle sizes. In both cases, a series of screen sizes is used, the fractions retained or passed by each size being reported. Knowledge of the size consist or overall fraction relationship rather than just one size is required. For example, in pulverized coal firing, combustion efficiency (carbon loss) is normally more affected by larger size consist, whereas grinding power is more closely related to the finer size percentages.

Another physical property related to pulverizer performance is ease of grinding or grindability index, which is determined by power required in laboratory pulverization of a prepared sample of the test coal for comparison with a standard. In the Hardgrove method, the standard is 100, decreasing numbers indicating progressively harder grinding coals.[18]

Oil fuels are reported in an ultimate analysis together with higher heating value and sample density, viscosity and flash point. Density can be stated in terms of standard specific gravity, referred to water, or degrees API, the two terms being readily convertible.[19] Additional properties are pour point, sediment, and the presence of solid impurities such as metallic salts. These properties may have bearing on pumping, storage, slagging and corrosion problems.

In general, the ultimate analysis is sufficient to determine fuel-air relationships for byproduct liquid fuels such as pulp mill black liquor, refinery wastes, pitch and others. However, operating problems may require special tests in addition to the standard physical property determinations mentioned.

Gaseous fuels are usually combinations of saturated and unsaturated hydrocarbons, and their analysis is reported as a mol or volume per cent of these constituents. Common analysis techniques are low temperature distillation, mass-spectrometer and adsorption methods. High heating value at standard volumetric conditions and saturated or dry can be calculated from this constituent analysis using standard heating values of constituents. The classical method of heating value determination, by calorimeter, is feasible where gas samples of large volume can be provided easily. For instance, recording calorimeters are commonly found at transmission line entry points to users' plants for billing purposes.

Fuel–Air Proportioning

Combustion air flow measurement and regulation are a requisite in good opera-

---

[17] See Chapter 13, Fuel Properties of Coal.
[18] See Chapter 16, Pulverizers, for additional information.
[19] Degrees API = 141.5/(specific gravity at 60/60 F) − 131.5.

tion because of the desire to burn a fuel with optimum air quantity. Some air in excess of the theoretical quantity for complete combustion is always required, the amount depending upon the fuel and firing method. Although ideally the lowest excess air is desirable, there are many conditions under which high excess air results in more economical plant operation. For example, if constant steam temperature is to be maintained at low ratings, increased gas mass flow may be required over heat transfer surfaces, and this can only be accomplished by increasing excess air or recirculating gas.

From an operating point of view it is not necessary to know the quantities of air required and fuel products formed in terms of weight or volume rates. The operator wants to know these quantities relative to the theoretical amounts for the fuel rate being burned. Therefore, operating indexes are designed to show the per cent excess air or relative per cent total air quantities. However, for engineering design purposes these air and gas rates are necessary to properly size fans, ducts and heat transfer equipment.

Air flow measurement in routine operation is accomplished through pressure or draft differential sensing of a gas or air side component, or by means of flue gas analysis. In either case field calibration of the metering equipment is ultimately based upon test flue gas analysis. Flow measurement by pitot tube techniques is somewhat restricted in boiler air-flue gas flow problems because duct configuration and low static-impact pressure difference generally limit the resulting accuracy. More importantly the flue gas analysis method is superior because of its simple interpretation for overall air flow. However, pitot measurements become necessary for study of air or flue gas distribution within a system.

The fundamental method of volumetric flue gas analysis is by orsat apparatus, in which a known volume of gas is sequentially exposed to absorbent solutions for carbon dioxide and oxygen. Measurement of sample volume between stages indicates the constituent volume percentages and the remaining nitrogen. Trace gases such as argon are included with nitrogen, while sulfur compounds such as sulfur dioxide and trioxide are absorbed together with carbon dioxide. For most fuels, their effect on the gas analysis results is negligible in excess air determination.

The resultant gaseous products for complete combustion of a fuel using several excess air values are calculated from the ultimate fuel analysis and chemical combining equations. Plotting the volume percentages of carbon dioxide and oxygen thus formed permits excess air determination by volumetric gas analysis. As a matter of fact, within certain restrictions, the excess air can be determined without knowing the fuel analysis because the available oxygen in products is a direct measure of excess air, and when compared to the nitrogen will indicate per cent excess air. Moreover, for conventional fuels oxygen measurement alone is sufficient to indicate excess air with acceptable accuracy, as indicated in the explanations accompanying Fig. 12–4.

The practical uniformity of this oxygen–excess air relationship over a wide range of fuels makes it extremely useful in both single and combination fuel firing and is responsible for the widespread use of flue gas oxygen analyzers for operating and test purposes. These devices employ either catalytic combustion of a known gas and the uncombined oxygen in a flue gas

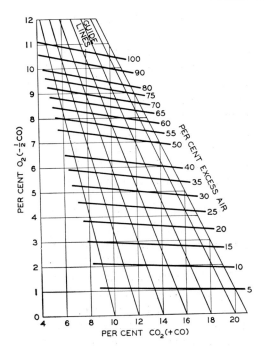

Fig. 12–4. Percentage relationship of O_2, CO_2 and excess air

laboratory analysis of small samples by mass spectrometer and adsorption techniques. In either case, the samples must be collected with extreme care to avoid sample contamination if misleading results are to be avoided. For example, the sampling probe should be a quenching type since hot probe materials may act as combustion catalysts in the flue gas thus indicating no combustibles where they are present, or conversely, probes and sample containers should be free of oil films, high vapor pressure stopcock grease and the like, since these materials may cause traces of combustibles when there are none in the flue gas.

Temperature Measurements

Temperature measurement is accomplished by several methods depending upon temperature level, fluid stratification, physical accessibility and accuracy desired.[20]

Classification of techniques commonly used in steam generator testing is generally as follows:

1. Filled system thermometers
2. Thermoelectric and electrical resistance effects

These two methods are direct in that they involve fluid temperature level attainment by the sensing element. Indirect techniques, such as utilization of optical or radiation effects accompanying temperature level of the fluid, are infrequently used because of calibration difficulties arising from variations in these effects with different fuels and furnace equipment.

Of the filled system thermometers, mercury and other liquid in glass thermom-

sample within a temperature sensitive electrical circuit, or magnetic field distortion due to paramagnetic qualities of the oxygen in the flue gas sample. In both cases, the effect is proportional to sample oxygen content, permitting calibration of the instrument output signal in terms of oxygen per cent.

In modern fuel burning practice, unburned gaseous combustibles in flue gas are generally nonexistent; however, they can occur with certain operating conditions. The extremely low quantities to be found even in such cases (less than 0.10 per cent) are usually beyond the accuracy of orsat work and require detection by chemical reaction–calorimetric methods or

20 For additional detailed information, see ASME Power Test Codes, Instruments and Apparatus, Part 3, "Temperature Measurement," PTC 19.3–1961.

eters use volume expansion and are the most common examples of the first class. Their usage in gas-air work is restricted to ambient level temperatures, and, when stratification does not exist, in ducts. Gaseous-bulb type instruments, commonly found in operating instrumentation, are a variation of the volume expansion class and employ measurement of the accompanying pressure change. This type instrument permits remote indication, but it is a fixed position device and usually requires field calibration by another means.

The most versatile temperature measurement devices are those in the second group. Both thermoelectric and electric resistance type techniques are readily adaptable to remote measurement, thus enabling monitoring of many points from a single location. Of the two, the thermocouple is more widely used because of its simplicity and low cost.

Thermocouple measurement employs the thermoelectric effect, a phenomenon whose alternate effects were first observed respectively by Seebeck and Peltier in 1821 and 1834. An electromotive force (emf) is developed if a circuit comprising two different wires has the two junctions at different temperatures. The magnitude of the emf depends on the wire materials and is proportional to the temperature difference between the junctions. Thus knowing the temperature at one junction and considering the wire materials, the temperature at the other junction can be determined. The effects of intermediate metals and temperatures are defined by specific laws.[21]

Numerous metals are available for thermocouple materials, selection of the most suitable being based on emf developed, expected mechanical life in the atmosphere and temperature involved, calibration constancy and cost. The most common types are copper–constantan,[22] iron–constantan, chromel–alumel, and platinum–platinum–rhodium; their upper limit temperature ratings for general service are 400, 1100, 1800 and 2700 F respectively.

Detailed specifications covering temperature–emf relationships and standard accuracy limits have been developed by several engineering societies.[23]

Experience with chromel–constantan thermocouples also indicates suitability of this combination for measurements up to 1600 F with high emf developed.

Thermocouple emf can be measured with either a millivolt galvanometer or a null-balance potentiometer. However, in the galvanometer system, the thermocouple circuit resistance is an additional factor and complicates the measurement, whereas in the null-balance system no current flows in the thermocouple circuit, the measurement being of the opposing emf. The latter system, being simpler, is more widely used.

The *resistance bulb* method involves known temperature–electrical resistance change characteristic of a material, usually nickel or platinum, using a Wheatstone bridge type measuring circuit. This method can be made extremely accurate and is used in temperature standards work. However, the high cost of sensing

---

[21] For additional information, see "Thermoelectric Thermometry," a 92-page monograph by Paul H. Dike, published by Leeds and Northrup Company, Philadelphia 44, Penna.

[22] Chromel and alumel are chromium–nickel and aluminum–nickel alloys respectively. Constantan is a copper alloy.

[23] For example, see Instrument Society of America, Recommended Practice — Thermocouples and Thermocouple Extension Wires, RP 1.1–1.7, and ASA and ASTM publications on thermocouples.

elements and measuring circuit restricts its use to laboratory calibration work or field test work where high precision is required, such as measurement of fractional parts of degrees.

Use of Probes. Flue gas temperature measurement is most commonly made with thermocouple probes. This requires the hot junction to reach fluid temperature level, which means the fluid contacting the thermocouple must be flowing at a sufficient rate to supply heat lost by conduction from the hot junction along lead wires and radiation to colder surfaces. The magnitude of these heat losses will depend upon probe design, including probe temperature and relative orientation of the hot junction, and temperature differential between the hot junction and the heat receiving surfaces. Physical properties of flue gas also have an effect.

In general, thermocouple measurement of gas–air temperature in most ducts is simplified for the following reasons.

1. Temperature level is below 700 F and does not require water cooling of probes for mechanical strength.
2. Ducts are insulated to prevent heat loss and their interiors are essentially at fluid temperature.

At a temperature level of 700 F, an error of 15 deg F is commonly found with bare thermocouples in proximity to economizer heating surface at 500 F.

At gas temperatures higher than 700 F water cooling of probes is necessary for mechanical strength reasons, and the lead wire conduction heat loss increases. More significantly, higher temperature levels correspond to areas with heat transfer surfaces such as economizer, waterwalls, superheater and reheater, the surface temperatures of which vary between 500 and 1100 F. As a result, the radiation error of a bare thermocouple junction increases severely until at the furnace outlet with gas temperature of 2000 F the bare thermocouple error is about 200 deg F.

To compensate for the radiation and conduction heat loss in furnace gas temperature work, the thermocouple junction is shielded with a thin ceramic cylinder through which a high gas flow is induced. The shield in turn is subject to the same heat loss effects, and by increasing the number of annular shield layers the thermocouple junction can be brought to within ± 5 deg F of true gas temperature. The limit to the size and number of shield openings is usually determined by the fuel. Serious plugging occurs with high ash coals in a short period when shields with small openings are used.

Another type of furnace gas temperature measuring device is the orifice probe, in which the hot gas is drawn through two metering orifices in series with deliberate cooling of the gas occurring between them. By measuring the two orifice flow rates and cold gas temperature, the initial gas temperature can be calculated since weight flow is constant and the orifice flow differentials indicate volume flow which is a function of temperature. The advantage of this type measurement is that it eliminates thermocouple radiation error. It does have the disadvantage, however, of requiring a more complicated measuring system and involves calculation.

Solid and Gaseous Emission

Considerations of corrosion and erosion of surfaces, formation of deposits and community air pollution from stack emission evoke interest in gaseous and particulate products of combustion. In attempting to control these effects, test work becomes necessary to establish the character of the emissions and control methods required.

In addition to the usual gaseous combustion products, gases such as oxides of nitrogen and of sulfur are formed, which are of significance from the standpoint of air pollution. Detection is by chemical methods. Also, dew point temperature elevation due to the presence of sulfur trioxide in flue gas is important for air heater and dust collector corrosion and plugging.

Particulate stack emissions vary with fuel and firing method. For example, fly ash from coal-fired units may range in size from less than ten microns to 50 mesh. Aside from the nuisance value of fly ash emission, any combustible contained in it represents a heat loss which must be minimized. In addition to measuring this loss, dust loading and analysis provide performance data on the plant dust collecting equipment.

Fly ash samples are taken with a sharp-edged nozzle pointed upstream, through which a gas sample is withdrawn. For accurate sampling the withdrawal rate must equal the undisturbed point flow rate in the duct; i.e., the sampling must be carried out isokinetically. The fly ash is separated from the gas sample either by cyclone, filter or electrostatic precipitator, depending upon the circumstances of the particular test. Suitable precautions must be taken to obtain a large enough sample, and to avoid settling or condensation in connecting lines if the separator is external to the duct.

Because of velocity and concentration stratification in most ducts, traversing is essential to obtain representative samples and data. The number of sampling points required for traversing must be determined by a preliminary study and varies with the degree of stratification encountered and accuracy desired.

Recommended sampling locations are

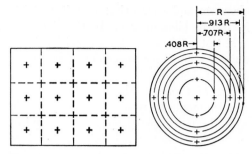

Fig. 12–5. Position locations for duct sampling

obtained by dividing the total duct area into equal areas, as shown in Fig. 12–5. Sampling is at the centers of these areas. Obviously, the degree of subdivision required depends upon the stratification existing. As a rule of thumb, sampling points spaced approximately three feet apart in rectangular ducts have been satisfactory in many cases. In general, this spacing should be decreased for sampling locations close to heat absorption surfaces.

The best sampling location is usually a matter of convenience, since straight runs of duct are seldom encountered and the combined effect of upstream and downstream turns is often erratic. With severe stratification installation of straightening vanes may be desirable. However, their orientation must be determined from analytical considerations and model studies.

By doubling or quadrupling the number of sampling points, accuracy can be improved somewhat. This also increases the sampling time and effort, and improvement may not always be commensurate with the additional work required. One other approach exists which may be useful if stratification is not too severe. If the stratification is confined largely to one side, say to the top, a compromise procedure would be to subdivide the top row of squares only.

Efficiency and Heat Losses

The desire to achieve process completion with maximum economy is basic in any technical effort. One of the measures of performance in steam generators is overall or gross efficiency which is defined as the ratio of heat output to heat input.[24] Also, a heat balance diagram as shown in Fig. 12–6, indicates the corollary to be: efficiency = 100 − per cent losses.

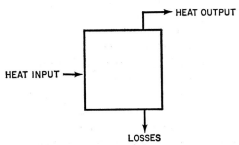

From the heat balance diagram
Input = Output + Losses
By definition

$$\text{Per Cent Efficiency} = \frac{\text{Output}}{\text{Input}} \times 100$$

$$= \frac{\text{Input} - \text{Losses}}{\text{Input}} \times 100$$

$$= \left(1 - \frac{\text{Losses}}{\text{Input}}\right) \times 100$$

$$= 100 - \left(\frac{\text{Losses}}{\text{Input}} \times 100\right)$$

$$= 100 - \text{Per Cent Losses}$$

Fig. 12–6. Basic heat balance diagram and efficiency relationships

Present day units are large, and the water–steam and fuel quantities associated with them are so great that their measurement with high accuracy is extremely difficult. Weighed water and fuel tests are seldom feasible on these units, and the results with operating instrumentation are subject to commercial meter accuracies. Hence, the *input-output method* is often unsuitable for an accurate test of very large stationary boilers.[25]

Efficiency measurement by the *heat loss method* has several advantages over the input–output method in addition to being less costly. It is more informative since it establishes the individual losses for comparison with expected performance.

Regarding accuracy, the total losses are only 10 to 20 per cent and fuel sampling and analysis errors affect the end results slightly, whereas in the input-output method these errors are at least four or five times as signficant. Moreover, the basic losses measurements are simple: fuel analysis, exit gas temperature, entering air temperature and refuse combustible content. Minor items in the heat losses can be obtained from sources such as ASME Power Test Code PTC–4 which contains detailed instructions on test procedure and results calculations.

Drafts and Pressure Losses

Draft and pressure losses in steam generators are recorded in both routine and special test operation because they indicate the system resistance which fans and exhausters must overcome.

Test measurement is usually of draft differential rather than draft alone. Aside from convenience in direct reading, a restriction must be observed in that draft measurement is with reference to some atmospheric pressure. Since atmospheric pressure changes with elevation (approximately one inch water gage per 100 ft) all draft gages must be at the same eleva-

[24] The terms input, output, and losses used here are categorical. For detailed definitions and procedures, the reader is referred to ASME Power Test Codes for Steam Generating Units, PTC 4.1 — 1964 and the diagrams appearing opposite page 12–1 and on page 12–23, Fig. 12–10.

[25] A comparison of the two methods, with emphasis on smaller boilers where fuel and water can be weighed, is found in ASME Paper 60–WA–298, "Efficiency Determination of Marine Boilers: Input-Output Versus Heat-Loss Method" by L. Cohen and W. A. Fritz, Jr.

tion or readings corrected for elevation; otherwise an error of as much as 10 per cent can be introduced.

Measurement is with inclined and U-tube liquid manometers. Duct walls and casing connections are usually suitable; the maximum error due to impact would not exceed one velocity head which is less than 0.1 in. water gage in most cases. The most common source of error in draft measurement is condensation and ash plugging in connecting lines. The importance of adequate line pitch, drain connections and blowout fittings cannot be overemphasized.

Measurements Related to Heat Absorption

Water and Steam Flow

Both steam output and feedwater flow are obtained by pressure differential measurement across flow nozzle or thin plate orifice sections. The two flows are equal except for loss such as blowdown, injection leakoff, etc. However, of the two, feedwater measurement is generally more reliable than steam flow because orifice coefficients are more positively established for the former.

The recording flow meters found in most plants employ commercial orifices or flow nozzles. Overall accuracy is usually plus or minus two per cent of full scale, unless the installation has been calibrated against a special test orifice. These test orifices are plant primary standards, usually installed in low pressure-temperature condensate points in the feedwater cycle to avoid undue extrapolation of original calibration data. Their calibration is performed with laboratory weigh tanks, and extrapolation of flow coefficients to the condensate con-

ditions of flow, temperature and pressure is usually accomplished on the basis of Reynolds number and other dimensionless criteria.

While a few central stations have reheat steam flow meters, it is more common to determine this quantity from primary steam-water flow, high pressure heater heat balance and the appropriate turbine gland corrections.

For test of heat absorption surface characteristics it is usually sufficient to use the operating feedwater recorder because these characteristics are essentially constant for rating changes within meter accuracy, and the fuel-air-gas flow data are related to this base value by heat balance.[26]

Another method of flow measurement sometimes used is pitot tube technique. Variations of the standard air-gas type are usually preferred for manufacturing reasons, and these are commonly used in some circulation studies where a low resistance measuring element is required. These devices are usually not suitable for total unit flow measurement because of structural and flow pattern uncertainty reasons.

Weigh tanks are rarely found in large utility installations nowadays because of unit size and consequent cost. Their functions are being filled by calibrated flow nozzles and orifices. However, the weighing facilities are necessary as primary references in university and standards laboratories where the nozzle calibration work is performed.

Temperature Measurement

The most common methods of temperature measurement are thermocouples, resistance bulb elements and thermometers.

---

[26] An excellent reference on flow measurement is the ASME research publication, "Fluid Meters — Their Theory and Application," Fifth Edition, 1959.

The general statements on this subject made previously under gas and air measurements apply to steam and water measurements also.

However, some aspects present more serious problems than in the gas-air work. Since in this case the fluid pressures are also high, the measuring elements are rarely exposed directly to the fluid stream. Measurement is commonly made by bottoming contact with a metal well which projects into the stream and provides the necessary mechanical strength. Several well designs are shown in the ASME Power Test Code, Supplements on Instruments and Apparatus–PTC 19.3 and in a paper by J. W. Murdock.[27]

Another method of fluid temperature determination is surface temperature measurement of the containing steam or water line. However, this method is only possible where there is no heat transfer because of temperature gradient effects from hot gas and steam-film. In these zero heat flux areas the tube wall gradient usually presents no problem in measurement, although even here precautions should be taken against boundary effects.

Thermocouples are commonly peened directly into the tube metal or attached by welding the hot junction to the metal. In a well application spring loading of the element is most practical. In both these cases the thermocouple is grounded and measurement of a number of points must be by separate circuits since series connections can form unknown loops using boiler metal as a third wire.

Pressure and Pressure Differentials

The fundamental pressure and pressure differential measuring device is the visible liquid column. Although its use is limited to column heights which are practical, the foolproof simplicity of the method is the reason for its retention as a reference. Glass-faced mercury manometers are used for pressure differential work up to line pressures of 2000 psig, especially for orifice-flow nozzle differential measurements. Some range flexibility exists through use of liquids whose densities are between those of water and mercury. A variation of the visible column, used for pressures over 2000 psig, is a column inside a tube or jacket with a float indicating liquid level through mechanical linkage or magnetic pointer.

Dead weight instruments employ incremental weights acting on a given sized piston which floats when the liquid and weight pressures are equal. In deadweight gages the liquid pressure is line pressure, its value determined from the weight total. In deadweight testers the liquid is in a closed system, the pressure acting on the instrument to be calibrated and the weight piston from which the pressure value is determined.

The most common steam-water pressure measuring device is the Bourdon gage, the simplest form of which is a bent-flattened tube that tends to straighten itself when internal pressure is applied. Motion of the tube end is transmitted through linkage to a pointer which sweeps a graduated scale. The concept of mechanical motion or distortion due to fluid pressure is common to all pressure elements; the differences occur in the way this force is transduced into a signal. Development of this idea is found in diaphragms, bellows and cylinders whose motions are linked to and described by pointers, strain gage wires, varying resistance bridges, differential transformers, and

[27] See "Power Test Code Thermometer Wells" by J. W. Murdock, *Trans.* ASME, *Journal of Engineering for Power*, Vol. 81, Series A, 1959, pp. 403–416.

other mechanical or electrical signal generators.

Such combinations of devices are known as pressure transducers. Their combined sensitivity, linearity, repeatability and hysteresis are characteristics to be evaluated in selecting a combination for any specific application. Accelerated development of these devices has resulted from a need for automation in both testing and operation of industrial equipment.

Additional Performance Measurements

The steam generator structure is the means by which heat liberated in combustion of the fuel is absorbed by the steam-water fluid. Since the process is one of heat flow it must be apparent that temperatures of the various equipment items are the basic criteria for design once the desired pressure is stated.

The thermocouple is by far the most used piece of test apparatus in steam generator study. Its adaptability for remote measurement of many widely separated points permits investigations and control otherwise impossible. Usage is not limited to pressure parts but includes structural parts as well.

Aside from temperature considerations, steam generator equipment is subjected to abrasion and erosion and to vibration forces. The first two are generally long term processes requiring correlation of metallurgical laboratory studies with prolonged operating experience. The main function of field test activity in this area is to establish the magnitudes of existing factors such as temperature, gas flow velocity patterns, ash-fuel character and concentrations.

With the increase in unit size and desire for balance between strength and weight, vibration forces have received considerable attention because of their destructive effects. Standing waves in flue gas passages induce structural and pressure parts vibrations. Test activity in this area is required for corrective work and to provide design criteria to avoid susceptible arrangements. Gas vibrations are measured with traversing pressure transducers and oscillographic measuring circuits or mechanical vibration graphing devices, depending upon conditions. The latter are also used for structural and casing members.

Another problem related to temperature factors is equipment expansion between hot and cold positions. These movements are generally measured with trams or dial gages depending upon the application. For instance, waterwall headers on certain units are expected to move downward three inches or more, and other parts lesser amounts, and unrestrained movement is essential.

Automatic Data Collection

The advent of boilers in the multimillion pounds of steam per hour range has increased the complexity of boiler testing. A desire to reduce the manpower and the time required for data collection has prompted the use of automatic data logging equipment. A data logger is essentially a system to select and measure a number of analog input signals and convert them either to a graphic display or a digital printout. On steam generators the signals are low level direct current quantities such as thermocouple emf, pressure transducer output and the like. The measurement can be simultaneous, as in the case of a multi-channel system, or sequential, as in the case of a single channel system. A coded tape output may also be provided if the final data reduction is by computer.

No clear distinction can be made between data loggers and computers. Loggers usually perform some computations and computers always have logging functions. However, for convenience a logger can be arbitrarily defined as primarily a device for accepting and recording analog inputs.

Data Logger Types

Most data loggers fall into two basic categories: those designed for (1) transient testing and (2) for steady state testing. The former types can accept 100–500 points per second. The latter feature relatively slow speed logging of 0.5–10 inputs per second.

The single channel high speed data logger successively scans a large number of data points by means of mercury-wetted switches. The analog signals are measured and a record is ultimately provided through readout of some intermediate memory system such as a high speed magnetic tape.

High speed data loggers are relatively expensive and their use is justified where an almost instantaneous "look" is necessary. Multi-channel data loggers have been developed for use where simultaneous readout of data points is required. Typical use would be recording of high frequency signals, which in some areas of transient testing may be 100 cycles per second.

Slow speed data loggers incorporate mechanical stepping switches for sequential reading and are suitable for logging of steady state or slowly changing conditions. The slow speed scanning permits printout as data is taken with data display on recorder chart, typewritten log sheet and coded tape.

A data logger suitable for special requirements for field test work should be capable of making the following steady state measurements: (1) temperatures, (2) pressure and pressure differential, (3) flue gas oxygen analysis, (4) draft and air pressure loss, (5) position indication.

C–E Data Logger — Inputs and Components

Physical quantities such as temperature, position, pressures and per cent oxygen can be converted to analog signals through the use of suitable transducers. In the C–E Data Logger three types of thermocouples are used for temperature measurements. A strain gage bridge circuit actuated by pressure bellows is the sending device for pressures and pressure differential. Position indication is made by voltage divider circuits operated by a mechanical linkage. The above signals are transmitted to the data logger by means of cables with multi-pin electrical plugs on each end. The mating receptacles are furnished on the boiler at erection time, thus reducing field set up time. The pressure points to be logged are connected to the data logger by individual cables which supply the excitation and return the analog signal from the transducers.

The basic components of a portable field test data logger are shown schematically in Fig. 12–7. Logging cycles are controlled by switches on the analog console, with a choice of continuous or fixed interval operation. There is also provision for log on demand, manual point advance, continuous single point monitoring and delete features.

The signal converter is an electromechanical null balance potentiometer

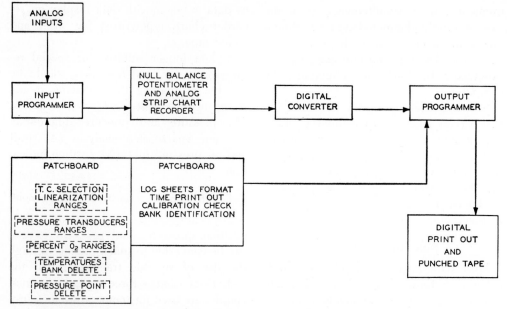

Fig. 12–7. Schematic diagram of basic components of C–E Data Logger

which balances an internal signal against an unknown input. An encoder located on the potentiometer shaft translates shaft position into 0–1000 divisions. This coded signal is fed into a translater which actuates the typewriter and tape punch.

An output programmer in the digital console of the C–E Data Logger sets the typewritten format, and the correct sequence of digits. The typewriter is manually operable between log cycles for typing in auxiliary information.

Besides the digital printout of data points, each log cycle contains the number of the log, time of start and finish, and a calibration check.

Accuracy

Overall accuracy of the C–E Data Logger is one quarter per cent of full scale, independent of primary measuring devices. This logger accuracy compares favorably with the manual measuring devices usually employed during field tests.

Data Reduction by Electronic Digital Computers

Increases in boiler sizes and advances in testing technology have accordingly added to the complexity of analyzing test results. The vast amount of data recorded during a comprehensive test program on a boiler would require up to several thousand man hours to convert to a form necessary for analysis. To eliminate the many hours of averaging, converting, tabulating and plotting, electronic digital computers can be programmed to accomplish these tedious tasks in a fraction of the time and at a fraction of the cost.

Data reduction by computer is accomplished by either of two methods: frequently used reduction processes that are programmed directly into the machine for use at any time; or infrequently used processes which are set up by means of a shorthand machine language that the computer converts into a temporary program.

While the first method is fairly complicated and requires extensive training to accomplish, the second is reasonably simple and can be performed after minimum instruction.

Raw test data is received at the computer center as coded-punched tape, typed log and handwritten form. There it is converted to punched cards for record purposes and for further conversion to magnetic tape for introduction into the computer. The data on the magnetic tape is used in either of the two previously mentioned types of programs to obtain various results ranging from simple averaging of sets of readings through complicated calculation and plotting routines or iterative-problem solving. Some of the test data reduction programs are summarized below.

Gas Temperatures

Flue gas temperatures measured anywhere in the boiler are accepted by this program. The temperature data can be from traversing probes or stationary rakes as shown in Figs. 12–8 and 12–9. The computer will accept data in the form of either millivolts from thermocouples or degrees and, in the case of the former, converts each reading to degrees. The program, in general, follows this sequence:

1. Averages "in" and "out" readings if traverse method is used to obtain data
2. Interpolates between preset intervals for intervening readings
3. Corrects elevation of traverse to account for droop of probe, if applicable
4. Calculates an arithmetic average of the test insert
5. Calculates "strip averages" of the plane where two or more inserts are contained per plane
6. Calculates a "plane average" based on the strip averages
7. Interpolates readings of 1 and 2 above to obtain a temperature grid with one foot intervals, vertically and horizontally, within the plane boundaries

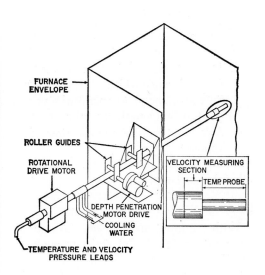

Fig. 12–8. Traversing probe

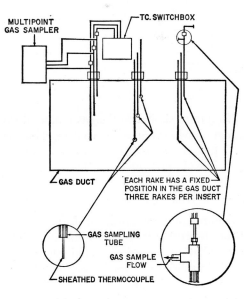

Fig. 12–9. Stationary rake

8. Tabulates 1, 2, 3, 4, 5 and 6 above.

9. Plots, to scale, a contour diagram of 7 above

Gas Velocities and Mass Flows

Gas velocities are usually measured by means of some type of directional pitot tube, the resulting data being in inches of water differential and angular degrees of flow. The computer program for reduction of this data is similar to the gas temperature program in regards to averaging, interpolating and tabulating, with the additions listed below:

1. Correlates gas temperatures from the previous program and the new flow data to calculate the mass flows for each reading

2. Calculates the mass flow normal to the plane from the flow angle and actual mass flow

3. Calculates a weighted temperature average of the insert and of the plane, based on the normal mass flow and the gas temperatures of the previous program

4. Plots contours of gas mass flow for each plane

5. Plots a profile of the gas flow angles for each insert

Gas Analysis

Programs similar to the gas temperature program will average, interpolate, tabulate and plot contours of either oxygen or carbon dioxide present in the flue gas.

Furnace Wall Heat Absorption

Information for study of furnace wall heat absorption is usually obtained either by radiation panels mounted on water-cooled probes or by measuring metal temperatures on the fire side and on the casing side of the furnace wall tubes. In either case, the heat absorption rates are calculated and tabulated and the absorption rate contours are plotted similar to temperature and mass flow contours.

Combustion Characteristics of a Fuel

Fuel analyses from fuel samples are processed to give a tabulation of the following:

1. Higher heating value (including calculated value for gaseous fuels)

2. Products of combustion: wet air, dry air, wet products and dry products, in weight per chemical heat input (lb per million Btu)

4. Products of combustion: O_2, CO_2, SO_2, N_2 and H_2O, in per cent by weight

4. Products of combustion: O_2, CO_2, SO_2 and N_2, in per cent by volume, dry

5. Mean and instantaneous specific heats of the flue gas at several excess airs and temperatures ranging from 0 F to 2400 F

In addition to these tabulations, plots of 2, 4, and 5 are produced.

Temperature Versus Variable Plots

Several adaptions are used with this program, the most common being:

1. Element steam or metal temperatures versus furnace width

2. Steam or metal temperatures versus gas touched length of a tube

3. Any temperature versus time (response)

Both tabulations and plots are provided in all of these examples.

Efficiency

With the input of necessary gas and air temperatures, fuel and fly ash analysis, unit heat losses and efficiency are calculated and tabulated.

ASME Power Test Codes

Since its first publication in 1915, ASME Power Test Code 4.1, Steam Generating Units, has been a recognized guide for procedures of boiler testing. Fig. 12–10 as well as the boiler boundary diagram opposite page 12–1 and the forms on pages 12–24 and 12–25 are reproduced from the 1964 edition of PTC 4.1.

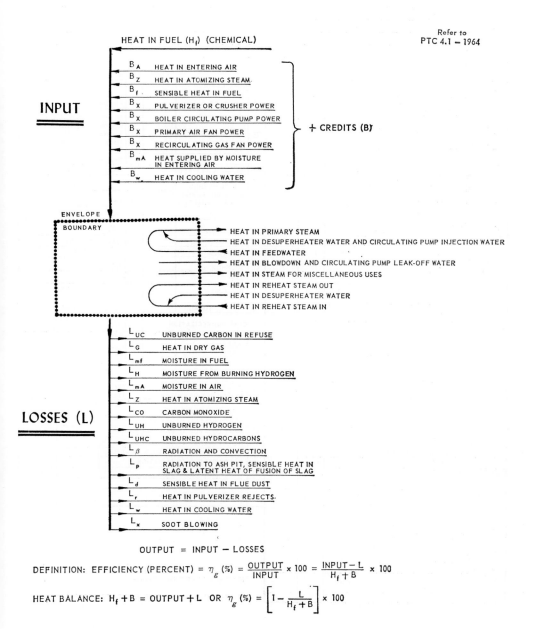

Refer to
PTC 4.1 — 1964

HEAT IN FUEL (H_f) (CHEMICAL)

INPUT

B_A	HEAT IN ENTERING AIR
B_Z	HEAT IN ATOMIZING STEAM
B_f	SENSIBLE HEAT IN FUEL
B_X	PULVERIZER OR CRUSHER POWER
B_X	BOILER CIRCULATING PUMP POWER
B_X	PRIMARY AIR FAN POWER
B_X	RECIRCULATING GAS FAN POWER
B_{mA}	HEAT SUPPLIED BY MOISTURE IN ENTERING AIR
B_w	HEAT IN COOLING WATER

+ CREDITS (B)

ENVELOPE
BOUNDARY

HEAT IN PRIMARY STEAM
HEAT IN DESUPERHEATER WATER AND CIRCULATING PUMP INJECTION WATER
HEAT IN FEEDWATER
HEAT IN BLOWDOWN AND CIRCULATING PUMP LEAK-OFF WATER
HEAT IN STEAM FOR MISCELLANEOUS USES
HEAT IN REHEAT STEAM OUT
HEAT IN DESUPERHEATER WATER
HEAT IN REHEAT STEAM IN

LOSSES (L)

L_{UC}	UNBURNED CARBON IN REFUSE
L_G	HEAT IN DRY GAS
L_{mf}	MOISTURE IN FUEL
L_H	MOISTURE FROM BURNING HYDROGEN
L_{mA}	MOISTURE IN AIR
L_Z	HEAT IN ATOMIZING STEAM
L_{CO}	CARBON MONOXIDE
L_{UH}	UNBURNED HYDROGEN
L_{UHC}	UNBURNED HYDROCARBONS
L_β	RADIATION AND CONVECTION
L_p	RADIATION TO ASH PIT, SENSIBLE HEAT IN SLAG & LATENT HEAT OF FUSION OF SLAG
L_d	SENSIBLE HEAT IN FLUE DUST
L_r	HEAT IN PULVERIZER REJECTS
L_w	HEAT IN COOLING WATER
L_x	SOOT BLOWING

OUTPUT = INPUT − LOSSES

DEFINITION: EFFICIENCY (PERCENT) = η_g (%) = $\dfrac{\text{OUTPUT}}{\text{INPUT}} \times 100 = \dfrac{\text{INPUT} - \text{L}}{H_f + B} \times 100$

HEAT BALANCE: $H_f + B$ = OUTPUT + L   OR η_g (%) = $\left[1 - \dfrac{L}{H_f + B}\right] \times 100$

Fig. 12–10. Heat balance of a steam generator

SUMMARY SHEET

ASME TEST FORM
FOR ABBREVIATED EFFICIENCY TEST

PTC 4.1-a (1964)

	TEST NO.	BOILER NO.	DATE
OWNER OF PLANT	LOCATION	
TEST CONDUCTED BY	OBJECTIVE OF TEST	DURATION
BOILER, MAKE & TYPE	RATED CAPACITY	
STOKER, TYPE & SIZE		
PULVERIZER, TYPE & SIZE	BURNER, TYPE & SIZE	
FUEL USED	MINE	COUNTY	STATE	SIZE AS FIRED

PRESSURES & TEMPERATURES / FUEL DATA

	PRESSURES & TEMPERATURES				COAL AS FIRED PROX. ANALYSIS	% wt		OIL	
1	STEAM PRESSURE IN BOILER DRUM	psia							
2	STEAM PRESSURE AT S. H. OUTLET	psia		37	MOISTURE		51	FLASH POINT F*	
3	STEAM PRESSURE AT R. H. INLET	psia		38	VOL MATTER		52	Sp. Gravity Deg. API*	
4	STEAM PRESSURE AT R. H. OUTLET	psia		39	FIXED CARBON		53	VISCOSITY AT SSU* BURNER SSF	
5	STEAM TEMPERATURE AT S. H. OUTLET	F		40	ASH		44	TOTAL HYDROGEN % wt	
6	STEAM TEMPERATURE AT R. H. INLET	F			TOTAL		41	Btu per lb	
7	STEAM TEMPERATURE AT R.H. OUTLET	F		41	Btu per lb AS FIRED				
8	WATER TEMP. ENTERING (ECON.) (BOILER)	F		42	ASH SOFT TEMP.* ASTM METHOD			GAS	% VOL
9	STEAM QUALITY % MOISTURE OR P.P.M.				COAL OR OIL AS FIRED ULTIMATE ANALYSIS		54	CO	
10	AIR TEMP. AROUND BOILER (AMBIENT)	F		43	CARBON		55	CH_4 METHANE	
11	TEMP. AIR FOR COMBUSTION (This is Reference Temperature) †	F		44	HYDROGEN		56	C_2H_2 ACETYLENE	
12	TEMPERATURE OF FUEL	F		45	OXYGEN		57	C_2H_4 ETHYLENE	
13	GAS TEMP. LEAVING (Boiler) (Econ.) (Air Htr.)	F		46	NITROGEN		58	C_2H_6 ETHANE	
14	GAS TEMP. ENTERING AH (If conditions to be corrected to guarantee)	F		47	SULPHUR		59	H_2S	
	UNIT QUANTITIES			40	ASH		60	CO_2	
15	ENTHALPY OF SAT. LIQUID (TOTAL HEAT)	Btu/lb		37	MOISTURE		61	H_2 HYDROGEN	
16	ENTHALPY OF (SATURATED) (SUPERHEATED) STM.	Btu/lb			TOTAL			TOTAL	
17	ENTHALPY OF SAT. FEED TO (BOILER) (ECON.)	Btu/lb			COAL PULVERIZATION			TOTAL HYDROGEN % wt	
18	ENTHALPY OF REHEATED STEAM R. H. INLET	Btu/lb		48	GRINDABILITY INDEX*		62	DENSITY 68 F ATM. PRESS.	
19	ENTHALPY OF REHEATED STEAM R. H. OUTLET	Btu/lb		49	FINENESS % THRU 50 M*		63	Btu PER CU FT	
20	HEAT ABS/LB OF STEAM (ITEM 16 – ITEM 17)	Btu/lb		50	FINENESS % THRU 200 M*		41	Btu PER LB	
21	HEAT ABS/LB R.H. STEAM (ITEM 19 – ITEM 18)	Btu/lb		64	INPUT-OUTPUT EFFICIENCY OF UNIT %		ITEM 31 × 100 / ITEM 29	
22	DRY REFUSE (ASH PIT + FLY ASH) PER LB AS FIRED FUEL	lb/lb			HEAT LOSS EFFICIENCY		Btu/lb A.F. FUEL	% of A.F. FUEL
23	Btu PER LB IN REFUSE (WEIGHTED AVERAGE)	Btu/lb		65	HEAT LOSS DUE TO DRY GAS			
24	CARBON BURNED PER LB AS FIRED FUEL	lb/lb		66	HEAT LOSS DUE TO MOISTURE IN FUEL			
25	DRY GAS PER LB AS FIRED FUEL BURNED	lb/lb		67	HEAT LOSS DUE TO H_2O FROM COMB. OF H_2			
	HOURLY QUANTITIES			68	HEAT LOSS DUE TO COMBUST. IN REFUSE			
26	ACTUAL WATER EVAPORATED	lb/hr		69	HEAT LOSS DUE TO RADIATION			
27	REHEAT STEAM FLOW	lb/hr		70	UNMEASURED LOSSES			
28	RATE OF FUEL FIRING (AS FIRED wt)	lb/hr		71	TOTAL			
29	TOTAL HEAT INPUT (Item 28 × Item 41) / 1000	kB/hr		72	EFFICIENCY = (100 – Item 71)			
30	HEAT OUTPUT IN BLOW-DOWN WATER	kB/hr						
31	TOTAL HEAT OUTPUT (Item 26×Item 20)+(Item 27×Item 21)+Item 30 / 1000	kB/hr						
	FLUE GAS ANAL. (BOILER)(ECON) (AIR HTR) OUTLET							
32	CO_2	% VOL						
33	O_2	% VOL						
34	CO	% VOL						
35	N_2 (BY DIFFERENCE)	% VOL						
36	EXCESS AIR	%						

*Not Required for Efficiency Testing

† For Point of Measurement See Par. 7.2.8.1-PTC 4.1-1964

ASME TEST FORM

CALCULATION SHEET   **FOR ABBREVIATED EFFICIENCY TEST**   PTC 4.1-b (1964)

OWNER OF PLANT	TEST NO. BOILER NO. DATE	

30 HEAT OUTPUT IN BOILER BLOW-DOWN WATER = LB OF WATER BLOW-DOWN PER HR × $\dfrac{\boxed{\text{ITEM 15} \quad \text{ITEM 17}}}{1000}$ = ... kB/hr

24

If impractical to weigh refuse, this item can be estimated as follows

DRY REFUSE PER LB OF AS FIRED FUEL = $\dfrac{\text{\% ASH IN AS FIRED COAL}}{100 - \text{\% COMB. IN REFUSE SAMPLE}}$

$\begin{array}{l}\text{CARBON BURNED}\\\text{PER LB AS FIRED}\\\text{FUEL}\end{array} = \dfrac{\boxed{\text{ITEM 43}}}{100} - \left[\dfrac{\boxed{\text{ITEM 22}}}{} \times \dfrac{\boxed{\text{ITEM 23}}}{14.500}\right] = ...$

NOTE: IF FLUE DUST & ASH PIT REFUSE DIFFER MATERIALLY IN COMBUSTIBLE CONTENT, THEY SHOULD BE ESTIMATED SEPARATELY. SEE SECTION 7, COMPUTATIONS.

25

$\begin{array}{l}\text{DRY GAS PER LB}\\\text{AS FIRED FUEL}\\\text{BURNED}\end{array} = \dfrac{11CO_2 + 8O_2 + 7(N_2 + CO)}{3(CO_2 + CO)} \times \left(\text{LB CARBON BURNED PER LB AS FIRED FUEL} + \dfrac{3}{8}\,S\right)$

$= \dfrac{11 \times \boxed{\text{ITEM 32}} + 8 \times \boxed{\text{ITEM 33}} + 7\left(\boxed{\text{ITEM 35}} + \boxed{\text{ITEM 34}}\right)}{3 \times \left(\boxed{\text{ITEM 32}} + \boxed{\text{ITEM 34}}\right)} \times \left[\boxed{\text{ITEM 24}} + \dfrac{\boxed{\text{ITEM 47}}}{2.67}\right] = ...$

36

$\begin{array}{l}\text{EXCESS}\\\text{AIR}†\end{array} = 100 \times \dfrac{O_2 - \dfrac{CO}{2}}{.2682N_2 - (O_2 - \dfrac{CO}{2})} = 100 \times \dfrac{\text{ITEM 33} - \dfrac{\text{ITEM 34}}{2}}{.2682(\text{ITEM 35}) - (\text{ITEM 33} - \dfrac{\text{ITEM 34}}{2})} = ...$

HEAT LOSS EFFICIENCY			Btu/lb AS FIRED FUEL	$\dfrac{\text{LOSS}}{\text{HHV}} \times 100 =$	LOSS %
65	HEAT LOSS DUE TO DRY GAS	$=\begin{array}{l}\text{LB DRY GAS}\\\text{PER LB AS}\\\text{FIRED FUEL}\end{array} \times C_p \times (t_{lvg} - t_{air}) = \dfrac{\text{ITEM 25}}{......} \times 0.24 \dfrac{(\text{ITEM 13}) - (\text{ITEM 11})}{......} =$	......	$\dfrac{65}{41} \times 100 =$	......
66	HEAT LOSS DUE TO MOISTURE IN FUEL	$=\begin{array}{l}\text{LB H}_2\text{O PER LB}\\\text{AS FIRED FUEL}\end{array} \times [(\text{ENTHALPY OF VAPOR AT 1 PSIA \& T GAS LVG}) - (\text{ENTHALPY OF LIQUID AT T AIR})] = \dfrac{\text{ITEM 37}}{100} \times [(\text{ENTHALPY OF VAPOR AT 1 PSIA \& T ITEM 13}) - (\text{ENTHALPY OF LIQUID AT T ITEM 11})] = ...$		......	$\dfrac{66}{41} \times 100 =$	......
67	HEAT LOSS DUE TO H$_2$O FROM COMB. OF H$_2$	$= 9H_2 \times [(\text{ENTHALPY OF VAPOR AT 1 PSIA \& T GAS LVG}) - (\text{ENTHALPY OF LIQUID AT T AIR})]$ $= 9 \times \dfrac{\text{ITEM 44}}{100} \times [(\text{ENTHALPY OF VAPOR AT 1 PSIA \& T ITEM 13}) - (\text{ENTHALPY OF LIQUID AT T ITEM 11})] = ...$		......	$\dfrac{67}{41} \times 100 =$	......
68	HEAT LOSS DUE TO COMBUSTIBLE IN REFUSE	$= \dfrac{\boxed{\text{ITEM 22}}}{......} \times \dfrac{\boxed{\text{ITEM 23}}}{......} = ...$		......	$\dfrac{68}{41} \times 100 =$	......
69	HEAT LOSS DUE TO RADIATION*	$= \dfrac{\text{TOTAL BTU RADIATION LOSS PER HR}}{\text{LB AS FIRED FUEL}} - \dfrac{\text{ITEM 28}}{............}$		......	$\dfrac{69}{41} \times 100 =$	......
70	UNMEASURED LOSSES **			......	$\dfrac{70}{41} \times 100 =$	......
71	TOTAL			......	......	......
72	EFFICIENCY = (100 − ITEM 71)			......	......	......

† For rigorous determination of excess air see Appendix 9.2 – PTC 4.1-1964
* If losses are not measured, use ABMA Standard Radiation Loss Chart, Fig. 8, PTC 4.1-1964
** Unmeasured losses listed in PTC 4.1 but not tabulated above may by provided for by assigning a mutually agreed upon value for Item 70.

Elements of central station coal handling

13

Fuel Properties of Coal[1]

COAL is the most important of all the fossil fuels used for steam generation. It is widely available throughout much of the world, and the quantity and quality of coal reserves are better known than those of other fuels. Many studies have been made of coal availability and utilization and should be consulted for more detailed information.[2]

Formation of Coal

The formation of coal is the result of a natural chemical process in which plants absorb carbon dioxide from the atmosphere. Sunlight, moisture and other factors convert carbon dioxide into compounds containing carbon, hydrogen and oxygen, such as sugars, starch, cellulose, lignin and other complex substances that go to make up the plant structure. Under favorable conditions, vegetation is converted into some of the many forms of coal now known to mankind.

Many kinds of coal are found in the natural deposits. No hard and fast lines can be drawn between them, for many transitions from one to the other are found. In some of the western deposits of the United States, transitions from the extremes of lignite to anthracite are found in a single bed. It is generally assumed that differences in rank of coal are not caused by different source materials but by the agencies of coal formation. This is certainly true in the general sense that vegetation forms the raw material for all ranks.

Geologists usually name time, pressure and temperature as the agencies of coal formation whereby peat may be changed into different types of coal. Chemists include microorganisms as an additional important factor.

Time, it must be remembered, is in itself no agent; it is merely the duration or period during which an agent has an opportunity to act. It becomes important, however, because many organic chemical reactions are slow. In fact, it is believed that reactions are going on slowly in most complex organic substances. In a short period the results of such reactions would

1 Information from First Edition revised and supplemented by James Jonakin.
2 The numerous publications of the U.S. Bureau of Mines and the U.S. Geological Survey provide comprehensive information. A valuable private study is *Energy in the American Economy, 1850–1975* by S. H. Schurr and B. C. Netschert, The Johns Hopkins Press, 1960, especially the evaluation of coal reserves, resources and uses, pp. 57–83 and pp. 302–346. A very useful compendium of engineering information is *Fuels and Combustion Handbook*, edited by A. J. Johnson and G. H. Auth, McGraw-Hill, 1951. Current statistics and related information may be found in "Bituminous Coal Facts," a biennial publication of the National Coal Association, Washington 5, D.C.

be negligible, but over periods of thousands and millions of years the total results must be large. Time was probably the greatest single factor in the process of formation, but other factors must also be sought, because there are coals of the same age and, in fact, in the same bed, of different rank.

Pressure is generally considered to be the factor of next importance, because coal of higher rank is generally found in regions that have been under high pressure. Anthracite, for example, is associated with earth folding or mountain formation, which processes bring about great internal pressure. Experimentally, it has not been determined that pressure alone can change organic substances chemically.

Heat has also played an important part in this great natural chemical industry. The temperature need not be high, for long time brings about a relatively great change even at the low temperatures prevailing in the crust of the earth.

Man completes the cycle by burning the various products of the natural process to carbon dioxide, and then nature starts all over again. Time is of no concern to nature, which consumes millions of years in the making of products that man consumes in an instantaneous chemical reaction.

There is no satisfactory definition of coal. It is a mixture of organic chemical and mineral materials produced by a natural process of growth and decay, accumulation of debris both vegetal and mineral, with some sorting and stratification, and accomplished by chemical, biological, bacteriological and metamorphic action. The organic chemical materials produce heat when burned; the mineral matter remains as the residue called ash.

Classification of Coal

Coals are classified according to rank which refers to the degree of progressive alteration in the transformation from lignite to anthracite.

For the purposes of the power plant operator the following ranking of coals is suitable:

> Anthracite
> Bituminous
> Subbituminous
> Lignite

The foregoing terms, however, are extremely broad and they fail closely to define rank. Many investigators have attempted to set up some scientific system of classification that would accurately define the boundary lines of variation. Some of the better known bases for classification are those of Persifor Frazer, Jr., who made the earliest published classification of American coals in 1877; M. R. Campbell and S. W. Parr, who both published papers on the subject in 1906; David White, with publications in 1909 and 1913; and O. C. Ralston, whose graphic studies of some 3000 coal analyses were made in 1915. Each one of these will serve to type a coal within narrow limits, but the suitability of a given coal for a specific purpose is best established by actual trial in the equipment for which it is selected.[3]

The American Society for Testing and Materials has established perhaps the most universally applicable basis for classifying coal according to fixed carbon and heating value (Btu) calculated to a mineral-

[3] The engineering background for these coal classifications is discussed in three papers originally published in ASME *Transactions*: "Classification and Heating Value of American Coals" by William Kent, Vol. 36, 1914, pp. 189–209; "Constitution and Classification of Coal" by A. C. Fieldner, Vol. 49–50, 1927–28, FSP 50–51; and "Burning Characteristics of Different Coals" by Henry Kreisinger and B. J. Cross, Vol. 49–50, 1927–28, FSP 50–52.

Table 13–1   ASTM Classification of Coals by Rank[a]

Class	Group	Fixed Carbon Limits, per cent (Dry, Mineral-Matter-Free Basis)		Volatile Matter Limits, per cent (Dry, Mineral-Matter-Free Basis)		Calorific Value Limits, Btu per pound (Moist,[b] Mineral-Matter-Free Basis)		Agglomerating Character
		Equal or Greater Than	Less Than	Greater Than	Equal or Less Than	Equal or Greater Than	Less Than	
I. Anthracitic	1. Meta-anthracite	98	...	...	2	...	...	...
	2. Anthracite	92	98	2	8	...	...	Nonagglomerating[c]
	3. Semianthracite	86	92	8	14	...	...	...
II. Bituminous	1. Low volatile bituminous coal	78	86	14	22	...	...	...
	2. Medium volatile bituminous coal	69	78	22	31	...	...	Commonly agglomerating[e]
	3. High volatile A bituminous coal	...	69	31	...	14 000[d]	...	
	4. High volatile B bituminous coal	...	...	...	...	13 000[d]	14 000	
	5. High volatile C bituminous coal	...	...	...	...	11 500	13 000	
		...	...	...	...	10 500	11 500	Agglomerating
III. Subbituminous	1. Subbituminous A coal	...	...	...	...	10 500	11 500	Nonagglomerating
	2. Subbituminous B coal	...	...	...	...	9 500	10 500	...
	3. Subbituminous C coal	...	...	...	...	8 300	9 500	...
IV. Lignitic	1. Lignite A	...	...	...	...	6 300	8 300	...
	2. Lignite B	...	...	...	...	...	6 300	...

[a] This classification does not include a few coals, principally nonbanded varieties, which have unusual physical and chemical properties and which come within the limits of fixed carbon or calorific value of the high-volatile bituminous and subbituminous ranks. All of these coals either contain less than 48 per cent dry, mineral-matter-free fixed carbon or have more than 15,500 moist, mineral-matter-free British thermal units per pound.
[b] Moist refers to coal containing its natural inherent moisture but not including visible water on the surface of the coal.
[c] If agglomerating, classify in low-volatile group of the bituminous class.
[d] Coals having 69 per cent or more fixed carbon on the dry, mineral-matter-free basis shall be classified according to fixed carbon, regardless of calorific value.
[e] It is recognized that there may be nonagglomerating varieties in these groups of the bituminous class, and there are notable exceptions in high volatile C bituminous group.

Reprinted from "Specifications for Classification of Coals by Rank," ASTM D 388–64T, by permission of American Society for Testing and Materials.

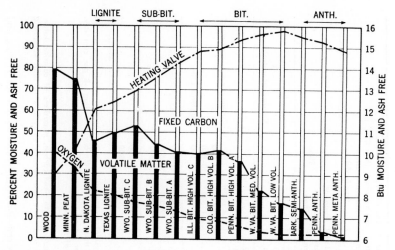

Fig. 13—1.   Diagram showing progressive change from vegetal matter in coals of various ranks as based on ASTM method for classification

matter-free basis. This scheme, Table 13–1, represents a further development of the proposals of S. W. Parr. The high-rank coals are classified according to fixed carbon on the dry basis, and the low-rank coals according to Btu on the moist basis. Agglomerating and slacking (weathering) indices are used to differentiate between certain adjacent groups.[4]

In commercial practice it frequently suffices to calculate to a dry ash-free basis. The ash, however, does not correspond to the mineral matter in coal. Thus, in problems of classification of coal according to rank, if the ash-free basis is used, significant errors may be introduced. Remarkably uniform results, however, are obtained from heating values of coals of a given rank and source when calculated to a dry mineral-matter-free basis.

The agglomerating index, or caking quality of a coal, is used in ASTM classification by rank to indicate the dividing line between noncaking coals and those having weakly caking properties. The noncaking designation is applied only to coals

that produce a noncoherent residue which can be poured out of the crucible as a powder or flakes that will pulverize easily with thumb and finger pressure.

The slacking, or weathering, index is a measure of the disintegrating characteristics of a coal sample when exposed to certain standard conditions of humidity, temperature, and immersion.

The transformation of vegetal matter, through wood and peat to lignite and finally to anthracite, results in a reduction of volatile matter and oxygen content, together with a simultaneous increase in carbon content. This is illustrated in Table 13–2 in which analyses of various coals are classified according to rank, as defined by the ASTM Standards, together with wood and peat as representing the earliest stages of transformation. These data have also been used to portray graphically several important relationships in Fig. 13–1. All coal analyses used are taken from U.S. Bureau of Mines publications, and the wood analyses are a composite of two species.

---

[4] ASTM Designation D 388–64T. This and other ASTM Standards may be obtained from the Society at 1916 Race Street, Philadelphia 3, Pennsylvania.

Table 13-2   Progressive Stages of Transformation of Vegetal Matter into Coal

Fuel Classification by Rank	Locality	Moisture (as-received)	Analysis on dry basis									Heating value Btu (dry basis)
			Proximate			Ultimate						
			VM	FC	Ash	S	H_2	C	N_2	O_2		
Wood	Minnesota	46.9	78.1	20.4	1.5		6.0	51.4	0.1	41.0		8835
Peat		64.3	67.3	22.7	10.0	0.4	5.3	52.2	1.8	30.3		9057
Lignite	North Dakota	36.0	49.8	38.1	12.1	1.8	4.0	64.7	1.9	15.5		11038
Lignite	Texas	33.7	44.1	44.9	11.0	0.8	4.6	64.1	1.2	18.3		11084
Subbituminous C	Wyoming	22.3	40.4	44.7	14.9	3.4	4.1	61.7	1.3	14.6		10598
Subbituminous B	Wyoming	15.3	39.7	53.6	6.7	2.7	5.2	67.3	1.9	16.2		12096
Subbituminous A	Wyoming	12.8	39.0	55.2	5.8	0.4	5.2	73.1	0.9	14.6		12902
Bituminous High Volatile C	Colorado	12.0	38.9	53.9	7.2	0.6	5.0	73.1	1.5	12.6		13063
Bituminous High Volatile B	Illinois	8.6	35.4	56.2	8.4	1.8	4.8	74.6	1.5	8.9		13388
Bituminous High Volatile A	Pennsylvania	1.4	34.3	59.2	6.5	1.3	5.2	79.5	1.4	6.1		14396
Bituminous Medium Volatile	West Virginia	3.4	22.2	74.9	2.9	0.6	4.9	86.4	1.6	3.6		15178
Bituminous Low Volatile	West Virginia	3.6	16.0	79.1	4.9	0.8	4.8	85.4	1.5	2.6		15000
Semianthracite	Arkansas	5.2	11.0	74.2	14.8	2.2	3.4	76.4	0.5	2.7		13142
Anthracite	Pennsylvania	5.4	7.4	75.9	16.7	0.8	2.6	76.8	0.8	2.3		12737
Meta-anthracite	Rhode Island	4.5	3.2	82.4	14.4	0.9	0.5	82.4	0.1	1.7		11624

Origin of Ash in Coal

Coal, as mined, contains varying quantities of mineral matter, which, when the coal is burned, results in the residue known as ash. The largest fraction of this mineral matter was brought in by wind and water; only a small fraction was inherent in the original vegetation. The ash analysis does not indicate the nature or distribution of the mineral matter but, nevertheless, provides information which is useful in both the study and the utilization of coal. Examination of many analyses of coal ash shows, in almost all cases, that oxides of silicon, aluminum, iron, calcium and magnesium account for 95 per cent or more of the ash. Of the other components present, oxides of sodium and potassium are important insofar as they act as fluxes in fusing the ash.

In some areas the quantity of mineral matter brought in was large and much of it dispersed into the vegetal deposits. As a result, the coal seams thus formed have a high ash content which is distributed throughout the coal substance.

While these may be either high-rank or low-rank coals, they are definitely low grade and cannot be economically upgraded by cleaning methods.

Coal Sampling

A sample must represent the bulk of the coal from which it is taken. The items that should be most representative are ash and moisture content. The weight of the gross sample and the method of collecting and handling it depend on the size of the coal, the moisture and ash content, and the purpose for which the sample is collected. The method of collecting the sample should be so chosen as to insure representative ash and moisture content. After the sample is collected, it must be handled in such a way that the moisture content does not change. If the coal is very wet, considerable loss of moisture may occur during the handling. It may be necessary to stabilize the moisture in the gross sample by air drying before crushing and quartering are undertaken. In such cases, the air-drying moisture loss must be determined. Collecting and handling the sample require care and ingenuity on the part of the sampler.

The standard method for sampling coals is ASTM D 492–48. The procedures described in this method are designated as (1) commercial sampling procedures and (2) special purpose sampling procedures. Both procedures are divided into the following ash groups:

> Ash, per cent
> Under 8
> 8.0 to 9.9
> 10.0 to 14.9
> 15.0 and over

The methods prescribe a minimum number of increments and the minimum weight per increment required for eight size groups in each of the four ash classifications. An increment is that quantity of coal obtained by a single motion and in flowing coal which should represent a complete cross section of the stream.

The commercial sampling procedure is intended for an accuracy such that if a large number of samples were taken from a single sample lot of coal, the test results in 95 out of 100 cases would fall within 10 per cent of the average ash content of these samples. The number and size of the increments vary with the coal size and the ash content.

In the special purpose sampling procedure, in order to obtain a greater accuracy, the number of increments required for the commercial sample are increased as follows:

To increase accuracy Increase minimum
of collection of gross number of increments
sample for commercial sample

± 5 per cent of the ash
content of the coal
sampled .... 4 times

± 3.33 per cent of the
ash content of the coal
sampled .... 9 times

For the determination of total moisture
in coal either a standard moisture sample
or a special moisture sample may be taken.
In the case of performance tests which require special accuracy the special moisture sample is used.[5]

Coal Analysis

Two types of coal analysis are in general use: the proximate and the ultimate
analysis, both expressed in per cent by
weight.

The proximate analysis gives information on the behavior of coal when it is
heated; that is, how much of the coal goes
off as gas and tar vapors, called the volatile matter, and how much remains as
fixed carbon. The proximate analysis is
easy to make and supplies useful information to assist in the selection of coal for
industrial purposes. Along with the determination of volatile matter and fixed
carbon are also given the moisture and ash
contents and the heating value in Btu.
Sulfur is given as a separate determination.

The ultimate analysis gives the elements
of which the coal substance is composed.
These elements include carbon, hydrogen, nitrogen, oxygen and sulfur. Ash content is determined as a whole, and, when
desirable, separate analysis is made on the
ash.[6]

Coal analysis may be given on several
bases and it is customary to select the
basis to suit the application. Thus for the
purposes of classification the dry or moist
and mineral-matter-free bases are generally used. In combustion calculations the
as-received basis is applicable.

As-Received

The as-received analysis of a fuel represents the actual proportions of the constituents in the fuel sample as received at
the laboratory. The sample itself may be
fuel as-fired, as-mined or in any other
given condition.

Moisture-free (Dry)

Moisture content is variable, even in
the same coal, under different conditions
of handling and exposure. For example:
coal, as received at a plant, may contain
an amount of moisture different from that
received at the laboratory for analysis, and
both may vary with weather conditions.
Also, in a plant burning pulverized fuel,
the coal may carry one percentage of
moisture as delivered to the raw-coal
bunker, another as delivered to the pulverizer, another as delivered to the pulverized-fuel bunker, and still another as fired.
Furthermore, when a laboratory determines an ultimate analysis as wet, as-
received, or as-fired, the moisture is reported as hydrogen and oxygen and added
to the hydrogen and oxygen of the coal
itself. Obviously, therefore, many engineers prefer to work with the analysis,
heating value, air weight and gas weight
expressed per pound of dry coal.

For these reasons, performance figures
are often based on moisture-free (dry)
coal so that these figures may be corrected

---

[5] Detailed information on procedures for collecting coal samples for both the ash and moisture
determination may be found in ASTM Standard Methods D 492–48 and D 271–64.
[6] For detailed information on analysis procedures refer to ASTM Standard Methods D 271–64.

from a common base, for the actual moisture content when test results are obtained, or the values compared.

Calculations to dry basis are made as follows:

$$\text{Per cent dry} = \frac{\text{per cent as-received} \times 100}{100 - \text{per cent moisture}}$$

Dry Mineral-matter-free

The ash does not correspond in percentage to the mineral matter in the coal. Consequently errors are introduced which become of significance in problems of classification of coals according to rank. Two formulas are available for making such calculations from the as-received basis.

Parr Formulas:

Dry, MM-free FC =
$$\frac{FC - 0.15S}{100 - (M + 1.08A + 0.55S)} \times 100$$

Dry, MM-free VM = 100 − Dry, MM-free FC

Moist, MM-free Btu =
$$\frac{Btu - 50S}{100 - (1.08A + 0.55S)} \times 100$$

Note: The above formula for fixed carbon is derived from the Parr formula for volatile matter.[7]

Approximation Formulas:

Dry, MM-free FC =
$$\frac{FC}{100 - (M + 1.1A + 0.1S)} \times 100$$

Dry, MM-free VM = 100 − Dry, MM-free FC

Moist, MM-free Btu =
$$\frac{Btu}{100 - (1.1A + 0.1S)} \times 100$$

where
  MM = mineral matter
  FC = percentage of fixed carbon
  VM = percentage of volatile matter
  M = percentage of moisture
  A = percentage of ash
  S = percentage of sulfur

The formulas can be used to check analyses and frequently to identify the source and rank of the fuel. For example, the heating value of coals of a given rank and source are remarkably uniform when calculated on a dry, MM-free basis.

In commercial practice it frequently suffices to calculate to a dry, ash-free basis as follows:

$$\text{Dry, ash-free FC} = \frac{FC}{100 - (M + A)} \times 100$$

Dry, ash-free VM = 100 − Dry, ash-free

Items of Proximate Analysis

Coal as mined and shipped contains varying amounts of water. Accurate determination of this water is not as simple as one would expect, since the sample frequently can lose moisture on exposure to the atmosphere. This is particularly true during the reduction of the sample for analysis. In order to prevent this loss it is customary to air-dry the entire sample under specified conditions previous to fine grinding for analysis. The moisture is then determined by a standard procedure of drying in an oven and the loss in weight is corrected for the air-drying loss. The moisture in coal does not represent all of the water present since water of decomposition (combined water) and water of hydration are not given off under the conditions of test. The moisture content of coals

---

[7] Two bulletins published by the University of Illinois Engineering Experiment Station, Urbana, are the original sources of the Parr Formulas: "Unit Coal and the Composition of Coal Ash" by S. W. Parr and W. F. Wheeler, Bulletin 37, 1909, and "The Classification of Coal" by S. W. Parr, Bulletin 180, 1928.

varies widely and is subject to fortuitous circumstances. In the high-rank eastern coals it is frequently under 5 per cent. Midwestern coals may have as much as 12 per cent and lignite in North Dakota as high as 45 per cent as mined. The finer sizes will often retain more moisture than the coarse sizes of the same coal subjected to rainfall or wet-washing.

Volatile Matter

The volatile matter is that portion which is driven off in gas or vapor form when the coal is subjected to a standardized temperature test. It consists of hydrocarbons and other gases resulting from distillation and decomposition.

Fixed Carbon

The fixed carbon is the combustible residue left after driving off the volatile matter. It is not all carbon, and its form and hardness are an indication of the coking properties of a fuel, and therefore, a guide in the choice of combustion equipment. In general, the fixed carbon represents that portion of the fuel that must be burned in solid state, either in the fuel bed on a stoker, or as solid particles in the pulverized fuel furnace.

Ash

Ash is the non-combustible residue after complete combustion of the coal. The weight of ash is usually slightly less than that of the mineral matter originally present before burning. However, for high calcium content coals, the ash can be higher than the mineral matter due to retention of the oxides of sulfur.[8]

Sulfur

Sulfur is separately determined, and its amount is useful in judging the noxiousness and corrosiveness of the products of combustion of a fuel. Combustion of sulfur forms oxides, which combine with water to form acids that may be deposited when the waste gas is cooled below its dewpoint temperature.

Heating Value

The heating value of a solid fuel is expressed in Btu per lb of fuel on as-received, dry, or moisture- and ash-free basis. Heating values as determined in calorimeters are termed higher or gross heating values, and include the latent heat of the water vapor in the products of combustion. In actual operation of boilers, the water vapor in the waste gas is not cooled below its dewpoint, and this latent heat is not available for making steam. The latent heat is sometimes subtracted from the higher, or gross, heating value to give the lower, or net, heating value.

This deduction in Btu per lb of fuel is equal to the total pounds of water vapor per lb of fuel (moisture in the fuel, plus vapor formed by combustion of hydrogen of the coal substance) multiplied by the latent heat of evaporation at the partial pressure of the vapor in the exit gas. The value used varies from 1040 to 1080 Btu per lb of water vapor. Lower heating values are standard in European practice, and higher heating values are standard in American practice. For anthracite and bituminous coal gross heating value can be calculated approximately by Dulong's for-

---

[8] This is discussed in "Effect of Sulfur Retention on Determined Ash in Lower Rank Coals" by W. H. Ode and F. H. Gibson, U.S. Bureau of Mines, Report of Investigation 5931, 1962.

mula from ultimate analysis, as follows:

Heating value =
$$14{,}600\ C + 62{,}000\left(H - \frac{O}{8}\right) + 4050\ S$$

where: C, H, O and S are carbon, hydrogen, oxygen and sulfur in coal, respectively, expressed in fraction of a pound.[9] For low-rank coals the heating values obtained by this formula are generally too low.

Ash-Softening Temperature

When coal ash is heated, it becomes soft and sticky, and as the temperature continues to rise, it becomes fluid. Coals with ash that softens and fuses at comparatively low temperature are likely to give trouble from clinkers in the fuel bed and from slag deposit on boiler tubes and superheaters. When coal is burned in pulverized form, in slagging bottom furnaces, low fusion-temperature ash may be desirable for easy removal of the ash from the furnace in a liquid state. However, the slagging of the boiler and superheater may be troublesome. The fusion temperature of ash is useful information in the selection of coal for a given type of equipment and, conversely, for selecting or designing equipment for a given coal.

The ash-softening temperature is determined by placing a cone made of ash to be tested in a laboratory furnace, maintaining a reducing atmosphere which is gradually brought up in temperature. During the rise of temperature, the behavior of the ash cone is observed. As the cone softens, the point may become blunt or bend over. This is the initial deformation temperature. The softening temperature is defined as the temperature at which the cone has fused down to a spher-

ical lump. This is the temperature usually given in the tables. As the temperature continues to rise, the cone flattens down until it becomes a layer of fluid ash. Fig. 13–2 illustrates the cone shape at three temperature points discussed.

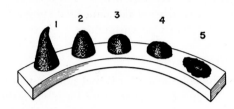

Fig. 13–2.   Fusibility of ash cones
Cone 1, initial deformation temperature
Cone 3, softening temperature
Cone 5, fluid temperature

Softening and fluid temperatures are affected by the condition of furnace atmosphere. A reducing atmosphere generally lowers the temperature, while an oxidizing atmosphere raises it. In a fuel bed, there is usually a reducing or partly reducing atmosphere. In a pulverized coal furnace, there may be a partly reducing atmosphere near the bottom. However, at the top of the furnace, among the boiler tubes, and in the superheater, the atmosphere is oxidizing. When ashes of different coals are tested for comparison, care should be taken to keep the furnace atmosphere the same. This is particularly important with ash having a low softening temperature.

Items of Ultimate Analysis

Ultimate analysis is needed for the computation of air requirements, weight of products of combustion and heat losses on boiler tests. The air requirements and the weight of products of combustion are used in the determination of fan size. The following are items of ultimate analysis:

[9] See *Fuels and Combustion Handbook* by A. J. Johnson and G. H. Auth, McGraw-Hill, 1951, p. 365.

Total Carbon

Total carbon includes both the carbon in the fixed carbon and in the volatile matter, and will be proportionately greater than the fixed carbon as the volatile content of the coal increases. All this carbon appears in the products of combustion as CO_2 when the fuel is completely burned.

Hydrogen

All hydrogen in the fuel is burned to water and, together with the moisture in fuel, appears as water vapor in the waste gas. In the publications of the U.S. Bureau of Mines, ultimate analysis of coal on as-received basis includes moisture in the hydrogen and oxygen items. The weight of the water vapor in the products of combustion is nine times the hydrogen item.

Nitrogen

Nitrogen in most solid fuels is low and of no importance, as it is incombustible.

Oxygen

The oxygen content of fuels is a guide to the rank of the fuel. The amount of oxygen is high in low-rank fuels like lignite. Oxygen in fuels is in combination with carbon or hydrogen and, therefore, represents a reduction in the potential heat of a fuel. High oxygen fuels have low heating values.

Miscellaneous Tests

Grindability of Coal

The grindability index indicates the ease with which coal can be pulverized, and is useful in estimating the capacity of a given mill when pulverizing various coals. The index is a comparative value, which is high for soft coals and low for hard coals.

The Hardgrove Method (ASTM Standard Method D 409–51) is based on a test with an apparatus devised by R. M. Hardgrove. The index of 100 applies to a particular coal designated as standard. Coals softer than this standard have indexes higher than 100. The Hardgrove apparatus, which is a miniature of a commercial type of pulverizer, subjects a relatively small quantity of specially prepared coal to a short period of grinding. The percentage of material produced by the grinding and passing through a 200-mesh sieve divided by the number of revolutions is directly proportioned to the grindability index.[10]

Degree of Fineness Required

For pulverized-fuel-firing, low-volatile coals should be pulverized to a higher degree of fineness than high-volatile coals, because less of the combustible is distilled off and burns as gas, and more remains in the solid particle and burns slowly as fixed carbon. Thus, a fineness of 60 per cent through 200-mesh sieve may be entirely satisfactory with high volatile coals, whereas 75 per cent or more may be required with low-volatile coals. However, most of the low-volatile eastern coals are of granular structure and naturally soft. They are easily pulverized, and therefore the necessary higher degree of fineness does not necessarily reduce the capacity of the pulverizer.

Determination of Fineness of Pulverized Coal

The fineness of pulverized coal is determined by passing the coal through standard sieves (ASTM D 197–30). Five

---

[10] See Chapter 16, Pulverizers, for additional information.

sizes of sieves are used for this purpose, Nos, 16, 30, 50, 100 and 200. These sieves have approximately 16, 30, 50, 100 and 200 meshes to the inch, with openings of 0.0468, 0.0234, 0.0117, 0.0059 and 0.0029 in., respectively.[11] When fineness is specified, usually only the percentage passing through No. 200-sieve is given; it is 60 per cent for high-volatile coals, and 75 per cent for low-volatile coals. Anthracite is pulverized to 80 or 85 per cent through 200-sieve. While it is desirable for good combustion to have the percentage through 200-sieve as high as economically possible, it is important that the percentage greater than No. 50-sieve be small, because much time is required to burn this oversize coal. For good combustion results, this oversize coal should not exceed two per cent.

Free Swelling Index

The behavior of a coal on burning cannot be predicted accurately from the proximate or ultimate analysis. Consequently, laboratory tests are proposed from time to time, the objective of which is an index to the behavior of coal in the fuel bed, coke oven or other method of utilization. One such test which seems to serve a useful purpose is the standard method for free-swelling index of coals (ASTM D 720–57).

The results may be used as an indication of the coking characteristics of coal.

The test is very simple involving the heating of a one-gram sample of a coal freshly ground to pass a No. 60-sieve under certain fixed conditions. The shape of the residue is then compared with a series of standard profiles which are numbered in half units from 1 to 9. The larger the index, the greater is the swelling of the coal. The test not only serves to give some indication of the tendency of an unknown coal to coke but is useful in determining the extent to which oxidation may have destroyed the coking power of known coal.

Typical Coal Analyses

Table 13–3 shows the form in which the analyses are given in the U.S. Bureau of Mines publications.[12]

Bulletin 446 of the U.S. Bureau of Mines contains the proximate analysis and softening temperatures of ash of several hundred coals from various states. The coals are identified by county, mine, coal bed, and rank.

Table 13–4 gives the proximate analysis, softening temperature of ash, and the grindability of typical coals of the United States. The coals are identified by state county, mining district or seam, and the proximate analysis of the coal.

---

[11] For detailed information see ASTM Designation E 11–61, Specification for Sieves for Testing Purposes.

[12] The most complete collection of reliable analyses of coals of the United States is contained in publications of the U.S. Bureau of Mines. These publications also contain information on the thickness of seams, number of partings, method of sampling, and methods of making analyses. Information Circular 7923, "Fusibility of Ash of United States Coals" by Roy Abernathy and E. Cochrane, 1960, gives fusion temperature of ashes of a large number of coals. Information on analyses of coal as sold is available through the Bituminous Coal Division of the Department of the Interior. These publications can be obtained from the Superintendent of Documents, U.S. Government Printing Office, Washington 25, D.C. A helpful guide to this literature is "List of Publications Issued by the Bureau of Mines from July 1, 1910 to January 1, 1960, with Subject and Author Index" by Hazel J. Stratton. For analyses of coals outside the United States, see Chapter 15, World Fuel Reserves.

Table 13-3 Chemical Analyses

Coal, Pennsylvania, Somerset County, Upper Kittaning Bed, No. 3 Mine

Condition or basis	Proximate, per cent				Ultimate, per cent*					Heating Value, Btu/lb
	Mois-ture	Volatile Matter	Fixed Carbon	Ash	Carbon	Hydro-gen	Oxygen	Nitro-gen	Sul-fur	
As-received	3.39	20.61	66.53	9.47	77.29	4.59	5.61	1.73	1.31	13,619
Dry		21.33	68.87	9.80	80.00	4.36	2.69	1.79	1.36	14,098
Moisture- and ash-free		23.65	76.35		88.69	4.83	2.99	1.98	1.51	15,629

* In the ultimate analysis, moisture on an as-received basis is included in the hydrogen and oxygen.

Description of Coals

Anthracite

Pennsylvania anthracite is dense, shiny black in color, and homogeneous in structure, with no marks of layers. It is hard, very brittle and burns with a short, clear, bluish flame. It is principally used for heating homes and in gas producers. The small sizes, formerly a refuse, are burned on traveling grate stokers and in boilers fired by pulverized coal.

The so-called western, and particularly the Arkansas, anthracites are really semi-anthracites. They are dense, but softer than the Pennsylvania anthracite, shiny gray in color, and somewhat granular in structure. The grains have a tendency to break off in handling the lump, and produce a coarse sandlike slack. They burn with a short, clear, bluish flame.

Semianthracite is of dark gray color and distinctly granular structure. The grains break off easily in handling and produce a coarse slack. The granular structure has been produced by small vertical cracks in horizontal layers of comparatively pure coal separated by very thin partings. The cracks are the result of heavy downward pressure, and probably shrinkage of the pure coal due to drop in temperature. The coal burns with short clear flame.

Bituminous Coal

The low-volatile bituminous coals are of grayish black color and distinctly granular in structure. The grain breaks off very easily, and handling reduces the coal to slack. Any lumps that remain are held together by thin partings. Because the grains consist of comparatively pure coal, the slack is usually lower in ash than the lumps. The coal cakes in the fire, burns with short, clear flame, and is usually regarded as smokeless. The Pocahontas and East Broad Top are coals representative of this class.

Medium-volatile bituminous coals come principally from the Appalachian region, and include the best steam coals. They are the transition from high-volatile to low-volatile coal and, as such, have the characteristics of both. Many of them have the granular structure, are soft, and crumble easily. Some of them have homogeneous structure, with very faint indications of grains or layers. Others are of more distinct laminar structure, are hard, and stand handling well. They cake in the fire, and smoke when improperly burned.

High-volatile A bituminous coals come entirely from the Appalachian region. They are mostly homogeneous in structure, with no indication of grains, but some show distinct layers. They are hard and stand handling with little breakage.

The moisture, ash and sulfur content is low, and the heating value high. They include the best steaming and coking coals. They cake in the fire and smoke when improperly burned.

High-volatile *B* bituminous coals are of distinct laminar structure; thin layers of black, shiny coal alternate with dull, charcoal-like layers. They are hard and stand handling well. Breakage occurs generally at right angles and parallel to the layers, so that the lumps generally have a cubical shape. They make good steaming coal, and some of them are good coking coals. They cake in the fire and smoke when improperly burned.

The high-volatile *C* bituminous coals occur mostly in the Interior province and particularly in the Illinois coal fields. They are of distinct laminar structure, are hard and stand handling well. They generally have high moisture, ash and sulfur content. They are fair steaming coals and some of them make good coke. Although under certain conditions these coals will cake in the fire, they are considered as free-burning coals.

Subbituminous coals occur mainly in the Rocky Mountains, the Great Plains and the Pacific Coast provinces. They are brownish black or black color. Most of them are of a homogeneous structure with smooth surfaces, and with no indication of layers. They have high moisture content, although appearing dry. When exposed to air they lose part of the moisture and crack with an audible noise. On long exposure to air, they disintegrate. In the fire they have no caking property and crumble into small pieces. They are free-burning coals.

Lignite

Lignites are of brown color, and of a laminar structure in which the remnants of woody fibres may be quite apparent. In some of the lignite seams of North Dakota, preserved stumps of trees may be found which can be whittled into curly shavings with a pocket knife. Freshly mined lignite is tough, although not hard, and it requires a heavy blow with a hammer to break the large lumps. However, on exposure to air it loses moisture rapidly and disintegrates. Even when it appears quite dry, the moisture content may be as high as 30 per cent. Owing to the high moisture and low heating value, it is not economical to transport it long distances. It can be burned quite efficiently on traveling-grate and spreader stokers, and in pulverized form. Because of the tendency of the lignite to disintegrate, the fuel bed must not be agitated since agitation speeds up the disintegration.

Peat

Peat is not a commercial fuel in the United States, but in countries such as Ireland, where there is little coal, it is used to a considerable extent. It always occurs at or near the surface of the ground. It is taken out of the peat bog drenching wet and is placed on the nearby ground for air drying. It dries into cakes which can be moved to the place of use.

Commercial Sizes of Bituminous Coals

Bituminous coal is usually sized at the tipple as it is loaded into railroad cars for shipment. Because of the difference in the fracturing characteristics of various coals, and because of the difference in the market demands for certain sizes, the sizing practice varies in different fields. In some cases, the coal is shipped as run-of-mine without any sizing. The following are the sizes, together with their principal uses, produced by some mines:

Table 13-4 Ash Softening Temperature, Grindability, and Proximate Analysis of Typical Coals of the United States

State and county	Mining district or seam	Typical analysis — as-received						Approx. ash-softening temp. F	Grindability (Hardgrove)
		M	Vol.	FC	Ash	Sul.	Btu		
ALABAMA, Jefferson	Mary Lee	2.6	28.1	58.4	10.9	1.0	13,300	2850	62–87
Walker	Mary Lee	3.4	30.8	57.8	13.0	0.7	12,360	2880	51–65
ARKANSAS, Franklin	Denning	2.2	14.3	74.0	9.5	1.9	14,000	2200	99–102
COLORADO, El Paso	Colo. Springs	22.3	33.3	38.2	6.2	0.4	8,625	2225	38–39
Las Animas	Trinidad	2.3	29.8	58.7	9.2	0.5	13,780	2445	44–54
ILLINOIS, Franklin	Franklin	10.0	32.8	49.3	7.9	1.0	11,857	2375	53–63
Williamson	Williamson	8.8	32.6	51.4	7.2	1.1	12,177	2310	52–59
Sangamon	Springfield	13.1	36.5	41.1	9.3	3.8	10,935	2115	54–68
St. Clair	Belleville-Saunton	11.2	39.3	39.2	10.3	4.2	11,223	1995	57–62
Peoria	Peoria	15.4	34.4	38.5	11.7	3.0	10,422	1970	65–67
Fulton	Fulton	16.3	35.5	37.0	11.2	2.9	10,220	1930	51–68
INDIANA, Clay, Greene, Vigo	No. 3	11.5	38.2	40.5	9.8	4.6	11,550	2125	62–66
Greene, Sullivan	No. 4	13.5	33.6	45.4	7.5	0.9	11,740	2580	53–60
Greene, Sullivan, Gibson	No. 5	11.2	35.7	42.6	10.5	4.2	11,370	2095	60
Greene, Sullivan, Knox	No. 6	14.9	31.6	46.2	7.3	2.2	11,325	2065	60–65
IOWA, Appanoose, Wayne	Mystic	7.3	36.0	47.5	9.2	3.8	11,500	2050	60–70
Marion	......	6.5	39.0	46.7	7.8	5.0	10,200	......	......
Monroe	......	5.3	41.0	46.2	7.5	5.2	11,750	......	......
Polk	......	10.3	38.2	39.7	11.8	5.0	10,500	2000	62–66
Boone	......	12.3	38.2	43.8	5.7	4.8	10,500	2200	61
KANSAS, Cherokee	Cherokee	5.0	33.1	52.9	9.0	4.6	12,930	1950	61
Leavenworth	Leavenworth	11.5	35.3	40.0	13.2	4.2	10,900	1965	70

(Continued)

Table 13-4 (continued)

State and county	Mining district or seam	Typical analysis — as-received						Approx. ash-softening temp. F	Grind-ability (Hardgrove)
		M	Vol.	FC	Ash	Sul.	Btu		
Clearfield	Lower Kittaning	2.7	21.1	67.9	8.3	1.8	13,940	2485	106
Somerset	Lower Freeport	3.1	24.8	65.2	6.9	1.6	14,025	2480	87
	Upper Kittaning	2.8	17.3	71.0	8.9	1.4	13,810	2300	95-100
Westmoreland	Lower Kittaning	2.8	16.2	73.0	8.0	1.7	13,990	2500	115
Allegheny	Redstone	2.1	33.2	53.6	11.1	2.4	13,140	2600	60-70
TENNESSEE, Campbell	Upper Freeport	2.5	34.0	54.5	9.0	2.2	13,400	2350	55-60
Bledsoe	Jellico	3.5	36.3	52.9	7.3	1.6	13,630	2065	45-55
	Sewanee	3.2	29.3	59.7	7.8	0.8	13,500	2400	50-60
TEXAS, Bowie S. W. to La Salle	Lignite Fields	33.4	40.4	17.2	9.0	1.1	7,600	2250	53-79
UTAH, Carbon	Castlegate	5.5	39.2	47.8	7.5	0.6	12,500	2200	43-49
Summit	Wasatch	14.0	38.0	43.0	5.0	1.4	10,700	2240	47-50
VIRGINIA, Tazewell	Pocahontas	2.9	21.2	71.5	4.4	0.5	14,550	2400	99-105
Wise	Norton	1.4	34.1	58.5	6.0	0.8	14,250	2600	62
WASHINGTON, Kittitas	Clealum (Cle Elum)	8.0	34.6	44.7	12.7	0.4	11,410	2500	49-52
Kittitas	Roslyn	3.7	34.3	48.6	13.4	0.3	12,250	2470	52
Pierce	High Vol. Carbonado	3.8	36.0	51.2	9.0	0.5	13,400	2700	69
Pierce	Med. Vol. Carbonado	3.8	29.3	49.9	17.0	0.5	11,500	2700	55
WEST VIRGINIA, Monongalia, Marion, Harrison	Fairmont	1.8	37.6	54.1	6.5	2.2	13,850	2300	50-70
Fayette	New River	2.1	22.5	72.2	3.2	0.6	14,860	2500	90-100
Mercer	Pocahontas	2.6	17.8	75.0	4.6	0.6	14,635	2375	105
Kanawha, Fayette	Kanawha	1.8	35.8	55.7	6.7	0.9	13,500	2800	40-60
Mingo	Thacker	2.4	35.8	56.4	5.4	0.9	14,100	2500	56

Table 13–4 (continued)

State and county	Mining district or seam	Typical analysis — as-received						Approx. ash-softening temp. F	Grindability (Hardgrove)
		M	Vol.	FC	Ash	Sul.	Btu		
EAST KENTUCKY, Floyd, Letcher, Pike, Perry, Breathitt	Elkhorn	3.4	36.8	55.8	4.0	0.8	14,000	2425	50–60
Knott, Letcher	Hazard No. 4	3.8	36.7	55.3	4.2	0.7	13,755	2800	45–55
Harlan	Harlan	3.2	36.9	56.0	3.9	0.8	13,960	2720	47–58
WEST KENTUCKY, Union, Webster,	Eastern Interior								
Hopkins, Muhlenburg	Seam No. 9	4.8	36.7	49.5	9.0	3.3	12,490	2106	60–65
MARYLAND, Allegany	Georges Creek	2.6	19.1	71.4	6.9	1.2	14,135	2410	95–100
MICHIGAN, Saginaw	Saginaw	9.0	34.0	53.2	3.8	1.0	12,750	2200	50–67
MISSOURI, Adair	Bevier	11.8	34.5	40.7	13.0	4.8	11,150	1985	72–75
MONTANA, Carbon	Red Lodge	11.4	35.3	42.8	10.5	1.7	9,900	2145	50–55
Carbon	Bear Creek	9.4	35.6	45.6	9.4	2.4	10,700	2050	47–56
NEW MEXICO, McKinley	San Juan	11.5	39.1	42.6	6.8	0.7	11,300	2100	29–41
Santa Fé	Cerillos	3.7	35.0	49.5	11.8	1.0	12,800	2350	65
NORTH DAKOTA, Most Middle and Western Counties	(General)	36.0	29.0	28.0	7.0	0.6	6,600	2050	50
OHIO, Morgan, Noble, Washington, Harrison	Meigs Creek	4.0	36.0	48.5	11.5	4.2	12,250	2400	67
Belmont	Pittsburgh No. 8	5.9	37.8	46.8	9.5	4.2	12,055	2000	50–60
OKLAHOMA, Pittsburg	McAlester	2.0	37.3	56.2	4.5	0.8	13,500	2230	47–67
PENNSYLVANIA, Luzerne & Lackawanna	Northern Coal Field	3.0	6.1	82.0	8.9	0.7	13,000	3010	25–30
	Southern Coal Field	4.0	6.4	80.5	9.1	0.9	12,800	3000	35–45
Dauphin, Schuylkill, Carbon,	Upper Kittaning	2.6	16.2	71.9	9.3	2.1	13,865	2275	85–87
Cambria	Lower Kittaning	2.3	18.7	72.4	6.6	1.4	14,400	2640	107
Cambria	Upper Freeport	2.8	21.6	67.4	8.2	1.4	13,930	2375	87
	Lower Freeport	2.9	22.4	67.0	7.7	1.6	13,960	2465	99

Run-of-mine coal consists of the product as it comes from the mine without screening. It is sold chiefly for steam-raising purposes and locally for domestic heating.

5-in. lump is that size of coal coming from the mine that will not pass through a 5-in. round-hole screen. It is sold for hand-firing in domestic and industrial uses.

5 × 2-in. egg is that size of coal which passes through a 5-in. round opening and is retained on a 2-in. round-hole screen. It is used for domestic, hand-firing and gas producers.

2 × 1¼ in. nut is that size of coal which passes through a 2-in. round hole and is retained on a 1¼ in, round-hole screen. Its use is domestic, hand-firing, and for small industrial stokers and gas producers.

1¼ × ¾-in. stoker coal is that size of coal which passes through a 1¼-in. round hole but is retained on a ¾-in. round-hole screen. Its use is domestic and for small industrial stokers.

¾ × 0-in. slack is the coal that passes through a ¾-in. round-hole equivalent screen. It is used for industrial stokers and pulverizers.

Commercial Sizes of Anthracite

The sizing of anthracite is definitely established, and all mines prepare sized coal. Because of its complete smokelessness, the larger sizes are used mostly for heating purposes in hand-fired furnaces. Some of it is also used in gas producers. The small sizes, known as buckwheat, are byproducts of the preparation of the larger sizes, and are burned on traveling-grate stokers or as pulverized coal for making steam in central stations and industrial plants. No. 1 and No. 2 buckwheat sizes

are sold for use with domestic stokers. A low selling price is necessary in order that the small anthracite may compete with good bituminous steaming coal. Its use is generally limited to plants within short hauling distances, with low freight cost. Table 13–5 gives the dimensions and the trade names of the standard sizes of anthracite.

A limited amount of anthracite is recovered by river dredging. There is a high proportion of fines which are generally burned on traveling grate stokers or in boilers fired by pulverized coal. Fuel properties of this recovered anthracite are very similar to that of the freshly mined fuel with the exception that it runs slightly higher in ash content and slightly lower in heating value.

Storage of Bituminous Coal

Coal in storage is subject to fires by spontaneous combustion caused by oxidation of the coal. Experience shows that the fires in a coal storage pile can be avoided or greatly minimized if access of air into the pile is prevented or greatly reduced. If there is no oxygen in the coal pile, oxidation cannot take place.[13]

Air finds its way into the storage pile through the void spaces between coal pieces. These voids occur mostly where larger coal pieces are separated from fines. Therefore, when coal is stored, separation of sizes must be avoided. The coal should be spread in horizontal layers one to two feet thick and packed down tightly, so that the spaces between the larger pieces are completely filled with fines. Thinner layers pack better than thick ones. The spreading of the coal in layers and packing it down can be done with cater-

---

[13] A useful reference is a publication of the Ohio Coal Association entitled "Storage of Coal." Another source of information is Chapter 18, Handling and Storing Solid Fuels, from *Fuels and Combustion Handbook* by A. J. Johnson and G. H. Auth, McGraw-Hill, 1951.

Table 13—5   Standard Sizes and Names of Anthracite

| Trade name of size | Broken | Egg | Stove | Chestnut | Pea | Buckwheat | | | |
						No. 1	No. 2 (Rice)	No. 3 (Barley)	No. 4
Passing through round hole — in.	4⅜	3¼	2⁷⁄₁₆	1⅝	1³⁄₁₆	⁹⁄₁₆	⁵⁄₁₆	³⁄₁₆	³⁄₃₂
Retained on round hole — in.	3¼	2⁷⁄₁₆	1⅝	1³⁄₁₆	⁹⁄₁₆	⁵⁄₁₆	³⁄₁₆	³⁄₃₂	³⁄₆₄

(Silt is refuse smaller than No. 4 buckwheat.)

pillar tractors or bulldozers. Uniformity of mixture of sizes, and packing, should be extended to the sides of the coal pile which are exposed to wind pressure. To reduce still further the access of air into the coal pile, the surface should be covered with a layer of several inches of fine coal. This layer of fine coal should, in turn, be covered with coarse coal to prevent the dust layer from being blown away by wind or washed down by rain.

If air enters the coal pile, approximately the same volume of gas must escape somewhere through the top. On a cool morning, the escaping gas is indicated by a haze of steam. These steamy places are the leaky spots in the coal pile surfaces, where the coal-dust covering is imperfect. These leaky spots can be eliminated by additional packing and dust covering.

The ground for storage of coal should be level, clean and well drained. The sides of the storage pile should have a slope of from 30 to 35 degrees from horizontal. Steeper slopes are more difficult to pack and make airtight; they are also subjected to greater wind pressure and to more erosion by rain and wind.

The best size of coal for storage is screenings that have a sufficient proportion of fines for close packing. It is impractical to store run-of-mine coal, because the presence of large lumps makes

packing of coal impossible. If run-of-mine coal must be stored, it should be passed through a crusher to reduce the lumps to suitable size. Screened lump coal can be stored without packing. The large empty voids between the lumps provide sufficient ventilation to carry away the heat generated by the oxidation of the coal, which is small because of the relatively small exposed surface of the lumps.

The fire hazard of coals high in moisture and sulfur content is great. If they must be stored, the packing and sealing should be carried to the limit. The ideal storage for such coals would be containers that could be sealed tight. Coal storing would then become coal preserving. Underwater storage is sometimes used with coal of this type.

Storing of coal on hot sunny days should be avoided, because the sun heats the surface of the coal to high temperature. If these warm surfaces are covered with a layer of coal, the heat is retained and may be a contributing factor in starting a fire.

Burning Characteristics of Coals

The most outstanding burning characteristic of coal is the property of *caking* exhibited by some coals and its opposite, *free-burning*, shown by others. This property, more than any other factor, governs the selection of coal-burning equipment.

As important as this characteristic is, it must be admitted that there is no test which will permit its precise evaluation in the laboratory. While there is no difficulty in distinguishing between caking and free-burning coals, there are many shades and gradations of difference between the two extremes, and frequently these gradations are of the greatest interest to the consumer. The free-swelling index test described earlier is an approach to the problem.

Caking Coals

Caking coals, when heated in the furnace, pass through a plastic state during which the individual pieces fuse together into large masses of semicoke, which is impervious to flow of air. The air can pass only through cracks formed between the masses of semicoke. The very active combustion in these cracks widens them into crater-like fissures, which allow passage of a large volume of air, much of which is not used in combustion, while, in the centers of the masses of coke, the fuel remains inactive, owing to lack of air. The masses of coke must be broken with fire tools or by the action of the stoker. For this reason, caking coals are burned on an underfeed type of stoker which has moving rams or other means for breaking the masses of semicoke. Caking coals cannot be burned successfully on traveling grate stokers, because these stokers have no means for breaking the masses of semicoke.

Free-Burning Coals

In the free-burning coals the individual pieces do not fuse together but burn separately, or after fusion the mass breaks up quickly into fragments. The air flows in small streams through the irregular passages between the pieces of fuel, and combustion is nearly uniform over the entire grate area. The fuel bed needs no agitation, so that the traveling grate stoker is well adapted for burning such coals.

Most of the coals of the Eastern province are caking, whereas most of the coals of the Interior province are free-burning. The subbituminous coals and the lignites are classed as free-burning coals. They lack completely the fusion property of the caking coals and, in addition, the larger pieces disintegrate in fire into small pieces. With any agitation of the fuel bed, the small pieces sift through the grate and may cause fire in the ashpit. The traveling grate or spreader types of stoker are the best suited burning equipment for these fuels because there is no agitation of the fuel bed.

Another term for caking is agglomerating, and the agglomerating index is used in classification of coals to indicate the dividing line between non-caking coals and those having weakly caking properties. The test is essentially the same as the free-swelling index already discussed, the non-caking designation being applied only to coals that produce a noncoherent residue which can be poured out of the crucible as a powder or flakes that will pulverize easily with thumb and finger pressure. In practice, coals that approach this border line will be free-burning; hence it is apparent that the term caking has a different meaning to the scientist interested in coal classification than to the fuel engineer burning the coal.

Both caking and free-burning coals can be burned without difficulty and equally well in boilers fired with pulverized coal. In general the caking coals fall within the range of the high-volatile A, medium-volatile and low-volatile bituminous coal groups (ASTM Classification). Within these groups wide variations in behavior will be found.

Coking versus Caking

Coking coals are those which make good coke suitable for metallurgical purposes. Coke is produced when coking coal is heated in a coke oven, out of contact with air, and the greater part of the volatile matter is driven off. It consists mostly of the fixed carbon and ash of the original coal.

The term coking coals is sometimes used instead of caking coals. The caking process in a boiler furnace is confused with the coking process in the coke oven. There are many caking coals which do not make good coke in a coke oven, and there are some free-burning coals that make good coke.

Caking and coking coals have generally lower oxygen content than free-burning and noncoking coals. This, however, is true only to a certain extent.

When a caking coal is exposed to the action of air over a long period of time it picks up oxygen and loses much of its caking property. It is known that the outcrop coal of a caking-coal seam shows little of the caking property. The rate of oxygen pickup increases rapidly as the temperature is raised, as shown in Fig. 13–3. This principle is used in a stoker design greatly to reduce the caking property of coals. The coal is heated in the presence of air as it is moved into the furnace.

The caking characteristic is much more pronounced when the coal contains a large proportion of fines than it is with screened or lump coal. Some of the caking coals could pass as noncaking if the slack were screened out of them.

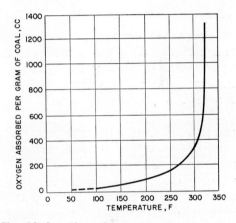

Fig. 13–3. Chart showing increase in rate of oxygen pickup resulting from heating coal while exposed to air

CONC. SULFITE LIQUOR

14

Natural Gas, Oil and Byproduct Fuels[1]

FOSSIL FUELS may be classified as in Table 14–1 into solid, liquid and gaseous fuels. Each of these fuels may in turn be further classified as natural fuels and manufactured or byproduct fuels. These classifications are not mutually exclusive and necessarily overlap in some areas.

Obvious examples of natural fuels are coal, crude oil and natural gas. Residual oils which are fired in boilers might be considered as a byproduct of the refining of crude oil. Wood, although a natural fuel, is rarely burned in boilers except in the form of sawdust, shavings, slabs and bark which remain as a byproduct after lumbering and pulping operations. Coal is the natural fuel from which coke, coke oven gas, char, tars, chemicals and industrial gases may be converted by carbonization. Coal may also be gasified to

Table 14–1   Classification of Fuels

Type of Fuel	Natural Fuels	Manufactured or Byproduct Fuels
Solid	Coal	Coke and coke breeze
		Coal tar
	Lignite	Lignite char
	Peat	
	Wood	Charcoal
		Bark, saw dust and wood waste
		Petroleum coke
		Bagasse
		Refuse
Liquid	Petroleum	Gasoline
		Kerosene
		Fuel oil
		Gas oil
		Shale oil
		Petroleum fractions and residues
Gaseous	Natural gas	Refinery gas
	Liquefied petroleum gases (LPG)	Coke oven gas
		Blast furnace gas
		Producer gas
		Water gas
		Carburetted water gas
		Coal gas
		Regenerator waste gas

[1] Information from First Edition revised and supplemented by D. J. Frey.

obtain industrial gases for heating, chemical reduction, and hydrogenation and synthesis reactions.[2]

In this book fuels are discussed primarily from the point of their usefulness and economic utilization in the generation of steam. Since coal is the most important fuel fired in boilers, the preceding chapter, Fuel Properties of Coal, is appropriately devoted to it. Yet the reader must not lose sight of the increasing contribution of natural gas and crude petroleum to the energy market of the United States as shown graphically in Fig. 14–1 for the years 1900 through 1960. More than any-

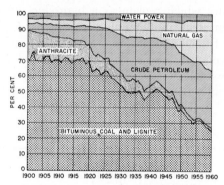

Fig. 14–1. Changes in United States energy production, 1900–1960

thing else this reflects the greatly increased use of petroleum products for automotive and aviation industries, plus the widespread consumption of oil and natural gas as domestic and industrial fuels.

This chapter is organized in major sections dealing with gaseous, liquid and solid fuels. Discussions of natural, manufactured and byproduct fuels are interspersed throughout the chapter, together with mention of important fuel properties

and end uses in boiler firing. The chapter title was chosen to focus attention upon natural gas, oil and byproduct fuels and to emphasize their importance as sources of thermal energy for steam generation.

Gaseous Fuels

Gaseous fuels are ideally suited for steam generation purposes because of the ease of control, the presence of little or no solid residue and the low excess air requirement which contributes to high efficiency.

Properties of fuel gas considered to be of prime importance are composition, heating value, and specific gravity.

Analysis

The analysis of fuel gas is expressed in terms of volume percentages of the component gases. Determinations can be made by selective absorption in chemical solutions, by separation of components through distillation, by infrared or mass spectrometry, or by means of gas chromatography. Typical analysis of various gases are given under their specific headings.

Heating Value

The heating value refers to the quantity of heat released during combustion of a unit amount of fuel gas. Determinations are made with a continuous flow (constant pressure) gas calorimeter. The heating value as determined in calorimeters is termed *higher heating value* and is the quantity of heat evolved when the products of combustion are cooled to 60 F and the water vapor produced is completely condensed to a liquid at that temperature. The *lower heating value* is the same as

[2] For what might be described as a classic treatment of this subject, see Chapter II, Fuels, in *Steam Power Plant Engineering* by G. F. Gebhardt, Sixth Edition, 1928 Revision, John Wiley & Sons, New York; an authoritative approach of more recent origin may be found in the chapter, Fuels and Their Utilization, by Richard C. Corey from *Riegel's Industrial Chemistry*, edited by James A. Kent and published by Reinhold, New York, 1962.

the gross heating value except that the water produced is not condensed but retained in the vapor form at 60 F.

The heating value of manufactured gas is expressed as Btu per cu ft when measured at 60 F and 30 in. Hg, saturated with water vapor. The values for natural gas, however, are commonly reported at a pressure of 14.7 psia or 30 in. Hg, at a temperature of 80 F, and generally on a dry basis.

The heating values of gaseous mixtures can be calculated by multiplying the mole fractions of the component gases by their respective heating values; the sum of the products is the heating value of the mixture.

Specific Gravity

Various methods for determining the specific gravity of a fuel gas are available but three methods have been adopted as standards by ASTM:[3]

Direct Weighing Method. This involves the determination of the weight differential between two equal volumes of gas and air, both at identical conditions of temperature and pressure.

Pressure Balance Method. In this method, a flask containing the gas is counterbalanced on a beam enclosed in a container. The beam is brought to balance by adjusting the air pressure within the container which varies the buoyancy of the flask. The procedure is repeated with air in the flask and the specific gravity determined from the ratio of the required absolute pressures.

Displacement Balance Method. The instrument consists of a balance beam on each end of which two bells are suspended in a sealing liquid. One bell, containing air, is open to the atmosphere through holes in its top; the other bell, containing the gas, is open to the atmosphere through a 59 in. gas column connected to the space under the bell. An unbalanced force is produced which is equal to the pressure differential above and within the gas filled bulb. The magnitude of this force is an indication of the specific gravity.

Natural Gas

Natural gas is perhaps the closest approach to an ideal fuel because it is practically free from noncombustible gas or solid residue. It is found compressed in porous rock and shale formations, or cavities, which are sealed between strata of close-textured rocks under the earth's surface. When these so-called gas bearing sands of a pool are tapped by drilling wells, the gas is found to be under rock pressure, which may be as high as 2000 psig. As gas is withdrawn, this pressure gradually decreases until it eventually becomes so low that the field must be abandoned.

Natural gas consists mainly of methane, with smaller quantities of other hydrocarbons, particularly ethane, although carbon dioxide and nitrogen are usually present in small amounts. Sometimes there are also appreciable amounts of hydrogen sulfide present. This is generally removed at the field before transmission.

Oxygen is present only when there has been an infiltration of atmospheric air. In the California fields, a high percentage of carbon dioxide may be encountered, while in certain Kansas and Oklahoma fields relatively large percentages of nitrogen are present. Natural gas from some Texas fields may contain as much as one per cent helium. Table 14–2 shows analyses of natural gas from several widely separated fields, and Table 14–3 provides similar information on natural gas distrib-

[3] See "Standard Methods of Test for Specific Gravity of Gaseous Fuels," ASTM D 1070–63.

Table 14–2   Natural Gas From Various Gas Fields*

Location and Field	Components of gas — per cent by volume									Higher heating value, Btu per cu ft, dry†	Sp gr
	Methane	Ethane	Propane	Butane	Pentane	Hexane plus	CO_2	O_2	N_2		
California Kettleman North Dome (b)	87.20	3.20	3.50	2.00	1.70	—	0.40	—	—	1212	0.690
California Kettleman North Dome (a)	93.00	4.60	1.80	0.20	—	—	0.40	—	—	1080	0.602
California, Rio Vista	94.20	2.95	0.80	0.15	0.10	—	0.30	—	1.50	1038	0.590
California, Ventura (b)	83.60	5.40	6.10	3.20	1.40	—	0.30	—	—	1260	0.706
California, Ventura (a)	92.70	4.70	2.20	0.10	—	—	0.30	—	—	1083	0.604
Illinois — Indiana	97.00	—	—	—	—	—	1.00	0.60	1.60	983	—
Kansas — Cunningham	62.30	21.20	—	—	—	—	0.20	0.30	16.00	1101	—
Kansas — Hugoton	77.00	3.90	2.60	2.00	0.50	0.10	0.10	0.10	13.60	1005	0.698
Kansas, Otis	71.80	13.90	—	—	—	—	0.30	0.20	13.80	976	—
Kentucky	83.40	13.30	—	—	—	—	0.80	0.40	2.10	1083	—
Louisiana, Monroe	91.28	1.52	0.70	0.41	0.19	0.15	0.30	—	5.45	997	0.6075
Louisiana, Paradis	92.18	3.33	1.48	0.79	0.25	0.05	0.90	—	1.02	1067	0.6153
Michigan	75.80	17.50	—	—	—	—	0.10	0.30	6.30	1081	—
Mississippi, Owinville	95.74	0.27	0.07	0.10	0.03	0.18	1.28	—	2.33	989	0.5855
Ohio, Canton	86.10	10.80	0.60	—	—	—	0.10	0.40	2.00	1082	0.620
Ohio, Hinckley-Medina	80.20	16.80	0.20	—	—	—	0.20	0.10	2.50	1118	0.650
Oklahoma, Hugoton	75.30	6.40	3.70	1.40	0.30	0.30	—	—	12.50	1043	0.710
Oklahoma, Hughes County	79.00	17.50	—	—	—	—	0.20	0.30	3.00	1114	—
Oklahoma, Keyes	51.50	17.50	—	—	—	—	1.40	0.20	29.40		—
Pennsylvania, Greene County	85.41	8.10	3.34	1.53	0.62	—	0.10	—	0.90	1171	0.667
Pennsylvania, Leidy	96.80	2.50	0.20	—	—	—	0.20	—	0.30	1031	0.5751
Pennsylvania, Western Penn.	85.60	13.30	0.30	—	—	—	0.10	0.10	0.60	1112	0.6271
Texas, Agua Dulce (b)	90.98	4.56	1.88	1.04	0.41	0.34	0.12	—	0.67	1109	0.6307
Texas, Agua Dulce (a)	93.00	4.14	1.03	0.19	0.04	0.07	0.49	—	1.04	1051	0.5986
Texas, Carthage (b)	90.29	4.47	1.45	0.87	0.38	0.39	0.88	—	1.27	1093	0.634
Texas, Carthage (a)	91.73	4.01	0.94	0.24	0.02	0.14	0.87	—	2.05	1038	0.6073
Texas, East Texas	63.28	22.49	11.15	0.09	0.08	0.19	0.67	—	2.05	1336	0.7941
Texas, Hugoton (b)	76.90	6.07	3.69	1.34	0.46	0.13	—	—	11.41	1046	0.698
Texas, Hugoton (a)	79.00	6.31	2.20	0.07	0.07	—	—	—	12.35	967	0.659
Texas, Keystone (a)	86.20	11.90	1.66	0.24	—	—	—	—	—	1133	0.630
Texas, Keystone (b) (6 formations)	78.77	10.92	6.07	2.38	0.70	0.43	0.40	H_2S-0.31	—	1279	0.730
Texas, Panhandle (b)	81.76	5.63	3.44	1.51	0.26	0.43	0.10	—	6.87	1090	0.681
Texas, Panhandle (a)	81.50	5.96	3.66	1.23	0.05	—	0.10	—	7.50	1061	0.669
Texas, Pledger	94.24	2.85	0.98	0.60	0.30	0.48	0.10	—	0.45	1086	0.613

Texas, Tom O'Connor	90.77	4.48	1.88	1.16	0.43	0.32	0.11	—	0.85	1117	0.632
Texas, Wasson (b)	69.52	9.71	6.48	3.20	1.40	0.66	5.60	—	3.14	1238	0.805
Texas, Wasson (a)	76.87	10.14	2.25	0.12	0.04	0.04	6.02	—	3.54	1030	0.684
West Virginia, Northern	85.86	8.51	3.15	1.14	0.44	—	0.10	—	0.80	1158	0.647
West Virginia, Terra Alta	98.75	1.07	0.04	0.14	—	—	—	—	—	1027	0.561
West Virginia, Wyoming County	97.75	1.80	0.35	0.10	—	—	—	—	—	1036	0.568

† 30 in. Hg, 60 F. To convert to a saturated basis, deduct 1.73 per cent; i.e., 17.3 from 1000, 19 from 1100.
(a) After processing plant (b) Before processing plant.
* Analyses obtained from major companies operating in the field or taking gas from it.

Table 14-3   Natural Gas Distributed in Various Cities in the United States*

City	Components of gas — per cent by volume									Higher heating value, Btu per cu ft, dry†	Sp gr
	Methane	Ethane	Propane	Butane	Pentane	Hexane plus	CO_2	O_2	N_2		
Abilene, Texas	68.60	19.83	2.71	0.25	—	—	0.47	0.58	7.56	1124	0.719
Akron, Ohio	92.60	4.00	0.90†	—	—	—	0.20	—	2.30	1040	0.600
Alburquerque, New Mexico	93.60	4.17	1.13	0.11	0.03	—	Trace	0.96	—	1055	0.593
Atlanta, Georgia	93.50	2.40	0.60	0.34	0.15	0.02	0.70	—	2.40	1024	0.595
Baltimore, Maryland	93.80	3.60	0.90	0.70	—	—	0.60	—	0.40	1062	0.602
Birmingham, Alabama	94.07	1.79	0.46	0.21	0.09	0.10	0.80	—	2.48	1013	0.582
Bismarck, North Dakota	93.09	2.73	0.30	—	—	—	—	—	3.88	988	0.589
Brooklyn, New York	94.53	3.53	0.89	0.28	0.08	0.19	0.50	—	—	1065	0.597
Butte, Montana	87.38	3.02	1.09	0.11	0.06	—	1.98	—	6.36	990	0.630
Canton, Ohio	92.60	4.00	0.90†	—	—	—	0.20	—	2.30	1052	0.614
Cheyenne, Wyoming	74.76	4.19	5.28	1.14	0.24	0.11	0.49	—	13.79	973	0.708
Cincinnati, Ohio	92.80	4.30	1.10	0.36	0.10	0.12	0.70	—	0.50	1049	0.606
Cleveland, Ohio	92.60	4.00	0.90	—	—	—	0.20	—	2.30	1040	0.600
Columbus, Ohio	95.70	2.90	—	—	—	—	1.30	—	0.10	1037	0.609
Dallas, Texas	85.00	7.10	2.40	0.50	0.40	—	0.60	—	4.00	1079	0.650
Denver, Colorado	74.76	4.19	5.28	1.14	0.24	0.11	0.49	—	13.79	973	0.708
Des Moines, Iowa	75.64	6.85	3.79	0.24	1.04	—	0.10	0.10	12.24	1018	0.684
Detroit, Michigan	75.50	12.50	—	—	—	—	0.10	0.50	11.50	1003	0.667
El Paso, Texas	86.60	7.29	2.48	0.61	—	—	—	—	3.02	1086	0.635
Ft. Worth, Texas	87.11	6.88	2.21	0.30	0.12	—	—	—	3.38	1076	0.629
Houston, Texas	92.50	4.80	2.00	0.30	—	—	0.27	—	0.13	1031	0.623

(Continued)

Table 14–3   Natural Gas Distributed in Various Cities in the United States* (Cont'd)

City	Components of gas – per cent by volume									Higher heating value, Btu per cu ft, dry†	Sp gr
	Methane	Ethane	Propane	Butane	Pentane	Hexane plus	CO_2	O_2	N_2		
Kansas City, Missouri	79.21	4.54	2.71	1.53	0.48	0.12	0.10	—	11.31	1024	0.684
Little Rock, Arkansas	94.00	3.00	0.50	0.20	0.20	—	1.00	—	1.10	1035	0.590
Los Angeles, California	80.20	10.20	3.60	0.50	0.10	0.10	—	—	5.30	1109	0.674
Louisville, Kentucky	89.40	8.30†	—	—	—	—	0.40	0.70	1.20	1075	0.610
Memphis, Tennessee	92.80	4.20	0.80	0.20	0.10	0.10	1.00	—	0.80	1049	0.600
Milwaukee, Wisconsin	72.80	6.60	3.60	0.80	0.02	0.02	—	—	16.20	958	0.698
Minneapolis, Minnesota	74.49	12.76	—	—	—	—	0.19	0.20	12.36	994	0.688
New Orleans, Louisiana	93.75	3.16	1.36	0.65	0.66	—	0.42	—	—	1072	0.612
New York City	91.50	5.50	0.80†	0.30	—	—	0.80	0.60	0.80	1063	0.600
Oklahoma City, Okla.	83.95	11.72	2.01	0.75	0.25	0.12	0.10	0.15	11.40	1133	0.650
Omaha, Nebraska	74.23	7.28	3.77	1.46	—	—	—	—	13.26	1028	0.697
Parkersburg, West Virginia	91.40	7.70	0.20	—	—	—	0.03	—	0.40	1068	0.600
Phoenix, Arizona	83.90	9.31	2.70	0.55	0.21	—	—	—	3.33	1107	0.651
Pittsburgh, Pennsylvania	90.12	5.64	1.39	0.48	0.07	0.04	0.68	—	1.58	1071	0.617
Provo, Utah	97.38	0.63	—	—	—	—	0.15	—	1.84	995	0.566
Pueblo, Colorado	74.76	4.19	5.28	1.14	0.24	0.11	0.49	—	13.79	973	0.708
Rapid City, South Dakota	93.09	2.73	0.30	—	—	—	—	—	3.88	988	0.589
St. Louis, Missouri	88.30	9.00	—	—	—	—	0.80	—	4.90	1058	0.613
Salt Lake City, Utah	92.00	3.80	—	—	—	—	0.20	—	4.00	1003	0.630
San Diego, California	81.97	10.00	3.35	0.61	0.14	—	—	—	3.93	1104	0.663
San Francisco, California	86.30	6.90	3.00	0.40	0.20	—	0.40	—	2.80	1100	0.640
Toledo, Ohio	95.70	2.90	—	—	—	—	1.30	—	0.10	1037	0.609
Tulsa, Oklahoma	80.07	10.44	3.09	0.52	0.33	0.10	0.20	0.10	5.15	1108	0.675
Waco, Texas	93.81	1.94	0.64	0.34	0.13	0.19	0.96	—	1.99	1023	0.597
Washington, D. C.	94.60	3.20	0.70	0.50	—	—	0.50	—	0.50	1051	0.590
Wichita, Kansas	79.62	6.40	1.42	1.12	0.48	0.14	0.10	0.10	10.62	1051	0.660
Youngstown, Ohio	92.60	4.00	0.90	—	—	—	0.20	—	2.30	1040	0.600

* Average analyses obtained from the operating utility company or from the major pipeline supplying the city. The gas supply may vary considerably from these averages. Also, as new supplies may be received from other sources, the analyses may change in the future.

† 30 in. Hg, 60 F. To convert to a saturated basis deduct 1.73 per cent; i.e., 17.3 from 1000, 19 from 1100.

uted in representative cities throughout the United States.[4]

Dry and Wet Natural Gas. The characteristics of a natural gas are influenced by the underground conditions existing in the localities where it is found. Most frequently these areas contain oil deposits and, as a result, the gas may be impregnated with heavy saturated hydrocarbons, which are liquid at ordinary pressures and temperatures. This "wet" gas is then dried by stripping from it those liquids which constitute the so-called "casinghead" gasoline. Where sulfur is present in the oil deposit, the gas will frequently contain hydrogen sulfide.

"Dry" natural gas, produced by wells which are remote from oil-bearing areas, is gas containing less than 0.1 gal of gasoline vapor per 1000 cu ft. In view of the foregoing, it is well to remember that the terms *wet* and *dry*, when associated with natural gas, refer to its gasoline content, not to its moisture content.

Natural gases are also classified as either "sweet" or "sour." The *sour* gas is one which contains some mercaptans and a high percentage of hydrogen sulfide while the *sweet* gas is one in which these objectionable constituents have been removed. Analysis of these gases are shown in Table 14–4.

Heating Value. The higher or gross heating value of natural gas is usually around 1000 Btu per cu ft, and it can be computed by adding together the heat contributed by volumetric percentages of the various component gases. This method will usually result in a lower value per cubic foot than that obtained by calorimetric determinations, because the unsaturated hydrocarbons are frequently grouped and reported with C_2H_6. For the same reason, the corresponding density, under standard conditions of 60 F and 30 in. Hg, will also be lower. The calculated Btu per pound, however, will be close to its actual value, because of the compensating effect of the lower calculated density.

Liquefied Petroleum Gas (LPG)

The term *liquefied petroleum gas, LPG,* is applied to certain hydrocarbons which are gaseous under normal atmospheric conditions, but can be liquefied under moderate pressure at normal temperatures. LPG is derived from natural gas and from various petroleum refinery

Table 14–4   Natural Gas From Arkansas Fields

Constituents	Raw-sour gas*	Sweetened-sour gas**
Carbon dioxide	5.50	0.00
Methane	77.73	88.83
Ethane	5.56	6.35
Propane	2.41	2.75
Butane	1.17	1.34
Pentane	0.39	0.45
Hexane and higher	0.24	0.28
Hydrogen sulfide	7.0	0.0004
Higher heating value Btu per cu ft at standard conditions	—	1159

* From Big Creek field
** From McKamie field

[4] These analyses were provided by the American Gas Association, 420 Lexington Avenue, New York 17, N. Y.

sources such as crude distillation and cracking. The hydrocarbons in LPG are mainly of the paraffinic (saturated) series, principally propane, isobutane and normal butane.

The California Natural Gasoline Association, as shown in Table 14–5, has divided LPG mixtures into six standard grades based on physical properties such as vapor pressure and specific gravity.[5]

The greatest use of LPG is as a domestic fuel with an appreciable amount being consumed in synthetic rubber production and chemical industries. It has a limited use in steam generating units as an ignition and warm-up fuel but is generally prohibited for economic reasons as a primary fuel.

Refinery Gas

Refinery gas, blended refinery gas, yard gas and still gas are some of the names applied to the byproduct gaseous fuels encountered in refinery operation when crude oil is processed into gasoline and other similar products. These gases are "rich" but variable in composition as a result of differences in the characteristics of the oil refined and the extent of cracking to which the oil has been subjected.

Their heating value is higher than natural gas, owing to the larger percentage of heavier hydrocarbons present. There are also present some illuminants, or unsaturated hydrocarbons, from the cracking operation. The wide range in their characteristic analyses is shown in Table 14–6.

For use in steam generating units, the gases from several types of operations are mixed, or blended, usually averaging approximately 1500 Btu per cu ft. They may constitute a large percentage of the fuel supply for the generation of steam used in refinery processes and power generation.

Coke Oven Gas

Coke oven gas is obtained during the high temperature carbonization of bituminous coal to make coke. Substantially all volatile matter in the raw coal is distilled off, and the vapors thus obtained contain fixed gases, liquids and solids. Various methods of cooling, separation and extraction are used to recover the liquids and solids. Some of the fixed gases are then used to heat the coke ovens, while the remainder is available for boiler, process or domestic fuel.

The quality of coke oven gas depends

Table 14–5   CNGA Standard Grade for LPG Mixture

CNGA Standard Grade	Max Vapor Pressure Psig at 100 F	Range of Allowable Sp Gr 60/60 F $H_2O = 1.0$	Composition
A	80	0.585–0.555	Predominantly butanes
B	100	0.560–0.545	Butane-propane mixture, largely butanes
C	125	0.550–0.535	Butane-propane mixture, proportions approximately equal
D	150	0.540–0.525	Butane-propane mixture, propane exceeds butane
E	175	0.530–0.510	Propane-butane mixture, largely propane
F	200	0.520–0.504	Predominantly propane

[5] This originally appeared in Bulletin TS–441 of the California Natural Gasoline Association in 1945 and was reprinted as Table 4 on page 33 of *Gaseous Fuels,* edited by Louis Shnidman and published by American Gas Association, Second Edition, 1954.

Table 14-6   Typical Analyses of Refinery Gas

Per cent by volume

Constituents															
Oxygen O_2	1.2	—	0.4	—	4.1	—	—	—	—	—	—	—	2.3	1.2	—
Nitrogen N_2	7.7	7.1	5.0	—	—	—	—	—	—	—	—	—	8.7	7.7	—
Carbon Dioxide CO_2	—	0.5	—	—	—	—	—	—	—	—	—	3.3	—	—	26.9
Carbon Monoxide CO	0.3	1.4	0.2	—	—	—	—	—	—	—	—	1.5	—	9.3	—
Hydrogen H_2	—	21.2	—	—	—	40.9	1.2	—	—	—	—	5.6	—	—	—
Hydrogen Sulfide H_2S	—	—	—	—	—	—	—	2.2	—	—	—	—	—	—	—
Methane CH_4	36.3	44.6	86.4	52.4	43.6	40.5	31.0	41.6	4.3	92.10	5.0	30.9	30.3	36.3	30.9
Ethane C_2H_6	22.9	14.5	4.0	22.2	19.8	10.6	22.1	20.9	82.7	1.9	12.0	19.8	13.4	22.9	15.5
Propane C_3H_8	26.8	8.9	3.0	17.8	22.3	5.5	28.5	19.7	13.0	4.5	30.0	38.1	19.1	26.8	10.8
Butane C_4H_{10}	4.3	1.4	1.0	4.6	7.5	1.6	12.4	9.1	—	1.3	34.0	0.6	14.7	4.3	2.0
Pentane C_5H_{12}	0.5	0.4	—	—	—	0.9	4.8	6.5	—	0.2	19.0	—	1.8	0.5	—
Illuminants as Ethylene C_2H_4	—	—	—	3.0	2.7	—	—	—	—	—	—	0.2	9.7	—	13.9
Heating value Btu per cu ft	1590	966	1148	1550	1592	—	—	1809	1781	1104	2814	1625	1759	—	1226

(In the last column the value 26.9 is bracketed ←— 26.9 —→ across the O_2, N_2, CO_2, CO and H_2 rows.)

upon the character of the coal processed, the duration of the coking operation, the maximum temperature reached, and to some extent, upon the conditions of operation. At very high carbonizing temperatures, the volatile matter of the coal is thermally cracked to a greater extent than at normal temperatures (1800 to 2100 F), thereby lowering the heating value of the gas discharged, but simultaneously increasing the thermal yield of gas.

Typical analyses of coke oven gas are shown in Table 14–7. The higher heating value is approximately one half of that for natural gas. It ranges from 460 to 650 Btu per cu ft and, to a certain extent, is indicative of the maximum temperature existing in the carbonizing retorts.

Producer Gas

Producer gas is formed through the partial combustion of coal or coke by passing air through the hot fuel bed. Because of the use of air, the nitrogen content of the gas is high, generally 50–55 per cent by volume, and the heating value is rather low, ranging from about 140 to 180 Btu per cu ft. The ranges of component gases in this fuel are given below:

Component	Per Cent by Volume
CO	20–30
H_2	8–20
CH_4	0.5–3
CO_2	3–9
N_2	50–56
O_2	0.1–0.3

Water Gas (Blue Gas)

Water gas is made in a cyclic process, in which coke is "blown" with air to raise its temperature and then "blasted" with steam. The steam reacts with the hot carbon endothermally as follows:

$$C + H_2O \longrightarrow CO + H_2$$

The gas is sometimes called "blue gas" because of the characteristic blue flame with which it burns, the coloring being due to the high percentage of hydrogen and carbon monoxide. A typical analysis of this gas is:

Component	Per Cent by Volume
CO_2	5.4
CO	37.0
H_2	47.3
CH_4	1.3
N_2	8.3
HHV, Btu per cu ft	287

Carburetted Water Gas

Water gas is often enriched with fuel oil to raise its heating value. The enriched gas is termed *carburetted water gas*. The process involves the injection of oil into the carburetting chamber during the steam blow; the water gas, passing into the carburetor, picks up the oil vapor which is then cracked into gases. The composition and heating value of the carburetted water gas varies with the amount of oil used, the latter property varying between 400 and 700 Btu per cu ft. Table 14–8 shows typical analyses of this gas.[6]

Regenerator Waste Gas

The lighter hydrocarbons or gas oils produced in the petroleum coking processes are further refined in catalytic cracking units. These units fall into two general types: fluid units, in which fine powdered catalyst flows through the equipment with flow characteristics resembling a liquid, and moving bed units, which use either spherical or pelleted catalyst circulated by elevators or gas lifts.

[6] This table originally appeared in the *Gas Chemists Handbook,* Third Edition, 1929, and may also be found on page 45, *Gaseous Fuels,* edited by Louis Shnidman, Second Edition, 1954.

Table 14–7   Coke Oven Gas

Constituents	Per cent by volume						
CO_2	1.8	2.3	1.0	3.13	0.75	1.4	2.6
CO	6.3	9.4	4.8	11.93	6.0	5.1	6.1
O_2	0.2	0.6	—	—	—	0.5	0.6
H_2	53.0	49.3	53.5	42.16	53.0	5.7.4	47.9
N_2	3.4	6.5	3.7	—	12.1	4.2	3.7
CH_4	31.6	28.4	34.0	37.14	28.15	28.5	33.9
C_2H_4	3.7	3.5	3.0	5.64	—	2.9	5.2
Higher heating value Btu per cu ft	580	550	557	645	466	526	588

Table 14–8   Analyses of Carburetted Water Gas

Component	From Coke	From Anthracite
Carbon dioxide and hydrogen sulfide	0.9	3.3
Nitrogen	6.8	4.2
Hydrogen	37.4	38.4
Carbon monoxide	35.0	31.0
Methane	8.1	12.7
Ethane	1.30	1.05
Ethylene	6.7	6.9
Propane	0.25	0.08
Propylene	1.5	0.87
Butane	0.0	0.0
Butylene	0.75	0.45
Liquid hydrocarbons	1.30	1.05

The cracking of the feed occurs in what is termed a chemical reactor vessel. The preheated catalyst is maintained in a fluid state and during the cracking reaction the catalyst becomes coated with a coke deposit. This material must be removed in order to maintain catalyst activity.

The spent catalyst is continuously removed from the reactor and transported to a regenerator vessel. In this unit compressed air is used to fluidize the catalyst and burn off the carbon. To keep compression costs to a minimum, as well as to keep the temperature inside the regenerator restricted to a level which will not destroy catalyst activity, the smallest amount of air is used that will effectively clean the catalyst. This combustion process therefore normally produces an appreciable percentage of carbon monoxide.

A typical analysis of *regenerator waste gas* and the range of the various constituents are given in Table 14–9. The gas, although at temperatures as high as 1125 F, has a heating value of not over 40 Btu per cu ft.[7]

Table 14–9   Typical Analysis of Regenerator Waste Gas

	Per cent by Volume	Range — Per cent
Carbon monoxide	6.9	3–9
Carbon dioxide	8.1	7–11
Oxygen	0.8	0.3
Nitrogen	65.8	56.75
Water vapor	18.4	7–33

Blast Furnace Gas

Blast furnace gas results from various reactions occurring throughout the blast furnace. This gas contains relatively high percentages of carbon monoxide, along with carbon dioxide, nitrogen and water vapor. Its heating value varies between

[7] See Chapter 23, Natural Circulation Boilers, section on waste heat boilers, and "Tangential Firing of Regenerator Waste Heat Gas in CO Boilers" by J. G. Singer and S. S. Blackburn, Jr., ASME Paper 60–WA–327.

90 and 110 Btu per cu ft and is dependent principally upon the quality of coke used, speed of combustion and character of the ore treated. The combustible in blast furnace gas consists of about 30 per cent carbon monoxide, 2 to 3 per cent hydrogen and a trace of methane. The inert gas consists of about 9.0 per cent of carbon dioxide and 59.0 per cent nitrogen; when washed it carries a considerable amount of water in suspension as fine droplets as well as water vapor. An average figure for the amount of gas produced by a blast furnace is 150,000 cu ft per ton of iron, or about 160,000 cu ft per ton of coke charged. Approximately 10 per cent is lost through leakage, and 30 per cent is required to preheat the blast. As it leaves the "top," this gas is hot and contains considerable dust having a high iron oxide content. Much of the dust is removed and then sintered for return to the blast furnace as a part of the ore charge.

Liquid Fuels

Fuel Oil

Fuel oil used for steam generation in power plant boilers may be defined as petroleum or any of its liquid residues remaining after the more volatile constituents have been removed.

Petroleum is sometimes burned in its crude form. In this condition, most of it will contain lighter gasoline fractions which lower the flash point and present a fire hazard. Through limited fractional distillation, or topping, the lighter gasoline can be removed and a safe fuel oil can be produced. If the refining process is carried through extended fractional distillation and cracking, such fuels as gasoline, kerosene, gas oil, light fuel oils, lubricating oil, heavy fuel oil, residual tar, pitch and petroleum coke are produced.

Properties of Fuel Oil. The term fuel oil may conveniently cover a wide range of petroleum products. It may be applied to crude petroleum, to a light petroleum fraction similar to kerosene or gas oil, or to a heavy residue left after distilling off the fixed gases, the gasoline and more or less of the kerosene and gas oil. To provide standardization, specifications have been established, Table 14–10, for five grades of fuel oil.[8]

Grades No. 1 and No. 2 are sometimes designated as light and medium domestic fuel oils and are specified mainly by the temperature of the distillation range. Grade No. 6 which is designated as heavy industrial fuel oil and sometimes known as Bunker C oil is specified mainly by viscosity. The specific gravities of Grades 4, 5, and 6 are not specified because they will vary with the source of the crude petroleum and the extent of the refinery operation in cracking and distilling.

Despite the multiplicity of chemical compounds found in fuel oils, the typical analyses of these fuels, as shown in Table 14–11, are fairly constant.

Specific Gravity. This is the ratio between the weight of any volume of oil at 60 F and the weight of an equal volume of water at 60 F. The common designation is *Sp Gr 60/60 F* and is expressed as a decimal carried to four places.

Gravity determinations are readily made by immersing a hydrometer into the sample and reading the scale at the point to which the instrument sinks in the oil. The specific gravity is either read direct or the gravity is measured in degrees API.

---

[8] See "Tentative Specifications for Fuel Oils," ASTM Designation D 396–64 T, from which Table 14–10 is reprinted.

Table 14—10 Detailed Requirements for Fuel Oils[a]

Grade of Fuel Oil[b]	Flash Point, F Min	Pour Point, F Max	Water and Sediment, per cent by volume Max	Carbon Residue on 10 per cent Bottoms, per cent Max	Ash, per cent by weight Max	Distillation Temperatures, F 10 per cent Point Max	90 per cent Point Max	Min	Saybolt Viscosity, sec Universal at 100 F Max	Min	Furol at 122 F Max	Min	Kinematic Viscosity, centistokes At 100 F Max	Min	At 122 F Max	Min	Gravity, deg API Min	Copper Strip Corrosion Max
No. 1 { A distillate oil intended for vaporizing pot-type burners and other burners requiring this grade of fuel	100 or legal	0	trace	0.15	...	420	550	...	...	...	...	...	2.2	1.4	...	...	35	No. 3
No. 2 { A distillate oil for general purpose domestic heating for use in burners not requiring No. 1 fuel oil	100 or legal	20[c]	0.10	0.35	...	d	640[e]	540[e]	37.93	32.6	...	...	(3.6)[e]	(2.0)[e]	...	...	30[g]	...
No. 4 { An oil for burner installations not equipped with preheating facilities	130 or legal	20	0.50	...	0.10	...	...	...	125	45	...	...	(26.4)	(5.8)	...	...	...	...
No. 5 { A residual-type oil for burner installations equipped with preheating facilities	130 or legal	...	1.00	...	0.10	...	...	...	...	150	40	...	...	(32.1)	(81)	...	...	...
No. 6 { An oil for use in burners equipped with preheaters permitting a high-viscosity fuel	150	...	2.00[f]	...	...	...	...	...	...	...	300	45	...	...	(638)	(92)	...	...

[a] Recognizing the necessity for low sulfur fuel oils used in connection with heat treatment, nonferrous metal, glass, and ceramic furnaces and other special uses, a sulfur requirement may be specified in accordance with the following table:

Grade of Fuel Oil	Sulfur, max, per cent
No. 1	0.5
No. 2	1.0
No. 4	no limit
No. 5	no limit
No. 6	no limit

Other sulfur limits may be specified only by mutual agreement between the purchaser and the seller.

[b] It is the intent of these classifications that failure to meet any requirement of a given grade does not automatically place an oil in the next lower grade unless in fact it meets all requirements of the lower grade.

[c] Lower or higher pour points may be specified whenever required by conditions of storage or use. However, these specifications shall not require a pour point lower than 0 F under any conditions.

[d] The 10 per cent distillation temperature point may be specified at 440 F maximum for use in other than atomizing burners.

[e] When pour point less than 0 F is specified, the minimum viscosity shall be 1.8 cs (32.0 sec, Saybolt Universal) and the minimum 90 per cent point shall be waived.

[f] The amount of water by distillation plus the sediment by extraction shall not exceed 2.00 per cent. The amount of sediment by extraction shall not exceed 0.50 per cent. A deduction in quantity shall be made for all water and sediment in excess of 1.0 per cent.

[g] In the states of Alaska, Arizona, California, Hawaii, Idaho, Nevada, Oregon, Utah and Washington, a minimum gravity of 28 deg API is permissible

Table 14–11   Typical Analyses and Properties of Fuel Oils*

Grade	No. 1 Fuel Oil	No. 2 Fuel Oil	No. 4 Fuel Oil	No. 5 Fuel Oil	No. 6 Fuel Oil
Type	Distillate (Kerosene)	Distillate	Very Light Residual	Light Residual	Residual
Color	Light	Amber	Black	Black	Black
API gravity, 60 F	40	32	21	17	12
Specific gravity, 60/60 F	0.8251	0.8654	0.9279	0.9529	0.9861
Lb per U.S. gallon, 60 F	6.870	7.206	7.727	7.935	8.212
Viscos., Centistokes, 100 F	1.6	2.68	15.0	50.0	360.0
Viscos., Saybolt Univ., 100 F	31	35	77	232	—
Viscos., Saybolt Furol, 122 F	—	—	—	—	170
Pour point, F	Below zero	Below zero	10	30	65
Temp. for pumping, F	Atmospheric	Atmospheric	15 min.	35 min.	100
Temp. for atomizing, F	Atmospheric	Atmospheric	25 min.	130	200
Carbon residue, per cent	Trace	Trace	2.5	5.0	12.0
Sulfur, per cent	0.1	0.4–0.7	0.4–1.5	2.0 max.	2.8 max.
Oxygen and nitrogen, per cent	0.2	0.2	0.48	0.70	0.92
Hydrogen, per cent	13.2	12.7	11.9	11.7	10.5
Carbon, per cent	86.5	86.4	86.10	85.55	85.70
Sediment and water, per cent	Trace	Trace	0.5 max.	1.0 max.	2.0 max.
Ash, per cent	Trace	Trace	0.02	0.05	0.08
Btu per gallon	137,000	141,000	146,000	148,000	150,000

* Technical information from Humble Oil & Refining Company.

Formerly, the gravity of oil was measured in degrees Baumé but confusion developed over the use of the two so-called Baumé scales for light liquids. To overcome this, the American Petroleum Institute, the U.S. Bureau of Mines, and the U.S. Bureau of Standards agreed to recommend, in 1921, that only one scale be used in the petroleum industry, and that it be known as the API scale. The relation between specific gravity and deg API is expressed by:

$$\text{Sp Gr } 60/60 \text{ F} = \frac{141.5}{131.5 + \text{Deg API}}$$

Heating Value. This may be expressed in either Btu per gallon at 60 F or Btu per pound. The heating value per gallon increases with specific gravity, because there is more weight per gallon, and ranges from about 135,000 to 150,000 Btu. The heating value per pound of fuel oil varies inversely with the specific gravity, because lighter oil contains more hydrogen; it ranges from 18,300 to 19,500 Btu.

The exact determination of the heat content of fuel oil is made in a bomb calorimeter. However, there is an approximate relationship between specific gravity and higher heating value:

For an uncracked distillate or residue,
Btu per lb (Higher) = 17,660 + (69 × API gravity)
For a cracked distillate,
Btu per lb (Higher) = 17,780 + (54 × API gravity)

Viscosity. This is defined as the measure of the resistance to flow. The greater this resistance, the longer it takes a given volume of oil to flow through a fixed orifice. The Saybolt Universal viscosity is expressed in seconds of time that it takes to run 60 cc through a standard size orifice at any desired temperature. Viscosity is commonly measured at 100 F, 150 F and 210 F. The oil is held at constant temperature within ± 0.25 deg F during the test period.

Fuel oil is very viscous, and it takes a long time to make a determination with the Saybolt Universal viscosimeter. For this reason, the viscosity of fuel oil is usually measured with a Saybolt Furol viscosimeter, which is the same as the Saybolt Universal except that the orifice is larger. Viscosity of 62 seconds Saybolt Furol is 600 seconds Saybolt Universal.[9]

Another measure of viscosity sometimes used is the so-called Engler degree or specific viscosity. The Engler degree is the quotient of time of outflow of 200 cc of oil, divided by the time of flow of 200 cc of water; that is, the viscosity of oil is compared with that of water.

Viscosity of fuel oil decreases as the temperature rises and becomes nearly constant above about 250 F. Therefore, when fuel oil is heated, to reduce the viscosity for good atomization, there is little gain in heating the oil beyond 250 F. Moreover, since burners operate most efficiently with oil of constant viscosity, it is desirable to operate in the viscosity range where temperature variations have the least effect. This is illustrated in Fig. 14–2 for Bunker C oil, Grade No. 6. The viscosity-temperature relationships for the five grades of fuel are shown in Fig. 14–3. Typical analyses are shown in Table 14–10.

The relationship between specific gravity, degrees API, density in lb per gal, Btu per lb, and Btu per gal for petroleum products is graphically shown in Fig. 14–4. Also included are the ranges in deg API for gasoline, kerosene, gas oil and fuel oils. Knowing the value of any one of these characteristics, it is possible to determine all the others quickly. For example, assume the deg API to be 75, then the intersection of this value with the degree API curves is at a point A, through which a horizontal line is drawn to intersect the remaining curves. Then, by referring to their respective scales, it is possible to read the specific gravity B as 0.685, the density C as 5.675 lb per gal, and the higher heating value at D as 20,550 Btu per lb, or at E as 116,800 Btu per gal. Of particular interest is the fact that, although the high specific gravity fuel oils (15 deg API) have a lower heating value per pound than the lower specific gravity gasoline (60 deg API), nevertheless the total heat per gallon, the basis on which they are purchased, is considerably greater.

Flash and Fire Point. Flash point of fuel oil is the lowest temperature at which sufficient vapor is given off to form a momentary flash when flame is brought near the surface. The values vary with the apparatus and procedure used and both must be specified. Flash point specifications for the five grades of fuel oil are given in Table 14–10. Fire point is the lowest temperature at which the oil gives off enough vapor to burn continuously.

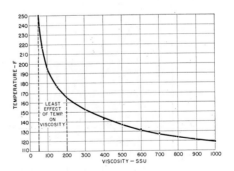

Fig. 14–2. Viscosity versus temperature, No. 6 fuel oil

---

[9] For additional information see ASTM D 2161–63 T, "Method for Conversion of Kinematic Viscosity to Saybolt Universal Viscosity or to Saybolt Furol Viscosity."

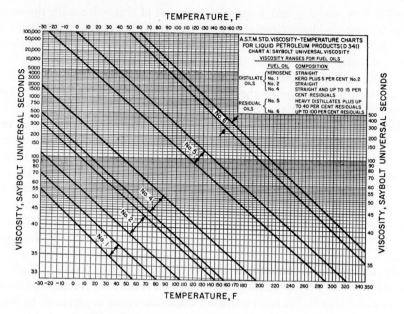

Fig. 14–3. Viscosity ranges for fuel oils

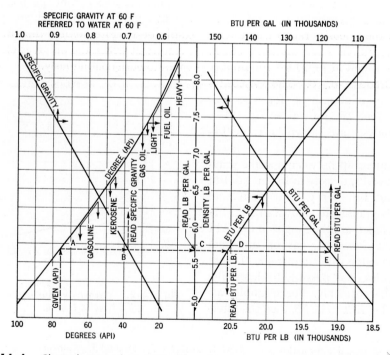

Fig. 14–4. Chart showing the relationships of important characteristics of liquid fuels

Sulfur and Ash. Sulfur is a very undesirable element in fuel oil because its products of combustion are acidic and cause corrosion in economizers, air heaters and gas ducts. Because of the high hydrogen content in fuel oil, and the resulting high water vapor content in the products of combustion, a given amount of sulfur in fuel oil does more damage than the same amount of sulfur in coal.

Fuel oil contains all the solid impurities originally present in the crude oil. If these solids contain a large proportion of salt, they are very fusible, stick to the boiler and superheater tubes and can cause considerable trouble.

Oil Refinery Refuse Fuels. Byproducts from refinery operation consist of a wide variety of refuse fuels. There are solids, such as asphaltic pitch and petroleum coke. The liquids, termed *sludge*, often have a high specific gravity and contain variable amounts of solid matter in suspension.

The characteristics of the sludge are governed by those of the crude oil used and the manner in which it is processed. Much of the suspended solids may be carbonaceous, in the form of small particles of oil coke.

Perhaps the most troublesome of sludges, because of its frequent and widely varying characteristics, is *acid sludge*. Its gravity may range between 5 and 14 deg API, and its viscosity is indeterminate. It contains changing quantities of weak sulfuric acid that may run as high as 40 per cent, and this, together with the suspended carbonaceous material and flux, which must be added in variable amounts to make the sludge flow, causes the heating value to vary between 8000 and 17,500 Btu per lb.

Alkaline sludges, such as soda tar and neutralized sludge, are less troublesome to fire since they are less variable in character than acid sludge.

Solid Fuels

Coke

Coke is the residue remaining following the destructive heating or carbonization of certain bituminous coals in the absence of air.[10] During the carbonization process, the water and most of the volatile matter in the coal is driven off, leaving a solid, porous residue consisting essentially of carbon and ash. Coke is produced through two processes: high temperature carbonization, employing temperatures of 1800 to 2200 F, and low temperature carbonization which is carried out at temperatures of 1000 to 1400 F. The resultant cokes are quite different in both composition and physical characteristics; high temperature coke is a hard, finely cellular, carbonaceous mass of high strength and containing three per cent or less volatile matter. Low temperature coke is a noncoherent, granular structure with a volatile matter content of 7 to 20 per cent. The properties of the low temperature coke render it unsuitable for metallurgical purposes; however, due to its higher reactivity, it makes an excellent smokeless fuel.

Nearly all the coke produced in this country is carbonized at high temperatures in byproduct ovens of the slot type. The volatile products of the process, consisting essentially of gas, ammonia, tar and light oil, are recovered and separated into their various fractions.

A comparison of cokes produced in several carbonizing processes is presented in Table 14–12.

10 The properties of coking coals were previously discussed in Chapter 13, Fuel Properties of Coal.

Table 14–12   Analyses of Typical U.S. Coke, as Fired

	Proximate analysis per cent				Ultimate analysis per cent							Heating value Btu per lb		Atmos. air at zero excess air, lb/10⁶ Btu	CO₂ at zero excess air, per cent
	Moisture	Vol. matter	Fixed carbon	Ash	Moisture H_2O	Carbon C	Hydrogen H_2	Sulphur S	Oxygen O_2	Nitrogen N_2	Ash	Higher	Lower		
High temperature coke	5.0	1.3	83.7	10.0	5.0	82.0	0.5	0.8	0.7	1.0	10.0	12200	12095	796	20.7
Low temperature coke	2.8	15.1	72.1	10.0	2.8	74.5	3.2	1.8	6.1	1.6	10.0	12600	12258	763	19.3
Beehive coke	0.5	1.8	86.0	11.7	0.5	84.4	0.7	1.0	0.5	1.2	11.7	12527	12453	805	20.5
Byproduct coke	0.8	1.4	87.1	10.7	0.8	85.0	0.7	1.0	0.5	1.3	10.7	12690	12613	801	20.5
High temperature coke breeze	12.0	4.2	65.8	18.0	12.0	66.8	1.2	0.6	0.5	0.9	18.0	10200	9950	805	20.1
Gas works coke: Horiz. retorts	0.8	1.4	88.0	9.8	0.8	86.8	0.6	0.7	0.2	1.1	9.8	12820	12753	807	20.6
Vertical retorts	1.3	2.5	86.3	9.9	1.3	85.4	1.0	0.7	0.3	1.4	9.9	12770	12659	810	20.4
Narrow coke ovens	0.7	2.0	85.3	12.0	0.7	84.6	0.5	0.7	0.3	1.2	12.0	12550	12493	802	20.6
Petroleum coke	1.1	7.0	90.7	1.2	1.1	90.8	3.2	0.8	2.1	0.8	1.2	15060	14737	773	19.5
Pitch coke	0.3	1.1	97.6	1.0	0.3	96.6	0.6	0.5	0.3	0.7	1.0	14097	14036	813	20.7

Coke Breeze

A certain amount of degradation occurs in the handling of coke; the resultant fines which pass through a ¼ inch sieve are termed *coke breeze.*

Petroleum Coke

Petroleum coke is a byproduct of a process in which residual hydrocarbons are converted to lighter, more highly valued distillates. Two processes are in use: *delayed coking* and *fluid coking.*

Delayed Coking. In this process the reduced crude oil is heated rapidly and flows to isolated coking drums where it is coked by its own contained heat. The process requires several drums to permit removal of the coke in one drum while the others remain on stream. The residual product which solidifies in these drums is termed "delayed coke." When first removed from the drum it has the appearance of run-of-mine coal, except that the coke is dull black.

The analysis of the coke varies with the crude from which it is made. The components range as follows:

Moisture	3–12 per cent
Volatile matter	10–20 per cent
Fixed carbon	88–71 per cent
Ash	0.2–3.0 per cent
Btu per lb (Dry)	14,100–15,600
Sulfur	2.9–5.4 per cent

Fluid Coking. Two large vessels are used in fluid coking. One is known as a reactor vessel, and the other, a burner vessel. In this process, fluid coke is both the catalyst and secondary product. The seed coke is first heated in the burner vessel, either by adding air and burning a portion of the coke, or by burning an extraneous fuel such as oil. The heated seed coke then flows into the reactor vessel where it comes in contact with the pre-

heated residual oil and the lighter fractions of the oil are flashed off. The coke which is produced both deposits in uniform layers on the seed coke and forms new seed coke. Thus there is a constantly accumulating coke reservoir which is tapped off and is available as a boiler feed.

The coke thus formed is a hard, dry, spherical solid resembling black sand. It is composed of over 90 per cent carbon with varying percentages of sulfur and ash, depending on the source of the crude oil. Typical analyses are as follows:

Fixed carbon	90–95 per cent
Volatile matter	3–6.5 per cent
Ash	0.2–0.5 per cent
Sulfur	4.0–7.5 per cent
Btu per lb, higher	14,100–14,600

Coal Tar

Coal tar is a byproduct in the carbonization of coal. The tar compounds are extremely complex and number in the hundreds. The solid material which is insoluble in benzene is contained as colloidal and coarse dispersed particles and is known as "free carbon." The composition of the tar is dependent on the temperature of carbonization and, to a lesser extent, on the nature of the coking coal. The following is an example of coal tar analysis and its physical properties:

Carbon	per cent	89.9
Hydrogen	per cent	6.0
Sulfur	per cent	1.2
Oxygen	per cent	1.8
Nitrogen	per cent	0.4
Moisture	per cent	0.7
Gravity	deg Baumé	1.18
Viscosity at 122 F	SSF	900
Flash point	F	156
Heating Value	Btu per lb	16,750

Coal tar is burned in boilers only when it cannot be sold for other purposes at a higher price than its equivalent fuel value. At ordinary temperature, the viscosity of tar is very high and must be heated for pumping. It burns like a fuel oil and the same equipment can be used.

Coal Tar Pitch

Coal tar pitch is used to a small extent for generation of steam. It is the residue resulting from the distillation and refining of coal tar. The pitch is solid at ordinary atmospheric temperature but becomes liquid at about 300 F. It is generally burned in pulverized form; in a few cases, it is melted and burned like oil or coal tar. When it is burned in pulverized form, care must be taken to keep it cool during the pulverization and while it is being delivered to the furnace. In some cases, it is preferred to coal. Because of its very low ash content, the stack gas is practically free from dust, and therefore there is no flue dust nuisance. When burned in liquid form, it must be kept very hot to prevent congealing. Table 14–13 shows analyses of coal tar pitch.

Wood

Wood is a complex vegetable tissue composed principally of cellulose, an organic compound having a definite chemical composition. It would therefore seem reasonable to assume that equal weights of different dry wood species will have practically the same heat content. However, owing to the presence of resins, gums and other substances in varying amounts, this heat content is not uniform.

Ultimate analyses showing the chemical composition of several different wood species are given in Table 14–14. These do not indicate the amount of resins or similar substances present, but it will be noted that the heat content, on the dry basis, is

Table 14–13   Coal Tar Pitch

Proximate Analysis				
Per cent	Moisture 2.2	Vol. Matter 48.2	F.C. 48.9	Ash 0.7

Ultimate analysis — Per cent	
Carbon	90.1
Hydrogen	4.9
Sulfur	0.9
Oxygen	0.6
Nitrogen	0.6
Moisture	2.2
Ash	0.7
Heating value (dry)	16,200 Btu per lb

greatest in the cases of such highly resinous woods as fir and pine.

The moisture content of freshly cut wood varies from 30 to 50 per cent. After air drying for approximately a year, this is reduced to from 18 to 25 per cent.

Most wood, as commercially available for steam generation, is usually the waste product resulting from some manufacturing process. Its moisture content as received at the furnace will depend on (1) extraneous water from source or storage or handling in the rain and (2) whether it is "sap wood" or "heart wood," as well as on the species and on the time of year in which it is cut.

The use of wet wood for steam generation falls into three broad classifications, each of which has its own specific combustion problems. Into the first classification fall the sawmills in which the fuel is produced. For their own use, byproduct fuel is usually made up of sawdust, shavings, bark and other wood waste in varying percentages depending on the nature of the operation, resulting from the production of lumber, the method of storing and disposing of waste wood, and the arrangement of available fuel burning equipment. In the second classification are those plants which purchase their wood

Table 14-14 Typical Analyses of Wood, Dry

	Per cent by weight						Heating value Btu per lb		Atmos. air at zero excess air lb/10⁶ Btu	CO₂ at zero excess air, per cent
	Carbon C	Hydrogen H₂	Sulfur S	Oxygen O₂	Nitrogen N₂	Ash	Higher	Lower		
SOFTWOODS**										
Cedar, white	48.80	6.37	—	44.46	—	0.37	8400*	7780	709	20.2
Cypress	54.98	6.54	—	38.08	—	0.40	9870*	9234	712	19.5
Fir, Douglas	52.3	6.3	—	40.5	0.1	0.8	9050	8438	719	19.9
Hemlock, Western	50.4	5.8	0.1	41.4	0.1	2.2	8620	8056	705	20.4
Pine, pitch	59.00	7.19	—	32.68	—	1.13	11320*	10620	702	18.7
white	52.55	6.08	—	41.25	—	0.12	8900*	8308	722	20.2
yellow	52.60	7.02	—	40.07	—	1.31	9610*	8927	709	19.2
Redwood	53.5	5.9	—	40.3	0.1	0.2	8840	8266	707	20.2
HARDWOODS**										
Ash, white	49.73	6.93	—	43.04	—	0.30	8920*	8246	709	19.5
Beech	51.64	6.26	—	41.45	—	0.65	8760*	8151	728	20.1
Birch, white	49.77	6.49	—	43.45	—	0.29	8650*	8019	714	20.0
Elm	50.35	6.57	—	42.34	—	0.74	8810*	8171	717	19.8
Hickory	49.67	6.49	—	43.11	—	0.73	8670*	8039	712	19.9
Maple	50.64	6.02	—	41.74	0.25	1.35	8580	7995	719	20.3
Oak, black	48.78	6.09	—	44.98	—	0.15	8180*	7587	713	20.5
red	49.49	6.62	—	43.74	—	0.15	8690*	8037	711	19.9
white	50.44	6.59	—	42.73	—	0.24	8810*	8169	713	19.8
Poplar	51.64	6.26	—	41.45	—	0.65	8920*	8311	715	20.0

* Calculated from reported higher heating value of kiln-dried wood assumed to contain eight per cent moisture.

The terms **hard and **soft** wood, contrary to popular conception, have no reference to the actual hardness of the wood. According to the Wood Handbook, prepared by the Forest Products Laboratory of the U.S. Department of Agriculture, hardwoods belong to the botanical group of trees that are broad leaved whereas softwoods belong to the group that have needle or scalelike leaves, such as evergreens; cypress, larch and tamarack are exceptions.

fuel supply, usually composed of chips with little or no sawdust and shavings. Paper mills are in the third classification, as they must dispose of the wet wood refuse produced in their wood preparation plants. Their principal problem is one of wet bark disposal.

Bark. This is a common waste product in paper mills, resulting from debarking tree trunks used in making paper. The bark is peeled off the trunks in long ropelike strips. This shape and size, combined with the high moisture content, make the handling of the fuel difficult.

Bark as received from the barking drums contains 80 per cent or more moisture, and in this condition is of no value as a fuel. This fact is best illustrated by Table 14–15, the data for which have been prepared on the basis of a dry bark heating value of 8750 Btu per lb. Thus, at 80 per cent moisture the heating value is only 1750 Btu per lb (as received), and for every pound of dry substance there are 4 lb of water which must be evaporated before any heat is available. Under these conditions, the bark will not support its own combustion, and it will be necessary

Table 14–15   Relationship of Bark
Moisture to Heat Content

Moisture — per cent	Btu per lb	Lb water per lb dry substance
0	8750	0.00
20	7000	0.25
40	5250	0.67
50	4375	1.00
60	3500	1.50
70	2625	2.30
80	1750	4.00
90	875	9.00

Table 14–16   Analyses of Hogged Fuels

Kind of fuel		Western Hemlock	Douglas Fir	Pine Sawdust
Moisture as received	Per cent	57.9	35.9	—
Moisture air dried	"	7.3	6.5	6.3
Proximate analysis, dry fuel				
Volatile matter	Per cent	74.2	82.0	79.4
Fixed carbon	"	23.6	17.2	20.1
Ash	"	2.2	0.8	0.5
Ultimate analysis, dry fuel				
Hydrogen	Per cent	5.8	6.3	6.3
Carbon	"	50.4	52.3	51.8
Nitrogen	"	0.1	0.1	0.1
Oxygen	"	41.4	40.5	41.3
Sulfur	"	0.1	0	0
Ash	"	2.2	0.8	0.5
Heating value, dry	Btu per lb	8620	9050	9130

Table 14–17   Unit Weight and Moisture Content of Wood (as-received basis)

Type of Wood	Moisture — per cent	Weight — lb per cu ft
Drum Barker (pressed)	63.4	19.3
Regular paper mill waste wood	56.9	21.5
Hemlock	53.7	19.4
Douglas fir	44.4	17.4

Table 14—18   Typical Analyses of Bagasse

| | Per cent by weight | | | | | Heating Value Btu per lb | | Atmos. air at zero excess air lb per 10⁶ Btu | CO₂ at zero excess air, per cent |
	Carbon C	Hydrogen H_2	Oxygen N_2	Nitrogren N_2	Ash	Higher	Lower		
Cuba	43.15	6.00	47.95	—	2.90	7985	7402	625	21.0
Hawaii	46.20	6.40	45.90	—	1.50	8160	7538	687	20.3
Java	46.03	6.56	45.55	0.18	1.68	8681	8043	651	20.1
Mexico	47.30	6.08	35.30	—	11.32	9140	8548	667	19.4
Peru	49.00	5.89	43.36	—	1.75	8380	7807	699	20.5
Puerto Rico	44.21	6.31	47.72	0.41	1.35	8386	7773	625	20.5

to supply heat from some other source if the wet material is to be disposed of in a boiler furnace.[11]

Hog Fuel.   In the manufacture of lumber the amount of material removed from the log to produce sound lumber is approximately as follows: 18 per cent in the form of slabs, edging and trimming; 10 per cent as bark; and 20 per cent as sawdust and shavings. While the total waste material will usually average 50 per cent, distribution of different types of waste may vary widely from the approximations given above, owing to mill conditions as well as finished product. The mills frequently use either the sawdust or a mixture of sawdust and shavings for steam production purposes, because these can be burned without further processing. The remainder of the so-called waste products requires further size reduction in a "hog" to facilitate feeding, rapid combustion, transportation and storage. These newly sized products, together with varying percentages of sawdust and shavings present, constitute *hog fuel*. The percentage of sawdust and shavings present may be quite high if the fuel is to be burned at the sawmill. Table 14–16 on page 14–22 shows typical analyses of hogged fuel.

One of the large paper producers conducted a series of tests to determine the moisture content, as well as the unit weight, of waste wood produced in his mill. The results of these tests, shown in Table 14–17, are an illustration of the wide variation in weight that will exist between units of hog fuel because of moisture and different wood-species content.

Hog fuel, as normally delivered to the furnace, contains variable amounts of moisture, which may be taken as approximately 50 per cent, and most of which is in the cellular structure of the wood.

Storage of logs in the mill pond, water lubrication of saws and exposure to rain due to outdoor storage of the hog fuel all contribute to the high total moisture content. In addition, the hog fuel, on dry-wood basis, contains approximately 81 per cent volatile matter and somewhat less than 18 per cent fixed carbon. The noncombustible residue, in the form of wood ash, is only a small fraction of one per cent.

Bagasse

Bagasse is a refuse of cane from which the sugar juice has been extracted. It has a fibrous structure like that of wood, and also a similar analysis. The most variable item is moisture, which normally ranges from 40 to 60 per cent. The relatively high ash in bagasse is due to silt picked up in the harvesting of the cane. Examples of bagasse from various countries are given on page 14–23 in Table 14–18.

Fuel Burning Applications

Emphasis in this chapter and in the preceding chapter on coal has been primarily placed upon fuel properties. Equipment design must necessarily be related to these fuel properties and is discussed in many sections of this book. Chapter 16 deals with the pulverization of solid fuels and Chapter 18 with their firing by means of stokers. The fuel burning systems discussed in Chapter 17 are capable of handling solid, liquid, and gaseous fuels.

Chapters 23 through 29 all provide examples of boilers in which the various fuels can be burned to generate steam. In addition, Table 14–19 lists many byproduct fuels and waste gases and tells how they are utilized and where additional information may be found.

[11] See Chapter 27, Boilers and Recovery Units for Pulp and Paper Industry, section on burning wood waste and bark, for additional information.

Table 14—19   Recovery of Energy from Byproduct Fuels and Waste Gases

Byproduct fuel or waste gas	Category		Equipment Utilized	Chapter References
	State	Heat Content		
Coke breeze	Solid	Chemical	Traveling grate stokers with steam generation	14, 18
Coke oven gas	Gaseous	Chemical	Turbulent or tangential burners with steam generation	14, 17
Blast furnace gas	Gaseous	Chemical	Turbulent or tangential burners with steam generation	14, 17, 23
Reverberatory waste gas	Gaseous	Sensible	Waste heat boiler with optional firing	23
Open hearth waste gas	Gaseous	Sensible	Waste heat boiler with optional firing	23
Gas turbine exhaust	Gaseous	Sensible	Economizer or waste heat boiler with optional firing	5, 19, 23
Catalytic regenerator waste gas	Gaseous	Chemical and sensible	Tangential burners with steam generation	14, 17, 23
Lignite char	Solid	Chemical and sensible	Turbulent or tangential burners with steam generation—pulverizers	14, 16
Fluid coke (Petroleum)	Solid	Chemical	Turbulent or tangential burners with steam generation—pulverizers	14, 16, 17
Delayed coke (Petroleum)	Solid	Chemical	Turbulent or tangential burners with steam generation—pulverizers	14, 16, 17
Refinery gas	Gaseous	Chemical	Turbulent or tangential burners with steam generation	14, 17
Acid sludge and tar	Liquid	Chemical	Turbulent or tangential burners with steam generation	14, 17
River anthracite	Solid	Chemical	Traveling grate stokers with steam generation	13, 18
Cement and lime kiln waste gas	Gaseous	Sensible	Waste heat boilers	23
Municipal and industrial waste	Solid	Chemical	Incinerator stokers with optional waste heat recovery	31
Waste wood and bark	Solid	Chemical	Spreader stokers or tangential firing with steam generation	14, 18, 27
Black liquor	Liquid	Chemical and sensible	Chemical recovery units	27
Bagasse	Solid	Chemical	Spreader stokers with steam generation	14, 18
Coffee grounds and rice hulls	Solid	Chemical	Pneumatic injection or tangential burners with steam generation—pulverizers	18, 23
Furfural residue	Solid	Chemical	Spreader stokers with steam generation or pulverized for use in turbulent or tangential burners	14, 18
Boiler stack gases	Gaseous	Sensible	Low level economizer	5, 19

CODE NUMBERS

The first figure of the code number indicates the class of coal, determined by volatile-matter content up to 33% V.M. and by calorific parameter above 33% V.M.
The second figure indicates the group of coal, determined by coking properties.
The third figure indicates the subgroup, determined by coking properties.

GROUP (determined by coking properties)			Code numbers by Class (0–9)										SUBGROUPS (determined by coking properties)		
GROUP NUMBER	Free-swelling index (crucible-swelling number)	Roga index	0	1 (A | B)	2	3	4	5	6	7	8	9	SUB-GROUP NUMBER	Dilatometer	Gray-King
3	>4	>45					435	535	635				5	>140	$>G_8$
3	>4	>45				334	434	534	634				4	>50–140	G_5–G_8
3	>4	>45				333	433	533	633	733			3	>0–50	G_1–G_4
3	>4	>45				332 a | b	432	532	632	732	832		2	$\leqq 0$	E–G
2	2½–4	>20–45				323	423	523	623	723	823		3	>0–50	G_1–G_4
2	2½–4	>20–45				322	422	522	622	722	822		2	$\leqq 0$	E–G
2	2½–4	>20–45				321	421	521	621	721	821		1	Contraction only	B–D
1	1–2	>5–20			212	312	412	512	612	712	812		2	$\geqq 0$	E–G
1	1–2	>5–20			211	311	411	511	611	711	811		1	Contraction only	B–D
0	0–½	0–5		100 A | B	200	300	400	500	600	700	800	900	0	Nonsoftening	A

(Column headers abbreviated: GROUPS — ALTERNATIVE GROUP PARAMETERS; SUBGROUPS — ALTERNATIVE SUBGROUP PARAMETERS)

CLASS PARAMETERS

CLASS NUMBER	0	1	2	3	4	5	6	7	8	9
Volatile matter (dry, ash-free)	0–3	>3–10 (>3–6.5 | 6.5–10)	>10–14	>14–20	>20–28	>28–33	>33	>33	>33	>33
Calorific parameter a							>13,950	>12,960–13,950	>10,980–12,960	>10,260–10,980

CLASSES (Determined by volatile matter up to 33% V.M. and by calorific parameter above 33% V.M.)

As an indication, the following classes have an approximate volatile-matter content of:
Class 6   33–41% volatile-matter
7   33–44% "
8   35–50% "
9   42–50% "

Note: (i) Where the ash content of coal is too high to allow classification according to the present systems, it must be reduced by laboratory float-and-sink method (or any other appropriate means). The specific gravity selected for flotation should allow a maximum yield of coal with 5 to 10 percent of ash.
(ii) 332 a... >14–16 % V.M.
     332 b... >16–20 % V.M.

a/Gross calorific value on moist, ash-free basis (30°C, 96% relative humidity) B.t.u./lb.

Fig. 15–1. International classification of hard coals by type

15

World Fuel Reserves[1]

ENERGY demands throughout the world are increasing at such a rapid rate that man is taxing the fuel resources upon which he now depends. The use of fuels in the last century alone has amounted to almost half the total used in the preceding nineteen centuries. The present rate of consumption is expected to continue at an accelerated pace into the future. An active worldwide hunt goes on for new fuel reserves, and engineers continue to search for new ways to get more efficient conversion of fuels currently available. Efforts are also directed toward harnessing such sources of energy as the sunlight, the constant movement of the tides, the heat beneath the surface of the earth, the fission of heavy nuclei and the fusion of light nuclei.[2]

The most commonly used sources of energy throughout the world are coal, oil, natural gas and water power. Since the end of World War I the United States has seen a transformation in its overall energy pattern from a predominantly coal economy to one geared primarily to petroleum and natural gas. Table 15–1 summarizes this transition in energy consumption. In 1920 coal fuels supplied 78 per cent of the energy requirements of the United States, but in 1962 they accounted for only 22 per cent.

Despite the larger percentages of the energy market shared by oil and gas, coal remains the most important fuel for power generation and should continue to play an important role in the future in competition with nuclear energy and other possible sources. Coal reserves are in much greater supply than those of other fossil fuels, and this is one of the principal reasons why coal will continue to play a major role in the energy market.

Table 15–2 lists world coal and oil reserves plus water power estimates. Since natural gas reserves are difficult to predict, no figures for such reserves are listed.

International Coal Classification

Because of the increased international trade in coal following World War II, the Coal Committee of the Economic Commission for Europe established a Classification Working Party in 1949 to develop an international system for classi-

---

[1] Information from First Edition revised and supplemented by R. P. Hensel.
[2] For an overall picture, see *Energy Sources — The Wealth of the World* by Eugene Ayres and Charles A. Scarlott, New York, 1952, 344 pp.

Table 15–1   Consumption of Energy Fuels and Waterpower Energy
in the United States (Calculated)*

Year	Total Energy Consumed (Trillion) (Btu)	Percentage Contributed					
		Bituminous Coal and Lignite	Anthracite	Crude Oil	Petroleum Products Net E, Exported I, Imported	Natural Gas (and Liquids)	Water Power
1920	19,782	67.4	11.0	15.3	E 2.0	4.4	3.9
1925	20,899	62.6	7.8	22.2	E 2.3	6.4	3.3
1930	22,288	53.5	7.7	27.6	E 2.2	9.9	3.5
1935	19,107	48.9	6.8	30.4	E 1.6	11.2	4.3
1940	23,908	47.2	5.2	32.1	E 0.7	12.4	3.8
1945	31,541	46.5	4.2	32.3	E 1.8	14.1	4.7
1950	34,153	34.8	3.0	36.0	I 1.2	20.3	4.7
1955	39,956	27.8	1.5	39.9	I 0.9	26.1	3.8
1960	44,960	22.2	1.0	38.2	I 3.2	31.5	3.9
1962	47,882	21.2	0.8	37.3	I 3.8	32.8	4.1

* Source: **Minerals Yearbook**, Vol. II, Fuels, published by Bureau of Mines, U.S. Department of Interior, 1962.

Table 15–2   Fossil Fuel and Water Power Reserves

	Coal1		Petroleum2		Water Power3	
	Millions of metric tons	Per cent	Millions of metric tons	Per cent	Millions of hp	Per cent
Africa						
Algeria	110		109			
Nigeria	527		8			
Union of S. A.	68,000					
United Arab Rep.			23			
Libya			109			
Others	1,213		5			
Total	69,850	1.5	254	5.0	271.7	40.9
Asia						
China	1,011,600		*		22.0	
India	62,935		12		39.0	
Indonesia	2,748		156		6.0	
Iran			578			
Iraq			398			
Japan	10,155		1		7.2	
Kuwait			992			
Pakistan	557					
Saudi Arabia			938			
U.S.S.R.	1,200,000		461		78.0	
Others	5,214		287		9.7	
Total	2,293,209	49.4	3,823	74.8	161.9	24.4
Europe						
France	12,718		4		6.0	
Germany	286,300		10		2.0	
Italy	979		5		6.0	
Norway	1,980				10.0	
Poland	80,018		*		1.4	
Sweden	99				4.0	
Yugoslavia	21,718		4		4.0	
United Kingdom	170,686				0.7	
Czechoslovakia	18,950		*		*	
Belgium	5,988					
Netherlands	3,400		4			
Total	602,836	13.0	27	0.5	34.1	5.1

* Listed with U.S.S.R.

Table 15–2   (continued)

	Coal		Petroleum		Water Power	
	Millions of metric tons	Per cent	Millions of metric tons	Per cent	Millions of hp	Per cent
North America						
Canada	86,926		89		32.0	
Mexico	4,306		39		8.5	
United States	1,505,876		536		36.1	
Total	1,597,108	34.4	664	13.0	76.6	11.5
Central & South America						
Argentina			36		5.4	
Brazil	3,810		5		28.0	
Chile			3		3.6	
Colombia	12,000		14		5.4	
Venezuela	3,068		266		4.3	
Peru			6		6.4	
Trinidad			8			
Bolivia			3		3.6	
Other					14.8	
Total	18,878	0.4	341	6.8	71.5	10.8
Australia	58,684	1.3	2		1.0	0.2
Other					47.1	7.1
World Total	4,640,565	100.0	5,111	100.0	664.0	100.0

1 **Coal Reserves of the United States,** U.S. Geological Survey Bulletin No. 1136, Jan. 1, 1960, pp. 91–92.
2 **The Oil and Gas Journal,** Dec. 30, 1963, pp. 102-103.
3 **Energy Sources — The Wealth of the World** by E. Ayres and C. A. Scarlott, McGraw-Hill, 1952.

fying coal. The system for classification of hard coals was published in 1956 as a document of the United Nations.[3] The results of a study by the U.S. Bureau of Mines, applying this system to American coals, were published in 1958, followed in 1960 by a study relating to brown coals and lignites.[4]

Fig. 15–1 shows this system which classifies coals according to their volatile matter content, calculated on a dry, ash free basis, resulting in nine classes of coals. As volatile matter is not an entirely suitable parameter for classifying coals containing more than about 33 per cent of this constituent, the calorific value on a moist, ash free basis is used for such coals. The nine classes of coal, based on volatile matter content and calorific value, are divided into groups according to their caking properties, as measured by tests when the coal is heated rapidly. The coal groups are further subdivided according to coking properties which are determined by tests in which the coal is heated slowly.

A three figure code number is used to express the classification of a coal. The first figure indicates the *class* of coal; the second figure, the *group;* and the third figure, the *subgroup.*

[3] "International Classification of Hard Coals by Type," United Nations' Economic Commission for Europe, E/ECE/247, E/ECE/COAL/110, August 1956.
[4] "The International Systems of Hard Coal Classification and Their Application to American Coals" by W. H. Ode and W. H. Frederic, U. S. Bureau of Mines, Report of Investigations 5435, 1958, 19 pp., and "International System for Classifying Brown Coals and Lignites and Its Application to American Coals" by W. H. Ode and F. H. Gibson, U. S. Bureau of Mines, Report of Investigations 5695, 1960, 20 pp.

Coal Deposits of the World

Coal is found on all continents and in most countries throughout the world. However, there are a number of countries, such as Brazil, Argentina, Italy and Sweden whose resources are so meager in proportion to their energy demands as to be inconsequential. By far the largest world coal reserves are located in the Northern Hemisphere.

Coal Deposits of North America

Alaska

Alaska is known to have extensive coal reserves ranging from lignite to anthracite. In 1913 these reserves were estimated at more than 21 billion tons, but by 1959 the estimate of known reserves was increased to nearly 95 billion tons.

Alaska is divided into six regions, all of which contain a part of the coal reserves. These regions include Northern Alaska and Seward Peninsula; Yukon Basin; Cook Inlet — Susitna; Southwestern Alaska; Copper River — Alaska Gulf; and Southeastern Alaska. The most important fields in terms of production are the lower Matanuska Valley field in the Cook Inlet region and the Nenana field in the Yukon region. Table 15–3 shows typical analyses of coals for several Alaska regions.

Canada

Canada has large deposits, located in the Atlantic and Pacific Coast regions, in the mountains of British Columbia, in Alberta, and in the plains region of the interior. The Canadian coals embrace practically all kinds, ranging from anthracite to lignite. Good steam and coking coals are mined on the Atlantic seaboard. Those of British Columbia are mainly bituminous, but there are some lignites and small deposits of anthracite. The coking coals from these areas are well adapted to metallurgical uses. The Province of Alberta is liberally supplied with areas of bituminous coals and lignites. Some of the bituminous coals yield good coke. Saskatchewan has only lignites.

Table 15–4 gives the analyses of typical Canadian coals. The data for this table have been taken from publications of the Canada Department of Mines. These analyses are reported on an as-received basis.

United States

The United States Geological Survey has divided the coal-bearing areas of this country into six main provinces designated as (1) Eastern, (2) Interior, (3) Gulf, (4) Northern Great Plains, (5) Rocky Mountain, and (6) Pacific Coast. The provinces are subdivided into coal regions, coal fields, and coal districts. These provinces and coal fields are shown in Fig. 15–2.

The Eastern Province. This includes the anthracite regions of Pennsylvania and Rhode Island; the Atlantic Coast region, containing the Triassic fields of Virginia and North Carolina; and the Appalachian region extending from Pennsylvania through eastern Ohio, Kentucky, West Virginia, western Virginia, and Tennessee into Alabama. The Appalachian region is the largest deposit of the high-grade bituminous and semibituminous coals. The Triassic deposits of central Virginia and North Carolina occur in irregular pockets rather than in seams and are at present of

Table 15–3 Analyses of Typical Alaskan Coals

Region, town or district, and mine	Proximate analysis, as-received					Higher heating value, as-received	Approx. ash-softening temp. F.
	M	Vol	F.C.	Ash	S		
Northern Alaska Region							
Wainwright	20.7	31.8	44.3	3.2	0.3	9760	——
Yukon Region							
Broad Pass Field							
Colorado Station							
Costello Creek	14.3	35.5	36.9	13.3	0.5	9470	——
	15.8	38.7	38.2	7.3	0.5	10090	——
Eagle	19.8	33.1	22.7	24.4	0.2	6270	——
Nenana Field							
Suntrana	22.3	37.2	34.0	6.5	0.1	8640	2140
Kuskokwin Region							
Nelson Island	3.9	23.8	54.1	18.2	0.4	11440	2710
Southwestern Alaska Region							
Chignik Bay							
Alaska Packers'							
Association	7.1	31.5	39.6	21.8	1.3	9850	——
Cook Inlet Region							
Cook Inlet Field							
Bluff Point	22.4	37.1	31.5	8.4	0.3	8340	2010
Matanuska Field							
Anthracite Ridge	4.0	8.5	31.3	6.2	0.5	13410	2330
Chickaloon	2.0	17.8	62.1	18.1	0.7	12090	2800
	1.9	20.8	66.9	10.4	0.7	13260	2060
Coal Creek	1.5	19.3	56.3	22.9	0.8	11400	2830
	1.6	22.9	69.7	5.8	0.6	14380	2450
	4.1	13.8	70.5	11.6	0.6	12600	2240
Eska	4.9	41.6	48.0	5.5	0.5	13030	——
	4.9	38.0	39.6	17.5	0.4	11150	——
	3.7	41.0	44.4	10.9	0.5	12410	2570
Jonesville	3.5	36.8	38.4	21.3	0.2	10450	2370
	5.0	40.7	46.3	8.0	0.3	12440	——
Moose Creek	3.9	40.0	49.7	6.4	0.2	12920	2660
Alaska Gulf Region							
Bering River Field							
Katalla	5.0	13.7	77.5	3.8	0.9	14190	2240
Southeastern Alaska Region							
Admiralty Island							
Harkrader	3.8	35.2	39.6	21.4	1.3	10630	2250

little commercial value, because of expensive mining and rather low-grade quality of coal.

The Interior Province. This province includes all the bituminous coal area of the Mississippi Valley region and the coal fields of Texas and Michigan. This province is subdivided into the Northern region consisting of the coal field of Michigan; the Eastern region, comprising the fields of Illinois, Indiana and western Kentucky; and also the Western region embracing the coal fields of Iowa, Missouri, Nebraska, Kansas, Arkansas, Oklahoma, and the southwestern region of Texas. With some exceptions, the bituminous coals of this province are of lower rank and grade than those of the Eastern province. However, owing to the close proximity to large markets, the coal industry of this province is continuously expanding.

Table 15–4   Analyses of Typical Canadian Coals

Province	Mining District or Seam	Typical analysis — as-received						Approx. ash-softening temp. F	Grindability (Hardgrove)
		Mois.	Vol.	F.C.	Ash	Sul.	Btu		
Nova Scotia	Bras d'Or	5.3	32.2	50.7	11.8	5.3	12,015	2060	66
	Springhill	2.8	29.9	57.6	9.7	1.6	13,225	2250	84
	Stellerton	2.5	29.1	54.8	13.6	1.0	12,625	2400	67
	Joggins	5.0	32.9	43.1	19.0	7.6	10,565	2010	66
	Sydney (Dominion)	4.0	32.4	55.4	8.4	2.9	13,340	2025	69
New Brunswick	Minto	3.2	29.7	47.8	19.3	7.6	11,610	2030	70
Saskatchewan	Souris (Bienfait)	35.0	26.0	33.0	6.0	0.4	7,380	2180	50
	Souris (Estevan)	35.3	24.4	30.8	9.6	0.2	6,725	2125	43
Alberta	Camrose	28.5	26.6	37.9	7.0	0.4	8,060	2090	—
	Crows Nest	2.5	24.9	57.8	14.8	0.6	12,490	2850	70
	Drumheller	18.2	30.7	44.2	6.9	0.5	9,790	2110	33
	Edmonton	25.5	27.4	40.2	6.9	0.4	8,600	2110	35
	Wabamun	21.8	26.5	39.5	12.2	0.2	8,005	2335	47
	Lethbridge	10.2	35.3	44.4	10.1	0.6	10,900	2240	43
	Sheerness	27.5	28.5	38.1	5.9	0.5	8,300	2150	45
British Columbia	Crows Nest	1.5	24.0	66.0	8.5	0.6	13,930	2560	100
	Comox	3.5	31.5	51.4	13.8	2.4	12,770	2170	65
	Nicola Valley	8.0	33.9	43.3	14.8	0.5	11,020	2850	51

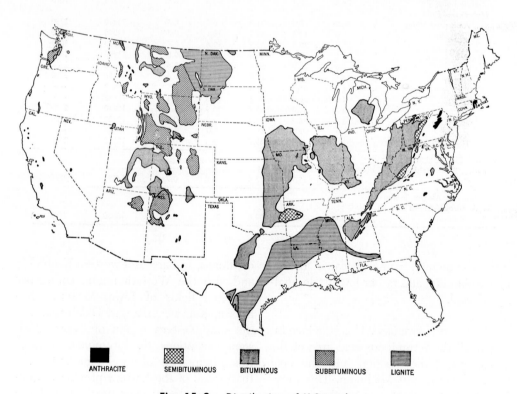

ANTHRACITE   SEMIBITUMINOUS   BITUMINOUS   SUBBITUMINOUS   LIGNITE

Fig. 15–2.   Distribution of U.S. coals

The Gulf Province. This consists of the Mississippi region in the east and the Texas region in the west. The Mississippi region includes the lignite fields of Alabama, Mississippi, and Louisiana. The Texas region comprises the lignite fields of Arkansas and Texas. Up to the present, the coal production of this province has been small and commercially unimportant. Lignite is mined at a few places west of the Mississippi. Abundance of fuel oil and natural gas, which are available for all kinds of use, has been the main retarding force of lignite mining development. When the supply of these other fuels is diminished or becomes restricted to more important uses, the lignite may become an important fuel for many industrial uses.

The Northern Great Plains Province. This includes all the coal fields of the great plains east of the eastern front range of the Rocky Mountains. In this province are immense lignite areas of the two Dakotas, and the bituminous and subbituminous fields of northern Wyoming and northern and eastern Montana. With a few exceptions, the coals are of low rank; and owing to lack of nearby markets, mining has been developed only on a small scale.

The Rocky Mountain Province. This comprises the coal fields of the mountainous districts of Montana, Wyoming, Utah, Colorado, and New Mexico. It possesses a great variety of coals, ranging from lignite through subbituminous and high grade bituminous coals to anthracite. Considerable progress has been made in the coal industry of this province.

The Pacific Coast Province. This is largely limited to the State of Washington, which contains the largest coal fields on the Pacific Coast. It also embraces the small fields of Oregon and California. The coals of Washington range from subbituminous through bituminous to anthracite. However, because of rather high ash content, mining has been developed only to a small extent. Washington coal must compete with a higher grade coal from Vancouver Island.

The coals of Oregon and California rank somewhat lower than those of Washington. Those of California consist mainly of non-coking bituminous coals in the southern part of the State, lignite in the northern, and subbituminous in the center. The fields are scattered and limited in area, and the coal must compete with oil.

East Dominates in Quality, West in Quantity. From the viewpoint of quantity, the largest coal reserves in the United States occur in the three western areas known as the Northern Great Plains, Rocky Mountains, and Pacific Coast provinces, whose deposits far surpass in quantity those of the two eastern provinces. The Fort Union region of Wyoming, Montana, and the Dakotas possesses the largest quantity of coal known in any single coal bearing area, aggregating 1,104,103,000,-000 tons. The next greatest reserve area is that of the Green River region of Wyoming and Colorado, with deposits amounting to 665,649,000,000 tons. The third is that of the Appalachian region of the east, with reserve totaling 550,989,000,000 tons.

Notwithstanding their relatively restricted resources, it is in the Eastern and Interior provinces that the real wealth of coal lies. The coals of the central and northern fields of the Appalachian region supply the bulk of the coke produced, furnish power for the concentrated industrial activities of the northern and eastern sections of the country, constitute the heaviest portion of shipments to Canada and provide most overseas export.[4]

Mexico

Mexico has considerable coal deposits, but very little information is available as to their extent and quality. Abundance of oil, available as fuel for making steam, has retarded the development of the coal mining industry.

The State of Coahuila contains the only highly developed coal fields in Mexico. They are situated in the northern part, near the frontier, on the Rio Grande and its tributaries. The fields consist of five basins centering around Sabinas. The Sabinas Basin, which is about 35 miles long and 15 miles wide, is the most important. The coal areas lie along the Mondova Division of the National Railways of Mexico from Piedras Negras to Saltillo.

The Sabinas mines produce bituminous coal which contains 60 to 70 percent fixed carbon and makes good coke for metallurgical purposes.

Coal Deposits of South America

South America's coal deposits are very small, compared to those of North America. The only countries of South America where deposits of any economic importance are known to occur are Chile, Colombia, Peru, and Brazil. Owing to inaccessibility of most of the deposits and lack of transportation, coal mining has not been developed. Lack of capital and skilled labor also contributes to the retardation of development. However, within recent years, considerable improvement has been made.

Chile

Chile is the largest producer of coal in South America, because the deposits occur in the low lying land along the ocean, and hence are easily accessible. The Province of Concepcion and the deposits near the Bay of Arauco have thus far yielded the best coal in Chile. Table 15–5 gives the proximate analyses of the representative coals of these regions.

Chilean coal is used by the steamship companies of the west coast of South America; by the government railways; for domestic purposes; and for making gas. With a mixture of foreign coking coals, fairly good metallurgical coke can be produced.

Peru

Coal deposits occur in almost every department of Peru. The most important ones are located in the department of Junin. The mines at Goyllarisquisga and Quishuarcancha account for the bulk of the Peruvian production. The seams are generally thick, but the quality of coal is low. The analyses of Table 15–6 are typical of Peruvian coals.

Brazil

The principal explored and developed coal deposit of Brazil extends southward from Southern São Paulo, through the states of Parana, Santa Catharina, and Rio Grande do Sul, to the Uruguay frontier. The coal is classified as bituminous, but is of low-grade because of its high ash content. It is not easily separated from the shale partings and must be crushed to small size to make washing effective. Table 15–7 shows analyses from four Brazilian mines.

[4] For further information on coals of the United States, see Chapter 13, Fuel Properties of Coals.

Table 15—5 Analyses of Typical Chilean Coals

	Moisture	Vol. matter	F.C.	Ash	Sulfur	Btu
Lota Mines	3.42	39.64	55.44	1.50	0.73	14,260
Schwager Mines	2.88	41.29	52.25	3.58	0.97	14,300
Lebu Mines	2.22	44.02	45.94	7.82	4.00	13,230
Rios Mines	2.04	42.06	37.86	18.04	4.00	11,400
Arauca Mines	3.42	41.32	40.95	14.31	5.40	11,930
Buen Retiro	1.68	46.70	43.96	7.66	5.80	13,680
Mafil Mines	12.68	35.58	39.96	11.78	0.64	10,100
Quila Coya Mines	1.70	6.12	78.90	13.28	0.89	12,600

Table 15—6

Proximate Analyses of Goyllarisquisga Coal

Kinds of Coal	Vol. matter	F.C.	Ash	Btu
Goyllarisquisga coal	36.8	30.7	32.5	9,930
Goyllarisquisga steam coal washed	44.9	37.1	18.0	12,425
Goyllarisquisga coking coal	40.6	40.8	18.6	12,300
Quishuarcancha raw coal	36.7	35.7	27.6	9,980

Table 15—7

Proximate Analyses of Coal from Four Brazilian Mines

	Moisture	Vol. matter	F.C.	Ash	Sulfur
Butia Mine	11.51	32.02	42.88	13.59	1.35
Jacuhy Mine	9.58	19.42	49.82	21.18	0.85
Tubarao Mine	1.90	29.10	40.79	28.21	1.10
Cresciuma Mine	1.50	27.96	46.90	23.64	1.63

Argentina

The presence of coal bearing strata has been known in various sections of the Republic, chiefly on the western frontier but, so far, there has been very little active exploitation. The known coal is generally high in ash and of low grade.

Colombia

Colombia has considerable coal deposits, but no comprehensive survey has yet been made of their extent and quality. The fields of the Canca River Basin are the most extensively operated. The principal mines are located close to the city of Cali. The coal in this region is mostly of bituminous rank and of good grade. It is somewhat friable, steams easily and cokes well.

The Cauca Basin coal is of the following proximate analysis (moisture free):

Vol. matter	F. C.	Ash	Sulfur
23	68 to 70.5	5.4 to 7.6	0.8

The coal produced in the Bogotá region is good bituminous coal of the following proximate analysis (moisture free):

Vol. matter	F. C.	Ash	Sulfur	Btu
23.4 to 31.2	63.7 to 70.1	7.6	0.8 to 0.9	14,202 to 14,500

Mining methods are generally primitive and the cost of production is high.

Venezuela

Coal occurs in regions north of the Orinoco and Apure rivers and in the Llanos. The deposits are in detached basins, some of which cover hundreds of miles. Although most of the coal is of bituminous and lignite rank, in the Coro district of the State of Falcon some deposits of semianthracite occur.

The most important known coal deposits occur in the Barcelona and Coro districts. It is mined by primitive methods to supply local demands. The following is the proximate analysis of the Barcelona coal:

Moisture	Vol. matter	F. C.	Ash	Sulfur	Btu
3.0	36.1	57.5	3.4	1.4	13,680

The coal is very friable; it makes good illuminating gas and good coke.

Coals from the Falcon district are harder than those mined in the Barcelona field. The heating value averages 10,900 Btu.

Ecuador

Considerable coal deposits occur in various sections of Ecuador, but no commercial-scale mining is carried on. The bulk of the deposits contains low-grade lignite, high in ash. In some localities coals of better quality, approaching anthracite, have been found. However, the general low quality, high cost of mining, and lack of transportation are factors against exploitation of Ecuadorian resources.

Coal Deposits of Europe

Great Britain

Great Britain has been long regarded as one of the principal coal producing nations of the world, and has been surpassed in developed resources and production only by the United States, and more recently by Russia. The most important factors in its prominence were its geographical location and the high quality of its coal.

The fields of Great Britain may be grouped into three principal areas designated as the southern, the central, and the northern coal fields. The southern area embraces the fields known as South Wales, Forest of Dean, Bristol and Kent. The central area includes the fields of Lancashire, North Wales, Yorkshire, Derbyshire, Nottinghamshire, Staffordshire and Warwickshire. The northern area comprises the fields of Northumberland, Durham, Cumberland, and the fields of Scotland.

The coal of the southern area varies, from the bituminous coal through the well-known Welsh steam coal to anthracite of notable purity. The bulk of the central-area coal field lies in the south of Lancashire. Coals in this field are classed as gas coal, and contain 30 to 35 per cent volatile matter. Some of them yield good coke. In the northern area, the Durham and Northumberland fields are among the most important in Great Britain. The character of the coal varies considerably. It is of exceptionally fine quality for steam, coking, household, manufacturing, and gas producing purposes. Table 15–8 gives the proximate analyses of typical British coals.

Ireland

Of the four developed coal fields in Ireland, that of Lunster is the most important. It is anthracite of good quality and is used locally for house coal and general purposes. Its analysis is as follows:

Vol. matter	F. C.	Ash
4.5	92	3.5

Germany

German deposits contain bituminous

Table 15—8   Analyses of Typical British Coals

Area	Mining District or Seam	Typical analysis — as-received						Approx. ash-softening temp. F	Grindability (Hardgrove)
		Mois.	Vol.	F.C.	Ash	Sul.	Btu		
South Wales	East Glamorgan	0.9	12.2	84.1	2.8	0.7			
South Wales	East Glamorgan	1.2	17.9	77.9	3.0	0.7			
South Wales	Northeast Glamorgan	0.7	11.0	86.3	2.0	0.8			
South Wales	Monmouthshire	1.0	20.5	76.3	2.2	0.8			
South Wales	Southwest Glamorgan	0.9	10.0	86.5	2.6	1.0			
South Wales	East Carmarthen (Anthracite)	0.9	4.3	93.1	1.7	0.8			
South Wales	N.E. Glamorgan (Anthracite)	1.3	4.9	91.5	2.3	1.0			
South Wales	Brecon (Anthracite)	1.0	5.8	90.5	2.7	1.5			
Central Area	Arley	1.1	36.3	59.0	3.6	2.3			
Central Area	Trencherbone	2.4	34.8	60.0	1.9	0.9			
Central Area	Wigan Six-foot	4.6	30.7	61.5	3.2	1.1			
Central Area	Mountain Mine	1.7	26.6	70.5	1.1	0.4			
Central Area	King	1.2	35.5	60.2	3.1	2.4			
Durham and Northumberland	Bowers West Hartley	2.7	29.4	65.4	2.5	0.7			
	Garesfield	1.1	27.7	67.8	3.4	0.6			
	Wallsend	5.9	32.4	59.1	2.6	1.1			
	Bolden	2.0	31.3	64.7	2.0	0.9			
Typical Ranges of Coals Supplied to Power Stations									
	Northumberland	6.3– / 12.2	23.4– / 30.0	34.0– / 50.0	13.5– / 32.2	1.2–3.1	7950– / 12,160	2140–2700+	62–78
	Yorkshire	4.7– / 11.8	20.9– / 28.8	35.0– / 52.4	16.4– / 31.4	1.0–3.1	8120– / 10,910–	2400–2700+	60
	East Midlands	6.8– / 11.5	26.5– / 30.5	40.5– / 45.0	15.0– / 25.0	0.9–2.0	9700– / 10,900	2260–2400	50–56

coal and lignites. The principal districts where bituminous coal occurs in greatest abundance are: the Lower Rhine and Westphalia, Silesia, the Rhenish district and the Saar district. In central north Germany, lignite occurs in the Rhine Province and in Saxony.

The Westphalian and Rhine district fields include the Ruhr Basin, the most important coal field in Germany. These coal districts are connected with those of southern Holland, Belgium, and northern France. The coal ranges from medium to high volatile, and the ash varies considerably from mine to mine. The bulk of the entire German output comes from the Lower Rhenish Westphalian fields.

The Silesian district extends through the province of Silesia, which, geographically, is divided between Germany, Poland and Czechoslovakia. The bulk of the coal of this district is of first class coking quality, and is widely used in steel industries.

The Saar district stretches through parts of Alsace-Lorraine. The coals are hard and stand transportation well, but they contain considerable ash, particularly in small sizes, which are usually washed. The coal is used for household, steam and railway purposes. Constituents of analyses of these range as follows:

Moisture	Vol. matter	F. C.	Ash	Btu
3 to 8	27.5 to 36.7	47 to 60	7 to 11	10,800 to 12,600

The German lignite is soft, and crumbles easily. It contains about 50 per cent moisture. The chief use of this fuel is in generation of electrical power, which is transmitted over a large part of southern Germany. Table 15–9 lists typical analyses of German coals.

France

French coal deposits consist of a large number of small fields distributed over the northern, central, and southern parts of France. The most important are the fields of Nord and Pas-de-Calais. The coals in these districts vary from anthracite to long-flame bituminous, with a good proportion of coking coal.

The coal deposits in the center and south of France are rather limited in extent, and are scattered throughout these regions. The Fuveau Basin contains lignite. The French bituminous coals are divided into two classes: low volatile, ranging from 9 to 19 per cent volatile matter; and high volatile ranging from 20 to 38 per cent volatile matter. The ash in these two classes ranges from 4 to 12 per cent. Analyses of typical French and Belgian coals are shown in Table 15–10 on the following page.

Belgium

Belgium has two large fields, known as the South Basin and the North Basin and also called the Campine coal fields.

The South Basin extends through the valley of the Samber and Meuse rivers, running east to the German frontier and west to the French border. This Basin supplies a large part of the coal production. The Campine Basin stretches in a westerly direction from the German border, through the Provinces of Limburg and Antwerp. The Basin has large reserves but has not been fully developed. The Belgian coals range from high-volatile bituminous to anthracite. A considerable part has good coking qualities and is also suitable for gas making.

Table 15–9 Analyses of Typical German Coals

Area	Mining District or Seam	Typical analysis — as-received						Approx. ash-soft-ening temp. F	Grind-ability (Hard-grove)
		Mois.	Vol.	F.C.	Ash	Sul.	Btu		
Bavaria	Pechglanzkohleaus Peissenberg	13.9	37.1	34.8	14.2	0.9	9,350†		46–65
Saar Basin	Zeche Viktoria	14.7	21.9	31.9	31.5		7,240†	2570	54
	Zeche Duhamel	29.0	22.1	32.5	16.4		7,070†	2310	72
Ruhr Basin	Hamborner Bergbau, Schacht Westend	6.0	12.7	64.6	16.7	1.3	11,800	2550	60–70
Ruhr Basin	Zeche Furst Leopold Baldur, Dorsten	6.4	26.3	44.8	22.5	2.9	10,280	2370	45–55
Ruhr Basin	Zeche Diergardt Mevissen Stinneskonzern	1.1	9.8	80.0	8.1	1.1	13,740	2520	55–60
Ruhr Basin	Zeche Jbbenburen Westflox	8.6	9.3	73.7	8.4	1.7	12,650	2420	66
Upper Silesia	Stein Kohle	9.0	25.9	53.6	11.5		11,520	2340	45–60
Austria (Brown Coal)	St Stephanbei St. Andra	31.1	29.0	26.1	13.8	0.7	6,730	2330	30–45
Greece (Brown Coal)	Aus Ptolemais	6.2	42.1	24.4	27.3	1.0	6,030	2580	62
Central Germany	Espenhain	32.1	33.9	20.2	13.8	2.8	6,740	2180	60–80
Rhine	Frimmersdorf — Westfeld	60.7	20.0	16.7	2.6	0.2	4,240		
Polen	Turow	40.6	26.9	17.8	14.7	1.3	5,390	2800	76

† Net, or low heating value; other values are higher heating value

Table 15–10 Analyses of Typical French and Belgian Coals

Area	Mining District or Seam		Typical analysis — as-received						Approx. ash-soft-ening temp. F	Grind-ability (Hard-grove)
			Mois.	Vol.	F.C.	Ash	Sul.	Btu		
HOUILLERES DU BASSIN DU NORD ET DU PAS DE CALAIS										
Auchel	Marles	VI	1.2	25.3	47.0	26.5	—	11,260	2100	86
Bethune	Bethune	VII	1.0	17.1	34.6	47.3	0.6	7,395	1920	75
	Noeuds-les-Mines	VI	1.5	25.1	40.7	32.7	—	9,826	2120	87
Bruay	Bruay	VII	1.8	27.4	42.9	27.9	—	10,332	1940	83
Douai	Douai	V	1.1	17.9	55.0	26.0	—	11,120	2280	95
	Somain	IV	0.9	13.7	60.1	25.3	0.7	11,320	2150	106
Henin-Lietard	Henin-Lietard	II	1.0	9.7	65.8	23.5	—	11,555	2280	79
Lens	Lens	IV	1.0	17.1	64.3	17.6	0.6	12,550	2010	89
	Lens	VII	0.9	22.7	40.4	36.0	—	9,420	2010	—
Oignies	Oignies	II	0.9	9.1	66.0	24.0	—	11,405	2280	78
Valenciennes	Anzin	IV	1.6	9.2	44.3	44.9	—	7,685	2190	71
	Agache	II	0.9	8.4	63.1	27.6	0.5	10,950	—	81
HOUILLERES DU BASSIN DE LORRAINE										
Petite Rosselle	Simon	VII	3.3	40.1	50.7	5.9	—	12,600	1970	—
	St. Charles	VIII	1.8	25.7	37.7	34.8	—	8,530	1970	76
	Wendel	VII	3.2	26.9	40.4	29.5	1.1	9,225	2060	57
Sarre & Moselle	Merlebach	VII	2.8	39.2	51.9	6.1	—	12,855	1920	—
	La Houve	VIII	3.2	25.1	36.7	35.0	1.3	8,235	2060	—
Faulquemont	Faulquemont	VII	4.0	36.6	50.8	8.6	—	12,890	2010	
HOUILLERES DU BASSIN DE BLANZY										
	Blanzy	VI	1.8	25.3	60.6	12.3	—	13,285	2060	—
	Blanzy	IV	0.7	14.3	72.6	12.4	1.4	13,475	1970	—

Netherlands

The most important of the Netherlands coal areas lies in the Province of Limburg, where it links up with the Campine Basin of Belgium, and extends in a northwest direction into the Province of North Brabant. The coals are used for domestic and industrial purposes and gas making; some make high class coke.

Russia

There are three main coal fields in European Russia: the Donetz Basin, the Ural Basin, and the Moscow coal fields.

The most important, from the standpoint of production and quality, is the Donetz Basin. It lies directly north of the Sea of Azov, in Ukraine. In this Basin, both anthracite and high grade bituminous coal occur. The anthracite deposit is very extensive. The anthracite is hard and lustrous, and breaks into lumps suitable for household use without producing much fines. The estimated reserves of anthracite are about two and a half times those of bituminous. The quantity of good coking coal is comparatively small; hence the utilization, on a considerable scale, of anthracite for blast furnaces and steam boilers, and for export. The fact that reserves of coal, iron, manganese, and limestone are all available within a short distance creates an unusual economic situation in the Donetz territory. There are over twenty-five workable seams in the Donetz Basin, and the nature and chemical composition vary over a wide range, from high volatile bituminous coals to anthracite.

The Ural fields rank next in importance to the Donetz Basin. Owing to insufficient transportation facilities, these fields have been developed only to a small extent. Coal so far found in this region has not produced coke.

The Moscow field has the largest reserve, but the coal is of low-rank and low-grade. It is lignitic in character, and has high moisture, ash and sulfur content. The sulfur occurs as pyrites, which make the coal hard to pulverize and lowers the fusion temperature of ash. Removal of the pyrites from the coal would improve its quality and reduce the difficulty from slagging.

Coal also occurs in the Konban territory and in the Province of Kontais in the Caucasian region. It is said to yield a dense, strong coke for metallurgical purposes.

Since about 1930, there has been a considerable development in the use of local low grade fuels, such as peat and oil shale, for generation of power. These developments were made in the effort to avoid long hauls of higher grade fuels. Thus, in the Leningrad district and in White Russia, oil shale and peat are used for generation of power. Oil shale is also used in the Volga Region. The shale contains 50 to 55 per cent of ash, which is used as cement for construction purposes. The heating value of the shale is 3200 to 3600 Btu per lb as fired.

Tables 15–11 and 15–12 give the analyses of Russian coals of different regions. the moisture item is given on an as-fired basis. The ash is expressed on dry basis, and the rest of the items on moisture-and ash-free basis.

Coal Deposits of Asia

Siberia

The largest coal deposit in Siberia is the Kuznetsk Basin in south central Siberia. Next in importance are the Irkutsk region, and the Karagandinask and the Saghalin deposits. The Kuznetsk Basin has

Table 15–11   Analyses of Selected Russian Coals, Shale and Peat

Province or District	Location or name of coal	As-fired moisture	Dry ash	Moisture and ash free						Btu	Approx. ash-softening temp. F
				S	C	H₂	N₂	O₂	Volatile		
	Near Moscow	33.0	27.5	3.3	68.9	5.2	1.3	21.3	45.0	12,060	2640
Northern Section	Vorkutsk	6.5	16.0	0.8	85.6	5.3	2.3	6.0	29.5	15,210	2190
Ukraine	Aleksandrisk	55.0	24	3.6	67.6	6.0	0.8	22.0	57.0	12,150	2175
Ukraine	Kirovsk	45.0	45.0	3.7	62.5	5.2	1.0	27.6	56.0	10,062	2660
Grusine	Tkribulsk	12.0	30.0	1.2	78.4	5.9	1.5	13.0	40.0	13,950	2730
Grusine	Tkvarchelsk	7.0	30.0	1.2	81.5	5.9	1.7	9.7	35.0	14,750	2510
Ural	Kizelevsk	4.0	27.5	5.2	80.0	5.6	1.2	5.1	40.0	14,860	2515
Ural	Cheliabinsk	19.0	27.0	1.4	72.3	5.1	1.7	19.5	39.0	12,520	2110
Ural	Bogoslovsk	30.0	20.0	0.5	70.0	4.7	1.5	23.3	43.0	11,710	2190
Ural	Egroshinsk	6.0	24.0	0.6	90.0	3.7	0.6	5.7	8.0	14,780	2730
Ural	Poltavsk	9.0	20.0	0.2	95.0	0.8	0.5	3.5	3.5	13,860	2570
Ural	Bredinsk	7.5	20.0	0.7	93.5	1.7	0.7	3.3	4.0	14,340	2550
Kazachsky	Karagandinsk	7.0	21.0	1.0	85.5	5.2	1.4	6.9	25.0	15,050	2625
		27.0	16.0	0.7					40.0	13,000	—
Kazachsky	Berchogursk	6.0	40.0	4.4	77.8	6.6	1.4	9.8	47.0	14,240	2640
Kirgiz	Kizil-Kia	27.0	15.0	1.2	76.5	4.2	1.0	17.1	33.0	12,600	2010
Kirgiz	Syliutka	21.0	15.0	0.5	77.7	4.0	0.8	17.0	29.0	12,660	2265
Kirgiz	Kok-Yankak	14.0	19.0	1.9	77.5	5.0	1.0	14.6	35.0		2300
Siberia	Minusinsky	12.0	12.0	0.5	79.0	5.5	2 2	12.5	42 0	14,050	2355
Siberia	Kansky	32.0	15.0	0.7	73.1	4.9	1.3	20.0	44.0	12,440	
Siberia	Cheremkovsky	12.0	12.0	0.8	78.5	5 7	1.6	13.4	45.0	13,850	2190
Trans Baikal	Chernovsky	33.0	11.0	0.7	75.5	5.0	1.3	17.5	40.0	12,960	2065
Trans Baikal	Bukachachisky	14.0	17.0	0.6	80.0	5.5	1.1	12.8	39.0	14,100	2350
Far East	Kirdinsky	33.0	19.0	0.3	71.0	4.3	1.2	23.2	41.0	11,530	2265
Far East	Raychikinsky	38.0	14.0	0.3	70.0	4.3	1.1	24.3	41.0	11,440	2190
Far East	Artemovsky	26.0	19.0	0.6	71.5	5.5	1.5	20.9	49.0	12,510	2190
Far East	Suchansky	6.0	29.0	0.6	86.0	5.0	1.4	7.0	32.0	14,950	2310
		11.5	53.5						81.0		2372

Table 15–12   Analyses of Donetz Basin Coals

Kind of Coal	As-fired moisture	Dry Ash	Moisture and ash free						Btu	Approx. ash-softening temp. F
			S	C	H₂	N₂	O₂	Volatile		
Long flame	12.0	22.5	3.5	77.0	5.6	1.6	12.3	44.0	13,900	2100
	8.0	16.0	2.5	82.0	5.5	1.5	8.5	39.0	14,600	2120
High volatile coking	3.5	15.5	2.8	85.0	5.1	1.5	5.6	30.0	15,200	—
High volatile steam	5.0	20.0	4.8	83.0	5.1	1.5	5.6	32.0	15,140	2050
Medium volatile coking	3.5	17.0	3.1	85.2	4.7	1.5	5.5	22.0	15,300	—
Medium volatile steam	3.5	4.5	3.6	86.5	4.8	1.5	3.6	21.0	15,220	—
Low volatile coking	3.0	12.5	2.3	89.0	4.5	1.5	2.7	16.0	15,600	—
Low volatile steam	3.0	16.5	3.1	88.0	4.5	1.5	2.9	16.0	15,400	2050
Short flame	4.0	14.0	2.2	90.0	4.2	1.5	2.1	12.0	15,380	2085
Anthracite	2.0	11.5	0.8	94.6	1.8	1.0	1.8	3.5	14,590	2125

undergone a considerable development within the last few years. It contains coking coal, which is being used in the production of steel in the Magnitogorsk steel plants. Analysis of these coals is shown in Table 15–13.

Table 15–13 Analyses of Kuznetsk Basin Coals

Kind of Coal	As-fired moisture	Dry Ash	Moisture and ash free						Btu	Approx. ash-softening temp. F
			S	C	H_2	N_2	O_2	Volatile		
Anzhero-Sudzhesky	4.0	12	0.7	91.0	4.3	1.9	2.1	15.0	15,490	2100
Leninsky	6.0	11.0	0.7	83.0	5.8	2.7	7.8	39.0	14,880	2426
	9.0	7.5	0.5	79.0	5.5	2.4	12.6	40.0	14,500	2085
Kamerovsky	4.0	12.5	0.3	85.7	5.4	2.1	6.5	33.0	15,030	—
	7.0	13.0	0.4	88.5	4.5	1.8	4.8	18.0	15,230	—
Prokopiersky	6.0	11.0	0.5	89.0	4.6	2.2	3.7	20.0	15,250	—
Kiselevsky	4.5	9.5	0.5	89.3	4.3	2.3	3.6	17.0	15,310	—
	7.0	10.0	0.5	89.3	4.3	2.3	3.6	18.0	15,210	2730
Osinovsky	7.0	11.0	0.5	86.5	5.5	2.7	4.8	30	15,410	—
	5.0	18.0	0.7	89.0	4.1	2.0	4.2	10.0	12,130	2550

Turkey

Considerable deposits of coal and lignite occur in Turkey, the most important so far being those in the northwestern regions of Anatolia. Commercial development, however, has been practically confined to the Erigli Basin. The Erigli coal, when properly cleaned, is suitable for most purposes, and compares favorably with the bulk of European bituminous. It contains 40 to 45 per cent volatile matter, and is utilized by steamships, railways and factories.

China

Coal deposits of China are extensive, coal being found in almost every province. One very large area is in northern China, extending over most of the southern part of Shansi, and one in the south extending over southern Hunan, Kweichow, Yunnan and Szechwan. In variety, Chinese coals range from hard anthracite to lignites of pronounced woody structure. The bituminous coals are of medium and high volatile rank, the medium volatile being rather high in ash. These coals are used for power production, locomotives and bunkering. Table 15–14 gives the proximate analyses of many Chinese coals.

India

India's coal fields are of large extent, and probably contain enormous reserves. The coals vary greatly in quality. Even the best average 10 per cent ash, while some have ash as high as 25 per cent. The ash is generally finely disseminated throughout, and renders washing difficult. The coals in Raniganj and Jharria fields yield coke satisfactory for the steel industries.

Japan

Coal is widely distributed throughout all the islands and territories of the Japanese Empire. The regions of Kyushu and Hokaida are by far the most important for quantity and quality. The Japanese coals range from anthracite to lignite, but the bituminous outweighs all other in quantity and value. The greater portion of bituminous is of the high volatile rank containing 5 to 9 per cent ash with a Btu range of 12,000 to 13,000. Most of the coal belongs to the coking class, but is rather soft and crumbles easily. Table 15–15 gives

Table 15–14 Proximate Analyses of Chinese Coals

Province	Location	Name of Mine	Moist.	Ash	Vol. Matter	F.C.	Heating Value Btu As Received
Hunan	Ningshian	Chingsi	6.00	8.00	30.60	55.4	13,354
Hupeh	Tayeh	Tayeh	1.32	12.20	10.40	76.02	13,541
Hupeh	Tzequai	Hsian Shi	4.81	14.72	25.69	54.68	12,562
Kiangsi	Pingshian	Kiangsi	0.92	4.90	33.53	60.65	14,328
Kiangsi	Po-Loo	Kiangsi	3.10	10.20	41.20	45.50	11,800
Kiangsi	Kao Keng	Kiangsi	1.00	8.90	24.40	65.70	14,300
Kiangsi	Kian	Tienho	1.50	6.16	30.50	61.84	11,106
Anhwei	Hweiyuan	Hweinan	2.14	9.75	39.13	49.98	12,840
Anhwei	Dahtung	Dahtung	3.30	8.87	36.64	51.19	12,827
Anhwei		Tatung	0.30	7.92	42.95	48.83	13,347
Anhwei		Wheichow	0.41	13.56	27.59	58.44	13,000
Kiangsu	Hsiaohsien	Dahchung	2.00	16.17	22.02	59.81	12,723
Chekiang		Changshin	1.15	16.57	36.25	46.03	12,780
Szechwan	Kiangwei	Kiayang	0.40	18.22	27.30	54.08	12,699
Szechwan	Weiyuan	Weiyuan	2.19	8.20	30.13	59.48	13,986
Szechwan	Pahsien	Kianchwan	1.21	13.18	18.42	67.19	13,644
Kweichow	Tungtze	Nantung	1.02	12.21	19.12	67.65	13,647
Kweichow	Kweiyang	Kweichow	1.84	15.36	20.11	62.69	11,938
Yunnan	Shuanwei	Shuanming	0.86	12.68	26.73	59.73	13,425
Yunnan	Kweiyang	Niaokah	2.79	16.90	25.82	54.49	12,200
Sikang	Shuanwei	Paikaowan	0.72	10.86	24.76	63.66	13,898
Jehol	Kaiyuan	Peipiao	3.25	11.00	30.50	55.25	13,203
Suiyuan	Wheilie		4.82	24.82	16.44	53.92	11,146
Liaoning		Fushun	6.68	10.20	39.87	43.25	12,058
Liaoning	Sian	Sian	6.75	1.74	38.54	52.97	13,900
Kirin	Muling	Muling	3.00	10.00	28.00	59.00	13,450
Jehol	Chaoyang	Pilpiao	3.00	7.00	32.00	58.00	12,918
Jehol	Fusing	Fusing	12.33	7.25	30.02	50.40	11,869
Hailungkiang	Tangyuan	Hullkong	2.01	6.22	35.04	56.73	13,113
Hailungkiang	Lubing		20.93	3.69	36.35	39.03	9,542
Hopeh	Tsingsing	Tsingsing	0.49	7.66	23.20	68.65	14,217
Hopeh	Lintsing	Lintsing	1.55	10.00	30.13	58.32	12,434
Hopeh	Wanping	Mentuogo	2.30	15.00	7.60	75.10	12,704
Hopeh	Wanping	Chaitang	0.26	5.24	16.93	77.57	14,861
Honan	Anyang	Liuhokou	1.11	11.44	19.82	67.63	13,504
Honan	Yuhsien	Yuhsien	1.02	16.30	17.48	65.20	13,007
Honan	Yihloh	Yihloh	0.67	14.13	20.60	64.60	13,356
Honan	Liho	Chung Fu	1.10	9.90	8.50	80.50	13,160
Honan	Shen Hsien	Ming Sung	4.03	27.54	18.41	50.02	9,312
Shantung	Yih Hsien	Chunshin	0.65	9.95	27.18	62.22	13,860
Shantung	Poshan	Poshan	0.25	8.50	11.15	80.10	14,259
Shantung	Poshan	Poshan	4.50	17.00	16.80	61.70	11,928
Shansi	Dahtung	Dahtung	3.69	7.33	29.98	59.00	14,216
Kansu	Yung Don	Yung Don	5.59	3.76	33.18	57.47	13,847
Hunan	Tzehsin	Sianguan	2.76	9.95	22.44	64.85	12,569
Hunan	Siangtan	Tankiashan	3.46	25.18	28.42	42.94	10,532

Table 15–15   Typical Analyses of Japanese Coals

Area	Mining District or Seam	Typical analysis — as-received					Grind-ability (Hard-grove)
		Mois.	Vol.	F.C.	Ash	Btu	
Kyushu	Tagawa	3.9	31.1	29.6	35.4	8,290	45
	Iizuka	2.2	36.6	39.1	22.1	10,910	44
	Hiyoshi	3.0	29.0	43.5	24.5	10,660	49
	Kokura	6.1	29.4	25.4	39.1	7,210	37
	Onoura	2.4	34.1	39.7	23.8	10,660	46
	Yamano	2.2	21.3	25.2	51.3	6,230	43
	Meiji-Saga	2.2	42.6	39.8	15.4	12,200	47
	Shinhokusho	3.6	34.3	38.8	23.3	10,740	51
	Miike	1.0	40.9	41.2	16.9	12,700	56
	Takamatsu	4.4	31.4	34.5	29.7	9,250	38
Yamaguchi	Okinoyama	8.5	26.7	20.6	44.2	6,050	43
	Sanyo	2.2	6.3	59.8	31.7	9,850	72
	Heigen	7.8	27.8	18.1	46.3	6,070	46
Zyoban	Zyoban	5.3	37.2	41.9	25.6	10,030	39
	Ibaragi	9.8	32.2	17.1	40.9	6,280	37
	Takahagi	8.4	27.2	12.8	51.6	4,730	42
Hokkaido	Sunagawa	1.6	30.0	30.4	38.0	8,280	49
	Bihai	3.6	37.3	44.0	15.1	11,650	47
	Yubetsu	2.4	34.1	41.9	21.6	11,200	53
	Oyuberi	1.1	41.4	51.2	6.3	14,450	59
	Taiheiyo	7.2	29.7	25.1	38.0	9,500	37
	Akama	2.6	30.9	35.7	30.8	9,720	54
Hokkaido	Hahoro	12.9	39.2	31.1	16.8	10,200	36
	Horonai	3.4	42.8	45.6	8.2	12,810	38

the proximate analyses of many Japanese coals.

Coal Deposits of Africa

Union of South Africa

The Union of South Africa is by far the most extensive coal-producing region on the African continent. The Transvaal leads in the size of deposit and in the quality of coal, which is mostly of the medium volatile rank. The analyses range as follows:

Moisture	Vol. matter	F. C.	Ash	Sulfur
1 to 6	21 to 26	51 to 60	12 to 21	0.5 to 2.0

Natal

The Natal district may be regarded as the eastern extension of the Transvaal fields, extending from Newcastle on the north to about twelve miles north of Lady-smith on the south. This field is traversed extensively by igneous dykes, which in many places have driven off the volatile matter and given the coal an anthracite character. Natal coal, where thus affected, is considered the best in South Africa. It is an excellent steam coal, and much of it yields a good coke, but some of it is high in sulfur. The following are typical analyses from the Dundee colliery:

Moisture	Vol. matter	F. C.	Ash	Sulfur
—	16.63	70.53	8.66	4.18

from the Navigation colliery:

0.5	15.2	71.6	11.4	1.3

Orange Free State

The Orange Free State fields may be regarded as the southern extension of the

Table 15–16 Typical Analyses of Australian Coals

Area	Mining District or Seam	Typical analysis — as-received						Approx. ash-soft-ening temp. F	Grind-ability (Hard-grove)
		Mois.	Vol.	F.C.	Ash	Sul.	Btu		
QUEENSLAND									
1. Ipswich	Bluff, Wright, Lagoon	7.4	26.3	44.6	21.7	0.3	10,130	2740	59
2. Rockhampton	Callide	12.6	24.8	49.5	13.1	0.1	9,700	2610	83
3. Rockhampton	Kianga	5.0	30.6	56.6	7.8	0.5	13,000	2470	72
VICTORIA									
4. Gippsland	Yallourn (brown coal)	66.3	17.7	15.3	0.7	0.1	3,700	2550	
5. Gippsland	Yallourn (Briquette)	13.0	44.8	40.4	1.8	0.2	9,570	2370	
6. Gippsland	Morwell	63.0	10.4	24.8	1.8	0.2	4,255	2510	
7. Western District	Bacchus Marsh	59.9	20.2	17.2	2.7	0.6	4,400	2650	
8. Western District	Anglesea	45.5	25.2	27.8	1.5	1.9	6,480	2910	
9. Gippsland	Wonthaggi	11.7	30.9	43.0	14.4	0.4	11,040	2420	59
WESTERN AUSTRALIA									
10. Collie	Muja (open cut)	29.9	23.2	44.1	2.8	0.7	8,530	2370	70–77
10A Collie	Collie	25.0	25.3	42.5	7.2	0.8	8,660	2320	80–85
SOUTH AUSTRALIA									
11. Leigh Creek	Main Basin	33.8	21.1	28.4	16.7	0.2	5,960	2070	
12. Leigh Creek	Telford Basin	30.6	22.0	31.0	16.4	0.2	6,045	1330	92
13. Leigh Creek North	Basin, Lobe D Upper	37.5	22.5	32.5	7.5	0.4	6,600	1300	92
14. Leigh Creek North	Basin, Lobe D Lower	36.0	21.5	29.5	13.0	0.4	6,200	1280	92
15. Leigh Creek North	Basin, Lobe C	29.0	22.0	28.0	21.0	3.4	5,600		92
NEW SOUTH WALES									
16. Newcastle (Northern)	Great Northern	6.0	29.0	46.7	18.3	0.4	10,880	2920	48
17. Newcastle (Northern)	Wallarah	8.0	29.0	51.3	11.7	0.5	11,620	2920	51
18. Lidell (Northern)	Liddell	7.5	35.8	50.0	6.7	0.5	12,740	2840	59
19. Maitland (Northern)	Big Ben	5.5	34.4	49.6	10.5	0.8	12,430	2830	59
20. Maitland (Northern)	Greta	6.0	37.4	45.6	11.0	0.9	12,400	2730	45
21. Illawarra (Southern)	Wongawilli	4.0	22.4	48.6	25.0	0.5	10,700	2920	80
22. Illawarra (Southern)	Bulli	4.0	22.0	62.4	11.6	0.4	12,920	2550	75
23. Lithgow (Western)	Lithgow	6.5	29.5	46.3	17.7	0.5	11,200	2920	50

Transvaal fields. The coal has an average composition as follows:

Moisture	Vol. matter	F. C.	Ash	Sulfur
5.6	28.4	50.4	15.6	1.5

It is noncoking coal but fairly good for steaming purposes.

Rhodesia

In Rhodesia, the Wankie field is the most important. The coal has excellent steaming and coking qualities. The average analysis is:

Moisture	Vol. matter	F. C.	Ash
0.7	21.0	66.8	11.5

Coal Deposits of Oceania

Australia

Australia is rich in bituminous coal deposits. The most important fields lie in New South Wales and Queensland. The great basin of New South Wales contains coals which differ in their quality: those from the Newcastle district are especially adapted to the manufacture of gas, and to household purposes; those from the Illawarra and Lithgow districts are excellent for steaming purposes. The Greta seams are extensively operated, and constitute the most important coal-mining district in Australia. The coal is hard and clean, and burns rather quickly.

The Queensland coal varies considerably in analysis in different areas. Some of it approaches anthracite in character, while some is practically gas coal.

Victoria has a small amount of bituminous coals, but a considerable deposit of lignite. The bituminous makes a first class house coal and is also used for steaming purposes. The seams are rather thin, making mining expensive. The lignites contain 40 to 60 per cent of water when mined, but about one half of the water is lost by air drying.

The only known coal deposit of any importance in Western Australia is the small Collie Basin. The coal from this district is bright and clean but rather friable when dry. It is used by railways and for bunkering; some of it is also used for household purposes.

Typical analyses of Australian coals are shown in Table 15–16 on page 15–19.

New Zealand

Coal ranging from anthracite to lignite occurs in many sections of New Zealand. The Buller-Mokihinui is the best known bituminous field. The coal is of good quality and makes an excellent steam fuel. It is coking, but the coke produced is not rated high.

Philippine Islands

Coal is mined in eight localities in the Philippine Islands, namely: Bataan, Cebu, Zamboanga, Politti, Masbati, Mindoro, Luzon and Mindanao. The basins are small and discontinuous. The deposits contain lignite, subbituminous and bituminous coals. The bulk of the lignite is black, and seldom displays a woody structure or brown color. The bituminous coals are black, hard and lustrous. They are generally noncoking.

16

Pulverizers[1]

ONE OF THE MOST significant engineering achievements of the twentieth century is the commercial perfection of methods of firing coal in pulverized form. In fact, the development is one of the cornerstones making possible the extremely large modern steam generating unit with its high thermal efficiency, reliability and safety. This is graphically illustrated in Fig. 16–1 which shows the remarkable increase in boiler capacity after World War I when pulverized coal firing achieved widespread adoption in the central station industry.

Practically every coal mined in the United States and throughout the world is being burned with complete success in pulverized form. Many other types of low grade, waste and byproduct solid fuels may also be fired economically and efficiently in this manner. Pulverized fuel firing has contributed to the reduction of labor costs in steam power plants, and at the same time it has increased flexibility of operation and made practicable the utilization of an extremely wide range of fuels.

Over the years the concept of pulverized coal firing has attracted the attention

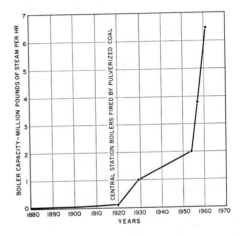

Fig. 16–1. Increase in boiler capacity showing effect of introduction of pulverized coal firing to central stations in 1919

of some of the finest engineering minds. Sadi Carnot was familiar with early nineteenth-century French experiments and provided a critical thermodynamic analysis of the pyréolophore, an engine fired by powdered coal, in his 1824 engineering classic, *Reflections on the Motive Power of Fire*.[2] Rudolf Diesel conducted his first

[1] Material contributed by A. Bogot and L. J. Andresen.
[2] See the paperback edition of the Carnot *Reflections*, including the extended footnote reference on page 56 and the related illustration of the pyréolophore, invented by Claude and Nicephore Niepce in 1806, Dover Publications, New York, 1960.

experiments on the internal combustion engine bearing his name with pulverized coal as the primary fuel, this work having taken place during the 1890's when pulverized coal firing was achieving its first real commercial success in the cement industry.[3] Thomas A. Edison, in the early 1900's, made improvements in the firing of pulverized coal in cement kilns, greatly increasing their efficiency and output.[4]

In all fairness, however, recognition must be given to hundreds of engineers of lesser renown who have made equal or greater technical contributions. Since the first information attributed to the Niepce brothers was published in France in the early 1800's, there have been many examples of engineers whose visions of future developments in pulverized coal technology have far exceeded the materials and technical understanding of their time. Pulverized coal firing has largely developed as an *empirical art,* and its progress has been marked by the efforts of devoted engineers whose success may be attributed to persistence in the face of many discouraging obstacles. Theoretical understanding has generally *followed* rather than preceded practical accomplishment in the field of pulverized coal firing.

The elements of engineering reasoning which have stimulated invention and improvement of devices to burn coal in pulverized form include the following: (1) Coal is widely available for com-

bustion purposes. (2) Burning gas appears to be a simpler process than consumption of large pieces of coal. (3) If coal can be finely divided and burned like a gas, it becomes an even more attractive fuel, promising greater boiler efficiency and simplicity of combustion.

As evidence of the foregoing, these words were written many years before the first successful commercial applications of pulverized fuel:

"A stage in the use of carbon, evidently approximate to the gaseous condition, is that of bringing it into the state of a very fine powder before mingling it with air. The plan of using fuel ground up into fine dust had been attempted many years ago in America, and is now being elaborately worked out by Mr. Crampton, Mr. J. Bourne, and also several inventors in America. Injected into the combustion chamber, it is at once turned into gas; and if no simpler and cheaper method of thus increasing the areas of contact between the fuel and the air for combustion could be found, it would constitute a great improvement. . . ."[5]

Developments in Perspective

What obstacles did engineers have to overcome to make practicable the huge pulverized coal furnaces of today? Perhaps one of the best ways to appreciate the difficulties is to read the words of one of the outstanding British mechanical engi-

---

[3] A basic reference is *Theory and Construction of a Rational Heat Motor*, London, 1894, an original work of Rudolf Diesel translated by Bryan Donkin; *A History of Western Technology* by Friedrich Klemm, Scribner's, New York, 1959, gives an interesting insight into the creative work of Diesel as an engineer, pp. 342–347.

[4] For accounts of this work see *Powdered Coal As a Fuel* by C. F. Herington, New York, 1918, pp. 68–72, and *Edison — His Life and Inventions* by F. L. Dyer, T. C. Martin and W. H. Meadowcroft, New York, 1929, Vol. II, pp. 953–957, plus list of Edison patents dealing with burning portland cement and grinding coal, pp. 998–1003.

[5] From an article entitled "Gaseous Fuel" which was published in *The Engineer* (London), Vol. 44, October 19, 1866, page 273.

neers of the nineteenth century, John Bourne, whose first patent for the firing of coal dust was awarded in 1857 but whose work in this field apparently dates back to 1845.

". . . For all practical purpose, the beginning of thermodynamics in combustion is carried on in atmospheric air, and coal is the fuel with which the combustion has to be performed. Notwithstanding the persistent attempts, however, which have been made during the last century to establish an efficient and unobjectionable method of burning coal, it cannot be said that any substantial progress has been made towards the establishment of a uniform and satisfactory system. . . . On the whole, the subject of the efficient and economical utilization of coal must be admitted to be still in a most unsatisfactory condition.

"Impelled by these considerations, I instituted, between the years 1868 and 1878, an elaborate series of experiments in the hope of being enabled to devise means of burning, as a useful fuel, the small coal at present wasted. . . . Many years before I had proposed the use of coal dust instead of coal in furnaces, both because coal dust was virtually a waste material, and because by reason of its minute subdivision the combustion of the dust ought to be very rapid, whereby it was concluded the size of the furnace might be correspondingly reduced. . . ."

"Although therefore the problem of burning coal dust was one of apparent simplicity, it was in reality found to be a most difficult one to solve. No doubt by

making the dust extremely fine, and by using only the dust of highly bituminous coal, the problem was so far simplified as to permit a simple solution, for such dust will burn in much the same way as vapor of petroleum. Such limitations to the problem, however, deprived its solution of all practical utility, as bituminous coal, reduced to so impalpable a condition as to burn like a gas, was necessarily very costly. . . ."[6]

While economics was a negative factor in this instance, it was the rapid increase in the price of oil in the United States in the 1890's that was the principal incentive for developing the use of pulverized coal for firing cement kilns, the first industrial application to achieve outstanding commercial success. E. H. Hurry and H. J. Seaman of the Atlas Portland Cement Company began a series of experiments relating to the use of pulverized coal in 1894, and in the following year it was successfully applied to a rotary cement kiln. Since that time pulverized coal has been the dominant fuel in the cement industry.

In terms of current usage of pulverized coal for the largest central stations, the *accident* of its pioneering application to the cement industry has proved of incalculable value. It is certain that the vast experience which the cement industry had accumulated in crushing rock and grinding cement clinker contributed to the rapid acceptance of pulverized coal in that industry. Likewise, the cement industry was accustomed to handling solid materials in large quantities and had de-

[6] These excerpts are from pages 306 and 323 of one of the many books by John Bourne, this one published in London in 1878 under the incredibly long title, *Examples of Steam, Air & Gas Engines of the Most Recent Types as Employed in Mines, Factories, Steam Navigation, Railways and Agriculture, Practically Described with an Account of All the Principal Projects for the Production of Motive Power from Heat Which Have Been Propounded in Different Times and Countries.* Additional information is found on pages 191–197 and 306–325 plus pages lxxi–lxxvi in the appendix of that book.

veloped techniques for transporting them in mechanical conveyors and as fines entrained in fluids. Both methods of transport are now integral parts of coal handling and fuel burning systems in the modern central station.

By the time of World War I, powdered coal — the term then generally used for what is now designated as pulverized coal — had gained sufficient acceptance for ASME to sponsor a symposium bringing together the accumulated experience in the several fields of application. Those who take the time to read the printed record of this symposium will get a much clearer understanding of the empirical nature of progress and a new appreciation of the wide variety of equipment available for various types of pulverized coal firing.[7]

Despite an increasing number of applications which spread from the cement industry to the metallurgical industry, to the steam locomotive and to several stationary boilers, and notwithstanding the steadily increasing rate of consumption as shown in Fig. 16–2, pulverized coal really had not achieved its full potential by the end of World War I. All of the elements for outstanding success appeared to be present, but someone was needed to integrate the many ideas and

provide a new forward thrust for pulverized coal firing in the central station industry. No one can lay more claim for initiating this impetus than John Anderson, chief engineer of power plants of what is now Wisconsin Electric Power Company.

It may be well to attempt to recreate the exciting engineering atmosphere in Milwaukee in the years 1918 through 1921, the locale and time of pioneering pulverized coal installations in the existing Oneida Street Station and the bold new concept of Lakeside Station. In an outstanding example of the merging of men, money and materials to achieve engineering advancement, John Anderson effectively enlisted the support and active participation of exceptionally able engineers from his own organization, the public utility industry, equipment suppliers and the U.S. Bureau of Mines. Solid financial backing and the necessary equipment and instruments were available for a thorough program of engineering development and full scale testing.[8]

Milwaukee provides an outstanding object lesson for those engineers who are skeptical of the value of the empirical approach and who prefer to do their theorizing isolated from practical reality. Two of the participants in the pulverized

---

[7] See "Symposium on Powdered Fuel," *Trans.* ASME Vol. 36, 1914, pp. 85–169, including "Pulverized Coal Burning in the Cement Industry" by R. C. Carpenter, "An Installation for Powdered Coal Fuel in Industrial Furnaces" by William Dalton and W. S. Quigley, "Pulverized Coal for Steam Making" by F. R. Low, and the informative topical discussion on powdered fuel covering 16 items. Albert W. Raymond who developed the widely used Raymond Roller Mill was one of the participants who furnished data based upon operating experience.

[8] Probably the outstanding coverage of events in Milwaukee is to be found in *Power*. The issue of March 2, 1920, Vol. 51, contains three articles and an editorial: "Pulverized Coal Under Central Station Boilers" by John Anderson, pp. 336–339; "Pulverized Fuel at Oneida Street Plant" by Paul W. Thompson (Detroit Edison Company), pp. 339–340; "Four Day Test on Five Oneida Street Boilers Burning Pulverized Coal," pp. 354–357; and "Pulverized Coal at Milwaukee," pp. 341–342, a perceptive and prophetic editorial. In the issue of Sept. 7, 1920, Vol. 52, pp. 358–360 there is an article entitled "The New Lakeside Pulverized Coal Plant, Milwaukee," followed on April 18, 1922, Vol. 55, pp. 604–610, by an illustrated description entitled "Largest Station Using Pulverized Coal."

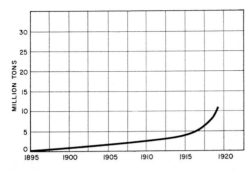

Fig. 16–2. Growth in use of pulverized coal between 1895 and 1919

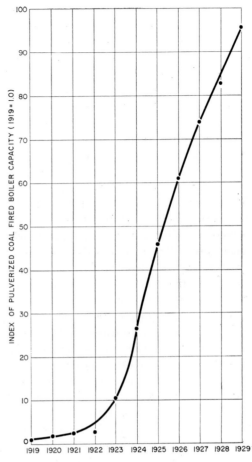

Fig. 16–3. Index of growth of pulverized coal fired installations between 1919 and 1929

coal tests in Milwaukee, after the passage of two decades, recalled the accomplishments in these terms:

"To determine the best method of burning powdered fuel John Anderson did two things: (1) He made a large scale trial installation of pulverized coal. (2) He provided the means for testing this fuel system and of analyzing the results which could be obtained with pulverized coal. He also indicated the lines of development along which the system could advance.

"The impartial attitude of those conducting the tests and the thorough manner in which they were carried out inspired the confidence of power users who were interested in steam generation and caused them to realize that pulverized coal offered possibilities well worthy of consideration. . . .

"In reviewing the work done in Milwaukee, one is impressed by the great number of fundamentals which were investigated. . . . The effect of fineness on combustion, drying coal in the pulverizer, the excess air in the flue gas, the temperature and heat absorption in the furnace, methods of obtaining a thorough account of the distribution of the heat and ash from the coal, and the elimination of dust from the flue gases were all studied before pulverized coal became the commonly used fuel it now is for firing power plant boilers."[9]

[9] These excerpts are from "Milwaukee's Contribution to Pulverized Coal Development" by Henry Kreisinger and John Blizard, *Mechanical Engineering*, Vol. 62, October 1940, pp. 723–726, 737. For an elaboration see an article by another participant who succeeded John Anderson as chief engineer of power plants, namely, "Developments in Burning Pulverized Coal — Thirty Year Review of Experience in Milwaukee Plants" by F. L. Dornbrook, *Mechanical Engineering*, Vol. 70, December 1948, pp. 967–974.

The results of the experimental developments and extensive testing at Milwaukee were widely publicized, following the traditional pattern of the electric utility industry in freely sharing its technical experiences. The resulting stimulus expressed itself in several ways. The first and most obvious was demonstrated by the heightened interest of management leaders in the use of pulverized coal for central stations and large industrial power plants. Graphical evidence of this is shown in Fig. 16–3, which is a plot of the rapid increase in boiler capacity fired by pulverized coal for the years 1919 through 1929. Secondly, and possibly of even greater long run significance, there was the stimulation of engineering research in understanding the physical phenomena and mechanisms of pulverized coal firing.

Much American research in this field stems from the establishment of the U.S. Bureau of Mines in 1910 and its extensive program of boiler and equipment testing.[10] But there was also earlier work in this country and abroad on the inflammability of dust clouds which caused explosions in coal mines. Empirical progress in the art of pulverized coal firing helped to link these two areas of research and brought forth a series of reports and investigations ranging from power plant tests to studies of particle flow and the thermodynamics of combustion.

Two outstanding test reports that deserve to stand as engineering classics, those based on experimental work at the Oneida Street and Lakeside Stations, contain much basic information on pulverized coal firing and established a pattern for much subsequent research, including many of the activities of the ASME Furnace Performance Factors Committee.[11]

Studies on velocities and characteristics of pulverized coal particles were reported by E. Audibert[12] and John Blizard,[13] who a few years earlier had published a comprehensive study of the state of the pulverized coal art.[14] Research linking studies of inflammability of coal mine dust to desired combustion properties appears in an article by Henri Verdinne.[15] W. Nusselt published results of research on coal particle ignition times in 1924,[16] and P. Rosin reported on studies of heat liberation based on thermodynamic data in 1925.[17] The first of a series of papers on boiler heat transfer studies

[10] See Chapter 18, Stokers, Footnote 6, for a listing of important papers on combustion and heat transfer by Henry Kreisinger and his colleagues in the U.S. Bureau of Mines.

[11] "An Investigation of Powdered Coal as Fuel for Power Plant Boilers — Tests at the Oneida Street Power Station" by H. Kreisinger, J. Blizard, C. E. Augustine and B. J. Cross, Bulletin 223, 1923; "Tests of a Large Boiler Fired with Powdered Coal at the Lakeside Station" by H. Kreisinger, J. Blizard, C. E. Augustine and B. J. Cross, Bulletin 237, 1925, U.S. Bureau of Mines.

[12] "Etude de l'Entrainment du Poussier de Houille par l'Air," *Revue Industrie Minerale,* Vol. 4, 1922, pp. 1–32.

[13] "The Terminal Velocity of Particles of Powdered Coal Falling in Air or Other Viscous Fluid," *Journal* of the Franklin Institute, February 1924, pp. 199–207.

[14] "Preparation, Transportation and Combustion of Powdered Coal" which was originally published by the Canadian Department of Mines in 1921 and republished by the U.S. Bureau of Mines as Bulletin 217 in 1923.

[15] "The Technique of Powdered Fuel Firing," *Fuel in Science and Practice,* Vol. 2, 1923, pp. 146–151.

[16] "Der Verbrennungsvorgang in der Kohlenstaubfeuerung," *VDI,* Vol. 68, 1924, pp. 124–128.

[17] "Die thermodynamischen und wirtschaftlichen Grundlagen der Kohlenstaubfeuerung," *Braunkohle,* Vol. 24, 1925, pp. 241–259.

at Yale University by W. J. Wohlenberg and his colleagues was also published by ASME in 1925.[18]

Despite the extensive theoretical studies that were made in the 1920's, much of the progress was achieved on an empirical basis of trial and error with boiler installations of ever increasing size. This was particularly true in the development of pulverizers, where the theory of the underlying principles had not advanced very rapidly. Even today the laws for crushing materials are subject to much dispute.

Rittinger's law of crushing dates back to a book published in Germany in 1867. It states that the work required to produce material of a given size from a larger size is proportional to the new surface produced. This expression finds more general acceptance than Kick's law which was first published in 1885 and states that the energy required to effect crushing or pulverizing is proportional to the volume reduction of the particle. While Rittinger's law is a closer approximation, neither can be used for comparing efficiencies of different coal pulverizers.[19]

The energy required to effect pulverization is dissipated in a number of ways and cannot be accounted for in the specific manner applicable to a boiler or power plant heat balance. For this reason the design and application of pulverizers retain many of the elements of an engineering art.

Principal Types of Pulverizers

To effect the particle size reduction for the proper combustion in pulverized coal firing, machines known as *pulverizers* or *mills* are used to grind or comminute the fuel. Grinding mills use either one, two or all three of the basic principles of particle size reduction, namely, *impact*, *attrition* and *crushing*. With respect to speed, these machines may be classified as low, medium and high. The four most commonly used pulverizers are the ball, the ring roll and ball race, and the impact attrition type, and their speed characteristics are shown in Table 16–1.

Table 16–1   Pulverizer Types

Speed:	Low	Medium	High
Type:	Ball or Tube Mill	Ring Roll Mill Ball Race Mill	Impact or Hammer Mill Attrition Mill

Ball Mills

A *ball* or *tube mill* (usually called ball when the length does not exceed the diameter) is basically a hollow horizontal cylinder, rotated on its axis, whose length is slightly less to somewhat greater than its diameter. The inside of the cylindrical shell is fitted with heavy cast liners and is filled to a little less than half, as shown diagrammatically in Fig. 16–4, with forged steel or cast alloy balls varying from one to two inches in diameter. Rotating slowly, 18 to 35 rpm, or about

---

[18] "Radiation in the Pulverized Fuel Furnace" by W. J. Wohlenberg and D. G. Morrow, *Trans. ASME*, Vol. 47, 1925, pp. 127–176.

[19] For a discussion of these laws, see *Micromeritics — The Technology of Fine Particles* by J. M. Dallvale, Second Edition, New York, 1948, pp. 474–475. The original references for the crushing laws are: *Lehrbuch der Aufbereitungskunde* by Peter Ritter von Rittinger, Berlin, 1867 and *Das Gesetz der proportionalen Widerstande und seine Anwendung* by Kick, Leipzig, 1885. See also treatment of Kick's law by Stadler, *Trans. Inst. Mining Met.*, London, Vols. 19 and 20, 1910 and 1911.

20 rpm for an eight foot diameter mill, the balls are carried about two thirds of the way up the periphery and then continually cascaded towards the center of the mill. Coal is fed into the cylinder through hollow trunnions, Fig. 16–5, and intermingles with the ball charge. Pulverization which is accomplished through continual cascading of the mixtures results from (1) impact of the falling balls on the coal, (2) attrition as particles slide over each other as well as over the liners and (3) crushing as balls roll over each other and over the liners with coal particles between them. Larger pieces of coal are broken by impact and the fine grinding is done by attrition and crushing as the balls roll and slide within the charge.

Hot air flow is induced through the mill in order to dry the coal and remove the fines from the pulverizing zone. In most designs used for firing boilers or industral furnaces, an external classifier is used to regulate the size consist or degree of fineness of the finished product. The oversize or rejects from the classifier, sometimes called tailings, already dried in the pulverizing and classifying process are returned to the grinding zone with the raw coal thus reducing the average moisture content of the mixture. This recirculation of dried tailings reduces the tendency for wet coal to plug the feed end of this type of mill.

Low maintenance, reliability and quick response to change in fuel demand are inherent characteristics of the ball mill. During operation, the relatively large quantity of pulverized coal in the grinding zone acts as a storage reservoir from which sudden increases in fuel demand are supplied.

The power consumption of ball type mills, per ton of coal pulverized, is high,

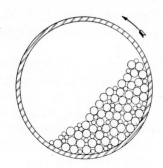

Fig. 16—4. Diagram of ball mill with ball charge

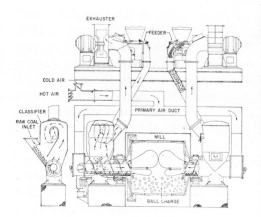

Fig. 16—5. Arrangement of ball mill

particularly at partial loads. Physically, they are relatively large per unit of capacity and therefore require considerable floor space. Because of their size and weight, first cost is quite high. The absence of a high circulating load within the mill results in an overproduction of fines within the mill charge. The use of an adequate classifier permits the removal of a coarser product from the grinding zone and reduces the production of extreme fines. The comparatively poor mixing of heated air with the partially pulverized material, reduces the drying efficiency of this type of mill. High moisture coals pro-

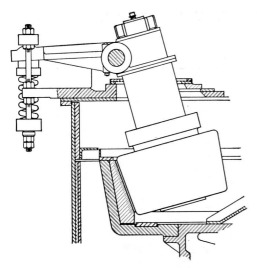

Fig. 16–9. Diagram of bowl type ring roll mill, suction firing

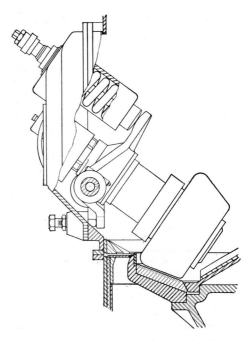

Fig. 16–10. Diagram of bowl type ring roll mill, pressurized firing

an adequate temperature to produce a satisfactory mill outlet temperature, they can handle very wet coals with but a small reduction in capacity. The high ratio of circulating load (classifier rejects returning to the grinding zone for further size reduction) to output, with the resulting rapid reduction of average moisture content, facilitates the grinding process. Mills of the above types require less power than any others.

Physically, these mills are compact and occupy a relatively small amount of floor space per unit of capacity. Some designs of ring roll mills are extremely quiet in operation. Fineness of the product is relatively uniform throughout the life of the grinding elements.

Maintenance is equal to or less than that of the ball mill and is considerably less than that of the impact mills. First cost for a given capacity lies between that of the ball and impact mill. These mills are not very suitable from a cost standpoint in sizes below 3000 lb per hour capacity.

Several references have been made previously to the ability of the various types of pulverizing equipment to grind different coals economically and efficiently. This capability is a reflection of the grinding pressures available, the method of application of this force, speed of moving elements, abrasion, power and size limitations of the particular units. A list of commercially pulverized materials which could be produced by the mill types described could be extended indefinitely. Hence Table 16–2 is limited mainly to combustible materials which are of primary concern in this presentation.

C-E Raymond Roller Mill

The period between 1895 when the first pulverizers were installed in a Penn-

Table 16–2   Types of Pulverizers for Various Materials

Type of Material	Ball or Tube	Impact and Attrition	Ball Race	Ring Roll
Low volatile anthracite	x	–	–	–
High volatile anthracite	x	–	x	x
Coke breeze	x	–	–	–
Petroleum coke (fluid)	x	–	x	x
Petroleum coke (delayed)	x	x	x	x
Graphite	x	–	x	x
Bituminous coal (low volatile)	x	x	x	x
Bituminous coal (medium volatile)	x	x	x	x
Bituminous coal H.V."A"	x	x	x	x
Bituminous coal H.V."B"	x	x	x	x
Bituminous coal H.V."C"	x	–	x	x
Subbituminous coal "A"	x	–	x	x
Subbituminous coal "B"	x	–	x	x
Subbituminous coal "C"	–	–	x	x
Lignite	–	–	x	x
Lignite and coal char	x	–	x	x
Brown coal	–	x	–	–
Furfural residue	–	x	–	x
Sulfur	–	x	–	x
Gypsum	–	x	x	x
Phosphate rock	x	–	x	x
Limestone	x	–	–	x
Rice hulls	–	x	–	–
Grains	–	x	–	–
Ores — hard	x	–	–	–
Ores — soft	x	–	x	x

sylvania cement plant and 1919 when a succesful boiler installation was made at Oneida Street Station in Milwaukee was a testing time for this type of equipment. Early during this period the C-E Raymond Roller Mill was developed to pulverize coal for storage systems serving metallurgical furnaces and cement kilns, and by 1919 several hundred of these mills were being operated successfully. A catalog published in 1900 stated, "The Raymond Roller Mill crushes and grinds the material by gravity and centrifugal force," and described it as a slow speed machine with great capacity and one that requires less power per ton of a product than any other mill. A listing of projects for which the Raymond Roller Mill, Fig. 16–11, was supplied reads like a history of pulverized coal applications, including cement kilns, railroad and coal mine stationary plants, malleable iron furnaces, copper reverberatory furnaces and open hearths. Hence when pulverized coal gained a foothold in the central station industry after World War I this machine was a fully developed and standardized pulverizer which was specified for many of the pioneering installations.

The early mills were built for a maximum capacity of six tons per hour of 55 grindability coal when grinding to a fineness of 65 per cent minus 200 mesh. By 1930 the maximum capability of this mill design had been increased to 15 and then to 25 tons per hour. Practically all of these mills used external dryers to predry the coal before use in the pulverizer. The economic disadvantages of these dryers helped to bring about internal

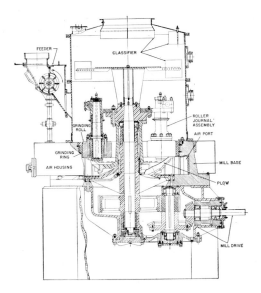

Fig. 16—11. Cutaway view, C-E Raymond Roller Mill

mill through directional ports located below the ring and picks up the partially ground coal. The rotating parts set up a swirling motion in the coal and air stream. This action establishes a classifying zone in the upper space of the mill housing. As a result, the coarser particles are held to the periphery and then, flowing downward along the walls, are returned to be reground. The finer particles, having less inertia, move toward the center in the direction of the air flow and are thus removed from the mill.

These mills are excellent dryers because hot air, in flowing through the grinding zone, is intimately mixed with the coal. They are used primarily in indirect firing systems, where low output temperatures are necessary to prevent overheating the pulverized coal going into storage. However, they are not as well adapted for direct firing because of the temperature limitations under which they must be operated. There is always some coal in the bottom of the mill which, when exposed to high temperature for any length of time, may ignite through overheating. Using flue gas with high CO_2 content as a drying means eliminates this danger but interferes with ignition.

If little or no drying is to be done in the mill, practically all air in the system is recirculated. When, however, there is an appreciable amount of drying required, a large percentage of the air, carrying the moisture removed from the coal, must be vented from the system. If this is not done, the relative humidity will gradually build up to the saturation point, and then no further drying is obtainable. Under extreme conditions, it may be necessary to continually remove from the system as much as 70 per cent of the total air. To accomplish this, the dust laden air is drawn through a cyclone collector. Ap-

mill drying which is now the accepted practice. However, the original feature of air separation and classification inherent in the Roller Mill has become the accepted current standard of roll race pulverizer design.

Mills are usually direct driven by a variable speed motor. The vertical shaft maximum speed varies from 115 rpm to 80 rpm depending upon mill size, number and size of rollers used, the grindability of the coal being pulverized and its final fineness. Coal enters the mill just above the grinding ring through one or two feeders. Pendulum type roll assemblies are pivotally mounted in the mill spider which, in turn, is attached to the rotating vertical shaft. The rollers exert a crushing force upon the coal, the intensity of which will vary with the mill speed. Any coal falling past the rolls to the mill bottom is scooped up by rotating plows and carried back to the grinding zone. Air enters the

proximately 98 per cent of the dust is thus collected and then discharged, through a rotary valve or air locks, either directly to a storage bin or to a distributing conveyor. The remaining two per cent of the dust which is extremely fine (all minus 200 mesh) returns to the mill exhauster. A vent connection is located in the duct between the exhauster and mill. At this point the air to be vented is drawn off by a vent fan and discharged through a cyclone concentrator. This concentrator is essentially of the same construction as the cyclone collector, except that the dust, instead of being completely separated, is concentrated in 10 to 15 per cent of the air. This dusty air is then removed through the bottom of the concentrator and returned to the mill system. The remaining air is vented to the atmosphere. Approximately 70 to 80 per cent of the dust entering the concentrator is collected in this manner. Hot air or gas is supplied to the mill and this quantity must be vented. A complete grinding and drying system is shown diagrammatically in Fig. 16–12.[20]

In cases where half the air is vented, approximately one per cent of the coal milled will go to the concentrator. Of this amount, about 80 per cent is returned, so that the total system dust loss is about 0.2 per cent. When grinding 15 tons per hour this represents a loss of 60 lb. As the moisture in the coal feed increases, more air must be vented. Thus, the system approaches its maximum drying capacity, and as a result the efficiency of both cyclone and concentrator is increased. Although more air is vented under these conditions, the dust loss is usually reduced.

In a mill drying system, care must be exercised to avoid excessive drying be-

cause the dust loss will be too great. Storage system drying arrangements, their complications and economics, together with the accompanying vent problems, brought about the adoption of the simpler, ventless, direct fired equipment.

Table 16–3 shows the four most commonly used sizes of C-E Raymond Roller Mills for storage systems. Capacity is based on 55 grindability coal pulverized to 70 per cent minus 200 mesh.

C-E Raymond Impact Mills

The increase in possibilities for direct pulverized coal firing resulted in the development in 1923 of a series of C-E Raymond Impact Mills. Two basic designs were adopted: one for the smaller ca-

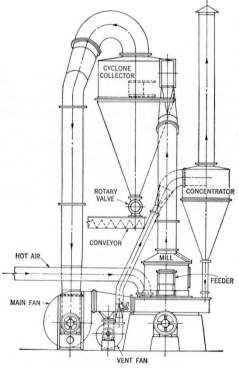

Fig. 16–12.   Equipment for a complete grinding and drying system

[20] This process is discussed in more detail in Chapter 30, Flash Drying Systems.

Table 16–3   C–E Raymond Roller Mill Sizes

Mill Size	Capacity lb per hour	Mill motor	Fan motor	Approx. Kw per ton
No. 5	11,000	75 hp–450 rpm	50 hp–1200 rpm	16.3
No. 10	18,500	125 hp–450 rpm	75 hp–1200 rpm	15.25
No. 15	30,500	200 hp–450 rpm	100 hp–1200 rpm	13.5
No. 25	50,000	300 hp–600 rpm	150 hp–1200 rpm	12.5

pacities, Fig. 16–13, in which the grinding elements, classifying means and fan were all mounted on a common shaft rotating at 1800 rpm and the other, Fig. 16–14 for the larger outputs which utilized an integral fan but external classifier. Both designs were provided with a mill housing clearance space or tramp iron pocket for accumulation and periodic removal of foreign material. The whizzer or rejector blades for fineness control were first used on these mills. These mills are excellent drying pulverizers because high temperature air can be utilized and there is very violent turbulence of the mixture passing through the pulverizer. They are best suited to soft, relatively nonabrasive coals and for use on small boilers and furnaces. Life of grinding elements is very short, and maintenance and mill power are quite high. Table 16–4 lists various sizes and capacities.

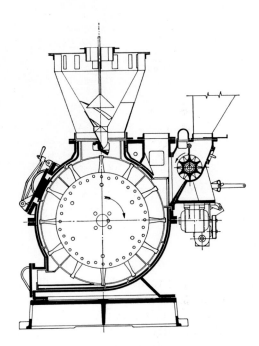

Fig. 16–14.   C-E Raymond Impact Mill with external classifier and exhauster integrally mounted

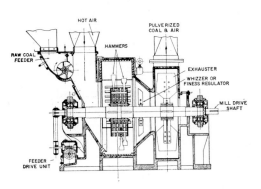

Fig. 16–13.   C-E Raymond Impact Mill

Table 16–4   C–E Raymond Impact Mill Sizes

Mill Size	Classifier	Lb per hr capacity based on 100 grindability coal 70 per cent minus 200 mesh
32	Whizzer	1600
40	Whizzer	2300
50	Whizzer	4800
55	External	5000
72	External	8300
82	External	11,000
90	External	14,700

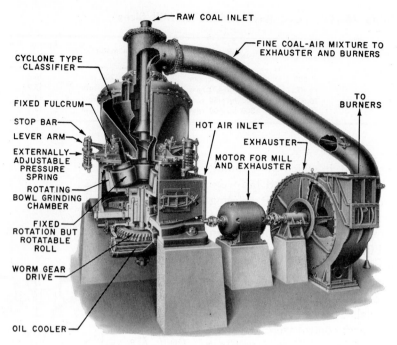

RAW COAL INLET

FINE COAL-AIR MIXTURE TO
EXHAUSTER AND BURNERS

CYCLONE TYPE
CLASSIFIER

TO
BURNERS

FIXED FULCRUM

STOP BAR

LEVER ARM

HOT AIR INLET

EXTERNALLY
ADJUSTABLE
PRESSURE
SPRING

EXHAUSTER

MOTOR FOR MILL
AND EXHAUSTER

ROTATING
BOWL GRINDING
CHAMBER

FIXED
ROTATION BUT
ROTATABLE
ROLL

WORM GEAR
DRIVE

OIL COOLER

Fig. 16–15. C-E Raymond Bowl Mill

C-E Raymond Bowl Mill

The inability to use the roller mill for direct firing, and the limitations of the impact mill for this purpose were responsible for the development in the mid-1930's of the C-E Raymond Bowl Mill. Two designs of this roll race mill are available. One shown previously in Fig. 16–9, is operated under suction and is used for firing balanced draft furnaces, while the second, Fig. 16–10, is operated as a pressurized unit and is primarily used for firing furnaces under pressure.

The C-E Raymond Bowl Mill, shown in a cutaway view in Fig. 16–15, consists essentially of a replaceable grinding ring carried by a rotating bowl.[21] The ring rim speed is approximately 1050 to 1300 ft per min. Fixed position journal assemblies, carrying rotatable tapered rolls, are mounted so that the roll face is approximately parallel to and in close proximity to the inside surface of the grinding ring. Stops are provided to prevent metal to metal contact between these two surfaces. Pressure for grinding is applied through externally adjustable compression springs. An integral stationary multivaned classifier, the outlet of which is usually connected to the mill exhauster, is located above the grinding chamber. Classifier vanes are externally adjustable. All mill components are suitably enclosed in reinforced cast iron or heavy welded steel housings which meet the requirements of the National Board of Fire Underwriters Code, NBFU No 60.[22]

[21] Mechanical design features are described and explained in Chapter 11, Manufacture and Machine Design, section on Machine Design of Bowl Mills, p. 11–23.
[22] This Standard for the Installation and Operation of Pulverized Fuel Systems may be obtained from the National Board of Fire Underwriters, 85 John Street, New York 38, New York.

In operation, a rotary overshot feeder having variable speed control delivers coal into the revolving bowl. Centrifugal action imparted to the coal by bowl rotation, forces the coal to the grinding ring face where it is crushed by the rotating rolls. The partially pulverized coal is thrown from the bowl rim to the annular hot air passage around the bowl. A single pass of coal between rolls and ring provides partial pulverization so that the product contains between 15 and 25 per cent minus 200 mesh material, depending on physical conditions of the grinding elements and characteristics of coal. A series of deflectors immediately above the bowl rejects the larger particles back into the grinding zone. Pyrites and tramp iron, because of their weight and the low airstream mass velocity around the bowl, fall to the mill bottom where pivoted scrapers carry them to a reject spout. The rising air current around the bowl carries the intermediate and fine fractions of coal up into the classifier inlet vanes, where they are deflected and a spinning action is imparted. The setting of the adjustable vanes determines the degree of spin and thus the coarseness of the material thrown to the inner wall of the classifier cone. This coal returns to the bowl for regrinding while the fines pass from the classifier to the mill exhauster through connecting fuel lines to the furnace. The coarse material returned for regrinding has already been dried, and the total quantity of this material may be three to five times the raw feed input. Mixing in the grinding zone with the wet incoming feed provides a considerably lower average moisture content for the material actually being ground.

There are a number of factors affecting the fineness for a given classifier vane setting:

1. The finer the product entering the classifier, the finer will be the leaving product.

2. High grindability coal produces more fines per pass through the grinding zone and the classifier will deliver a finer product.

3. High spring pressure on the rolls will produce more fines entering the classifier.

4. Badly worn grinding elements increase the quantity of oversize material delivered to the classifier.

5. High moisture and inadequate drying reduces fineness of material delivered to the classifier.

6. The volume and velocity of air flowing through the mill will have a minor influence on product fineness.

The above indicates the definite need for an externally adjustable, high efficiency classifier. The bowl mill classifier permits fineness changes of 20 to 30 per cent on the minus 200 mesh product; i.e., from 60 to 65 per cent minus 200 mesh to 85 or 90 per cent minus 200 mesh. This adjustment is possible on an operating mill. Fineness effect on mill capacity is shown in Fig. 16–16. As the load in the bowl changes, the rolls move away or towards the ring, automatically increasing or decreasing spring pressure, in quick response to input variations. Manual or automatic control may be used to effect required changes in coal feed rate and mill air flow. The former is accomplished by adjusting feeder speed and the latter by damper regulation. Mill outlet temperature is maintained by adjustment of dampers in both the hot and cold tempering air supply.

Bowl mills are usually direct driven through an integral worm gear unit. This drive is quiet in operation and is designed for a large single reduction allowing for the use of a high speed motor on a low speed mill, permitting the use of a single

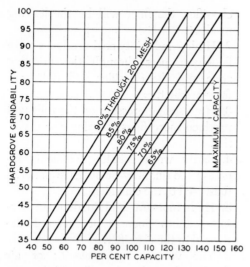

Fig. 16—16. Mill capacity versus grindability and fineness

drive shaft for both mill and exhauster. The use of a single motor for both these components results in a compact installation and produces economics in electrical and physical requirements.

The lubrication system of the mill is quite simple. The drive is completely bath or integral force feed lubricated. The roller assemblies and exhauster bearings are bath lubricated. All lubrication is accomplished with the mill in service; no shutdowns are required.

Bowl mills are available in numerous sizes. Application and capacity ranges are shown in Table 16–5. Capacities are based on the use of 55 grindability coal pulverized to 70 per cent through 200 mesh having a moisture content of 12 per cent on Midwestern (low rank bituminous coals) or 8 per cent on Eastern (high rank bituminous coals).

Grindability of Coal

In order to predict mill performance on a specific coal with some degree of accuracy, if no previous tests have been run, the ease with which coal can be pulverized must be known. A measure of this ease of pulverization is referred to as the *grindability index*. This grindability index is not an inherent property of coal, such as moisture, ash or heating value. Actually it is a representation of the relative ease of grinding of the coal when tested in a particular type of apparatus. Consistency of grindability test results permits them to serve their purpose. The proper interpretation of these results and their application to a particular type of pulverizer is the responsibility of the pulverizer manufacturer.

Grindability may readily be determined by pulverizing a small air dried sample of properly sized coal in a miniature mill. These results may then be converted into a grindability index factor which, by referring to suitable correction curves, can be used to interpret mill capacity.

Table 16–5   C–E Raymond Bowl Mill Sizes

Bowl Mill Type	RB	RPS
Furnace firing	Suction	Pressure
Size designation	#312–#753	#423–#863
Capacity, lb per hr	3550–59,100	12,000–106,000
Motor size, mill and exhauster hp	40–500	100–900
Motor speed rpm	1800–900	1200–900

The Hardgrove method was developed to measure the quantity of new material that will pass a 200 mesh sieve. The apparatus for this method, as shown in Fig. 16–17, is extremely simple. A 50 gram sample of air dried coal, sized to minus 16 and plus 30 mesh, is placed in the mortar of the test machine along with some one inch diameter steel balls. After a weighted upper race has been placed on the ball and coal charge and turned 60 revolutions, the sample is removed and screened. The quantity passing the

200 mesh sieve determines the grindability index as indicated by the following empirical equation:

$$\text{Grindability, } G = 6.93\,W + 13$$

where W is the weight in grams of that portion of the sample passing through the 200 mesh sieve.[23]

Factors Affecting Capacity

Frequently, too much emphasis is placed on grindability while other factors such as moisture which also affect mill capacity are almost entirely overlooked. The capacity of a pulverizer is not directly proportional to the grindability index of the coal. Corrections must also be made for fineness of product and moisture of the raw feed.

Usually a reference to moisture in coal pertains to the total moisture content. This is comprised of what is commonly termed "inherent" moisture and "surface" moisture. Inherent moisture varies with coal type or rank, and mine location and would more accurately be called "bed" or "cellular" moisture. The surface moisture is, in reality, the difference between total moisture and this "bed" moisture. Definitions of total and surface moisture are found in ASTM Method D 271–64.

Performance of both the combustion and pulverizing processes are adversely affected by surface moisture. This surface moisture produces agglomeration of the fines in the pulverizing zone and reduces mill capacity because of the inability to remove the fines efficiently and as quickly as they are produced. Agglomeration of the fines has the same effect as coarse coal in the combustion process, for the surface available for the chemical reaction is reduced. Since mill drying is the accepted method of preparing coal for pulverized fuel burning, sufficient hot air at an ade-

[23] For further information, see ASTM D 409–51.

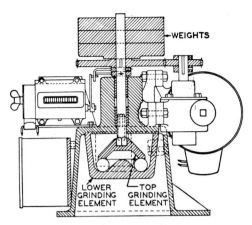

Fig. 16–17 Hardgrove grindability machine

quate temperature is necessary in the milling system. Curves as shown in Figs. 16–18 and 16–19 indicate the air temperatures required to dry coal of varied total moistures and varied air-coal mixtures.

The mill capacity is dependent upon having sufficient heated air available to dry the coal. If there is a deficiency of hot air, the mill output will be limited to the drying and not the grinding capacity of the mill. Thus, it may be possible to obtain more capacity with a relatively dry coal of lower grindability than with a high moisture coal of higher grindability.

As stated previously, mill capacity is not directly proportional to grindability. Thus, if the actual capacity of a pulverizer with 50 grindability is 10,000 lb per hour, then with 100 grindability it will be about 17,000 lb per hour, and not 20,000 lb per hour. This is because of the differences between a commercial pulverizer and a grindability test machine. The latter is of the batch rather than the continuous type and has no provision for continuous removal of fines. Its crushing pressure is also considerably less, and therefore some of its energy is dissipated in particle deformation prior to particle fracture.

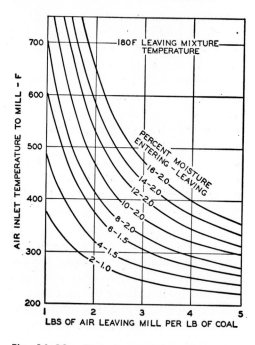

Fig. 16–18.   Temperature of air to mill — eastern coals

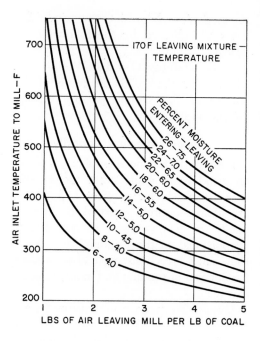

Fig. 16–19.   Temperature of air to mill — midwestern coals

Hence the test equipment does not indicate a direct proportion of capability between hard and soft materials. However, the value of these tests is not reduced, because correction factors developed by pulverizer manufacturers on commercial equipment provide for overcoming these discrepancies. A correction curve for variations in fineness and grindability was shown earlier in Fig. 16–16, and an additional correction for moisture is indicated in the curve Fig. 16–20.

Factors Affecting Fineness Requirements

The fineness to which coal should be pulverized depends on many factors.

Coking coals when exposed to furnace temperatures tend to swell and form light weight, porous cenospheres which may be carried out of the furnace before they are entirely burned. Carbon loss is then excessive unless the degree of pulverization is high. On the contrary, free burning coals do not require the same high fineness because the swelling characteristic is absent.[24]

High volatile coals, which ignite more readily and contain less fixed carbon than those of a low volatile content, do not require the same degree of fine pulverization.

Large furnaces may operate satisfactorily on high volatile coal as coarse as 60 per cent minus 200 mesh, while small water cooled furnaces burning low volatile coal may require a fineness of 80–85 per

[24] See Chapter 13, Fuel Properties of Coal, for additional information.

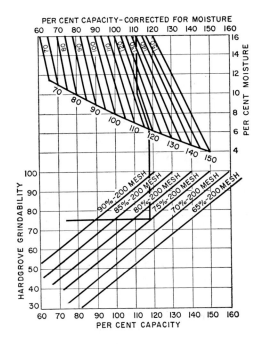

PER CENT CAPACITY-CORRECTED FOR MOISTURE

Fig. 16–20. Mill correction factors — moisture

cent through 200 mesh to keep carbon loss down to a reasonable level. Carbon loss is influenced not only by the fineness of pulverization but also by the quantity of excess air used in the burning process, burner and furnace design, disposition of furnace volume, length of flame travel and furnace turbulence and temperature. Generally, however, small furnaces require finer pulverization than do larger units burning similar fuels.[25]

Since the advent of pulverized coal firing, fineness specifications have, with increased experience and knowledge, changed considerably. Initially, specifications called for 95 per cent of minus 100 mesh and 85 per cent minus 200 mesh. Now individual requirements dictate a

variation in the minus 200 mesh of from 65 to 85 per cent. The minus 100 mesh specification is rarely used. Instead, the plus 50 mesh, which is usually designated as not to exceed 2 per cent is frequently specified. The relationship between the plus 50 mesh and minus 200 mesh varies with the size and type of pulverizer, the efficiency of its classifier and with the hardness of the coal being pulverized. The harder the coal, the greater will be the spread between the percentage passing through the two sieves.

Standards for Measuring Fineness

When solid fuels are burned in suspension it is essential that the fuel air mixture contain an appreciable quantity of extremely fine particles to insure rapid ignition. In order to obtain maximum combustion efficiency it is desirable to have a minimum amount of coarse particles in this same fuel air mixture. The former is usually expressed as percentage through a 200 mesh screen (−74 microns), while the latter is designated as percentage retained on a 50 mesh screen (+300 microns).

The mesh of a screen is designated by the number of openings per linear inch. Thus a 200 mesh screen has 200 openings to the inch or 40,000 per square inch. The size of opening is governed by the diameter of the wire used in making the screen. The U.S. Standard and W.S. Tyler are the most commonly used screen sieves. The mesh and the opening of these and other international screens are shown in Table 16–6 and Fig. 16–21.

Classification and Size Consist

In some reactions, such as setting of

---

[25] See Chapter 17, Fuel Burning Systems, for additional information.

cement, surface area is of extreme importance. In the combustion of pulverized coal, however, while it is important to have a large percentage of fine particles having a larger surface area, it is equally necessary to eliminate the oversize on the coarser screen. Regardless of the percentage of minus 200 mesh, as little as 5 per cent plus 50 mesh may produce furnace slagging and increased combustible loss, even though combustion conditions are excellent for the finer coal. The small amount of oversize represents very little additional surface if it is pulverized to all minus 50 mesh and all plus 200 mesh.

As an illustration, assume a typical screen analysis of coal sample from the Pittsburgh No. 8 seam, pulverized to 80 per cent minus 200 mesh:

> 99.5 per cent minus   50 mesh
> 96.5 per cent minus 100 mesh
> 80.0 per cent minus 200 mesh

This represents a surface area of approximately 1500 sq cm per gram, with over 97 per cent of the surface in the minus 200 mesh portion.

By overgrinding and poor classification it would be possible, on a commercially sized mill to have a sample of the following analysis:

> 95 per cent minus   50 mesh
> 90 per cent minus 100 mesh
> 80 per cent minus 200 mesh

This is not a satisfactory grind, because of the high percentage retained on the 50 mesh, even though the surface area is still 1500 sq cm per gram.

Therefore, good classification of coal is important. As a rule, it will lower the surface area of any grind. Thus, for a fixed percentage passing the 200 mesh

Table 16–6   Comparison of Sieve Openings

U.S. Standard Sieve			W. S. Tyler Sieve		
Mesh	Inches	Mm.	Mesh	Inches	Mm.
20	0.0331	0.84	20	0.0328	0.833
30	0.0234	0.595	28	0.0232	0.589
40	0.0165	0.420	35	0.0164	0.417
50*	0.0117	0.297	48*	0.0116	0.295
60	0.0098	0.250	60	0.0097	0.246
100*	0.0059	0.149	100*	0.0058	0.147
140	0.0041	0.105	150	0.0041	0.104
200*	0.0029	0.074	200*	0.0029	0.074
325	0.0017	0.044	325	0.0017	0.043
400	0.0015	0.037	400	0.0015	0.037

* Commonly used screens in pulverized coal practice for combustion purposes.

sieve, well classified coal will have less plus 50 mesh and also less surface area. However, a soft coal, such as Pocahontas, when ground to the same percentage passing the 200 mesh, will have slightly more plus 50 mesh and approximately 50 per cent more surface area.

Sampling Pulverized Coal

It is apparent that product fineness has a considerable bearing on pulverizer performance. Fineness samples should, therefore, be periodically analyzed. In a storage system this sample may be taken directly from the mill cyclone discharge.

On a direct fired system obtaining the sample is more difficult since it must be taken from a fuel line. A sample device, consisting of a small cyclone collector, sample jar and sampling nozzle with connecting hose may be utilized.

As in all sampling, it is essential that a sample, as representative of the whole as possible, be obtained.[26] It should be taken in the straightest possible line, as far removed from bends or offsets as the piping layout will allow, and should be obtained

---

[26] See Chapter 12, Power Plant Tests and Measurements, section on sampling in ducts and piping.

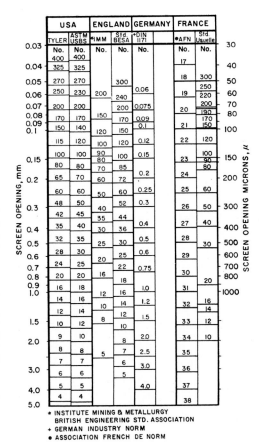

Fig. 16—21. Comparison of international screen openings

* INSTITUTE MINING & METALLURGY
BRITISH ENGINEERING STD. ASSOCIATION
+ GERMAN INDUSTRY NORM
• ASSOCIATION FRENCH DE NORM

thoroughly mixed. Fifty grams of this sample are placed on the top sieve of a nest of 50 mesh, 100 mesh and 200 mesh sieves and the nest then shaken until the procedure is completed.

Abrasion

Pulverizing requires power and results in an eventual loss of grinding element material. Balls, rolls, rings, races and liners gradually erode and wear out as a result of abrasion and metal displacement in the grinding process. Both power and maintenance make up the major cost of the pulverizing operation.

"Pure coal" is in itself relatively non-abrasive; however, such foreign materials as slate, sand and pyrites, commonly found in coal, as mined, are quite abrasive and these are the elements which produce the rapid and excessive wear in pulverizing apparatus. The economics of coal cleaning to remove abrasive foreign materials is dependent on many variables and must be determined for each individual application.

The resistance of a smooth plane surface to abrasion is called its hardness and is commonly recorded in terms of 10 common minerals according to Mohs' scale

at two points in the pipe at right angles to each other, both points being in the same plane perpendicular to the axis of the fuel line. If possible, the samples should be taken ahead of any distributors which might be in the system.

The sample is obtained by traversing the pipe across its entire diameter. The entire pipe diameter must be traversed and the rate of movement must be uniform. Samples in both directions must be taken for the same period of time.

The contents of the sampling jars are

Table 16—7   Mohs' Scale of Hardness

1 — Talc
2 — Gypsum
3 — Calcspar
4 — Fluorspar
5 — Apatite
6 — Feldspar
7 — Quartz
8 — Topaz
9 — Sapphire
10 — Diamond

of hardness, Table 16–7. There is no quantitative relation between these, the diamond being much greater in hardness above sapphire, than sapphire is above talc. Starting with the sapphire, and going down the scale the approximate relative hardness would be, sapphire 100, topaz 30, quartz 18, feldspar 12, apatite 7, fluorspar 3½, calcspar 2½, gypsum ½. Hardness of selected common materials is shown in Table 16–8.

Table   16–8   Common Materials and Their Mohs' Hardness

Coal	0.5 to 2.5
Slate	0.50 to 6.0
Mica	2.0 to 6.0
Pyrite	6.0 to 6.5
Granite	6.5
Marble	3.0
Soapstone	1.0 to 4.0
Kaolin clay	2.0 to 2.5
Beach sand	6.5 to 7.0
Iron ore	0.50 to 6.5
Window glass	5.5 to 6.0
Carborundum	9.5
Thumb nail	2.5
Copper coin	3.0
Knife blade	5.5
File	6.5
Emery	7.5

Coal Preparation

Coal should be properly prepared for its safe, economical and efficient use in a pulverizing system. Controllable continuity of flow to the pulverizer must be maintained steadily. Organic foreign materials such as wood, cloth or straw should be removed since they may collect in the milling system and become a fire hazard or may impair material or air flow patterns in the mill. Although many mills are de-

signed to reject, or are not adversely affected by small inorganic or metallic materials, larger metallic objects should be removed by a magnetic separator installed in the raw coal conveying system. These objects may otherwise obstruct the flow of coal through the pulverizer coal feeder or seriously damage the pulverizer.

The raw coal should be crushed to a size that will promote a uniform flow rate to the mill by the feeder. Favorable size consist will minimize segregation of coarse and fine fractions in the bunker, and result in more uniform rate of feed to various pulverizers being supplied from a given bunker. Fine, high surface moisture coal, when mixed with relatively dry lump coal, accentuates the segregation problem in bunkers. Crushing by size reduction of the dry lumps exposes additional dry surfaces for the adsorption of moisture from the wet fines, thereby producing a more uniform size and moisture distribution in the raw coal mass. Direct firing of pulverized coal is the method most commonly used for steam generation. In this application an uninterrupted and uniformly controllable supply of pulverized coal to the furnace is a most essential requisite. A steady and continuous flow of raw coal to the pulverizer will insure this.

Closely sized, double screened (say ¾ × ¼ in.) coal makes an ideal feed, since it permits water to drain off and flows freely from bunkers. However, such favorable sizing can be obtained only at a considerable price premium and this invariably precludes its use. In most cases, power

Table 16–9   Raw Coal Sizing for Pulverizers

Unit Pulverizer Capacity, tons per hr	1½ to 10	10 to 18	18 to 55
Raw Coal Sizing, in.	¾ X 10	1 to 1¼ X 0	1¼ to 1½ X 0

plants will receive coals classified as run-of-mine or screenings with lumps. It is therefore necessary that crushing equipment be installed in order to provide uniform raw feed sizing. Requirements of pulverizers and their feeders are shown in Table 16–9.

Coal Crushers

Although there are numerous types of crushers commercially available, the type most commonly used for smaller capacities is the swing hammer type of crusher. This has proved satisfactory for overall use and has demonstrated reliability and economy.

hammer type, speed, wear and bar spacing. The latter is usually somewhat greater than the desired coal size. These crushers produce a uniform coal sizing and break up pieces of wood and foreign material with the exception of metallic items. They are provided with pockets to catch foreign material that is too hard to crush.

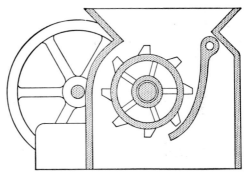

Fig. 16–23. Roll crusher

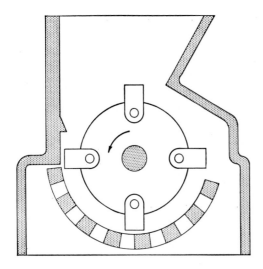

Fig. 16–22. Swing hammer crusher

The swing hammer crusher, Fig. 16–22, consists of a casing enclosing a rotor to which are attached pivoted hammers or rings. Coal is fed through a suitable opening in the top of the casing and crushing is effected by impact of the revolving hammers or rings directly on, or by throwing the coal against, the liners or spaced grate bars in the bottom of the casing. The degree of size reduction depends on

Roll crushers, Fig. 16–23, have been used but are not entirely satisfactory because of their inability to deliver a uniformly sized product. Probably the most satisfactory crusher for large capacities is the Bradford breaker. This design, Fig. 16–24, consists of a large diameter, slowly revolving (approximately 20 rpm) cylinder of perforated steel plates, the size of the perforations determining the final coal sizing. These openings are usually 1¼ to 1½ in. diameter. Breaking action of the coal is accomplished as follows: the coal is fed in at one end of the cylinder and carried upward on projecting vanes or shelves. As the cylinder rotates, the coal cascades off these shelves and breaks as it strikes the perforated plate. Since the coal dropping distance is relatively small, coal crushing occurs with the production of very few fines. Coal broken to

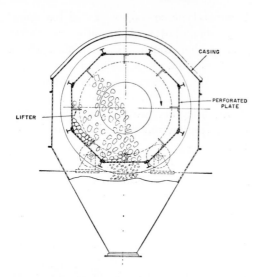

Fig. 16–24.   Bradford breaker

Table 16–10   Approximate Equivalent Round and Square Testing Screens

Screens	
Square Openings (No. or In.)	Round Openings (In.)
No. 8	⅛
No. 4	¼
⅜	½
½	⅝
⅝	¾
¾	⅞
⅞	1
1	1¼
1⅛	1⅜
1¼	1½
1½	1¾
1¾	2
2	2⅜
2¼	2¾
2½	3
3	3½

the screen size passes through the perforations to a hopper below. Rock, wood, slate, tramp iron and other foreign material is rejected. This breaker produces a relatively uniform product and uses very little power.

Table 16–10 shows equivalent sizes of round and square screens.

Coal Feeders

A coal feeder is a device used to supply the pulverizer with an uninterrupted flow of raw coal to meet system requirements. This requirement is especially important in a direct fired system. There are several types, including the table feeder, belt feeder and overshot roll feeder.

The table feeder utilizes a rotating table or disc onto which the coal is fed from a spout above. Rotation of the disc carries the coal around to a fixed scraper or plow blade. The rate of coal feed is determined by the speed of the table or the height of the orifice at the raw coal inlet. This type is subject to stoppage from small quantities of cellulose materials,

foreign matter or tramp iron, and the smaller sizes have difficulty in handling wet coal. They usually require more closely controlled raw coal sizing.

The belt feeder uses a short endless belt running on two separated rollers receiving coal from above at one end, discharging it at the other. Feed rate is controlled by varying the speed of the driving roll. A levelling plate fixes the depth of the coal bed on the belt.

The overshot roll feeder, Fig. 16–25, has a multibladed rotor which rotates about a fixed hollow cylindrical core. This core has an opening to the feeder discharge and is provided with heated air to minimize wet coal accumulation on surfaces and aid in coal drying. A hinged, spring-loaded levelling gate mounted over the rotor is used to limit the discharge from the rotor pockets. This gate permits the passage of oversize foreign material.

The roll feeder and the belt feeder, by virtue of their design, may be considered highly efficient volumetric feeding devices.

Feeders may be integrally or separately mounted and usually have separate drives.

Closed Circuit Grinding

When a large piece of coal is reduced to a number of smaller ones by any method, a larger number of finer particles will be produced simultaneously. Therefore, it is not possible for a pulverizer to produce a product that will all pass a 50 mesh screen without also obtaining a large percentage of material finer than 200 mesh. Thus if a quantity of coal, at one stage of pulverization, contains 50 per cent of material that will pass through a 50 mesh sieve, and if this minus 50 mesh material is removed from the grinding zone, it will contain a smaller percentage of minus 200 mesh material than if it had been permitted to remain in the grinding zone until the total quantity had been reduced to pass a 50 mesh sieve.

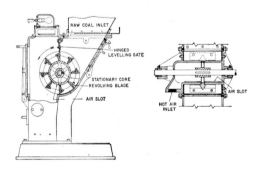

Fig. 16–25. Overshot roll feeder

An abundance of fine particles is necessary to insure prompt ignition of coal in suspension burning.[27] Energy is required in the production of this fine material. However, when grinding finer than necessary, power is wasted and the pulver-

izing equipment must be larger than actually required. Removal of the fines from the pulverizing zone as rapidly as they are produced and return of the oversize for regrinding eliminates unnecesary production of fines and reduces energy requirements. Better product sizing and increased capacity result from the above, which is termed closed circuit grinding. The pulverizing system component which accomplishes this size control is known as the classifier.

Mill Drying

Early coal pulverizing installations received undried coal and utilized ambient air in the mill system. No heat was added to the system and therefore coal feed was limited to that of very low moisture content. Maximum pulverizer capabilities were not realized. Later on, external coal dryers were added to the system. Because of the lack of cleanliness, high first cost, fire hazard and space requirements, these dryers were supplanted with what has become the universally accepted practice of mill drying.

Three methods of supplying and firing pulverized coal have been developed. These are the storage or bin and feeder system, the direct fired system and the semidirect system.

In a *storage system*, Fig. 16–26, coal is pulverized and is conveyed by air or gas to a suitable collector where the carrying medium is separated from the coal which is then transferred to a storage bin. It is there fed as required to the furnace. Hot air or flue gas introduced into the mill inlet provides the system drying requirements. Air vented from the system carries with it the moisture evaporated from the fuel.

---

[27] See Chapter 17, Fuel Burning Systems, for a more complete discussion of the combustion of pulverized coal.

In a *direct fired system,* Fig. 16–27, coal is pulverized and is transported with air, or air slightly diluted with gas, directly to the furnace where the fuel is consumed. Hot air or diluted furnace gas supplied to the pulverizer furnishes the heat for drying the coal. In addition to the functions of drying and transporting the pulverized fuel to the furnace, this air is also part of the combustion air and is known as a primary air. Inasmuch as a reduction in oxygen concentration in this primary air stream affects rapidity and stability of ignition, it is necessary, when using hot gas to draw it from a point of low CO_2 concentration and high temperature. This obviates the use of flue gas for drying in a direct firing system.

In a *semidirect system,* Fig. 16–28, a cyclone collector is utilized between the pulverizer and furnace to separate the conveying medium from the coal. The coal is fed directly from the cyclone to the furnace in a primary air stream which is independent of the milling system. The drying medium therefore can be the same as in a storage or bin system.

The drying capability of a given pulverizer design depends on the extent of circulating load within the mill, the ability to rapidly mix the dry classifier returns with incoming raw wet coal feed, the air weight and the air temperature which the design will tolerate. Some pulverizers are designed so that they will operate satisfactorily with inlet air temperatures up to 825 F while others are capable of using air at a maximum of 600 F.

Source of Heated Air

The best source of hot air for mill drying is either a regenerative or a tubular air heater. Those used in connection with large boiler installations usually provide sufficiently high temperature for almost

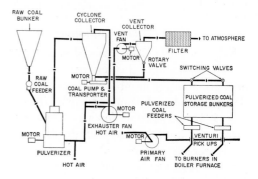

Fig. 16–26.   Storage system

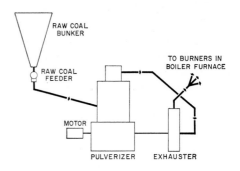

Fig. 16–27.   Direct fired system

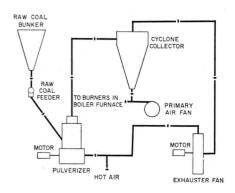

Fig. 16–28.   Semidirect system

any fuel moisture condition. On small installations, where the moisture is not high, steam air heaters may provide the heat necessary for drying the coal. For higher moisture conditions, it may be necessary to supplement this with furnace gas. Direct fired air heaters, properly interlocked and protected may also be used to supplement air heating requirements.

Moisture contained in fuel must be evaporated before ignition can take place. For rapid ignition, therefore, surface moisture must be removed before the fuel is injected into the furnace. This same drying process facilitates pulverization. The extent of mill drying required depends upon the type of fuel and its surface moisture.

High rank bituminous coals have a relatively dense structure and appear dry only when containing less than two or three per cent total moisture. The inherent moisture of these fuels varies from one to two per cent. Extremely low rank fuels such as lignite are of a relatively porous or cellular structure and contain inherent moisture of from 15 to 35 per cent. These same fuels with three per cent surface moisture (18 to 38 per cent total moisture) still appear dry. Dakota lignites have been succesfully fired when entering the furnace containing 35 per cent moisture, while Texas lignites have been fired at 28 per cent moisture. Weld County Colorado lignites, however, are limited to approximately 17 per cent moisture. It is apparent from the above that for both the pulverizing and ignition processes it is necessary to reduce the total moisture contained in the fuel to inherent moisture level.

If a particular pulverizer design requires low air flow for fineness maintenance, wet coal cannot be utilized without a considerable reduction in mill capacity. The design should permit use of high temperature incoming air in sufficient volume to maintain a condition of relative humidity below saturation at the mill output temperature. A pulverizer designed for a larger volume of low temperature inlet air for normal moisture fuel will require the admission of large quantities of cold tempering air when grinding dry coals. Since this air does not pass through the boiler air heater, overall unit efficiency will be reduced.

The type of fuel and the kind of system being used will determine the mill outlet temperature. It will be noted from Table 16–11 that mill outlet temperatures for storage systems are lower than for direct or semidirect firing, since most coals will not store safely at the temperatures used in direct firing. Storage bin fires caused by

Table 16–11 Allowable Mill Outlet Temperatures, F

System	Storage	Direct	Semidirect
High rank, high volatile bituminous	130*	170	170
Low rank, high volatile bituminous	130*	160	160
High rank, low volatile bituminous	135*	180	180
Lignite	110	110–140	120–140
Anthracite	200	—	—
Petroleum coke (delayed)	135	180–200	180–200
Petroleum coke (fluid)	200	200	200

* 160 F permissible with inert atmosphere blanketing of storage bin and low oxygen concentration conveying medium.

Table 16–12   Comparison of Suction and Pressure Systems

Fans	Suction	Pressure
Type	Exhauster	Blower
Construction	Meets NBFU No. 60 Code	Light gauge steel plate
Material handled	Coal-air mixture	Air only
Fan air temperature	Constant, 150–180 F	Variable depending on coal moisture content, 300 to 600 F
Allowable maximum air temperature to mill	700 F to 825 F	600 F
Relative fan efficiency	1.0	1.30
Fan wear	Moderate	Low to none
Feeder under pressure	No	Yes
Fan design requirements	Constant cfm Constant head	Variable cfm Head varies with temperature
Coal distribution to fuel pipes	Excellent utilizing riffle divider	More difficult to obtain
Control of air	By damper positioning only	Flow measurement read to position damper
Drive	Direct and integral with mill at mill speed	Separate from mill, requires additional motor or v-belt drive
Wearing liners required	Yes	No, but may, depending on air source
Seal air blower required	No	Yes

spontaneous combustion of the fuel may result from inadequate mill outlet temperature control. These may be inhibited by maintaining an oxygen deficient atmosphere, such as flue gas inerting, over the bin coal level.[28]

Capacity of a mill is based on its coal input, and its output on a given coal on a dry basis will decrease with increasing moisture content. Thus in selecting a mill size, if too much reduction of capacity is experienced with high moisture fuels, the mill can be too large under normal conditions of moisture or too small under excessive moisture conditions.

Exhauster and Blowers

All coal pulverizing systems utilize air or gas for drying, classification and transport purposes. Two methods are utilized for supplying the air requirements and overcoming system resistance. In a direct firing system, one method utilizes the fan, downstream of the pulverizer, while the other has the fan on the upstream side. The former is then known as a suction system and the fan handles dust laden air, while the latter is known as a pressure system and the fan handles clean air. Advantages and disadvantages are found in each system and are shown in Table 16–12. Fig. 16–29 provides for performance curves for both systems as applied to a 40,000 lb per hr pulverizer.

In a suction system the exhauster accounts for approximately 40 per cent of the total power requirements (mill plus fan), while in a pressure system the blower is approximately 50 per cent of the total.

---

[28] Oxygen limits for various fuels are shown in NBFU No. 60, Standard for the Installation and Operation of Pulverized Fuel Systems.

With direct firing the exhauster or blower volume requirement will depend upon the pulverizer size, and is usually fixed by the base capacity of that pulverizer.

The air-coal relationship is also shown in Fig. 16–29. The pressure or total head requirement is a function of the pulverizer and classifier resistance and the fuel distributing system and burner resistances. These resistances are in turn affected by the system design, the required fuel line velocities and density of the mixture being conveyed as shown in Table 16–13.

In a storage system the fan is located down stream of the dust collector and handles only a very small quantity of extremely fine (−200 mesh) dust at a relatively constant temperature (approximately 130 F). These fans are therefore designed for high efficiencies and need not be designed for a head higher than their operating temperature requires under operating conditions.

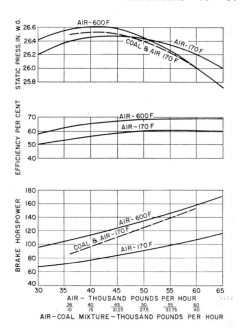

Fig. 16–29.   Fan performance curves for suction and pressure mills

Pulverizers — Primary Air Fans

These fans are used only with a bin and feeder system. In this system, the air used in the pulverizer for drying, classifying and conveying is separated from the coal in a cyclone collector. The pulverized coal is either dropped or mechanically or pneumatically conveyed to storage hoppers or bunkers. Mechanical, controllable feeders at the bunker outlets deliver the

required quantity of coal to burner fuel lines. At or near these feeders, the coal is reentrained in air (known as primary air) in proper proportions for transport to the burners.

According to the source of the air handled, there are installations where the primary air is taken from the room or preheated air duct, or both and installations where the vented air from the pulverizer system is used as all or part of the primary air.

Table 16—13   Typical Fuel Line Velocities

Piping Position		
Density, lb of air per lb of coal	1.2–2.5	2.5 and over
Horizontal velocity, fps	80–90	75–80
Vertical velocity, fps	60–80	45–60

Primary Air from Room or Air Duct

On installations of the first classification, only the air necessary to carry the coal to the burners and to provide the required velocity of coal-air mixture at the burners is used. This quantity depends, therefore, on the type of burner employed, the type of piping system employed (whether fuel lines be sloping, horizontal or vertical), the type of coal and, in some cases, the burner and furnace arrangement. A minor degree of flame control and regulation of furnace conditions can be accomplished through variations in the primary air quantity and discharge velocity at the burners.

Primary Air Temperature

Pulverized coal feeder and fuel piping arrangements determine the primary air temperature that can be used. This may be as high as 500 F. Since any tempering air admitted to the system reduces the quantity of air passing through the air heater, thus reducing the overall unit efficiency, a minimum amount of tempering air should be used in the primary air system.

The temperature of the air that the fan must handle will depend on its location. If heated air is to be used without tempering, either of two arrangements may be employed: a separate air heater for primary air may be used with the fan handling cold air or the fan may receive heated air from the main air heater and discharge it to a primary air duct at the required pressure.

When full preheat cannot be used, tempering is usually carried out at the suction side of the fan by dampering the preheated air and placing an adjustable cold air opening between this damper and the fan inlet. If equipment arrange-ment permits, a dampered cold air attachment from the forced draft fan may be made at this location. The temperature of the air handled by the fan with such an arrangement should be the maximum that can be used with the particular feeder and piping arrangement.

If vented air is to be used when available, the temperature will depend on that of the vent, the position of the vent in the return air line, and on whether or not preheated or cold air is added to the primary air at the fan inlet. The vented air will usually have a 70 to 90 per cent relative humidity, a temperature of 110 to 160 F and will contain coal fines vented from the collectors.

Volume Specifications

Generally speaking, the quantity of primary air required may be estimated with a greater degree of accuracy than that of the secondary air or flue gas, since it is not necessarily affected by changes in excess air supplied to nor leakage air into the furnace or setting. It is, however, affected to some extent by burner, furnace and piping design. It is also affected by the type of fuel being burned, particularly with respect to volatile content and fuel ignitability. For these reasons and because so many factors, including the skill of the operators are involved, definite values cannot be set for a given burner over its entire operating range. The maximum requirements at full burner capacity can, however, be quite accurately calculated for use in estimating fan volume.

Pressure Specifications

The fan pressure depends on the system resistance resulting from delivering the quantities of fuel and air required through the given arrangements of fan, ducts and piping; upon the source and temperature of the air handled and the pressure in the furnace to which the mixture is delivered. When the fan handles cold air, delivering it either directly or through an air heater to the feeder, the pressure at the fan inlet will be atmospheric and the total static pressure will be the sum of the resistances between the fan and the furnace including allowances for acceleration. When the fan handles heated air, received under pressure directly from the hot air duct, then the pressure available at the fan inlet may be subtracted from the total static pressure requirements calculated between fan and furnace, except when this heated air is tempered with air from the room. When the hot air is at a temperature in excess of that allowable for direct use, the available positive pressure, unless tempering is done from a connection to the forced draft fan discharge, is dissipated by dampering, and the tempering air flow is induced by a negative pressure of 0.5 to 1.0 in. wg at the fan inlet.

When the primary air fan handles vented air, the pressure required at the inlet will depend on the venting arrangement. If a vent fan is omitted, the primary air fan may be required to draw the air from the pulverizing system return air line from a point either under positive or negative pressure.

The velocities in primary air piping are high and the effect of changes in velocity cannot be neglected in these calculations.

If the pressure required to accelerate the coal at the feeder has been determined by test and if accurate calculation of all other losses has been made, a 10 per cent excess in pressure requirements should be adequate for fan selection.

Pulverizers — Vented Air Fans

In order to pulverize and classify coal economically and properly, it must either be dry when delivered to the pulverizer or must be dried during the pulverizing operation. This drying is accomplished by supplying hot air or flue gas to the pulverizing system. In a storage system, either all or a portion of the drying medium is discharged from the system by venting. This is done to remove the moisture which has been evaporated from the fuel. Aside from the adverse effects in the pulverizer resulting from lack of drying, a storage system requires the removal of moisture in order to eliminate or minimize difficulties in handling, storing and feeding of the pulverized fuel. The drying medium supplies a major portion of the heat to evaporate the fuel moisture and, in so doing, approaches saturation. Some of this almost saturated mixture, approximately equal to the weight of hot drying medium supplied, must be removed or vented from the system. The amount vented will depend on the pulverizer output, the moisture removed from the fuel, the initial temperature of the drying medium, the temperature of the vented material and the efficiency of the drying system. This latter may be measured in terms of relative humidity. The vented mixture may be disposed of in either one of two ways: by venting to the atmosphere directly or through the boiler stack, or by using it as part of the air supply to the burners or furnace. In the first case, since the vent contains some extremely fine coal (up to two per cent of the amount being pulverized) it cannot economically be vented directly without first removing most of the coal. This may be done in cyclone concentrators, bag filters, air washers or a combination of these. In the second case, the air need not be cleaned. In any case, however, there is sufficient resistance in the venting system to require a separate fan unless the primary air fan is designed for the additional pressure requirements.

Vent fans are called upon to handle air that is dusty and relatively close to saturation. Vented air piping must be designed for high velocities since the quantities vented will vary with the moisture in the fuel, and all pockets or horizontal runs, where coal can collect and perhaps become ignited, should be avoided. A minimum slope of 60 deg for these lines is desirable.

The vent fan must handle a quantity equal to the weight of hot air supplied for mill drying, plus the mill leakage and the moisture removed from the fuel.

Volume Specifications

In determining the volume on which to base selection of the vent fans, it is necessary to consider the effect of moisture on density of the mixture. Allowance should be made for the possible use of more air for drying in the pulverizer than theoretically required in order to compensate for lower available inlet temperatures or higher than specified coal moisture content. For fan selection the specified volume should be based on a 20 per cent excess factor above actual air requirements. The fan manufacturer should be given the temperature and density of the mixture to be handled under the most adverse conditions.

Pressure Specifications

On the inlet side of a vent fan, allowance must be made for pressure at the point of take off in the return air system and for resistance of the inlet line. On the discharge side, the vent line itself may represent a large part of the resistance, but, depending on where the air is vented, it may also be necessary to include the

vent concentrator resistance or bag filter or scrubber resistance as well as the furnace pressure. The pressure drop in the concentrator, bag filter or scrubber will depend on the design used and seemingly slight changes in the proportions of any of these items may greatly affect their efficiency and pressure drop. Where flue gas rather than preheated air is used for drying, a hot gas fan can be used to supply the drying medium to the pulverizer system. In some instances it may be desirable to omit the hot gas fan and rely on the vent fan to furnish the additional suction head required to induce an adequate flow of gas from its point of take off in the boiler passes to the point of ingress to the pulverizing system. The pressure loss in the hot gas system would also be included in the head requirements of the vent fan.

If there is any possibility that the fan may be called on to handle the above mentioned 20 per cent excess volume, then it should be selected for 40 per cent excess pressure.

Direct Firing Arrangements

Past references to direct firing systems presupposed firing into a furnace operated under suction. Fig. 16–30 shows the arrangement of equipment for a suction type mill when applied to a furnace of this design. Fig. 16–31 shows a pressure type mill for a similar furnace. Typical pressures, temperatures, damper and control requirements are indicated. Reference has previously been made in Table 16–12 to the varying conditions under which the exhauster or blower operates. With a suction mill, the coal feeder discharges against a negative pressure, whereas in the pressurized mill, the feeder discharges against a positive pressure of 18 to 21 in. wg. No coal feeder can act as a seal,

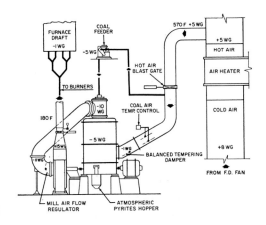

Fig. 16–30. Balanced draft furnace with suction mill

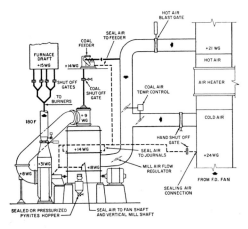

Fig. 16–32. Pressurized furnace with semipressurized mill

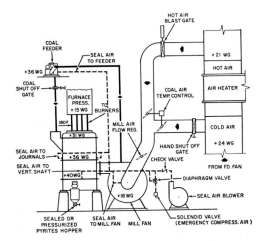

Fig. 16–31. Balanced draft furnace with pressurized mill

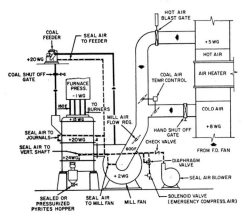

Fig. 16–33. Pressurized furnace with pressurized mill

and therefore, the head of coal above the feeder inlet must be utilized to prevent backflow of the pulverizer air. A roll type feeder, although not acting as a tight seal, can prevent excessive backflow of mill air in the event of coal stoppage above the feeder.

Although pulverized coal has been fired into pressure operated metallurgical furnaces for many years, its adaption to boilers operating under pressures sufficient to overcome the draft losses of the furnace, heat recovery and dust collecting equipment without the use of an induced draft fan is comparatively recent. Furnace pressures may be in the range of 8 to 20 in. wg.

Figs. 16–32 and 16–33 and Table 16–14 illustrate and compare two methods of pulverizer application to pressurized furnaces with typical pressures, temperatures, dampers and control requirements

Table 16–14   Pressurized Furnace Firing

Direct Firing Pressurized System using Exhausters or Blowers		
Mill pressure	Moderate	High
Type of fan	Exhauster	Blower
Location of fan	Outlet of pulverizer	Inlet of pulverizer
Materials handled	Air and pulverized coal	Air only
Casing construction	Meets NBFU No. 60 Code	Light gauge steel plate
Relative fan efficiency	1.00	1.3
Fan wear	Moderate	Low to none
Feeder pressure	Moderate	High
Need for sealing air blower	None	Required
Mill inlet temperature limit	825 F	600 F for standard fan
Coal distribution to burners	Excellent	More difficult to obtain
Temperature of material through fan	Constant	Variable depending on moisture, 300 to 600 F in fuel
Fan design for cfm	Constant — 130 to 180 F	Maximum required by temperature for Maximum H_2O to be encountered
Seal air blower required	No	Yes

indicated. Sealing air is shown where required. Fig. 16–32 illustrates the use of an exhauster located downstream of the pulverizer and acting as a booster fan in the system, while Fig. 16–33 illustrates a blower upstream of the pulverizer acting as a booster fan. Both systems utilize the unit forced draft fan as the source of primary air. The latter arrangement requires a seal air blower and the feeder operates against a pressure approximately 22 in. wg. greater than in the former arrangement. In all cases where the mill operates under pressure, an enclosed hopper valved at both inlet and outlet is required for the accumulation of pulverizer rejects.

Less total power is required for the system shown in Fig. 16–32 than for that of Fig. 16–33, since the fan on the former, although handling material and operating at a lower efficiency, operates at a much lower temperature than the fan on the latter system.

Safety and Controls

The production and handling of pulverized fuels can be hazardous. Fine particles in suspension or deposition are readily volatilized and become combustible with the result that under certain conditions explosions may take place. Notwithstanding these dangers, the industry has achieved a remarkable safety record since the inception of pulverized coal firing. All pulverizing equipment and related auxiliaries are designed in accordance with NBFU Standard No. 60 mentioned previously, including strength of equipment, valving and inerting in order to protect property and life.

To supplement the above recommendations, various controls and safety devices are utilized for the correct and proper operation of the equipment. They include permissive interlocks for the proper sequential operation of equipment, flow alarms to indicate cessation of coal flow to and from feeders, adequate temperature control of coal-air mixture leaving the mill, control of air flow through the pulverizing system to prevent fuel settling in transport piping and load limiting devices to prevent overfeeding the mills. Anticipating actions and more responsive feedback may often be included with the above in pulverizer control systems.

17

Fuel Burning Systems[1]

THE PRIMARY FUNCTION of *fuel burning systems* in the process of steam generation is to provide controlled, efficient conversion of the chemical energy of the fuel into heat energy which is then transferred to the heat absorbing surfaces of the steam generator.

Fuel burning systems function to do this by introducing the fuel and air for combustion, mixing these reactants, igniting the mixture and distributing the flame envelope and the products of combustion. These steps are essential to the successful controlled and efficient conversion of chemical energy to heat energy.

An ideal fuel burning system fulfilling these functions would have the following characteristics:

1. No excess oxygen or unburned fuel in the end products of combustion
2. A low rate of auxiliary ignition energy input to initiate and sustain continuity of the combustion reaction
3. A satisfactory and economical reaction rate between the fuel and oxygen
4. A compatible and effective method of handling and disposing of the solid impurities introduced with the fuel
5. Uniform distribution of the product weight and temperature in relation to the parallel circuits of heat absorbing surface
6. A wide and stable firing range

7. Fast response to demands for a change in firing rate
8. A high degree of equipment availability with low maintenance requirements

A fuel burning system is an interconnection of devices which appropriately prepares fuel and air for combustion, properly directs their introduction into the furnace, provides conditions for stable ignition and combustion and suitably removes the products of combustion from the furnace.

Subsystems and Their Functions

The fuel burning system should function so that the fuel and air input is ignited continuously and immediately upon its entry into the furnace. The total fuel burning system required to do this consists of *subsystems* for air handling, fuel handling, ignition and combustion product removal plus the main burners and the boiler furnace.

Air Handling

This subsystem should be capable of supplying properly prepared air to the main burners on a continuous and uninterrupted basis. It should be capable of providing any required air-fuel ratio over the entire operating range of the fuel burning system.

[1] Material contributed by V. Z. Caracristi and T. H. Cooper.

Fuel Handling

This subsystem should be capable of supplying properly prepared uncontaminated fuel to the main burners on a continuous and uninterrupted basis. It should be capable of providing any required air-fuel ratio over the entire operating range of the fuel burning system.

Ignition

This subsystem should be capable of providing initial ignition of any fuel input and air-fuel ratio over the entire operating range of the fuel burning system. Its primary function is to ignite the furnace input continuously and immediately. At very low boiler operating rates the ignition subsystem may be used to provide supplemental ignition energy to extend the stable operating range of the fuel burning system.

Main Burners

These should be designed and constructed so as to be capable of properly regulating and directing the flow of air and fuel into the furnace to provide stable combustion. The main burners function to insure self-ignition of the furnace input on a continuous and immediate basis. The range of stable burner operation should be determined by testing the related subsystems and establishing limits beyond which auxiliary ignition is required to achieve stable combustion.

Boiler Furnace

In terms of fuel burning systems and subsystems, the boiler furnace should be designed and constructed so as to promote a flow pattern of incoming fuel and air such that stable combustion can be achieved over the entire operating range. An important design consideration is to minimize stratification of gases and to eliminate dead pockets or zones which cannot be properly purged.[2]

Combustion Product Removal

This subsystem should be capable of removing furnace gases over the entire operating range of the fuel burning system while maintaining furnace pressures within design limitations. A primary function is to remove inert combustion products so that the furnace fuel and air input can be continuously and immediately ignited. The capacity of this subsystem for removal of combustion products can impose a limitation on the rate of furnace input.

The Combustion Process

The rate and degree of completion of a chemical reaction such as the combustion process are importantly influenced by temperature, concentration, preparation and distribution of the reactants, catalysts and mechanical turbulence. All of these factors have one effect in common: to increase contacts between molecules of the reactants.

Higher temperatures, for instance, increase the velocity of molecular movement permitting harder and more frequent contact between molecules. A temperature rise of 200 deg F at some stages can increase the possible rate of reaction by a million fold.

At a given pressure, three basic factors limit the maximum temperature that can be realized for increased opportunity for

---

[2] For additional considerations see Chapter 6, Heat Transfer, section on the boiler furnace, and Chapter 19, Fundamentals of Boiler Design.

contact. These are the heat absorbed by the combustion chamber enclosure, by the reactants in bringing them to ignition temperature and by the nitrogen in the air used as a source of oxygen.

The concentration and distribution of the reactants in a given volume is directly related to the opportunity for contact between interacting molecules. In an atmosphere containing 21 per cent oxygen, the amount present in air, this rate is much less than it would be with 90 per cent oxygen. This is another harmful effect of the presence of nitrogen in the air used as the oxygen supply for oxidizing the fuel. Distribution and concentration of reactants assumes even greater importance as the reaction proceeds toward completion. Because of the dilution of reactants by the inert products of combustion, the relative distribution, and hence opportunity for contact, approaches zero.

Preparation of the reactants and mechanical turbulence greatly influences the reaction rate. It is primarily this factor that is available to the designer of a fuel burning system to provide the desirable reaction rate.

The beneficial effect of mechanical turbulence on the combustion reaction becomes apparent when it is realized that agitation can improve relative distribution and impart energy permitting greater opportunity for molecular contact. Agitation assumes greater significance when it can be achieved in the later stages of the combustion process at a time when the relative concentration of the reactants is approaching zero.

Before the combustion reaction can occur, the mixture of reactants must of course be ignited. The mechanism of establishing ignition of any fuel-air mixture is to elevate its temperature to the point where its rate of oxidation and subsequent release of heat equals or exceeds the rate at which heat is extracted from the products of combustion.[3]

Fundamental Concepts of Ignition Energy

The functional requirement of a fuel burning system is to supply an uninterrupted flammable furnace input and ignite it continuously as fast as it is introduced and immediately upon its appearance in the furnace. Thus, no explosive mixture can accumulate in the furnace, since the furnace input is effectively consumed and rendered inert. *Ignition* takes place when the flammable furnace input is heated above the ignition temperature.

Supplying correct ignition energy for the furnace input is a substantial task. There are many factors which establish the *range* of combinations of ignition energy quantity, quality and location that can provide a satisfactory furnace input ignition rate at any instant. Unfortunately, these factors are of rapidly changing value, and what constitutes sufficient ignition energy at one instant may be insufficient the next. From the rate ignit-

---

[3] The interested reader will find the following two volumes at opposite ends of a spectrum encompassing various levels of discussion of the combustion process. *Fuels and Combustion Handbook* by A. J. Johnson and G. H. Auth (McGraw-Hill, 1951) represents a practical and empirical approach to the subject and contains a great deal of useful information for engineering design and operation. *Combustion, Flames and Explosion of Gases* by Bernard Lewis and Guenther von Elbe (Second Edition, Academic Press, 1961) constitutes an advanced approach from the viewpoint of physical chemistry and gives minimal attention to power plant applications. An effort should be made to understand both approaches and to recognize their strengths and limitations.

ing standpoint, ignition energy is never in excessive supply. The more stable a fire is, the more likely that ignition energy is being supplied in substantial excess of the minimum necessary to maintain input ignition.

Factors Determining Required Ignition Energy

Six major factors determine the total ignition energy required.

1. *Fuel quality.* Low grade fuels can require substantially more heat (auxiliary and inherent ignition energy) to raise the total fuel mass up to the required ignition temperature than do high grade fuels. High moisture concentrations in a fuel will require very large quantities of heat to convert the water to steam before the fuel can be burned.[4]

2. *Fuel preparation.* If the fuels are not suitably prepared (too coarse or too cold, for example), they can require much more ignition heat on a rate basis. This occurs because a higher percentage of the total fuel mass must be brought up to the ignition temperature before substantial inherent ignition energy (heat) is released.[5]

3. *Air preparation.* If the air is not suitably prepared (too cold or diluted with inert materials, for example), it can require much more ignition energy to bring the total oxygen-bearing mass (O_2 + inert) up to the ignition temperature.

4. *Burner product distribution.* If the main burner distributes fuel and air so that a noncombustible product is provided where the auxiliary or inherent ignition energy is still adequate to ignite a combustible furnace input, the best ignition energy will be ineffective.

5. *Total fuel-air ratio.* If the main burner fuel-air ratio is far off from premix flammable ratios, even though the diffusion firing technique for furnace combustion is used, it may require much more ignition energy because the excess ingredient (fuel or air) acts as an inert, consuming heat without being able to react chemically and release heat in return.

6. *Main burner mass flow rate.* If the main burner mass flow rate is substantial, it will require a comparable ignition energy input rate to provide satisfactory ignition, since the same percentage of the flammable main burner fuel and air mixture must be raised to the ignition temperature regardless of flow rates. Since igniters normally supply only a small percentage of the total fuel input, large amounts of inherent ignition energy[6] are essential to maintain ignition at high furnace input rates.

Supply of Ignition Energy

There are several reasons, however, why auxiliary ignition energy for lightoff is not always supplied in greatly excessive amounts as a safety factor to cover indeterminate ignition requirement factors.

Ignition energy usually is supplied in the form of heat. Large amounts of heat may not always be desired in practical boiler operation, particularly at low loads.

---

[4] Specific fuels are discussed in some detail in Chapter 13, Fuel Properties of Coal, and Chapter 14, Natural Gas, Oil and Byproduct Fuels.

[5] This is also discussed in Chapter 16, Pulverizers.

[6] A subsequent section of this chapter is concerned with the fundamental concepts of inherent ignition energy.

Ignition energy can be expensive. Most stations must utilize more costly fuel for auxiliary ignition purposes than is used for main burner firing. If the amount of premium fuel used is large, the costs can be substantial.

Furnaces are best fired up to avoid pressurizing by igniting the input in suitable and proportionate steps. Furnace walls for water tube boilers are not capable of withstanding a high furnace pressure. A proportionately large block increase in furnace input can be smoothly, adequately and continuously ignited, but the sudden increase in average furnace temperature calls for a quick increase in specific volume if the furnace pressure is to remain the same. Since few furnaces can vent the excess material fast enough, the specific volume cannot increase sufficiently and so the furnace pressure increases. Fig. 17–1 shows the step ignition process. Note that the scales are logarithmic. Experience has shown that firing by this system will minimize furnace pressurizing.

The best ignition systems supply ignition energy proportional to but in excess of that required. There are two sources of ignition energy presently used to accomplish this: auxiliary and inherent.

Fundamental Concepts of Auxiliary Ignition Energy

An auxiliary ignition system should be a controllable means of providing adequate ignition energy in the form of electrical sparks, hot gases or flame for a larger burner system. This should be independent of but functional with the main burner supplies.

The functional requirement of an auxiliary ignition system is to provide more ignition energy than that required by the interlocked main burner flows to be ignited or to remain ignited. An auxiliary ignition system should provide a reliable, safe method for igniting and stabilizing each planned main flame envelope in a furnace, without manual manipulation of the ignition energy. In this way the main burner fuel will be continuously ignited (providing sufficient air is being supplied with the fuel) as fast as it is introduced. The heat produced by igniters can be sufficient to warm a furnace.

Some auxiliary ignition systems utilize premium fuel (gaseous or light liquids) in a fuel subsystem supplying the igniter burner which prepares and distributes this fuel to a combustion zone located near or in close proximity to the point where the main burner flow first enters the furnace and forms a flammable mixture. Examples are shown on Fig. 17–2. The ignition fuel is usually ignited by a spark while it is supplied with oxygen from the main burner air flow or the furnace atmosphere, supplied originally from the main burner system.

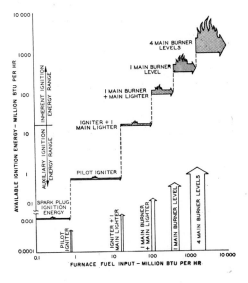

Figure 17–1. Plot of the step ignition process.

Factors Affecting Auxiliary Ignition Energy

The following factors affect the usable, effective and available auxiliary ignition energy supplied.

1. *Ignition fuel quantity and quality.* Some ignition fuels burn "hotter" than others. More ignition fuel flow only means potentially more auxiliary ignition energy. Twice as much ignition fuel does not necessarily mean that the igniter can ignite twice as much furnace input.

2. *Oxygen supply available for ignition fuel.* If insufficient or excessively diluted oxygen is supplied to the ignition fuel, the igniter effectiveness will be greatly reduced.

3. *Combustion efficiency.* If the igniter fuel is not burned up prior to or during initial contact with the ignitable main burner zone, it cannot provide satisfactory ignition. It would be possible for this volatile fuel to be the focal point of an explosion.

4. *Ability to deliver auxiliary ignition energy to the proper zone.* If the auxiliary ignition energy is not put in the place where it can be effective, no amount of ignition energy will make up for it.

5. *Form of ignition energy.* Of the various methods possible for raising flammable material up to the ignition temperature, such as the use of flame or products of combustion, one may be more effective for certain fuels or burner systems than the others.

6. *Zone affected by the ignition energy.* Certain fuels or burner systems may require the formation of a sizable ignition zone to achieve suitable ignition. Time may be necessary for volatilization to occur before ignition can be started. Thus, ignition energy may be needed to drive off the volatiles and then raise the volatiles and oxygen to the ignition temperature. Higher furnace input rates and longer ignition times will require a larger ignition zone.

Ideal and Practical Auxiliary Ignition Systems

The *ideal* auxiliary ignition system would be capable of measuring the resultant ignition energy required and then supplying more than necessary. Although it is difficult to measure all of the ignition factors, they must be carefully evaluated

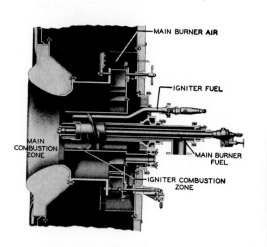

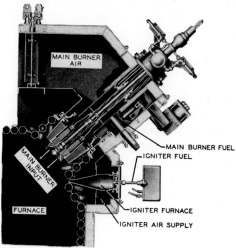

Figure 17–2. Typical auxiliary ignition systems.

so that only the actual amount of safety available is expected from an ignition subsystem.

An ignition subsystem that can quantitatively measure the ignition effect it is supplying can be used as a main burner "flame detector." When this auxiliary ignition subsystem is on, and its product is measured to be more than that required, the main burner can be then turned on, and it will be and remain ignited.

A *practical* auxiliary ignition system can only fulfill its basic purpose when the factors previously described are within specific limits, such that the ignition energy supplied is always more than the ignition energy required. Furnace operation is either within or without these limits, and this dictates that given igniters will be able to ignite or that they will not. If the igniters can ignite, they will be an essential part of any safe fuel burning system. If the igniters cannot reliably ignite, they will be a major contributor to the explosion hazard. The only criterion for operating an ignition system is that it should not be turned on or kept on when an explosive accumulation is in the furnace. However, when the furnace is nonflammable (air-rich, fuel-rich or inert), as during firing, any igniter operation, no matter how poor, will be safe.

Igniter Operation and Design

Igniter operating periods should be defined and insured by appropriate sequential interlocks so that no igniter operation can occur during unsafe conditions. Likewise, and equally as important, igniter operation should not be prohibited at any time when furnace atmospheres are nonflammable. Unnecessary limitations on igniter operation reduce the total safety that igniters can provide by keeping them off when they could improve an unstable situation, as well as preventing or complicating maintenance. This not only reduces igniter availability but may also decrease confidence in the ignition system.

If step ignition is used and it is known that each step can ignite the furnace input range intended for it, safe firing can be insured. Thus, it may be more simple, practical and reliable to monitor the ignition energy at an early step, such as a pilot igniter.

The range of required igniter operation is of prime importance. For instance, any igniter must reliably ignite the fuel-air mixture from the main burner under ideal minimum flow conditions. It is quite another problem, however, to instantaneously and smoothly ignite maximum fuel flow from a burner under maximum air flow conditions. While this may be an extremely difficult test of an ignition system, it may be absolutely essential to safe boiler operation.

Fig. 17–3 shows a type of igniter with a simple quantitative flame safeguard device as an integrated component. This igniter incorporates a separate interlock system for itself, since it is a burner-furnace combination, so that it is practically impossible for a flame-on indication to be sent from the igniter unless the flame is on and above the minimum satisfactory output level. The ultimate in a combined igniter-burner system design would preclude furnace explosions by always consuming furnace reactant supplies before the required amount for a serious explosion could accumulate.

Fundamental Concepts of Inherent Ignition Energy

Inherent ignition energy is heat that a fuel burning system retrieves from the products of combustion and uses to ignite the furnace input. This heat may be in the form of flame or products of combustion as shown in Fig. 17–4. Normally this source provides considerably more ignition energy than the auxiliary ignition system. Without ample inherent ignition energy, the flame will not be complete or stable when the auxiliary ignition is removed. All flexible firing systems are capable of stable operation over a wide range using only inherent ignition energy. Normally this range can be extended through the use of auxiliary ignition energy. To define operating limitations, proper evaluation of the inherent ignition energy is essential.

Generally, burner systems are judged by their inherent ignition characteristics. The stability of the fire and the unassisted operating range are related to the available inherent ignition energy. However, it is easier to check on the flame stability over the operating range of a burner system than it is to measure the inherent ignition energy, which is the cause. Unfortunately, this energy supply is not ideally suited to its need. When the fur-

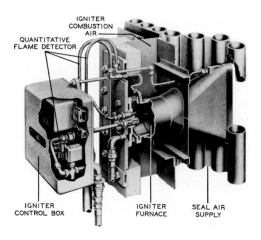

Figure 17–3.   Igniter with separate interlock system.

nace input is optimum, so that the minimum ignition energy is required, the maximum inherent ignition energy will be available. When the furnace input needs substantial ignition energy, the minimum inherent ignition energy is available, Fig. 17–5. The less powerful but readily available and controllable auxiliary ignition energy system therefore acquires added use as a stabilizing tool at conditions where inherent ignition energy is inadequate. This is in addition to its function of supplying initial ignition of the furnace input.

Inherent Ignition Energy and Its Functional Relationships

An inherent ignition supply is *functional* with the main flame. The same factors which determine the quality and quantity of the main combustion account for the quantity, quality and effectiveness of the inherent ignition energy. They are fuel and air preparation, input and mixing patterns, input quantity and fuel-air ratio.

Depending upon the type of inherent ignition energy used, changing individual factors will achieve different results. Some burner systems have ample inherent ignition energy at highly air-rich conditions and need assistance at fuel-rich inputs. Certain other burners do not need finely divided fuel as much as others. Each given burner system has a *range* of combinations of the factors stated above where the effective inherent ignition energy supply exceeds the ignition energy required. This range should be established and interlocked for each burner system.

The inherent ignition energy effectiveness, while functional with the form of ignition energy, will also be variable with the combustion efficiency. If an inherent

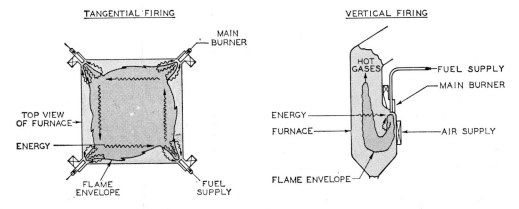

Figure 17–4. Inherent ignition energy for tangential and vertical firing.

ignition energy system utilizes hot products of combustion, its effectiveness (heat transfer) will be reduced at off-ratio firing even though the same proportion of burned gases is being circulated to the furnace input. If an inherent ignition energy system utilizes flame (radiant heat), short or nonluminous fires caused by an improper furnace input may limit its effectiveness although the same proportion of flame may be directed back to the furnace input.

When the auxiliary ignition system is off, a furnace flameout can only be caused directly through insufficient inherent ignition energy or through improper furnace inputs which then result in insufficient inherent ignition energy.

Thus all flameouts, where some fuel and air are being supplied, actually result from inadequate ignition energy. As Fig. 17–5 indicates, it is usually more advantageous to improve the furnace input and require less ignition energy (while obtaining more inherent ignition energy) than it is to supply auxiliary ignition energy.

Practical Burner Design

In a practical burner and fuel burning system as applied to a boiler, all of the fundamental factors influencing rate and completeness of combustion must be considered in conjunction with obtaining a high degree of heat transfer efficiency.

There are two basic methods of producing a total flow pattern in a combustion

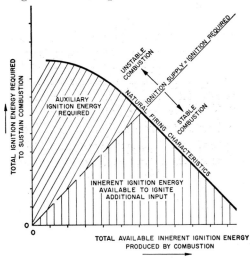

Figure 17–5. Inherent ignition energy versus total required ignition energy.

chamber to provide successful reactant molecular contacts through mechanical turbulence. One, providing multiple flame envelopes, is to divide and distribute fuel and air into a multiplicity of similar streams and treat each pair of fuel and air streams independently of the others. The second, resulting in a single flame envelope, is to provide interaction between all streams of air and fuel introduced into the combustion chamber.

The first of these methods requires accurate subdivision of the total fuel and air supplied to a common combustion chamber and provides little opportunity for sustained mechanical mixing or turbulence throughout the entire combustion chamber volume. The necessity of obtaining and sustaining good distribution of fuel and air is a technical as well as an operating problem. There must be sufficient opportunity for contact of fuel and oxygen molecules as well as uniform distribution of product temperature and mass in relation to the combustion chamber. The single flame envelope technique provides interaction between all streams of fuel and air introduced into a common chamber. It permits more time for contact between all fuel and air molecules, and mechanical turbulence is sustained throughout the entire volume of the combustion chamber. This avoids stringent distribution accuracy requirements.

Vertically Fired System

The burner nozzle and combustion chamber flow mechanism of a vertically fired system is shown in Fig. 17–6. An illustration of a typical burner air and fuel nozzle is shown in Fig. 17–7. This type of fuel burning system was developed initially for pulverized coal before the advent of water cooled combustion chamber wall surfaces. Because a large percentage of the total combustion air is withheld from the fuel stream until it projects well down into the furnace, this arrangement has the advantage that the fuel stream is heated separately from the main body of combustion air, providing good ignition stability. The delayed introduction of the main body of combustion air provides needed turbulence at a point in the fuel stream where partial dilution has taken place. The furnace flow pattern that passes the product gases immediately in front of and between the fuel nozzles provides a ready source of inherent ignition energy for raising the primary fuel stream to the ignition temperature. The path of entrained solid fuel particles is such that the larger particles with the lowest surface area to weight ratio have the longest residence time in the combustion chamber.

This type of firing is particularly well suited for solid fuels which are difficult to ignite, such as those with less than 15 per cent volatile matter. The delayed introduction of air does not provide desired results with the high volatile solid or liquid fuels and cannot be effectively used with gaseous fuels. Thus, where high volatile fuels are used, provision must be made for providing air more rapidly to the air fuel input. This change of air introduction alters the furnace flow pattern and the effectiveness of the furnace chamber surface. From the flow pattern produced in the furnace it is apparent that the fuel introduced to a burner nozzle, Fig. 17–7, can only obtain oxygen from parts a', a'', a'''. Therefore, the distribution of fuel and air to each section of the furnace must be uniform and symmetrical if opportunity for contact and uniformity of product mass and temperature is to be established. Physical factors limit the maximum capacity of each fuel

VERTICAL FIRING

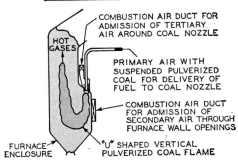

Figure 17–6. Flow pattern of vertical firing.

nozzle to approximately 50,000,000 Btu per hr, and the furnace width becomes too great for high capacity central station boilers.

Horizontally Fired System

The burner fuel nozzle, method of air introduction and the flow pattern produced by a horizontal turbulent type burner system are shown in Fig. 17–8 and a typical burner of the same type, in Fig. 17–9. This type of burner was developed to provide a method of introducing fuel and air to obtain higher capacities per fuel nozzle than was practical with the vertically fired system. With this type burner, the air is introduced into the throat area with a rotation which produces a secondary flow in the central zone. The fuel concentrated in the vortex has a relatively long residence time to reach ignition temperature with a relatively low mass of air to be simultaneously heated. While the mechanical turbulence in the immediate area of the throat is intensive, it does not persist for any appreciable distance out into the vastly greater volume of the combustion chamber. Rapid ignition and combustion must be obtained to utilize

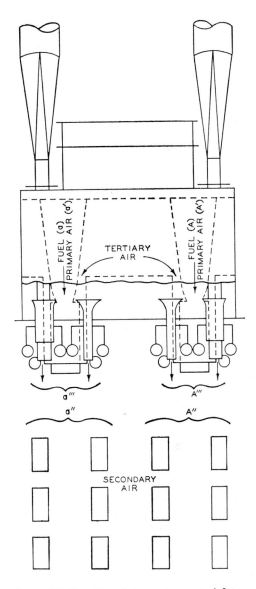

Figure 17–7. Air admission in vertical firing.

this turbulence before reduction in reactant concentration occurs. With this type of firing system it is impossible for the fuel introduced in burner A to mix suitably with the air from burner B. The proportioning of fuel and air to each nozzle

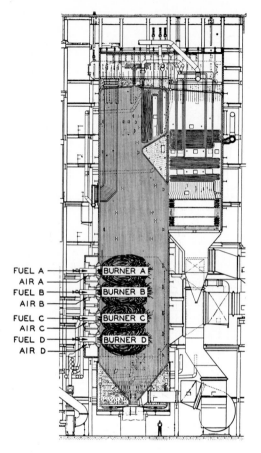

FUEL A
AIR A
FUEL B
AIR B
FUEL C
AIR C
FUEL D
AIR D

BURNER A
BURNER B
BURNER C
BURNER D

Figure 17—8. Flow pattern of horizontal firing.

throat area and by centering the fuel introduction nozzle in the throat opening.

Peripheral fuel distribution of liquid and gaseous fuels is usually accomplished through the geometry of the burner tip. In many burners this is done by arranging the tip orifices uniformly around the circumference of a circle on the tip or nozzle. Mechanical oil atomizers with a single tip orifice utilize an internal design that imparts a high angular velocity spin to the fluid which provides the quality of atomization and distribution required. In the case of pulverized coal, which is transported in mechanical suspension by a portion of the combustion air, adjustable vanes, Fig. 17–9, in the fuel inlet nozzle promote good peripheral fuel distribution.

Tangentially Fired System

The burner system in a tangentially fired boiler and the flow pattern it produces are shown in Fig. 17–10. An illustration of a typical tilting tangential type burner arrangement is shown in Fig. 17–11. This burner system was developed to

and air assembly must be uniform if opportunity for contact and uniform product mass and temperature in relation to the combustion chamber are to be established. Because of the limited time and volume through which mechanical turbulence is established and maintained, the peripheral distribution of air and fuel at each burner and the throat area is of extreme importance. Reference to Fig. 17–9 indicates how this peripheral distribution of air is accomplished by the yoke adjustment of the ring dampers, by the area reduction from the inlet vane area to the

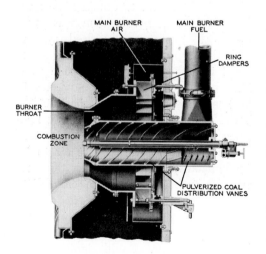

MAIN BURNER AIR   MAIN BURNER FUEL

RING DAMPERS

BURNER THROAT

COMBUSTION ZONE

PULVERIZED COAL DISTRIBUTION VANES

Figure 17–9. Burner for horizontal firing.

Figure 17—10. Flow pattern of tangential firing. Note size of man, location of pulverizers, and the amount of interconnecting fuel piping and ductwork.

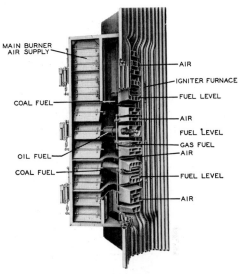

MAIN BURNER
AIR SUPPLY

COAL FUEL

OIL FUEL

COAL FUEL

AIR
IGNITER FURNACE
FUEL LEVEL
AIR
FUEL LEVEL
GAS FUEL
AIR
FUEL LEVEL
AIR

Figure 17—11. Tilting tangential burner.

incorporate the advantages of the single flame envelope technique previously described for an extremely wide range of fuels. Excellent control over the furnace flow pattern allows adjustment of the rate at which air is supplied to the fuel as well as the energy then available to mix these reactants.

Fuel streams are essentially injected into the furnace between air streams. Control of the input distribution and velocity provides control over the furnace flow pattern and thus the combustion process. The fuel is normally fired on a level basis so that proper interaction of the separate streams is obtained. Good results are obtained even when distribution is so unbalanced as to shift the flame envelope off exact center. Even if one corner is blanked off entirely, combustion can be stable and efficient. Involved efforts to provide exact symmetrical streams are unnecessary.

Additional Burner Functions

In practice a burner design may be utilized to accomplish other ends aside from efficient combustion of fuel. For instance, the burner system may be used to control slag fluidity or steam temperature in an operating steam generator.[7] It is possible to accomplish these very desirable aims with little or no sacrifice in burner performance as long as the basic principles of the mechanism of combustion are ad-hered to. One example of control by burner design is illustrated in Fig. 17–12 showing how tilting tangential burners permit selective utilization of the furnace heat absorbing surfaces. Another example of regulation of combustion chamber effectiveness is the use of gas recirculation at various points and in variable quantities in proper relation to the overall mass flow pattern. This is illustrated in Fig. 17–13.

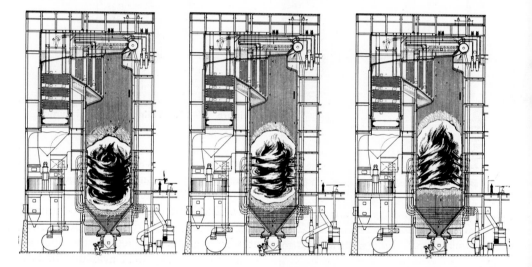

Figure 17–12.   Selective furnace utilization and steam temperature control by tilting tangential burners.

Interlocks and Safety Systems

Present day economics of power plant operation have accelerated the trend to larger steam generating units, and remote control of their fuel burning systems. Increase in the number and size of furnaces in service, has effected an exponential rise in repair costs and down time due to furnace accidents as a result of malfunction or operator error in manipulation of the fuel firing system. Designers now recognize furnace explosion protection must be considered an integral part of the complete fuel burning system.

The fuel burning system must incorporate evaluating and decision making capability over all regulating and interlocking devices controlling the fuel and air supplies, as well as the ignition energy, introduced into the furnace. Design criteria of paramount consideration to the fuel sys-

---

[7] Control of steam temperature is discussed in Chapter 22, Controls and Instruments.

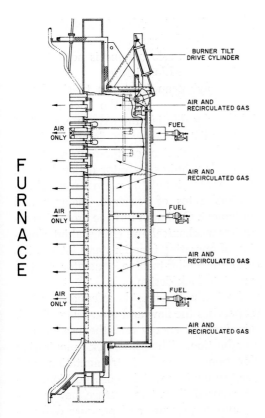

AIR AND
RECIRCULATED GAS

AIR AND
RECIRCULATED GAS

AIR AND
RECIRCULATED GAS

AIR AND
RECIRCULATED GAS

BURNER TILT
DRIVE CYLINDER

FUEL

FUEL

FUEL

AIR
ONLY

AIR
ONLY

AIR
ONLY

F
U
R
N
A
C
E

Figure 17—13. Burner with gas recirculation.

tems designer are *safety, reliability and availability.*

The basic control of the combustion process is the rate of admission of fuel and air. The combustion control and the load control modifies and regulates the fuel burning process through many control variables and feedbacks including, but not limited to, deviation limits, turbine safety runbacks, load change, emergency minimum fuel cut-back, flame scanning, trip functions, interlocks and automation functions, etc.

It is implicit in this control arrangement, to maintain and assure safe furnace firing conditions. The fuel burning system must be integrated with the combustion control and load control of the boiler-turbine-generator. Sound engineering analysis dictates the overall integration be under the boiler and fuel systems designers' control to fulfill the basic design concepts of *safety, reliability and availability.*

Furnace Explosions

Furnace explosions are rare and unlikely. The total number of unit operating hours relative to the hours lost due to explosions is extremely large. This desirable situation exists because (1) furnaces are provided with an explosive accumulation during a minute percentage of their operating life and (2) only a small part of those explosive charges provided receive suitable ignition to actually cause an explosion.

However, furnace explosions are hardly ever prevented. Often they are avoided by fortuitous circumstances (beyond operator control) that thwart the timely sequence of events necessary. Although many assumptions can be made that various circumstances will probably exist to interrupt the explosion sequence, reliance upon fortunate conditions is an unrealistic approach to "protecting" a furnace. To prevent furnace explosions, assertive control is essential.

It is essential in designing a furnace safeguard system to have a good understanding of the causes of furnace explosions. The primary control of the combustion process, for suspension burning, is the independent rate of fuel and air admission to a combustion chamber. The dynamic response of the reaction, however, is dependent on the diffusion of the fuel and air to a flammable limit, and the elevation of this diffused mixture to its kindling temperature. The aerodynamic diffusion of fuel and air results from the rate and method of admission. This admission flow pattern produces diffusion mechanically by interscrubbing of the fuel and air mass. Molecular diffusion is also present as a result of increased temperature.

Furnace explosions result from a rapid rate of volume increase when too great a quantity of fuel and air reacts almost simultaneously in an enclosure having a limited volume and strength. The normal furnace enclosure design pressure is generally limited to approximately three to four psig rupture pressure. Avoiding furnace pressures in excess of this pressure is therefore necessary to prevent furnace rupture. The basis for any furnace explosion prevention system must be to limit the quantity of flammable fuel and air mixture that can exist in the furnace at any one instant. The rate of maximum pressure rise possible during the reaction is also a function of the available oxygen per unit volume of reactants. The effect of any oxygen density dilutant (nitrogen, increased temperature, decreased pressure, excess fuel, inert gases) reduces the possible explosion pressure.

Furnace explosion protection control action should be directed to limiting the quantity of diffused flammable fuel-air mixture that can be accumulated in a furnace enclosure in proportion to the total furnace volume and mechanical strength.

While fuel and air are being admitted to a furnace, there are only three possible methods of preventing excessive flammable fuel-air diffused accumulations.

1. Igniting all flammable mixtures as they are formed prior to their excessive accumulation.
2. Diffuse all flammable mixtures with sufficient additional air, prior to ignition, to a point beyond the diffused flammable mixture ratio; and to ac-

complish this with sufficient degree of diffusion before a critical percentage of the furnace *volume* is occupied by the flammable mixture.
3. Supplying an inert gas to simultaneously diffuse with the fuel and air, thereby diluting the oxygen content of the mixture below the flammable limit.

Implementation of these preventative methods requires operator action beyond the capabilities of the normal manual operators' rates of response, memory and judgment. Optimum furnace protection requires mechanical and electrical interlocking of operating functions and integration into the boiler-turbine generator control and interlock design.

Basically, the fireside safeguard system supervises the flow and processing of fuel, air, ignition energy and the products of combustion. The interlock monitoring functions through instrumentation and control devices which sense position, motion, speed, flow, temperature, power consumption, pressure and pressure differentials. This supervisory control must be integrated into the generating unit primary control system and should not be modified or overrode.

Satisfactory boiler operation requires that the four ingredients be properly prepared, ratioed, directed and sequenced so that the furnace never can contain an explosive mixture. At the same time the combustion process must be supervised to check the results. Combustion must be kept efficient or the unconverted chemical energy may accumulate and subsequently become explosive.

Furnace Combustion Supervision

In the prevention of furnace explosions, the detection of the absence of flame, while fuel is being admitted, rather than the presence of flame is the only proper criterion for any control action initiated by a flame monitoring system. The ideal in furnace combustion supervision of a firing chamber would be a single device which could be relied upon implicitly to react when a flame did not exist.

Flame monitoring hardware must be reliable, sensitive to discern the minimum flame envelope and have fail-safe characteristics to avoid unnecessary trips. Reaction time of the flame detecting device must be an absolute minimum to prevent the accumulation of diffused flammable reactants in the furnace chamber, following a loss of flame, before the furnace protection system can respond with corrective action to prevent a furnace explosion. To be applicable for utility service, the flame monitoring device must be equally responsive to flame envelopes of coal, oil and gas.

When furnace heat input consists of a multiplicity of individual flame envelopes, each must be treated as a separate source of furnace-fuel admission and monitored accordingly. When these separate fuel admission nozzles combine to form a single flame envelope, the total fuel input should be treated as a unit.

Flame monitoring to aid in the prevention of furnace explosions is based on the detection of "no-flame" to initiate proper operation action. While this is but a part of the overall furnace safeguard system, it nevertheless must be an integral component, integrated into the boiler-turbine generator control as designed by the systems engineer.

Furnace Inerting

The following factors influence the effective composition change of an explosive charge:
1. The facility for mixing.
2. Inert material in the fuel.

3. Fuel-air ratio (a near stoichiometric ratio develops the highest explosion pressure).
4. The kind of fuel.

A furnace explosion requires (1) a suitable explosive accumulation within the furnace and (2) sufficient energy for ignition. The ignition requirements for an explosive charge are minute, making it impossible to protect against all possible sources of ignition, such as static electricity discharges, hot slag, hot furnace surfaces, etc. Therefore, the practical positive prevention of a furnace explosion is the prevention of an explosive accumulation.

The factors determining the magnitude of a furnace explosion — mass, change in composition, reaction time — are related in the *explosion factor*.

$$\text{Explosion Factor} = \frac{\text{Mass}}{\text{Furnace Volume}} \times \frac{\text{Composition Change}}{\text{Elapsed Time}}$$

For each furnace there is a limiting explosion factor. If the conditions yield an explosion factor exceeding this limit, an explosion or catastrophe results. Any lesser reaction will yield a furnace puff or upset.

In order to protect a furnace from an explosion, the burner safety system must insure a minimum reactive mass accumulation with a minimum available composition change and with a maximum reaction time required. Only composition control of the furnace atmosphere offers complete coverage in minimizing the explosion factor. Furnaces always contain sufficient mass to have an explosion and control of the time factor is impossible. Therefore, the composition change must be controlled to reliably prevent furnace explosions.

The mechanics of furnace explosions,

although defining the actual process, do not describe the furnace operations which provide the explosive accumulations. Ideal furnace operation continuously converts reactive furnace inputs into unreactive products as fast as the inputs enter the furnace. This precludes furnace explosions. However, in practical furnace firing, improper or unfavorable operations that create explosive situations are difficult to completely avoid.

A damaging furnace explosion is an event dependent upon several preceding, correctly timed events. The furnace explosion event itself is the rapid change in composition of the furnace atmosphere (not the furnace inputs). The change in furnace composition is not spontaneous, and a suitable ignition source, which can be substantially less than that required for continuous furnace input ignition, must be supplied *after* the furnace explosive composition is attained.

The potentially reactive furnace composition accumulation must be formed from an earlier buildup process. This process is the introduction of reactive inputs which are not converted by combustion to nonreactive or inert products. This buildup process must continue long enough to create a damaging accumulation. The accumulation composition, which must be within the limits of flammability for that fuel, is formed in one or more basic ways.

1. A flammable input into any furnace atmosphere (loss of ignition).
2. A fuel-rich input into an air-rich atmosphere (fuel interruption).
3. An air-rich input into a fuel-rich atmosphere (air interruption).

Furnace firing systems are designed to start up air-rich by introducing fuel into an air filled furnace. The input air-fuel reactant composition is introduced and controlled functionally, the integral auxiliary ignition system having satisfied permissive main fuel interlocks as to its adequacy to provide more ignition energy than that required by the main fuel to be ignited or to remain ignited. Additional air is introduced above or below the input flammable reactants to diffuse the mixture, beyond the flammable limits, if it has not been ignited and reacted to inert products of combustion, before a critical percentage of the furnace volume is occupied by the flammable mixture.

It has been established that steam is an effective inert and a steam inerting system can be suitably applied to most burner-furnace arrangements. Following the air-rich start up technique, steam from the unit will be available to inert the furnace inputs.

1. Emergency trip — fuel already in the lines and burners continues to flow into the furnace.
2. Fuel-rich trip protection — after fuel tripping, the danger of an explosion increases as continuing air flow diffuses with the fuel-rich furnace composition. At some point in this buildup, the furnace composition may attain explosive proportions as it proceeds from fuel-rich to air-rich.
3. After the furnace atmosphere composition has reached that of the inerted furnace input, the inert can be stopped, thereby changing the furnace input to 100 per cent air. Thus, furnace input inerting is used to provide and maintain nonexplosive furnace atmospheres. The inerting process is initiated automatically as furnace conditions are evaluated and action determined by the integrated burner-boiler-turbine control system.

18

Stokers[1]

STOKERS are *mechanical* devices to burn solid fuels. They perform the primary function of converting chemical energy in the fuel to thermal energy which may be absorbed by boiler surfaces to produce high temperature water or to generate steam. Stokers are designed in a manner that permits (1) continuous or intermittent fuel feed, (2) fuel ignition, (3) adequate supply of required air for combustion, (4) free passage for the resulting gaseous products and (5) disposal of noncombustible materials. The foregoing may be accomplished in a number of ways, but the most important types of stokers are classified as underfeed, crossfeed and overfeed.

The *underfeed stoker*, Fig. 18–1, is characterized by the fuel and air having the same relative direction. Both fuel and primary air enter the active burning zone from beneath the fuel bed. Underfeed stokers are built in *single retort* and *multiple retort* designs.

The *crossfeed stoker*, Fig. 18–2, is a mechanical arrangement that allows the fuel to enter the furnace at right angles to the primary air flow. The *traveling grate stoker* is the most common crossfeed type.

The *overfeed stoker*, Fig. 18–3, is arranged in a manner that permits fuel to

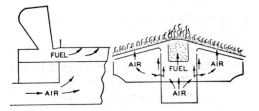

Fig. 18–1. Underfeed stoker

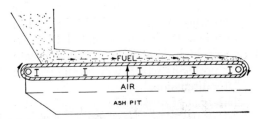

Fig. 18–2. Crossfeed stoker

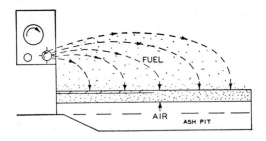

Fig. 18–3. Overfeed stoker

[1] Material contributed by Joseph F. Mullen.

18 – 1

enter the active combustion zone from above and opposite to the direction of primary air flow. A portion of the fuel burns in suspension and the remainder on the grate. The principal type is the *spreader stoker*.

Underfeed stokers of the single retort design are built in capacities ranging from 5000 to 50,000 lb of steam per hour on a maximum continuous basis. Multiple retort stokers, although no longer widely used, have been built in sizes ranging from 40,000 to 300,000 lb of steam per hour.

Crossfeed stokers of the traveling grate design are used in sizes from about 10,000 to 300,000 lb of steam per hour. A similar upper limit applies to spreader stokers.

Stokers are proportioned on the basis of grate heat release rates which may range from 200,000 Btu per hr sq ft for small single retort stokers to 1,000,000 Btu per hr sq ft or more for large spreader stokers where part of the fuel is burned in suspension. It should be noted that extremely high heat release rates create other problems which will be the subject of later discussion.

This area of projected grate surface determines the boiler cross section. Furnace volumes are proportioned on the basis of heat release rates which may range from 25,000 to 50,000 Btu per hr cu ft, depending upon installation size, type of stoker, probable load factor, amount of heat absorbing area and other considerations.[2]

Historical Development[3]

The first known attempt to fire coal by means of a mechanical stoker is credited to James Watt. A patent issued to him in 1785 described a device combining a coal hopper, a grate for fuel burning and provision for refuse disposal. The first known application of underfeed firing was devised in 1816 by John Isaac Hawkins and Emerson Dowson. A retort having a hinged sloping cover at one end was filled with coal. The retort was then pushed into the furnace through a door, the bottom of the retort resting on the grate. A hand operated piston forced the coal out of the retort and onto the grate, under the fuel bed. This crude manual device, the initial application of underfeed firing, employed the fundamental principle on which all modern underfeed stokers are based.

The idea of a spreader stoker for overfeed firing dates back to 1822 when John Stanley of Great Britain was awarded a patent for a design in which two rolls acted as a combined crusher and rotary feeder. In this manner a regulated quantity of sized coal was supplied to a rotating distributor which acted as a mechanical shovel, firing continuously without the necessity of opening the furnace doors. Stokers of this type were extensively used in England during the 1850's. The first record of a spreader stoker designed in the United States is found in a patent issued to James Hemington of Richmond, Indiana, in 1857.

In 1833 John Juckes was granted a patent for an improved underfeed stoker, and ten years later another patent was issued to him for a mechanism to burn coal on a continuously moving, nonagitating type of grate, the forerunner of the crossfeed

---

[2] See Chapter 19, Fundamentals of Boiler Design, for further information.

[3] This section is adapted from the First Edition of *Combustion Engineering*. Otto de Lorenzi, its editor, gained wide recognition for his knowledge of and contributions to stoker design. Practically all of the topics of this chapter are discussed at greater length in Chapters 3, 4, 5, 6 and 30 of the First Edition.

Table 18-1   Significant Dates in the Development of Mechanical Stokers

Design Improvements, Including Smoke Prevention Devices

Date	Name	Description
1685	Delasme (France)	Hand fired furnace with combustion air taken through fire in downward fashion, in accordance with the coking principle
1785	James Watt	Vertical hopper with coal piled up at front of grate and manually pushed to the rear, giving volatile gases a chance to distill slowly; germ of the idea for a coking stoker; devised to prevent smoke
1796	Thompson (Great Britain)	Fire brick coking arch and method of admitting excess air
1800	John and James Roberton	Hand fired furnace including a coal hopper, fuel burning structure and refuse disposal space; patent explained basis of the coking method of burning coal
1814	Thomas Tindall	First use of mechanical draft in conjunction with a stoker
1834	John George Bodmer	Vibratory grate
1839	Charles Wye Williams	Use of blower and bridgewall arch to mix combustion air and gases to prevent smoke
1841	Robert Hall	Water cooling of portions of stoker mechanism to prevent destruction of metal

Underfeed Stokers

Date	Name	Description
1816	John Isaac Hawkins and Emerson Dowson	Discovered principle of the underfeed coking stoker
1822	William Brunton	Peristaltic grate embodying a slow moving reciprocating ram, mechanically driven, plus provisions for variable combustion air zones
1833	Richard Holme	Devised a practical underfeed stoker
1838	John Juckes	Improvements in underfeed stoker
1844	Myron Frisbie	Fuel introduced from beneath through a central aperture
1889	Evan Jones	Use of a steam operated ram to push coal into the furnace underneath the fuel bed
1898	W. R. Wood	Single retort using a spiral screw for feeding coal
1904	E. E. Taylor	Multiple retort stoker

Traveling Grate Stokers

Date	Name	Description
1819	William Brunton	Revolving grate coking stoker, including automatic coal feeding and automatic ash and clinker discharge
1834	John George Bodmer	Traveling grate stoker constructed of a series of fire bars attached to an endless chain passage over rollers; also guillotine coal feed device
1841	John Juckes	Chain grate stoker with fire brick arches and fuel gate regulator
1893	E. B. Coxe	Traveling grate stoker, including air distribution system, for burning small sizes of anthracite

Spreader Stokers

Date	Name	Description
1822	John Stanley	Incorporated coal crusher and revolving fan with four arms to project and scatter fuel over grate
1857	James Hemington	Patented device with blades to feed sawdust and other materials into a furnace
1904	James and William Regan	Developed a variable speed rotary feeder on the overthrow principle
1911	George L. Swift	Devised an underthrow feeder with means for regulating the trajectory of fuel particles

Sources of Historical Information

Mechanical Stokers by Joseph G. Worker and Thomas A. Peebles, New York, 1922, pp. 1–12

Mechanical Stoking by David Brownlie, London, 1923, pp. 16–31

"John George Bodmer, His Life and Work, Particularly in Relation to the Evolution of Mechanical Stoking" by David Brownlie, **Transactions** of the Newcomen Society, Vol. 6, 1925, pp. 86–110

Combustion Engineering, edited by Otto de Lorenzi, First Edition, New York, 1947, Chapters 3, 4, 5 and 6

stoker. The first successful traveling grate stoker was invented by Eckley B. Coxe and was initially developed to burn anthracite, the first commercial installation having been made in 1893 in an industrial power plant.[4]

Improvements in underfeed firing were made by Evan W. Jones who obtained two patents for a stoker employing a steam operated ram, one in 1889 dealing with the feeding of cord wood into a furnace and the other in 1892 being an adaptation for coal burning. Walter R. Wood made substantial advances in the design of the single retort underfeed stoker in the period between 1898 and 1906. Many of these features are embodied in modern stokers of the underfeed type.

Although the patents of John Stanley and James Hemington disclosed many of the design elements of the spreader stoker prior to the Civil War, there is little evidence of any substantial progress in the art until 1904 when a patent was issued to James and William Reagan. That stoker used a variable speed rotary feeder and a constant speed distributor with radial blades, set at an angle, to throw coal uniformly over the length and width of the grate. In contrast to the *overthrow* principle upon which the Reagan stoker operated, George L. Swift was granted patents in 1911 and 1915 for stokers of the *underthrow* type.

As shown in Table 18–1, Significant Dates in the Development of Mechanical Stokers, most of the principles of mechanical stoking were understood and applied before 1860. Subsequent improvements have enabled the burning of almost every conceivable type of solid fuel in plants ranging from small industrial installations to moderate sized central stations. Although the relative importance of stokers as a means of firing coal has decreased, particularly in central stations where unit boiler-turbine-generator size has far exceeded the output capabilities of stokers, they remain an important type of commercial firing equipment for industrial and institutional power plants and for the burning of a wide variety of waste, refuse and byproduct fuels. Stokers are also used to a limited extent for coal carbonization, briquetting and ore beneficiation operations.[5]

Stokers and the Combustion Process

In a historical sense the greatest impetus for the development of stokers came from two sources: (1) objections to smoke emission resulting from hand firing and imperfect combustion and (2) limitations on steam output of boilers inherent in

---

[4] It is interesting to note the use of this topic as a portion of an ASME presidential address. See "Use of Small Sizes of Anthracite for Generating Steam" by Eckley B. Coxe, *Trans.* ASME, Vol. 15, 1894, pp. 36–42. The basic design reference is "A Furnace with Automatic Stoker, Traveling Grate and Variable Blast, Intended Especially for Burning Small Anthracite Coals" by Eckley B. Coxe, *Trans.* of American Institute of Mining, Metallurgical and Petroleum Engineers, Vol. 22, 1894, pp. 581–606. An account of the performance of the first industrial installation may be found in the *Proceedings* of the New England Cotton Manufacturers' Association, April 1895.

[5] Accounts of stoker applications are found in Chapter 19, Fundamentals of Boiler Design; Chapter 21, Combustion and Boiler Calculations, Example 1, Stoker Fired Industrial Power Plant Boiler; Chapter 26, Shop Assembled Boilers; Chapter 27, Boilers and Recovery Units for the Pulp and Paper Industry; Chapter 28, Marine Boilers; Chapter 29, High Temperature Water Boilers; Chapter 30, Flash Drying Systems; Chapter 31, Refuse Incinerators. Characteristics of stoker fuels are discussed in Chapter 13, Fuel Properties of Coal and Chapter 14, Natural Gas, Oil and Byproduct Fuels.

manual stoking. Early in the course of the improvement of the steam engine the demands for steam began to exceed the physical capabilities of even gangs of men. Hand firing was not only taxing in a physiological sense but was often carried out under adverse conditions of uncomfortably high ambient temperatures and in extremely dirty surroundings. Many whose personal experience involved a tour of duty with the coal shovel and poker were strongly motivated to make inventions and improvements to put an end to this sort of human drudgery. Hence it is not surprising that the dominant influence in stoker innovations was the creation of a "mechanical fireman." Even a casual review of the technical literature, including some of the basic stoker patents, discloses a record of amazing mechanical ingenuity in stoker design from the time of James Watt onward.

But the stoker is not only a machine. Of at least equal importance, it is a means to initiate the combustion process on a comparatively large but controlled scale. In a gross sense this process is visible and obvious, and in pragmatic terms the test of a stoker is its ability to consume a fuel, release thermal energy at a suitable rate and dispose of waste material with minimal complications. However, if the combustion process in a fuel bed is analyzed closely and more critically, it presents a real intellectual challenge. By comparison to the vast engineering literature dealing with stoker applications, relatively little

attention has been given to the theoretical considerations underlying the physical and chemical phenomena that take place when solid fuels are fired by means of stokers. Yet much information of value in other areas of power engineering can be derived from an understanding of the chemical transformations and heat processes that result from stoker operation.

In view of the manner in which the mechanical stoker evolved from hand firing, it seems fitting that one of the classical American studies of combustion should deal with the latter. This paper, "Combustion in the Fuel Bed of Hand Fired Furnaces," is one of many resulting from the research work of Henry Kreisinger and his colleagues in the U.S. Bureau of Mines. It was preceded by three important publications which represent the earliest comprehensive scientific (as distinguished from empirical or practical) approaches to heat transmission in a boiler furnace.[6]

An example of what would now be characterized as fundamental engineering science applied to the special case of stokers is found in a theoretical investigation of reactions and temperatures in an underfeed fuel bed. The results, which were presented in an ASME paper by Martin A. Mayers, indicate the significance of various chemical and physical factors in determining combustion characteristics of fuels. Yet this is more than an abstract analysis for its own sake, for the theoretical characteristics of pure underfeed combustion have been shown to duplicate

---

[6] See "Combustion in the Fuel Bed of Hand Fired Furnaces" by Henry Kreisinger, F. K. Ovitz and C. E. Augustine, U.S. Bureau of Mines Technical Paper 137, 1916, 76 pages. The three publications on boiler heat transmissions are "The Flow of Heat Through Furnace Walls" by W. T. Ray and Henry Kreisinger, Bulletin No. 8, 1911, 32 pages; "The Transmission of Heat into Steam Boilers" by Henry Kreisinger and W. T. Ray, Bulletin No. 18, 1912, 180 pages; and "Heat Transmission Through Boiler Tubes" by Henry Kreisinger and J. F. Barkley, Technical Paper No. 114, 1915, 36 pages. These are all published by the U.S. Bureau of Mines and may be consulted in depository libraries throughout the United States.

with considerable fidelity the experimental determinations of these same characteristics.[7]

For the purpose of this discussion, use will be made of a simplified fuel bed as shown in Fig. 18–4. The bed is considered to be a continuous solid of a porous nature such that air can be blown through it. In effect, this focusses attention on the fuel bed as a whole, rather than on the individual pieces of which it is composed.

As a basis of what transpires in this simplified concept of an underfeed fuel bed, it is postulated that heat flows through a fuel bed in two ways. The first is by convection provided by the air supplied for combustion and the resultant gases; the second, by a process obeying the laws of metallic conduction. It should be understood that the latter process is not limited as to heat transfer mechanism, although it probably occurs through radiation between adjacent particles. For this analysis it is sufficient that a property equivalent to thermal conductivity exists for the fuel bed as a whole and that it can be meas-

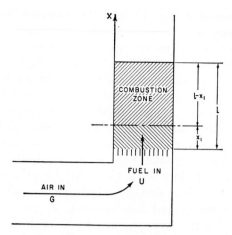

Fig. 18–4.   Simplified fuel bed

If there is a flow of fuel through the bed, it will be considered positive if in the positive x-direction. Ignition is supposed to take place at some plane designated by $x = x_1$, where x_1 may have any value from 0 to l, and combustion takes place from there to the end of the bed, $x = l$. The differential equation for the temperature of the bed may then be formulated in the following terms:

$$\frac{\delta}{\delta x}\left(k\,\frac{\delta T}{\delta x}\right) - \frac{\delta}{\delta x}\left(\rho UT\right) - \alpha(T - T_a) = \frac{\rho}{d}\,\frac{\delta T}{\delta t} + X(T) - \phi(x, x_1)$$

(Eq. 18–1)

ured. This process is responsible for heating the incoming fuel up to its ignition temperature.

Referring again to Fig. 18–4, the x-direction is taken as the direction of air (or gas) flow through the bed, usually vertically upward, and the bed extends from zero to l, which need not be constant. Variation of the properties of the bed in the x-direction only will be considered.

where T represents the temperature of the fuel; T_a that of the air or gas stream; k the thermal conductivity of the bed; ρ the heat capacity of the fuel; U the rate of fuel flow through the bed; d its bulk specific gravity; and α represents the heat transfer coefficient between fuel and the air stream. The term $X(T)$ represents the heat absorbed in endothermic reactions such as coking or cracking, while ϕ represents the

[7] The reader who is skeptical of the applicability and potency of differential equations in their relation to steam power equipment will find this paper a revelation. See "Temperature and Combustion Rates in Fuel Beds" by Martin A. Mayers, *Trans.* ASME, Vol. 59, 1937, pp. 279–288. Much of the information in the preceding and following paragraphs is adapted from this source.

heat liberated by combustion and is given by

$$\phi\,(x,\,x_1) = \begin{cases} 0,\ \text{when } 0 \lessgtr x < x_1 \\ \mu_1 h_1 p_1\,(x,\,x_1) - \mu_2 h_2 p_2\,(x,\,x_1),\ \text{when } x_1 \leq x \leq l \end{cases} \qquad \text{(Eq. 18–2)}$$

where μ_1 and μ_2 represent the rates of the reactions (A), $C + O_2 \rightarrow CO_2$ and (B), $C + CO_2 \rightarrow 2\ CO$, respectively, at unit concentration of the reacting gases—they also refer to unit volume of the bed just as α; h_1 and h_2 are the quantities of heat liberated or absorbed in the reactions (A) and (B) referred to unit weight of the reacting gases; and p_1 and p_2 represent the fractional concentrations of O_2 and CO_2, respectively.

In Eq. 18–1 the first term represents the gain of heat by an element of volume due to conduction; the second represents the loss to an element due to the heat carried away by the fuel flowing through it; the third represents the loss due to the transfer of heat from the solid fuel to the air or gas stream; and the fourth represents the heat absorbed in local rise in temperature. Thus the left hand side of Eq. 18–1 represents the net gain of heat in an element of volume due to transport processes, while the right hand side represents the net absorption of heat by reaction and by increase of temperature, so that the equation is simply a heat balance.

The temperature of the air stream satisfies the equation

$$Gc_p\,\frac{\delta T_a}{\delta x} - \alpha(T - T_a) = 0 \qquad \text{(Eq. 18–3)}$$

where G represents the rate of air or gas flow, and c_p is the specific heat of the gas. This equation states that the heat absorbed in raising the temperature of the gas passing through an element of volume is equal to the heat transferred to the gas from the fuel.

The concentrations of the various constituents of the gas stream satisfy the set of equations

$$\left. \begin{aligned} G\frac{\delta p_1}{\delta x} + \mu_1 p_1 &= 0 \\[4pt] G\frac{\delta p_2}{\delta x} + \mu_2 p_2 &= \mu_1 p_1 \\[4pt] G\frac{\delta p_3}{\delta x} &= 2\ \mu_2 p_2 \end{aligned} \right\} \begin{aligned} &\text{when } x_1 < x \leq l \\[10pt] &\text{(Eq. 18–4)} \end{aligned}$$

where p_3 represents the concentration of CO. The significance of these equations is exemplified by the second, which states that the rate of increase in quantity of CO_2 in the gas stream, given by the term $G\,(\delta p_2/\delta x)$, plus the rate of loss by reaction to form CO, given by $\mu_2 p_2$, is equal to the rate of formation of CO_2 from O_2, given by the term $\mu_1 p_1$.

Eqs. 18–1 to 18–4, inclusive, with suitable boundary conditions, are sufficient to determine a general solution for a one dimensional case of temperature rise and combustion rates in a hypothetical underfeed fuel bed such as shown previously in Fig. 18–4. This analysis can be extended to cover the three dimensional case, but certain additional physical and computational simplifications must be made in order to find solutions for the differential equations. A slight variation of the analysis makes it applicable to overfeed fuel beds, namely changing the sign of the combustion rate, U, in Eq. 18–1. Covering the other basic method of stoker firing, the same type of analytical investigation, although it becomes more complicated, is applicable to the solution of the temperature rise and combustion rates in crossfeed fuel beds.

This analysis predicts a limitation on the maximum rate of burning in underfeed combustion due to the limited rate at which heat can be conducted down through the bed against the air flow. Although this limitation had been observed experimentally, there was no satisfactory explanation until the formulation of the preceding analytical interpretation of underfeed combustion.

Principal Stoker Types

It is now time to turn from an overall view of stokers in historical perspective and from a consideration of combustion and heat transfer phenomena in stokers to a more detailed description of the principal types. In accordance with the classifications expressed at the beginning of the chapter, this section begins with underfeed designs and continues on to traveling grate and spreader stokers.

Underfeed stokers, either single or multiple retort, consist essentially of a trough or troughs into which coal is pushed by rams or screws. Part of the combustion air is introduced into the fuel bed through tuyeres or grate bars. Movement of the fuel discourages the formation of large coke masses. Volatile matter is distilled off the coal in these troughs or retorts and burns above the incandescent fuel bed. The partly coked and somewhat caked coal then falls into the air admitting tuyeres or grate bars where the fixed carbon is burned out. Progressively the fuel is pushed sidewise or forward until the refuse is discharged to the ashpit.

Single Retort Stoker

In a single retort underfeed stoker, Fig. 18–5, the fuel is introduced in the retort, and the incoming coal progressively forces fuel out of the retort and onto the side grates. This feeding action from the retort outward places the entire fuel bed under compression and automatically closes any holes that may tend to form in the fuel bed, thus overcoming one of the commonest obstacles to efficient firing.[8]

Fig. 18–5. Underfeed stoker, single retort type

Ease and simplicity of operation are characteristic of the single retort stoker. All adjustments are made from the stoker front, and practically the entire fuel bed is visible and accessible through the furnace doors located in the stoker front, adjacent to the furnace side walls. Cleanout doors provide access to the air chambers under the stoker, so that siftings which accumulate there may be cleaned out easily and conveniently as a detail of operating routine.

The most common single retort underfeed stoker is driven by a steam cylinder

---

[8] The flow of heat in an underfeed stoker is surprisingly complex. A detailed description is found in a portion of a paper entitled "Flow Processes in Underfeed Stokers" by Martin A. Mayers, *Trans.* ASME, Vol. 63, 1941, p. 485. See also "Radiation from the Grate in a Water Tube Boiler," *Sulzer Technical Review,* No. 4, 1930, pp. 6–15.

and piston mechanisms built into the stoker front. This simple and compact design is applicable wherever minimum steam pressure is not less than about 50 psig. Many types of electric drive are also available, including a hydraulic transmission or a gear transmission. The choice between types of stoker drive depends upon operating and space conditions and the preference of individuals who select the equipment. Both the steam drive and the electric drive are readily adaptable to standard types of automatic control for adjusting rates of coal feed and air supply according to changes in steam pressure.

Air Supply and Distribution. Air for combustion is supplied by a forced draft fan. In the electrically driven stoker, the fan may be directly connected to the stoker drive motor operated at constant speed and fitted with an inlet damper controlling the air supply. When a separate fan is used, its location and drive arrangement may be selected to suit the local conditions. A damper is furnished for installation in the duct connecting the fan to the main air chamber of the stoker, located directly beneath the retort, and a cleanout door is provided in the duct for easy access.

Forced draft is supplied to the entire grate area, which is divided into several pressure zones parallel to the retort, each under separate damper control. Air pressure is compensated to the thickness of the fuel bed, the greatest pressure being applied to the thickest portion over the retort.

Multiple Retort Stoker

The multiple retort stoker, Fig. 18–6, is an extension of the single retort stoker. It is nothing more than a series of single retort stokers built into the same machine with appropriate mechanism provided to operate the various components in unison.

The fuel bed on a multiple retort stoker is of two distinct types. In the underfeed section, there are parallel rows of hills and valleys, extending from front wall to the discharge ends of the retorts. The hills occur over the relatively inactive retort areas, because they have no provisions for air admission. The coal is supplied through a reciprocating feed, and this produces a certain amount of segregation in the fuel bed. The coarse coal finds its way to the tuyeres near the front. The fines travel the length of the retort.

Fig. 18–6. Multiple retort stoker

High combustion rates in a thin active fuel bed exist over the tuyeres through which the air is admitted. To shake down and level out these alternately thick and thin parallel ribbons is the function of the overfeed section. As this irregular mass of burning fuel reaches the overfeed section, it is quickly shaken down to uniform thickness by the reciprocating action of the grates in this area. The fuel bed is now level, compact, homogeneous, and extremely active because of the stroke control and the admission of correct air quantities. As a result, the fuel bed may be burned out uniformly across the stoker width by the time the fuel reaches the dump grates or ash discharge section.

The difference in fuel bed characteristics described above makes it necessary to provide complete air zoning. Below the underfeed section, lateral air zones are formed by sets of dampers installed under the tuyere section. In addition to these, a separate zone is provided for the overfeed section. Thus, there are means for proportioning the air supply to all sections of the fuel bed as may be required.

Traveling Grate Stokers

No type of fuel burning equipment yet developed has a wider application in the burning of solid fuels than the traveling grate stoker. Every type of fuel that is mined, with the single exception of caking bituminous coals, can be burned successfully on various designs of these machines. In addition, such waste and byproduct fuels as coke breeze, anthracite dredged from river bottoms, garbage and municipal refuse are burned efficiently and effectively. The traveling grate stoker may also be employed as a part of chemical process operations to produce coke and carbon dioxide.[9]

There are two types of surface commonly used for traveling grate stokers. Known as *chain grate* and *bar grate*, both perform the same function of carrying the fuel fed by gravity from a hopper, supporting it throughout the combustion period and depositing the refuse in the ashpit. A chain grate surface, Fig. 18–7, consists of a series of links strung on rods in a staggered arrangement and moved by sprockets or drums. As shown in Fig. 18–8, bar grate surface consists of rows of keys strung on bars which are in turn carried by chains driven by sprockets. Each has its advantages: chain grates tend less to retain siftings and clinker accretions; bar grates are less affected by wear and easier to repair.

Certain fundamental principles have been developed in the design of furnaces for traveling grate stokers. In order to burn fuel satisfactorily, ignition should occur and become stable as soon as possible after the fuel enters the furnace. If ignition is unstable for any reason, reliable performance of the unit, even at a fixed rate of operation, may not be maintained, and any effort to meet an increase in load may result in a complete loss of the fire.

Once the ignition of a fuel is well established, combustion should be maintained at as high a rate as is practical over each stoker compartment that is in active use. The furnace should be designed to make this possible. If this is not accomplished, losses will result in unburned gas and in carbon carried into the ash pit. A large traveling grate stoker installed in a central station is shown in Fig. 18–9.

Fuel Burning and Air Flow. The amount of fuel burned for a given load condition is determined by the heating value, the fuel bed thickness and the grate speed. The fuel bed thickness is determined by the admission gate height. The grate speed is controlled by a variable speed drive either operated manually or automatically from the combustion control system. Usually, the gate position will remain fixed except for capacities beyond the speed range of the stoker. With a given fuel bed thickness, say 4 to 5 in. with bituminous coal, the speed of the traveling grate stoker will be adjusted so that ignition under steady state conditions is maintained at the forward end of the stoker. Burning should never be allowed

---

[9] See Chapter 31, Refuse Incinerators. An interesting process application is described in an article entitled "From Flue Gas to Dry Ice" by A. J. Granata, *Combustion*, Vol. 21, September 1949, pp. 49–50.

Fig. 18–7.   Chain grate surface

Fig. 18–8.   Bar grate surface

Fig. 18–9.   Large traveling grate installation

to take place behind the coal gate. The line of ignition should not be permitted to extend beyond the first compartment.

In most traveling grate stokers of the progressive burning type, that is, where burning takes place from the front to the rear of the stoker, a multiplicity of stoker compartments with individual air control is incorporated in the design. For a given load condition, the total air flow is determined by an orsat analysis. The distribution of this air between compartments is adjusted manually and in proportion to the amount of fuel that is burned over each compartment. The amount of air to each compartment increases to a maximum over the first or second compartment, depending on fuel bed thickness and grate resistance, and decreases to a minimum as the fuel is consumed just prior to being discharged as ash into the ash pit at the rear of the stoker.[10]

Spreader Stokers

Spreader stokers use the combined principles of pulverized coal and stoker firing in that fines are burned in suspension and the larger particles are burned on the grate. Feeding and distributing mechanisms continually project coal into the furnace above an ignited fuel bed. With this method of firing, the chemical characteristics of the coal have little effect on the fuel bed. Strongly caking coals show little tendency to mat and burn with the same ease as the free burning variety. Flash drying of the incoming fuel, rapid release of volatile, and suspension burning of the fuel are factors which make this method of firing so widely applicable. Practically all types of coal have been successfully burned on spreader stokers, as have a wide variety of cellulose fuels, including bagasse, wood chips, bark, hogged wood, sawdust, shavings, coffee grounds and furfural residue.

[10] Results of a comprehensive investigation on fundamentals affecting the burning of solid fuels on traveling grate stokers are found in "Combustion of Solid Fuels in Thin Beds" by E. P. Carman, E. G. Graf and R. C. Corey, U.S. Bureau of Mines Bulletin No. 563, 1957, 92 pages.

The modern spreader stoker, Fig. 18–10, consists essentially of one or more mechanical firing units mounted on a front plate. These are comprised of a hopper, a feeder that regulates the flow of coal in proportion to the load and a distributor rotor that spreads the coal into the furnace and distributes it on the grate.

The fuel bed consists of a thin level fire on top of a uniform layer of ash. It is non-agitated and intensely active. Under proper operating conditions, there is never more than a few minutes supply of coal on the grate. This thin active fuel bed lays on a cooled nonagitated ash bed, and as a result of these conditions, even though the fusion temperature of the ash may be very low, few or no clinkers are formed. Furthermore, this protective layer of ash, together with uniform air flow to all portions of the grate, keeps the grate castings relatively cool. As a result, preheated air with temperatures of 300 to 350 F may be used without causing unreasonably high grate maintenance.

Feeder Design. The design of the feeder, the principal parts of which are identified in Fig. 18–11, is of the utmost importance, for upon it depends the uniformity with which fuel is supplied to the distributor. When the coal is fine and dry it will tend to feed too rapidly; when it is wet the particles may cohere, or they may stick to the feeder causing an erratic supply of fuel to the distributor. For all conditions, including these governing extremes, the feeder provides a positive control of the amount of fuel fed. The feeding unit permits positive regulation of the fuel supply over a wide range by either manual or automatic control.

The coal is measured out of the feeder at a rate necessary to carry the boiler load. It then falls in a practically continuous stream into the path of the revolving dis-

Fig. 18–10.   Spreader stoker

tributor blades. These blades are usually mounted in rows parallel with the axis of the distributor rotor. The crisscrossing of fuel streams from a single distributor, or from a combination of distributors, results in a consistently uniform distribution of fuel on the grate, which may be of the dumping or continuous discharge type.

Dumping Grate. In the dumping grate design, Fig. 18–12, the depth of ash on a spreader stoker will vary from none at all immediately after the fire is cleaned to four inches or more just before cleaning. The resistance to air flow becomes greater as the thickness of accumulated ash increases. However, the effect of comparatively wide variations in fuel bed and ash bed resistance is minimized by restricting the air openings in the grate surface so that they represent less than ten per cent of the total area. By so doing, a high fixed

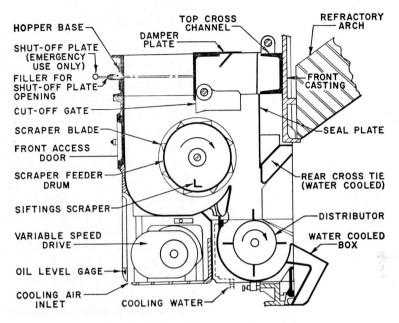

Fig. 18—11. Feeder for spreader stoker

Fig. 18—12. Spreader stoker, dumping grate design

resistance through the grate, plus a comparatively low variable resistance through the ash layer, is provided. Thus, the variations in ash layer present little or no problem in the practical application of automatic control.

A forced draft fan is used to supply air to the fuel through an undergrate plenum chamber, which also serves as an ash pit. The grate, as well as the plenum chamber, is sectionalized laterally, corresponding to the number of feeder units. Each air zone is under individual damper control, and therefore, fires can be cleaned one section at a time. This is accomplished quickly and with no loss in capacity. The grates may be hand operated or equipped with either steam or air operated dumping mechanisms. It is not unusual to dump a complete section and start a new fire in a matter of a few minutes.

Continuous Discharge Grate. When the ash content of the fuel is ten per cent or above, the spreader stoker grate is usually of the continuous discharge type, Fig. 18–13. This design incorporates the spreader and the distributor units with

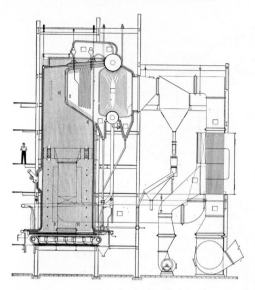

Fig. 18—13.   Spreader stoker, continuous discharge grate

the continuously moving fuel supporting surface of a traveling grate stoker. The conventional traveling grate stoker, as previously described, carries the fuel into the furnace from a hopper and discharges the refuse at the opposite end of the stoker. In the continuous discharge spreader stoker, the grate may travel toward the feeder units and discharge the refuse into a pit located at the stoker front, or it may travel away from the feeders and discharge the refuse at the rear. The grate speed is regulated so that a uniformly thick ash bed is maintained at the discharge end at all ratings. The substitution of a continuous ash discharge for periodic cleaning makes it possible to operate at high sustained combustion rates.

The furnace is usually of the open type characteristic of stationary spreader design. An air chamber is located below the fuel supporting surface, either between the upper and lower runs of the grate, or the plenum may be below the upper and

return runs of the grate, the air passing through keys or cored members. A short zone section is provided at both the front and rear under separate damper controls. Uniform air pressure is maintained under compartmented sections of the active stoker area, and suitable seals in the front and rear prevent loss of the air.

Many factors enter into any economic study to determine the choice between the dumping grate or the continuous ash discharge type of spreader stoker. The boiler unit may be narrower with the continuous ash discharge type, and this may result in a considerable reduction in first cost. This is particularly true where high ash coals are the principal fuels, because with the dumping type of stoker, the combustion rate must be kept low in order that the time intervals between cleaning periods may be long enough to insure a practical operating cycle.

If the capacity of a given unit is sufficiently large to justify the application of either the dumping grate or the continuous ash discharge type of stoker, then a dumping grate type is definitely indicated when ash in the coal is less than seven per cent. The continuous ash discharge type should be used when the ash content is greater than ten per cent.

Flexibility of Operation. One of the outstanding characteristics of spreader stoker firing is the ability to handle rapid swings in load with little or no change in steam temperature and pressure. It is not unusual for a spreader stoker installation to go from 25 per cent of rated capacity to 100 per cent of capacity in a minute or less. By the same token, if the fuel is shut off, the fire will almost immediately go out. On the dump grate stokers this makes it possible to shut the coal off on one feeder unit, leaving the air on to consume whatever coal may be on the grate. The length of time to consume this coal which may be on the grate is less than a minute. The air is then shut off under that particular section and the ash is dumped to the pit. When the grates are closed, the coal is started up again, and by radiation and hot gas convection from the adjacent bed, ignition takes place almost immediately on the coals that range in volatile from approximately 25 to 42 per cent. When this entire grate surface is ignited, the air is put back on under that particular section and the fuel is put on automatic control and the next section is dumped. Each section, as previously noted, can be dumped in a matter of minutes. When one unit is on manual control during the dumping cycle, the remaining units on a spreader stoker operation will immediately pick up the load and feed more coal to compensate for the absence of fuel in the unit that is being dumped. This takes place without loss of capacity or steam pressure.

Stoker Design and Operation

There are certain general considerations which have an important effect upon stoker design and operation. It therefore seems appropriate to turn away momentarily from specific types of stokers to consider two of them: *coal sizing* and *overfire air*. Both of these are related to continuity of stoker operation and to the controlled emission of ash particles, as limited by air pollution regulations.

Likewise, they have a bearing on the type and extent of stoker maintenance.[11]

Coal Sizing

A problem that has long confronted consumers of coal, and particularly those having stoker installations, is the matter of size consist and the designation of coal size. It is not uncommon to find coals of the same size designation but an entirely different screen analysis, these differences being largely due to the mining and processing practices of a particular coal producer.

Coal as sold commercially may have size designation in the form, ¾ in. by 0 in., 1½ in. by 0 in., and so on. According to ASTM D 431–44, "Standard Method for Designating the Size of Coal from Its Screen Analysis", the upper limit of coal size is defined by the screen that will retain a total of less than five per cent of the sample. The lower size limit is defined as the largest screen of the series that will pass a total of less than 15 per cent of the sample. It should be noted that ASTM Standard D 431 does not recognize the 0 in. size which is used in commercial practice.

Fig. 18–14 shows a plot of coal size specification, making use of a graphical form developed by the U. S. Bureau of Mines.[12] On this form a true broken coal size will plot as a straight line. For a coal which is designated commercially as

---

[11] For more details on operation and maintenance of stokers, see the First Edition of *Combustion Engineering*, Chapter 30, Operation and Maintenance of Equipment, or consult operating instructions prepared by manufacturers for specific stokers.

[12] See Information Circular No. 7346 published in 1946 by the U.S. Bureau of Mines, "A Graphical Form for Applying the Rosin and Rammler Equation to the Size of Distribution of Broken Coal" by W. S. Landers and W. T. Reid; an earlier and basic reference is "The Laws Governing the Fineness of Powdered Coal" by P. Rosin and E. Rammler, *Journal* of the Institute of Fuel, Vol. 7, October 1933, pp. 29–36.

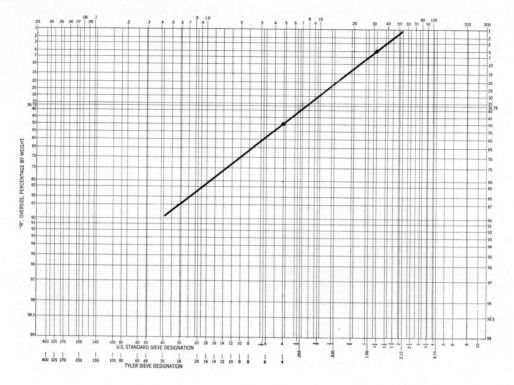

Fig. 18–14. Plot of a coal size specification

1¼ in. by 0 in., with not more than 50 per cent through a ¼ in. round hole screen, two points are established. One is at five per cent plus 1¼ in. and the second, at 50 per cent plus ¼ in.[13]

This graphical form has a number of applications. It may be used to designate coal size for screen analysis, to compare screen analyses from various producers and to blend coals of varying sizes in order to have an end product meeting specific requirements. It has also been employed to plot particle size distribution of stack discharges and the contents of boiler and dust collector hoppers. An example of the

latter is shown in Fig. 18–15, which also includes a plot of the original coal as fired.

The slope of the straight line curve may be termed the distribution coefficient and represented by n. This coefficient decreases as the size distribution becomes wider. For particles of exactly the same size, the plot would be vertical and the slope n would be infinite. The absolute size consist, x, is a measure of the size of the material, has the dimension of length, and is determined by the sieve opening on which 36.79 per cent $(100/e)$ of the sample by weight would be retained. The

[13] According to ASTM Standard D 431–44, ¼ in. round hole screen is roughly equivalent to No. 4 sieve; ⅛ in. round hole, to No. 8; ¹⁄₁₆ in. round hole, to No. 16; ¹⁄₃₂ in. round hole, to No. 30.

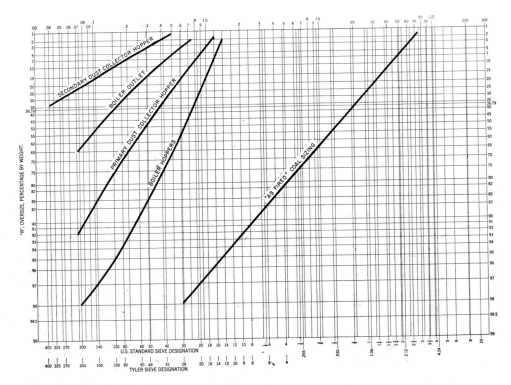

Fig. 18—15. Plot of size distribution as fired and in several boiler locations

use of these two parameters, the distribution constant and the absolute size constant, makes it possible to reconstruct complete sieve analyses and to make a direct comparison of the size consist of two or more fuels.

With any fuel, regardless of type, whether it be burned on an underfeed, a traveling grate or a spreader stoker, the importance of segregation of sizes cannot be overemphasized. If all the fines are on one side of the stoker and all the coarse coal on the other, there will be a tendency for the fines to mat over and the coarse coal to burn rather freely. Under these circumstances, because of maldistribution of air through the fire, there may be over-

heating of the grate surface and other stoker parts. Bad burning characteristics are also indicated by a ragged fire. The most important consideration is that different sizes of coals be thoroughly mixed before they are fed to stokers of any type.

Overfire Air

Overfire air, sometimes referred to as secondary air, is quite commonly used in furnaces in which bituminous coals are burned. It helps to eliminate smoke and improve combustion efficiency by blowing air into the furnace where it is needed and mixing it with the unburned gases and smoke. Turbulent mixing of air and gas is desirable, and the pressure and the volume of the air used should be sufficient to produce that condition.

The quantity of overfire air should be between 5 and 15 per cent of the total quantity of air needed for combustion of the fuel. The amount of overfire air will be a function of the coal rank, and the amount of excess air in the furnace proper. Air at pressures below 6 in. wg. is not always effective in creating turbulence. Relatively small jets of air at pressures up to 25 or 30 in. wg., have been used in some installations for improving combustion conditions in the furnace, and for reducing visible smoke and cinder carryover. Extreme care must be used in employing these pressures, since the penetration is a function of the static pressure and the volume of air per nozzle.[14]

Stoker Fuel Characteristics and Specifications

Single retort underfeed stokers are designed to burn strongly or moderately caking bituminous coals, certain free burning bituminous coals and — to a lesser extent — other grades of coal and waste fuels. In practical applications, fuels ranging from lignite to anthracite are being burned successfully. However, this type of stoker is most widely used for burning Eastern caking and mildly caking bituminous coals and many of the Midwestern free burning coals, especially those having an ash fusion temperature sufficiently high for successful utilization in the relatively thick fuel beds that characterize underfeed burning. For satisfactory stoker operation, coal sizing is as important as coal analysis. The size of

coal best suited for single retort stokers is that designated commercially as 1 in. to 1½ in. nut and slack, preferably containing not more than 50 per cent slack. Slack is defined as coal of a size that will pass through a ¼ in. round hole screen.

For multiple retort underfeed stokers the ideal coal should vary in size from 2 in. to slack, with not more than 50 per cent slack content that will pass through a ¼ in. round screen. This coal must be distributed uniformly across the stoker hopper; the volatile content should preferably be between 20 and 30 per cent; ash content should range between 6 and 8 per cent; and the ash softening temperature should be above 2400 F in a reducing atmosphere. Iron content of the ash should not be more than 20 per cent as Fe_2O_3 for this range of softening temperatures and not more than 15 per cent if the softening temperature is between 2200 and 2400 F.

The fuels most widely used on traveling grate stokers are anthracite, semianthracite, noncaking or free burning bituminous coal, subbituminous coal, lignite and coke breeze. Some bituminous coals of the caking type may be burned on traveling grate stokers if the coal is of an optimum size, has been allowed to weather and is tempered to approximately 15 per cent moisture.

Coal sizing for traveling grate stokers may be related to the ASTM Classification of Coal by Rank (D–388–64T) as shown in Fig. 18–16. For anthracite (Rank I–2), the size of No. 3 buckwheat (barley) should be all through ¾₆ in. round hole screen and not more than 20 per cent

---

[14] Basic data for the application of overfire jets may be found in the following technical papers: "Overfire Air Jets" by R. B. Engdahl and W. C. Holton, *Trans.* ASME, Vol. 65, 1943, pp. 73–86; "Design Data for Overfire Jets" by R. B. Engdahl, *Combustion*, Vol. 15, March, 1944, pp. 47–51; and "Overfire Air Jets in European Practice" by Wilhelm Gumz, *Combustion*, Vol. 22, April 1951, pp. 39–47.

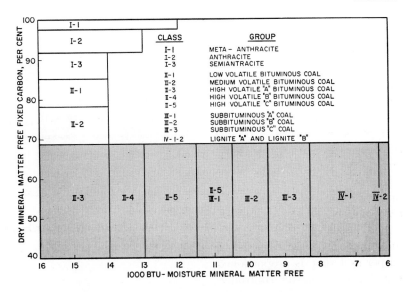

Fig. 18—16. ASTM classification of coal by rank

through $\frac{3}{32}$ in. screen; No. 4 buckwheat should pass through $\frac{3}{32}$ in. round hole screen with not more than ten per cent through a $\frac{3}{64}$ in. screen and not more than one per cent through a 100 mesh screen. For coals of ASTM Ranks II–4, 5; III–1, 2, 3 and IV–1,2 the size should be one inch nut and slack with not more than 50 per cent slack through a $\frac{1}{4}$ in. round hole screen and tempering to 15 per cent moisture. For friable coals of ASTM Ranks II–1,2,3 the sizing should be $1\frac{1}{4}$ or $1\frac{1}{2}$ in. nut and slack with not more than 50 per cent slack through a $\frac{1}{4}$ in. round screen. For nonfriable coals of ASTM Ranks II–1,2,3 the sizing should be $\frac{3}{4}$ in. nut and slack with not more than 50 per cent slack through a $\frac{1}{4}$ in. round hole screen. If coke breeze is burned on traveling grate stokers, it should contain 8 to 10 per cent moisture and not less than one per cent volatile matter; the entire quantity should pass through a $\frac{5}{8}$ in. round mesh with not more than 50 per cent nor less than 25 per cent through a $\frac{1}{8}$ in. round hole screen.

Spreader stokers were developed to burn the lower grades of coal, but they are capable of handling all ranks from semianthracite to lignite, plus numerous waste and byproduct fuels. As might be expected, spreader stoker performance is best when quality and sizing are good. The thin, quick burning fuel bed requires a relatively small size fuel. The spreader stoker will burn fuel ranging from slack or carbon, all through $\frac{1}{8}$ or $\frac{1}{4}$ in. screen, to $1\frac{1}{4}$ or $1\frac{1}{2}$ in. nut and slack. Considerable range in size consist is necessary for satisfactory distribution, and if there is a good balance between coarse and fine particles the burning rate and ash bed thickness are practically uniform over the entire grate surface.

Spreader Stokers for Bagasse Burning

Bagasse is the refuse that remains after sugar is extracted from cane. In many modern sugar mills conventional fuels are used only for startup and emergency conditions, the great bulk of process heating and power generation requirements being furnished by bagasse burning.[15]

The spreader stoker is the most widely accepted means of burning bagasse. A special type of feeder and distributor is required in order to bring about the successful burning of this bulky and fibrous fuel. Drum type rotary feeders, a typical example of which is shown in Fig. 18–17, are attached to the bottom of a bunker from which they feed bagasse to the spreader or distributor unit located at the bottom of an inclined chute, Fig. 18–18. The drum type feeder operates on a controlled volumetric basis, and the amount of bagasse fed per unit time is proportioned to the demand from a master controller. Each spreader unit is served by an individual feeder.

Distributors may be of the mechanical or pneumatic type. A mechanical distributor is essentially a rotating drum with suitably placed blades at such an angle as to maintain uniform bagasse distribution over the grate surface. The speed of the rotating drum is adjusted to suit the bagasse conditions and the length of throw required to maintain uniform grate coverage.

In the case of the pneumatic distributor, the bagasse is projected from the feeders by means of air jets which distribute the fuel uniformly over the grate surface. The fuel enters the furnace in a thin, uniform and widely dispersed stream. Much is burned in suspension while the remainder is consumed after dropping to the grate.

As in the case of spreader stokers firing coal, the grate surface may be of the dumping or continuous ash discharge

Fig. 18–17.   Rotary feeders for bagasse firing

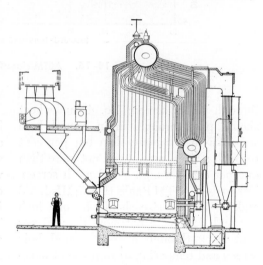

Fig. 18–18.   Spreader   stoker   for   bagasse firing

type. Spreader stokers of the dumping grate design are usually applied in areas where bagasse is relatively free of foreign material and favorable labor operating costs exist. If the bagasse contains a large amount of extraneous material such as dirt and sand from the harvesting opera-

[15] The first applications of spreader stokers for burning bagasse are described in two articles by H. G. Meissner: "Burning Bagasse at Cuban Sugar Centrals," *Combustion*, Vol. 19, January 1948, pp. 26–31; "Experience with Burning Bagasse on Spreader Type Stokers," *Combustion*, Vol. 20, September 1948, pp. 44–45.

tion, and if labor costs are quite high, the additional investment for a continuous ash discharge spreader stoker may be justified.

In general bagasse has a higher moisture and volatile content than coal, and the combustion process involves three phases: drying, distillation of volatiles and burning of fixed carbon. These take place in rapid succession. In order to get complete combustion of the volatile gases formed, a high percentage of the air supply must be furnished as overfire air introduced close to the surface of the fuel where there can be ready mixing with the volatile gases.

Material that is carried out of the furnace and settles in boiler hoppers is called "bagassilo" and represents a major disposal problem in many sugar mills. One solution is to reinject this material into the hottest and most active region of the furnace in order to consume the remaining carbon and to minimize the amount to be disposed.

Genesis of boiler design in an engineering conference

19

Fundamentals of Boiler Design[1]

WATER TUBE BOILERS range in capacity from small low pressure heating units generating a few thousand pounds of steam per hour to large central station boilers operating in the supercritical pressure region and serving turbine-generators in the million kilowatt range. In slightly different terms, capacity may be magnified more than a thousand times from the smallest to the largest, pressure may extend from just above atmospheric to values of 5000 psig or higher, and steam temperatures may vary from the boiling point to a highly superheated condition at 1200 F or above.

What are the common elements in boilers having such a diversity of design parameters? To answer this question it may be well to define the *primary function of a boiler. This is simply to generate steam at pressures above the atmospheric.* Steam is generated by the absorption of heat produced in the combustion of fuel. In some instances, such as waste heat boilers, heated fluids serve as the heat source.

Generation of steam by heat absorption from products of combustion suggests that a boiler must have a pressure parts system to convert incoming feedwater into steam;

a structure within which the combustion reaction may take place, at the same time facilitating heat transfer and supporting boiler components; means of introducing fuel and removing waste products; and controls and instruments to regulate and monitor operation. The elements a boiler designer has to work with are — using other terminology — such things as drums, headers and tubing which make up the pressure parts system and enclose the furnace in which combustion takes place; burners and related fuel and ash handling equipment; and fans to supply combustion air and exhaust waste gases. Various types of instruments and controls link these elements together in a physical and an operational sense.

These elements vary with the size and purpose of the power plant in which the boiler is installed. A large central station in which high thermal efficiency is a primary requisite has many more refinements and auxiliaries than a small heating plant in which minimum capital investment may be an important criterion. *No matter how many of these elements may be present, however, the boiler designer must integrate them so that the boiler as a whole*

---

[1] Material contributed by L. J. Marshall.

can function as a carefully adjusted, complex system which is capable of efficient operation over a wide load range.

Criteria Affecting Boiler Design

In addition to the basic elements which are of concern to the boiler designer there are many other factors which must be taken into consideration. Some of these are linked to the type of power plant and its thermodynamic cycle; others are related to fundamental considerations of engineering science; the remainder have to do with such things as fuels, manufacturing techniques and controls. All of them have a bearing on the practicality and economy of a particular boiler design. Table 19–1 lists many of these criteria and

Table 19–1   Criteria Affecting Boiler Design

Size and type of plant	Chapters 1, 2 and 3
Method of operation	Chapter 4
Thermodynamic cycle	Chapter 5
Heat transfer	Chapter 6
Fluid flow	Chapter 7
Feedwater quality	Chapter 8
Materials and metallurgy	Chapter 9
Structural design	Chapter 10
Manufacturing processes	Chapter 11
Testing results	Chapter 12
Fuels	Chapters 13, 14 and 15
Fuel burning equipment	Chapters 16, 17 and 18
Auxiliaries	Chapter 20
Calculations	Chapter 21
Controls and instruments	Chapter 22
Specific boiler types	Chapters 23 through 29

the chapters in which these topics are illustrated and discussed at some length and with additional details.

As will be seen in Chapters 23 through 29 which deal with specific boiler applications, these design criteria have a more pronounced effect on some types of boilers

than on others. For example, in combined circulation boilers operating at supercritical pressures, metallurgy and water treatment have far more stringent requirements than for shop assembled boilers. The latter, however, have been responsible for many improvements in shop fabrication techniques, and the designer takes advantage of this, for example, by specifying panel wall construction for central station boilers.

It should be apparent that choice of fuel and method of firing affect boiler design in many ways. A central station boiler intended for automatic operation has far more control sophistication than an industrial boiler having operators in constant attendance. Pressurized operation affects structural design requirements, and the list could be continued at some length. *It is an understatement to write that boiler design involves the interaction of a great number of variables.*

All of this serves as a reminder that "the boiler designer" is generally not one person but a team of specialists whose leader is capable of coordinating their efforts into a unified whole. Notwithstanding the many advantages of design specialization, there is always the possibility that overall objectives may be lost sight of or subordinated to narrow interests. Hence it is particularly important that the *fundamentals of boiler design* be thoroughly comprehended so that advantage may be taken of the broad perspective that they offer. The specialist who can understand the relationship of his work to the design and operation of the boiler as a whole can be a more effective member of the design team than the one who is oblivious to the significance of these other areas. If he is capable of seeing the boiler in the total power plant picture, he becomes even more useful to the design effort.[2]

Boiler Output

The output or capacity of a boiler is often expressed in pounds of steam per hour or in the power output of a turbine generator in those cases where a single boiler provides the entire steam supply for an electric generating unit. Neither term is a true measure of the thermal energy supplied by the boiler.

Actual boiler output in terms of heat energy depends on several factors other than quantity of steam. These include temperature of feedwater entering the economizer, steam pressure and steam temperature at the superheater outlet, and the quantity, temperature and pressure of steam entering and leaving the reheater. Similarly, because boiler output is affected by turbine and generator efficiencies, generator output in kilowatts or megawatts is not entirely a true measure of the energy output of the boiler alone.

An acceptable standard has long been needed to express true boiler output. Over the years the expression, mB, referring to million Btu per hour, has been recommended but has received only limited usage notwithstanding its very accurate representation of boiler output.

Boiler Functions

In addition to its primary function of generating steam under pressure, the modern boiler may be required to perform some or all of the following functions:

1. Provide steam of exceptionally high purity by removing impurities from the saturated steam.

2. Superheat the steam generated in the boiler to the desired temperature and maintain this temperature constant over a specified range of load.

3. In power plants operating on the reheat cycle, resuperheat the steam which is returned to the boiler after expanding through the high pressure stages of the turbine and maintain the desired reheat temperature constant over a specified range of load.

Boiler Efficiency

One of the best ways to comprehend the significance of boiler efficiency is by means of the Sankey diagram which is generally associated with the evaluation of thermodynamic cycles. Fig. 19–1 shows the distribution of heat energy in a coal fired reheat boiler for a central station. It can be seen that the primary source of heat is the fuel (A) but that preheated air also contributes to the total heat in the furnace. The amount of heat in the preheated air corresponds to that extracted from the exhaust gases by the air preheater.

Of the total heat entering the furnace the major portion is absorbed as sensible and latent heat in the heating surfaces of the furnace, economizer, superheater and reheater. This portion (B) represents the boiler output in the form of superheated and reheated steam. Losses account for the remainder of the heat supplied to the furnace. They comprise the heat contained in the flue gas leaving the air preheater (sensible heat in the dry gas and moisture in air plus sensible and latent heat in the

---

[2] For a personalized account of teamwork in boiler design, see Chapter 25, Combined Circulation Boilers, section entitled The Second Generation of Supercritical Pressure Boilers.

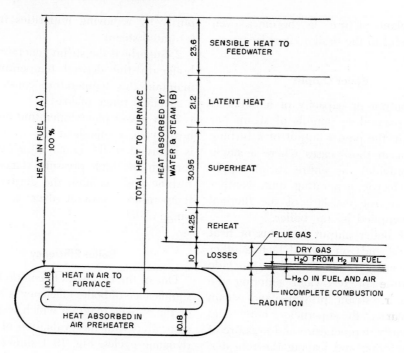

Fig. 19–1. Boiler heat balance

moisture in the fuel) and losses due to incomplete combustion and radiation from the boiler.

For central station boilers of the reheat type, losses account for about ten per cent of the total heat supplied in the fuel, thereby realizing boiler efficiencies of 90 per cent or higher. By referring to Fig. 19–1 it becomes quite evident that boiler efficiency may be represented by the ratio of heat absorbed by water and steam (B) to the heat in fuel (A).

It is well to think of boilers in the context of complete power plants. Fig. 19–2 shows the amount of energy available for power generation using a fire tube boiler, an industrial boiler and subcritical and supercritical pressure boilers. It should be noted that condensing losses decrease sub-

stantially and regeneration of air and feedwater become increasingly important in the most advanced central station boilers. While station auxiliary power requirements increase from two to eight per cent, the Sankey diagrams show that the useful energy for generating power rises from nine to 41 per cent.

Heat Absorbing Surfaces

The objective of the boiler designer is to arrange heat transfer surface and fuel burning equipment in such a manner as to optimize thermal efficiency and economic investment. He has a choice of a number of types of surface for absorbing and recovering heat. Waterwalls, superheaters and reheaters all absorb heat from the fur-

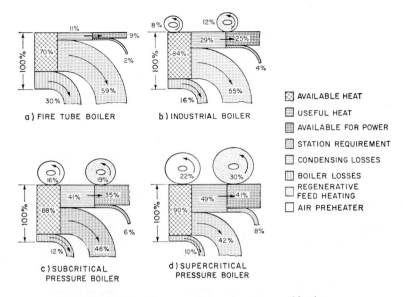

Fig. 19–2. Sankey diagrams for various types of boilers

nace gas as they perform their respective functions of heating water to the saturation point and of superheating and resuperheating steam. Air heaters and economizers recover heat from the furnace exit gases in order to preheat combustion air and increase the temperature of incoming feedwater.

The boiler designer must proportion heat absorbing and heat recovery surfaces in such a manner as to make best use of the heat released by the fuel. Waterwalls, superheaters and reheaters are exposed to convection and radiant heat, whereas convection heat transfer predominates in air heaters and economizers.

The relative amounts of these types of surface vary with the size and operating conditions of the boiler. A small low pressure heating plant with no heat recovery equipment has quite a different boiler arrangement from a large high pressure central station operating on a reheat re-

generative cycle and incorporating heat recovery equipment.

Fig. 19–3 shows how the proportion of energy absorbed varies with different types of boilers. It is evident that in a heating plant boiler operating with a minimum of feedwater heating and no superheater most of the heat absorbed is utilized in evaporating water to steam. In a large utility or central station boiler with feedwater heaters and heat recovery equipment, heat for evaporation is comparatively small, whereas that for superheating and reheating accounts for more than half of the total input.

There is an interesting contrast between the box-like low pressure heating boiler shown in Fig. 19–4 and the tower-like central station boiler shown in Fig. 19–5. The former has a considerable amount of evaporative surface in the form of waterwalls, closely spaced tubing joining the two drums. The latter incorporates super-

BOILER SERVICE	FUEL	CAPACITY LB PER HR	PRESSURE	STEAM TEMPERATURE-F	REHEAT TEMPERATURE-F	FEEDWATER TEMPERATURE-F	BOILER EFFICIENCY
HEATING	OIL	60,000	125	SAT	—	212	80.20
SMALL INDUSTRIAL	OIL	100,000	650	750	—	300	85.60
MEDIUM INDUSTRIAL	COAL	220,000	650	750	—	265	87.25
LARGE INDUSTRIAL	COAL	600,000	1500	880	—	275	88.00
SMALL UTILITY	OIL	1,580,000	1890	1005	1005	472	85.20
LARGE UTILITY	COAL	3,785,000	2620	1000	1000	480.5	90.04

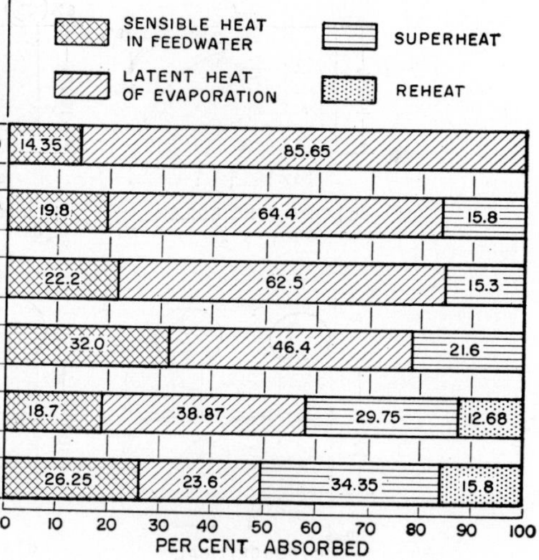

Legend: SENSIBLE HEAT IN FEEDWATER · LATENT HEAT OF EVAPORATION · SUPERHEAT · REHEAT

Chart values (PER CENT ABSORBED):
- HEATING: 14.35 | 85.65
- SMALL INDUSTRIAL: 19.8 | 64.4 | 15.8
- MEDIUM INDUSTRIAL: 22.2 | 62.5 | 15.3
- LARGE INDUSTRIAL: 32.0 | 46.4 | 21.6
- SMALL UTILITY: 18.7 | 38.87 | 29.75 | 12.68
- LARGE UTILITY: 26.25 | 23.6 | 34.35 | 15.8

PER CENT ABSORBED (0 10 20 30 40 50 60 70 80 90 100)

Fig. 19–3.   Heat absorption by various types of boilers

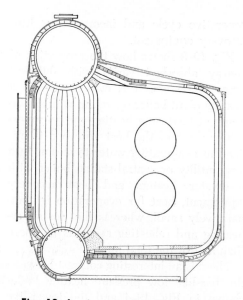

Fig. 19–4.   Low pressure heating boiler

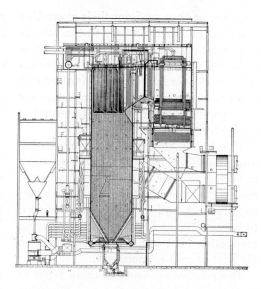

Fig. 19–5.   Central station reheat boiler

heater and reheater surface plus an air heater and an economizer in addition to a single drum and waterwalls.

Fig. 19–3 shows how the percentage of heat absorption differs from one type of a boiler to another. The boiler service designations in the left hand column are related to the heating and large utility boil-

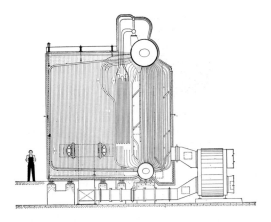

Fig. 19–6. Small industrial boiler

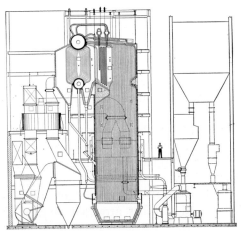

Fig. 19–7. Medium industrial boiler

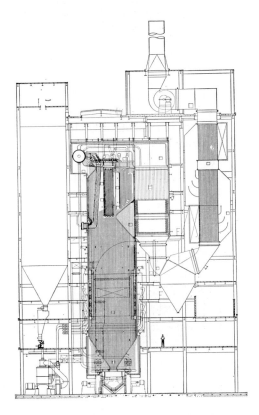

Fig. 19–8. Large industrial boiler

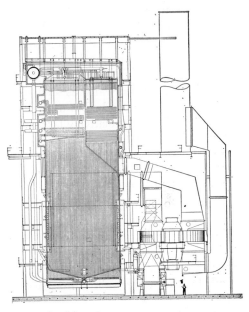

Fig. 19–9. Small central station boiler

medium industrial boiler shown in Fig. 19–7; a large industrial boiler shown in Fig. 19–8; and a small utility or central station boiler in Fig. 19–9. Capacities, fuel fired, outlet steam conditions, incoming feedwater temperatures and boiler efficiencies are all listed in Fig. 19–3.

ers previously mentioned and to a small industrial boiler shown in Fig. 19–6; a

Waterwalls

Practically all modern power boilers are equipped with waterwalls. In large central station boilers, waterwalls completely cover the interior surfaces of the furnace, thus providing practically complete elimination of exposed refractory surface. In addition, the waterwalls serve as the sole means of heating and evaporating the feedwater supplied to the boiler from the economizer.

Waterwalls usually consist of substantially vertical tubes arranged tangent or approximately so and are connected at top and bottom to headers. These tubes receive their water supply from the boiler drum by means of downcomer tubes connected between bottom of drum and lower headers. In a typical central station boiler, roughly 50 per cent of the heat released by the combustion of fuel in the furnace is absorbed by the waterwalls, as shown in Fig. 19–3. Heat so absorbed is utilized in evaporation of all or a relatively large percentage of the water supplied to the boiler. The steam generated and a substantial quantity of accompanying water is discharged from the top of the waterwall tubes into the upper waterwall headers and thence passes through riser tubes to the boiler drum. Here the steam is separated and the accompanying water together with the incoming feedwater is returned to the waterwalls through the downcomers.

Waterwalls serve as a durable furnace lining. By their use, a continuous metallic surface is provided which is capable of absorbing and transferring a large quantity of heat without deterioration, thus minimizing furnace maintenance and appreciably increasing availability of the boiler.

Superheaters and Reheaters

The function of the superheater is to increase the temperature of the steam generated in the boiler. Steam enters the superheater at saturated temperature in a practically dry saturated condition, and consequently the absorption of heat appears as sensible heat in increasing the steam temperature.

The reheater receives superheated steam which has partly expanded through the turbine. The function of the reheater is to re-superheat this steam to a desired temperature.

Designs of superheaters and reheaters vary depending largely on the duty to be performed. For relatively low final temperatures, superheaters of the convection type are generally used. Fig. 19–10 is a typical example of this type. For higher duties and correspondently high final steam temperatures, surface requirements are greater and of necessity elements are located in high gas temperature zones. For such requirements, platen, panel or wall superheaters or reheaters of the radiant type are used. Fig. 19–11 designates the several types of superheater and reheater surface in a reheat boiler.

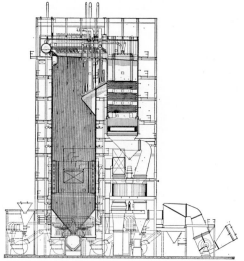

Fig. 19–10.   Convection type superheater in central station boiler

It should be noted that the convection section is arranged to provide essentially counterflow of steam and gas with steam entering at the bottom and leaving at top of pass while gas flow is opposite. In this manner, maximum mean temperature difference is maintained between the two media resulting in minimizing the heating surface in the primary section.

Fig. 19–11 shows in detail radiant panel and platen type superheaters. As shown in Fig. 19–12 panel elements are few in number and are very widely spaced to permit large radiant absorption. Platen sections located after the panel elements are spaced on wide enough centers to avoid accumulations or bridging of slag on or between tubes. This spacing provides high heat absorption by radiation and convection.

Fig. 19–11 also shows a section of a radiant wall reheater. Here tubes are vertical and spaced together to form continuous wall. This type of surface is generally located in the upper part of furnace for the purpose of providing protection against overheating during startup or during low load operation.

A top view of the superheaters and the reheaters of Fig. 19–11 is shown in Fig. 19–12. This provides the reader with an opportunity to visualize the spacing of platen, pendant and convection surface and to get a better idea of the tremendous number of individual tubes required for superheating and reheating in a large central station boiler.

Design Considerations

In addition to the basic design conditions of evaporation, steam pressure and steam temperature, the designer must consider a number of other factors, all of which influence the overall design. These factors and the manner in which each of them affects the boiler as a whole are discussed below.

Fuels

Coal is to a large extent the base fuel in power generating stations in this country although natural gas and oil are used where costs are favorable. In contrast to gas, coal contains ash which consists of a number of objectionable chemical elements and compounds. Oil generally contains only small amounts of ash. The objectionable constituents of the ash, however, may have a far reaching effect on the design.

Ash is of concern since at the high temperatures resulting from the burning of fuel in the furnace, fractions of the ash become partially fused and sticky. Depending on the quantity and fusion temperature, the partially fused ash may adhere to surfaces contacted by the ash-containing combustion gases, causing objectionable buildup of slag on or bridging between tubes. Chemicals in the ash may attack materials such as alloys used in superheaters and reheaters.

In addition to the deposits in the high temperature sections of the unit, the air heater which is the coolest part may be subject to corrosion and plugging of gas passages due primarily to sulfur compounds in the fuel acting in combination with moisture present in the flue gas.

Furnaces

Furnace design must take into consideration water heating and steam generation in the wall tubes as well as the processes of combustion. Practically all large modern boilers are designed with walls comprised of water cooled tubes to form complete metal coverage of furnace enclosure. In addition, areas outside of the

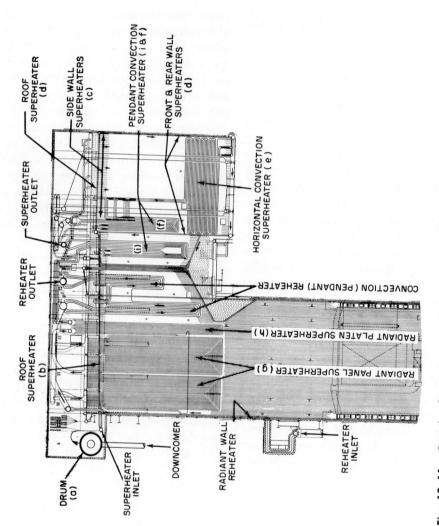

Fig. 19—11.   Details of arrangement of superheaters and reheaters in a central station boiler

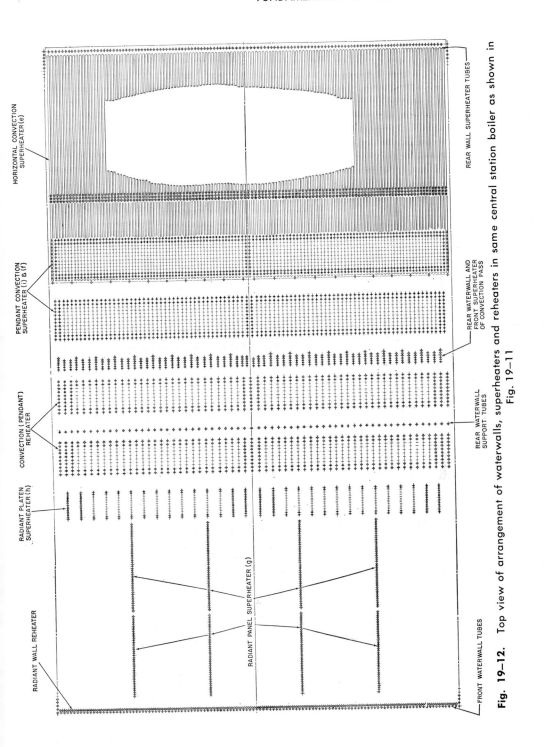

Fig. 19–12. Top view of arrangement of waterwalls, superheaters and reheaters in same central station boiler as shown in Fig. 19–11

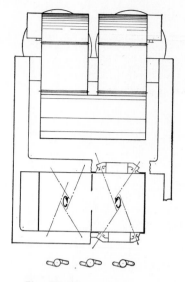

Fig. 19–13. Furnace with division walls

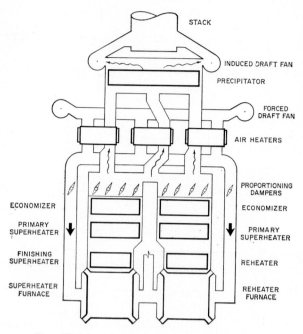

STACK

INDUCED DRAFT FAN

PRECIPITATOR

FORCED DRAFT FAN

AIR HEATERS

PROPORTIONING DAMPERS

ECONOMIZER

ECONOMIZER

PRIMARY SUPERHEATER

PRIMARY SUPERHEATER

FINISHING SUPERHEATER

REHEATER

SUPERHEATER FURNACE

REHEATER FURNACE

Fig. 19–14.   Arrangement of twin furnaces

furnace which form enclosures for sections of superheaters, reheaters and often economizers are also designed in a manner similar to the furnace using either water or steam cooled tube surfaces. Present practice is to use tube arrangements and configurations which permit practically complete elimination of refractories in all areas that are exposed to high temperature gases.

Tube diameter and thickness are of concern from the standpoints of circulation and metal temperatures. Natural circulation boilers generally use larger diameter tubes than controlled circulation or once-through boilers. This practice is dictated largely by the need for more liberal flow area to provide the lower velocities necessary with the limited head available. The use of small diameter tubes becomes advantageous in high pressure boilers since the lesser tube thicknesses required result in lower outside tube metal temperatures. Small diameter tubes are advantageously used in controlled or forced circulation boilers where pumps provide adequate head for circulation and maintenance of desired velocities.

Factors such as velocity of water and water steam mixtures, quality of water and steam mixtures are of particular concern in high heat absorption areas of high pressure boilers.

While it is not possible for the designer to provide complete freedom from corrosion and plugging, nevertheless, there is much that can be accomplished to minimize these objectionable features. In the furnace, factors such as size, shape, amount of water cooling, and elimination of all refractories, are given due consideration with respect to fuel analysis. Provisions for continuous cleaning of surfaces and areas by the installation of proper types, numbers, and location of soot blowers, and the installation of ash hoppers in

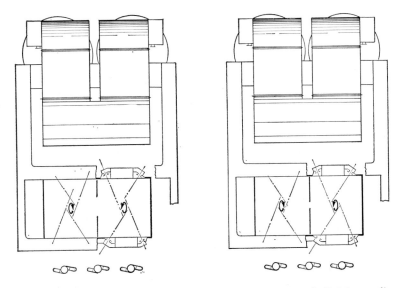

Fig. 19–15. Arrangement of twin furnaces, each one with division walls

proper locations are means of maintaining continuously clean surfaces. In connection with the superheaters and reheaters, particular importance is placed on the arrangement and spacing of tubes and selection of materials for tubes and supports.

The desire to reduce power generating costs has resulted in demands for higher capacity turbine-generators with steam supplied by a single boiler. This has resulted in the use of another technique for increasing furnace heating surface, namely, the addition of partitions in a single furnace or the use of twin furnaces, the waterwalls of which connect to a single boiler drum. Fig. 19–13 illustrates an example of a divided furnace and Fig. 19–14, a twin furnace. Both arrangements provide means to reduce the space occupied by the boiler by reducing the overall furnace dimensions. In extremely large furnaces, both features are employed, namely twin furnaces, each of which is provided with a partition wall. Fig. 19–15 illustrates such a design.

Another factor of particular interest to designers of large coal-fired boilers is gas velocity. The depletion of high quality coal has resulted in the utilization of lower grade coals containing high percentages of ash. The abrasive character of some fractions of the ash has caused erosion of metal surfaces of boilers designed in accordance with past practice. Thus, proper gas velocity and the avoidance of localized concentration of ash in the gas stream is an important consideration.

Circulation

In practically all types of boilers, the difference in density between steam and water is utilized to provide or to assist in providing water circulation. Generally, the waterwall downtakes serve as the high density leg of the U-tube. The waterwalls or the boiler bank containing mixture of steam and water constitutes the low density leg. The available head for providing circulation is also affected by frictional and entrance and exit losses in the several

Table 19–2   Logical Postulates of Combined Circulation

(1) Heat Absorbing Circuits + Drum = Natural Circulation (with recirculation)
(2) Natural Circulation + Circulating Pumps = Controlled Circulation (with recirculation)
(3) Heat Absorbing Circuits — Drum — Recirculation = Once-Through Circulation
(4) Heat Absorbing Circuits + Pump + Once-Through Circulation + Recirculation = Combined Circulation
(5) Combined Circulation = Elements of Natural, Controlled and Once-Through Circulation

circuits. It is thus evident that adequate circulation can only be provided if losses are low enough to make sufficient circulating head available. Generally, boilers are designed in such a manner that steam discharged from the waterwall headers and to the drum is accompanied by a limited quantity of water. The presence of water in the tubes insures that the water and steam mixture will not exceed the saturation temperature corresponding to existing pressure. Also due to low film resistance as a result of this mixture circulating through the tubes, temperature of the inside surface of tubes is close to that of the water and steam in the tubes.

Increasing steam pressures and the use of higher capacities have reached the point where available head no longer is sufficient to provide adequate circulation. Thus, the limitations of natural circulation have been realized. It is for this reason that controlled circulation incorporating circulating pumps came into use. More recently, forced circulation boilers of the once-through type have been designed and installed for subcritical as well as supercritical pressures. Advantages of once-through and controlled circulation are linked together in combined circulation as explained and illustrated in Fig. 19–16 and Table 19–2.

Metallurgy

The selection of materials for superheaters and reheaters in boilers designed for high pressures and temperatures in excess of 1000 F requires the use of high-strength alloy tubing. In addition to matters of strength and oxidation resistance in superheater and reheater materials, the use of high steam pressure requires increased tube thicknesses in all tubes subject to steam pressure. Furthermore, the thicker tubes are subject to higher outside metal temperatures. Since chemical action is accelerated at higher temperatures, the tube metal is more subject to external corrosion. This is of particular concern when burning fuels containing objectionable impurities. The designer takes account of such conditions in selecting material and tube sizes.

Controlled Steam Temperature

The desire to maintain turbine efficiency over a wide range of load and to avoid fluctuations in turbine metal temperatures has resulted in a need to maintain constant steam and reheat temperatures over the anticipated operating load range. In order to satisfy this requirement it is necessary that the boiler be equipped with means for controlling and maintaining constant steam and reheat temperatures over the desired range. If uncontrolled, steam temperatures rise with in-

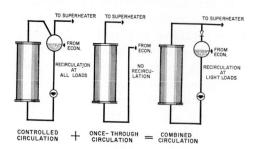

Fig. 19–16.   Elements of Combined Circulation

creasing steam output. This is characteristic of convection type superheaters which necessarily account for the major share of the heat absorbed by the superheater.

It is desirable from the standpoint of economy of heating surface and corresponding cost and in the interest of operation with minimum metal temperatures to design superheaters and reheaters to provide desired steam temperature at maximum output. To satisfy this condition the means of control must be capable of raising and maintaining full steam and reheat temperatures over the full control range.

Two means have been developed to accomplish this objective. Tangential tilting burners have been widely used. They effect a reduction in furnace heat absorption at reduced outputs thus causing an increase in furnace outlet gas temperature and making more heat available to the superheater, correspondingly increasing steam and reheat temperatures. A second means referred to as gas recirculation diverts a portion of the flue gas from the main stream at a point following the superheater. The diverted gas passes through a recirculating fan and is discharged to the lower part of the furnace. Gas thus recirculated mixes with the flue gas in the furnace, causing a reduction in heat absorption. Thus, heat available to the superheater is increased as is the gas quantity passing over the superheater surface. Both of these factors operate to increase steam temperature.

Both of the above means of control have the desirable feature of permitting superheaters and reheaters to be designed for full temperature at maximum load. In this manner additional surface is not required in order to raise temperatures at lower loads. Other means which provide control on the basis of reducing temperatures to desired levels have been used but find only limited application. These require that superheater and reheater surfaces be sufficient to provide full temperatures at the lowest point of the control range.

The first is gas bypass which reduces quantity of gas passing through the superheater. The heat available to the superheater is reduced as a result of the portion of the gas bypassed around it. The reduced gas flow together with the lowered gas velocity effects a reduction in heat absorption which in turn brings about a reduction in steam temperature.

A second control means used to effect a reduction in steam temperature incorporates a water spray. This method, referred to as spray desuperheating, produces a reduction in temperature by injecting solid water into the oversuperheated steam. The reduction in temperature is the result of the heat transferred to water from superheated steam in evaporating and raising its temperature to that of the steam. The injection points of the spray water are generally located between rather than following individual sections of the superheater. In this way, outlet elements of the final superheater are not subjected to excessive temperatures.

Boiler Drum

The boiler drum serves two functions, the first and primary one being that of separating steam from the mixture of water and steam discharged into it. Secondly, the drum is used to house the equipment used for purification of steam after being separated from the water.

The quantity of water contained in the boiler below the water-level is relatively small compared to the total steam output. Consequently, regardless of the drum size, the matter of water storage is not significant. Primarily the drum size is determined by the space required to accommodate steam separating and purifying equipment. Drum diameter and length should be sufficient to provide accessibility for installation and inspection. Length generally depends on furnace width, or in the case of high capacity units, it may be controlled by the space required for the steam separating devices.

Determination of Heating Surface

The amount of heating surface to be provided in each of the several elements of the boiler depends on a number of factors. The manner in which each of these factors influences the heating surface determinations is discussed below. It is of course necessary that surface be adequate to satisfy design and operating requirements. Also of importance are proper applications and arrangements of surfaces to insure effective utilization. The latter is to a large degree dictated by economic considerations.

The present practice of using steam and reheat temperatures of 1000 F and higher not only requires the use of expensive alloys in sections of these elements attaining metal temperatures of 1100 F and higher but also requires the use of large amounts of tubing. It is thus important to give careful consideration to designs which provide the desired performance and reflect economic considerations.

Furnace

Heat generated in the combustion of fuel appears as sensible and latent heat in the products of combustion. Roughly 50 percent of the heat so generated is absorbed by water circulated through tubes forming the furnace wall lining. Heat absorbed generates steam by the evaporation of part of the circulated water.

To a limited degree the furnace heat absorbing surface is dictated by the size and dimensions required for proper combustion of the fuel. Other limitations are often imposed such as ash content and fusion temperature, in the case of coal firing. For coals containing low fusion temperature ash, the gas temperature leaving the furnace may be limited by considerations of slag accumulations and bridging between tubes of boiler or superheater. For this reason, also for the purpose of possibly limiting metal temperatures, furnace outlet temperature is an important factor to the designer. While these factors are of concern, designing for high steam and reheat temperatures requires major consideration since sufficient heat must be available in the gas leaving the furnace to provide the desired steam temperatures. When factors such as mentioned above place limitations on furnace outlet temperature, practicable sizes of convection type superheaters and reheaters may not provide the desired temperatures. Thus the question of whether or not to incorporate radiant type superheater surface may be determined by the permissible gas temperature at the furnace outlet.

Furnace size and arrangement as well as the type and arrangement of burners all influence the furnace outlet temperature. The major part of the heat absorbed in the furnace is by radiation but the absorption rate is affected by so many other factors that it is not generally considered practical to calculate absorption by theoretical means. Accordingly, empirical means based on actual operating data have been adopted for practical usage.

In general, furnace sizes of small boilers are determined by combustion and burner requirements: furnace outlet temperature requirements, to a large extent, determine the quantity of heat to be absorbed by furnace walls. With the present trend to continually larger central station boilers the conventional single furnace design becomes excessive in size. It is for this reason that twin and divided furnaces have come into use. Widely spaced water cooled or steam cooled (radiant superheater) panels similar to arrangements of Fig. 19–11 have also been used, the latter functioning as radiant heat absorbing surface.

Welded Panel Walls

Designing furnaces for pressurized firing is becoming general practice for both central station and industrial types of boilers. This practice is justified by economic considerations of reduced investment due to the elimination of induced draft fans and also by a reduction in fan power. The use of pressurized furnaces requires particular attention to problems of design with respect to furnace tightness since outward leakage of furnace gases cannot be tolerated.

Waterwalls arranged with tangent tubes have generally been provided with skin casings consisting of thin steel sheets welded together in the form of an envelope placed behind and in contact with the waterwall tubes. It is this welded enclosure that provides the seal against furnace leakage. However, this type of construction requires a considerable amount of field fabrication and welding. In order to lessen the amount of this work and to decrease the time required for boiler erection, an improved design referred to as panel wall construction has been developed.

Panels consist of a number of tubes joined together by a process of fusion welding and are made in widths of approximately five feet. The tubes are spaced about three eighths to one half inch apart by means of bars which are then fused together with the tubes to form a continuous metal furnace lining.[3]

Superheaters and Reheaters

As previously discussed in this chapter, the amount of heat absorbed by superheaters and reheaters in high pressure boilers designed for high steam temperatures represents a large fraction of the total absorption of the boiler. For reasons of maintaining metal temperatures within safe limits, it is desirable to limit the use of panels and radiant wall type superheaters to furnace areas of relatively low heat absorption. Accordingly, a limit is placed on the amount of radiant surface which should be used. This limitation in surface results in limiting the total heat absorption in radiant surface to a relatively small fraction of the total superheater and reheater absorption. Thus the balance or major portion of the absorption must be obtained in convection type surface where the transfer of heat results in an increase in the temperature of steam and a reduction in temperature of gas.

The magnitude of the steam temperature rise and gas temperature drop requires that a large portion of the surface be arranged for substantially counterflow of steam and gas. The minimum temperature difference at the gas outlet of the superheater, even with counterflow, is largely an economic consideration and may determine whether or not radiant superheaters should be incorporated. Generally all or part of the convection reheater is placed between sections of the superheater. The relatively large temperature difference in the high temperature

[3] For further information see the description of a fusion panel welder in Chapter 11, Manufacture and Machine Design, section on manufacturing case studies and the discussion on strength of furnace walls in Chapter 10, Stress Analysis and Structural Design.

section or sections of the superheater permit parallel flow arrangements. Thus the surface at the outlet ends of these sections is subjected to lower gas temperatures, resulting in lower metal temperature at the steam outlet ends of these sections than would be the case with counterflow arrangements.

Economizers

Economizers provide a means for improving boiler efficiency by extracting heat from flue gases discharged, depending on the design, from the superheater section or the evaporative section of the boiler. In the economizer, heat is transferred to the feedwater which enters at a temperature appreciably lower than that of saturated steam. Generally the economizers are arranged for downward flow of gas and upward flow of water. Water enters from a lower header and flows through the horizontal tubing which comprises the heating surface. Return bends at the ends of the tubing provide continuous tube elements, the upper ends of which connect to outlet header which in turn is connected to boiler drum by means of tubes or large pipes. Tubes forming the heating surface are closely spaced and may be plain or provided with extended surface such as fins. They are generally arranged in staggered relationship in the gas pass to obtain high heat transfer and also to lessen the space requirements.

Designing the economizer for counterflow of gas and water results in maximum mean temperature difference for heat transfer. Upward flow of water assists in avoiding water hammer which may occur under some operating conditions. Economizers are generally designed with water leaving temperature below that of saturated steam for normal operating conditions to avoid steam generation.

As shown in Fig. 19–17 economizers of a typical central station boiler are located in the same pass as the primary or horizontal sections of the superheater or superheater and reheater, depending on the arrangement of the surface. As shown the same enclosure forms the walls surrounding both types of surface.

Walls are generally covered with vertical steam or water cooled tubing depending on the particular design. If steam is used it is introduced at a temperature close to that of saturation. If water is used it is supplied from the economizer outlet and enters at the bottom lower portion usually of two opposite walls. Economizers are often applied to industrial type boilers. In these cases they are equipped with casing separate from the boiler although one side may be common to both boiler and economizer as in Fig. 19–18.

Tubing forming the heating surface is generally low carbon steel. Since steel is subject to corrosion in the presence of even extremely low concentrations of oxygen it is necessary to provide practically 100 per cent oxygen free water. In central stations and other plants it is common practice to provide for oxygen removal by means of deaerators.

Small low pressure boilers may be equipped with economizers made of cast iron which is not as subject to oxygen corrosion. Design pressure for this material is limited however to approximately 250 psig. Cast iron tubes, while used to some extent in the past, find very little application today.

Another application of economizers, referred to as low level heat recovery, has recently come into limited use in high efficiency central station boilers. Here low temperature condensate provides the cooling medium to absorb heat from flue gas discharged from conventional air heaters. In economizers used for this purpose one

Fig. 19–17. Construction view of economizer in a central station boiler

justified and the extent to which gas temperature can be lowered.

Low level heating surface of the conventional type is subject to corrosion since metal temperature is appreciably lower than the dew point of the gas. Consequently a type of surface which resists corrosion is required. Cost of such surface is an important consideration.

Air Heaters

For many years air heaters have been used almost universally on central station and large industrial boilers. In recent

or more low pressure condensate stage heaters is omitted and feedwater heating is accomplished by absorption of heat from flue gas. While some reduction in efficiency of the regenerative heating cycle results from the reduced amount of bled steam nevertheless the overall plant efficiency is increased by lowering the exit gas temperature from the boiler. While it is generally not economical to design heat recovery equipment to obtain exit gas temperature below the range of 260 to 300 F, studies have indicated that the use of low level economizers are sometimes justified in reducing exit gas temperature to as low as 200 F. In one such application condensate enters economizer at 166 F and leaves at 202 F. Gas enters at 270 F and leaves at 204 F. It is evident that the relatively small temperature difference obtained between gas and water requires a large amount of heating surface. Economic considerations will obviously dictate whether low level economizers are

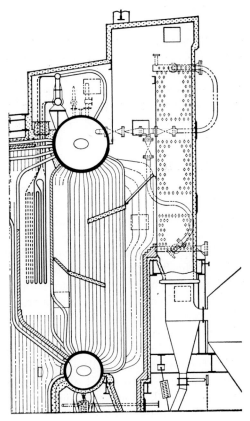

Fig. 19–18. Economizer applied to industrial boiler

years the demand for higher plant efficiency, largely because of increasing fuel costs, has resulted in the use of larger air heaters to provide higher efficiency.

Of the three types of air heaters used in the past, namely, plate, tubular and regenerative (Ljungstrom), the latter type is used quite extensively, particularly on large boilers. The plate type has been largely discarded. Tubular heaters find a wide application in the industrial field for small boilers where high heat recovery is not justified.

Air heaters improve efficiency by extracting heat from the flue gas thus reducing the flue gas loss by reducing the exit gas temperature. The limit in this respect is an economic one since cost of surface is an increasing function with reduction in gas temperature.

While improvement in efficiency is the primary reason for the use of air heaters, other benefits derived from hot air are improvement and stabilizing of combustion; also, with pulverized coal firing hot air is used as the medium for drying the coal during pulverization.

Designing for Low Exit Gas Temperature

While improved efficiencies are obtainable by the use of added surface to reduce exit gas temperature from an air heater, this practice results in lowering cold-end metal temperatures and also lowering dew point of the flue gas. Consequently, conventional steel tubes or plates are subject to corrosion from sulfuric acid as a result of moisture condensation in the presence of sulfur and moisture in the gas.

A number of means for minimizing the rate of corrosion as well as provision for replacement of corroded surface, have been developed. Since corrosion occurs on the lowest temperature surface, air heater designs have been developed which incorporate replaceable cold end sections. Other means for minimizing corrosion are aimed at increasing the metal temperature. One arrangement provides such means by directing a portion of the preheated air to the inlet of the forced draft fan and recirculating it through the air heater. Thus the temperature of the air leaving the fan and entering the air heater is increased, correspondingly increasing the cold end metal temperature.

Another scheme which has been used to a limited extent is the application of air bypass which causes part of the air to be bypassed around the heater. Because of reduced air flow, metal temperatures within the air heater are higher because of the influence of the higher gas to air ratio. Also because the overall recovery is less as a result of the reduced air flow, gas outlet temperature is increased correspondingly causing an increase in the cold end metal temperature.

Still another means of increasing cold end metal temperature, one which is prevalent today, is the use of steam air heaters located in the cold air duct between the forced draft fan and the air heater. These effect an increase in temperature of air entering the heater correspondingly causing an increase in the metal temperature. Steam bled from the turbine is utilized as the heating medium in the steam air heater. Steam is bled at a pressure corresponding to the desired temperature. In supplying heat to the cold air, steam is condensed and the condensate returned to the appropriate stage of the feedwater bleed heating system.

Tubular Air Heaters

Fig. 19–19 shows typical application of a tubular air preheater to an industrial boiler. This heater is arranged for vertical gas flow through tubes. Air flows horizontally across tubes which are generally in staggered relationship. Air passes over the heating surface several times, the effect of which is to provide counterflow. Tube sheets are provided at top and bottom through which the tubes pass and to which tubes are attached. Structural support is provided by members which are attached to top of upper tube sheet or located below the lower tube sheet.

Fig. 19–20 shows a two section air heater which is applicable where cold end section is subject to corrosion. Thus the short tube cold end section is replaceable at a relatively low cost if corrosion is prevalent.

Regenerative Air Preheater

The Ljungstrom continuous-regenerative-type air preheater was developed in Sweden in the 1920's in conjunction with the design of a steam turbine locomotive. Although the regenerative principle was previously well known, it had only been partially utilized in the design of refractory-type checker regenerators for open hearth steel furnaces. In the United States the first Ljungstrom installations for industrial power boilers were made in 1923.

The preheater assembly consists of a housing divided into two end or outside compartments, and one middle compartment in which the heating surface, contained in a slowly moving rotor, is installed. The outside compartments are divided by partitions which confine the hot gas to one side of the apparatus, while the air to be heated is on the other side. For each revolution of the rotor there is a complete cycle of exchange in which heat from the hot gas is continually absorbed by the regenerator method of heating surface, and then given up as the rotation moves into the path of the air to be heated.

A typical unit of the vertical flow design

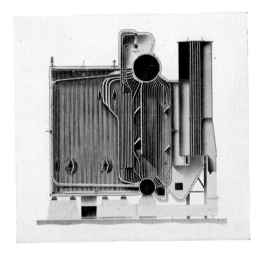

Fig. 19–19. Tubular air preheater applied to industrial boiler

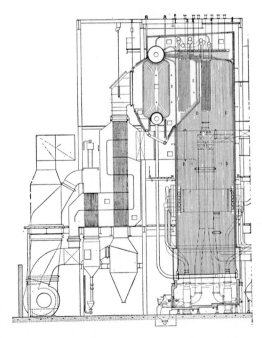

Fig. 19–20. Two section tubular air preheater with replaceable cold end, left

is shown in Fig. 19–21. The air for combustion enters at the lower left side, passes upward through the heating surface, and discharges at the upper left side into the hot air ducts. The hot flue gas enters at the upper right side, flowing continuously downward through the heating surface into the lower right chamber, counterflow to the air, and is then exhausted to the stack by either natural or induced draft. Upward flow of the gas and downward air flow may be used if required. Horizontal flow design may also be furnished with the flow passages either side by side or with one stream passage vertically over the other depending on layout requirements.

Both the vertical flow design and the horizontal flow design are commonly used for preheaters applied to large power boilers or furnaces where the temperature of the entering gas does not exceed 1000 F. Designs are available in a number of standard sizes, between the largest and the smallest, and can therefore be easily adapted to meet almost any capacity requirement. For entering gas temperature in excess of 1000 F, special designs are available.

Heating Surface. The rotor which carries the heating surface is a structure of sector shaped cells into which the heating surface of regenerative mass is fitted. The heating surface is divided into a number of groups, or baskets, of smaller size, easily handled and quickly inserted. The seals are mounted on the plates forming the rotor. These plates are fabricated to permit easy application and adjustment of the seals. The structure is strong and light in weight, and is sufficiently flexible to operate without difficulties under conditions of large temperature gradients through the rotor in the axial direction.

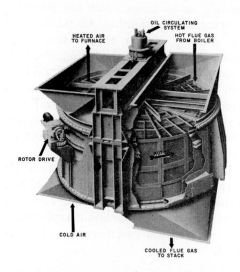

Fig. 19–21. Arrangement of Ljungstrom regenerative type air preheater

The heating surface employed in the Ljungstrom preheater is made of combinations of flat or formed thin sheets. The formed sheets may be corrugated, notched or undulated with the ribs, when in combination, forming longitudinal passages of the most desirable contour for the predetermined spacing. The design and arrangement of surface provides only point contact between adjacent plates. The gas and air flow are turbulent, but at the same time the smooth path for their travel through the rotor offers low resistance. As an approximate rule, it may be stated that one inch in height of standard Ljungstrom heating surface will recover about as much heat as a foot length of surface in a standard plate heater, or two feet in a tubular heater with equivalent resistance to gas and air flow. The compact arrangement of light metal sheets permits a large amount of effective heating surface to be placed in a relatively small rotor.

Normally, the heating surface is divided

into two or more layers as shown in Fig. 19–22. The depth of the layers is proportioned according to the requirements of operating conditions. Many advantages result from the ability to layer the surface, some of which are the following:

1. The low cost of replacing a fractional part of the heating surface makes it possible to justify using lower exit gas temperatures, with resultant higher efficiencies than otherwise practical, particularly if the moisture and sulfur content of the gas is high.
2. Variation in spacing of the surface throughout the preheater sections may be used to satisfy different operating demands.
3. The sheets used in each layer may be of different materials, each of which is best suited to the temperature and other conditions which exist in its particular zone of application.

The rotor is motor driven through reduction gears to a pinion shaft and then, finally, through a pinion gear to a pin rack mounted on the rotor periphery. The rotor turns from approximately one to three rpm and the actual power required to drive it varies from ½ to 5 hp, depending on the preheater size.

Air Leakage. Leakage of air into the gas in a Ljungstrom preheater may be divided into three kinds:

1. Leakage into the gas chamber resulting from entrainment in the rotor passages.
2. Leakage at the periphery of the rotor through the clearance space between the rotor and the housing and then into the gas passage.
3. The third source of leakage is across the radial seals into the gas passage.

The total leakage in a Ljungstrom is only a small percentage of the air provided

Fig. 19–22. Heating surface of Ljungstrom regenerative type air preheater

by the forced draft fan. The greatest pressure differential and the denser air exists at the cold end of the preheater, where the gas exits and the air enters. Therefore, the largest portion of the leakage is at this end, and does not pass through the preheater; thus the performance as to either heat recovery or draft loss is not measurably affected.

Since the draft and air resistances, previously indicated, are not measurably affected by leakage, the only additional power imposed upon the forced and induced draft fans is that for the slightly increased volumes. This is partially offset in the induced draft fan by the temperature decrease resulting from dilution by the cool leakage air. The total increase in fan power input resulting from leakage in the Ljungstrom preheater corresponds roughly to a loss in heat as represented by an approximate drop of three degrees Fahrenheit in the flue gas temperature.

Ljungstrom Preheater Installations. The broadest application for continuous regenerative preheaters has been to power boilers in stationary plants. Either the vertical or horizontal type may be used.

The vertical type preheater is generally used on indoor installations where the hot gas may either enter the bottom of the unit and flow upward or have a top inlet with downward flow.

The horizontal type preheater is generally used on outdoor installations where the fans and preheaters are located at ground level.

For small or medium sized units it is customary to use one preheater per boiler. However, in the case of high capacity installations, it is quite common to apply two to four preheaters per boiler. From an operating standpoint, this has the advantage of permitting better arrangement of both the preheaters and the ducts serving it.

Heat recovery equipment is now available for small industrial steam and process plants. The package Ljungstrom air preheater can be practically installed on industrial boilers with evaporation rates as small as 25,000 pounds of steam per hour and with all types of fuel burning process equipment.

The package type operates on the same principle of continuous regenerative heat recovery as the larger Ljungstrom. The heating elements are factory installed in two layers. The cold end elements are packed in easily reversible baskets to permit extended life in the corrosion zone. A side door in the preheater permits easy removal or reversal of the baskets.

The package Ljungstrom air heater is available in horizontal or vertical models which make it adaptable to any plant arrangement. The cleaning equipment available with package Ljungstrom air preheaters is the same as for the larger units.

The units are delivered completely assembled and ready for operation. Erection consists of setting the preheater in place and making the necessary duct and power connections.

20

Boiler Auxiliaries[1]

BOILER AUXILIARIES comprise a group of components which are secondary to the design of the boiler itself but which are absolutely essential to its operation. They are not to be dismissed as nuisance items or necessary evils. Together, they represent a very sizable portion of the overall boiler cost, and as such they merit considerable attention. Many engineers spend their careers in the design, manufacture, sale and use of this important auxiliary equipment.

In this chapter major emphasis is on auxiliaries for central station boilers, but many of the same considerations apply to boilers of smaller size. The principal boiler auxiliaries which will be discussed include fans, soot blowers, observation ports and access doors, equipment for pressurized firing, equipment for ash and soot removal, ducts, boiler casing and its related setting and insulation, pumps, and valves.

A *boiler auxiliary* may be defined as a piece of equipment which is an integral part of, or is required for the operation of, the boiler. This is in distinction to equipment which may be considered auxiliary to the remainder of a steam power plant. For example, fans, observation ports and access doors, ducts, casing, setting and insulation fall wholly within the category of boiler auxiliaries. Compressors for air soot blowers and certain pressurized firing requirements, as well as piping and sluicing or vacuum equipment for soot and ash removal, are part of the overall power plant equipment and are not boiler auxiliaries as defined in this chapter. Pumps within the boiler circuit are boiler auxiliaries, but feedwater pumps are part of the power plant cycle. In general, those valves required for boiler operation are boiler auxiliaries, but steam stop valves, turbine throttle valves and most other power plant valves are not.

Regardless of definition, the listed boiler auxiliaries are either built by the boiler manufacturer, purchased by him, or furnished by the boiler user. Observation ports, access doors, soot hoppers and casings are made by the boiler manufacturer. Commonly, the ducts on the boiler side of the air heater also fall in this class, and the ducts beyond the air heater are furnished by the user. Soot blowers, settings, insulation, boiler circulating pumps and boiler valves are usually purchased by the boiler manufacturer. Fans, piping for pressurized firing, ash hoppers and dust collectors are purchased either by the boiler manufacturer or user.

For purposes of illustrating the physical

[1] Material contributed by D. G. Hubert except as noted.

20 — 1

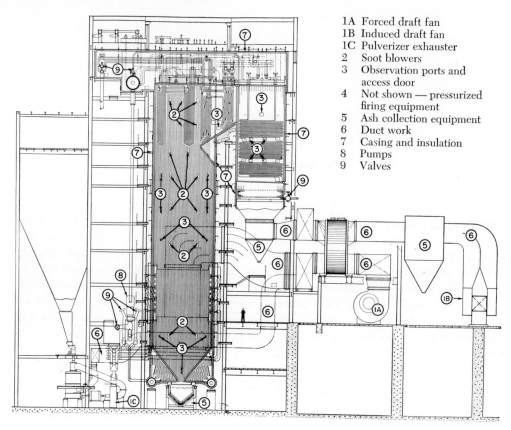

1A Forced draft fan
1B Induced draft fan
1C Pulverizer exhauster
2   Soot blowers
3   Observation ports and access door
4   Not shown — pressurized firing equipment
5   Ash collection equipment
6   Duct work
7   Casing and insulation
8   Pumps
9   Valves

Figure 20–1.   Location of boiler auxiliaries in a large central station boiler of the controlled circulation type.

location of boiler auxiliaries, a controlled circulation boiler designed for central station service has been chosen. In Fig. 20–1 all of the auxiliaries discussed in this chapter are indicated by number with the exception of special equipment for pressurized firing.

Fans[2]

Practically all large boilers, regardless of fuel and method of firing, employ mechanical draft fans. *Forced draft fans,* shown in Fig. 20–1 as *1–A,* are used to supply air for combustion. *Induced draft fans,* shown in Fig. 20–1 as *1–B,* are used to remove products of combustion. *Gas recirculation fans* are used for steam temperature control. When burning bituminous coal on stokers, it is common practice to provide overfire air which is supplied by a separate *over-*

---

[2] This section contributed by P. H. Vaughan and adapted, in part, from the First Edition.

fire air fan. Pulverized coal firing with the storage system generally introduces three other fans: a *pulverizer exhauster* to handle the coal and air mixture between the pulverizer and the collector and to recirculate air back to the pulverizer; the *vent fan* which is used to vent air and evaporated moisture from the system; and the *primary air fan* which again mixes air with and carries the coal to the burners. In direct fired systems, the pulverizer exhauster, shown in Fig. 20–1 as *1–C*, performs the combined functions of exhauster, vent fan and primary air fan.[3]

The problem of specifying the required operating conditions for fans at various load points is generally left to the boiler manufacturer. The fan manufacturer assumes limited responsibility for producing the volume and pressure specified to him. The word *limited* is used because standard fan test codes specify certain conditions which can be maintained in a formal testing setup but which are seldom if ever duplicated in an actual installation.[4] It is thus practically impossible to determine comparable performance of laboratory and field conditions. Furthermore, the connections made to a fan may affect its performance to such an extent that it would be unwise to select it without large pressure and volume tolerances unless it were shop tested with inlet and outlet connections identical to those to be used under service conditions. In this connection it is always desirable to submit the layout of ductwork connected to fans to the fan manufacturer for evaluation and comments.

Forced Draft Fan

The requirements of a forced draft fan, designated as *1–A* in Fig. 20–1, are calculated from the fuel fired and the excess air. For pressure firing, the calculation is quite accurate as all air passes through the forced draft fan. For balanced draft units, the calculation is more complicated as the excess air measurement does not usually correspond to the air through the forced draft fan. Other sources of air flow into the unit are setting infiltration and tempering air.

Infiltration and Tempering. Infiltration is determined by tightness of setting including expansion joints, observation and access doors, ash pits, etc. It will vary with life, operation and maintenance of the unit. Tempering air is determined by the moisture in the fuel. It is high with dry coal and low with wet coal. In assigning values for infiltration and tempering it should be noted that too high an estimate of air flow through the fan and air preheater results in low predicted exit gas temperature and over-guarantee of boiler performance. To avoid this it is usual to assign normal values of infiltration and to assign a value of tempering air as required by the specified coal. Variations from these quantities resulting in more air flow through the forced draft fan are then cov-

---

[3] Fans have been used for ventilation and in steam power plants for more than three centuries. Their origin is believed to be the grain fanning mill developed by the Chinese. Two books of historical interest are *A Treatise on Ventilation — Natural and Artificial* by Robert Ritchie, London, 1862, 207 pages and *Mechanical Draft — A Practical Treatise* edited by Walter B. Snow and published by B. F. Sturtevant Co., Boston, 1898, 385 pages.

[4] See "Standard Test Code for Centrifugal and Axial Fans" of the American Society of Heating, Refrigerating and Air Conditioning Engineers and the National Association of Fan Manufacturers, *NAFM Bulletin*, No. 110, 1952.

ered by the extra tolerance allowed for balanced draft unit fan selection over and above the tolerance used for fan selection on pressure fired units.

Vent Air and Outward Leakage. On storage system units, where heated air is taken from the main preheated air duct for mill drying and is not returned to the system by venting to the primary air fan or furnace, the quantity so used must be added to the combustion air handled by the forced draft fan. Outward air leakage from ducts, compartments and air seal points should also be added to the combustion air handled by the forced draft fan.

Effect of Air Temperature. The temperature and elevation of the fan above sea level both affect the density of the air, which in turn affects the capacity of the fan. If air preheater protection such as a steam coil is provided ahead of the fan, the air temperature leaving must be considered. If hot air recirculation is used for air preheater protection, then both temperature and extra volume must be considered.

Pressure Specification. On balanced draft units the required static head is the sum of all series resistances in the secondary air system, including cold air duct, steam air heater, air preheater, air metering device, hot air duct, dampers and burner pressure drop. On pressure fired units the additional loss from the furnace to the stack outlet must also be included in determining total system resistance. Where stack effect is present, it must also be considered in determining total head requirement of the fan.

Selection. The volume and static pressure calculated in accordance with the foregoing gives the actual required fan capacity under good operating conditions, with assumed excess air, steady load, tight

setting, normal fuel and commercially clean surfaces such as might be expected during an acceptance test. These actual conditions are needed to evaluate power consumption at the various loads, select the control equipment and provide a fan that will operate at maximum efficiency at the desired normal output of the steam-generating unit.

These actual calculated operating conditions, however, should not be used as maximum requirements in purchasing the fan. The outward leakage corrections may be exceeded or the infiltration on a balanced draft unit may actually be less than estimated; or it may be necessary and desirable at times to operate with more excess air; or the actual temperature at the fan may be higher than anticipated; or lastly, the fan may not be up to expectations, because of poor inlet and discharge conditions. Therefore, for specifying conditions for fan selection liberal excess factors are generally applied to both volume and pressure as follows:

Balanced draft unit, 25 per cent excess volume, 50 per cent excess static pressure.

Pressure fired unit, 20 per cent excess volume, 25 per cent excess static pressure.

These values may, of course, be modified if extreme conservatism was used in arriving at the so-called actual requirements, or if they were calculated for an unusual peak load well above the desired maximum continuous rate of operation.

Interpreting Excess Factors. It will be noted that excess factors for selecting forced draft fans are not the same for balanced draft and pressure fired units. These excesses are largely based on experience, but in each case an analysis of them will indicate that they are a composite of individual excesses covering the variables applying to the particular fan duty. The reason for the different fan volume-pressure excesses will be apparent when the method of allowing individual excesses for each of the variables is examined: for excess air, an excess is applied to the volume with double the excess applied to the static; for windbox pressure, the excess is applied to static pressure only; for Ljungstrom air preheater leakage, the excess is applied to the volume only; for dirtying surfaces, the excess is applied only to the static head; for setting leakage, the excess applies mostly to the volume. Out of these and others the overall fan tolerance can be built up.

Induced Draft Fan

The induced draft fan, designated as 1–B in Fig. 20–1, is usually positioned at the outlet of the terminal heat recovery apparatus. It may be located either ahead of or after the dust collector. In some instances it is furnished as an integral part of, and built into, the stack base. This fan must therefore handle the gas resulting from combustion of the fuel as well as all infiltration occurring up to the fan inlet, including leakage in the air preheater.

Volume Specifications. The volume requirements of induced draft fans are figured at the calculated density existing at the fan inlet. The density is based on the flue gas temperature entering the fan. It should also be corrected for elevation above sea level and for moisture in the flue gas on some fuels, such as natural gas, wood or bagasse. On most other fuels, for ordinary fan calculations, the error will be of low magnitude if the specific volume of wet gas is taken as equal to the specific volume of dry air at the same temperature.

The weight of the flue gas on which the volume is based is calculated from the fuel requirements and excess air. This gas weight should include moisture from fuel, from combustion of hydrogen, and from

the air or any other source, such as water seals or jets in the ash pit.

The fly ash carried in the flue gas from a pulverized coal fired unit does not appreciably increase the total volume of the mixture handled, even though it does increase density. The presence of ash may increase the power requirements of the drive for a given speed and capacity. However, since ash carried will generally be less than five grains per cu ft no allowance need be made other than for fan excess factors recommended below.

Pressure Specification. The induced draft fan must provide a static head equal to the series resistance from the furnace to stack outlet, including resistance of superheater, reheater, boiler bank, economizer, air preheater, dust collector and all ductwork. Besides resistances, net stack effect furnace to stack outlet must be included together with required furnace draft in arriving at the total draft requirement of the induced draft fan.

Selection. The volume and static pressure calculated in accordance with the foregoing give the actual required fan capacity under good operating conditions, with assumed excess air, commercially clean surfaces and normal leakage values. As in the case of the forced draft fan, the above conditions are needed for evaluating power, setting controls and providing a fan that will operate at maximum efficiency at desired normal output of the boiler, but the actual calculated operating conditions should not be used as maximum requirements in purchasing the fan. Operation at higher excess air may be advisable; higher amounts of gas recirculation may be used; leakage and infiltration may be higher than estimated; surfaces may be dirty, which will increase temperature as well as resistance; lastly the fan may not perform up to expectations because of poor inlet and discharge connections. Therefore, for specifying conditions for induced draft fan selection, liberal excess factors are generally applied to both volume and pressure, as follows: twenty per cent excess volume and thirty per cent excess static pressure. These figures may, of course, be modified if extreme conservatism was used in arriving at the so-called actual requirements, or if they were calculated for an unusual peak load well above the desired maximum continuous rate of operation.

Gas Recirculation Fan

The gas recirculation fan normally draws flue gas from a point located between the economizer and the air preheater. It discharges to a point in the furnace usually near the bottom of the furnace. When it is used to control steam temperature on coal fired units a dust collector is normally installed upstream of the fan. Frequently it is installed on coal fired units for use only with oil as a second fuel, and in this case the dust collector is omitted.

Volume Specifications. The volume requirements of the gas recirculation fan are determined by the amount of recirculation necessary to make steam temperature. This is usually maximum at control load or below on the unit. In many cases gas recirculation is also required to make steam temperature at full boiler load. Specifying the flue gas volume to be handled together with the gas temperature is a matter for the superheater designer to determine. However, it must be given at both the upper and lower end of the operating range of the gas recirculation requirement.

Pressure Specifications. Gas recirculation flow results in pressure drops throughout the gas recirculation system, including ducts, dampers and dust collector. Since the amount of gas recirculated adds to, and is common with the main gas flow through the superheater, reheater and economizer it also increases the drops through these items. It is these latter items which generally dominate in establishing the total head requirements of the recirculation fan.

At control load or some other partial boiler load, gas recirculation requirements are maximum. But because the main gas flow is low the total head requirements of the recirculation fan are moderate. At full boiler load, little or no gas recirculation may be required. However, since the main gas flow through the boiler is high, the pressure differential across the superheater, reheater and economizer is high and the recirculation fan is required to produce a high static head to balance this differential. In selecting the fan, the relationship of fan head to the above differential is critical for should the situation ever exist at any point over the operating range of the fan where the fan could not develop enough head to overcome the differential developed by the boiler, back flow of furnace gas will result through the fan with very serious consequences.

To protect against the above condition it is usual to specify as a minimum point on the fan characteristic a pressure at least one inch (water gage) above the maximum superheater-reheater-economizer differential at full load on the boiler. Sizing of the fan will normally be dictated by control load requirements. The following are usual excess percentages applied to the calculated requirements at this load: fifteen to twenty per cent volume excess and twenty to twenty-five per cent static pressure excess.

In some cases where there are high recirculation requirements at full boiler

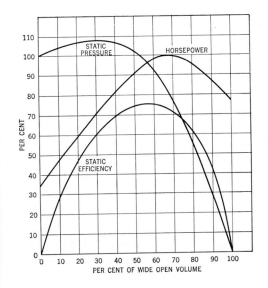

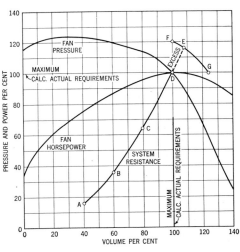

Figure 20–2. Typical constant speed characteristics for a fan with backward curved blades.

Figure 20–3. Use of characteristic curves as applied to problems of fan selection.

load, fan size may be determined by the requirement at full load. Where there is a question which point will govern the fan selection, both points should be given to the fan manufacturer together with the excesses shown above.

Fan Characteristic Curves

A typical set of constant-speed characteristic curves for a fan having backwardly inclined blades is shown in Fig. 20–2. The performance of a single fan of a given type may be used to determine the characteristics of a complete line of sizes, by application of the theory of similitude. Each separate type, however, must be tested independently. The curves shown are drawn for one speed only, and therefore, when the fan is driven by constant speed motor, it will operate somewhere on the characteristic curves, depending on

the resistance imposed by the system through which the air is being passed. The system resistance, therefore, acts as an automatic control on the fan and will limit the amount of overload that can be developed, regardless of the flatness or the pressure characteristics. The amount of overload will depend also on the shape of the horsepower curve.

Backwardly inclined blades will give a nonoverloading characteristic, but all other types have an increasing power right up to the wide open volume. The power required in wide open volume for radial tip, straight radial blade, and forwardly curved blades will be, respectively, approximately two times, two and a half times and three times the power required at the point of maximum static efficiency.

The characteristic curves for any other speed or air density may be constructed by application of the laws of fan performance.[5]

Fig. 20–3 illustrates the application of characteristic curves to a fan problem where points A, B, C and D represent calculated requirements at four load points on a given boiler. The line through them defines the system resistance. The point where this line intersects the static pressure characteristics of any fan, at any speed, will determine the point on the characteristic at which the fan will operate, if both curves are plotted for the same density. However, the fan can operate only on its characteristic curve, and if any error has been made in calculating point D, in volume or pressure, that point will not fall on the characteristic curve, and the fan may not meet the requirements when operating at that particular speed.

For example, if 10 per cent more volume is needed at the same pressure point, D will be displaced to the right, but the available pressure at the fan head at the same time drops 14 per cent and the fan cannot satisfy the requirements. Similarly, if the volume were correct but 10 per cent more pressure were needed, the volume that the fan would deliver at this increased pressure would be only about 90 per cent of the requirements, since the fan can operate only on its characteristic curve for a given speed and density.

To provide excess capacity it is customary to specify the volume and pressure to an excess of the actual calculated requirements and thereby obtain a larger fan. Suppose a portion of the pressure characteristic of this larger fan, operating at the same speed and density, is represented by Line FG in Figure 20–3. Then it is apparent that this size fan would be selected by the manufacturer if the purchaser specified 24 per cent excess volume with no excess pressure, or 20 per cent excess pressure with no excess volume. At the same time, the fan would satisfy the requirements of Point E, which require 8 per cent excess volume and 17 per cent excess pressure. The only advantage in attempting to define Point E on the extrapolated system resistance curve, instead of Point F or G, is that the power requirement given by the manufacturer will then represent a closer estimate of the larger fan under actual operating conditions than if Point F or Point G had been defined for fan selection. The fan finally chosen will, however, be capable of satisfying the requirements of all three points, if sufficient power is available from the drive.

Types of Fans

From the point of view of fluid mechanics, fans represent a class of turbomachines designed to move fluids such as air, gases and vapor against low pressure. From the point of view of mechanical design, a very light casing construction is used for fans since inlet pressures are atmospheric or lower. Simplified hydraulic forms and welded steel plate construction are generally encountered in fans.

Direct connected drives are used almost exclusively in power plant work. Control is obtained through the use of variable speed motors, hydraulic couplings, spe-

---

[5] For further information, see *Fan Engineering*, edited by R. D. Madison and published by Buffalo Forge Co., and *Air Conditioning and Engineering* published by American Blower Corp. A useful article is "Fan Laws Simplify Performance Calculations" by R. D. Moyer, *Power*, Vol. 90, pp. 77–80, August 1946.

cially designed inlet dampers or plain louvered dampers.

Fans are broadly classed as either axial or centrifugal, according to the direction of flow through them.

Vane Axial Fans. Under the category of the axial type falls all fans where air flow parallels the rotational axis of the impeller. They range from the simple propeller fan to the vane axial fan which is coming into increasing use for power plant applications.

The vane axial fan is a highly developed type employing variable pitch, air foil shaped impeller blades, straightening vanes, a streamlined hub and body section and a venturi shaped housing.

Within its normal operating range it has a very broad band of high operating efficiency, but at low loads it becomes unstable in operation. In the single stage design it is particularly suitable for high volume, moderate pressure applications. It tends to be noisy if designed to operate at too high rotative speeds.

Centrifugal Fans. Most mechanical draft fans used in power plants are of the centrifugal type. These employ blades mounted on an impeller rotated within a spiral or volute housing. Blade design determines fan characteristics.[6] A velocity vector diagram at blade tip will indicate that backward curved blades produce low resultant velocities for a given tip or peripheral speed, and that forward curved blades give high velocity. Radial blades and radial tipped blades lie between these two extremes. The backward curved blade type, therefore, operates at higher motor speeds than the other types for a given duty and is well adapted to direct drive with motors or steam turbines.

There are both a reason and a field for each type, and the final selection is best left to the manufacturer who will guarantee satisfactory operation. Besides the operating conditions of volume, pressure and temperature specified by the purchaser, many other factors must be considered, such as method of drive, speed of drive, method of control, speed limitations, allowable noise and vibration, corrosion or erosion due to materials contaminating the gas, range of operation and point of most likely continuous operation.

Often the selection will be a flat backward inclined or air foil shaped blade for use in forced draft service. These fans have nonoverloading horsepower characteristics and are suited to motor operating speeds of 1200 or 1800 rpm. Induced draft fans for moderate pressure are generally of the forward curved blade type and operate preferably at motor speeds of 720 or 900 rpm but not exceeding 1200 rpm. This type fan is somewhat more compact for a given fan duty. However, there is a pronounced dip in the characteristic curve, and where parallel fan operation is planned, care must be exercised in the system design to prevent hunting of the fans. For high pressures, straight radial blade or radial tipped induced draft fans are sometimes offered, operating at the same speeds as above. Both the radial and radial tipped fans are well suited to service where ash erosion is present.

Gas recirculation is a particularly severe type of service on high ash, coal fired units. Radial and radial tipped blade fans are often used for this service. Vent fans, primary air fans and pulverizer exhausters are invariably of the straight blade type and operate up to 1800 rpm, depending on

---

[6] For examples, see Chapter 12, Centrifugal Fans, of *Turboblowers* by A. J. Stepanoff, published by John Wiley, 1955.

the pressure requirements. Fans having backward curved blades are sometimes offered for induced draft service for gas or oil firing because they permit the use of higher motor speed and give higher efficiency than any other centrifugal type. However, if there is any dirt in the gas, it may cause trouble by depositing on the back of the blades.

Capacities of centrifugal fans range from a few hundred cubic feet per minute to over 100,000 cfm and cover a range of specific speeds from 150 to 5000, based on static heads in feet of fluid. Wide variations in fan efficiency may result from different methods of speed control.

Soot Blower Systems[7]

To provide satisfactory cleaning of heat absorbing surfaces in the boiler unit, soot blower applications should be coordinated with boiler design and the entire system engineered to accommodate the specified fuel. The fuels most commonly used for steam generation are coal, oil and natural gas. Each requires special consideration and the number and location of all soot blowers is based on the characteristics of the ash of the fuel being used. The percentage of ash in the fuel, the softening temperature, the fluid temperature and the chemical composition of the ash all have a direct bearing on the selection of soot blowers.

Natural gas is a clean burning fuel with a small percentage of entrained dust which is deposited on the heat absorbing surfaces. The quantity is not objectionable and does not require the application of soot blowers for cleaning.

Oil fuel has a low ash content which produces a thin water soluble deposit on the walls of the furnace cavity which is removed by annual water washing and does not require the use of soot blowers in this area. In the superheater and reheater sections soot blowers are required because the ash deposit accumulates due to the decreasing temperature of the combustion products and the narrower spaced heat absorbing surfaces.

Of the major fuels, coal requires the most extreme application of soot blower systems. The ash deposition resulting from the combustion of the coal varies throughout the unit and may be classified as three types. Molten ash is generally encountered in the burner zone of the furnace cavity. Sintered ash is deposited at the furnace outlet and the first convection pass, and in the last pass of the unit a dust-like ash is prevalent. The removal of the different type ash is accomplished by specific type blowers.

The ash deposited on the walls of furnace chambers is removed by a short single nozzle retractable blower. The ash in the vertical pendant sections of the superheater is removed by a long retractable soot blower of single nozzle design which traverses the complete width of the units. These can be introduced from both sides or from one side only. Commercial blowers are available up to forty feet in length. In the rear pass where the dry dusty ash is present, rotary blowers of multiple nozzle design are used. This is normally the low temperature superheater section and the economizer. The multiple nozzle lance tube is stationary and is mounted twelve to fifteen inches above the tube bank to be cleaned, and extends full length up to

---

[7] This section has been contributed by E. P. Petit.

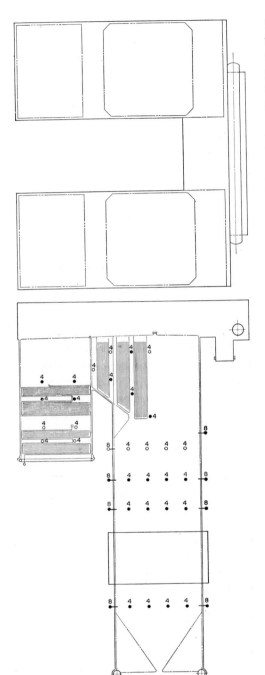

Figure 20–4. Twin furnace, pulverized coal fired boiler showing location of existing and possible future soot blowers.

twenty feet. For lengths greater than twenty feet long retractable blowers are used for economical design of the supply piping. The lance is supported by means of bearings which are attached to the top row of tubes and are equally spaced.

For cleaning applications other than those already mentioned, special types of blowers are commercially available. Regenerative and tubular air heaters, waste heat boilers of various designs, low level economizers, and gas ducts require special cleaning equipment.

The cleaning medium is specified by the ultimate user as compressed air or steam, the decision being based on plant economics. Experience has shown equal cleaning ability for both mediums and the boiler designer or boiler manufacturer has no preference. The same is true of the power drives for individual blowers which can be either air or electric motor operated.

Depending upon the size and capacity of the boiler unit and the number of blowers installed, various modes of soot blower operation can be employed. Small industrial boilers using few soot blowers cannot economically justify the use of automatic control systems and hand operated blowers are used. Large industrial and central station boilers can justify various degrees of automatic control. Control systems are available of special design to suit the cleaning requirements of the individual boiler. These systems range in scope from simple push button stations to automatic pre-programed cleaning cycles. The elaborate systems used in central stations incorporate boiler diagrams with indicating lights for each blower, pressure gauges and transmitters, meters, protection devices and boiler failure alarms.

Fig. 20–4 shows the outline of a pulverized coal fired boiler having a capacity of nearly 4,000,000 lb of steam per hr and consisting of two furnaces, each with identical superheater, reheater and economizer. Each furnace is 40 ft wide and 152 ft high. A side elevation is shown, and the furnace and rear pass are 40 ft and 33 ft deep, respectively, from front to rear. The solid circles are soot blowers presently installed in the side walls, and the short horizontal lines represent similar blowers in the front and rear walls of the furnace. The open circles indicate blowers that may be installed in the future if required. All blowers in the furnace walls, below the nose of the arch, are short retractables. All others are long retractables. There are 104 of the former and 32 of the latter initially installed, and provision is made for 24 additional short retractables and 28 long retractables.

Observation Ports and Access Doors

Observation doors are provided for visual access to the furnace, to view firing conditions and furnace cleanliness. Each opening is a source of potential leakage, and the number of observation doors selected should be kept to a minimum consistent with good operating practice. The type of door used will depend on whether the furnace is suction or pressure fired. Pressurized furnaces require a means of aspirating to prevent furnace gas emission when the door is open.

Fig. 20–5 shows the same boiler as in Fig. 20–4. Observation ports in the side walls are shown as solid circles and in the front and rear walls as short horizontal lines. Access doors in the superheater, reheater, economizer and roof and bottom housings are shown as squares in the side walls and as rectangles in the front and

rear walls. There are 102 observation ports and 68 access doors.

Equipment for Pressurized Firing

On balanced draft units there is a slight negative pressure in the furnace, so that any leakage is air leakage inward. With pressurized firing, all of the fluid friction in all air and gas passages in the entire unit is overcome by the pressure produced by the forced draft fan since there is no induced draft fan.

This means that there is a positive pressure in the furnace, equal to the sum of the friction losses in all equipment beyond the furnace, all the way to the stack. Any leakage is gas and dust leakage outwards, and this is intolerable. Potential leakage points exist at literally hundreds of places, including soot blowers, observation ports, air heater seals, damper shafts, retractable oil guns, ignitors, and certain parts of the coal pulverizers.[8] In some cases, mechanical seals are redesigned to assure no leakage. In other cases, air at a pressure higher than furnace pressure must be introduced, permitting a small amount of inward leakage.

Observation ports on balanced draft units are actually doors which can be opened when the boiler is in operation. On pressurized units, the port has a heat resistant glass insert for viewing the furnace. To assure no outward leakage, and to keep the glass clean, air is piped to a special fitting on the frame of the port. The same is true of retractable soot blowers, since the opening around the moving blower lance requires an air seal.

Fig. 20–6 again shows the same boiler as in Figs. 20–4 and 20–5. The soot blowers and observation ports are shown, with-

---

[8] For changes in design resulting from pressurized firing, see Chapter 11. Manufacture and Machine Design, section on Machine Design of Bowl Mills.

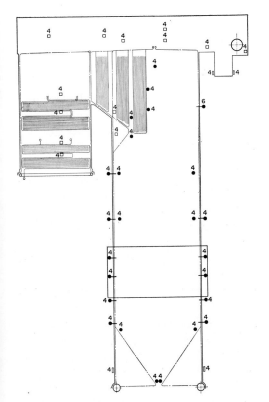

Figure 20–5. Location of observation ports and access doors.

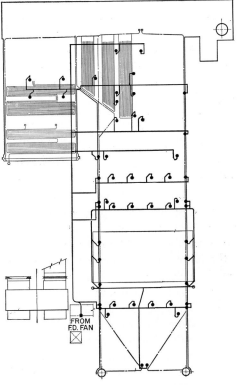

Figure 20–6. Air piping system for soot blowers and observation ports.

out distinction between them, and part of the extensive air piping system is shown. The source of air, not shown, is a duct coming from the forced draft fan outlet, where the highest pressure exists. Piping ranges in size from 14 in. OD at the source down to one inch at the smallest opening. Air quantities are about 10 cfm for each port, 15 cfm for each short retractable blower and 50 cfm for each long retractable blower. Larger quantities are required at retractable oil guns and pulverizers. The air piping must be designed to take care of the various expansion movements of the boiler.

Sometimes it is necessary to open an observation port to replace a broken glass or clean out the opening, and to remove a soot blower for maintenance, both while the boiler remains in operation. Aspirating air connections are provided at the wall openings, and compressed air at 80 to 100 psig is piped to the opening. This may be done by temporary connections or by permanent piping. Observation ports are designed with an interlock so they cannot be opened unless the aspirating connection is under full air pressure.

In addition to the above provisions, the entire boiler casing and much of the ductwork must be structurally designed to limit the deflections caused by the higher pressure on the large areas.

Equipment for Ash and Soot Removal

The ash which enters the unit as part of the coal must be almost completely removed to limit the nuisance from the stack. Fig. 20–1 shows three places where this is done.

A considerable portion of the ash drops to the bottom of the furnace into the ash hopper. This device is usually filled with water to cool the ash and assist in its removal. Gates at the lower part of the hopper allow the water and ash to pass into sluicing trenches below the floor or into a piping system including a pump. The mixture may then pass through processing equipment and on to an outside storage area or pond. Many ash hoppers are equipped with clinker grinders to break up the larger chunks.

Of the ash which passes through the unit as fly ash, a small portion can be collected in soot hoppers, such as the one shown below the rear pass in Fig. 20–1. This eliminates some of the ash passing through the air heater, reducing the possibility of plugging the heater.

A very large part of the ash is removed in the dust collector, shown between the air heater and the induced draft fan in Fig. 20–1. Dust collectors are generally either mechanical or electrostatic or a combination of both.

Mechanical dust collectors which are generally available today remove between 65 and 85 per cent of the dust passing through them. Most of them depend upon the centrifugal effect of many short radius turns in the stream of dust laden gas and the cyclone effect. Some use multiple vertical tubes in which both effects are utilized. Others use larger cyclones with recirculation ducts and fans. Efficiency is closely related to particle size, and mechanical dust collectors are most effective with the larger particles. Draft loss generally runs between three and four inches water gage, and increased efficiency is usually obtained at the expense of increased draft loss.

Electrostatic dust collectors or precipitators, as they are usually called, can achieve efficiencies well above 90 per cent, have low draft loss (on the order of 0.5 in. wg) and generally cost more than mechanical collectors. Electrostatic precipitators apply high voltage charges to the suspended particles, collect these particles on plates and remove the precipitated material to external receptacles or hoppers. The gas stream is not deflected or disturbed as much as in mechanical collectors, thereby accounting for the low draft loss of the electrostatic device which is effective on a wide range of particle sizes.[9]

In some cases, both mechanical and electrostatic collectors are used, in series. The efficiency of a combined arrangement, where E_m, E_e and E_c are the efficiencies of the mechanical, the electrostatic and the combination, respectively, in per cent, is as follows:

$$E_c = 100 \left[1 - (1 - E_m/100) (1 - E_e/100) \right]$$

---

[9] For a comprehensive book based on extensive research, design and operating experience, see *Industrial Electrostatic Precipitation* by Harry J. White, Addison Wesley, 1963, 376 pages.

Soot is removed from dust collector hoppers as well as from the hopper before the air heater and other soot hoppers by means of a valve and piping system connected to the hopper outlets. A vacuum system is one device for transporting the material thus collected.

Ducts

The boiler ductwork system consists of the following principal elements:

1. Air system
   a. Main air
   b. Primary air
   c. Recirculating air

2. Gas system
   a. Main gas
   b. Recirculating gas

In the simplest arrangement of a gas fired boiler there is a *main air duct* from the forced draft fan to the air heater and to the burners and a *main gas duct* from the economizer outlet to the air heater to the induced draft fan to the stack. If the furnace is pressurized and without an induced draft fan, the main gas duct runs directly from the air heater to the stack.

For a pulverized coal fired boiler there will be, in addition, a *primary air duct* from the main hot air duct to the pulverizers. The function of this duct is to dry the coal and transport it to the burners. From the point of takeoff of the primary air, the air going to the burners is called secondary air even though it is a major portion of the air supply. Fig. 20–1 shows a pulverized coal fired boiler with the number 6 indicating all ductwork.

Fig. 20–7 is the same boiler as shown previously in Figs. 20–4, 20–5 and 20–6 but this time presented with the ductwork clearly outlined. All air for this unit is taken from the top of the boiler room to regain some of the heat lost by radiation and enters the forced draft fan at *1*. The main air goes to the air heater at *2* and to the burner box at *3*. The exit gas goes from the economizer at *9* through the air heater at *2* and on to the precipitator and stack beyond *10*.

The primary air taps off the main hot air duct at *4* and goes to a distributing manifold at *5* and to the individual pulverizers at *7*. On a balanced draft unit, cold tempering air is drawn from the room into the mill by a slight suction and mixed with the hot air for the correct drying temperature. However, the subject unit is pressurized, and the cold air must be taken from the forced draft fan discharge at *8* and mixed with the hot air at *6*.

A schematic arrangement of ductwork and control dampers for the same unit is shown in Fig. 20–8. The same ducts and identifying numbers are used as in Fig. 20–7, plus one additional duct. Direction of flow is indicated by arrows. Control dampers are shown by short diagonal lines and the letter *D*. The damper at *3* represents many air distributing dampers at the burners. The dampers on both sides of point *6* control the proportion of hot and cold air to achieve the right temperature and are automatically operated together in opposite directions. The dampers at *7* control the total quantity of primary air to the pulverizers. Two of several pulverizers are shown. Not shown are various shutoff dampers for isolating air heaters and pulverizers.

The additional duct in this figure is the recirculating air duct from *10* to *11*. Moisture in the gas, derived from moisture in the coal and air and hydrogen in any fuel, combined with acid from sulfur in coal and oil, will cause corrosion of the cold end air heater elements, with high dew point and low gas temperatures at low boiler

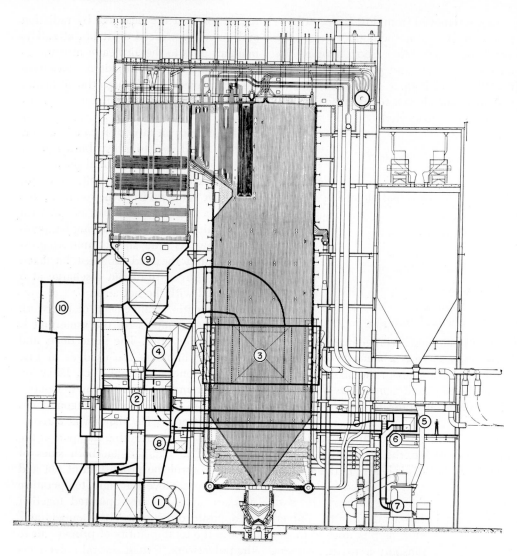

Figure 20–7.   Ductwork included in a large central station boiler.

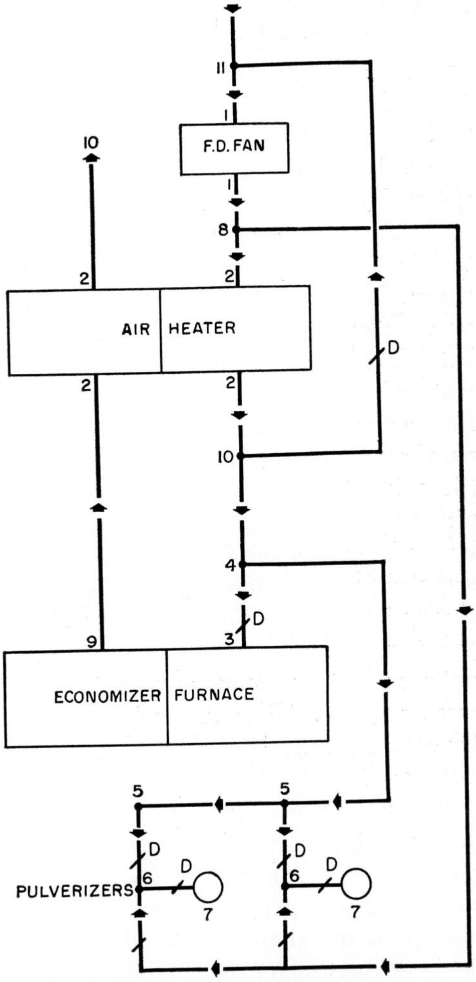

of hot air. An alternative method is a steam coil placed in the main air duct between the forced draft fan and the air heater.

For the same size unit and the same amount of heat released by the fuel, oil firing requires much larger heating surfaces in the superheater and reheater than for coal firing. Much of this relatively expensive surface can be eliminated by increasing the gas mass flow through the convection passes, using gas recirculation. This is common on pure oil fired units and is required on combination coal and oil units. The gas recirculating duct system is shown schematically in Fig. 20–9. Nos. 3 and 9 are taken from Fig. 20–8 and other numbers are added. Gas is tapped off the main gas duct at *12*, passes through the gas recirculating fan at *13* and enters the bottom of the furnace at *14*. Damper *D* controls the flow and is part of the steam temperature control system.

The gas recirculation fan is necessary to overcome the pressure differential between the furnace and the economizer outlet. If for any reason the fan is shut down

Figure 20–8. Schematic arrangement of ductwork and control dampers.

loads. To prevent this, the air from the forced draft fan is preheated before entering the air heater. The recirculating air duct shown, with control damper, accomplishes this by introducing a small amount

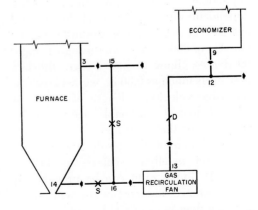

Figure 20–9. Schematic arrangement of gas recirculating duct system.

while the boiler is in operation, high temperature furnace gas would flow backward through the fan and ducts, which are not designed to withstand such temperatures. Therefore shut off damper S between *16* and *14* automatically shuts when the fan stops. However, even the best shutoff damper has some leakage, so higher pressure air is tapped off the main duct at *15*. The shutoff damper S between *15* and *16* is ordinarily shut, but opens automatically with closing of the other shutoff damper. There will then be a small flow of air from *15* to *16* and in both directions from *16*, thus protecting all equipment.

In the design of gas and air ducts, consideration should be given to distribution and turbulence, as well as resistance, particularly in proximity to fans, air heaters and dust collectors. Undue turbulence at the inlet or outlet of fans may result in serious loss in fan efficiency and capacity. Lack of attention to uniformity of gas and air flow entering and leaving air heaters and dust collectors may result in loss of efficiency of this equipment.

Frequently there are so many bends and changes in section, in gas and air ducts, that the resistance may be practically independent of lengths, and almost wholly dependent on the design of bends and changes in section. For example, at the velocity of 3000 ft per min through a single 90 degree elbow of bad design, the loss may be as much as 0.50 in. wg. whereas, at the same velocity, a length of 200 ft of straight duct of reasonable size would be required for the same loss.

The design of the inside and outside corners of an elbow is of utmost importance. If liberal radii can be provided, a low resistance, low cost elbow will result. If space does not permit the use of a long radius elbow, turning vanes should be used.

Casing, Setting and Insulation

No. 7 in Fig. 20–1 indicates the enclosure for the entire boiler envelope, including the housings above the furnace and convection passes and at the furnace bottom. All walls are formed on the inside by plain tubes nearly tangent or by finned tubes. Where these tubes and fins are not welded together to form a gas tight enclosure, a light gage skin casing is attached to the back side of the tubes to accomplish the same purpose. Next, one or more layers of insulating block or blanket is attached. In some areas, refractory material is required if exposure to the furnace or gas pass is unavoidable. In unusual cases, such as burning very low volatile pulverized coal where maintaining ignition is difficult, refractory material may be used to cover the furnace side of large areas of the tubes in order to reduce heat absorption in the walls and maintain high gas temperatures. In some stoker fired units, refractory arches are used for the same purpose. All of this refractory and insulation material constitutes the boiler setting.

Outside the wall insulation it is common practice to install a metal casing for protection and appearance. This may consist of medium gage flat steel plate, fabricated in the shop and installed in the field, or very light gage corrugated or ribbed steel or aluminum lagging cut and applied in the field. Occasionally, a plastic outer casing is used, the term here referring to a hard surface but flexible cement coating over the insulation.

Insulation, either block or blanket, is also required for all hot ducts and pipes in order to prevent heat loss and protect plant personnel. This applies generally to all ductwork except cold air ducts, all steam and feedwater pipes. The high temperature tubes, headers and pipes inside the boiler roof housing must likewise be protected to hold down the temperature in this enclosure. Also such equipment as air heaters and induced draft fans must be insulated. In some cases, such low gas temperature devices as dust collectors, particularly if located outdoors, must be insulated to prevent inside condensation and resultant corrosion.

Pumps

The principal pumps, and usually the only ones with which the boiler designer is closely concerned, are the boiler circulating pumps.[10] However, of the many pumps in the power plant, two others are of great interest to the boiler designer: the feedwater pump and the fuel oil pump. If the feedwater pump is a constant speed pump, either driven by a separate motor or from the main turbine shaft, its characteristic will produce about the right pressure at full load but a very high pressure at low load. This means extra duty for the feedwater regulator which is sometimes furnished by the boiler manufacturer. Adequate pressure will be available for superheater desuperheaters, but spray valves in the steam temperature control system are affected.

If the feedwater pump is motor driven with a variable speed device, outlet pressure will match boiler system resistance and feedwater regulators may or may not be used. If they are not used, superheater spray water pressure is low at low loads, and this must be considered in the design of spray control valves. Also, if feedwater regulators are not used, and boiler circulating pumps are of the type requiring injection water at shaft seals, there may

not be enough pressure at low loads for this purpose, and booster pumps may be required in the injection water lines.

If feedwater pumps are variable speed using a separate turbine drive, the steam is taken from one of the bleed points on the main turbine at or above the point of reheat return. This reduces the quantity of steam in the reheater and affects the design of the reheater.

The type of fuel oil pump, whether centrifugal or constant displacement, has a definite effect on the design of the oil burner control system.

Valves

Some indication of the scope of the valves required on a large central station boiler may be afforded by a glance at Table 20–1. These are the valves furnished for the same 4,000,000 lb per hr boiler shown in Figs. 20–4, 20–5, 20–6, 20–7 and 20–8. They do not include the valves for the boiler circulating pump system nor the soot blower system.

Sizes in the valve list are nominal sizes of piping to which the valves are connected. The overall physical dimensions of a 14 in. valve, for example, may run to several feet, and its weight may exceed one ton.

Since boiler valves are subject to extremes of temperature and pressure as well as widely varying conditions of operation, close attention must be given by the valve manufacturer to the materials of construction. For valve parts these may range from low carbon steel through the low and medium chrome alloys to stainless steel, in both castings and forgings. Because of the severity of service, most boiler valves have seats and discs of Stel-

---

[10] For further discussion of these, see Chapter 24, Controlled Circulation Boilers, and Chapter 25, Combined Circulation Boilers.

lite which is a tungsten, chromium, cobalt alloy having exceptional hardness at high temperatures.

Safety valves are subject to the regulations of the ASME Boiler and Pressure Vessel Code.[11] For boilers operating below the critical pressure it is customary to set superheater safety valves so that they will pop before boiler safety valves. This assures maximum possible flow through the superheater, thus protecting the tubes.

Feedwater valves consist of stop and check valves near the economizer inlet. Ordinarily these valves are wide open. Blowoff valves are located at low points in the boiler, such as the lower waterwall supply drums, for rapid removal of sludge collected at these points. Continuous blowdown and chemical feed valves serve to limit and control concentration of impurities in the water in the main steam drum.

Sampling valves provide a continuous record of steam and water purity.

On Controlled Circulation Boilers there is a large motor operated gate valve at the inlet of each boiler circulating pump and one or two stop-check valves at the outlet. There are also many smaller valves for various services at the circulating pumps.

The boiler referred to in the valve list of Table 10–1 also has one water gage and two remote water level indicators with alarms and recorders for determining drum water level. On the same boiler there are also five steam pressure gages, one on the drum, two on the superheater and two on the reheater.[12]

Boilers operating at supercritical pressures involve special considerations that differ from ASME Boiler and Pressure Vessel Code requirements for subcritical pressure boilers.[13]

Table 10–1   Valve List

Purpose	Number	Sizes
Safety valves	20	$2\frac{1}{2}''–3''–6''$
Feedwater valves	4	$14''$
Blowoff	16	$2''$
Continuous blowdown	4	$2''$
Vent	48	$1''–2''$
Drain	40	$1''–1\frac{1}{2}''–2''$
Chemical feed	2	$1''$
Sampling	40	$1''$
Miscellaneous	51	$\frac{1}{2}''–1''–1\frac{1}{2}''–2''–2\frac{1}{2}''$
Total	225	

[11] For specific information on safety valves, see Section I, *Rules for Construction of Power Boilers*, P–269 through P–290, published by The American Society of Mechanical Engineers, New York.

[12] See P–291 through P–298 of Section I of the ASME Boiler and Pressure Vessel Code for further information.

[13] Most of these installations are treated as special cases, and special approval may be necessary from the local authority having jurisdiction.

21

Combustion and Boiler Calculations[1]

ANY DESIGN PROCEDURE necessarily involves calculations, and boiler design is no exception to this rule. This chapter is primarily concerned with the principal calculations that might be required for two distinctively different types of steam generating units, but similar procedures are followed for various other boiler applications. One example is based on a stoker fired industrial boiler and the other on a gas fired boiler for a central station operating on the reheat cycle. These calculations are subdivided into sections concerned with the combustion process, proportioning of heat transfer surface, determination of boiler heat balance and selection of materials for high temperature service. A concluding section deals with the use of a digital computer for boiler performance calculations.[2]

The reader should recognize that these calculations are not all inclusive. Depending upon the particular circumstances involved in a specific boiler design, more or fewer calculations may be required. Where certain design parameters extend into areas of little or no experience, far more detailed investigations and calculations of heat transfer and fluid flow may be required.

Historical Perspective

Calculations tend to become routine, with the consequence that their origin and significance are readily overlooked. Yet they do not generally come into being at one time, and the evaluation of calculations may give a clue to their past and present importance. This seems particularly true for combustion calculations which deal with a common physical phenomenon whose subtleties are not always fully appreciated.

Although observation of fire dates back to man's earliest existence on earth, it was not until about the year 1800 that a quantitative understanding of the combustion process was achieved. One could trace the development of many hypotheses concerning the nature and properties of fire, including some that were expressed in supernatural terms of fear and awe. Even the existence of the now discredited phlogiston theory of combustion did not prevent enterprising engineers from designing and constructing boilers to generate steam for the earliest steam engines.

Phlogiston was a hypothetical mysterious substance, sometimes presumed to have the property of negative weight,

---

[1] Material contributed by P. H. Vaughan.
[2] Other parts of the book which incorporate calculation procedures include Chapter 10, Stress Analysis and Structural Design; Chapter 30, Flash Drying Systems; Chapter 31, Refuse Incinerators.

which combined with a body to render it combustible. G. E. Stahl (1660–1734) first proposed the phlogiston theory in 1697, and it dominated the chemical thought of the eighteenth century. Even such a perceptive observer as Joseph Priestly (1733–1804), who in 1774 discovered the unique power of oxygen for supporting combustion, accepted the phlogiston theory. Antoine L. Lavoisier (1743–1794), in the years between 1775 and 1781, substituted for it the theory of oxygenation and provided experimental evidence that combustion was the union of the substance burned with the oxygen of the atmosphere.

In 1755 Joseph Black (1728–1799) discovered carbon dioxide, and in 1781 Henry Cavendish (1731–1810) demonstrated the compound nature of water. At about this same time Lavoisier made the precise measurements and formulated the volume and weight relationships that underlie the modern theory of combustion.

These and other scientific developments linked combustion theory to the principles of mechanics established by Galileo and Newton. In another respect, however, combustion calculations are based upon the relationships expressed in the perfect gas laws. In 1660 Robert Boyle (1627–1691) published a treatise entitled *Experiments Touching the Spring of Air* in which he showed that at constant temperature the volume of any given mass of gas is inversely proportional to the pressure. More than a century later, about 1781, J. A. C. Charles (1746–1823) demonstrated that the product of the pressure and the specific volume of a gas is directly proportional to the absolute temperature, a relationship also stated independently in 1802 by L. J. Gay-Lussac (1778–1850). Beyond this, in 1811 Amedeo Avogadro (1776–1856) established that the number of molecules in a unit volume under standard conditions is the same for all gases. During this same period John Dalton (1766–1844) enunciated the law of partial pressures, and in 1803 his study of the physical properties of gases led to formulation of the atomic theory, including the law of combining weights. Related to the foregoing is the observation made by Gay-Lussac in 1808 that gases always combine in volumes that bear simple ratios to each other.[3]

Combustion Calculations

The preceding section presents the evolution of the historical development of the fundamental laws that underlie modern combustion calculations. The engineer makes use of these laws whenever he calculates the quantities of fuel, air and gas

---

[3] For additional historical information the interested reader is referred to *A History of Science* by W. C. Dampier, Third Edition, Macmillan, New York, 1942 (also available in shorter form in a paperback edition from Meridian Books, New York), *A Textbook of Heat* by H. S. Allen and R. S. Maxwell, Macmillan, London, 1939, and St. Martin's Press, New York, and *A History of Physics* by Florian Cajori, Macmillan, New York, 1929 (available in a paperback edition from Dover Publications, New York).

required for a given steam output from a boiler. The gas weight resulting from combustion of fuel is required to determine proper arrangement and proportioning of boiler heating surface. The air weight is used in sizing burners and air heaters, and both air and gas weights are required to proportion fans, ducts, air heaters, dust collectors and stacks.

The four fundamental laws upon which modern combustion calculations are based are listed below. They are used explicitly or implicitly in the relationships and calculations that follow.

1. Law of conservation of matter
2. Law of conservation of energy
3. The perfect gas law
4. The law of combining weights

Combustion Fundamentals

To the engineer primarily concerned with boiler design and performance, combustion may be considered as the chemical union of the combustible of a fuel and the oxygen of the air, controlled at such a rate as to produce useful heat energy. The principal combustible constituents are elemental carbon and hydrogen together with their compounds. In the combustion process, the compounds and elements are burned to carbon dioxide and water vapor. Small quantities of sulfur are present in most fuels. While sulfur is a combustible and contributes slightly to the heating value of the fuel, its presence is generally detrimental due to the corrosive nature of its compounds.

Air, the usual source of oxygen for combustion, is a mixture of oxygen, nitrogen and small amounts of water vapor, carbon dioxide, argon and other elements. For the purpose of combustion calculations, the last four items are usually included with the nitrogen. The composition of dry air may therefore be assumed to be as shown in Table 21–1.

Table 21—1   Properties of Air

Volumetric analysis of **dry air**
  21 per cent oxygen
  79 per cent nitrogen

Gravimetric analysis of **dry air**
  23.15 per cent oxygen
  76.85 per cent nitrogen

Lb dry air per lb oxygen $= \dfrac{1}{0.2315} = 4.32$

Lb nitrogen per lb oxygen $= \dfrac{76.85}{23.15} = 3.32$

Molecular weight of dry air $(0.21 \times 32) + (0.79 \times 28)$
  $= 28.84$

Density dry air at standard conditions, 32 F, 14.7 psia
  $= 28.84 \div 359 = 0.0808$ lb per cu ft

Water vapor in air at 80 F and 60 per cent relative humidity $= 0.013$ lb per lb of air*

* This is an industry standard established by the American Boiler Manufacturers Association and commonly used for combustion and boiler calculations.

The ratio of 3⅓ parts of nitrogen to each part of oxygen is of particular interest in Table 21–1. The presence of such a diluted source of oxygen is of considerable concern and significance in the design of burners and the proportions of the boiler furnace.[4] Adequate time must be allowed and suitable turbulence provided to obtain intimate contact of oxygen and combustible, and this process must be carried out at sufficient temperature to complete the combustion process.

[4] See Chapter 6, Heat Transfer, and Chapter 17, Fuel Burning Systems.

In an ideal situation the combustion process could take place with the exact proportions of oxygen and combustible that are called for in theory. Actually it is impracticable and commercially unjustifiable to operate a boiler at the theoretical level of zero per cent excess oxygen. In practice this condition is approached by providing an excess of oxygen in the form of excess air from the atmosphere. The amount of excess air varies with the fuel, loading condition and firing equipment.

Combustion Equations

For the purposes of combustion calculations, however, it is customary to write the combustion reaction equations on the basis of theoretical oxygen only, notwithstanding the presence of excess air and nitrogen. A partial list of these combustion equations is given in Table 21–2.

Table 21–2   Combustion Equations

Combustible	Molecular Weight	Equation	Heat Release Btu/lb (High)
Carbon	12	$C + O_2 \rightarrow CO_2$	14,100
Hydrogen	2	$H_2 + 0.5\,O_2 \rightarrow H_2O$	61,100
Sulfur	32	$S + O_2 \rightarrow SO_2$	4,000
Hydrogen sulfide	34	$H_2S + 1.5\,O_2 \rightarrow SO_2 + H_2O$	7,100
Methane	16	$CH_4 + 2\,O_2 \rightarrow CO_2 + 2H_2O$	23,880
Ethane	30	$C_2H_6 + 3.5\,O_2 \rightarrow 2CO_2 + 3H_2O$	23,320
Propane	44	$C_3H_8 + 5\,O_2 \rightarrow 3CO_2 + 4H_2O$	21,660
Butane	58	$C_4H_{10} + 6.5\,O_2 \rightarrow 4CO_2 + 5H_2O$	21,300
Pentane	72	$C_5H_{12} + 8\,O_2 \rightarrow 5CO_2 + 6H_2O$	21,090

All combustion calculations are based on fundamental relationships expressed in chemical equations as shown on Table 21–2. The equations not only indicate what substances are involved in the reaction but also the molecular proportions in which they take part.

Each molecule has a numerical value that represents its relative weight or molecular weight. This molecular weight is the sum of the atomic weights of the atoms composing the molecule. Thus carbon, C, has a molecular weight of 12; oxygen, O_2, has a molecular weight of 2 × 16 = 32; and carbon dioxide, CO_2, has a molecular weight of 12 + (2 × 16) = 44. It should be understood that these molecular weights are only relative values and may be expressed in any units. Table 21–2 gives the molecular weights of substances involved in combustion calculations.

It has been established that a molecular weight of any substance in the gaseous state and under the same conditions of temperature and pressure will occupy the same volume. This relationship is very significant. The volume will, of course, vary numerically for different units of weight and for different conditions of temperature and pressure. For combustion calculations, the pound and the cubic foot are the units commonly used and unless otherwise stated, the temperature and pressure are understood to be standard at 32 F and 14.7 psia. Thus a molecular weight of 32 lb of oxygen at 32 F and atmospheric pressure will have the same volume as a molecular weight of 44 lb of carbon dioxide under the same conditions. This volume is 359 cu ft.

Concept of the Mol

A molecular weight expressed in pounds is called a *pound mol*, or simply a *mol*, and the volume that it occupies is called a molal volume. Molal volume varies with changes in temperature and pressure according to gas laws previously mentioned and may be corrected to any desired conditions. Volume is directly proportional to the absolute temperature and inversely proportional to the absolute pressure. Since combustion processes in steam boiler furnaces usually take place at practically constant atmospheric pressure, pressure corrections are seldom necessary.

Returning to the combustion equation for carbon and oxygen and applying these concepts, it is now possible, as shown below, to write this equation in several ways. For purposes of molar analysis carbon may be treated as a gas.

$$(1) \ C + (1) \ O_2 = (1) \ CO_2 \qquad \text{(Eq. 21–1)}$$

$$1 \ \text{mol} \ C + 1 \ \text{mol} \ O_2 = 1 \ \text{mol} \ CO_2 \qquad \text{(Eq. 21–2)}$$

$$12 \ \text{lb} \ C + 32 \ \text{lb} \ O_2 = 44 \ \text{lb} \ CO_2 \qquad \text{(Eq. 21–3)}$$

$$1 \ \text{lb} \ C + 32 \div 12 \ \text{lb} \ O_2 = 44 \div 12 \ \text{lb} \ CO_2 \qquad \text{(Eq. 21–4)}$$

$$359 \ \text{cu ft} \ C + 359 \ \text{cu ft} \ O_2 = 359 \ \text{cu ft} \ CO_2 \qquad \text{(Eq. 21–5)}$$

$$1 \ \text{vol} \ C + 1 \ \text{vol} \ O_2 = 1 \ \text{vol} \ CO_2 \qquad \text{(Eq. 21–6)}$$

It will be noticed how each equation balances. There are the same number of atoms of each element and the same weight of reacting substances on each side of the equality sign but not necessarily the same number of molecules, mols or volumes. Thus, one molecule of carbon plus one molecule of oxygen gives only one molecule of carbon dioxide and two mols of hydrogen plus one mol of oxygen gives only two mols of water vapor.

It will be evident from a consideration of the mol-volume relationship that per cent by volume is numerically the same as per cent by mol.

Since a mol represents a definite weight as well as a definite volume, it serves as a means of converting analyses by weight into analyses by volume and vice versa. For example, as indicated in Table 21–1, air has an approximate volumetric analysis of 21 per cent of oxygen and 79 per cent of nitrogen. Since per cent by volume is per cent by mol, there is in one mol of air 0.21 mol of oxygen and 0.79 mol of nitrogen. The weights of oxygen and nitrogen corresponding to these mol fractions are $0.21 \times 32 = 6.72$ and $0.79 \times 28 = 22.12$ respectively. The total weight therefore of one mol of air or, in other words, the molecular weight of air is equal to the sum of the weights of the mol fractions or $6.72 + 22.12 = 28.84$. The per cent by weight of oxygen in air is then $6.72 \div 28.84 \times 100$, or approximately 23, and the per cent by weight of nitrogen in air is similarly $22.12 \div 28.84 \times 100$, or approximately 77. Furthermore, since the molecular weight of air is 28.84, a mol of air will weigh 28.84 lb, and since a mol is equivalent to 359 cu ft, the density of air under standard conditions is $28.84 \div 359 = 0.0808$ lb per cu ft. The density of any gas at any temperature is found by dividing the molecular weight of the gas by the molal volume at that temperature, the latter relationship being indicated in Fig. 21–1.

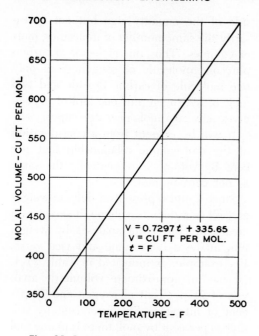

MOLAL VOLUME – CU FT PER MOL

V = 0.7297 *t* + 335.65
V = CU FT PER MOL.
t = F

TEMPERATURE – F

Fig. 21–1. Gas density determination

Methods of Combustion Calculations

Two methods of combustion calculations are presented in some detail in the pages that follow. The first is known as the *mol method* and is based on the chemical relationships previously explained. The second is a *graphical method* which uses charts and the firing of a million Btu as a basis of calculation.

Each of these methods is illustrated by two examples, the first being based on coal and the second on natural gas. These same two fuels are then used in parallel examples of boiler calculations. One is concerned with a stoker fired industrial boiler and the other with a gas fired boiler for a central station.

Mol Calculations — Solid or Liquid Fuel

Since for either solid or liquid fuel the combustible material is composed of the same three elements, carbon, hydrogen and sulfur, the basic combustion equations are:

$$C + O_2 \rightarrow CO_2$$
$$S + O_2 \rightarrow SO_2$$
$$H_2 + 1/2\ O_2 \rightarrow H_2O$$

Aside from a correction for carbon loss, sometimes included for the solid fuel, the basic calculation on the mol system is the same for either type fuel.

Fuel — Midwestern Illinois bituminous coal

Excess air — 20 per cent

Basis of calculation — 100 lb fuel as fired

Example I — Bituminous Coal

Fuel Analysis — As Fired

	Per Cent by Weight	*Mol Weight*
Carbon	63.50	12
Hydrogen	4.07	2
Sulfur	1.53	32
Oxygen	7.46	32
Nitrogen	1.28	28
Moisture	15.00	18
Ash	7.16	
Higher heating value	11,350 Btu per lb	

The calculation of air weight for combustion must be made on the basis of an oxygen balance since oxygen is the only element common to all combustion equations. Oxygen contained in the fuel must be deducted from the calculated quantity needed because it is already combined with carbon or hydrogen.

Air for Combustion

Oxygen for carbon	$63.5/12 = 5.292$ lb mol
Oxygen for hydrogen	$4.07/2{\times}2 = 1.017$ lb mol
Oxygen for sulfur	$1.53/32 = 0.048$ lb mol
	Total 6.357 lb mol
Oxygen in fuel	$7.46/32 = 0.233$ lb mol
Oxygen required	$= 6.124$ lb mol
Oxygen from excess air	$6.124 \times 0.20 = 1.225$ lb mol
	Total oxygen required $= 7.349$ lb mol

$$\text{Air required (7.349 lb mol } O_2)\ \frac{(100 \text{ lb mol air})}{(\ 21 \text{ lb mol } O_2)} = 35 \quad \text{lb mol}$$

$35 \times 28.85 = 1010$ lb air per 100 lb fuel

$35 \times 359 = 12{,}570$ cu ft measured at standard conditions per 100 lb fuel

Water vapor is always present in atmospheric air and when the volume of air to be supplied for combustion is calculated, allowances should be made for the water vapor which increases the volume of dry air by one to three per cent. The water vapor content of the atmosphere is considerably greater in summer than it is in the winter.

Weight of Products of Combustion. The weight of gaseous products of combustion is calculated from the volumetric analysis of flue gas. It is usually expressed in pounds of dry gas per pound of carbon. In this calculation, the concept of pound mol is also very useful.

Not only the weight of flue gas per 100 lb of coal but its analysis and volume can be calculated from the information given in the preceding example.

Lb mol CO_2 formed	5.292
Lb mol SO_2 formed	0.048
Total	5.340

Lb mol excess oxygen	1.225
Lb mol nitrogen introduced	
$(7.349 \text{ lb mol } O_2)\ \dfrac{(79 \text{ lb mol } N_2)}{(21 \text{ lb mol } O_2)} =$	27.600
Lb mol nitrogen in fuel $\dfrac{1.28}{28}$ $=$	0.046
Total lb mol dry flue gas	34.211

Since mol per cent and volume per cent are equivalent, the dry flue gas analysis can be calculated at once. In this calculation, SO_2 is combined with and reported as CO_2 since it will be absorbed by the water when an analysis is made by Orsat apparatus.

$5.340 \times 100/34.21 = 15.60$ CO_2 (per cent)
$1.225 \times 100/34.21 = 3.58$ O_2 (per cent)
$27.646 \times 100/34.21 = 80.82$ N_2 (per cent)

The volume of the dry gas at 32 F and 14.7 psia can be calculated as follows:

$34.21 \times 359 = 12{,}300$ cu ft per 100 lb coal

The weight of dry flue gas per 100 lb coal can be calculated from the preceding data.

Weight CO₂ = 5.292 × 44 =   232.50
Weight SO₂ = 0.048 × 64 =   3.07
Weight O₂ = 1.225 × 32 =   39.20
Weight N₂ = 27.646 × 28 =   775.00

$$\text{Total} \quad 1049.77 \text{ lb}$$

These calculations are subject to the allowances for unburned carbon. This is because not all the carbon is burned. Some of it drops into the ashpit and some is carried out of the furnace with the flue gas. On a boiler test, these carbon losses should be determined and expressed in percentage of coal in order that the unburned carbon may be deducted from the percentage of carbon in coal.

The above problem was calculated on a dry basis. However, in many combustion calculations, it is necessary to know the moisture content of combustion products. For this reason, the following example will be calculated on both dry and wet bases.

Mol Calculations — Gaseous Fuel

Fuel — natural gas
Excess air — ten per cent
Basis of calculation — one volume or one mol of fuel

Example II — Natural Gas

	Per cent by volume	Mol per mol of fuel	Molecular weights	
CH₄	74.0	0.74	16	11.84
C₂H₆	15.0	0.15	30	4.50
CO₂	5.0	0.05	44	2.20
N₂	6.0	0.06	28	1.68
		1.00		
Molecular weight of fuel				20.22

Mol relations from combustion equations — as found in Table 21–2 on page 21–4.

1 Mol	Mol O₂	Mol CO₂	Mol H₂O
CH₄	2	1	2
C₂H₆	3.5	2	3
CO₂	—	1	—
N₂	—	—	—

Mol per Mol of Fuel

		O₂	CO₂	H₂O	N₂
CH₄	0.74	× 2 = 1.480	× 1 = 0.740	× 2 = 1.480	—
C₂H₆	0.15	× 3.5 = 0.525	× 2 = 0.300	× 3 = 0.450	—
CO₂	0.05	—	0.050	—	—
N₂	0.06	—	—	—	0.060
O₂ from theoretical air		= 2.005	—	—	—
N₂ from theoretical air		—	—	— 2.005 × $\frac{79}{21}$ = 7.543	
Products at zero per cent excess air			1.090	1.930	7.603
10 per cent excess air		0.200			0.754
Products at 10 per cent excess air		0.200	1.090	1.930	8.357

Total air supplied = 2.205 × $\frac{100}{21}$ = 10.480 mol

Total dry products = 0.200 + 1.090 + 8.357 = 9.647 mol

Total wet products = 9.647 + 1.930 = 11.577 mol

Analysis of Products of Combustion

		Dry Gases		Wet Gases	
Per cent by volume	CO_2	$\dfrac{1.090 \times 100}{9.647} =$	11.30	$\dfrac{1.090 \times 100}{11.577} =$	9.42
Per cent by volume	N_2	$\dfrac{8.357 \times 100}{9.647} =$	86.63	$\dfrac{8.357 \times 100}{11.577} =$	72.17
Per cent by volume	O_2	$\dfrac{0.200 \times 100}{9.647} =$	2.07	$\dfrac{0.200 \times 100}{11.577} =$	1.73
Per cent by volume	H_2O			$\dfrac{1.930 \times 100}{11.577} =$	16.68
			100.00		100.00

*Molecular Weight and Volume
of Products of Combustion*

	Dry Gases		Wet Gases	
CO_2	$0.1130 \times 44 =$	4.97	$0.0942 \times 44 =$	4.14
N_2	$0.8663 \times 28 =$	24.25	$0.7217 \times 28 =$	20.21
O_2	$0.0207 \times 32 =$	0.66	$0.0173 \times 32 =$	0.55
H_2O	–	–	$0.1668 \times 18 =$	3.00
1 Mol		= 29.88	1 Mol	= 27.09

Weight

$$\frac{\text{Lb air}}{\text{Lb fuel}} = \frac{10.480 \times 28.84}{1 \quad \times 20.22} = 15.00$$

$$\frac{\text{Lb dry flue gas}}{\text{Lb fuel}} = \frac{9.647 \times 29.88}{1 \quad \times 20.22} = 14.25$$

$$\frac{\text{Lb wet flue gas}}{\text{Lb fuel}} = \frac{11.577 \times 27.90}{1 \quad \times 20.22} = 16.00$$

Volume (from Fig. 21–1)

	Assumed Conditions		Cu Ft	
$\dfrac{\text{Dry air}}{\text{Lb fuel}}$	100 F	14.7 psia	$\dfrac{10.480 \times 411}{20.22} = 213$	
$\dfrac{\text{Dry flue gas}}{\text{Lb fuel}}$	300 F	14.7 psia	$\dfrac{9.647 \times 555}{20.22} = 265$	
$\dfrac{\text{Wet flue gas}}{\text{Lb fuel}}$	300 F	14.7 psia	$\dfrac{11.577 \times 555}{20.22} = 318$	

Graphical Calculation Method —
Million Btu Basis

The million Btu method for combustion calculations is based on the concept that the weight of air required in the combustion of a unit weight of any commercial fuel is more nearly proportional to the unit heat value than to the unit weight of the fuel. Accordingly, the weights of air, dry gas, moisture, wet gas, and other quantities are expressed in pounds per million Btu fired.[5]

In connection with this calculation method, the following items will be discussed:

1. Fuel in products, W_f
2. Atmospheric air, W_a
3. Effect of unburned combustible
4. Products of combustion, W_g
5. Moisture in air, M_a
6. Moisture from fuel contained in products of combustion, M
7. Dry gas, W_{dg}
8. Carbon dioxide in products, CO_2

The first four items are necessary for the calculation of the gas and air quantities. Items 5 to 7 form the basis of heat balance calculations, either in the design or testing of a steam generating unit, whenever current forms of ASME Power Test Code are used.[6] The last item, carbon dioxide and its relationship to excess air, is important in combustion calculations because the CO_2 in the gases is what is actually measured in boiler tests, and from it the excess air is calculated. However, the equipment designer prefers to work with excess air even though he may appear to have based his estimates on the per cent of CO_2.

1. *Fuel in Products, W_f*, is defined as that portion of the fuel fired which, in gaseous form as separate elements or in chemical combination with other elements, reappears after combustion in the gaseous products of combustion. Since with the present method all quantities are to be those required for or resulting from firing 1,000,000 Btu, W_f must also be calculated on that basis. If a fuel contains no ash and if, in addition, it deposits no carbon in the furnace or on other heating surface, W_f is simply obtained by dividing 1,000,000 by the as-fired heat value of the fuel in Btu per pound. For the other cases where ash or solid combustible loss must be considered, the following equation may be used. A graphical plot of this equation is shown in Figure 21–2.

$$W_f = \frac{10^4 (100 - \% \text{Ash} - \% \text{Solid combustible loss})}{\text{Fuel heat value}}$$

where   (Eq. 21–7)

W_f = pounds per million Btu fired
% Ash = per cent by weight in fuel as fired
% Solid combustible loss = per cent by weight in fuel as fired
Fuel heating value (HHV) = high heating value as fired, Btu per lb.

---

[5] The original source of this information is a series of articles by W. S. Patterson and A. L. Nicolai. Six of these appeared in Vol. 13 of *Combustion*: August 1941, pp. 25–30; October 1941, pp. 39–42; December 1941, pp. 44–48; February 1942, pp. 38–42; April 1942, pp. 37–42; June 1942, pp. 32–37. The last two were published in *Combustion*, Vol. 14, August 1942, pp. 40–44 and Vol. 16, August 1944, pp. 43–47. Reprints of this series entitled "Combustion Calculations by Graphical Methods" are available from Combustion Engineering, Inc.
[6] In this chapter the specific power test code under consideration is PTC 4.1, Stationary Steam Generating Units. The latest edition published by ASME should be consulted for any additional information desired.

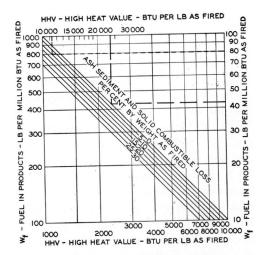

Fig. 21—2. Plot of fuel in products relationship

The higher heating value is the accepted standard in this country. It is obtained by calorimetric analysis of the fuel in a laboratory. Producers often sell fuel on the basis of its heating value and users generally check it periodically. In any event, manufacturers of steam generating equipment need to know it; if it is not furnished, they must make an independent test or calculate it from the fuel constituents. For solid and liquid fuels, empirical formulas must be used, but for gaseous fuels the sum of the heating values of the various combustible constituents may be employed. There may be considerable difference between the analysis "as received" and "as fired" even though nothing is intentionally done to the fuel between the time it is received and the time it is burned. However, certain fuels are purposely dried before they are fired, and others take on moisture hygroscopically or are purposely "tempered." In the storage system of pulverized coal firing, the moisture removed from the coal may actually be vented directly to a stack, but in the direct fired system, the moisture,

although removed from the coal, is fired with the coal and therefore does not truly alter the combustion quantities.

Likewise, with gaseous fuels, the heating value and analysis are generally reported on the volumetric basis and the temperature and the pressure conditions of the fuel are therefore an essential part of the analysis. Standard conditions are 60 F and 30 in. Hg.

2. *Atmospheric Air, W_a.* As mentioned earlier, all combustion requires oxygen which in commercial practice must be supplied from the atmosphere.

The theoretical weight of dry air, TW_{da}, may be calculated from the fuel analysis and the formula:

$$TW_{da} = \left[\frac{11.54(\%C) + 34.34\left(\%H - \dfrac{\%O}{8}\right) + 4.32(\%S)}{HHV \text{ as fired} \times 10^6} \right] \times 10^4$$

(Eq. 21–8)

where

    $11.54 = $ lb air to burn one lb C
    $34.34 = $ lb air to burn one lb H
    $4.32 = $ lb air to burn one lb S

Determination of air for combustion is a time-consuming task and shorter methods are usually desirable if accuracy can at the same time be maintained. The charts for the graphical method make allowance for all important variables in the analysis and for practical purposes are as accurate as if more laborious methods of calculation were used.

Curve A in the combustion calculation charts gives the relation of air quantity to per cent excess air for various fuels. The curve is based on atmospheric air, which simply means that an arbitrary amount of moisture has been added to the air. As a basis for boiler proposals, the American Boiler Manufacturers Association strongly recommends the use of 60 per cent relative humidity at 80 F, which is equivalent to 0.013 lb of water vapor per pound of air. To neglect this would introduce an error of approximately one per cent.

3. *Effect of Unburned Combustible.* With a well-designed burner and furnace, it is possible to complete combustion of all liquid and gaseous fuel so that no allowance need be made for loss of combustible in gas and air weight calculations.

In the combustion of solid fuels, even in pulverized form, it is not commercially feasible to burn all the available combustible. As a matter of fact, the relationship between the heat loss due to excess air and the heat loss due to unburned fuel may be such as to make it more economical to operate with a combustible loss considerably higher than the minimum loss which could be obtained.

The method employed to determine the solid combustible loss involves collection of fly ash and refuse from various hoppers. A dry sample of this collection is then burned in a muffle furnace and its loss of weight due to combustion is measured. This loss of weight can be readily expressed as the per cent by weight of the fuel as fired.

In the combustion of a fuel having pure carbon as the only combustible constituent, the air required may be accurately obtained by multiplying the curve reading (such as found later in Curve A of Figure 21–3) by the factor

$$C = 1 - \frac{\% \text{ solid combustible weight loss}}{100}$$

$$\text{(Eq. 21–9)}$$

This relationship holds because in this case the air for combustion is directly proportional to the carbon in the fuel. If, however, all the heat in the fuel does not come from the carbon alone, so that the air is not strictly proportional to the combustible weight loss, the factor C will not be exactly correct. It will be nearly correct for high-carbon, low-volatile fuels and will result in only a small error even for fuels low in fixed carbon and high in hydrogen, because the combustible loss with the latter is generally very small. However, the error involved by using Eq. 21–9 in all cases is quite within the limits of accuracy of all other combustion calculations.

For a heat balance, the combustible weight loss must be converted to per cent heat loss. This can be done conveniently by dividing the per cent solid combustible weight loss by the heat value of the fuel as fired and multiplying it by 14,600 which is the heat value for combustible in the refuse recommended by ASME Power Test Code PTC 4 for this calculation.

4. *Products of Combustion,* W_g. Having calculated the foregoing quantities W_f and W_a, the gaseous products of combustion may readily be determined by the addition of W_f and W_a, as previously corrected. Thus:

$$W_g = W_t + CW_a \qquad \text{(Eq. 21–10)}$$

where

W_g = Total gaseous products of combustion, pounds per 10^6 Btu fired

W_f = Fuel fired exclusive of ash or solid carbon loss, pounds per 10^6 Btu fired

W_a = Atmospheric air consumed, pounds per 10^6 Btu fired

C = Combustible loss correction factor

5. *Moisture in Air, M_a.* Since ASME Power Test Code PTC 4 allows the heat loss due to moisture in air to be reported as a separate item in the test heat balance of a steam generating unit, it has become the custom of engineers to include it in a predicted heat balance. In an actual test, the moisture in air can be determined from wet and dry bulb temperature readings, but for a predicted heat balance it must be assumed. It may vary from day to day even in the same locality, but the American Boiler Manufacturers Association has recommended an arbitrary value for use in preparing proposals. As mentioned above, this is taken as 0.013 lb of water per pound of dry air and is included in the atmospheric air W_a as read from the air-weight curve. When required as a separate item for heat-balance calculations, it will be sufficiently accurate to use an assumed value from the following equation:

$$M_a = 0.013 W_a \qquad \text{(Eq. 21–11)}$$

6. *Moisture from Fuel, M.* This is another item which is separately reported in an ASME Power Test Code, PTC 4, heat balance and likewise in a predicted heat balance. In the case of some fuels, such as natural and refinery gases, the heat loss due to this moisture may be the largest single item in the heat balance. M includes the combined surface and inherent moisture, M_f, plus the moisture formed by the combustion of hydrogen, M_h. The former will vary from zero or a mere trace in fuel oil to over 115 lb per million Btu fired in the case of green wood; the latter will vary from zero or a trace in lampblack to 100 lb per million Btu fired in the case of some refinery gases.

The charts for combustion calculations by graphical methods include curves for determining the moisture in the fuel. The curves are based on the following equations:

$$M_t = H_2O \frac{(10^4)}{(HHV)} \qquad \text{(Eq. 21–12)}$$

$$M_h = 9 \times H_2 \times \frac{(10^4)}{(HHV)} \qquad \text{(Eq. 21–13)}$$

where

M_t = Moisture in the fuel, pounds per million Btu fired

M_h = Moisture from combustion of H_2, pounds per million Btu fired

H_2 = Hydrogen in fuel, per cent by weight

HHV = High (gross) heating value of fuel, Btu per lb

7. *Dry Gas, W_{dg}.* The necessity of calculating the dry gas or the dry products as contrasted with, and in addition to, the total products, is due to ASME Power Test Code PTC 4. Dry gas loss is a separate item of the heat balance.

The dry gas may be determined by subtracting the water vapor from the total products, thus:

$$W_{dg} = W_g - (M_a + M) \qquad \text{(Eq. 21–14)}$$

where

W_{dg} = Dry gas, pounds per million Btu fired

W_g = Total products of combustion (Item 4)

M_a = Moisture in air (Item 5)

M = Moisture from fuel (Item 6)

8. *Carbon Dioxide in Products, CO_2.* The CO_2 in the gases leaving a furnace or boiler is used by the operators as a guide in adjusting the air supplied, so as not to use too much excess air and in this way decrease the efficiency. Conversely, however, if the CO_2 is maintained too high so that the excess air is too low, there

will be incomplete combustion of volatile fuel and a higher than normal loss in unburned fixed carbon.

Examples of Graphical Calculation Method

Charts for the graphical method of combustion calculations have been prepared for the fuels listed below and may be found where indicated:

1. Fuel oil (Appendix A)
2. Coal (Fig. 21–3 of following Example I — Solid Fuel)
3. Coke (Appendix A)
4. Wood and bagasse (Appendix A)
5. Natural gas (Fig. 21–4 of following Example II — Gaseous Fuel)
6. Refinery gas (Appendix A)
7. Blast furnace gas (Appendix A)
8. Coke oven gas (Appendix A)

The first four fuels are either solid or liquid, and Example I for bituminous coal is typical of the method of calculation for these fuels. The other four fuels are gases, and Example II for natural gas is typical of the gas fuels.

Example I — Solid Fuel — Midwestern Illinois Bituminous Coal

Coal Analysis

Carbon	63.50 per cent
Hydrogen	4.07 per cent
Sulfur	1.53 per cent
Oxygen	7.46 per cent
Nitrogen	1.28 per cent
Moisture	15.00 per cent
Ash	7.16 per cent

Higher heating value 11,350 Btu per lb

Assume that this coal is burned with 30 per cent excess air and that the expected solid combustible loss is 2.0 per cent by weight.

(1) *Fuel, W_f*

Ash sediment and solid combustible loss $= 7.16 + 2.0 = 9.16$ per cent For HHV $= 11,350$ and previous value of 9.16, read Fig. 21–2 or solve Eq. 21–7.

$W_f = 80$ lb per million Btu

(2) *Atmospheric Air, W_a*

$$\frac{C}{H_2 + 0.1\,O_2} = \frac{63.5}{4.07 + 0.1 \times 7.46} = 13.2$$

For 30 per cent excess air and

$$\frac{C}{H_2 + 0.1\,O_2} = 13.2, \text{ read Fig. 21–3.}$$

$W_a = 1000$ lb per million Btu

(3) *Unburned Combustible Factor, C.* For solid combustible loss of 2 per cent,

$$C =$$

$$1 - \frac{\text{Per cent solid combustible weight loss}}{100}$$

$$= 0.98$$

(4) *Total Products,* $W_g = W_f + C\,W_a =$ $80 + 0.98 \times 1000 = 1060$ lb per million Btu.

(5) *Moisture in Air,* $M_a = 0.013 \times W_a$ $= 0.013 \times 1000 = 13.0$ lb per million Btu.

(6) *Moisture from Fuel, M,* is the sum of M_f, the moisture in the coal as fired, and M_h, the water formed by combustion of hydrogen from curve D, Fig. 21–3, for 15 per cent moisture, 4.07 per cent of H_2 in fuel, and higher heating value of 11,350 Btu per lb. Read $M_f = 13$ lb per million Btu and $M_h = 32$ lb per million Btu. M = $M_f + M_h = 13 + 32 = 45$ lb per million Btu.

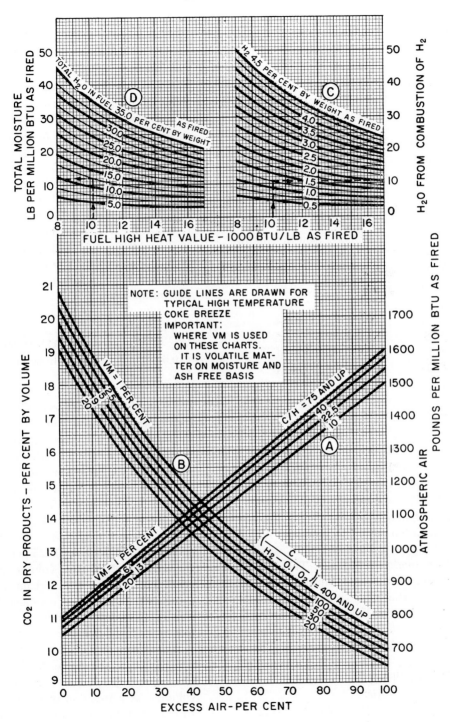

Fig. 21–3. Graphical calculation curves for coal — million Btu basis

(7) *Dry Gas,* W_{dg}

$W_{dg} = W_g - (M_a + M) = 1060 - (13.0 + 45) = 1002$ lb per million Btu

(8) *Per Cent* CO_2 *in Products.* By assuming 30 per cent excess air and

$$\frac{C}{H_2 - 0.1\,O_2} = \frac{63.5}{4.07 - 0.746} = 19.7,$$

read from Fig. 21–3, $CO_2 = 14.3$ per cent

Example II Gaseous Fuel — Natural Gas with Ten Per Cent Excess Air Fuel Analysis

	Per cent by volume
CH_4	93.87
C_2H_6	3.62
C_3H_8	0.93
C_4H_{10}	0.06
C_5H_{12}	0.94
H_2S	0.15
A	0.01
CO_2	0.41
O_2	0.01

Higher heating value at 60 F and 30 in. Hg is 1060 Btu per cu ft and 23,100 Btu per lb.

(1) *Fuel* W_f. For a higher heating value of 23,100 Btu per lb, read from Fig. 21–2, $W_f = 43$ lb per million Btu

(2) *Atmospheric Air,* W_a. From Fig. 21–4 with ten per cent excess air, $W_a = 812$ lb per million Btu

(3) *Unburned Combustible.* The general assumption when burning natural gas in stationary boiler furnaces is that the combustible loss is zero. Consequently, C may be taken as 1.

(4) *Total Products,* W_g

$W_g = W_f + C W_a = 43 + 812 = 855$ lb per million Btu

(5) *Moisture in Air,* M_a

$M_a = 0.013\,W_a = 0.013 \times 812 = 10.5$ lb per million Btu

(6) *Moisture from Fuel, M.* M_f, the entrained moisture, is zero and M_s, the saturation moisture, is negligible. M_h can be determined from Fig. 21–4, based on the known higher heating value of 1060 Btu per cu ft and the per cent by volume of the natural gas as fired. To do this it is necessary to add the volume percentages of the constituents as shown on the abscissae of the C family of curves of Fig. 21–4. These are as follows: $H_2S + 2\ CH_4 + 3\ C_2H_6 + 4\ C_3H_8 + 5\ C_4H_{10} + 6\ C_5H_{12} = 0.15 + 2 \times 93.87 + 3 \times 3.62 + 4 \times 0.93 + 5 \times 0.06 + 6 \times 0.94 = 208.4$ per cent by volume. On Fig. 21–4, read $M_h = 92$ lb per million Btu.

(7) *Dry Gas,* W_{dg}

$W_{dg} = W_g - (M_a + M) = 855 - (10.5 + 92) = 752.5$ lb per million Btu

(8) *Per Cent* CO_2 *in Products.* CO_2 can be determined from Fig. 21–4. To do this it is necessary to add volume percentages of the constituents as shown on the abscissae of the E family of curves. These are as follows: $CO_2 + CH_4 + 2\ C_2H_6 + 3\ C_3H_8 + 4\ C_4H_{10} + 5\ C_5H_{12} = 0.41 + 93.87 + 2 \times 3.62 + 3 \times 0.93 + 4 \times 0.06 + 5 \times 0.94 = 109.25$ per cent by volume. Next the volume percentage of H_2S in the fuel must be subtracted from the compensated sum of CO_2 and N_2 as follows: $8.5\ CO_2 + N_2 - 5.5\ H_2S = 8.5 \times 0.41 + 0.0 - 5.5 \times 0.15 = 3.49 - 0.82 = 2.67$ per cent by volume. Then read CO_2 in dry products (per cent by volume) as a function of excess air. In Fig. 21–4 this gives a value of CO_2 of 11.0 per cent,

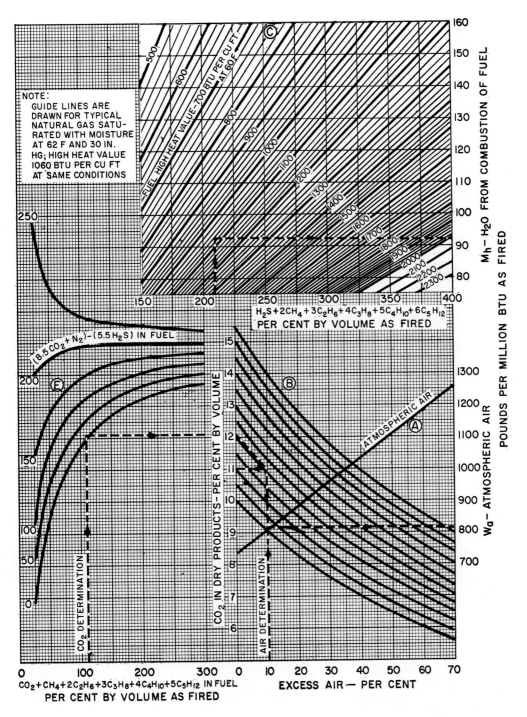

Fig. 21-4. Graphical calculation curves for natural gas — million Btu basis

Boiler Calculations

Boiler calculations cannot be started until certain basic decisions have been made. The purchaser must establish steam conditions and capacity and set forth any local requirements which may affect the geometry or arrangement of the boiler. Capacity is generally expressed in terms of a maximum continuous rating, with an overload or peak rating for a limited period of time.

In order to calculate boiler performance it is obviously necessary to know the fuel to be burned as well as a typical analysis. Economic studies should be made to determine merits of installing boiler auxiliaries and heat recovery equipment. Choice of balanced draft or pressurized firing must be made as well as the desirability of incorporating an air heater or an economizer or both. All of these decisions are a part of the preliminary design of power plants.[7]

Heat Output

Knowing steam temperature and pressure, the heat content (enthalpy, h, for superheated or saturated steam) in Btu per lb is obtained from steam tables.[8] The heat in the feedwater, h_f, is similarly read from these tables. Then, if W_s represents the steam produced in pounds per hour, the total boiler heat output, H_o, will be

$$H_o = W_s (h - h_f) \qquad \text{(Eq. 21–15)}$$

Heat Input

It is next necessary to evaluate the heat input to the furnace, H_i, since it is the input that enables the designer to determine the quantity of fuel to be burned and the amount of air that must be supplied for, and the weight of products formed by, combustion. The total heat input is given by

$$H_i = \frac{H_o}{e} \qquad \text{(Eq. 21–16)}$$

where e is the overall efficiency of the entire unit.

The value of e used at this point is in the nature of an experienced guess which should later be checked by a heat balance. Table 21–3 indicates the range of values

Table 21–3   Boiler Efficiency

Fuel	Per Cent Efficiency with Heat Recovery	Per Cent Efficiency without Heat Recovery
Coal (Pulverized)	87 to 90	80 to 82
Coal (Stoker)	83 to 85	76 to 78
Oil	87 to 89	80 to 82
Natural Gas	83 to 85	76 to 78

of efficiency frequently used in design of boilers.

Fuel Fired

With all fuels, it is necessary to determine the weight of fuel burned, usually in lb per hr, because the size of the fuel burning equipment is based on this quan-

---

[7] Factors which must be considered prior to making decisions upon which boiler performance calculations are based are discussed in Chapter 2, Elements of Power Plant Design, and Chapter 3, Design of Central Stations.

[8] Copies of C–E Steam Tables may be obtained from the General offices, Windsor, Conn.

tity. Having found the total heat input to the furnace, H_i, as explained before, the weight of fuel fired is determined by the following relationship:

$$\text{Fuel fired} = \frac{H_i}{H_f} \qquad \text{(Eq. 21–17)}$$

where H_f is the higher heating value in Btu per lb.

Excess Air for Combustion

Having arrived at the weight of fuel fired, the next item that must be fixed is the excess air coefficient.

Commercial fuels can be burned satisfactorily only when the amount of air supplied to them exceeds that which is theoretically calculated as required from equations showing the chemical reactions involved. The quantity of excess air provided in any particular case is dependent on the physical state of the fuel in the combustion chamber, on the size of the fuel particle, or, in the case of oil, on its viscosity; on the proportion of inert matter present; and on the design of furnace and fuel burning equipment. For complete combustion, solid fuels require the greatest, and gaseous fuels the least, quantity of excess air. Fuels that are finely subdivided on entering the furnace burn more easily and require less excess air than those induced in large lumps. Burners, stokers and furnaces which incorporate design features that produce a high degree of turbulence and commingling of the fuel with the combustion air require less excess air.

Table 21–4 indicates the range in values for the excess air, expressed in per cent of the theoretical air, that is commonly employed by the designer at the point where the products of combustion leave the furnace.

Table 21–4 Excess Air At Furnace Outlet

Fuels		Excess air, Per Cent
Solid fuels	Coal	10–40
	Coke	20–40
	Wood	25–50
	Bagasse	25–45
Liquid fuels	Oil	3–15
Gaseous fuels	Natural gas	5–10
	Refinery gas	8–15
	Blast furnace gas	15–25
	Coke oven gas	5–10

When testing for the operating efficiency of a steam-generating unit, the excess air is obtained indirectly by measuring the CO_2 in the products of combustion with an Orsat apparatus. For convenience, it is customary to base all calculations of air and products on the per cent CO_2 by volume, rather than on the excess air. Then, for any given fuel analysis it can be shown that there is a definite relation between the per cent CO_2 and the excess air in the dry products. This relation is brought out graphically by Figs. 21–3 and 21–4 and the combustion calculation charts in Appendix E.

Weight of Air and Combustion Products

Figs. 21–3 and 21–4 and Appendix E may also be used to establish weight of combustion air and products of combustion, as outlined earlier in this chapter in the section entitled Graphical Calculation Method — Million Btu Basis.

Principal Items Required

The following is a list of the principal items that must be known before proceeding with the calculation and selection of the various heat absorbing surfaces.

1. Excess air or CO_2 for efficient combustion
2. Total weight of products formed by combustion

For the design of firing and auxiliary equipment such as burners, stokers, pulverizers, air heaters, fans and ducts the following items are required.

1. Weight of fuel fired
2. Total weight of air to be supplied

The magnitude of any of these items depends largely on the characteristics of the fuel burned and, more specifically, on its analysis and calorific value. Therefore, familiarity with both combustion calculations as covered earlier in this chapter and with properties of fuels and their behavior in combustion is essential for correct design of steam generating equipment.[9]

Heat Transfer Values

Procedures are shown in the following examples for calculation of furnace, superheater, reheater, boiler and economizer surfaces. In the presentation, emphasis is on procedure rather than on rigorousness of treatment. To simplify the presentation, therefore, it has been found convenient to present general curves for heat transfer rate and to extrapolate particular values from these for use in evaluating the various types of surfaces.

Example I
Industrial Power Plant Boiler — Stoker Fired

This boiler is to be installed in a heating plant with a low load factor and is to be located in an area where solid fuel cost is relatively low. The stoker fired boiler shown in Fig. 21–5 is designed without heat recovery equipment and with a natural draft stack.

Specifications

Pressure at boiler outlet   125 psig

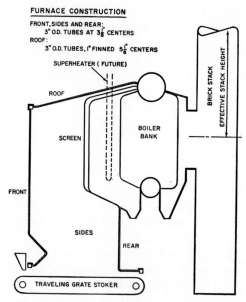

FURNACE CONSTRUCTION
FRONT, SIDES AND REAR:
    3" O.D. TUBES AT 3⅛ CENTERS
ROOF:
    3" O.D. TUBES, 1" FINNED 5⅝ CENTERS
SUPERHEATER (FUTURE)

Fig. 21–5.   Stoker fired boiler

Steam temperature, t_s Saturated (353 F)
Maximum continuous rating 115,000 lb per hr
Normal steam requirements 75,000 lb per hr
Feedwater temperature   220 F
Ambient air temperature   90 F
Heat recovery equipment   None
Type stoker   Traveling grate

Fuel Analysis (Same as Example I, Combustion Calculations)

	Illinois bituminous coal (free burning type)
Type	
Moisture	15.00 per cent
Carbon	63.50 per cent
Hydrogen	4.07 per cent
Nitrogren	1.28 per cent
Sulfur	1.52 per cent
Oxygen	7.46 per cent
Ash	7.16 per cent
Total	100.00 per cent
Higher heating value	11,350 Btu per lb
Ash fusion temperature	2150 F
Coking index	6

Coal size — one inch nut and slack with not more than 50 per cent through ¼ inch round mesh

[9] For additional information on fuels see Chapter 13, Fuel Properties of Coal, and Chapter 14, Natural Gas, Oil and Byproduct Fuels.

Basic Design Information

Maximum continuous rating	115,000 lb per hr
Enthalpy of steam (125 psig saturated)	1193 Btu per lb
Enthalpy of feedwater (220 F)	188 Btu per lb
Heat (enthalpy) added per pound	1005 Btu per lb
Total heat added (115,000) (1005) =	115.6×10^6 Btu per hr
Boiler efficiency (estimated)	76.5 per cent
Total heat fired $115.6 \times 10^6 \div 0.765 =$	151.0×10^6 Btu per hr
Fuel fired $151.0 \times 10^6 \div 11,350 =$	13,300 lb per hr

Sequence of Calculations

The calculations are arranged in the following sequence from fuel firing to discharge of waste gases from the stack.

1. Stoker selection
2. Furnace performance
3. Temperature drop across screen tubes
4. Exit temperature from boiler convection bank
5. Boiler convection bank draft loss
6. Stack diameter and height

Stoker Selection (Traveling Grate Type)

Stoker grate area selection is made on the basis of heat release per square foot. Stoker width is governed by fuel bed velocity and by economic considerations. In this case, a 15 ft wide stoker is selected to match the width of the boiler shown in Fig. 21–5.

Guides for selection of traveling grate stoker

Heat released at full load	500,000 to 550,000 Btu per sq ft hr
Allowable range of grate speed at full load	30 to 45 ft per hr

Calculated fuel bed velocity on basis of 6 inch fuel bed thickness and fuel density of 50 lb per cu ft.

Stoker area (approximate) $= \dfrac{151 \times 10^6}{525,000}$	288 sq ft
Stoker area (actual) (15 ft wide × 19 ft-6 in. long)	292 sq ft
Volume of coal fired $\dfrac{13,300}{50}$	266 cu ft per hr
Stoker speed $\dfrac{266 \text{ cu ft per hr}}{\frac{1}{2} \text{ ft fuel bed} \times 15 \text{ ft wide}}$	35.5 ft per hr
Stoker heat release $\dfrac{151 \times 10^6}{292}$	517,000 Btu per hr sq ft grate
CO_2 at furnace outlet (from Fig. 21–6)	14.3 per cent
Excess air at furnace outlet	30 per cent
Carbon loss (from Fig. 21–6)	2.5 per cent
Flue gas, Wg (from combustion calculation, Example I, coal firing)	1060 lb per 10^6 Btu
Flue gas leaving furnace (151 × 1060)	160,000 lb per hr

Furnace Performance

Furnace exit gas temperature is determined by empirical curves relating furnace temperature to net furnace heat release. Furnace net heat release is obtained by dividing net heat by *effective projected radiant surface,* EPRS, of the furnace which is the total envelope of the furnace multiplied by appropriate effectiveness factors for the various wall surfaces.[10]

Net heat is the effective heat in the furnace. It is obtained by deducting from the total heat fired the unavailable heat comprising losses from (1) carbon and (2) the latent heat of moisture from fuel. If an air heater is installed, the extra heat made available by preheated air must be added to determine the net heat.

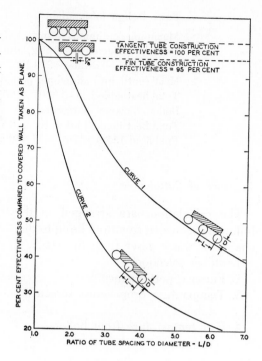

Fig. 21–7.   Effectiveness factors

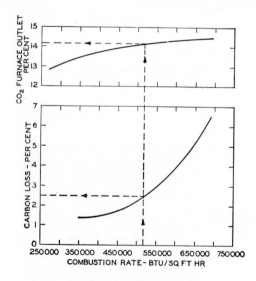

Fig. 21–6.   Carbon loss and CO_2 for traveling grate stoker

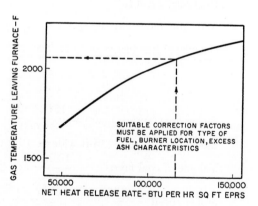

Fig. 21–8.   Heat release rate versus furnace exit temperature

---

[10] See Chapter 19, Fundamentals of Boiler Design, for factors affecting furnace geometry.

Net Heat at Maximum Continuous Rating

Total heat fired	151×10^6 Btu per hr
Carbon heat loss (2.5 per cent $\times$ 151 $\times$ 10^6)	3.8×10^6 Btu per hr
Moisture from fuel, M (from combustion calculation, Example I, coal firing and latent heat of vaporization of 1050 Btu per lb) $45 \times 1050 \times 151$	7.2×10^6 Btu per hr
Total deduction carbon and moisture from fuel losses	11.0×10^6 Btu per hr
Furnace net heat	140.0×10^6 Btu per hr

Furnace Effective Projected Radiant Surface, Sq Ft (EPRS)

To obtain the furnace EPRS, the furnace size and shape must be established together with the type of furnace wall surface to be used, as shown in Fig. 21–5. Effectiveness factors for various surfaces may be taken from Fig. 21–7.

Front wall	—	29 ft $\times$ 15 ft $\times$ 1 = 435
Roof	—	9 ft $\times$ 15 ft $\times$ 0.95 = 121
Rear wall	—	26 ft $\times$ 15 ft $\times$ 1 = 390
Side wall	—	128 ft $\times$ 2 ft $\times$ 1 = 256

Total EPRS = 1202 sq ft

Furnace net heat release

$$\frac{140.0 \times 10^6}{1202} = 117,000 \text{ Btu per sq ft hr}$$

Furnace exit gas temperature   (Fig. 21–8), $(2060 - 140) = 1920$ F

Fig. 21–8 is a general furnace temperature curve. In using it for this example a correction of approximately 140 deg F must be made to the curve reading.

Screen Tubes

A screen composed of a row or two of widely spaced tubes at the furnace outlet serves to cool the gaseous products of combustion before they enter the closely spaced convection surface. Performance of this heating surface is primarily a function of gas temperature and mass flow and is frequently expressed as gas temperature drop per row of tubes.

Two screen rows deep
3 in. OD tubes ($D = 3$) at 6¼ in. centers ($S_T = 6.25$)

Furnace width at screen	15 ft
Screen heights (average)	16 ft
Free gas area (from geometry of tube arrangement)	125 sq ft

$$\frac{S_T}{D} = \frac{6.25}{3} \qquad 2.08$$

$$G, \text{ mass velocity} = \frac{160,000}{125}$$

1280 lb per sq ft hr

Average gas temperature (assumed)	1850 F
$\triangle$T per row = 41 F	(Fig. 21–9)
$F_s = 1.90$	(Fig. 21–10)
$F_f = 1.02$	(Table 21–5)
Gas temperature drop 2 rows $41 \times 1.90 \times 1.02 \times 2 =$	160 deg F
Gas temperature leaving screen $1920 - 160 =$	1760 F

Table 21–5   Fuel and Excess Air Correction Factors for Screen Calculations

Fuel	Excess Air	F_f
Blast Furnace Gas	20	1.21
Natural Gas	10	1.05
Low Volatile Eastern Bituminous	20	0.98
High Volatile Eastern Bituminous	20	1.00
Midwest Bituminous	20	1.02
Wyoming Subbituminous	20	1.05
North Dakota Lignite	20	1.07
Wood – 30 per cent Moisture	30	1.10
Wood – 50 per cent Moisture	30	1.10
Bagasse – 50 per cent	30	1.12
Oil	15	1.03

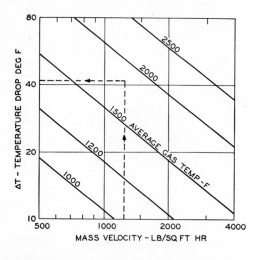

Fig. 21–9.   Temperature drop, screen tubes

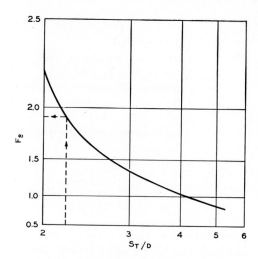

Fig. 21–10.   Correction factor, tube geometry

Boiler Convection Bank

On low pressure boilers of this type a boiler convection bank is required. This is a bank of tubes forming a part of the circulation system between the upper and lower boiler drums. The dimensions of the boiler convection bank are determined by the interrelated factors of tube size, spacing, boiler geometry and required performance.[11] In this particular unit, however, the width at the boiler convection bank is determined by the steam separation capabilities of the upper drum.

Tube diameter, D 2½ in. OD

In-line tube spacing arrangement

51 rows wide, 3½ in. width spacing, S_T
  (15 ft boiler width)

22 tubes deep, 3½ in. depth spacing, S_L

Effective boiler pass height   14 ft

Effective heating surface, S 10,300 sq ft
  $(51 \times 22 \times 14 \times 0.655)$

Free gas area, FGA 61 sq ft

$$FGA = (15 \times 14) - (51 \times \frac{2.5}{12} \times 14)$$

Gas weight, average through boiler bank, W_g
          163,000 lb per hr

Air leakage corresponding to an increase of approximately five per cent excess air is customarily assumed for boiler banks. Performance is based on the average of the gas weight entering and leaving the boiler bank.

Log mean temperature difference is evaluated from temperatures shown in Fig. 21–11 and the following equation.

$$LMTD = \frac{T_1 - T_2}{\mathrm{Log_e} \dfrac{T_1 - t_s}{T_2 - t_s}} = 682 \ \mathrm{deg} \ F$$

[11] See Chapter 19, Fundamentals at Boiler Design, for a discussion of these factors.

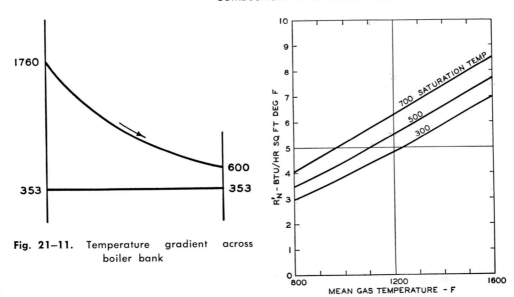

Fig. 21–11. Temperature gradient across boiler bank

Fig. 21–12. Transfer rate — nonluminous radiation

Evaluation of Nonluminous Radiation Transfer Rate, R_n

R_n = nonluminous radiation transfer rate
 = $R'_n \times F_b \times F_f$

Mean gas temperature = LMTD + t_s = 682 + 353	1035 F
R'_n (from Fig. 21–12)	4.2 Btu per hr sq ft deg F
Beam length, $L_b = 0.09 \dfrac{(S_T \times S_L)}{(D)} - 0.07 D$	0.26 ft
F_b, beam length correction (from Fig. 21–13)	0.22
Per cent moisture in products $= \dfrac{45}{1060} \times 100$	4.2
CO_2 (from combustion calculation, Example I, coal firing)	14.3
F_f, Fuel correction factor (from Fig. 21–14)	0.95
$R_n = 4.2 \times 0.22 \times 0.95$	0.9 Btu per hr sq ft deg F

Evaluation of Convection Transfer Rate, R_c

R_c = convection transfer rate = $R'_c \times F_d \times F_a$

In order to determine R'_c, it is necessary to calculate mass velocity, G, through boiler bank.

$$G = \frac{163,000}{61} \qquad 2670 \text{ lb per sq ft hr}$$

R'_c (from Fig. 21–15)   7.5

In order to determine F_d and F_a, it is necessary to know S_T, S_L, D and a temperature parameter.

$$\frac{S_T}{D} = 1.40$$

$$\frac{S_L}{D} = 1.40$$

Temperature parameter = ½ (Mean gas temperature + t_s) = 694 F

F_d (from Fig. 21–16)   0.96

F_a (from Fig. 21–17)   0.95

$R_c = 7.5 \times 0.96 \times 0.95$
                6.85 Btu per hr sq ft deg F

Evaluation of Total Heat Transfer Rate, R_t

R_t = total heat transfer rate = $R_c + R_n$

$R_t = 6.85 + 0.90 = 7.75$ Btu per hr sq ft deg F

Evaluation of Boiler Exit Temperature, T_2

$T_2 = T_1 -$ Gas Temperature Drop, $\triangle T$

$$\triangle T = \frac{R_t S}{W_g C_g} \text{ LMTD}$$

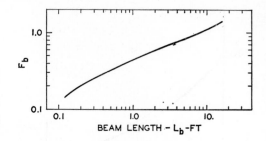

Fig. 21–13. Correction factor, beam length

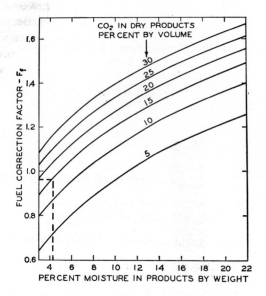

Fig. 21–14. Fuel correction factor

$C_g = 0.290$ for assumed average gas temperature of 1200 F. (See Appendix C, Engineering Data and Conversion Factors, for curves of values of instantaneous specific heat.)

$$\triangle T = \frac{7.75 \times 10,300}{163,000 \times 0.290} (682) = 1145 \text{ deg F}$$

$T_2 = 1760 - 1145 = 615$ F boiler exit
                gas temperature

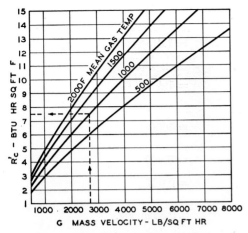

Fig. 21–15. Convection transfer rate

Fig. 21–16. Correction factor, tube geometry

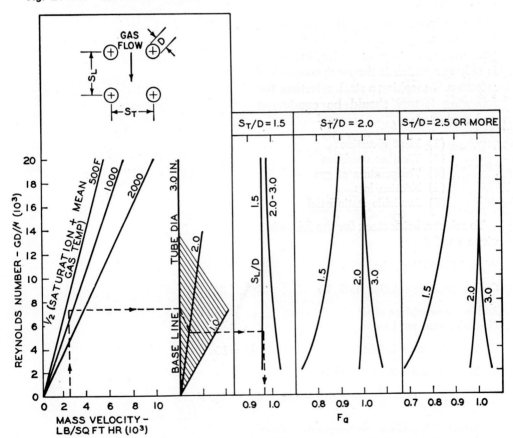

Fig. 21–17. Correction factors, Reynolds number and tube geometry

Draft Loss in Boiler Convection Bank

$$\frac{S_T}{D} = \frac{\text{Transverse Spacing}}{\text{Outside diameter of tube}} = \frac{3\frac{1}{2}}{2\frac{1}{2}} \qquad = 1.4$$

$$\frac{S_L}{D} = \frac{\text{Longitudinal Spacing}}{\text{Outside diameter of tube}} = \frac{3\frac{1}{2}}{2\frac{1}{2}} \qquad = 1.4$$

Reynolds number (from Fig. 21–18) $20,000 \times \dfrac{2\frac{1}{2}}{10}$ $\qquad = 5000$

Friction factor, f (from Fig. 21–19) $\qquad = 0.092$

Draft loss per restriction (from Fig. 21–20) $\qquad = 0.027$

Draft loss through bank $(0.027) \dfrac{(0.092)}{(0.100)}$ (22) $\qquad = 0.55$ in. wg.

Stack Calculation

For a given set of operating conditions, there are many sizes of stacks that will produce satisfactory operation, but there is only one which is the most economical selection. In making a stack selection, the following factors should be considered and evaluated:

    (1) Plant elevation
    (2) Weather condition
    (3) Temperature of gas
    (4) Friction loss
    (5) Available static head

To select a brick stack for the following given conditions:

$W_g = 166,000$ lb per hr

Gas temperature entering stack, Ts 615 F

Ambient temperature of air   90 F
Plant elevation, sea level

(1) Assuming stack height $H = 130$ ft

(2) Mean stack gas temperature =

$$Ts - \frac{H}{2} \times C = 615 - 130 \times \tfrac{1}{2} \quad = 550 \text{ F}$$

    where C is a linear gas temperature drop factor along the height of stack
    $C = 0.5$ deg F per ft for brick and lined stack or
    $C = 1$ deg F per ft for unlined steel stack

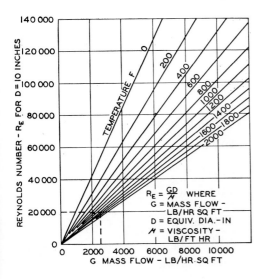

Fig. 21–18. Mass flow versus Reynolds number

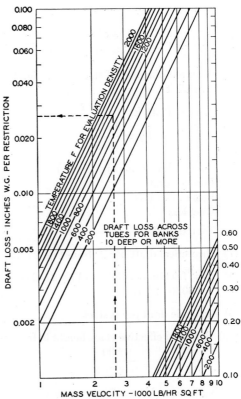

Fig. 21–20. Draft loss across tube banks

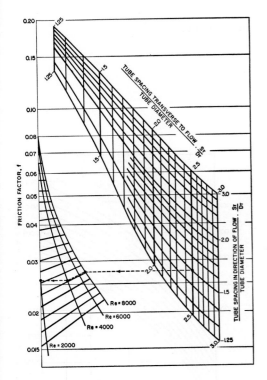

Fig. 21–19. Friction factors for in-line tube banks

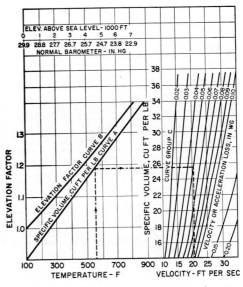

Fig. 21–21. Elevation factor and acceleration loss in stacks

(3) Specific volume (from Fig. 21–21)   = 25.4 cu ft per lb

(4) $\text{CFS} = \dfrac{25.4 \text{ cu ft per lb} \times 166,000 \text{ lb per hr}}{3600 \text{ sec per hr}} = 1170$

(5) Required diameter of stack from Fig. 21–22 is 8.4 ft
    Use 8½ ft

    Area 8½ ft stack   = 56.5 sq ft

    Actual velocity $= \dfrac{1170}{56.5}$ = 20.7 ft per sec

(6) Velocity loss (from Fig. 21–21)   = 0.050 in. wg
    Furnace draft   = 0.100 in. wg
    Boiler draft loss   = 0.550 in. wg
    Duct loss   = 0.100 in. wg

    Total draft loss   0.800 in. wg

(7) Theoretical draft per ft (from Fig. 21–23) $\doteq$ 0.00630 in. wg

(8) Static friction per ft (from Fig. 21–24)
    0.0030×0.12 = 0.00036 in. wg

(9) Available draft per ft stack   = 0.00594 in. wg

(10) Required effective stack height in ft
    $\dfrac{0.800}{0.00594}$ =   134 ft

    This value checks fairly well with the assumed H of 130 ft so that recalculation is not necessary.

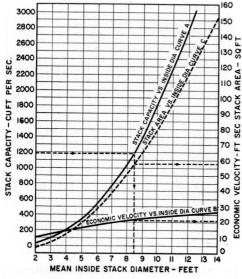

Fig. 21–22. Capacity and economic velocity versus stack diameter

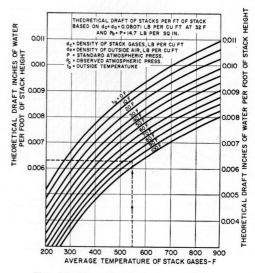

Fig. 21–23. Theoretical stack draft

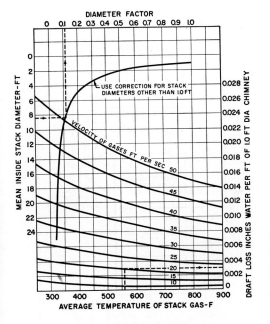

DIAMETER FACTOR

MEAN INSIDE STACK DIAMETER-FT

USE CORRECTION FOR STACK DIAMETERS OTHER THAN 1.0 FT

VELOCITY OF GASES FT PER SEC

DRAFT LOSS INCHES WATER PER FT OF 1.0 FT DIA CHIMNEY

AVERAGE TEMPERATURE OF STACK GAS-F

Fig. 21–24. Stack friction loss

Example II
Central Station Boiler — Gas Fired

This boiler is to be installed in a central station to meet the demands for additional power generating capacity. The most economical fuel available in the area served by the power company is natural gas. A radiant reheat boiler with a single furnace is selected to serve a 200,000 kilowatt turbine-generator.

Specifications

Pressure at superheater outlet	2000 psig
Steam temperature at superheater outlet	1000 F
Maximum continuous rating, W_s	1,584,000 lb per hr
Pressure at reheater outlet	488 psig
Steam temperature at reheater outlet	1000 F
Reheater steam flow	1,426,000 lb per hr
Pressure at reheater inlet	500 psig
Temperature at reheater inlet	680 F
Feedwater temperature	471 F
Ambient air temperature	80 F
Temperature control range	1,029,600 to 1,584,000 lb per hr
Heat recovery equipment	Economizer, air heater
Type unit	Radiant reheat, balanced draft

This boiler is designed to burn natural gas with ten per cent excess air and the same analysis as that shown in Example II, gaseous fuel, of the earlier section on combustion calculations, page 21–16.

Fuel Analysis (Same as Example II,
     Combustion Calculations)

Type	Natural Gas Per cent by Volume
CH$_4$	93.87
C$_2$H$_6$	3.62
C$_3$H$_8$	0.93
C$_4$H$_{10}$	0.06
C$_5$H$_{12}$	0.94
H$_2$S	0.15
A	0.01
CO$_2$	0.41
O$_2$	0.01
Total	100.00

Higher heating value 1060 Btu per cu ft
              23,100 Btu per lb

It has been impractical to develop a
completely standardized unit for installations of this type because the basic conditions for design are varied to meet specific
requirements of each individual boiler.
Experience has indicated that the unit
shown in the Fig. 21–25 is a satisfactory
choice to meet the conditions of the specifications.

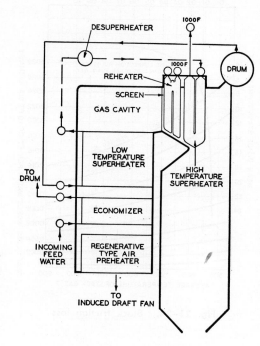

Fig. 21–25.   Gas fired boiler

Basic Design Information

Maximum continuous rating	1,584,000 lb per hr
Enthalpy of steam (1000 F, 2000 psig)	1474.5 Btu per lb
Enthalpy of feedwater (471 F, 2150 psig)	454.0 Btu per lb
Heat (enthalpy) added per pound of water and steam	1020.5 Btu per lb
Heat to water and steam (1,584,000) (1020.5) =	1620 × 10⁶ Btu per hr
Reheater steam flow	1,426,000 lb per hr
Enthalpy of steam leaving reheater (1000 F, 488 psig) =	1519.5 Btu per lb
Enthalpy of steam entering reheater (680 F, 500 psig) =	1344.5 Btu per lb
Heat (enthalpy) added per pound of steam to reheater	175.0 Btu per lb
Heat to reheater (1,426,000) (175) =	250 × 10⁶ Btu per hr
Total heat output 1620 × 10⁶ + 250 × 10⁶ =	1870 × 10⁶ Btu per hr
Boiler efficiency (estimated)	85 per cent
Total fuel heat input 1870 × 10⁶ ÷ 0.85 =	2200 × 10⁶ Btu per hr
Fuel fired 2200 × 10⁶ ÷ 1060 =	2.08 × 10⁶ cu ft per hr
Flue gas, W$_g$ (from combustion calculation, Example II, natural gas firing)	855 lb per 10⁶ Btu
Flue gas leaving furnace (855 × 2200)	1,880,000 lb per hr

Sequence of Calculations

The calculations are arranged in the following sequence, starting with the furnace and ending with the air heater.

1. Furnace performance
2. Gas and steam temperatures for high temperature superheater
3. Gas temperature and required heating surface for reheater
4. Gas temperature drop across screen tubes
5. Cavity gas temperatures
6. Gas temperature and required surface for low temperature superheater
7. Heating surface for finned economizer
8. Air heater performance

Furnace Performance

Furnace exit gas temperature is determined by the same method as described in Example I for an industrial power plant boiler. The gas temperature calculated is 2225 F.

High Temperature Superheater

Since this section is exposed to direct furnace radiation, it is desirable for it to perform as furnace surface. Therefore, the tubing is arranged almost tangent in the direction to the gas stream and on wide centers perpendicular to the gas stream. Some other reasons for having wide spacing are as follows:

1. A widely spaced section results in fewer tubes and higher steam flows per tube. This lowers the steam film coefficient which will decrease the metal temperature. Arranging the section for parallel flow also helps to reduce the metal temperature as this puts the coolest steam adjacent to the furnace outlet where the highest gas temperatures are found.

2. Since high gas temperatures also are required for finishing off the 1000 F reheat steam, a large gas temperature drop through the high temperature superheater is not desirable. Use of a minimum amount of widely spaced surface is therefore essential to limiting gas temperature drop in this section.

Known Data

Tube diameter	2⅛ in. OD
Width spacing, S_T	15⁵⁄₃₂ in.
Depth spacing, S_L	2½ in.
Effective heating surface, S	5600 sq ft
Free gas area, FGA	1010 sq ft
Number of assemblies, N	33
Number of tubes deep	18
Steam temperature leaving, t_2	1000 F
Steam pressure leaving, P_2	2000 psig
Steam pressure entering, P_1	2050 psig
Steam flow, W_s	1,584,000 lb per hr
Gas temperature entering, T_1	2225 F
Gas weight, W_g	1,880,000 lb per hr
Section is arranged for parallel flow.	

Calculation of Gas and Steam
Temperatures

Since this section receives direct radiation, the amount of heat obtained due to radiation is the first item to be determined. An average steam temperature in the front row of superheater tubes is assumed to be 900 F.

$$\frac{Q}{A} = 43{,}000 \text{ Btu per hr sq ft (from Fig. 21–26)}$$

A_R is exposed projected area of superheater

$$A_R = L' \times S_T \times N = 26.5 \times \frac{15.16}{12} \times 33$$

$$= 1105 \text{ sq ft}$$

L' is the average length of the superheater tube which is subject to furnace radiation

Total radiation from the furnace $= Q_{RT}$

$$Q_{RT} = \frac{Q}{A} \times A_R = 43{,}000 \times 1105$$

$$= 47.5 \times 10^6 \text{ Btu per hr}$$

The percentage of Q_{RT} absorbed by this section is found from Fig. 21–27 using a value of 18 tubes deep and

$$\frac{S_T}{D} = \frac{15.156}{2.125} = 7.13$$

The amount of furnace radiation absorbed in the superheater is 84 per cent.
Radiant heat absorbed by this section is designated as Q_{RS}.

$$Q_{RS} = 0.84 \, Q_{RT} = 0.84 \times 47.5 \times 10^6$$
$$= 39.9 \times 10^6 \text{ Btu per hr}$$

It is now possible to calculate the gas temperature leaving the superheater, T_2. To do this, the total heat absorbed by this section must be established. This requires that a value of steam temperature entering the superheater, t_1, be assumed. Since this calculation is normally a reiterative process, a close approximation of 872 F is chosen for t_1 in this example.

From the steam tables (Appendix D), the following information is obtained:

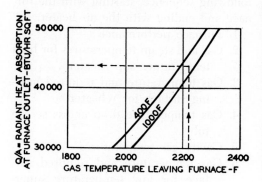

Fig. 21–26. Radiant heat absorption at furnace outlet

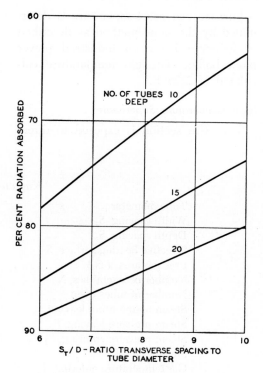

Fig. 21–27. Radiant heat absorbed by high temperature superheater

Enthalpy of t_2 at 2000 psig $= H_2 = 1474.5$ Btu per Lb
Enthalpy of t_1 at 2050 psig $= H_1 = 1387.7$ Btu per Lb
Heat absorbed per lb of steam, $\triangle H = 86.8$ Btu
Total heat absorbed by steam $= W_s \times \triangle H = 1,584,000 \times 86.8 = 137.3 \times 10^6$ Btu per hr

Q_c is the balance of heat absorbed by the steam.

Q_c = Total heat absorbed — Radiant heat absorbed
$= 137.3 \times 10^6 - 39.9 \times 10^6 = 97.4 \times 10^6$ Btu per hr

Since Q_c is also the heat given up by the gas, the following relationships may be written:

$$Q_c = W_g\, C_g\, \triangle T_g$$

$$\triangle T_g = \frac{Q_c}{W_g\, C_g} = T_1 - T_2$$

$C_g = 0.337$ for assumed average gas temperature of 2150 F

(See Appendix C, Engineering Data and Conversion Factors, for curves of values of instantaneous specific heat)

$$T_g = \frac{97.4 \times 10^6}{1,880,000 \times 0.337} = 154 \text{ deg F}$$

$$T_2 = 2225 - 154 = 2071 \text{ F}$$

This is a first trial value for T_2 and must be verified by additional heat transfer calculations.

Log mean temperature difference, LMTD, from Fig. 21–28. This is an approximate based on assumed t_1 and trial value of T_2

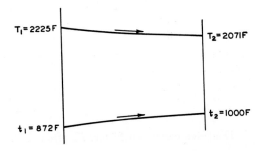
$T_1 = 2225F$ $T_2 = 2071F$
$t_1 = 872F$ $t_2 = 1000F$

Fig. 21–28. Temperature gradient across high temperatures superheater

$$LMTD = \frac{(T_1 - t_1) - (T_2 - t_2)}{\text{Log}_e \dfrac{(T_1 - t_1)}{(T_2 - t_2)}}$$

$$LMTD = \frac{(2225 - 872) - (2071 - 1000)}{\text{Log}_e \dfrac{(2225 - 872)}{(2071 - 1000)}} = 1220 \text{ F}$$

R_t (total overall transfer rate) $= R_n$ (Non-luminous radiation transfer rate) $+ R_c$
(Convection transfer rate)

In order to obtain R_n, the following items are required:

1. Mean gas temperature $= T_M$

2. Radiant beam length $= L_b$ (from Fig. 21–29)

3. Radiant beam length correction $= F_b$ (from Fig. 21–30)

4. Fuel correction factor $= F_f$ (from Fig. 21–31)

5. R'_n, Btu per sq ft deg F hr (from Fig. 21–32)

T_M = Average steam temperature + LMTD

$$T_M = \frac{t_2 + t_1}{2} + \text{LMTD} = \frac{1000 + 872}{2} + 1220$$

$$= 2156 \text{ F}$$

$L_b = 1.45$ ft

$F_b = 0.515$

$F_f = 1.2$ based on 12 per cent CO_2

$R'_n = 13.0$

$R_n = R'_n \times F_b \times F_f = 13 \times 0.515 \times 1.2$
$= 8.05$ Btu per hr sq ft deg F

In order to obtain R_c the following items are required:

1. Mass velocity of gas, G, lb per hr sq ft, based on flue gas flow, W_2, and free gas area, FGA.

2. R'_c, Btu per hr sq ft deg F (from Fig. 21–33)

3. Diameter correction factor, F_d (from Fig. 21–34)

$$G = \frac{W_2}{FGA} = \frac{1{,}880{,}000}{1{,}010}$$
$$= 1860 \text{ lb per sq ft}$$

$R'_c = 6.1$ Btu per hr sq ft deg F.

$F_d = 1$ for a 2⅛ in. OD tube

$F_a = 1$, since this is platen surface

$R_c = R'_c \times F_d \times F_a$

$R_c = 6.1 \times 1 \times 1$
$= 6.1$ Btu per hr sq ft deg F

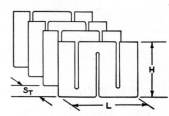

$$L_b = 1.7 \left(\frac{H' L' S_T''}{12 H' L' + S_T'' (L' + H')} \right)$$

L_b, L, H = FEET
S_T = INCHES

Fig. 21–29. Radiant beam length of platen type superheater

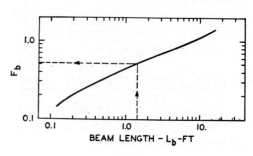

Fig. 21–30. Correction factor, radiant beam length

$$R_t = R_n + R_c = 8.05 + 6.1$$
$$= 14.15 \text{ Btu per hr sq ft deg F}$$

R_t, the overall heat transfer rate, is related to Q_c, the balance of heat absorbed by the steam, by the following equation:

$$R_t = \frac{Q_c}{S \times LMTD} = \frac{W_g C_g \triangle T_g}{S \times LMTD}$$

$$\triangle T_g = \frac{R_t \times S \times LMTD}{W_g C_g}$$

$$= \frac{14.15 \times 5600 \times 1220}{1,880,000 \times 0.337} = 153 \text{ deg F}$$

$$T_2 = T_1 - T_g = 2225 - 153 = 2072 \text{ F}$$

Since the first trial value of T_2 was found to be 2071 F, no further recalculation is necessary except to correct the entering steam temperature, t_1, for the calculated gas temperature drop of 153 deg. F.

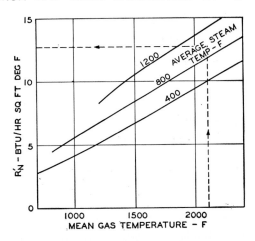

Fig. 21–32. Transfer rate, nonluminous radiation

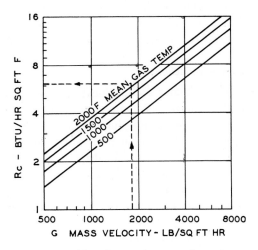

Fig. 21–33. Convection transfer rate

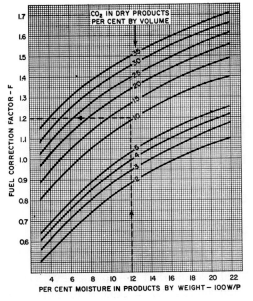

Fig. 21–31. Fuel correction factor, nonluminous radiation

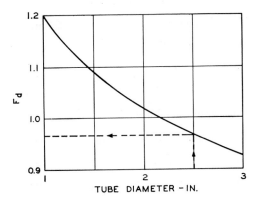

Fig. 21–34. Tube diameter correction factor

The value of Q_c may be expressed as follows from the preceding relationships:

$$Q_c = W_g C_g \triangle T_g = 1,880,000 \times 0.337 \times 153$$
$$= 96.8 \times 10^6 \text{ Btu per hr}$$

The total heat absorbed by the section is Q_T.

$$Q_T = Q_c + Q_{RS} = 96.8 \times 10^6 + 39.9 \times 10^6$$
$$= 136.7 \times 10^6 \text{ Btu per hr}$$

$$\text{Heat absorbed by the steam} = \frac{136.7 \times 10^6}{1,584,000}$$
$$= 86.3 \text{ Btu per lb}$$

Enthalpy, $H_2 = 1474.5$ Btu per lb

Heat absorbed $= 86.3$ Btu per lb

Enthalpy, $H_1 = 1388.2$ Btu per lb

The value of t_1 at 2050 psig and H_2 of 1388.2 is 873 F. This compares very favorably to the assumed value of t_1 of 872 F.

Reheater Section

The reheater section located in a moderately high gas temperature region is designed with an intermediate width spacing of 6 1/16 inches. Since in this example all of the reheating is done in a single section, both inlet and outlet steam conditions are known. For this reason the calculation can be made in a single step without assumption of intermediate temperatures.

Known Data

Tube Diameter	2⅛ in. OD
Width spacing, S_T	6¹⁄₁₆ in.
Depth spacing, S_L	4 in.
Free gas area, FGA	684 sq ft
Number of assemblies, N	83
Steam temperature leaving, t_2	1000 F
Steam pressure leaving, P_2	488 psig
Steam temperature entering, t_1	680 F

Steam pressure entering P_1	500 psig
Steam flow, W_s	1,426,000 lb per hr
Gas Weight, W_g	1,880,000 lb per hr
Gas temperature entering, T_1	2072 F

Calculation of Gas Temperature and Heating Surface

The reheater section is counter flow and its entering gas temperature, T_1, is the same as the gas temperature, T_2, leaving the superheater previously calculated.

To find gas temperature leaving reheater, T_2, and heating surface, S, required to raise steam temperature from 680 F to 1000 F, the following steps are required.

The amount of direct furnace radiation which passes through the superheater platen and is absorbed by the reheater is first determined. It is assumed that the reheater absorbs all the radiation which passes through the superheater platen.

$Q_{RR} =$ Direct furnace radiation absorbed by the reheater.

$$Q_{RR} = Q_{RT} - Q_{RS} = 47.5 \times 10^6 - 39.9 \times 10^6 = 7.6 \times 10^6 \text{ Btu per hr.}$$

Total heat absorbed by the reheater is now established from steam conditions in and out of the reheater. From this total is deducted the heat from furnace radiation, Q_{RR}, to obtain the value of Q_c for the reheater section.

Enthalpy of steam at 1000 F and 488 psig = $H_2 = 1519.5$ Btu per lb.

Enthalpy of steam at 680 F and 500 psig = $H_1 = 1344.5$ Btu per lb.

Heat absorbed by reheater per lb of steam = $\triangle H = 175.0$ Btu

Total heat absorbed by reheater = $W_s \triangle H = 1,426,000 \times 175.0 = 249.6 \times 10^6$ Btu per hr

Q_{RR} = 7.6×10^6 Btu per hr

Q_c = 242.0×10^6 Btu per hr

Since Q_c is also the heat absorbed from the gas, the following relationship, leading to the solution of T_2, may be expressed.

$$Q_c = W_g C_g \triangle T_g$$

$$\triangle T_g = \frac{Q_c}{W_g C_g} = T_1 - T_2$$

For solution of T_2 all values are known in the above equations except C_g which for an assumed temperature of 1875 F is 0.331.

$$\triangle T_g = \frac{242.0 \times 10^6}{1,880,000 \times 0.331} = 389 \text{ deg F}$$

$$T_2 = 2072 - 389 = 1683 \text{ F}$$

Heating surface S, is the only remaining unknown in connection with the reheater section. This can be determined from the following relationship:

$$S = \frac{W_g C_g \triangle T_g}{\text{LMTD} \times R_t}$$

LMTD from Fig. 21–35

$$\text{LMTD} = \frac{(T_1 - t_2) - (T_2 - t_1)}{\text{Log}_e \dfrac{T_1 - t_2}{T_2 - t_1}}$$

$$= \frac{1072 - 1003}{\text{Log}_e \dfrac{1072}{1003}} = 1020 \text{ deg F}$$

$$R_t = R_n + R_c$$

$$R_n = R'_n \times F_b \times F_t$$

$$T_M = t_{AVG} + \text{LMTD}$$

$$T_M = \frac{1000 + 680}{2} + 1020 = 1860 \text{ F}$$

$L_b = 0.88$ (from Fig. 21–36)

$R'_n = 10.7$ Btu per hr sq ft deg F
(from Fig. 21–32)

$F_b = 0.42$ (from Fig. 21–30)

$F_t = 1.2$ (from Fig. 21–31)

$R_n = 10.7 \times 0.42 \times 1.2 = $
$= 5.4$ Btu per hr sq ft deg F

$R_c = R'_c \times F_d \times F_a$
        Mass velocity, G, is required
        to evaluate R'_c

$$G = \frac{W_2}{FGA} = \frac{1,880,000}{684}$$

$$= 2750 \text{ lb per hr sq ft}$$

$R'_c = 7.72$ Btu per sq ft deg F
(from Fig. 21–33 based on $T_m = 1860$ F)

$F_d = 1$ (from Fig. 21–34)

$F_a = 0.93$ (from Fig. 21–37)

$R_c = 7.72 \times 1 \times 0.93$
$= 7.18$ Btu per hr sq ft deg F

$R_t = R_n + R_c \times 5.4 + 7.18$
$= 12.58$ Btu per hr sq ft deg F

$$S = \frac{W_g \times C_g \times \triangle T_g}{R_T \times \text{LMTD}}$$

$$= \frac{(1,880,000) \quad (0.331) \quad (389)}{(12.58) \quad (1020)}$$

$$= 18,900 \text{ sq ft}$$

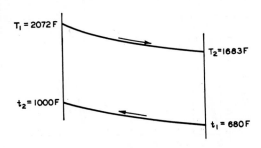

Fig. 21–35. Temperature gradient across reheater

$$L_b = 0.09 \left(\frac{S_T \, S_L}{D} \right) - .07D$$

L_b = FEET
S_T, S_L, D = INCHES

Fig. 21–36. Radiant beam
length, in-line tubes

Screen Tubes

On units of this type one or more rows of screen tubes are often found in the gas pass. They are necessary for reasons of construction such as hanging the rear wall or feeding the low temperature superheater inlet header. Although their presence does not contribute materially to performance, it is necessary to calculate the gas temperature drop over the screen in order to enter the next section with the proper gas temperature.

Known Data

Tube diameter	1½ in. OD
Width spacing, S_T	6⅟₁₆ in.
Number of rows, N	3
Free gas area, FGA	487 sq ft
Gas temperature entering, T_1	1683 F
Gas Weight, W_g	1,880,000 lb per hr

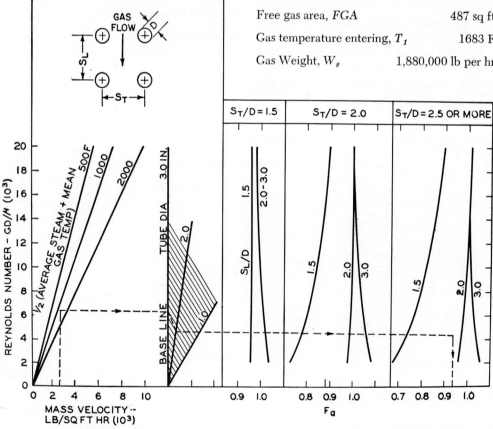

Fig. 21–37. Correction factor, Reynolds number and tube geometry

Calculation of Gas Temperature Drop

To find gas drop across screen tubes, mass velocity, G, is required.

$$G = \frac{W_g}{FGA} = \frac{1,880,000}{487} = 3860 \text{ lb per hr sq ft}$$

$$\frac{S_T}{D} = \frac{6.06}{1.5} = 4.04$$

Average gas temperature (assumed)   1660 F

$\triangle T_1$ for one row = 15 deg F (from Fig, 21–9, Example I)

$F_s = 1$ (from Fig. 21–10, Example I)

$F_t = 1.05$ (from Table 21–5, Example I)

$\triangle T$ for three rows = $\triangle T_1 \times F_s \times F_t \times N$

$\triangle T = 15 \times 1 \times 1.05 \times 3 = 47$ deg F

$T_2 = T_1 - \triangle T = 1683 - 47 = 1636$ F

Cavity

For small cavities such as the ones shown in Fig. 21–25 between the high temperature superheater section and the reheater section or between the reheater section and the screen, the cavity effects are negligible and the calculation may be omitted. On large cavities such as that following the screen, gas temperature drop is significant and therefore calculations are necessary. In making this calculation, heat transfer in the cavity may be assumed to be due entirely to non-luminous radiation.

Known Data

Cavity dimensions, ft	20 × 16 × 42.72
Gas weight, W_g	1,880,000 lb per hr
Gas temperature entering, T_1	1636 F
Temperature of walls, t	640 F

Calculation of Gas Temperature

Gas temperature drop, $\triangle T_g$, in the cavity may be found from the relationship:

$$\triangle T_g = \frac{S \; R \; LMTD}{W_g C_g}$$

The true LMTD for this cavity is difficult to determine due to the several different wall temperatures of the cavity. It will be satisfactory for this example to use the difference between assumed average gas temperature, T_{ave}, and saturation temperature, t_s, in place of a true LMTD value.

$$T_{ave} - t_s = 1600 - 640 = 960 \text{ F}$$

For use in evaluating R'_n and F_b, both mean gas temperature, T_M, and radiant beam length, L_b, must be found.

$$T_M = t_s + LMTD = 640 + 960 = 1600 \text{ F}$$

$$\text{Radiant beam length, } L_b = \frac{(0.85) \, (4) \, (V)}{S}$$

V = Volume of cavity cu ft

S = Projected area of cavity sq ft

$V = 20 \times 16 \times 42.72 = 13,650$ cu ft

$S = 2(20 \times 16) +$
$(20 \times 42.72) + (16 \times 42.72) = 3718$ sq ft

$$L_b = \frac{(0.85) \; (4) \; (13,650)}{3718} = 12.5 \text{ ft}$$

$$R'_n = 8.3 \; \frac{\text{Btu}}{\text{Hr F}}$$
(from Fig. 21–32 for $T_M = 1600$ F)

$F_b = 1.23$ (from Fig. 21–30 for $L_b = 12.5$)

$F_t = 1.2$ (from Fig. 21–31)

$R_n = R'_n \times F_b \times F_t =$
$8.3 \times 1.23 \times 1.2 = 12.24$ Btu per hr sq ft deg F

$$\triangle T_g = \frac{S \times R_n \times LMTD}{W_g C_g}$$

C_g for assumed average gas temperature in cavity of 1600 F is 0.322.

$$\triangle T_g = \frac{3718 \times 12.24 \times 961}{1,880,000 \times .322} = 72.1 \text{ deg F}$$

$$T_2 = T_1 - \triangle T_g$$

$$T_2 = 1636 - 72 = 1564 \text{ F}$$

Low Temperature Superheater

The low temperature superheater is located in a moderate gas temperature zone. For this reason, the surface may be closely spaced without concern for slagging or plugging. This is an especially important consideration where low grade fuels are involved. Also, because of the low heat head available a large amount of closely spaced surface must be installed to obtain the necessary heat pickup within a reasonable amount of space. In this example 2⅛ in. OD tubes are placed on 4½₂ in. width spacing. A closer spacing could have been used here if desired.

Known Data

Tube Diameter	2⅛ in. OD
Width spacing, S_T	4½₂ in. OD
Depth spacing, S_L	4½₂ in. OD
Free gas area, FGA	411 sq ft
Number of assemblies, N	125
Steam temperature leaving, t_2	873 F
Steam pressure leaving, P_2	2052 psig
Steam temperature entering, t_1	640 F
Steam pressure entering, P_1	2068 psig
Steam flow, W_s	1,584,000 lb per hr
Gas temperature entering, T_1	1564 F
Gas weight	1,880,000 lb per hr
Section is counter flow.	

Calculation of Gas Temperature and Surface. The gas temperature leaving the low temperature superheater may be obtained by deducting the gas temperature drop in this section, from the known gas temperature entering. The gas tempera-

ture drop, $\triangle T_g$, may be obtained from the following relationship:

$$\triangle T_g = \frac{\triangle H_e \times W_s}{W_g C_g}$$

Enthalpy of 873 F steam at 2052 psig = $H_2 = 1387.9$ Btu per lb

Enthalpy of 640 F steam at 2060 psig =

$H_1 = 1130.0$ Btu per lb
Total heat absorbed by the low temperature superheater is:

$$H_2 - H_1 = \triangle H_e$$

$\triangle H_e = 1387.9 - 1130 = 257.9$ Btu per lb
C_g is based on an assumed T_{ave} of 1210 F

$$\triangle T_g = \frac{257.9 \times 1,584.000}{0.310 \times 1,880,000} = 700 \text{ deg F}$$

$$T_2 = T_1 - \triangle T_g = 1564 - 700 = 864 \text{ F}$$

To determine the heating surface, S, in the low temperature superheater both the LMTD and the overall heat transfer rate, R_t, must be found.

$$\text{LMTD} = \frac{(T_1 - t_2) - (T_2 - t_1)}{\text{Log}_e \dfrac{(T_1 - t_2)}{(T_2 - t_1)}}$$

LMTD (from Fig. 21–38)

$$\text{LMTD} = \frac{(1564 - 873) - (864 - 640)}{\text{Log}_e \dfrac{(1564 - 873)}{(864 - 640)}}$$

$$= 415 \text{ deg F}$$

$$R_t = R_n + R_e$$

$$R_n = R'_n \times F_b \times F_t$$

$$T_M = \frac{t_L + t_1}{2} + \text{LMTD} = \frac{640 + 873}{2} + 415$$

$$= 1171.5 \text{ F}$$

$L_b = 0.55$ (from Fig. 21–36)

$F_b = 0.328$ (from Fig. 21–30)

$F_t = 1.2$ (based on 10 per cent excess air from Fig. 21–31)

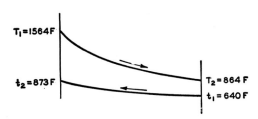

Fig. 21–38. Temperature gradient across low temperature superheater

$R'_n = 6.4$ (from Fig. 21–32)

$R_n = 6.4 \times 0.328 \times 1.2$
$= 2.52$ Btu per hr sq ft deg F

$G = \dfrac{W_g}{FGA} = \dfrac{1,880,000}{411} = 4575$ lb per hr sq ft

$R_c = R'_c \times F_d \times F_a$

$R'_c = 9.4$ Btu (from Fig. 21–33 based on T_M
$= 1171.5$ F)

$F_d = 1$ (from Fig. 21–34)

$F_a = 0.98$ (from Fig. 21–37)

$R_c = 9.4 \times 1 \times 0.98$
$= 9.2$ Btu per hr sq ft deg F

$R_t = R_n + R_c$

$R_t = 2.52 + 9.2$
$= 11.72$ Btu per hr sq ft deg F

$S = \dfrac{W_g \times C_g \times \triangle T_g}{R_t \times LMTD}$

$S = \dfrac{1,880,000 \times 0.310 \times 700}{11.72 \times 415}$

$S = 83,900$ sq ft

Finned Economizer

Economizer heating surface is located in the lowest gas temperature zone of any of the primary heating surface. Heat transfer is low, and for maximum pick up, closely spaced, finned tube surface (arranged in a staggered pattern) is used. In this problem it is necessary for the economizer to reduce the gas temperature to 700 F. It should be noted here, from a

practical standpoint, that a temperature of around 700 F is the maximum value the air preheater will accept and still produce a final gas temperature of 250 F as required for the assumed boiler efficiency of 85 per cent.

Known Data

Tube diameter	2 in. OD
Width spacing, S_T	4½/32 in.
Depth spacing, S_L	5 in.
Free gas area, FGA	420 sq ft
Number of assemblies, N	125
Water temperature entering, t_1	471 F
Water pressure entering, P_1	2090 psig
Water pressure leaving, P_2	2080 psig
Water flow, W_w	1,584,000 lb per hr
Gas temperature entering, T_1	864 F
Gas temperature leaving, T_2	700 F
Gas flow, W_g	1,880,000 lb per hr
Section is counter flow.	

Calculation of Heating Surface. Since the gas temperature leaving, T_2, has been established at 700 F the water temperature, t_2, may be obtained from the following relationship:

$$\triangle H = W_g\, C_g \triangle T_g = (H_2 - H_1)\, W_s$$

$$H_2 = H_1 + \dfrac{W_g\, C_g \triangle T_g}{W_s}$$

C_g at 782 F $T_{ave} = 0.291$

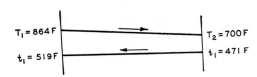

Fig. 21–39. Temperature gradient across economizer

Enthalpy of water entering, H_1, at 471 F and 2090 psig is 454 Btu per lb

$$\frac{W_g\, C_g\, \triangle T_g}{W_s} = \frac{1,880,000 \times 0.291 \times 164}{1,584,000} = 56.6 \text{ Btu per lb}$$

$H_2 = 454 + 56.6 = 510.6$ Btu per lb

The value of t_2 at H_2 of 510.6 Btu per lb and 2080 psig is 519 F

With all gas and water temperatures now established the LMTD can be obtained. R_t must also be obtained.

LMTD (from Fig. 21–39)

$$\text{LMTD} = \frac{(T_1 - t_2) - (T_2 - t_1)}{\text{Log}_e \dfrac{(T_1 - t_2)}{(T_2 - t_1)}}$$

$$\text{LMTD} = \frac{(864 - 519) - (700 - 471)}{\text{Log}_e \dfrac{864 - 519}{700 - 471}} = 282 \text{ deg F}$$

$$G = \frac{W_g}{\text{FGA}} = \frac{1,880,000}{411} = 4580 \text{ lb per hr sq ft}$$

$R_t = 7.85$ Btu per hr sq ft deg F (from Fig. 21–40 based on $T_{ave} = 782\,F$)

$$S = \frac{W_g \times C_g \times T_g}{R_T \times \text{LMTD}} = \frac{1,880,000 \times 0.291 \times 164}{7.85 \times 282}$$

$S = 40,500$ sq ft

Air Heater[12]

The air heater performance for this unit is as follows:

    Entering gas temperature, 700 F
    Leaving gas temperature, 250 F
    Entering air temperature, 80 F
    Leaving air temperature, 594 F

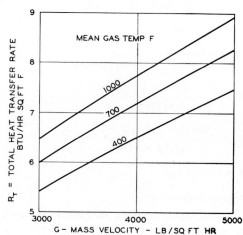

Fig. 21–40. Transfer rate, finned economizer

---

[12] A discussion of design considerations for air heaters may be found in Chapter 19, Fundamentals of Boiler Design.

Boiler Heat Balance Calculations

Earlier in this chapter at the beginning of the section dealing with boiler calculations, there was a discussion of the method of arriving at the total heat input, H_t, as expressed in Eq. 21–16. It was pointed out that initially the overall efficiency of the steam unit must be assumed, and then finally checked by means of a heat balance. That this check is essential, becomes apparent when it is realized that the weights of the fuel fired, the air supplied and the products formed are directly proportional to the heat input. It is these three quantities that largely determine the size of the furnace, boiler and auxiliary equipment.

Furthermore, the overall efficiency is of great importance to the purchaser, because it represents that portion of the heat energy in the fuel fired which is available in the steam for doing work. To him the efficiency is a measure of fuel consumption and therefore of the cost that will be incurred in producing the required amount of steam.

In design work, the combined or overall efficiency of the whole steam-generating unit is always arrived at by calculating the losses in per cent of the heat input. These losses are then added together and subtracted from 100 to obtain the efficiency.

The process of accounting for all the heat losses, as well as the heat available in the steam, is known as a *heat balance*. The heat balance method is frequently employed to test for the efficiency of an operating unit, but in contrast to the test engineer, who can measure these losses accurately, the designer must assign to

some of them values based on experience.[13]

The following losses are those which must be known before the efficiency can be determined:

(a) Loss in dry products of combustion
(b) Loss due to moisture in air
(c) Loss due to moisture from fuel
(d) Loss due to water vapor in gaseous fuels
(e) Loss due to moisture from hydrogen in fuel
(f) Loss due to unburned combustible
(g) Loss due to radiation
(h) Losses unaccounted for

Loss in Dry Products of Combustion

The dry gas, W_{dg}, is easily calculated by subtracting the water vapor in the products from the total products of combustion, W_g, or:

$$W_{dg} = W_g - (M_a + M_f + M_s) \quad \text{(Eq. 21–18)}$$

with all quantities of this expression in pounds per million Btu input. Knowing W_{dg}, the per cent dry gas loss is found from:

$$L_{dg} = \frac{W_{dg} \times 0.24\,(T_g - T_a)}{10^4} \quad \text{(Eq. 21–19)}$$

The moisture terms, M_a, M_f, and M_s, have been mentioned previously in the section on combustion calculations and will be discussed again in the following paragraphs.

Loss Due to Moisture in Air

It is obvious that, even in the same locality, the amount of moisture present in the air varies continuously. For design

[13] See Chapter 12, Power Plant Tests and Measurements, for additional information.

purposes, the American Boiler Manufacturers Association has established an arbitrary value of 0.013 lb of water vapor per lb of dry air, which corresponds to a relative humidity of 60 per cent at 80 F. Then, the pounds of vapor in the air per million Btu fired, M_a, can be found with sufficient accuracy from Eq. 21–11 shown earlier in the section on combustion calculations:

$$M_a = 0.013 \, W_a$$

where W_a, the *atmospheric* air (rather than *dry* air), is obtained from the charts in Figs. 21–3, 21–4 and Appendix E. The loss in per cent of the heat input equals:

$$L_a = \frac{M_a \, (0.47) \, (T_g - T_a)}{10^4} \qquad (Eq. \ 21\text{–}20)$$

In this equation, T_g is the temperature of the products of combustion as they leave the last heat transfer surface and go to the stack; and T_a is the ambient temperature, ordinarily taken as 80 F.

Loss Due to Moisture from Fuel

If H_2O represents both the surface and hygroscopic moisture in per cent by weight of fuel as fired, then the following relationship exists from Eq. 21–12:

$$M_f = \frac{H_2O \, (10^4)}{H_f}.$$

M_f may be obtained from the D family of curves in the combustion calculation charts shown in Fig. 21–3 for coal and in Appendix E for wood and coke.

For T_g higher than 575 F loss due to moisture from fuel equals:

$$L_f = \frac{M_f \, (1066 + 0.5 \, T_g - T_f)}{10^4} \qquad (Eq. \ 21\text{–}21)$$

and for T_g lower than 575 F this loss equals:

$$L_f = \frac{M_f \, (1089 + 0.46 \, T_g - T_f)}{10^4} \qquad (Eq. \ 21\text{–}22)$$

in which T_f corresponds to the temperature of the fuel as it goes to the furnace, customarily assumed to be 80 F.

It should be understood that M_f does not include water vapor as found in gaseous fuels.

Loss Due to Water Vapor in Gaseous Fuels

Moisture is also present in many of the gaseous fuels, particularly in blast furnace gas and coke oven gas, which are frequently dedusted by passing them through sprays of water. This moisture exists in the gas in two separate forms, which require different treatment in calculating the heat balance.

Washed gas contains *entrained* water in the form of suspended globules. In the most common case, where exceptionally clean gas is not required, the entrained moisture, M_f, averages 7 lb per million Btu.

There is no entrained water in unwashed gas.

In addition to the visible moisture in a liquid state, nearly all gaseous fuels contain some water vapor. In natural gas, the water vapor is there because of salt water that has been in contact with the gas in the ground, or because of *rehydration*. In refinery gas, blast furnace gas, and coke oven gas it is present either owing to the nature of the process of which these gases are byproducts, or because of subsequent cleaning operations.

The water vapor, M_s in pounds per million Btu is of such magnitude that it can usually be neglected in heat balance calculations for natural gas, refinery gas, or coke oven gas. For blast furnace gas at or close to 62 F, it may be taken as 10 lb per million Btu without serious error.

In a heat balance for gaseous fuels M_s must be considered separately from M_h and M_f, since it exists as a vapor which already has the latent heat of vaporization, and therefore requires no heat evolved by the fuel to vaporize it. In every respect it is similar to M_a, so that the per cent loss due to its presence is:

$$L_s = \frac{M_s (0.47)(T_g - T_a)}{10^4} \qquad \text{(Eq. 21–23)}$$

Loss Due to Moisture from Hydrogen in Fuel

Solid and Liquid Fuels. In all cases where the ultimate analysis of coal, coke, wood, bagasse or oil is given, the percentage of hydrogen by weight is known, and as shown previously in Eq. 21–13:

$$M_h = \frac{9 (H_2) 10^4}{H_f}$$

M_h may be obtained from the C family of curves in the combustion calculation charts shown in Fig. 21–3 for coal and in Appendix E for wood, coke and oil.

When only the proximate analysis is available, it is necessary to resort to an empirical relation between the hydrogen in the fuel and the volatile matter, such as is found on Fig. 21–41, for coal; or between M_h and the volatile matter, as on Fig. 21–42, for coke. The volatile matter and higher heating value must be converted to a moisture and ash-free basis before using these curves. The hydrogen read is likewise on a moisture and ash-free percentage. However, it is worth remembering that in deriving the hydrogen moisture from a proximate analysis, the loss due to water in the fuel may be in error as much as 1.5 per cent, a discrepancy which, as will presently be seen, may

be sufficient to nullify the unaccounted-for losses.

Gaseous Fuels. With natural gas, refinery gas, blast furnace gas, and coke oven gas, the analysis is reported in per cent by volume. For these fuels, it may be shown that, on burning, each gaseous constituent will form a volume of water proportional to one half of its hydrogen atoms. Then from this it is possible to derive the following representative formula:

$$M_h = \frac{46,700 (H_2 + 2\,CH_4 + 2\,C_2H_4 \ldots\text{. etc.})}{\text{Btu per cu ft at 62 F and 30 in. Hg}}$$
$$\text{(Eq. 21–24)}$$

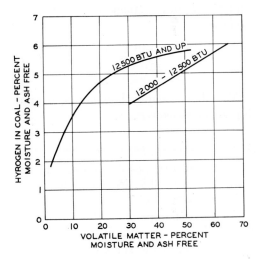

Fig. 21–41. Variation of hydrogen and volatile matter in coal

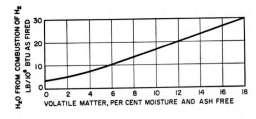

Fig. 21–42. Variation of hydrogen and volatile matter in coke

The higher heating value in Btu per cu ft is computed as previously outlined, and the values of H_2, CH_4, C_2H_4, etc., are in per cent by volume.

The C family of curves in the combustion calculation charts shown in Fig. 21–4 for natural gas and in Appendix E for refinery gas, blast furnace gas and coke oven gas are nothing more than plots of this equation.

For T_g higher than 575 F loss due to moisture from hydrogen in fuel equals:

$$L_h = \frac{M_h(1066 + 0.5\,T_g - T_a)}{10^4} \quad \text{(Eq. 21–25)}$$

and for T_g lower than 575 F this loss equals:

$$L_h = \frac{M_h(1089 + 0.46\,T_g - T_a)}{10^4} \quad \text{(Eq. 21–26)}$$

The above relationships apply to solid, liquid and gaseous fuels.

Loss Due to Unburned Combustible

There are two possible sources of unburned combustible loss. The first, and most important, is the one due to solid fuel which is trapped in the ash that is removed from ashpit and boiler hoppers or passes out of the stack with the products of combustion. This solid combustible loss varies considerably according to the character of the fuel and its ash content, the size of the fuel as supplied to the grate or burners, and the design of the burning equipment and furnace. Considerable judgment is required on the part of the designer in interpreting test data for this loss, which may be anywhere from a negligible quantity to 20 per cent.

The second source of unburned combustible loss is found in the incomplete combustion of the carbon in the fuel, as evidenced by the presence of CO in the products of combustion leaving the furnace. This loss is usually negligible in well-designed boilers; but when it occurs, it is not confined to any particular type of fuel. In designing steam-generating units, it is ordinarily assumed that the CO loss is zero, regardless of the fuel.

For purposes of design calculations only, liquid and gaseous fuels are generally presumed to burn with no combustible loss.

Loss Due to Radiation

This term includes all the heat lost to the surroundings, by either radiation, convection, or conduction through the setting, or the casing, of the steam generating unit. Because it is very difficult to measure in existing units, this heat loss cannot be accurately estimated in the design stage. It is, however, known to vary with the character of the setting wall, particularly with the extent of watercooling, and with capacity. This has prompted the American Boiler Manufacturers Association to issue Fig. 21–43 which gives the value for different types of wall construction up to furnace outputs of 20 billion Btu per hr.

Losses Unaccounted For

These losses are customarily included in a heat balance in order to provide a margin of safety or tolerance in the calculated efficiency. The American Boiler Manufacturers Association has established a value of 1.5 per cent for these losses.

Overall Efficiency

The overall efficiency, e, of a boiler is given by the following relationship:

e (per cent) = 100 − sum of losses (per cent)

(Eq. 21–27)

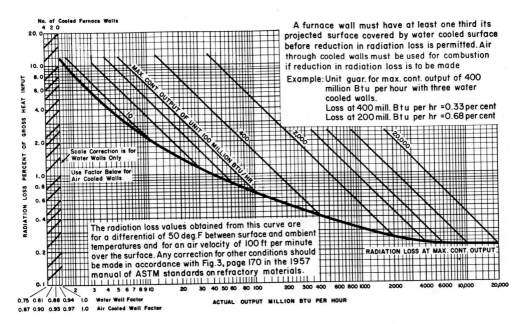

Fig. 21–43. Radiation loss for furnace walls

Example I
Industrial Power Plant Boiler — Stoker Fired

Data from Graphical Combustion Calculations, Bituminous Coal at 35 Per cent Excess Air

Dry gas, W_{dg}	1037 lb per 10^6 Btu
Moisture in air, M_a	13.0 lb per 10^6 Btu
Moisture from fuel, M_f	13.0 lb per 10^6 Btu
Moisture from H_2, M_h	32.0 lb per 10^6 Btu

Data from Boiler Calculations, Example I

Gas temperature leaving boiler, T_g	615 F
Air temperature, T_a	90 F
Fuel temperature, T_f	80 F
Carbon loss (unburned combustible)	2.50 per cent
CO in flue gas	0.0 per cent

Heat Balance

1. Loss in dry products of combustion, L_{dg} (Eq. 21–19)

$$L_{dg} = \frac{1037 \times 0.24 \times (615 - 90)}{10^4} = 13.05 \text{ per cent}$$

2. Loss due to moisture in air, L_a (Eq. 21–20)

$$L_a = \frac{13.0 \times 0.47 \times (615 - 90)}{10^4} = 0.32 \text{ per cent}$$

3. Loss due to moisture from fuel, L_f (Eq. 21–21)

$$L_f = \frac{13.0 \, (1066 + 0.5 \times 615 - 80)}{10^4} = 1.68 \text{ per cent}$$

4. Loss due to moisture from hydrogen, L_h (Eq. 21–25)

$$L_h = \frac{32.0 \, (1066 + 0.5 \times 615 - 90)}{10^4} = 4.11 \text{ per cent}$$

5. Loss due to unburned combustible   2.50 per cent

6. Loss due to radiation
(Fig. 21–43)   0.68 per cent

7. Losses unaccounted for   1.50 per cent

Total losses   23.84 per cent

Overall efficiency, e
(Eq. 21–27)   76.16 per cent

This value of 76.16 per cent agrees reasonably well with the estimated boiler efficiency of 76.5 per cent which was included in the basic design information near the beginning of the boiler calculations for Example I.

Example II
Central Station Boiler — Gas Fired

Data from Graphical Combustion Calculations, Natural Gas

Dry gas, W_{dg}	752.4 lb per 10^6 Btu
Moisture in air, M_a	10.5 lb per 10^6 Btu
Moisture from H_2, M_h	92.0 lb per 10^6 Btu

Data from Boiler Calculations, Example II

Gas temperature leaving air heater, T_g	250 F
Air temperature, T_a	80 F
Fuel temperature, T_f	80 F
CO in flue gas	0.0 per cent

Heat Balance

1. Loss in dry products of combustion, L_{dg} (Eq. 21–19)

$$L_{dg} = \frac{752.5 \times 0.24 \times (250 - 80)}{10_4} = 3.07 \text{ per cent}$$

2. Loss due to moisture in air, L_a (Eq. 21–20)

$$L_a = \frac{10.5 \times 0.47 \times (250 - 80)}{10^4} = 0.08 \text{ per cent}$$

3. Loss due to moisture from hydrogen, L_h (Eq. 21–26)

$$L_h = \frac{92.0\,(1089 + 0.46 \times 250 - 80)}{10^4} = 10.35 \text{ per cent}$$

4. Loss due to radiation
   (Fig. 21–43)   0.25 per cent

5. Losses unaccounted for   1.50 per cent

Total losses   15.25 per cent

Overall efficiency, e
   (Eq. 21–27)   84.75 per cent

This value of 84.75 per cent agrees reasonably well with the estimated boiler efficiency of 85.0 per cent which was included in the basic design information near the beginning of the boiler calculations for Example II.

Calculations for Materials Selection[14]

From the point of view of thermodynamics, power plant cycle efficiency is related to primary and reheat steam temperature. Increase in steam temperature results in a gain in cycle efficiency, everything else being the same. However, superheater and reheater outlet conditions are limited by the ability of materials to withstand physical stress and by economic breakeven points. In the high temperature region of boilers, allowable stress goes down as materials are exposed to high flue gas temperatures necessary to superheat and reheat steam to high temperatures. At the same time, more costly grades of alloy steel are required to withstand the physical stress of elevated temperatures and pressures.

As an example of the effect of increase in temperature, the allowable stress for a material known as SA–213 T–11 drops from 11,000 psi at 95 F to 7800 psi at 1000 F. Up to around 850 F it is usually possible to specify carbon steel, but beyond this point more costly alloys are required.

In view of these facts selection of materials is a most important consideration in superheater and reheater design. Proper material selection requires not only knowledge of metal temperature conditions but also of the economics of manufacture and fabrication of various steel alloys. A systematic procedure to calculate the metal temperatures of superheater and reheater tubing is outlined in the following.

Superheater and Reheater Metal Temperatures

Before proceeding to make metal temperature calculations, the designer assumes the following data to be known for the point in question:

[14] This section follows closely the development of Chapter 9, Heating and Cooling Inside Tubes, from *Heat Transmission* by W. H. McAdams (Third Edition, McGraw-Hill, New York, 1954) and "Superheater Metal Temperature" by G. Parmakian and N. S. Sellers, ASME Paper 54–A–181.

Gas temperature, T,
Steam temperature at the point in question, t_s
Mass velocity of gas, G_g
Mass velocity of steam, G_s
Tubing size and estimated thickness
Tubing material
Steam pressure
Heat absorbed, q, lb per hr

(1) Total heat transfer rate, R_t (as defined in previous section on boiler calculations)

$$R_t = R_c + R_n \qquad \text{(Eq. 21–28)}$$

(2) Total heat absorption rate per unit area, $\dfrac{q}{A_o}$

$$\frac{q}{A_o} = R_t \,(T_g - t_s) \qquad \text{(Eq. 21–29)}$$

By knowing R_t, t_s and T_g the heat absorption rate per unit area can be obtained.

If the superheater or reheater tube in question is subject to direct furnace radiation, this should be taken into consideration in the preceding equation.

(3) Steam side film conductance of heat transfer h_c

After the heat absorption per unit area is determined the next step is to establish steam side film conductance of heat transfer, h_c. By dimensional analysis and experimental work a general relationship is developed to calculate the film conductance for forced convection in fluids. This may be evaluated from the equation $(Nu) = a(Re)^b(Pr)^c$, where $a = 0.023$, $b = 0.8$, $c = 0.4$ and the terms are respectively Nusselt, Reynolds and Prandtl numbers. The correlation may then be expressed as follows:

$$\frac{h_c D}{k} = 0.023 \left(\frac{D\,G}{\mu} \right) 0.8 \left(\frac{c_p \mu}{k} \right) 0.4$$

$$\text{(Eq. 21–30)}$$

where D is an expression of applicable diameter, k is the thermal conductivity of the fluid, G is the mass velocity, μ is the absolute viscosity of the fluid and c_p is the specific heat at constant pressure. The values of a, b and c are determined experimentally and should be used with discretion, taking into consideration the latest results available in the heat transfer literature.

(4) Steam side film temperature drop, Δt_s

By knowing the heat absorption rate per unit area and steam side film conductance of heat transfer, the steam side film temperature drop can be obtained from the following relationship:

$$\triangle t_s = \frac{q}{A_o} \frac{1}{h_c} \frac{D_o}{D_i} \qquad \text{(Eq. 21–31)}$$

where D_o is the outside diameter of tube and D_i is the inside diameter of tube. The D_o/D_i term appears in the above formula because q/A_o was based on outside diameter of tube.

(5) Tube wall temperature drop, $\triangle T$

Temperature drop through tube can be calculated from the conduction equation:

$$\triangle T = \frac{q}{A_o} D_o \log_e \frac{D_o}{D_i} \frac{1}{2k} \qquad \text{(Eq. 21–32)}$$

k is the thermal conductivity of the tube in question.

The tube metal temperature at any given point in the tubing will be the sum of the steam temperature, film temperature drop and average tube wall temperature drop.

Metal Temperature Tolerances

The preceding represents an ideal case based on the assumptions that the steam flow rate and temperature and gas flow rate and temperature are uniform for all the elements. These conditions actually are never experienced in the performance of the steam generator. It is necessary therefore to provide so called "unbalances" or tolerances that are anticipated. These include the following:

(1) Desuperheater Allowance

This allowance is the number of degrees that the steam temperature will rise at the particular point upstream of the superheater when the full use of the desuperheater is made. Usually the design is such that little or no desuperheating is required. However, when a desuperheater is installed all pressure parts ahead of the desuperheater are designed to include the desuperheater allowance.

(2) Steam temperature unbalance

An allowance is made for the increase in average steam temperature at a given point caused by the unbalance distribution in steam flows, gas flows and gas temperatures.

(3) Film and metal drop unbalance

This allowance is considered to be the increase in the calculated average film and metal temperature drop caused by the unbalanced distribution in the gas flows and gas temperatures.

The maximum metal temperature at any given point in the tubing will be the sum of the steam temperature, film and metal temperature drops, desuperheater allowance — if any, steam temperature unbalance and film — metal drop unbalance.

After the metal temperature is established the selection of material may be made in accordance with the ASME Boiler and Pressure Vessel Code. Section I of the code covering Power Boilers gives details for calculating tube wall thickness and the allowable stress values for the various materials. In superheater and reheater design it has been found desirable to limit the use of various materials in accordance with Table 21–6 which is established on the oxidation resistance basis.[15]

Table 21–6   Maximum Metal Temperatures

ASME Specifications	Nominal Composition			Maximum Metal Temperature F
SA–213 Tp–347–H	18 Cr	8 N	1 Cb	1300
SA–213 T–9	9 Cr	1 MO		1175
SA–213 T–22	1½ Cr	1 MO		1100
SA–213 T–11	1¼ Cr	½ MO		1025
SA–213 T–1	Carbon Steel	½ MO		900
SA–213	Carbon Steel			850

Boiler Calculations by Digital Computer[16]

In the design of steam generating units one of the important problems is the calculation of required surface of convection heat transfer equipment such as superheaters, reheaters, economizers and air preheaters to meet specific guarantees of performance. A closely related problem is the determination and prediction of performance of existing or designed equipment under various operating conditions.

Regardless of which factors or variables are known in advance and which are computed, the same fundamental relations always exist. Basically, heat is transferred from the products of combustion, through the heat transfer surface of the section, to a colder fluid such as steam, water or air.

The method used for calculating the

---

[15] Materials properties are discussed at greater length in Chapter 9, Materials and Metallurgy.
[16] This section is based on a report prepared by C. Guarraia.

CUSTOMER CENTRAL STATION BLR — COMBUSTION ENGINEERING, INC.
SHEET NO. 1 CALC. NO. 26 BY N CH CONT. NO. 7 22
REMARKS MAX LOAD RH&SH SURF DATE 18EA OGR — ENGINEERING DEPT. - WINDSOR, CONN.

DESCRIPTION OF SECTION	SECTION NO.	SECT. TYPE	FLOW TYPE	H'T'D FLUID SEQU. NO.	GAS PASS NO.	GAS PASS AR'G'T	GAS WEIGHT LB/HR ENT'G	GAS TEMPERATURE °F ENT'G T_1	GAS TEMPERATURE °F L'V'G T_2	FUEL TYPE	EXCESS AIR %	HEATED FLUID WEIGHT LB/HR ENT'G	HEATED FLUID TEMPERATURE °F ENT'G t_1	HEATED FLUID TEMPERATURE °F L'V'G t_2	PRESSURE-PSIG ENT'G	PRESSURE-PSIG L'V'G	MOIST %	HEATING SURFACE SQ. FT. S
SH RADWALL	1	1	5	01	1	0	2075,000	2150	2150	8		1675,000	684.7	696.4	2780	2760	0	2,180
SH PLATEN	2	1	5	06	1	2	2075,000	2150	2013			1675,000	837.9	945.3	2700	2675	0	6,060
CAVITY 1	3	9	5	01	1	1	2075,000	2013	2004			1675,000	550.0	552.7	2780	2780	100.0	328
SH FINISH	4	1	5	07	1	2	2075,000	2004	1902			1675,000	945.3	1000.0	2675	2650	0	5,300
CAVITY 2	5	9	5	02	1	1	2075,000	1902	1883			1675,000	552.7	558.6	2780	2780	100.0	688
WW SCREEN	6	7	1	01	1	2	2075,000	1883	1849			1675,000					0	
RH FR PEND	7	3	5	04	1	2	2075,000	1849	1612			1440,000	809.0	1000.0	605	592	0	14,860
CAVITY 3	8	9	5	03	1	1	2075,000	1612	1606			1675,000	558.6	560.6	2780	2780	100.0	295
RH RE PEND	9	3	3	03	1	2	2075,000	1606	1527			1440,000	748.5	809.0	612	605	0	5,200
CAVITY 4	10	9	5	04	1	1	2075,000	1527	1524			1675,000	560.6	561.8	2780	2780	100.0	261
WW SCREEN	11	7	1	01	1	2	2075,000	1524	1479			1675,000					0	
SH ST WALL	12	1	5	02	1	2	2075,000	1479	1466			1675,000	696.4	697.6	2760	2755	0	915
RH PLATEN	13	3	3	02	1	2	2075,000	1466	1437			1440,000	727.8	748.5	616	612	0	2,010
STCLSDWL 1	14	1	5	03	1	1	2075,000	1437	1404			1675,000	697.6	701.9	2755	2755	0	2,415
SCREEN	15	7	1	01	1	2	2075,000	1404	1375			1675,000					0	
SH HORIZ	16	1	3	05	1	2	2075,000	1375	836			1675,000	702.3	837.9	2755	2700	0	109,625
STCLSDWL 2	17	1	5	04	1	1	2075,000	836	833			1675,000	701.9	702.3	2755	2755	0	1,271
RH HORIZ	18	3	3	01	1	2	2075,000	833	713			1440,000	649.0	727.8	624	616	0	95,433
ECONOMIZER	19	5	3	01	1	2	2075,000	713	635			1675,000	496.0	518.4	2820	2780	100.0	30,887

ENG 1001-T

Fig. 21–44. Typical printed results of digital computer

heating surface requirements and the performance of such convection equipment by means of a stored-program digital computer is based on the relationship that the heat given up by the combustion gases is equal to the heat transferred through the heating surface of the section, and this in turn is equal to the heat absorbed by the fluid being heated. If the section is also exposed to direct furnace radiation, the radiant heat must be subtracted from the total heat absorbed by the fluid to obtain the quantity absorbed by convection only. The relationship may be expressed as follows:

$$Q_T = W_g C_g (T_1 - T_2) = R_T S\ (LMTD)$$
$$= w_s c_s (t_2 - t_1) - Q_R \qquad \text{(Eq. 21–33)}$$

where the term Q_T is the quantity of convection heat including the nonluminous radiation portion, transmitted per hour; $W_g C_g\ (T_1 - T_2)$ represents the heat given up by the gas; $R_T S(LMTD)$, the heat transmitted through the heating surface; $w_s c_s\ (t_2 - t_1)$, the total heat absorbed by the fluid and Q_R the direct radiant heat to the section.

In the normal process of heat transfer design, the weights of the gases and of the heated fluids are known. The specific heats of the various fluids are known for any temperature under consideration. The radiant heat can be determined for any given arrangement of surface, gas temperature and heated fluid temperature. The transfer rate is determined from empirical formulas. Under these conditions the only variables that need to be considered in the solution of a heat transfer section are reduced to five which are as follows:

T_1 — Gas temperature entering
T_2 — Gas temperature leaving
t_1 — Heated fluid temperature entering

COMBUSTION ENGINEERING, INC.
ENGINEERING DEPT. - WINDSOR, CONN.

CUSTOMER _____ CENTRAL STATION BLR _____ CONT. NO. ____ 7 22
SHEET NO. **2** CALC NO **26** BY N CH _____ DATE 18EA OGR
REMARKS _____ MAX LOAD RHESH SURF

SECTION NO.	FREE GAS AREA SQ. FT.	TRANSFER RATE BTU/HR-FT²-°F R_c	R_N	R_T	FORM. OR EQ.	TUBE O.D. IN.	SPACING - IN. S_T	S_L	NO SCREEN N_z	TYPE OF SURFACE	CHANNEL FT. H^1	L^1	DIRECT RAD. SQ. FT. A_s	10^4 BTU/HR Q_s	GIVEN DATA T_1 T_2 t_1 t_2 S	ARRANGEMENT
1						1.75								98.8		
2	1220.0	5.61	6.87	12.48	2	2.12	18.18	2.1	0	00	28.5	4.0	1470	58.0		
3	1300.0	5.76	6.99	12.75	2	1.50	1.00	1.5	0	00		3.0				
4	1003.0	6.30	6.43	12.73	2	2.12	9.09	4.5	0	00						
5	1200.0	5.96	6.82	12.78	2	1.50	1.00	1.5	0	00		3.3				
6	828.0	6.87	6.62	13.49	2	3.00	9.09		1	00						
7	662.0	8.26	4.26	12.52	2	2.12	5.26	4.5	0	00						
8	940.0	7.02	5.64	12.66	2	1.25	1.00	1.2	0	00		3.2				
9	508.0	8.80	3.24	12.04	2	2.50	5.26	4.5	0	00						
10	820.0	7.63	5.11	12.74	2	1.25	1.00	1.2	0	00		2.9				
11	538.0	11.15	4.31	15.46	2	1.50	5.26		3	00						
12	481.0	10.44	3.63	14.07	2	2.00	5.26	5.2	0	00						
13	466.0	10.02	2.24	12.26	2	2.12	5.26	2.1	0	00	18.0	.5				
14	1000.0	5.69	7.17	12.86	2	2.00	1.00	2.0	0	00		6.6				
15	663.0	8.62	8.02	16.64	2	2.00	14.00		4	00						
16	465.0	8.45	1.64	10.09	2	2.00	3.53	3.2	0	00						
17	1000.0	4.72	2.86	7.58	2	2.00	1.00	2.0	0	00		2.8				
18	455.0	7.63	1.01	8.64	2	2.12	3.53	3.2	0	00						
19	385.0			8.58	2	2.00	3.13	5.0	0	02						

calculations for a central station boiler of the radiant reheat type

t_2 — Heated fluid temperature leaving
S — Heating surface

The solution of the heat transfer problems by means of the computer is accomplished by a technique of explicit formulation of these five variables. Depending on the conditions of performance given and on the arrangement of each section, one or more of the five variables may require a solution for the completion of the problem. To provide a suitable procedure for the processing of a system of transfer sections, a group of equations has been developed to make possible the solution of each variable when other variables in the sections are known. In the special cases when four or more of the variables are known, as in the case of test data, it is possible to solve explicitly for the transfer rate R. This item is then considered as a variable.

The computer program is designed to analyze each section in the heat transfer system and to select and solve the particular equations required for the section under consideration.

The computer calculates the performance of the heat transfer sections in a manner similar to that followed by an experienced calculating engineer.

Use of Input Forms

The input or basic design information and parameters is furnished by the engineer by filling in input forms. This basic data is then punched in cards and read into the computer. The steam tables, gas properties, various constants, and several temporary subroutines are then read in and executed. They are followed by the step-by-step computation program. The machine will then compute the required information. The results or output will be printed automatically on a final form as shown in Fig. 21–44.

The computer begins the actual calculations by examining the first heat transfer section for the number of known variables in the section. If sufficient variables are known, the computer selects the particular set of equations necessary for the computations and proceeds with the actual solution of the unknowns in that section. When the values thus calculated are common to other sections, as, for instance, the steam temperature at the junction of two sections or the gas temperature between two sections, such values are transferred to the corresponding common variables or mates of the other sections. The computer then proceeds with the examination of the next heat transfer section.

When the section lacks a sufficient number of known variables necessary for the solution, the program proceeds with the examination of the next section. If the next section has enough known variables, the unknowns are computed, then mated to the corresponding variables of other sections, if any. The program continues on to the next section until the last section has been considered. A test is then made to determine if all the unknowns in all the sections have been computed. If there are still some unknowns, the process is repeated, starting with the reconsideration of the first section, the second and so forth.

During each run of this loop in the program, consisting of the examination, computation and mating of the variables in all the sections in this problem, the total number of unknown variables may be reduced by virtue of the mating of corresponding temperatures from previously calculated sections. A section which cannot be solved during a loop of the process may be reduced or solved in a subsequent examination. This iterative process is continued until all the unknowns have been solved.

Use of Estimated Temperatures

If, in one complete iteration, no further reduction in the total number of unknowns is possible, an estimate of gas or steam temperature is made for the most suitable section. This estimate is treated as a known value for that section. The process of examination and completion of all the sections is then started all over again until all of the unknowns are solved. When the solution satisfies the estimate, the results are ready to be printed. If it does not satisfy, new estimates are made until there is complete convergence in the results.

Fig. 21–44 is an example of the output as printed out for a central station boiler design. It will be noted that 19 separate sections were processed by the computer. These sections consisted of seven stages of superheaters, four reheaters, seven evaporating surfaces and one economizer.

The first six columns of digits comprise the identification code for each section. The first column designates the number of the section in numerical ascending sequence with reference to the other sections in the system. The next column indicates the type or system of the heated fluid as for example, superheater, reheater, economizer or air heater. The third column designates the type of heat transfer arrangement, such as counter flow or parallel flow. This identification is required primarily for the calculations of the log mean temperature difference. The next two digits in the fourth column designate the position of the section in a heated fluid system in numerical sequence with reference to ascending heated fluid temperatures in the system. The next two columns identify the location of the section with respect to the physical arrangement of the section in a gas pass of the boiler under consideration.

The remaining items on the tabulations contain the complete performance of all the sections including the given design data and the results calculated by the computer.

Engineering calculations may be carried out in a data processing and computation center similar to that shown in Fig. 21–45.

Fig. 21–45. Digital Computer Installation

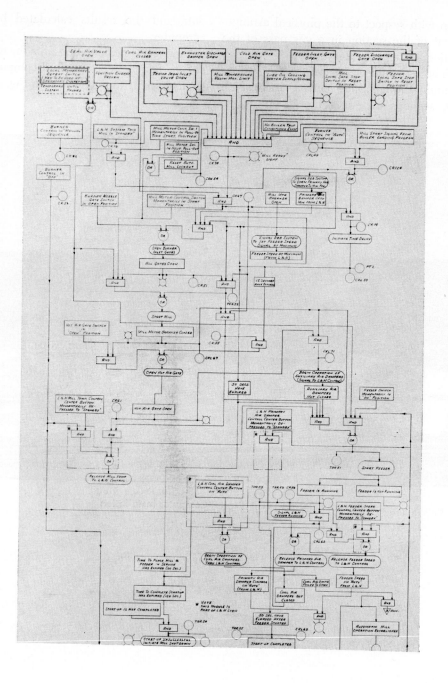

22

Controls and Instruments[1]

A POWER PLANT is composed of many processes and systems which interact with one another. An understanding of the physical processes of steam and nuclear power plants is an essential first step in the application of controls and instruments to their many interrelated systems. In a conventional power plant fired by fossil fuels these systems include fuel and ash handling; transport of air and products of combustion; flow of feedwater, steam and condensing water; and transmission and distribution of electrical power output. The physical processes range from combustion phenomena and heat transfer to change of phase in boiling and condensation, plus fluid flow phenomena and transformation of kinetic mechanical energy to electric energy.[2]

These processes and systems must be integrated and coordinated if a power plant is to function properly. The way that this is accomplished is through the use of various *control systems* and their related *instruments*. While this chapter will be primarily concerned with instrumentation and controls for boilers and their auxiliaries, many of the same considerations apply to nuclear reactors and to interconnected power generation systems.[3]

A Systems Approach to the Power Plant

It is important for the engineer to distinguish between the *objectives* of steam and power generation and the actual power plant *equipment* used in generation. The equipment provides the means whereby a specific objective of generating

[1] Material contributed by Joseph Lewis, R. D. Hottenstine and R. I. Brockett.
[2] See Chapter 1, Visualizing the Steam Power Plant.
[3] Three articles of related interest are "Systems Engineering for Automation of a Large Power Station" by W. L. Chadwick, *Electrical Engineering*, Vol. 81, August 1962, pp. 598–603; "Computer Controlled Power Systems, Part I, Boiler-Turbine Unit Controls" by Gordon D. Friedlander, *IEEE Spectrum*, Vol. 2, April 1965, pp. 60–81; and "Instrument Engineering — Its Growth and Promise in Process Control Problems" by G. S. Brown and D. P. Campbell, *Mechanical Engineering*, Vol. 72, February 1950, pp. 124–127, 136, plus related discussion, June 1950, pp. 587–589. Although the last of these articles did not receive deserved widespread attention among those interested in the technology of steam power plants, many of its qualities of foresight are preserved and amplified in three books of more recent publication: *Dynamic Behavior of the Production Process . . . . . Process Dynamics* by D. P. Campbell, Wiley, 1958, 316 pages; *A Methodology for Systems Engineering* by Arthur D. Hall, Van Nostrand, 1962, 478 pages; and *Techniques of Process Control* by Page S. Buckley, Wiley, 1964, 303 pages.

steam and power may be accomplished, but the same objective may be achieved by more than one type of equipment and by numerous combinations and arrangements of the equipment.

As an example, consider the means of heating a large industrial plant. To maintain the desired temperature conditions it might be possible to use a large number of separately fired space heaters or a central boiler room from which steam or high temperature water is distributed. Despite the common objective of maintaining a uniform temperature over a large manufacturing area, the required equipment varies substantially in size and appearance.

The problem of instrumentation and control differs for each of the combinations of equipment even though the ultimate objective of the process does not change. If the heating load is small enough to be supplied by a single hand fired space heater, the desired temperature can be maintained by varying the rate of firing. As the system becomes larger, however, it becomes necessary to regulate not one but a series of space heaters in an effective and efficient manner. Thus to maintain constant temperature the control problem becomes more complex, whether achieved manually or through some combination of instruments and controls.

If a boiler is used in a central heating plant, the situation becomes one not only of regulating temperature and firing rates but also of controlling several subsystems or subloops. One of these subsystems involves the transport of air and fuel to the furnace and removal of combustion products through the stack. Another handles the regulated flow of steam or high temperature water and its return to the boiler. In some systems these subsystems are themselves made up of additional subsystems.

The concept of the overall system of a heating plant may be extended to the three systems which constitute a gas fired central station. One of these systems starts at the gas well and incorporates the gas transmission stations and transport pipelines up to the gas burners of the boiler. The central station itself may be considered a second system similar to the heating plant, with an added output in the form of electrical energy. This in turn becomes a part of a third system, an electrical network which interconnects other central stations for the purpose of transmission and distribution of electrical power over a wide geographical area.

The Role of the Control Engineer

Because of the varied problems which face the control engineer and the growing complexity of the total control problem, rules of thumb and use of previously proved systems have severe limitations and cannot be expected to achieve optimum operation of the entire power plant. This is leading to an increasing awareness of the need to study the overall problem using a fundamental approach and making use of all available theoretical techniques. It is especially important that the control engineer be oriented to a process point of view.

The most important single process in steam and power generation is the *controlled release of thermal energy* in the boiler or nuclear reactor. This is the basic element around which control systems are designed. The systems of fuel supply and power transmission and distribution must be integrated with the thermal energy process.

A process like the release of thermal energy never operates in a condition of equilibrium.[4] It is being disturbed continually and continuously manipulated and corrected against these disturbances by manual and automatic action as well as by its own inherent characteristics. It is most important that the engineer thoroughly understand process behavior and not allow the complexity of equipment to obscure the control objectives. Adding of extra equipment to correct poor process performance is no substitute for proper design based upon a full understanding of the process.

A theoretical approach to the design of control systems is to formulate differential equations and other mathematical forms to provide an exact representation of the process as a function of time. It is then possible to use techniques from the field of servomechanisms to determine the required characteristics of feedback control systems based on the quantitative behavior of the process. For a central station this type of formulation involves great mathematical complexity, and various degrees of simplification must be made for practical applications.

Even with great amounts of simplification, however, it provides considerable assistance in understanding how a process is controlled and in arriving at a comprehensive design concept. The effects of internal and external disturbances can be studied and will lead to a better understanding of both the steady state, which guided equipment design, and transient conditions.

Power plant operation is subject to the limitations set forth by the first two laws of thermodynamics.[5] The first law governs the manner in which heat is generated and determines the amount. The second law governs the direction of the flow of heat.

Thermal processes may be manipulated either by controlling the rate at which heat energy is generated during the conversion to other forms of energy or by controlling the rate at which heat energy transfers from one point to another.

In the steam power plant the first method applies to combustion and nuclear reactions which may be varied or modulated according to the demands for steam and electrical output. The second comes into use by controlling flow directly, by recirculating and mixing products of combustion or heat transfer fluids, or by varying the amount of effective heat transfer surface exposed to radiant flames. When all of these methods of manipulating thermal processes come into action at one time, as they may in the operation of a power station, the physical and mathematical analyses become extremely complicated.

As an illustration, in an industrial plant, a boiler may be generating steam serving several different processes taking various amounts of steam. If a valve in a line serving steam to a process that requires a considerable amount of steam in relation to the amount being generated is opened rather suddenly, the disturbances may be severe. Steam flow from the boiler is increased requiring additional fuel, air and water flow. Steam pressure from the

---

[4] For an elaboration of this view, see the Preface to *Process Dynamics* by Donald P. Campbell, op. cit.
[5] This concept is treated at greater length in the work by D. P. Campbell, op. cit., Chapter 4, Thermal Process Dynamics, pp. 157–207.

boiler is decreased, affecting steam flow to the other processes. If these are controlled it probably will mean valves in lines carrying steam to these processes will open farther in an attempt to restore steam flow to the various processes to the desired quantity.

The question arises: how much additional fuel is required for the additional load? The first consideration is rather simple. The change in steam flow can be measured. The heat required for this steam can be calculated. The amount of additional fuel required to produce this amount of heat can be calculated. The fuel can be measured and the rate of fuel flow can be increased by the additional amount required for the additional steam flow, but this is not enough. The system has been disturbed and the desired plant pressures and temperatures must be restored quickly.

It is necessary to have equipment to measure disturbances and deviations from desired values and to transmit this information to other devices where the information is coordinated and translated into terms of action required to offset the disturbances and correct the deviations. This information must, in turn, be transmitted to the devices or servomotors that take the corrective action. All this must be done quickly, quantitatively, accurately. The various components must be designed well, made accurately and coordinated into a reliable system that is intended for the particular job to be done. Also the unit to be controlled must be designed and built so as to be controllable. *It is therefore essential that the control engineer, the boiler designer and the plant designer coordinate their work in such a way as to have an integrated power generation system.*

To illustrate the problems of control application and the methods now used in establishing the control system for a boiler, the subject will be treated in accordance with the following long established areas: (1) steam temperature control, (2) feedwater or drum level control and (3) combustion control.

Steam Temperature Control

The importance of steam temperature control has increased in recent years because the economics of power production have resulted in plant cycles which employ very high temperatures. More rigid standards for steam temperature control have resulted because the boiler designer must use more expensive alloy materials if the nominal steam temperature conditions are not accurately controlled. Significant losses in plant efficiency result if the temperatures fall below nominal turbine admission design values.

Two different types of heat transfer are normally encountered in superheating sections of a boiler. Those located in the furnace have a radiant characteristic, while those in areas where gas temperatures are comparatively low have a convection characteristic. Typical effects of load on steam outlet temperatures of radiant and convection superheaters are shown in Fig. 22–1.

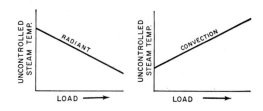

Figure 22–1. Steam temperature variation with boiler load

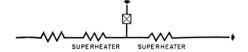

(1) Control by interstage desuperheater

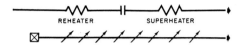

(2) Control by tilting burners with reheater

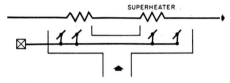

(3) Control by flue gas dampers

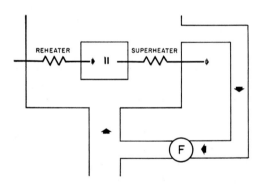

(4) Control by gas recirculation

Figure 22–2.   Methods of controlling steam temperature

Any combination of these characteristics may be utilized in a modern steam generator. The final configuration is a compromise between the control engineer, who would like an arrangement which would require the least amount of correction by the controlling system, and the design engineer, who must provide an economical design which can provide the specified outlet conditions.

Some of the basic methods which have been utilized to control steam temperatures are shown on Fig. 22–2.

Each of these systems has advantages and disadvantages which must be evaluated before a decision for its use can be made. The initial evaluations are of three types: system performance analysis, economic analysis and choice among several control systems and associated hardware. The outcome of these evaluations will depend on the economic conditions of the particular plant.

Spray Desuperheating

Spray type desuperheating at the boiler outlet provides an inexpensive control system and excellent controllability. However, its use is not practical because all the metal in the superheater would have to be designed to withstand maximum steam temperature, and this is not economical. To overcome this disadvantage an interstage desuperheater, shown at the top of Fig. 22–2, can be used. Fig. 22–3 shows the effect of interstage desuperheating on metal temperatures.

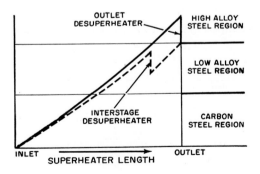

Figure 22–3.   Effect of interstage desuperheating

In order to show how basic equations are used to study a control system for a finishing superheater with interstage spray control, the following example is presented. An overall schematic diagram of the system to be analyzed is shown in Fig. 22–4. This system has a spray valve which is operated by a controller which receives its command from a set point and the final temperature detector. Each of these system units is described by differential equations, and the combined response of the system is then obtained. For purposes of simplification only the major characteristic of each system element is described in order to show the procedure and obtain the essential characteristics.

Fig. 22–5 shows an elementary tube section which is heated externally by radiation and conduction. The amount of heat transferred by these two processes will vary in different sections of the boiler. With constant heat input, however, the particular mode of heat transfer is not an important factor.

The dynamic equations which represent the action of this elementary tube section are derived from the basic continuity equation which states that the rate of change of stored heat energy is equal to the heat added per unit time minus the heat removed per unit time. When this is applied to the tube which is considered a lumped system of small length, l, the fol-

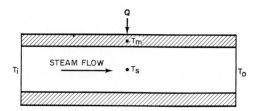

Figure 22–5.   Superheater tube section

lowing terms are obtained:

Rate of change of heat energy $=$ $M_mC_m(dT_m/dt)$, where M_m is weight of metal, C_m is specific heat of metal, T_m is metal temperature and t is time.

Heat added $= Q$

Heat removed $= Ah\ (T_m - T_s)$, where A is heat transfer area, h is the heat transfer coefficient (metal to steam) and T_s is the average steam temperature.

Combining these terms the following differential equation for the metal temperature is obtained for the lumped case:

$$M_mC_m\frac{dT_m}{dt} = Q - Ah(T_m - T_s) \qquad (22\text{–}1)$$

In a similar manner, the following terms and equation are derived for the flowing fluid heat balance.

Rate of change of heat $= M_sC_s(dT_s/dt)$, where M_s is the weight of steam and C_s is the specific heat of steam.

Heat added $= Ah(T_m - T_s) + W_sC_sT_i$, where W_s is the steam flow rate and T_i is the inlet steam temperature.

Heat removed $= W_sC_sT_o$, where T_o is the outlet steam temperature

$$M_sC_s\frac{dT_s}{dt} = Ah(T_m - T_s)$$
$$- W_sC_s(T_o - T_i) \qquad (22\text{–}2)$$

One additional equation is required to solve these equations. This equation is the equation which defines the average fluid temperature as a function of the inlet and

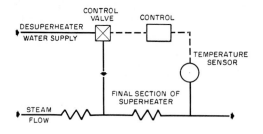

Figure 22–4.   Block diagram, interstage desuperheater

outlet temperatures. If the length of the heat exchanger is small so that the flowing fluid temperature rise is less than the average metal to steam temperature difference, the average steam temperature may be calculated as the simple average:

$$T_s = \frac{T_c + T_o}{2} \qquad (22\text{-}3)$$

In the event that the exchanger under study is so long that the temperature considerations above do not hold, an accurate analysis may be obtained by breaking the tube into several sections and writing equations for each section.

Some general conclusions may be drawn from these equations. Consider that Eq. 22-2 is rearranged in this form

$$\frac{M_s C_s}{Ah} \frac{dT_s}{dt} = (T_m - T_s) - \frac{W_s C_s}{Ah}(T_o - T_i) \qquad (22\text{-}4)$$

The controlling factors may be easily identified. The $M_s C_s / Ah$ factor may be considered a time scale factor since it multiplies the derivative term only and has the units of a time constant. The dimensionless factor, $W_s C_s / Ah$, will determine the steady state ratio between the heat transfer driving temperature difference $(T_m - T_s)$ and the fluid temperature rise $(T_o - T_i)$. The steady state condition is obtained when the derivative is set equal to zero.

Since the $W_s C_s / Ah$ factor controls the shape of the time response as well as specifying the steady state relative temperature, this term may be considered as the controllability factor of a heat exchanger such as a superheater section. If the heat added to the flowing fluid is assumed to be constant, the $W_s C_s / Ah$ factor will control the effect that a step change of inlet temperature will have on the derivative of the average temperature. Since the outlet,

average and inlet temperatures are linked by Eq. 22-3, the initial outlet temperature change depends on the average temperature change. When the $W_s C_s / Ah$ term is small, the section becomes difficult to control. A small factor in this equation would be indicative of a large temperature difference between inlet and outlet in the steady state. This would come about by a long small diameter tube. Since a long small diameter tube is indicative of a slowly changing process, rapid controller action would be slowed by the process so that overcorrection would be prevalent. This overcorrection is indicative of a tendency toward instability. Thus the $W_s C_s / Ah$ is a measure of the unit controllability.

Outlet Temperature Detectors

The outlet temperature detector may be as simple as a thermocouple and the appropriate reference junction or it may be a compound metal bar and the associated components. For this analysis a thermocouple or resistance thermometer type is assumed. Each of these will have output signals which follow behind changing input temperatures by some small amount. This type of action is approximated by a first order differential equation having a time constant τ_d. Since the output of the detector is assumed to be a voltage, a constant of proportionality, Kd, between temperature and voltage in the steady state is used. With these assumptions the detector equation is:

$$\tau_d \frac{de_d}{dt} = K_d T_o - e_d \qquad (22\text{-}5)$$

where e_d is the detector voltage output, T_o is the gas temperature sensed, d is the detector time constant and K_d is the steady state constant of proportionality.

Controllers

Controllers commonly have as many as three types of action in response to an error signal. These three actions are classified by the output response to a sudden change in input error as proportional, reset and rate action. The proportional action yields an output which is proportional to the error. The reset action yields an output which is proportional to the integral of error which appears as a reset action of the set point. The rate action yields an output which is a function of the rate of change of the error.

A common type of controller approximates proportional, reset, and rate action with the following differential equation:

$$\frac{ID}{10}\frac{d^2e_o}{dt^2} + \left(I + \frac{D}{10}\right)\frac{de_o}{dt} + e_o$$

$$= P\left[\frac{ID}{10}\frac{d^2(e_r - e_d)}{dt^2} + \left(\frac{I}{10} + D\right)\right.$$

$$\left. \times \frac{d(e_r - e_o)}{dt} + (e_r - e_d)\right]$$

$$(22\text{--}6)$$

where I is an adjustable constant for reset action, D is an adjustable constant for rate action, P is an adjustable constant of proportional action, e_o is the controller output signal, e_d is the detector input signal and e_r is the reference set voltage, a function of the desired temperature.

Spray Valve

An exact set of equations for the relation between valve position, inlet temperature and spray section outlet temperature is too complicated for this anaylsis. This would involve the pressure drop across the valve, the valve opening as a function of valve position, the spray water conditions and the superheater inlet steam and flow conditions. When a problem such as this is encountered, a practical approach is to assume each of the possible variables is constant and obtain the effects of each over a reasonable range. This reasoning leads to the simple equation below, where the range of K_T to be investigated must take into account the various effects mentioned above.

$$T_{in} = T_i - K_T\theta \qquad (22\text{--}7)$$

where T_{in} is the valve exit temperature or heater inlet temperature, T_i is the valve inlet temperature, K_T is the rate of change of valve exit temperature with valve opening and θ is the valve opening.

For this analysis it will be assumed that the valve positioner is separate from the controller and that this servo positioner has been designed such that a good approximation may be obtained by a second order differential equation with a damping ratio of one half. If this is the case, the following differential equation will represent the spray valve and positioner.

$$\tau n^2 \frac{d^2\theta}{dt^2} + \tau n \frac{d\theta}{dt} + \theta = -K_\theta e_o \qquad (22\text{--}8)$$

where e_o is the controller output voltage, θ is the valve position, τn is the valve servo time factor and K_θ is a steady state constant of proportionality between the input voltages and the valve position.

The total feedback control loop block diagram is shown in Fig. 22–6. The controller functions shown in this block diagram include proportional, reset and rate action. This block diagram may be studied mathematically or by simulating the system on an analog computer.

The results of utilizing an analog computer to analyze a control problem of this type are shown in Fig. 22–7. The first set of curves illustrates the effect of three different proportional settings in a single action control loop for a superheater. The dashed curve illustrates the uncontrolled tempera-

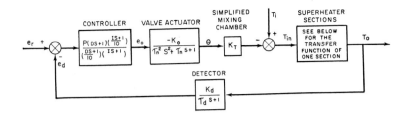

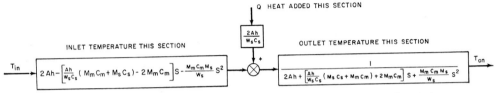

Figure 22–6. Block diagram and transfer function of one section of superheater

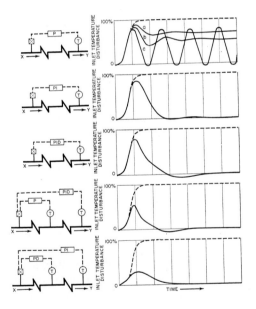

Figure 22–7. Superheater temperature control simulation by analog computer

illustrate the effects of increasing the proportional action, respectively, in the control loop. This procedure can be utilized to obtain the optimum setting for the process being controlled.

The second curve from the top of Fig. 22–7 illustrates the optimum setting which can be achieved by adding reset action to this loop. The middle curve is the best attainable with proportional, rate and reset actions. This is the same type of loop as represented by the block diagrams shown previously in Fig. 22–6.

If further improvement is desired, more complex control loops must be used. The lower two curves of Fig. 22–7 illustrate how this added degree of sophistication can be used to minimize deviation of response.

This study illustrates how the optimum control loop configuration for a particular method of control can be developed for a single disturbance. This study would have to be expanded to cover all expected disturbances, all controlling loops and all coordinating signals before a final design would result.

ture response at the outlet of the superheater when a disturbance is introduced at the inlet at time zero. The curves *a, b, c*

Drum Level Control

Where a boiler has a drum it is necessary to regulate the flow of feedwater and steam in such a manner as to hold the level of water in the drum at a constant level. Water level is affected by the pressure in the drum, by the temperature of the water and by the rate at which heat is being added.[6]

To get a picture of what happens in the drum with variation in load, assume a state of equilibrium with water at the desired level. If load is increased, causing a temporary drop of pressure in the drum, the steam bubbles and the water will increase, tending to make the water swell and raising the water level. At the same time the increase in load requires increased flow of feedwater to the drum, and this feedwater is comparatively cool by comparison to the near saturation temperature of water already in the drum. This increase in feedwater flow cools the water in the drum and causes the level to shrink or fall.

A water level control is designed to maintain the required amount of water in the steam generator over the operating conditions. In its simplest form, a valve controls feedwater flow so that the water level is maintained constant. The basic process which is being controlled here is an integrating process. The level is the integral of the inlet water flow and the outlet steam flow. This basic system is shown schematically in Fig. 22–8. The simplified block diagram with the appropriate transfer functions is shown in Fig. 22–9.

While this arrangement has certain advantages, it has two severe limitations. The first is that the drum area tends to be large compared to the amounts of water stored so that the level changes slowly. The second is that changes in water level due to changes in the density of the water with pressure changes will put severe transients on the system which is relatively slow acting. These density changes (swell) are usually a function of steam flow.

In order to anticipate the effect of rapid changes in steam flow, a steam flow signal is used to control the feed water and the level is used as an adjustment on the water flow. The level is an integral of the error between the steam flow and the water flow and serves to correct any errors in the balance between these two flows. This system is shown schematically in Fig. 22–10 followed by a related block diagram in Fig. 22–11.

In practice another detector is commonly added to anticipate level changes and take care of transients in the feedwater system. This measures the feedwater flow and is shown schematically in Fig. 22–12 and block diagram form in Fig. 22–13.

Although this is the most complicated of the three control systems illustrated, it provides more versatility in response characteristics. This has advantages in terms of speed of response and disadvantages because of opportunities for unstable actions. A combination of experience and study is required to determine which of the three systems of drum level control should be applied in specific cases.

---

[6] F. T. Thompson in 1964 wrote a doctoral thesis under the direction of the Department of Electrical Engineering of the University of Pittsburgh in which he analyzed various boiler components in terms of the overall physical processes of a central station. He also studied transient responses to power plant disturbances and proposed a method of control using stored energy in the economizer in the thesis entitled "A Dynamic Model for Control of a Drum Type Boiler System."

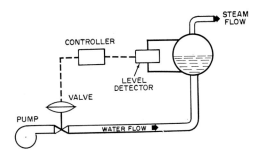

Figure 22–8. Water level controller — one detector

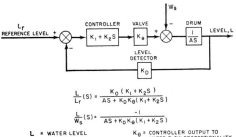

$$\frac{L}{L_r}(S) = \frac{K_0(K_1 + K_2 S)}{AS + K_D K_\theta(K_1 + K_2 S)}$$

$$\frac{L}{W_s}(S) = \frac{-1}{AS + K_D K_\theta(K_1 + K_2 S)}$$

L = WATER LEVEL	K$_\theta$ = CONTROLLER OUTPUT TO WATER FLOW PROPORTIONALITY
L$_r$ = REFERENCE LEVEL	
W$_s$ = STEAM FLOW	K$_2$ = CONTROLLER RATE ADJUSTMENT
A = AREA OF DRUM	S = LAPLACE OPERATOR
K$_1$ = CONTROLLER PROPORTION BAND ADJUSTMENT	K$_D$ = DETECTOR CONSTANT

Figure 22–9. Block diagram of water level controller — one detector

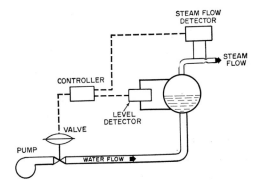

Figure 22–10. Water level controller — two detectors

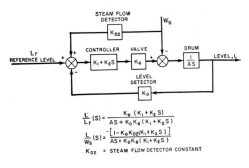

$$\frac{L}{L_r}(S) = \frac{K_\theta(K_1 + K_2 S)}{AS + K_D K_\theta(K_1 + K_2 S)}$$

$$\frac{L}{W_s}(S) = \frac{-[1 - K_\theta K_{D2}(K_1 + K_2 S)]}{AS + K_D K_\theta(K_1 + K_2 S)}$$

K$_{D2}$ = STEAM FLOW DETECTOR CONSTANT

Figure 22–11. Block diagram of water level controller — two detectors

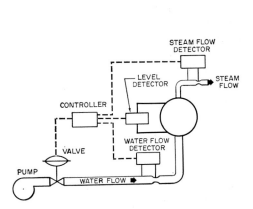

Figure 22–12. Water level controller — three detectors

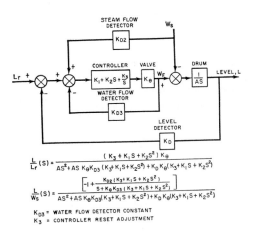

$$\frac{L}{L_r}(S) = \frac{(K_3 + K_1 S + K_2 S^2) K_\theta}{AS^2 + AS\, K_\theta K_{D3}(K_3 + K_1 S + K_2 S^2) + K_D K_\theta(K_3 + K_1 S + K_2 S^2)}$$

$$\frac{L}{W_s}(S) = \frac{-\left[1 + \dfrac{K_{D2}(K_3 + K_1 S + K_2 S^2)}{S + K_\theta K_{D3}(K_3 + K_1 S + K_2 S^2)}\right]}{AS^2 + AS\, K_\theta K_{D3}(K_3 + K_1 S + K_2 S^2) + K_D K_\theta(K_3 + K_1 S + K_2 S^2)}$$

K$_{D3}$ = WATER FLOW DETECTOR CONSTANT
K$_3$ = CONTROLLER RESET ADJUSTMENT

Figure 22–13. Block diagram of water level controller — three detectors

Combustion Control

The primary functions of an automatic combustion control system as applied to a steam generating unit are (1) to regulate air and fuel to the furnace in the proper ratio to result in optimum combustion and (2) to furnish fuel and air at a rate which will maintain the desired output.[7]

Combustion control systems vary widely. A small hand fired coal burning unit may require only a simple damper positioner to maintain steam pressure. In a large high pressure boiler there may be an elaborate system that not only measures and regulates the rate of fuel and air flow to maintain pressure but compensates for temperature, pressure and heating value of the fuel. Portions of this control system are interlocked so that certain steps must be taken in sequence and that a certain action can or cannot be taken except under specified conditions.

In this section combustion control will be considered from two distinctively different points of view. First, there will be an analytical presentation in which the transfer functions of the system are considered individually and then combined in a single block diagram. The second part of this section deals with a large gas fired boiler and includes a description of the combustion control system in terms of the actual hardware components.

Analytical Approach to Combustion Control

Fig. 22–14 shows the schematic of a simplified combustion control. This con-

trol has several transfer functions which are extremely complicated and will not be discussed in detail. However, the approach in the investigation will be to indicate an overall situation and to point out areas of possible further investigation.

Starting at the air inlet, the system functions will be discussed in order.

Air Control. This control system may become an involved analysis of the fan speed effects on damper effectiveness, as well as the damper position control. However, for the purpose of the present example it will be assumed that the air control system has been designed to give a minimum step response time and only a very little overshoot. If this is the case, the transfer function obtained for small sinusoidal variations can be approximated by a quadratic equation with a damping ratio slightly less than one.

$$\frac{\text{Air}}{\text{Air Demand}}(s) = \frac{1}{\tau_n^2 s + 2\,\delta\tau_n s + 1} \qquad (22\text{–}9)$$

where s is the Laplace transform, τ_n is the system characteristic time constant and δ is the damping ratio.

Fuel Control. From an overall point of view, the fuel control is also a positioning servo control. For the reasons stated in the previous paragraph the transfer function assumed is

$$\frac{\text{Fuel}}{\text{Fuel Desired}}(s) = \frac{1}{\tau_{n_2}^2 s^2 + 2\,\delta\tau_{n_2} s + 1}$$
$$(22\text{–}10)$$

In any particular installation, these

[7] See "The Development of Automatic Combustion Control Systems for Industrial and Power Station Boilers" by J. L. Hodgson and L. L. Robinson, *Proceedings* IME, Vol. 126, 1934, pp. 59–169 for the history and evolution of many designs. A fascinating account of the application of the process of creative thinking as exemplified in the Bailey boiler meter and related combustion control systems is found in "Invention and Sifting Out Engineering Facts" by E. G. Bailey, *Proceedings* IME, Vol. 160, 1949, pp. 196–207.

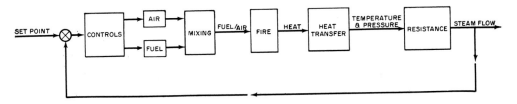

Figure 22–14. Schematic diagram of combustion control system

transfer functions should be calculated or measured much more precisely than suggested here, but these are reasonable approximations for this treatment.

Fuel-to-Air-Ratio. While this is a mathematical relationship, it is important from a control point of view. This ratio must stay within certain limits in order to stay away from dangerous furnace conditions.

Flame Propagation. In general the fire propagation through the furnace is rapid enough so that the dynamics of the fire are not important in the analysis of a feedback control system. In this case, the heat released may be considered proportional (with a proportionality factor, K) to the fuel present with a modification term which is a function of the fuel–air ratio.

$$Q = K(\text{Fuel}) + \mathfrak{F}(F/A) \quad (22\text{--}11)$$

Heat Transfer. The heat transfer equations were derived earlier in this chapter. It should be noted that the heat transferred to the tube metal may be from radiant or convection sources or a combination of the two.

Steam Pressure. While the analysis of the transfer functions of the steam pressure as a function of the inlet water flow, steam flow and heat added is complicated, simplifications may indicate the general char-

acteristics of the process. This analysis assumes that feedwater and steam flow are equal at all times and that the water in the system is at saturated conditions throughout the transient.

In an enclosed volume containing both steam and water, the pressure is a measure of the total energy in the system. If heat energy is added to the system, some of the water will be turned to steam and the increase in steam volume will be a measure of the heat added to the system.

The addition and removal of the same amount of water will not change the situation. If water is added and the same weight of steam is removed, the additional energy removed from the system by the steam must be taken into consideration. Over a short range the function of total energy in the system versus pressure may be considered a straight line. In this case the pressure becomes the integral of the energy added minus the integral of the energy removed. Therefore, the transfer function is:

$$P(s) = \frac{k_p}{s}(h_o - h_i) \quad (22\text{--}12)$$

where s is the Laplace transform; k_p, proportionality constant; P, pressure; h_i, inlet energy flow rate; and h_o, outlet energy flow rate.

Steam Flow Restrictions. Throughout a steam generation system, there are various pressure losses. However, for this analysis

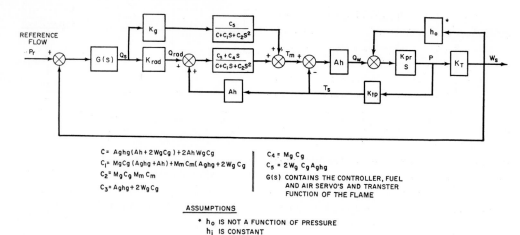

$$C = Aghg(Ah + 2WgCg) + 2Ah\,WgCg$$
$$C_1 = MgCg\,(Aghg + Ah) + Mm\,Cm(\,Aghg + 2Wg\,Cg$$
$$C_2 = Mg\,Cg\,Mm\,Cm$$
$$C_3 = Aghg + 2Wg\,Cg$$

$$C_4 = Mg\,Cg$$
$$C_5 = 2Wg\,Cg\,Aghg$$

G(S) CONTAINS THE CONTROLLER, FUEL
AND AIR SERVO'S AND TRANSTER
FUNCTION OF THE FLAME

ASSUMPTIONS

* h_o IS NOT A FUNCTION OF PRESSURE
h_i IS CONSTANT

Figure 22–15.   Block diagram of combustion control system

the only pressure loss which is considered will be the loss in the outlet control valve from the boiler. This valve will be used to adjust the flow of steam through the system by changing its opening. In addition to this external effect, there is the effect of steam pressure on steam flow. For small variations about a single point, this may be considered a simple proportionality constant and the transfer function is:

$$W_s = Kp \qquad (22\text{–}13)$$

where W_s is steam flow; K, proportionality constant; and p, valve pressure drop.

These transfer functions are combined into the block diagram, Fig. 22–15. This type of block diagram can be used for analysis and study of combustion control systems.

Descriptive Approach to Combustion Control

As an example of the descriptive approach to combustion control, consider the central station reheat boiler shown in Fig. 22–16. Assume that it is tangentially fired with natural gas through burners at each of the four corners, 9. The gas flow pattern is from the burners through the furnace, 1; a radiant superheater, 2; a reheater, 3; a

convection superheater, 4; an economizer, 5; a regenerative air heater, 6; and an induced draft fan, 7. A forced draft fan is indicated at 8. Fig. 22–17 shows principal central station systems in schematic form. Fig. 22–18 shows a schematic diagram

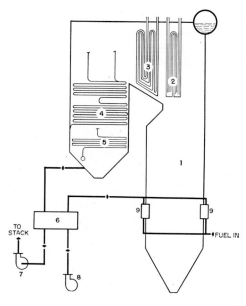

Figure 22–16.   Elements of central station boiler

of a simple combustion control system that can be applied to this unit. Steam pressure is measured in the steam line carrying steam from the unit. The point of measurement may be at the superheater outlet header or at some other point downstream. Other values which are metered are fuel flow (natural gas) and air flow. The latter may be measured at any point in the air duct from the forced draft fan inlet to the induced draft fan outlet providing the primary element is located in a place and under conditions suitable to satisfactory air flow measurement.

Assume that total air flow is measured in a single duct following the air heater. The device that measures the steam pressure sends out a control impulse or loading proportional to the deviation of actual pressure from the pressure it is set to maintain. In the illustration, this impulse or loading (which may be pneumatic, electric or hydraulic) acts on a gas valve drive unit and on forced draft fan damper drive unit to increase or decrease both fuel and air flow to the burners, depending on whether the pressure is low or high.

Flow meters measure fuel flow and air flow continuously. Each flow meter sends out an impulse or loading to a relay R_1

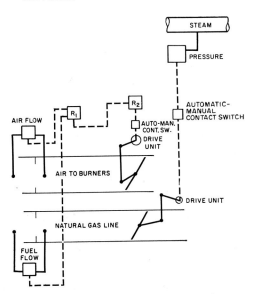

Figure 22–18. Components of combustion control system

that is proportional to the flow being measured. The flow meters and relay must be calibrated in such a way that if the rate of air flow is correct for the rate of gas flow, there is no effect on the position of the damper controlling the flow of air to the burners. If, however, the loadings from the flow meters to relay R_1 indicate an unbalance, i.e. that the rate of air flow is not optimum for the rate of gas flow, R_1 will send an impulse to R_2 which in turn will send an impulse to the drive unit to move the damper controlling the air flow to either open or close it until the ratio of the two flows is correct.

In summary, if the pressure and the ratio of air flow to fuel flow are both correct, the gas valve and air damper do not move. If the ratio is correct but pressure deviates from set point, both gas valve and air damper move and continue to do so until pressure is correct. If the ratio is upset during this action, the impulse from R_1 to R_2 will (1) cause rate of damper movement to change (if the drive unit has

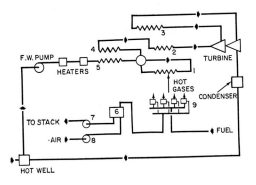

Figure 22–17. Schematic flow pattern of central station boiler

a variable speed) or (2) interrupt the damper movement if the air flow is greater than it should be or (3) continue to move the damper after the gas valve has stopped moving if more air is required.

The power for moving the drives may be pneumatic, electric, or hydraulic but not necessarily the same as for the control circuit.

Not all combustion control systems work exactly as outlined. In some, a deviation in pressure causes a change in flow of fuel only. It is a change in rate of fuel flow that causes a change in rate of air flow. In others, a deviation in pressure causes a change in air flow which in turn causes a change in fuel flow. While the foregoing describes a simple control arrangement, some systems merely position the fuel valve and air damper with a given position of valve and damper for a given pressure.

If oil is used for fuel, the basic system can be the same. With coal, it is not so easy to measure fuel flow, and air flow is frequently matched to steam flow. Instead of a valve in the fuel line some method is used to vary the rate of coal feed to the stoker, pulverizer, or possible pulverized coal to an air transport line. Some systems might vary the flow of air transporting the coal to the burners.

A large number of units are being designed for pressurized firing, omitting the induced draft fan and subjecting the entire furnace to positive pressure. On such a unit the above covers the basic principle of combustion control systems.

While the diagrams indicate that air flow is controlled by dampers in the duct carrying air to burners, and, therefore, furnace draft is controlled by positioning damper on induced draft fan, this is not necessarily so. Air flow can be controlled by regulation of dampers, inlet vanes, or

speed of either forced draft or induced draft fan. Likewise, furnace draft can be controlled by regulation of dampers, inlet vanes, or speed of either fan. If the forced draft fan is used for air flow, it is, of course, necessary to use the induced draft fan for furnace draft, and vice versa.

Combustion control systems become much more complex with the firing of multiple fuels (such as coal and oil; gas and bark; coal, oil and gas). Lack of duct length for measuring air flows, recirculation of gas for steam temperature control and multiple installations of fans and furnaces all add complications. The basic principle, however, is the same. This is to fire sufficient fuel to maintain a given condition (usually a constant steam pressure) and to regulate air to that quantity that results in optimum combustion.

In the system illustrated in Fig. 22–18 and previously described, if the impulse to the drive unit positioning the valve in the gas line were always the same for a given deviation of pressure from the desired pressure (set point), the system would be, as far as energy input and output pressure are concerned, merely approximate. The gas valve would assume a given position for a given deviation of pressure and if no more disturbances occurred, the system would, eventually, regulate fuel flow to produce required steam flow at the pressure corresponding to the valve position. In actual practice, however, while a given upset in steam pressure, that is, a given deviation in pressure does move the fuel valve a given amount proportional to the deviation (this is known as proportional band), a second feature of the control system, known as automatic reset starts to act and continues to act until the pressure measured equals the desired pressure (set point). Automatic reset serves the function of changing valve position in relation to the impulse or loading created by the deviation in steam pressure from set point and the loading going to the drive unit. The valve position can, therefore, be at any position required to give a rate of fuel flow to carry the load and hold pressure at desired value. A third function, rate action, can be and usually is built into the system. This feature has the effect of amplifying the impulse or loading to the drive unit depending on the rate of change of the deviation in pressure in order to prevent further change. The result is temporary overcorrection of valve position when the pressure is moving away from the set point and this eases the action when the pressure is approaching the set point.

Instruments

In all of the control systems previously described and analyzed, there is need for various types of measurement. Temperature, pressure, flow, level and other quantities must be determined reliably, quickly and accurately. To do this meters and instruments are required.

The importance of instruments and instrumentation was recognized long before automatic control came into widespread use. But their value is greatly accentuated as a result of such practices as firing multiple fuels, faster response of boilers which have little or no water reserve capacity, and the great increase in size of units operated at extremely advanced steam conditions. Developments relating to the completely automatic power plant, using ever more sophisticated control functions and analyses, put added burdens on the reliability and performance of power plant instrumentation.

The information desired from instruments is considerable and varied. As water is introduced into the boiler and converted to steam, it is customary to measure drum water level and temperatures and pressures at various places in the drum and superheater. Rate of feedwater and steam flow is also measured and integrated or totalled.

As air is introduced into the furnace to combine with fuel to release heat, it is desired to know air pressures and temperatures from the forced draft fan outlet through the air heater to windbox; pressure or suction in the furnace and through the various sections of the unit up to the stack may have to be determined. The rate of air flow and the amount of excess air or oxygen in the products of combustion are also desired. Knowledge of position of dampers and valves is frequently required. Various data regarding fuel such as rate of feed, total fuel over a given period and other data depending on the nature of the fuel may be required.

To get this information, there are available pressure gauges, draft gauges, thermometers, pyrometers, flow meters, analyzers such as oxygen and CO_2 meters, conductivity meters, water level meters and other instruments. Some of the instruments are indicating only and some, recording. There are also scanners, integrators, data loggers and digital computers. Among the indicators and recorders are large and miniature types. Among the recorders are circular chart and strip chart; single and multiple record. Remote transmitters are used with indicators, recorders and in control systems.

Following is a brief discussion of underlying principles of meters commonly used in the power plant.[8]

Pressure Gauges

The Bourdon tube, the spiral tube and bellows are three devices used to measure pressure other than very low pressure. Liquid or mercury filled U-tubes may be used to measure low pressure or suction, although light weight bellows and diaphragms are now more commonly used.

The Bourdon tube is a hollow cylinder, usually flattened, sealed at one end, and shaped somewhat like an interrogation point. The open end at the bottom of the interrogation point is fixed while the other end is free to move. The open end is connected to the source of pressure or point at which pressure is to be measured. Pressure tends to straighten the tube and the movements of the free end is a measure of the pressure.

The spiral is also made of a flattened hollow tube sealed at one end; fixed at the open end, free to move at the closed end. A smaller diameter and longer tube is used than for the Bourdon tube. It, too, tends to straighten out on the application of pressure.

The bellows is shaped as the name implies. If pressure is applied within the bellows, it tends to elongate. If it is sealed in a pressure tight chamber and pressure applied inside the chamber, an increase in pressure tends to compress the bellows. By doing both, it can be used as a differential pressure gauge. Sometimes springs

are used to oppose motion of the bellows and to calibrate it.

For low pressures and drafts (suction), liquid or mercury U-tubes or variation thereof are sometimes used. Depending on the pressure (or suction) either mercury or a colored oil is used. One end of the U-tube is connected to the source of pressure or suction, the other to atmosphere. The difference in the levels of the two legs represents the pressure or the suction head in linear units of the medium being used. If pressure is measured, the connected leg is depressed; if suction, the leg to atmosphere is depressed. Inclined draft gauges are of this variety.

Connecting one side of the U-tube to one point of pressure or suction in a system and the other side to a different point in the same system gives a drop or differential pressure between the two points. The instrument thus becomes a differential pressure gauge — a very important device. It is used for various readings such as draft loss across an air heater, fluid flow and liquid level.

Bellows and slack diaphragms are also used for low pressure and suction. They, too, can be used for differential pressure gauges.

Temperature[9]

There are a number of types of temperature measuring instruments, ranging from selfcontained glass stem mercury thermometers and expansion type dial thermometers, to electronic type pyrometers and resistance thermometers.

Expansion type thermometers depend on the expansion of a bimetal coil, or

---

[8] Many of these instruments are also discussed in Chapter 12, Power Plant Tests and Measurements.

[9] An interesting survey is found in "Review of Practical Thermometry" by R. P. Benedict, ASME Paper 57-A-203.

metal rod inside a protecting tube. The movement of the coil or rod is used to rotate a pointer on a dial connected to one end of the tube.

Another group of thermometers used widely in the power plant is known as long distance thermometers. They consist of a bulb for immersion in the medium, the temperature of which is to be measured, a capillary tubing extending from the bulb to the indicator or recorder, and bellows, helix, or spiral within the case of the indicator or recorder. The latter are designed as for pressure gauges. There are four classes of such thermometers: (I) liquid filled, (II) vapor filled, (III) gas filled, and (IV) mercury filled. Classes I and IV depend on expansion of the liquid or mercury. Classes II and III depend on pressure. To measure the expansion of pressure, the capillary tubing is connected to a hollow tube helix or bellows in the receiver. In all four classes it is imperative that the bulb, tubing, and helix (or bellows) be one continuous pressure tight system. This system is manufactured, calibrated and sealed that way, and the tubing can be neither lengthened nor shortened once the thermometer is made.

Resistance thermometers are used for temperatures up to 1000 F, but chart ranges to 1200 F may be obtained. They are based on the principle that a metal changes its resistance with a change in temperature. Not all metals are suitable however and the two metals usually used are nickel (up to 300 F) and platinum up to 1200 F (preferably not over 1000 F). The wire is wound non-inductively to form a bulb which is used to form one leg of a Wheatstone Bridge. The resistance of the bulb is then measured by adjusting the resistance in another leg of the bridge, or by changing the ratio of the resistance in two of the legs until the bridge is in balance. A galvanometer is sometimes used to detect an unbalance, although electronic amplifiers are used in the newer types.

The thermoelectric pyrometer or thermocouple used for temperature measurement is based on the principle that when two wires of dissimilar metals are welded together at one end and the welded end is heated, an electromotive force is produced proportional to the difference in the temperature found between the hot and cold end. If the temperature of the cold end is known and an instrument is used to measure the e.m.f. produced, the temperature of the hot end can be determined if the characteristics of the two metals are known.

Both thermoelectric pyrometers and resistance thermometers have a distinct advantage over gas filled, vapor filled or liquid filled thermometers, in that the resistance thermometer bulb and the thermocouple are individual items which are simply connected to a measuring device by means of electric wire. In the case of the resistance thermometer, copper wire is used although three conductor wire is required. In the case of thermoelectric pyrometers, it is customary to use what is called extension lead wire from the thermocouple to either the instrument or to a compensating junction box. This is due to the fact that the e.m.f. developed by the thermocouple is proportional to the difference between the temperature of the hot and cold ends. Instead of keeping the cold end constant, a compensating device is used to change the zero setting of the indicator or recorder in accordance with temperature of the cold end. The cold end of the thermocouple must, therefore, be brought to this compensating device which can be located either in the instrument or in a compensating junction box. If it is located in a compensating junction box, ordinary copper wire can be used from this point to the instrument.

Flow Meters[10]

There are various types of devices for measuring flow but in a steam power plant a vast majority are of the velocity head type. When a constriction is placed in a pipe to reduce the area there is an increase in velocity of the fluid flowing and some of the static head is changed to velocity head. By measuring the change in the static head and knowing the cross sectional area of both the pipe and constriction, it is possible to determine the rate of flow. Proper combinations of constrictions and meters which are measuring the change in static pressure will enable a manufacturer to calibrate the meter to read flow directly in any units desired. Since temperature and pressure do have an effect on the readings, changes in these values must be compensated for or a correction made in the reading.

When a constrictive device is used for steam flow measurement, it is customary to use either a thin plate orifice or nozzle. For liquid flow measurement, it is customary to use either a nozzle or a venturi tube, although orifice plates are sometimes used. For gas flow measurement in a pipe, orifice plates are probably used more than other devices. For measurement of air or flue gas through a boiler, drops across various sections such as the air heater or economizer can be used. In some cases this is not feasible and venturi sections may be built into the air ducts. One of the best

methods of obtaining a measureable differential for air flow is to use an airfoil as developed by I. G. McChesney.[11] This device gives a much higher differential with lower permanent pressure loss than other constrictive devices. It has the added advantage of being suitable for installation in a shorter section of duct than other types of constrictions.

In order to get the differential across the constriction or primary element it is necessary to use pressure taps. The location of these pressure taps in relation to the primary element is extremely important. The manufacturer of the flow meter equipment will give exact instructions as to the installation of the primary element and the exact measurement to be used from the primary element to the taps. The method of installing these taps is also important if good results are to be obtained.

There are various devices used for measuring the change in static pressure. It is to be remembered that this is a differential pressure and any differential pressure gauge could be used if it is suited to the particular application and range. It is, however, customary to use a modification of the mercury U-tube with a float riding in the mercury of one of the legs. The movement of this float is then measured either mechanically or electrically. The differential pressure across the primary element is proportional to the square of the flow. Many meters are designed to extract the square root and give an indication on a scale or chart that is graduated uniformly.

While velocity head meters are the ones usually used in the power plant, there are other types of flow meters. The area

---

[10] See *Fluid Meters — Their Theory and Application*, Fifth Edition, ASME, 1959, 203 pages.
[11] See "Air Metering for Combustion Control," *Combustion*, Vol. 21, August 1951, pp. 44–47.

meter is sometimes used for fuel oil flow. This type of meter is somewhat like a globe valve but instead of a valve stem holding the disc in a given position the disc is moved by the flow of the fluid. The meter forms the constriction which creates the velocity head. Magnetic flow meters which do not require a constriction in the line and therefore introduce no more pressure drop than an equal length of pipe are also available.

All of the above types of flow meters can be obtained with integrators, that is, with a device for totalizing the amount of flow continuously. In this way, total quantity of flow over a given period of time as well as instantaneous rate of flow can be determined.

Liquid Level Recorders and Indicators

There are many types of instruments used for measuring liquid level. For an open tank, floats are sometimes used. Another type is to blow air or steam at a given point below the surface of the liquid and measure the pressure of the air or steam balanced by the head of liquid. In a power plant, however, most liquid level instruments must indicate or record level of water under pressure. This is the case in measuring level of water in boiler drums, deaerators, feed water heaters and similar pressure vessels. In all of these cases, the equipment used is some form of differential pressure gauge. In the case of measuring drum level, a nozzle is connected to the drum near the bottom and one near the top. A condenser of some type is connected to the nozzle near the top of the drum so that a water leg of constant level is always maintained on the high pressure side of the differential pressure gauge. The nozzle at the bottom of the drum is connected to the low pressure

side of the differential gauge and the pressure on this side varies with the level of the water in the drum. The differential gauges are very similar to those used for flow meters, although, in the case of drum level there are a number of indicators so designed that the level is shown on a vertical indicating scale on the gauge board with a different color below the point of water level than above the water level. This makes the water level indication very easily visible from a distance.

Measuring water level under pressure while heat is being added, as in the case of drum level, involves many problems. A difference in temperature in the high pressure leg (cold water) and in the low pressure leg (hot water in the drum) can cause an error. It is possible to get water level indicators and recorders that compensate satisfactorily for pressure and temperature. In applying the use of such instruments to drum level, it is well to make a study of the ASME Boiler Code requirements.

Functional Instruments

In addition to being classified as to application, instruments can be classified as to function. Indicators show an instantaneous value of the units being measured. Integrators are devices for showing total quantities over a period of time and are very much like a counter that shows total mileage on a car.

Another type of instrument in extensive use is the scanner. With this type of device, an instrument is connected in sequence to given points but does not bother to indicate or record the value at any of these points unless one of them deviates from predetermined limits. What happens then depends to a great extent on the type of scanner used. In some cases the primary

Figure 22–19.   Portable data logger

element is immediately connected to a recorder and some kind of signal is given to show what point is being recorded. In the meantime the scanner continues to monitor the system as a whole. There are a number of types of scanning systems, which may be used to monitor temperatures of boiler tubes and turbine bearings.

Digital computers and data loggers are finding increasing use in power plants. With these devices many values may be measured and calculated on a continuous basis. Values may be recorded for test purposes, or the computer may be made an integral part of power plant operation. A test installation is shown in Fig. 22–19.

Television, generally of the closed circuit design, finds a number of applications in the centralized control room of steam power plants. It may be used to monitor stack exhaust conditions, to provide remote viewing of water level indicators and to give visual indication of combustion conditions in boiler furnaces.[12]

[12] The earliest known technical article to describe power plant installations is "Developments in Use of Television in Power Stations" by L. M. Exley, *Combustion*, Vol. 23, July 1951, pp. 43–46. This was supplemented by AIEE Technical Paper 52–285 by the same author, "Experience with Television for Direct Viewing of Furnaces," AIEE Trans., Vol. 71, 1952, Part III, pp. 999–1004.

23

Natural Circulation Boilers[1]

NATURAL CIRCULATION BOILERS, as a general type, comprise by far the largest number and the greatest ranges of capacities and steam conditions of the several basic designs now in service. While forced circulation boilers of several types, including controlled circulation, combined circulation and once through units, are used extensively in central stations operating at pressures above 2000 psig, many power plants are being designed for steam conditions ranging from 100 psig or less and saturation temperature to a point overlapping the use of forced circulation boilers. As they have been since the early development of the water tube boiler, natural circulation boilers are the dominant choice for these lower steam conditions. Some large industrial and central station installations are being built with natural circulation boilers supplying steam to turbines ranging from 50,000 to 200,000 kw, corresponding to steam generation on the order of 375,000 to 1,500,000 lb per hr at superheater outlet conditions up to 2000 psig with primary and reheat temperatures of 1000 F.

Some design features are common to all types of natural and forced circulation boilers. For boilers operating below the critical pressure of 3206.2 psia such factors and components as burners, furnace contours, superheaters, reheaters and air heaters are basically of the same design regardless of the general type of boiler application.

Fig. 23–1 shows one design of forced circulation boiler, the C-E Controlled Circulation Boiler.[2] The solid lines show the circulating system composed of the drum, downcomers, circulating pump which discharges into piping leading to the headers at the bottom of the boiler furnace, the risers or waterwall tubes and the connecting piping at the top of the boiler furnace discharging a mixture of steam and boiler water into the drum. Steam is separated from the boiler water in the drum and flows on to the superheater and reheater sections shown in dotted phantom lines. Feedwater from the economizer, also shown in phantom, enters the drum and mixes with the separated boiler water before entering the downcomers to begin the circulation cycle. Each time around the loop composed essentially of drum, downcomers and risers a certain proportion of steam is separated in the drum and is im-

---

[1] L. J. Marshall contributed the first section of this chapter; J. G. Singer and H. J. Blaskowski, the concluding section dealing with waste heat boilers.
[2] See Chapter 24, Controlled Circulation Boilers, for additional information.

mediately replaced by feedwater flowing in from the economizer.

Natural circulation boilers employ the effect of the density differential between water and steam to produce circulation. In boilers of the controlled and combined circulation type this natural force is augmented by pump output energy to insure positive circulation through waterwall tubes whose water input is controlled by orifices, the size of which may be varied to insure uniform circulation under variable boiler furnace conditions. In general, waterwall tubes of natural circulation boilers are larger than those of controlled circulation units in order to minimize friction losses and to take maximum advantage of limited head provided by density difference. As shown in Fig. 23–1 in the dotted phantom lines, the only differences between natural and controlled circulation boilers are in the circulating systems. Otherwise both types share the same kind of firing methods, means of superheating and reheating, heat recovery equipment and structural support.

Natural Circulation Boilers for Central Station Use

Fig. 23–2 shows a typical natural circulation boiler installed in a central station located in a natural gas producing area. There is a single furnace and the superheater stages are of the convection type, although radiant platens and radiant wall types are sometimes used. The boiler is designed to serve a 180,000 kw turbine-generator and has a rated output of 1,200,000 lb of steam per hour with superheater outlet conditions of 1850 psig, 1000 F. Either natural gas or oil may be burned in this boiler which is of the pressurized type, omitting the use of induced draft fans.

Tangential type burners are located in the four corners of the boiler furnace. There is a single water wall supply header located below the furnace bottom midway between the front and rear waterwalls. As shown in Fig. 23–2 boiler water is supplied by vertical downcomers connecting the drum to the bottom waterwall header. Lower ends of waterwall tubes of the front and rear walls connect directly to the same bottom waterwall header, and the upper ends connect through headers to the drum. Likewise, the side waterwalls are connected to headers at bottom and top. Tubes between the upper headers and the drum transport the mixture of steam and water discharged from the waterwalls to the drum where the steam is separated from the boiler water and passes on to the first stage superheater. To insure uniform distribution of steam and water, the connecting tubes are arranged uniformly along the drum and headers. The lower sections of the front and rear waterwalls bend inward to form an almost flat furnace floor.

The first stage superheater, as shown in Fig. 23–2, is located in the vertical pass at the rear of the furnace. Saturated steam from the drum passes through front and rear walls enclosing this section and then enters the lower superheater header. From this point the slightly superheated steam flows back and forth through the superheater tubes shown in the drawing, moving in a generally counterflow direction to the downward flow of the furnace flue gas from which the steam receives thermal energy by the heat transfer modes of convection and conduction. Leaving the first stage superheater, the steam then passes to the second stage which is a platen section located in the gas outlet of the boiler furnace where most of the heat is transferred by direct radiation. The third or

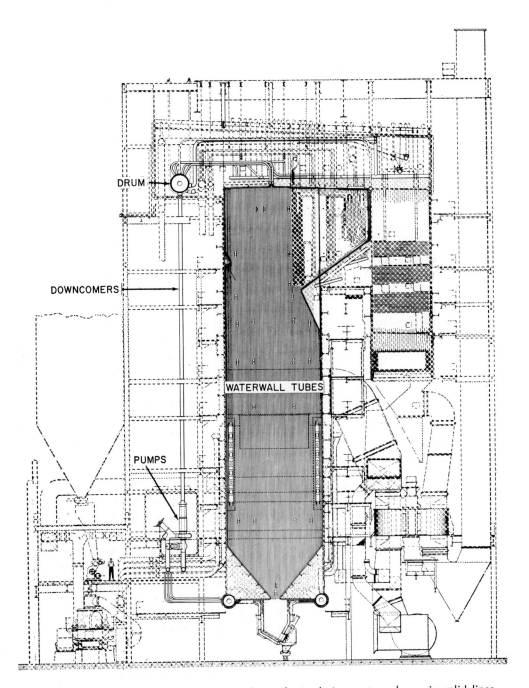

Fig. 23—1. C-E Controlled Circulation Boiler with circulating system shown in solid lines

outlet stage superheater is of the vertical pendant type in which heat transfer takes place by radiation and convection from the furnace gas and by conduction through the superheater tubing to the flowing steam. The reheater is located between the second stage platen superheater and the outlet third stage. The flow of furnace gas over the reheater and the third stage of superheating is essentially parallel to the flow of steam.

The economizer is located directly below the first stage superheater. Heat is transferred mainly by gas convection to the economizer surface which consists of tubes provided with welded vertical fins. Water flow in the economizer is essentially upward to provide approximate counterflow of furnace gas and feedwater. Outlet tube ends of economizer sections extend vertically upward to form the sidewalls of the horizontal first stage superheater and economizer enclosure. As shown in Fig. 23–2, these economizer tubes connect to headers above the roof, and connecting piping transports the feedwater from these headers to the drum.

A regenerative type (Ljungstrom) air preheater with a horizontal shaft is located at the central station basement floor elevation at the rear of the economizer. The gas ducts connecting the economizer to the air preheater and the latter to the stack are arranged with small hoppers in the horizontal sections where water used in cleaning air heaters and economizers is collected and drained from the system.

The entire natural circulation boiler, with the exception of the air preheater, is supported from steel located at the roof elevation.[3] Expansion joints are provided in the gas duct below the economizer and in the air ducts between the air preheaters and the windboxes of the tangential burners. Superheater and reheater connecting piping above the boiler roof as well as the superheater and reheater outlet headers, upper waterwall headers, riser tubing and the drum are completely housed by an insulated enclosure sometimes known as the doghouse.[4]

Another type of natural circulation boiler for central station use is shown in Fig. 23–3. Sometimes designated as the box type, this particular unit is designed to serve a 75,000 kw turbine-generator and has a rated output of 575,000 lb of steam per hour with superheater outlet conditions of 1850 psig, 1000 F, with reheat to 1000 F. The base fuel for this pressurized boiler is natural gas which is burned in tilting tangential burners, but fuel oil may also be fired and there is provision for future installation of pulverized coal firing equipment.

Superheaters and reheaters are of the horizontal type and are located in two passes above the boiler furnace. A single water cooled enclosure with four vertical waterwalls houses the boiler furnace, superheaters, reheater and economizer. Box type natural circulation boilers as shown in Fig. 23–3 are somewhat higher than the design shown previously in Fig. 23–2 but occupy less floor space and require less casing and fewer buckstays to protect the pressure parts against internal pressure. As in Fig. 23–2 an enclosure is located above the boiler roof to house some of the superheater headers, upper waterwall

---

[3] For additional information, See Chapter 10, Stress Analysis and Structural Design, section on Structural Design of Boilers.

[4] This construction is shown in Fig. 1–7 in the section, What Is a Boiler? of Chapter 1, Visualizing the Steam Power Plant.

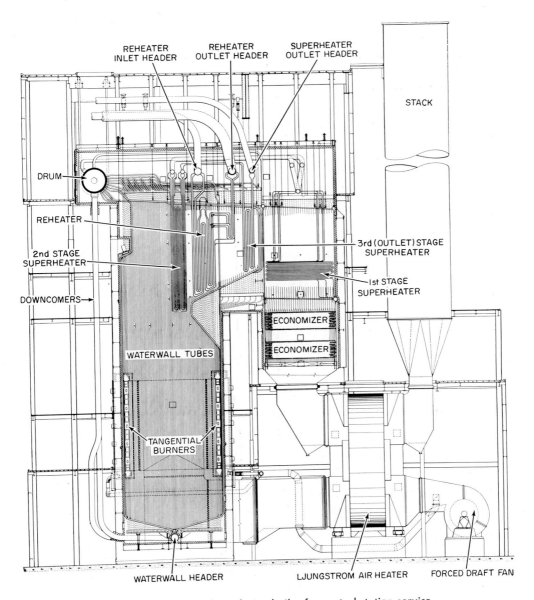

Fig. 23–2. Natural circulation boiler for central station service

headers, sidewall riser tubes and the drum. The primary or low temperature superheater is located in the rear pass and is arranged in two sections. Saturated steam enters the bottom of the lower section from the header located outside the boiler casing. Gas flows downward in this pass, and steam flow is generally upward to provide counterflow of steam and flue gas. After passing through the upper superheater section in the rear pass, steam continues through the vertical terminal tubes to a header located above the waterwall roof. It then continues by means of external piping to the inlet header of the high temperature section of the superheater located in the front gas pass. Substantially parallel flow of steam and gas is obtained in the high temperature section of the superheater.

The reheater is located in the front pass above the high temperature section of the superheater. Steam to be reheated enters the inlet header outside the setting directly below the drum and flows generally downward through the reheater in substantially counterflow relation to the gas flow.

The economizer is located in the rear pass just below the low temperature superheater, and the economizer elements are arranged parallel to those of the low temperature superheater. A counterflow arrangement of gas and feedwater is obtained by locating the economizer inlet header outside the casing and directly below the outlet header.

A regenerative type (Ljungstrom) air preheater with a horizontal shaft is located at the rear of the boiler with the gas inlet at approximately the same elevation as the gas outlet from the boiler.

Natural circulation boilers without reheaters are occasionally used in smaller central stations or in cases where minimum

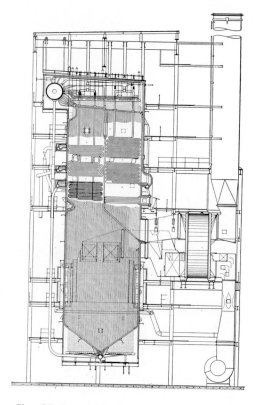

Fig. 23–3. Box type natural circulation boiler for central station service

capital investment is a more important consideration than high thermal efficiency, as in certain types of stripped down installations for electric power system peaking service. Fig. 23–4 shows a boiler of the same general box type as Fig. 23–3. Designed to serve a conventional regenerative cycle or nonreheat turbine-generator with a rating of 60,000 kw, this boiler is capable of generating 650,000 lb of steam per hour at superheater outlet conditions of 1322 psig, 960 F.

The chief difference between Figs. 23–3 and 23–4 is that the boiler of the latter has the high temperature superheater located in the same position as that

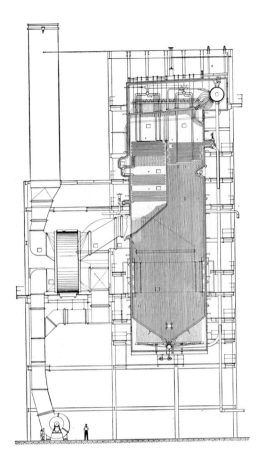

Fig. 23—4. Natural circulation boiler without reheater for central station service

tion required to provide the desired gas temperature to the air preheater results in increased duty in the form of temperature rise of the feedwater. In turn this requires additional heating surface as can be noted by comparing Figs. 23-3 and 23-4.

Natural Circulation Boilers for Industrial Applications

The industrial field covers a very wide range of capacities and steam conditions for which natural circulation boilers are used almost exclusively.[5] The number of large capacity industrial boilers designed for the high steam pressures and temperatures encountered in central stations is comparatively few. Likewise, there is a relatively limited market for industrial boilers in the capacity range from 150,000 to 400,000 lb of steam per hour. Under these widely varying conditions the boiler designer finds that no specific design is universally applicable. However, there are many standardized components with which the experienced engineer is familiar, and it is his design task to combine and synthesize these proved elements into a boiler which will meet the numerous requirements of the industrial boiler user. This is generally done by tailoring standardized boiler and firing components to meet specific operating needs.

Two types of standardization are used. The first applies to the larger ranges of boiler capacity and utilizes standard modular sections whose maximum sizes are determined by shipping requirements. These shop assembled sections are field erected with substantial savings by comparison to the cost of field assembly and erection of individual parts.

occupied by the reheater in the former. The omission of the reheater necessitates the use of additional economizer surface in the rear pass in order to reduce the exit flue gas temperature to the desired value at the air preheater. The economizer is in two sections and is located below the low temperature superheater in the rear pass. The additional economizer heat absorp-

[5] See the following section of this chapter. Waste Heat Boilers; Chapter 26, Shop Assembled Boilers; Chapter 27, Boilers and Recovery Units for Pulp and Paper Industry.

In the smaller ranges of steam capacities the second type of standardization takes the form of the completely shop assembled boiler shipped as a unit ready for operation upon arrival on the industrial site. While boilers burning fuel oil or natural gas are most commonly shop assembled, standardized units are also available for small stoker fired installations and for burning waste fuels.[6]

Fig. 23–5 shows a type of large natural circulation boiler used in industrial power plants. Burning pulverized coal fired through horizontal burners, this boiler has a steam output of 400,000 lb per hr with superheater outlet conditions of 865 psig, 825 F.

The boiler furnace is arranged with an ash hopper which is formed by side water-wall tubes which are sloped toward the center to form a slot running from front to rear through which the ash separated from the furnace gas is discharged. Burners are of the horizontal turbulent type located in the front left wall as shown in Fig. 23–5. The pulverizers are located on the basement floor below the burners. Coal and primary air are transported to the burners through approximately vertical pipes running from the pulverizer exhauster discharge.

The superheater is of the vertical pendant type and is located in the gas pass at the boiler furnace outlet. There is a convection tube bank running between the lower part of the main steam drum above to the upper part of a water drum located below. These tubes are closely spaced circumferentially and lengthwise of the drums. Gas from the furnace flows essentially horizontally over the superheater and the convection bank, the latter being provided with an ash hopper at the rear.

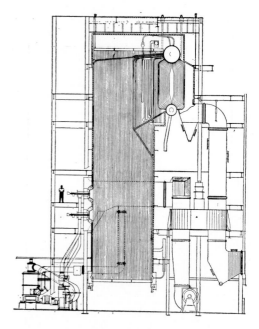

Fig. 23–5. Large natural circulation boiler for an industrial power plant

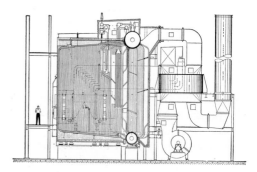

Fig. 23–6. Field erected industrial boiler

[6] For additional information on the design, shipping and installation of these boilers, see Chapter 26, Shop Assembled Boilers.

Beyond the convection bank the furnace or flue gas flows through a vertical duct to the regenerative type (Ljungstrom) air preheater mounted on a vertical shaft. After leaving the air preheater the flue gas passes through a dust collector and induced draft fan on its way to the stack. This natural circulation type industrial boiler is supported from above by structural steel in a manner similar to the central station boilers previously described.

Fig. 23–6 shows a boiler design widely used for industrial process steam and small power generation installations. The specified design conditions for this boiler are a capacity of 280,000 lb of steam per hour with superheater outlet conditions of 875 psig, 900 F. Natural gas and fuel oil may be burned in this boiler which serves a 22,000 kw turbine-generator in a municipal power plant.

This is a field erected boiler of which some components are standardized and shop assembled. In contrast to previously described boiler arrangements, the design in this case is of the low head type supported from the bottom rather than suspended from above. Boiler heat absorbing surface is located behind and occupies the entire height of one furnace wall. Tangential burners are located in the side walls close to the front and rear furnace waterwalls. Heat absorbing surface in the form of a vertical convection tube bank is located at the rear of the furnace. The superheater is of the pendant type in two vertical sections, of which the high temperature section is located at the boiler furnace outlet where gas flow is essentially perpendicular to the tubes. The low temperature section of the superheater is located between the furnace and convection tube bank where gas flow is downward and essentially parallel to the tubes. Baffles in the superheater sections and in the convection bank are arranged to direct the gases over the desired surface and provide required velocities. A combination of cross and parallel flow occurs in the convection bank.

Due to the low head characteristics of this boiler design, bottom support becomes practicable and simple with an appreciable reduction in the quantity of structural steel members. As shown in Fig. 23–6 both sections of the superheater are hung from above with the weight of tubing being supported by furnace roof tubes. In this boiler the headers of the low temperature superheater are supported on the upper drum, while those of the high temperature section are supported on the upper header of the side waterwall.

Fig. 23–7 shows a standardized field erected industrial boiler for gas and oil firing. It is designed and constructed to make use of standardized modular components which are shop assembled prior to field erection. Designed for pressurized firing, this boiler is one of a series which incorporates waterwalls consisting of panels composed of spaced tubes between which metallic fins are placed and welded to the tubes. The panels thus form completely tight waterwall sections.

This modular type boiler is similar in general arrangement to that shown previously in Fig. 23–6 in that it is bottom supported and can be designed for either horizontal or tangential firing. To meet specific industrial needs, a great variety of sizes can be made available by varying the depth, width, height and drum size of the boiler by the use of predetermined size increments. This provides for great flexibility and accounts for an output range from around 125,000 to 450,000 lb of steam per hour, plus operating pressures from 125 to 1000 psig and superheater outlet temperatures up to 900 F.

Fig. 23–8 shows a similar standardized boiler which is field erected for smaller outputs ranging from 60,000 to 125,000 lb of steam per hour. Operating pressures span the range from 125 to 700 psig, and steam temperatures to 700 F can be provided. Equipped with tangential type oil and gas burners, this pressurized boiler is bottom supported and is available in five sizes.

Another type of standardized field erected boiler is shown in Fig. 23–9. Designed in nine sizes to produce from 10,000 to 60,000 lb of steam per hour at superheater outlet conditions up to 475 psig and 600 F, this type of boiler is bottom supported and is intended to be operated with balanced furnace draft. Oil, gas or stoker firing may be utilized in this series of small natural circulation boilers.

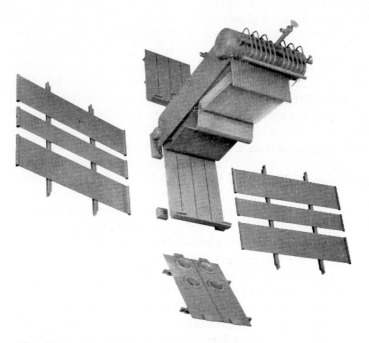

Fig. 23–7.   Standardized modular construction for field erected industrial boiler

Waste Heat Boilers

The design of boilers for the recovery of waste heat is closely related to the fuel fired and the industrial process involved. For the purposes of this discussion waste heat boilers will be defined in two categories: those actually fired by waste and byproduct fuels and those unfired units which recover sensible heat only from

Fig. 23–8. Standardized industrial boiler installed in an oil refinery

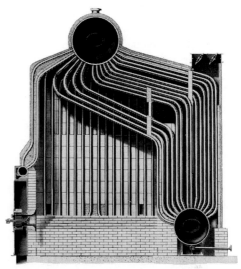

Fig. 23–9. Small natural circulation industrial boiler

industrial processes and combustion gas turbines. This section covers only a selected number from among many waste heat processes.[7]

Waste gases and byproduct fuels may be characterized as solid, liquid and gaseous in terms of the state in which they are fired. Solid waste fuels are generally handled and burned in stoker fired or suspended fuel fired arrangements; liquids, in atomized form. Except for spe-

cial cases these do not differ appreciably from the handling of coal or oil. Gaseous waste and byproduct fuels, on the other hand, may require special treatment, as outlined in this chapter.[8]

Refinery gas and coke oven gas, which are relatively clean gases differing from natural gases mainly in volumetric heat content, are excellent fuels that call for only minor changes in burner design. In general, fuel gases having heat contents higher than 500 Btu per cu ft are easily handled by burners of the same type as used for natural gas. With gases of heating value less than 250 Btu per cu ft, consideration should be given to burning systems of high volumetric capacity, such as tangential firing.

Waste gaseous fuels differ substantially

[7] For example, burning of bark, refuse wood and black liquor is the subject of Chapter 27, Boilers and Recovery Units for Pulp and Paper Industry.

[8] See Table 14–19, Chapter 14, Natural Gas, Oil and Byproduct Fuels, for a listing of byproduct fuels and waste gases together with the equipment used for combustion and heat recovery. This table also contains references to chapters where a more complete discussion may be found.

from natural gas because of large percentages of inert gases or dust carryover. Most problems involved with these gases are typified in the handling of steel and copper reverberatory gases, blast furnace gas, catalytic cracker regenerator gas and gases from cement kilns.

Most waste gases are characterized by a high inert gas content and by a solid carryover content. The degree to which the inerts are present and the quantity, size and character of the solids, strongly influence the boiler design for a given application.

Copper Reverberatory Gas

Boilers fired with smelter gases are required to operate continuously for prolonged periods of time. These gases which contain negligible amounts of combustible matter are made available to the steam generator at a temperature of about 2200 F. They contain varying quantities of sulfur dioxide and sulfur trioxide as well as droplets of slag and metal that may be molten as low as 1400 F.

To provide the maximum reduction in temperature of these hot gases with minimum contact with convection heating surface, boilers for this service are provided with ample cooling chambers or furnaces. To gain further insurance against plugging the narrower spaced convection bank, a wide spaced platen bank is sometimes installed at the furnace outlet. Sufficient hopper capacity to catch the carryover is required in both the furnace and boiler bank. Since the quantity of carryover is appreciable, care must be exercised to supply, judiciously locate and systematically operate soot-cleaning devices. To minimize outage because of possible corrosion difficulties, economizers are generally not used.

Blast Furnace Gas

Blast furnace gas, a dust laden byproduct of the iron reduction process, derives its value as a waste fuel from its high carbon monoxide content. Since this varies widely with the furnace charge, the heating value of the gas can range from 65 to 110 Btu per cu ft.

The dust carried over is mostly iron oxide. A large percentage of it is of a consistency and nature to foul gas mains, burners, boiler furnaces and convection heating surfaces, requiring their frequent cleaning. To extend and improve availability of equipment, the blast furnace gas may undergo as many as three stages of cleaning. The first stage is a simple mechanical separation; the second, a primary spray washing; and the third, either a more vigorous washing or an electrostatic separation. The dust load after the first stage of cleaning may range from 5 to 8 grains per cu ft. This is reduced to 0.3 to 1.0 grain per cu ft in the second stage and, in the final stage, to 0.005 to 0.01 grain per cu ft.

Boilers designed for steel making service must be rugged and have high availability. They must be capable of responding to very rapid load changes. When they are fired by blast furnace or coke oven gas, they are further subject to quick changes in the availability of these fuels. For this reason, supplemental burning of another fuel that can rapidly pick up load is required to establish continuity of steam generator operation.

There are many more variables to handle in designing a suitable boiler for blast furnace gas operation than for conventional fuels. As a first consideration, the quantity of solid carryover in the gas may permit the selection of a unit as simple and as compact as those used exclusively for natural gas or oil firing or may call for a unit of larger size, freely hoppered and provided with soot cleaning devices to the same extent as a pulverized coal fired boiler.

Secondly, the low heating value requires that 1500 to 1600 lb per hr of combustion products be generated for each million Btu fired as compared with 850 to 950 lb per hr of products per million Btu for such conventional fuels as oil and gas, and 950 to 1050 lb per hr of products per million Btu of coal fired. For a given evaporation, the quantity of products passing through a boiler varies considerably as fuels are changed. Since this is so, the control of the steam temperature for units having high temperature superheaters becomes a critical consideration. Design conditions are made more difficult because of the erratic availability of the blast furnace gas, which creates the need to hold steam temperature constant under conditions in which it would tend to swing as much as 100 deg F in seconds. This problem is normally handled by steam temperature control schemes of the spray or gas recirculation type.

There is an additional problem of handling the simultaneous burning of a number of fuels with blast furnace gas in the same furnace. Until recently, this was done by horizontally fired burners, which frequently proved to be an awkward way to handle the extra fuels especially where pulverized coal was one of the fuels to be burned. The application of tangential firing has resulted in a very simple arrangement, as shown in Fig. 23–10.

The selection of heat recovery equipment for blast furnace gas units designed for supplemental firing with other fuels involves a careful evaluation in order to achieve optimum recovery. Where air heaters are used, a bypass damper on the

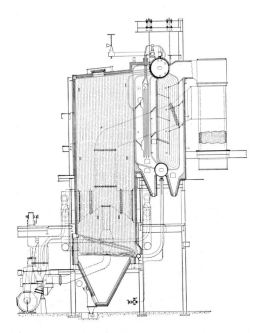

Fig. 23–10. Tangentially fired industrial boiler designed to burn blast furnace gas and coal

gas side is sometimes installed to bring about a more favorable draft loss relation since blast furnace gas has a much larger ratio of gas to air weight than other fuels.

Open Hearth Furnace Gas

One of the common methods of producing steel from pig iron utilizes the open hearth furnace. The exhaust gases leaving the furnace are passed through refractory checkerwork which serves as a regenerative type heater for the combustion air required for direct firing of fuel into the furnace. Two sets of checkerwork are included with each furnace, and slide gate dampers are used to exhaust air and gas alternately through the checkerwork.

The reversals of checkerwork, plus variations in the operation of the open hearth furnace itself, result in continuous changes of gas flow, dust loading and gas temperature. Ordinarily these gas temperatures range from 1000 to 1500 F, but where direct oxygen lancing of the furnace is utilized to increase the rate of steel production they may reach 2000 F.

Steam demands in a steel mill make the use of waste heat boilers a practical means of reducing the temperature of waste gases to around 600 F. This permits the use of electrostatic precipitators capable of removing dust particles as required by increasingly stringent air pollution laws. Because these gases are dirty and offer only sensible heat, they present special requirements for the boiler designer. To complicate matters further, flows and heat input may have wide fluctuations as previously noted. This means that heating surfaces must be arranged so as to minimize deposits and plugging of gas passages. At the same time positive circulation is essential to provide stability of boiler operation and to insure good steam quality.

Fig. 23–11 shows a controlled circulation boiler for the recovery of heat from open hearth furnace gas. Tube spacing at the inlet section near the bottom of the unit is comparatively wide to prevent slag adherence and to minimize abrasion. As the gas is cooled in passing through the boiler, the tube spacing is decreased. The boiler circulating pumps not only permit flexibility in the choice of tube size and spacing but also assure positive and stable circulation under steady and variable load conditions.

While originally applied to waste heat recovery from open hearth furnace gas, this design of controlled circulation waste

Fig. 23–11. Controlled circulation boiler for recovery of heat from open hearth furnace gas

heat boiler can be employed wherever exhaust gas conditions and limited physical space justify the advantages of the controlled circulation principle in reducing boiler size for a given steam output and waste heat throughput. Controlled circulation waste heat boilers find use in recovering heat from cement kilns and various metallurgical, mineral reduction and refining processes.

Basic Oxygen Process Gas[9]

The basic oxygen process for steel making has several advantages over the open hearth method. These include reduction in time required, increased rates of production and decreased costs. Oxygen is top blown into a vessel similar to a Bessemer converter, and the products of this reaction, mainly CO gas, are collected in a fume hood. The total cycle time varies with the oxygen blowing rate, but it usually consists of a 20 minute oxygen blowing time followed by a 25 minute charge time.

The primary function of the fume hood is to reduce the temperature of the dust-laden gases and direct them to the cleaning equipment prior to discharge to the atmosphere. The unit designed for this service uses controlled circulation principles and can be combined with convection surface to constitute a waste heat boiler as shown in Fig. 23–12. The unit is fabricated of small diameter tubing with fillet welds between adjacent tubes on the outside perimeter to form a continuous wall that is gas tight. The vessel cover is placed directly above the converter vessel and located in such a manner as to control entering ambient air. The amount of air admitted to the hood is controlled through the induced draft fan and is related to the quantity required to oxidize the carbon monoxide gas that is generated in the basic oxygen process as it is now being applied in the steel industry.

The dust produced in this steel making process is composed essentially of Fe_2O_3 with small amounts of FeO and Mn_3O_4. There are also traces of silicon, calcium, aluminum and phosphorus oxides. An in-

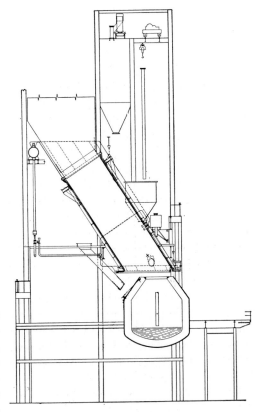

Fig. 23–12. Fume hood for waste heat recovery in the oxygen process for steel making

dication of the minute particle size is the fact that 85 per cent by weight of the particles in the fume are less than one micron, and 20 per cent are less than half a micron. The dust loading varies considerably during the oxygen blowing period and reaches a maximum after carbon monoxide evolution begins and temperature is highest.

The total weight of dust evolved during a blowing cycle has been found to vary

[9] This account is based on reports and technical papers prepared by A. J. Sefcik.

from one to two per cent of the metallic charge weight. The dust loading associated with the carryover for standard design purposes is seven to nine grains per standard cubic foot.

The gas emanating from the mouth of the vessel is composed mainly of carbon monoxide, and the total gas volume is directly related to the blowing rate. The carbon monoxide present must be totally burned in the hood to eliminate the possibility of an explosion in the associated duct work and dust collectors. An accepted design criterion is that the ratio of waste gas produced to oxygen blown is 25 to 1 under standard conditions. The amount of waste gas fluctuates with the excess air as shown in Table 23–1.

To insure complete oxidation of the carbon monoxide gas and more uniform heat absorption in the fume hood a tangential overfire air system has been developed. Controlled circulation is also necessary for this application since positive and complete circulation is required in areas of high heat absorption.

As shown in Fig. 23–12, feedwater is discharged into the steam drum where it mixes with circulated water from the unit. This water mixture enters the downcomers, and these are connected to circulating pumps which deliver water to a discharge manifold. The water then flows through supply tubes to the inlet headers of the fume hood and through the waterwalls to the outlet header. Risers from the outlet header to the steam drum complete the circuit. The unit has complete water cooling with convection surface located in the upper furnace area.

The application of waste heat boilers to the basic oxygen process is complicated by the cyclic operation which presents many obstacles to the design of an acceptable system for continuous steam generation. Supplementary fuel must be fired during the charging period, and it may sometimes be necessary during blowing and charging. The steam generated during the blowing cycle can be discharged into a header system and used elsewhere in the steel plant. One possibility of dampening the effect of the cyclic operations is to generate the steam at high pressure and store it in an accumulator. This steam can then be discharged at a constant rate and lower pressure during the charging cycle.

Refinery Regenerator Gas[10]

In the petroleum refining industry one of the major processes for producing gasoline is catalytic cracking. It is necessary to regenerate the catalyst continuously to maintain optimum output in steady flow catalytic processes. The process of regeneration involves the removal of coke deposited on the catalyst in the cracking operation. It is accomplished in a regenerator, a large vessel in which compressed air circulates and scours the hot catalyst to burn off the coke and return the catalyst to the reactor for reuse. To do this, large quantities of air must be raised to a pressure as high as 25 psig. At the same time, in order to minimize compression costs and to keep the temperature within the regenerator to a level which will not destroy catalyst activity, the quantity of air is limited to the smallest amount that will effectively clean the catalyst.

Under these combustion conditions an appreciable amount of carbon monoxide results. This gas, which may leave the re-

---

[10] This section has been adapted from ASME Paper 60-WA-327, "Tangential Firing of Regenerator Waste Gas in CO Boilers" by J. G. Singer and S. S. Blackburn, Jr.

Table 23-1 Waste Gas Volume and Composition

Combustion air, per cent	Excess air, per cent	Waste gas, cu ft per cu ft of O_2					Induced air, cu ft per cu ft of O_2	Waste gas composition, at peak of blow, per cent				Estimated hot gas temperature, F
		CO	CO_2	N_2	Air	Total		CO	CO_2	N_2	Air	
0	—	2	0	0	0	2	0	100	0	0	0	3000
25	—	1.5	0.5	0.94	0	2.94	1.19	51	17	32	0	3500
50	—	1	1	1.88	0	3.88	2.38	25.8	25.8	48.4	0	3800
75	—	0.5	1.5	2.82	0	4.82	3.57	10.4	31.1	58.5	0	4000
100	0	0	2	3.76	0	5.76	4.76	0	34.7	65.3	0	4200
125	25	0	2	3.76	1.19	6.95	5.95	0	28.8	54.1	17.1	3600
150	50	0	2	3.76	2.38	8.14	7.14	0	24.6	46.2	29.2	3200
175	75	0	2	3.76	3.57	9.33	8.33	0	21.4	40.3	38.3	3000
200	100	0	2	3.76	4.76	10.5	9.52	0	19.0	35.8	45.2	2700
300	200	0	2	3.76	9.52	15.3	14.3	0	13.1	24.6	62.3	2000
400	300	0	2	3.76	14.3	20.1	19.1	0	10.0	18.8	71.2	1600
500	400	0	2	3.76	19.0	24.8	23.8	0	8.1	15.2	76.7	1300
600	500	0	2	3.76	23.8	29.6	28.6	0	6.8	12.7	80.5	1100

generator at temperatures as high as 1125 F, contains a large amount of sensible heat, although it may have a heating value below 40 Btu per cu ft with a carbon monoxide content ranging from four to ten per cent. Regenerator waste gas cannot support its own combustion under ordinary conditions and requires a supplemental fuel, which is generally refinery gas, oil or natural gas.

Boilers have been designed to burn this regenerator gas and to supply steam at pressures and temperatures suitable for power generation and process use. At the same time these boilers are of considerable value because of their ability to reduce atmospheric pollution by oxidizing the carbon monoxide and hydrocarbon content of regenerator waste gas. A cross section of a typical design is shown in Fig. 23–13.

The amount of stabilizing supplementary fuel required to insure combustion of regenerator waste gas establishes the design criteria for what is known as a *minimum boiler*. This is a unit designed for continuous base load operation with a fixed quantity of waste gas and minimum supplementary fuel. In contrast to this, a unit may also be designed to take load

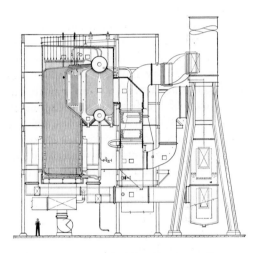

Fig. 23–13. Boiler for burning refinery regenerator gas

swings, with a maximum output as much as double the minimum load, making use of additional supplementary fuel. Such an increase in capacity is obtained at relatively small cost for the incremental amount of steam generation.

The main difference between boilers burning regenerator waste gas and conventional fuel fired units stems from the nature of the gas and the fact that its full flow must be handled by the boiler at all times. While a conventional boiler generally maintains a fixed fuel-air ratio throughout its load range and is capable of wide variation within this range, the boiler that handles regenerator waste gas begins with a minimum steam output corresponding to the minimum fuel fired for stable and complete combustion. Steam output can be varied from this minimum condition in only one direction, that is upward.

One of the most important features of the design of boilers for burning waste regenerator gas is the use of fixed tangential burners. The waste gas, stabilizing fuel and air are divided into several streams which are directed from the corners of the lower furnace so as to obtain cyclonic or rotary motion within the furnace. Concentration of the burners in the lower part of the furnace provides more heat for ignition as well as longer gas travel. Location of burners in quiescent corner positions assures positive ignition. The impinging and scrubbing action of the streams upon one another produces the turbulence and mixing of fuel and air necessary for rapid and complete combustion. With tangential firing the furnace is essentially the burner. Nearly all of the heat is released at the level of the burner nozzles, and complete burning takes place in a comparatively short vertical distance.

Gas Turbine Heat Recovery

The combustion gas turbine has become an important element in the production of electrical and mechanical power throughout the world. By burning liquid or gaseous fuels at relatively high temperatures and several atmospheres pressure, these machines generate energy without the condenser loss associated with steam power plants. Their thermal efficiency is nevertheless low because of high exit gas temperatures and the extremely high excess air percentages at which combustion is accomplished.

Gas turbines find wide application where power must be provided on a standby or peaking basis and for unattended service in remote locations. In many cases, it has been found desirable to improve the thermal efficiency of a gas turbine plant by adding heat recovery equipment, comprising boilers, economizers and regenerators, singly or in combination. Frequently it is found that the addition of either a fired or unfired steam generator to an existing gas turbine installation has economic justification. Many combined gas turbine-steam turbine power plants have been conceived and designed as such on the basis of higher thermal efficiency than a conventional steam power plant with the same steam conditions. The heat rate improvement can be as high as five per cent, depending on the steam temperature and pressure and the regenerative cycle chosen.

Gas turbines employ air-cooled stainless-steel combustion chambers operating at about 1500 F on a continuous basis. To obtain this relatively low combustion temperature, excess air in quantities higher than 300 per cent must be employed. With some gas turbines in which lower combustion chamber temperatures are used because of the nature of the fuel, the excess air may be as high as 500 per cent. The exhaust gas temperature is on the order of 600 deg F below the combustion chamber temperature.

There are three effects of these high excess air percentages and the 700 to 900 F turbine exhaust gas temperatures on the design of steam generating equipment: (1) straight waste heat recovery of sensible heat in the turbine exhaust must be accomplished at lower thermal heads than is the case with waste gas from reverberatory furnaces and the like; (2) as gas turbine combustion chamber temperatures are lowered, the exhaust stream becomes larger in quantity for a given gas turbine output at such a low temperature level that the recovery of waste heat may become uneconomical; (3) the use of gas turbine exhaust as highly preheated combustion air for a steam generating unit fired with any fuel, and without restriction as to steam conditions, becomes attractive. Many of the combined gas-steam turbine applications in operation or being studied involve both straight waste heat recovery by boilers or economizers and the use of turbine exhaust as the source of oxygen for fuel burning.[11]

Unfired Heat Recovery

Waste heat boilers for the recovery of sensible heat from gas turbine exhaust can be either of the natural or controlled circulation design. Such boilers can be built inside of what amounts to a continuation of the turbine exhaust duct. Gas velocities through these units are limited to about 100 fps by reason of excessive backpressure on the gas turbine.

The use of unfired boilers has been mainly for the production of process steam. In some applications, they have been used for power generation or space heating. It is characteristic of the simple-cycle, single-shaft gas turbine usually considered for this application that it produces substantially the same quantity of exhaust gas at all loads, but with sharply dropping exhaust temperature as kilowatt output decreases. The steam output of a boiler following such a gas turbine is then nearly directly proportional to the turbine electrical output. A superheater installed in such a boiler also has a drooping characteristic with decreasing load.

Gas turbine exhaust has been used in many instances for the purpose of adding heat to the feedwater of a steam cycle. This is accomplished by the use of extended surface economizers of the same design as utilized in power boilers.

Another arrangement has been investigated for use in areas where provision for the rapid handling of peak electrical loads has been found necessary. In this case, the gas turbine exhaust is passed over an economizer or stack gas cooler, which is installed in parallel with one or more of the feedwater heaters above the deaerator in a regenerative steam cycle. Under peak load conditions, the gas turbine is brought on the line and its products are exhausted to the stack gas cooler. The condensate circulated through the stack cooler is bypassed around one of the feedwater heaters. The extraction steam ordinarily required for this feedwater heater is then made available to the turbine. The arrangement permits the heat recovered from the gas turbine exhaust to be converted into additional power without the increased cost of steam generating equipment.

Boilers with Supplementary Firing

Gas turbine exhaust normally has 75 to 80 per cent of the oxygen found in free atmospheric air. It is a medium capable of concurrently supplying to the furnace of a steam generator both sensible heat and

---

[11] This topic is treated at greater length in many technical papers. One specifically concerned with boiler design is "Gas Turbine Boiler Applications" by H. J. Blaskowski and J. G. Singer, *Combustion*, Vol. 28, May 1957, pp. 38–44.

oxygen for the combustion of a fuel. The design and operation of boilers using turbine exhaust for combustion air will vary considerably, depending upon the ratio of the total exhaust flow to the amount necessary for oxidizing the supplementary fuel needed for a given evaporation. Combustion air preheaters are not used because of the already high level of preheat represented by the 700 to 900 F temperature of the exhaust gases.

Supplementary fired steam generators, Fig. 23–14, utilizing most of the oxygen content of the turbine exhaust, are of the same design and size as units using outside air through forced draft fans. The

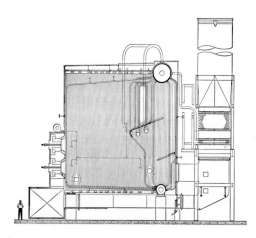

Fig. 23–14. Boiler designed for supplementary firing in conjunction with gas turbine cycle

stack temperature on such a unit can be dropped economically to within 100 deg F of the incoming feedwater temperature. In certain simple steam cycles where there is no lower feedwater temperature than

that leaving the deaerator, and this temperature exceeds 300 F, the stack temperature can be dropped to within 50 deg F of this water temperature by using an extremely large economizer. In such a cycle, gas turbine and boiler sizes must be matched closely in order to obtain a high ratio of feedwater flow to gas turbine exhaust flow.

For more advanced cycles it may be that the stack temperature cannot be dropped sufficiently low by an economizer alone to achieve optimum heat recovery. A stack gas cooler, which is actually another economizer that drops the gas temperature leaving the main economizer down to about the 300 F temperature level, may then be considered.

This stack gas cooler can be in series with the regenerative feedwater heaters, replacing either the highest pressure heater or some intermediate heaters. An alternate arrangement that results in improved combined cycle performance (at somewhat increased capital cost) is to put the stack gas cooler in parallel with the top four or five heaters. The possibility of external sulfur corrosion of the stack gas cooler should be considered where they are to operate in gases resulting from the combustion of high sulfur coals or oil. For feedwater or condensate temperature of 250 F and higher, finned tube economizers of standard steel construction can be employed. Low copper alloy steel can be used in the construction of economizers for feedwater temperatures of 225 to 250 F. Cast iron protected steel elements should be used for 150 to 225 F water temperature.

Since all gas turbine-boiler applications involve the recovery of sensible heat, the usual concept of boiler efficiency loses its significance. Customary practice, therefore, is to evaluate performance of combined-cycle boilers on the basis of stack temperature. The overall station heat balance is determined using the calculated value of fuel fired in the boiler (rather than boiler efficiency as such), in addition to the fuel fired in the gas turbine.

If it is desired, the relative efficiencies of several boiler designs using the same gas turbine exhaust flow and temperature can be calculated taking the sensible heat in the turbine exhaust (above a datum such as 80 F) as fuel fired, and assuming the turbine exhaust to be combustion air at the 80 F datum.

First million kilowatt C-E Controlled Circulation Boiler installed at Ravenswood Station of Consolidated Edison Company of New York

24

Controlled Circulation Boilers

THE COMBINED EFFECTS of higher steam temperature and pressure and the greatly increased size of boilers for central station service place severe limitations on boilers of the natural circulation type. The *controlled circulation boiler* incorporates a recirculating pump between the drum and waterwalls, thereby freeing the designer from dependence upon the difference in steam and water density to provide circulating head at advanced steam conditions, a differential that decreases rapidly in value as the critical pressure is approached.

The use of this pump means that the designer can be assured of positive circulation within a controlled circulation boiler even before heat is applied. Since the pump overcomes friction loss in waterwall tubes, small diameter tubes may be substituted for those of larger diameter required because of limited natural circulation head. This results in reduced tube weight, thinner tube thicknesses and lower thermal stress in tubes.

Another advantage of the use of the recirculating pump is that there is greater flexibility of boiler geometry and layout. When so desired the drum can be located below the top of the unit, saving in the amount of supporting structural steel required and providing the central station designer with additional alternatives in the layout of piping and auxiliary equipment. Likewise, there is more freedom in the arrangement of boiler heating surface, for with assured positive circulation, horizontal waterwall surface may be used to the extent desired. It is even possible to change the overall geometry of a controlled circulation boiler from the vertical "skyscraper" form to the horizontal "ranch house" arrangement.

Basis for Controlled Circulation

The basic elements of a controlled circulation boiler are shown schematically in Fig. 24–1. It employs a steam and water drum which receives a mixture of steam and water from the steam generating tubes and feed water from the economizer. Steam drum internals separate the steam from the excess boiler water. The saturated steam containing a minimum of impurities discharges from the top of the steam drum through a pipe or tubes into a saturated header and thence to the superheater portion of the boiler. The separated excess boiler water mixes with the feedwater in the steam drum, and the

[1] Material contributed by T. Ravese and E. M. Powell.

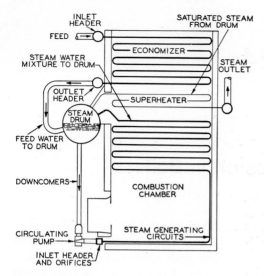

Fig. 24–1 Schematic arrangement of controlled circulation boiler

mixture is discharged to the steam generating tube inlet header by circulating pumps. Orifices in the inlet header control the flow of water to the steam generator circuits.[2]

It can be seen from this explanation that the basic difference between controlled and natural circulation boilers is in the introduction of a circulating pump between the downcomer system and the steam generating surface and the introduction of orifices for controlling distribution. The air heater, economizer, superheater and reheater are the same with both types. Circulation in the evaporative section of the boiler is produced primarily by a separate pump which usually runs at constant speed and is independent of feedwater flow and boiler output.

The use of a circulating pump makes it practicable to use small diameter waterwall tubes which have many inherent advantages. It is also possible to vary the shape and form of the steam generating

section and to locate it in any gas flow section of the boiler. Since circulation results from force imparted from a pump rather than from thermal head, the drum need not be located at the highest elevation of the boiler. The only limiting consideration of the height of the drum relative to the circulating pump is that the requirements for net positive suction head (NPSH) be met. These must be sufficient to avoid flashing of steam, cavitation and loss of pump capacity. Principal parts of a large controlled circulation boiler are identified in Fig. 24–2.

Circulating Pump and Piping System

A water circulating system diagram, Fig. 24–3, shows the schematic arrangement of the boiler circulating pump and downcomer piping system. Downcomers installed on the steam drum carry the excess recirculated boiler water mixed with the feedwater into the circulating pumps which are tied together through a common suction manifold. The purpose of the suction manifold is to insure a flow through all the downcomers regardless of the number or location of the circulating pumps in service. This feature is most important in that it minimizes the water level difference along the length of the steam drum. This is essential for good performance of steam drum internals and boiler circulating pumps.

It will be noted in the schematic arrangement that the downcomers are straight vertical pipes hung from the steam drum and that the circulating pumps are mounted between downcomers through a connecting suction manifold. This makes it possible to support the pumps from the structure and eliminates any need for external supports and pre-

---

[2] A basic reference is "The Controlled Circulation Boiler" by W. H. Armacost, *Trans.* ASME, Vol. 76, 1954, pp. 715–726.

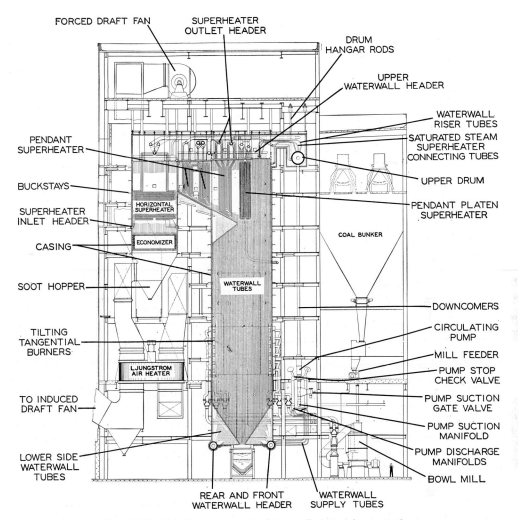

Fig. 24–2 Identified parts of C–E Controlled Circulation Boiler

vents undue stresses which may affect the alignment of the pumps.

The pumps are usually vertical and in most cases are driven by constant speed motors, although turbine drives may be used. Isolating valves are provided so that a pump can be shut down for inspection or maintenance without disrupting boiler operation. Sufficient boiler circulating pump capacity is usually installed so that full load boiler operation is possible for short periods with one less than the num-

ber of circulating pumps normally found in service.

A stop check valve is installed at each pump discharge to prevent recirculation through an idle pump, so that the valves need not be closed if the pump is available for service. Suitable bypass valves provide flow through the idle pump to maintain it hot and pressurized for immediate service. If the idle pump is kept on cold standby, then it must be pressurized and brought up to downcomer water temperature before it is placed in service. This operation requires approximately one hour, depending upon the pump size and recirculation flow rate.

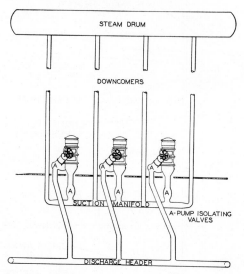

Fig. 24–3 Schematic arrangement of boiler circulating pumps and piping

Circulating Pump Types and Operation

Basically two types of circulating pumps are in use. One type employs a shaft soft packing gland or, if the operating pressure is too high, an injection type seal which will be explained later. The second type has no external seals since the motor is submerged; that is, it is contained within the same pressure tight vessel as the pump itself.

The temperature of the water pumped may sometimes be less than that of the saturated water at drum pressure, depending upon the subcooling effect of the feedwater if steam separation occurs in the steam drum without steam condensation. If the steam and feedwater are brought into direct contact for sufficient time in the steam drum, the temperature of the

water at the pump is that of the saturated water at the drum pressure. Boiler circulating pumps are always designed for this temperature condition since it exists during a boiler startup period when little or no feedwater is fed to the boiler and during an emergency or normal shutdown.

The suction pressure at the pump will be higher than drum pressure by the pressure equivalent of the difference in elevation minus the head loss in the piping to the circulating pump. It is very desirable that the piping loss be substantially less than the pressure increase due to elevation in order that flashing may be avoided and the pump operated without loss of capacity.

The pump head required for a typical controlled circulation boiler using waterwall tubes of 1 to 1¾ in. in diameter is 40 psi or less. A single stage impeller is adequate to supplement the limited effect of natural circulation and overcome the resistance of the installed orifices.

At least one pump must be in operation before the boiler is fired in order to provide positive circulation through waterwall tubes. If two or more pumps are required to handle the full capacity of the unit, two pumps can be started at once and additional pumps, if any, placed in operation after the load has been increased to the point where more circulating water is required.

The procedure for putting a controlled circulation boiler in service is identical with that for a natural circulation boiler except for starting a circulating pump before fuel firing begins. This results in uniform temperature rise in pressure parts during startup and avoids thermal shocks.

In the event of circulation loss through pump failure or power interruption, protective control equipment automatically shuts off the fuel supply to the boiler.

Description of Circulating Pumps

Pumping water at or near saturated temperature and at high pressure requires pumps of special design because of the possibility that water may flash rapidly into steam. For this service two types of boiler circulating pumps are in common use. One type employs a conventional drive, and shaft sealing is accomplished by a packing gland with suitable packing material or a shaft mechanical seal. This type is generally used in industrial applications, but for the higher pressures encountered in central station practice the shaft packing gland is supplemented by a sealing water labyrinth. The second type

of pump employs a submerged motor which is housed within the same pressure vessel as the pump itself and is therefore known as the glandless or zero leakage type of pump.

A pump with conventional drive commonly used in central station boilers is shown schematically in Fig. 24–4. The boiler operating pressure is too high for a shaft packing gland, and a cooling water labyrinth is provided for pressure breakdown to a value suitable for the soft packing. In accomplishing this result, water from the pump casing cannot be allowed to flow through the sealing water labyrinth because its temperature is too high, and flashing would occur in the seal, resulting in labyrinth erosion. Therefore, a source of cooler high pressure injection

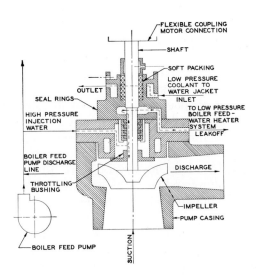

Fig. 24–4 Diagram showing circulating pump and sealing arrangements

water is required for sealing the pump as noted in Fig. 24–4. This water is taken from the boiler feed pump discharge before it has passed through the final feedwater heaters and when it is at a temperature and pressure suitable for addition to the circulating pump shaft packing.

When the boiler feed pump operates at constant speed, a source of pressure is available which is always greater than the boiler circulating pump pressure. At boiler steam flow rates substantially below normal, this pressure source of injection water provides too much injection pressure differential, and a pressure differential regulating valve is desirable for pressure control. When the boiler feed pump operates at variable speed, then at steam flow rates below normal this source of injection water may not provide sufficient injection pressure. In such cases a supplementary booster pump of limited capacity is provided with a takeoff point from the boiler feed pump discharge to supply the additional pressure necessary for sealing the boiler circulating pump. The booster injection pump is provided with a bypass system so that it need only be operated at partial loads as required.

The upward thrust due to the pump shaft extension through the soft packing gland is taken up by two sets of spherical roller or ball thrust bearings which are lubricated with oil circulated through an oil cooler by a pump mounted upon the main pump shaft. Radial ball bearings are mounted on the pump shaft above and below the thrust bearings to maintain shaft alignment. Thus no load is transmitted to the driving motor from the pump through the coupling. In some of the smaller sizes of pumps for industrial application the thrust load is transmitted to the motor in which case a motor thrust bearing of adequate size is provided.

The injection water requirement has led to the development of conventional motor driven mechanical shaft pressure seals and low gland leakoff. Water cooled mechanical shaft seals have proved reasonably successful for moderate steam pressures. A satisfactory mechanical shaft seal will not leak in excess of one gallon per hour during normal pump operation.

Another design allows leakage along the pump shaft through a labyrinth and pressure breakdown occurs in a shaft of reduced diameter, thus substantially reducing the quantity of flow past the labyrinth which has a very close shaft tolerance. This pump is designated as a low leakage type and is designed to operate with or without injection water. The pump bearings are water lubricated, and pump shaft thrust is transmitted to the motor thrust bearing designed for this service.

Developments in the atomic energy field have dictated the need for a completely leakproof pump. Designated as the zero leakage or glandless type, its use has been extended to controlled circulation boilers. This type of pump, shown in Fig. 24–5, has the motor housed within the same casing as the pump proper. The zero leakage pump is driven by a submerged motor which may have a canned rotor and stator immersed in full pressure but low temperature water. In the canned pump the stator operates dry and is enclosed in a very thin covering of nonmagnetic material. There is also a narrow "air gap" through which the high pressure cooling water circulates.

The submerged wet motor pump is similar to the canned type in construction with the exception that the stator winding insulation is exposed to water at pump pressure and must be suitable for this service. The insulating material is usually polyvinyl chloride or irradiated polyethyl-

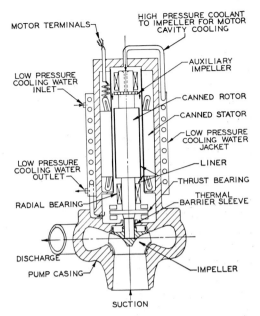

MOTOR TERMINALS

HIGH PRESSURE COOLANT
TO IMPELLER FOR MOTOR
CAVITY COOLING

AUXILIARY
IMPELLER

LOW PRESSURE
COOLING WATER
INLET

CANNED ROTOR

CANNED STATOR

LOW PRESSURE
COOLING WATER
JACKET

LINER

LOW PRESSURE
COOLING WATER
OUTLET

THRUST BEARING

THERMAL
BARRIER SLEEVE

RADIAL BEARING

DISCHARGE

PUMP CASING

IMPELLER

SUCTION

Fig. 24—5 Diagram showing zero leakage or glandless pump

ene. As with the canned pump the water is circulated by an auxiliary impeller through an external cooler which removes heat from the cooling water in contact with the motor and bearings.

A thermal barrier is equally important to the design of a wet or canned motor circulating pump. This is a section immediately above the main impeller, and its function is to retard the flow of heat from the circulated water or rotating assembly into the motor portion of the pump. The thermal barrier may consist of a hollow shaft with a close-fitting sleeve and bushing with extended surface over the neck portion of the pump and cooling jacket at the lower end of the motor or a plate section with suitable insulating material.

While the pump is operating there is ample cooling of the motor since the auxiliary pump on the main shaft provides the circulation of high pressure coolant through the cooler, bearings and

motor. However, when the pump is idle, pressurized and hot, then the only cooling provided is by natural circulation. During this period the effectiveness of the thermal barrier is most important. Submerged motor boiler circulating pump manufacturers take this into account in their design. All pumps of this type are capable of being maintained hot and pressurized without overheating the motor.

Circulation Ratio and Rate of Concentration

Circulation ratio is defined as the weight rate of water fed to the steam generating tubes divided by the weight rate of steam generated. If steam is condensed in the drum by coming in direct contact with the feed water, the weight of steam for the above calculation will be greater than the net output of the steam drum. In a boiler with drum internals capable of separating steam from water without condensing steam in the drum, the circulation ratio is the total pump circulation weight rate divided by the total steam weight rate leaving the steam drum.

The average weight of water per pound of steam leaving the steam generator circuits entering the steam drum is the circulation ratio minus one. For example, if the circulation ratio is four to one and the total steam generated is 1,000,000 lb per hr, the boiler circulating pumps must circulate 4,000,000 lb per hr of water through the boiler evaporating section.

In the controlled circulation boiler it is necessary to circulate only enough water and at a sufficient velocity so that the dissolved solids will remain in solution and enter the steam drum where the concentration is kept under close control by continuous blowdown. For the above example, if the total dissolved solids in the water entering the waterwall circuits amount to

600 ppm, they would concentrate to 800 ppm $\left(\dfrac{4,000,000}{3,000,000} \times 600 \right)$ in one passage through the evaporating circuits. This is true because the steam leaving the drum is essentially free of solids, that is, less than one part per million in large central station boilers. The efficiency of separation of impurities from the steam is well in excess of 99 per cent, and the recirculated boiler water (concentration 800 ppm) mixes with the feed water (concentration one ppm) in the steam drum so that the water pumped to the evaporating circuits is again practically 600 ppm.[3]

Table 24–1 provides data used to determine size and capacity of circulating pumps for a controlled circulation boiler rated at 1,584,000 lb of steam per hr and a circulation ratio of 4.35.

Strainers and Orifices for Steam Generating Tubes

Waterwall tube size in controlled circulation boilers varies generally from 1 to 1¾ in. in diameter. Flow control to the generating tubes is obtained by means of orifices positioned at the entrance to the circuit which may be composed of an individual tube or of two tubes joined at the inlet end where the orifice is located. Circuits comprising two tubes in parallel beyond the common inlet are called *bifurcated*.

It is desirable to provide strainers or screens between the circulating pump discharge and the orifices to prevent large particles of foreign material from plugging the orifices at the entrance to the generating circuits. Such strainers are installed in the inlet header or waterwall supply drum to which the steam generat-

Table   24–1   Data for Circulating Pumps

Rating of controlled circulation boiler, lb per hr	1,584,000
Number of pumps operating	3
Circulating ratio	4.35
Total circulation, lb per hr	6,900,000
Circulation per pump, lb per hr	2,300,000
Drum operating pressure, psig	2120
Saturated temperature in drum, F	645
Feedwater temperature to drum, F	499
Mixed water temperature, F	620
Mixed water specific volume, cu ft per lb	0.0243
Water horsepower, normal operation	162
Water horsepower, cold water	247
Pump efficiency, per cent	82
Pump brake horsepower, normal operation	198
Pump brake horsepower, cold water	301
Motor efficiency, per cent	90
Motor input, normal operation, hp	220
Motor input, cold water, hp	334
Motor input, normal operation, kw	164
Motor input, cold water, kw	249
Pump head, psi	40

ing tubes are connected. The strainers may be installed in individual tubes or for a group of circuits. Simplification dictates one strainer for a group of circuits whenever possible, and this has the added advantage that local fouling of a strainer will have a smaller effect on flow through any particular orifice. This arrangement of strainers is shown in Fig. 24–6 for circuits with orifices contained in a waterwall supply header and in Fig. 24–7 for circuits with orifices contained in a waterwall supply drum.

The strainers have a large number of small holes many times the area of the orifices and also smaller in size than the smallest orifice. This permits very fine particles to pass through the orifices without difficulty and also induces settling in the headers and drums of the larger particles. The strainers are made up in panels or sections permitting access to the orifices for inspection, removal and cleaning as required. As might be expected the need

---

[3] For additional information on steam separation and drum internals, see Chapter 8, Water Technology.

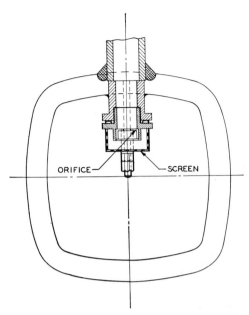

Fig. 24-6 Arrangement of screen and orifice assembly in header

of the strainers is most important during the initial startup of a new unit because it is during this period of operation that foreign material is brought into the boiler from preboiler cycle feedwater piping and auxiliary equipment. Accessibility to the strainer and orifice is also desirable to permit field alteration of orifice size as dictated by operating experience.

Orifices are shop fitted in an orifice mount which is assembled on an adapter in the boiler waterwall inlet header or waterwall supply drum. The adapter is also shop assembled and a keying arrangement insures that the orifice is installed in its proper tube circuit once the correctness of the initial installation of the orifice mount adapter has been established. In a 1,500,000 lb per hr controlled circulation boiler, five or six different sizes of orifices may be required to control and distribute the water properly to the steam generating tubes.

As long as the individual tubes of bifurcated elements are approximately the same length, and when each has almost the same heat absorption, each will receive practically the same amount of water. But two such elements in different parts of a furnace, where the heat absorption is different, can be designed for the same or different circulation ratios simply by selecting the proper orifice to suit the length of a circuit or the conditions under which it is expected to operate. By using only one orifice to serve two circuits, the total number of orifices and header or waterwall supply drum connections is cut in half and the quantity of water handled per orifice is twice as great, thereby permitting the use of a larger orifice for a given orifice pressure drop. Table 24–2 shows the results of actual flow field distribution tests on bifurcated elements supplied by a common orifice and located in radiant zones.

The data show that although the tubes are bifurcated with a common orifice the

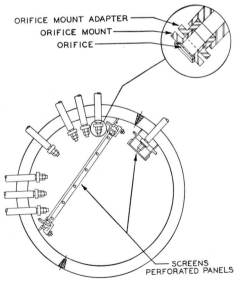

Fig. 24-7 Arrangement of orifices in drum

Table 24-2   Distribution of Flow in Bifurcated Furnace Circuits

Number of tests on each circuit				6				
Boiler steam flow — lb per hr				235,000 to 685,000				
Boiler steam drum pressure — psig				1546				
Front Furnace Wall								
Bifurcate number				73				
Furnace tube number				145	146			
Flow through each tube, per cent				49.4	50.6			
Inlet tube velocity, fps				3.4	3.5			
Rear Furnace Wall								
Bifurcate number		39		74		76		111
Furnace tube number	77	78	147	148	151	152	221*	222*
Flow through each tube, per cent	49.8	50.2	50.8	49.2	50.0	50.0	51.9	48.1
Inlet tube velocity, fps	5.0	5.0	5.0	4.9	5.0	5.0	5.0	4.7

* Denotes tubes in corner of furnace

flow through each tube is practically the same when the heat absorption of each tube is about the same. Even corner furnace tubes, where some difference in heat absorption might be expected, show good correlation.

Waterwall Tubes

Small sized tubing is used for waterwall tube circuits. To illustrate the advantages of small diameter tubing in a furnace, a waterwall composed of one inch tangent tubes may be compared to a wall of same width composed of three inch tangent tubes shown in Fig. 24–8. It is assumed that the tubes are exposed to the same radiant heat in each case and the furnace wall tubes operating at 2650 psig steam drum pressure. These tube sizes have been selected because they are in a range that could be used for this operating pressure. Pertinent data affecting circulation are in Table 24–3.

Table 24-3   Waterwall Tube Comparison

Tube diameter — inches	1.0	3.0
Tube thickness — inches	0.11	0.34
Velocity ratio	3.0	1.0
Tube weight ratio	0.325	1.0
Water weight ratio	0.339	1.0
Temperature gradient ratio	0.323	1.0

The calculations have been based on data plotted in Fig. 24–9 from tables of the ASME Boiler Code. The tube thicknesses, 0.34 and 0.11 for the large and small tubes respectively, are based on pressure stress only except that there is a limitation of 750 F maximum metal temperature.

Continuing these calculations further, Table 24–4 shows the results obtained with 100,000 and 200,000 Btu per hr sq ft heat absorption for waterwall tubes hav-

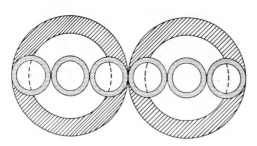

Fig. 24–8 Comparison of one and three inch waterwall tubing

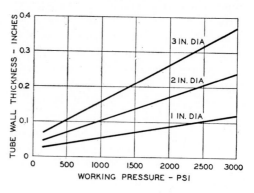

Fig. 24–9 Tube wall thicknesses at various working pressures

Table 24–4   Thermal Comparisons of Waterwall Tubes

Tube diameter — inches	1.0	1.0	3.0	3.0
Heat absorption — Btu per hr sq ft	100,000	200,000	100,000	200,000
Saturation temperature at 2650 psig	677	677	677	677
Temperature gradient — deg F	41	82	126	252
Hot face temperature — F	718	759	803	929

ing outside diameters of one and three inches.

These figures make no allowance for the small temperature drop through the inside film which would increase the hot face temperature nor for conduction in the rear of the tube which would lower it, but the large temperature difference between one inch and three inch tubes is clearly illustrated. The total stress in the three inch tubes would be much greater even though the stress directly due to pressure were nearly the same for both tube sizes.

The increased temperature gradient and the higher hot face metal temperature very definitely limit the rates of heat absorption to which the larger tubes may be exposed and still remain within allowable stress values. On the other hand, small diameter tubes in locations having radiant heat absorption rates of the 200,000 Btu per sq ft hr can operate with the mean tube metal temperature well within the limits set up by the ASME Boiler Code.

Experimental verification of this is shown by measurements made of temperatures at the crown of furnace wall tubes exposed to radiant heat in typical operating boilers. These measurements were made with thermocouples installed at several elevations of furnace wall tubes and instrumented in accordance with accepted methods. This made it possible to measure tube temperatures with varying heat absorption rates from a minimum to a maximum, depending upon the firing rate and furnace wall tube cleanliness.

The results of the tube temperature survey are compared in Fig. 24–10 for nat-

ural and controlled circulation units with approximately the same heat absorption rates. Tube temperature gradient including the film varied between a minimum of 22 deg F to a maximum of 113 deg F on the natural circulation unit whereas the range of similar temperature measurements gradient was 14 deg F to 53 deg F on the controlled circulation unit. Thus the temperature gradient through the furnace wall tube on the controlled circulation unit was less than half the range of the temperature gradient at approximately

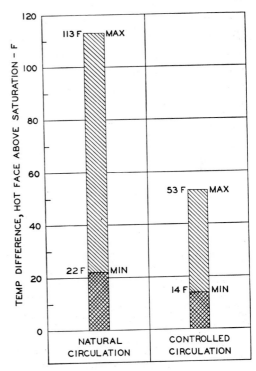

RANGE OF TEMPERATURE ABOVE
SATURATION TEMPERATURE

Fig. 24–10 Comparison of tube temperature gradients

the same heat absorption on the natural circulation unit. Accordingly the wall tube stress for the same operating pressure is less on the controlled circulation than on the natural circulation because the temperature stress is substantially less. These findings are confirmation of the temperature gradient calculations summarized in Table 24–4.

Thin wall tubes, which are used in controlled circulation boilers at pressure levels as high as 2800 psig, also make it possible to start up much more rapidly from the cold condition. Likewise, hot restarts can be made with less thermal shock because of the thinner tubes and the beneficial effect of the positive circulation induced by pumps which can be controlled independently of firing rates. These are important advantages in central stations where units may be "bottled up" during low load periods in the early morning hours or shut down entirely over weekend periods.

As an example of the ability of the controlled circulation boiler to respond rapidly during start up, Fig. 24–11 shows a rise in drum metal temperature averaging 220 deg F per hour during a test. This is in contrast to a comparable natural circulation boiler which, under similar conditions, would probably be limited to 100 deg F per hour. The data show that the maximum temperature variation in the drum shell is less than 70 deg F and that there are no sharp discontinuities which cause thermal shock.

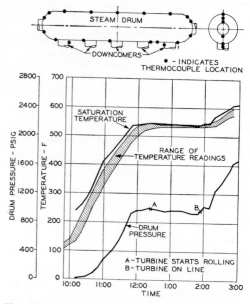

Fig. 24–11 Response of controlled circulation boiler to rapid start up

Installations

The first C–E Controlled Circulation Boiler in an American central station was placed in service in the Somerset Station of Montaup Electric Company in 1942. In the intervening years the principle of controlled circulation has been widely accepted for boilers of all types ranging from industrial, waste heat and marine units to the largest central station installations. The reliability, availability and safe operating records of controlled circulation boilers have justified their selection in power stations throughout the world.

25

Combined Circulation Boilers[1]

COMBINED CIRCULATION BOILERS are designed for use in the largest central stations operating at the most advanced steam conditions. They are the end result of engineering ingenuity as it manifests itself in the creative synthesis of design and operating experience with many types of natural and forced circulation boilers.

The opening section of this chapter deals primarily with the evolutionary development of once-through designs from their European origins as the Sulzer Monotube Boiler to their American modifications as the Combined Circulation Boiler. The concluding section, by contrast, is unconventional in that it is intentionally written in the first person plural to give a realistic personal touch to the actual team approach to the creation of a new engineering product, namely, the second generation of supercritical pressure steam generating units designated as the C-E Combined Circulation Boiler. By the use of this rhetorical device it is hoped that the reader will be able to grasp something of the feeling and atmosphere present when boiler design engineers work together cooperatively.

There is much too little understanding and comprehension of the human process whereby customer requirements are met by the interplay of competitive commercial factors and manufacturing know-how. The engineer plays a central role in this respect by bringing together accumulated design experience, knowledge of operating performance and the advancing impetus of new and creative ideas. In so many words, this account of the development of supercritical pressure boilers is intended to serve as a real life case study of the nature of *engineering design* as it is evidenced in the daily activities of one of the heavy capital goods industries.

Evolution of Once-Through Boiler Designs

For pressures up to the 2000 psig level, drum type natural circulation boilers have usually been accepted as the best technical and economic answer to the various requirements for steam generation. For pressures above 2000 psig, the difference

[1] Material for the opening section of this chapter has been contributed by J. I. Argersinger who was a member of the original technical team sent to Sulzer Brothers, Ltd., Winterthur, Switzerland, to adapt European once-through boiler design practice to American central station requirements. W. W. Schroedter, who led the engineering team responsible for translating the resulting design and operating experience into steam generating units of ever greater capacity, provided the concluding section of the chapter in the form of a personalized interpretation of the birth of the second generation of supercritical pressure boilers.

in density between water and steam is reduced to the point that many design and operating problems are handled more readily if mechanical means, such as a pump, are relied on to maintain circulation. In pressure ranging between 2000 and about 2800 psig, the controlled circulation design described in Chapter 24 has proved to be a most satisfactory solution. The once-through design is also successfully applied in this high pressure range, and it is of particular interest for pressures above the critical value of 3206 psia.

In a once-through boiler, as the name implies, there is no recirculation of water within the unit. In elemental form, the boiler is merely a length of tubing through which water is pumped. Heat is applied, and the water flowing through the tube is converted into steam and superheated to the desired temperature at the outlet. In actual practice, the single tube is replaced by a multiplicity of small tubes arranged to provide effective heat transfer in a manner quite similar to the arrangement in drum type boilers. It will be observed that the economizer and superheater operate on the once-through principle even in drum type boilers. The fundamental differences lies only in the heat absorbing circuits or evaporating portion of the unit. The word evaporating is used to include boiling at subcritical pressures and heating into the compressible vapor region at supercritical pressures.

In modern central station boilers the evaporating surface consists of waterwalls which form the major part, if not all, of the furnace enclosure. The principal distinguishing features of a once-through boiler are related to the design and operation of the waterwalls.

The distinctive design requirements stem partly from the temperatures that may exist in the waterwalls of a once-through unit. Figure 25-1 shows the distribution of water and steam temperature through typical boilers. In the drum type boiler of either the natural or controlled circulation type, the water entering the waterwall consists of the water from the economizer mixed with a much larger flow of recirculated water so that the mixture is cooled only slightly below saturation temperature. Thus the whole waterwall system operates at an essentially uniform temperature. In the once-through boiler, however, there is a considerable rise in temperature from waterwall inlet to outlet. The diagram shown in Figure 25-1 indicates average fluid temperatures typical of normal operation. Greater differences may exist during starting or upset conditions. Also there may be significant differences between individual tubes. All these differences produce relative thermal expansion movements in various parts of the furnace and between tubes, casing and buckstays. The furnace design and construction must take account of these differences, and this accounts for the first distinguishing characteristic of once-through boilers.

Because of the recirculation, the water flow entering the waterwalls of a drum type boiler is several times greater than in a once-through boiler. To provide proper velocities, the size and number of the waterwall tubes will be different. The arrangement or layout of the tubes may also be different in order to cover the same furnace wall area.

In operation, the waterwalls are exposed to high flame and gas temperatures and high rates of heat absorption even during startup and periods of very low firing rate. To prevent burnout of this surface, circulation of the working fluid must be provided any time the unit is fired. In a drum type boiler this require-

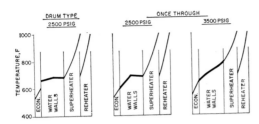

Fig. 25–1. Typical boiler fluid temperatures

ment is met by recirculation of the water in the boiler. Steam generated may be vented to atmosphere if it is not needed in other parts of the plant. In an elemental once-through boiler, the design does not permit internal recirculation, and a through flow must be established at least in the highly heated portions of the circuit. The operation of the power plant feedwater system including the boiler feed pump is needed to produce the through flow, and suitable means must be provided to dispose of the circulated flow without incurring an uneconomic loss of heat or working fluid. Such means normally take the form of the turbine bypass system which is the second distinguishing characteristic feature of a once-through boiler installation.

A Look Backward

The origins of the once-through boiler and the supercritical pressure cycle with which it is now commonly identified go back to an incredibly versatile American inventor, engineer and scientist who spent the last thirty years of his life in England. Jacob Perkins, who was born in Newburyport, Mass., on July 9, 1766 and died in London on July 30, 1849, designed a novel central heating plant for the Massachusetts Medical college in 1815, became a coin die maker, patented machinery and plates for engraving bank notes and in 1834 invented a refrigerating machine used to preserve food and make ice. It was, however, during his time as a successful manufacturer of fire engine pumps in Philadelphia that he became interested in and observed certain phenomena relating to the properties of water under high compression, and this was the beginning of a merging of scientific investigation and engineering ingenuity that culminated in the award of patents for novel high pressure boiler concepts in 1822 and 1827.[2]

As a personal acquaintance who was familiar with the high pressure steam engines of Oliver Evans, the distinguished but generally unrecognized American engineering innovator, Perkins naturally gave thought to using his recently acquired knowledge of the compressibility of water to improve methods of steam generation. He conceived the idea of an injection type boiler in which the amount of feedwater entering precisely equaled the amount of steam discharged. The boiler he built in 1822 was composed of a single copper chamber with a three-inch wall thickness and reportedly operated at pressures up to 7500 psig. His 1827 design constituted a continuous tube from inlet to the outlet

---

2 Jacob Perkins described the results of experiments by which he "proved that water was not only compressible but that the amount could be registered" to the American Philosophical Society in Philadelphia, and they were published in its *Proceedings* of April 16, 1819, just a few weeks before he left for England. During the Atlantic voyage Perkins conducted further experiments at great ocean depths, and these results together with additional work were reported to the Royal Society of London in a paper entitled "On the Compressibility of Water" which appeared in the 1821 volume of the *Philosophical Transactions* of that Society, pp. 324–329. Although it was misplaced and never published, a paper prepared by Perkins in 1822 for the Royal Society included information on the ratio of compressibility of water over a range from 10 to 2000 *atmospheres.*

steam chamber discharging to a steam engine cylinder. But Perkins was interested in steam rockets as well as improvements in the steam engine, and in 1824 he made the rather astonishing proposal of using steam at 50,000 psig and 1200 F to propel a cannon ball weighing a ton across the English channel. It is understandable that a contemporary, after describing the proposals and patent boiler of Perkins, could write:

". . . the method of heating the water subjected to this pressure, and the simple and effective manner of producing and continuing it, may possibly yet rank among the most important inventions of the time."[3]

Needless to say, though development work in high pressure steam was continued for many years by his son, Angier March Perkins, who also patented what was a pioneering high temperature water central heating system in 1831, the engineering concepts of Jacob Perkins were too far ahead of the times to gain any more than limited acceptance. It was not until 1889 that Leon Serpollet devised a successful once-through boiler of the flash type for steam automobiles. Interest in supercritical pressure generation lapsed for about a century until after the end of World War I when the concept was revived by a Mark Benson, a Czechoslo-

vakian chemical engineer who had emigrated to the United States.[4]

In 1923 when Benson proposed a turbine to operate at a steam pressure of about 1500 psig, throttle conditions of around 250 psig were in common use in American central stations, and the best record for thermal efficiency was slightly under 19,000 Btu per kwhr or about 18 per cent. To provide steam and circumvent the difficult problem of fabricating a thick walled drum, Benson conceived the idea of a once-through boiler to operate at critical pressure, with a reducing valve ahead of the final superheater. Along with improving thermal efficiency of central stations, the 1500 psig throttle pressure then presented a major technical and economic problem in fabrication of riveted boiler drums. It was largely for this reason that the boiler pressure was raised to the critical or nonboiling level of 3206 psia to avoid the formation of a two phase mixture and eliminate the need for a drum.

Several power plants of this type were built during the 1920's in England, Belgium and Germany, and they operated with varying degrees of success. Regulation of the boilers presented something of a problem, but the major drawback was the requirement for water of extremely high purity. The techniques of water treatment then available were simply not ade-

[3] A Descriptive History of the Steam Engine by R. Stuart, London, 1824, p. 207. Many of the engineering activities of Jacob Perkins and his sons are summarized in an illustrated article by C. G. R. Humphreys, "Perkins on High Pressure Steam", Combustion, Vol. 20, April 1949, pp. 48–52. Greville and Dorothy Bathe have written a scholarly biography, Jacob Perkins, His Inventions, His Times and His Contemporaries, Historical Society of Pennsylvania, 1943, 203 pages. Accounts of the patent boilers of 1822 and 1827 may be found in History and Progress of the Steam Engine by Elijah Galloway, London, 1836, pp. 243–248 and pp. 397–400; also A Practical Treatise on Boilers and Boiler-Making by N. P. Burgh, London, 1873, Chapter 4, Injection Boilers, pp. 190–204.

[4] For contemporary accounts of early developments, see "The Benson Super-Pressure Plant" by P. W. Swain, Power, Vol. 57, May 22, 1923, pp. 796–801; "The Benson Super-Pressure Plant — Its Scientific Basis" by P. W. Swain, Power, May 29, 1923, pp. 842–846; and "Steam Generation Under Critical Conditions" by David Brownlie, Transactions of the Institution of Chemical Engineers (London), Vol. 3, 1925, pp. 39–45 plus discussion, pp. 50–54.

quate for such an extreme increase in pressure. Impurities remaining in the feedwater deposited in the boiler tubes so rapidly that only limited periods of continuous operation could be achieved.

It was soon found that the once-through boiler could be used at subcritical pressures, thus reducing the feed pump power. The smaller amount of steel required in boilers of the Benson design, as compared to boilers of the drum type, provided sufficient incentive to persist in the development of once-through boiler design in Europe notwithstanding the other difficulties that had been encountered.

During the late 1920's the Swiss firm, Sulzer Brothers, Ltd. of Winterthur, also became interested in the once-through design, and developed the Monotube boiler for application below critical pressure.[5] Their program included the installation of a laboratory boiler in 1929. The first commercial installations were made about 1932. The decade of the 1930's marked the commercial acceptance of the once-through boiler in the European market for the pressure range from about 1200 to 2400 psig. Especially in Germany, the development has continued to increase

in scope and strength until, at present, a majority of the large, high pressure units being installed are of the once-through type.[6]

During the 1930's, there was likewise some interest in the United States. A few laboratory models and small commercial units were built.[7] Several factors combined, however, to delay any significant use for another twenty years. The somewhat lower relative cost of steel in this country lessened the economic advantage of the once-through type. A more rapid development in the art of welding permitted the construction of large drums for high pressure. During the industrial expansion of World War II, emphasis was placed on the use of known and proved designs to increase production and assure reliability. Following the war, improvements in drum type boilers, notably the controlled circulation type, encouraged further advances in pressure to the 2400 psig level and increases in steam capacity to the multimillion pound per hour range.

Shortly after 1950, spurred by rising fuel costs, American engineers again turned their attention to the attractive efficiency gains of the supercritical pressure cycle.[8]

[5] A basic reference is "Der Sulzer Einrohr Dampferzeuger" by Professor A. Stodola, *Zeitschrift des Vereines Deutscher Ingenieure*, Vol. 77, Nov. 18, 1933, pp. 1225–1232, and subsequently translated as "The Sulzer Single-Tube Steam Generator — Construction, Regulation, Regulating Trials", *Sulzer Technical Review*, No. 1, 1934, pp. 1–19.

[6] A comprehensive history of this development is found in *Die Entwicklung des Hochdruckdampfes in Deutschland* by Ernst-Otto Jochmann, VDI-Verlag, Dusseldorf, 1958, 164 pages. This includes a bibliography of 106 citations. An earlier but related work in English is *Steam Generators* by Dagobert W. Rudorff, London, 1938, 812 pages.

[7] See "Once-Through Series Boiler for 1500 to 5000 Lb. Pressure" by H. J. Kerr, *Trans.* ASME, *Fuels and Steam Power*, Vol. 54, No. 21, November 15, 1932, Paper RP–54–1a, and "Characteristics of a High-Pressure Series Steam Generator" by A. A. Potter, H. L. Solberg and G. A. Hawkins, *Trans.* ASME, Vol. 54, Paper RP–54–1b. One application is described in "Steamotive — A Complete Steam Generating Unit, Its Development and Test" by E. G. Bailey, A. R. Smith and P. S. Dickey, *Mechanical Engineering*, Vol. 58, December 1936, pp. 771–780.

[8] One indication was the presentation of a paper at the 1952 ASME Annual Meeting by Jacques Gastpar entitled "European Practice with Sulzer Monotube Steam Generators", *Trans.* ASME, Vol. 75, 1953, pp. 1345–1362. This was followed several years later by a paper entitled "The Monotube Once-Through Boiler for Conventional or Supercritical Pressures" by Arthur T. Hunter, *Proceedings* of the American Power Conference, Vol. 17, 1955, pp. 103–110.

Combustion Engineering, Inc. entered into a license and mutual technical assistance agreement with Sulzer Brothers, Ltd., in 1953 to gain the benefit of their experience of more than two decades with the once-through Sulzer Monotube boiler and its well developed system of controls. Marked advances in water technology, including ion exchange processes using demineralizing techniques, justified the confidence that continuous and reliable operation could be expected from large once-through boilers.

In 1953 and 1954 two large American electric utility companies announced plans to build supercritical pressure units: one for 125,000 kw with throttle steam at 4500 psig, 1150 F and double reheat to 1050 F and 1000 F; the other for 325,000 kw and throttle conditions of 5000 psig, 1200 F and double reheat to 1050 F in each stage. The latter unit, at the time of its announcement, had the distinction of setting four "firsts" in the central station industry, namely, high capacity, high steam pressure, high steam temperature and thermal efficiency.[9]

Subcritical Pressure Monotube Boilers

The Monotube boiler, as built for operation below the critical pressure, is a particular type of once-through boiler originally designed by Sulzer Brothers and further developed by Combustion Engineering in conjunction with Sulzer for application to American central stations. There are three fundamental features which distinguish the Monotube boiler:

1. The design and arrangement of the evaporating surface.
2. The use of a boiler water separator.
3. The boiler control system.

Taken together with the overall characteristics, these distinguishing features have produced a unit which has a high availability, operates continuously for extended periods of time and reliably and efficiently over a wide load range. This boiler also tolerates a certain degree of impurities in the feedwater because of the possibility of flushing the evaporating surface while on the line. Being capable of maintaining a constant steam temperature over a wide load range and during transient conditions, it also can be started quickly, cold or hot, with steam temperature matched to turbine starting requirements.

The design and arrangement of the evaporating surface give rise to the name "Monotube". In a modern boiler unit, the rate of steam generation is measured in hundreds of thousands or even in millions of pounds of steam per hour. It is obvious that, from a practical engineering viewpoint, such quantities of steam cannot be handled in one tube but must be handled by a large number of tubes in parallel. These tubes are connected together at each end by an inlet header and an outlet header. The headers must be so designed and proportioned with respect to the tubes, that the fluid will be distributed uniformly or equally to all tubes. The problem of achieving uniform distribution is much easier if the fluid consists of a single phase (entirely water or entirely dry steam) at the inlet header to a bank of tubes. For this reason the Monotube

---

[9] For an account of the original expectations of those responsible for the design and construction of the supercritical pressure units at Philo Station of Ohio Power Company and Eddystone Station of Philadelphia Electric Company, see "A New Power Generation Milestone" by Philip Sporn, *Electrical World*, June 29, 1953, pp. 72–76, 138, 140 and "New High Reached for Supercritical Pressure" by K. M. Irwin, *Electrical World*, November 15, 1954, pp. 114–119.

unit is designed and controlled, so that evaporation takes place entirely within a single bank of continuous tubes. The inlet header to the evaporating surface handles only water and the inlet header to the first superheater surface handles only dry steam. This is the basis for the name Monotube.

To handle the flow of water in the waterwalls or evaporating surface, and maintain a proper velocity for cooling the tubes, the number of tubes required is sufficient to cover only a small portion of the furnace periphery in a single pass. The tubes are therefore arranged to make several passes, perhaps in the order of 8 to 12, in covering the furnace walls.

Boiler Water Separator

In a unit for subcritical pressure a water separator is located at the outlet of the evaporating surface to insure that only dry steam will enter the superheater. The unit is normally controlled so that the steam entering the separator contains a small amount of moisture, perhaps five per cent. The moisture is withdrawn from the boiler unit and put into the feedwater heating system. The dry steam from the separator then passes into the superheater. The arrangement offers several advantages which otherwise would only be present in a drum type boiler.

1. With a separator a somewhat higher content of impurities can be tolerated in the feedwater. Most of the impurities will be concentrated in the water discharge from the separator, thus minimizing the formation of deposits in the boiler as well as the carryover of solids to the turbine.

2. A portion of the water withdrawn from the separator may be removed from the cycle as chemical blowdown. This permits control of the level of impurities in the cycle in the same manner as with blowdown on a conventional drum type boiler.

3. As a part of the feedwater control system, the water flow in some of the evaporating tubes is restricted so that these tubes operate with complete dryness and a slight degree of superheat at the outlet. Other tubes may also run dry for short periods of time due to changes or upsets in operating conditions. Moreover, with good water treatment, it is possible to operate the unit for considerable periods of time with evaporation being completed in the waterwalls and no water return from the boiler water separator. Under all these conditions, deposits will form in the outlet portion of the tubes. Such deposits are in general water soluble, and they can be washed out while the unit is in operation by merely increasing the feedwater flow slightly above the normal requirements.

4. A fourth feature of the water separator is that it makes it possible to restart the unit in a hot condition without chilling the hot metal in the superheater, steam piping, or turbine. The required minimum feedwater flow can be discharged from the separator until sufficient fire is established to generate steam which will then pass through the superheater. This is of particular importance in modern high temperature units where austenitic steel is used.

5. The action of the boiler water separator maintains dry saturated steam at the inlet to the superheater. This is actually the first step in steam temperature control. By maintaining the steam at the superheater inlet at a constant condition, it becomes easier to maintain a constant temperature at the superheater outlet under varying operating conditions.

Orifices and Throttling Valves

It is a feature of Monotube design that each tube in the evaporating section will have the same length, the same diameter, the same resistance to flow, and the same exposure to heat in various parts of the furnace as each of the other tubes in the system. The equalization is maintained as closely as possible within the limits of commercial design and fabrication. The flow system will, however, contain many tubes in parallel. There will be certain differences in flow and heat absorption between these tubes despite the best efforts of the designer, the builder and the operator. As a means for counteracting these differences, flow distribution devices are located at the inlet of the waterwall surface.

An orifice is located at the inlet of each waterwall tube. As originally installed, each orifice may be of the same size. Initial operation of the unit may indicate changes that are necessary in the size of certain orifices in order to obtain uniform steam quality at the outlet of the evaporating system.

In addition, the tubes are subdivided into groups with a throttling valve at the inlet of each group. For safety reasons, these valves are of the nonseating type. In effect, they are adjustable orifices which provide the operator with a ready means of changing the flow distribution while the unit is in operation. The valves are normally adjusted and left at a given setting, but they make it possible for the operator to wash out a group of tubes with the unit on the line, if operating conditions indicate this to be desirable or necessary.

Supercritical Pressure Monotube Boilers

When heating water and generating steam above critical pressure, there is no boiling and the change of phase from water to steam is not sharply defined. The transition takes place more or less gradually as heat is added to the fluid. The temperature rises continuously, although the specific heat and rate of temperature rise may vary considerably during the process. The fluid remains homogeneous while it becomes more compressible and assumes the characteristics of a vapor rather than a liquid.

Physical chemists postulate that in a typical liquid the molecules are arranged in relatively dense clusters. These clusters are of irregular and varying shape, with no set pattern. There may be some random interchange of molecules from one cluster to another. In a vapor, on the other hand, the molecules are much farther apart and there is no discernible pattern, the arrangement being completely random. During the boiling process at subcritical pressure, individual molecules break out of the dense liquid clusters and, as the physical surroundings permit, form a separate vapor phase. At supercritical pressure on the other hand, as heat is added to the liquid, the clusters gradually divide into smaller clusters and the spacing of molecules gradually becomes less dense until the transition to the wide spaced, random arrangement of a vapor is completed.[10]

The Monotube boiler design has been adapted to this supercritical pressure steaming process. Certain features of the design are no longer required, the most obvious being the boiler water separator.

---

[10] Mechanical engineers all too rarely concern themselves with some of the more complex concepts of physical chemistry. A pertinent exception is found in an appendix to a paper by Jerome Bartels, "Thermodynamics of Supercritical Pressure Steam Power Plants", *Trans.* ASME, Vol. 77, 1955, p. 755.

The most important result of this situation is that all impurities in the feed water must be either deposited in the boiler and superheater surfaces or carried over into the turbine. Feedwater purity now assumes an even higher degree of importance and only the best possible feedwater treatment can be considered acceptable. Since boiler blowdown is no longer available to remove impurities from the system, not only the makeup water must be purified but also at least a portion of the condensate. Otherwise the concentration of impurities in the system will gradually build up until intolerable conditions or tube failures will force an outage for cleaning or repairs. The use of condensate treatment or polishing replaces blowdown in a subcritical pressure boiler.

Other functions of the boiler water separator are replaced in other ways. A boiler extraction valve may be located ahead of the superheater to reduce the firing rate required during a cold start and to permit a hot quick restart without excessive chilling of the high temperature portions. If the boiler has been bottled up with hot steam in the superheater, the extraction valve may be opened at the time feedwater flow is established. This will reduce the flow of fluid into the superheater and minimize the temperature changes that take place while establishing a fire. Again this is of particular importance when austenitic steel is used in the superheater, main steam piping and turbine.

At supercritical pressure the change in specific volume from sub-cooled water to superheated steam is smaller than in the case of subcritical pressure operation. For this reason, the distribution of flow in a bank of parallel tubes is not so strongly influenced by variations in heat absorption, and the use of orifices or throttling valves to achieve stable distribution is not neces-sarily required. The design of the inlet portion of the waterwall system is thereby simplified.

The waterwall circuits themselves may be arranged in a manner similar to that for subcritical pressure units. Each tube of a given system will pass through all parts of the furnace in the same manner as each other tube, so that localized disturbances will have only a minor effect.

As already pointed out, in a strict once-through boiler, circulation in any part of the unit can be established only by operation of the feed pump and continuous admission of feedwater to the unit. To provide adequate cooling of the furnace wall circuits in the vicinity of the burners, it is necessary to establish a certain minimum water flow before the unit is fired. The quantity of this minimum flow is primarily a function of water velocity. It has been normal practice to design once-through units so that the desired minimum velocity will be obtained at a flow rate of approximately 30 per cent of maximum flow. It would, of course, be possible to obtain this velocity with a smaller percentage of flow, but the result would be to produce an excessively high pressure drop at full load. On the other hand, a higher flow rate during start up would require more extensive equipment for handling the startup flow and also a higher firing rate and greater fuel cost during the starting procedure. A minimum flow rate of approximately 30 per cent has therefore normally been accepted as a reasonable compromise.

Since the feedwater must be of high purity, it is expensive to produce and un-economical to waste. Therefore, some means must be provided to reclaim the water and as much as possible of the heat during the startup period. For this purpose, a turbine bypass system is customarily provided. For large supercritical pressure units, the bypass system may be a serious economic handicap. It represents a major investment in equipment that may be seldom used but nevertheless presents design, operating and maintenance problems.

The Second Generation of Supercritical Pressure Boilers

To this point we have considered the development and adaptation of C-E Sulzer Monotube Boilers for use in American central stations. We have noted that once-through circuits together with the related bypass system encounter certain limitations. We shall now see how the Combined Circulation Boiler originated out of technological study and engineering re-evaluation. Taking into account many conflicting technical and economic factors, we shall try to explain how this design solution encompasses a merging of creative ideas and the exercise of the art of management decision.

Technological advancement arises from a specific response to a direct challenge. It involves human endeavor interacting with the reality of technical environment. We can best understand the emergence of a new generation of boilers for supercritical pressure operation by taking a look at the framework of their working environment: the central station in terms of the background, practices and requirements of the electric utility industry in the United States.

At the time of this writing we are looking back over more than a decade of intense development, and we are also cautiously anticipating some of the most likely trends in the future of supercritical pressure steam generation. Although small in terms of historical perspective, this span of time nevertheless has been of great significance to our industry. It has demonstrated the engineering and leadership challenges which are present in a dynamic technical field and has brought forth inspiring responses in individuals as well as in teams. We will attempt to describe how the interests of electrical utility systems, consulting engineering organizations and equipment manufacturers have been linked together in the integrated design of large supercritical pressure boilers as we now know them.

Thermal Power Generation in the United States

As varied and complex as the environment posing the challenge may appear, we may nevertheless single out a few vital facts about the utility industry in the United States. Considered as a single national system, its size rated by installed capacity is indeed large when compared to installed capacity in any other industrial country. The thermal capacity installed in the United States, as a reference point for designers and builders of boilers, is shown in Figure 25–2. A national system as large as this must necessarily establish an environment of special impact on the industries serving it. This becomes clear in Figure 25–3, showing the yearly additions to the installed thermal generating capacity. On the basis of averaging out the cyclic pattern, boiler manufacturers were producing at an equivalent rate of about six million kilowatts a year in the early 1950's and at about ten million kilowatts a year in the early 1960's.

The singular stature of the utility industry in the United States is also illuminated by the fact that, based on 1961 statistics, this country produced 37 per cent of all the electric energy in the world for six per cent of the world population. Despite the rising United States population, the electric energy made available per person has been consistently increasing over the last decade, as shown in Figure 25–4.

We have merely used these statistics to point to a relationship between boiler design and the size of the industry. To be competitive, overall and component design must be basically very flexible and adaptive. It must lend itself to production procedures which are both cost saving and subject to industrial quality control. It is clear that boiler development generally and any effort towards boilers for supercritical pressure must take this into account as we will detail in the following sections.

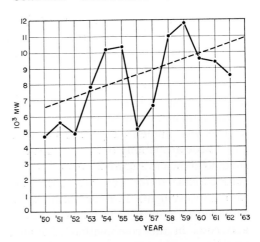

Fig. 25–3. Annual additions of installed thermal generating capacity

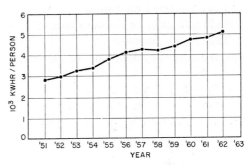

Fig. 25–4. Per capita electric energy use in the United States

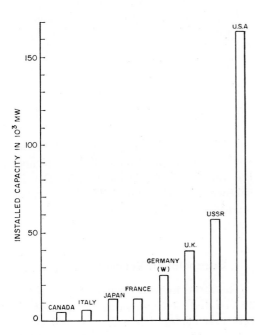

Fig. 25–2. Installed thermal capacity, 1961

Large Units

The most important and far reaching requirement has been one for larger and larger units. This trend results from two considerations. First, large systems need large unit increments to meet increased consumption. The gradually increased system capacity in turn generates the need to step up unit sizes. Second, the effort to produce power economically has been greatly influenced by the demonstrated reduction of unit cost as unit size increases. These benefits are also made available to an increasingly larger number of electric utility systems by pooling arrangements and strengthened interconnections.

The economics leading to this trend are significantly influenced by the comparitively wide availability of high grade fossil fuels, as shown in Figure 25–5, and the resulting demand for only moderate heat rate improvement. Further incentive is provided by improved turbine efficiencies and costs in the combination of higher pressures and larger sizes.

The single boiler-turbine-generator concept, almost universally adopted with the widespread introduction of the reheat cycle in the years following World War II, has been carried on throughout the past decade into units of the very largest sizes.

The rapid increase in size has also spurred the development of automatic

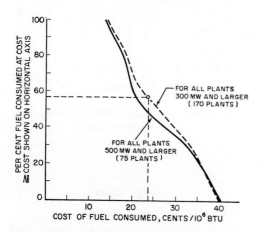

Fig. 25–5. Cost of fossil fuels consumed by U.S. central stations, 1961

controls and given further impetus to complete cycle and control integration of the single boiler-turbine-generator unit.[11]

Variety and Quantity

The variety and quantity of steam power production within a continent as large as that of the United States creates additional challenges.

Boilers are designed and built to meet specific requirements. Most important are fuel requirements which influence not only combustion systems and furnaces but general arrangements and surface design. Consideration must be given to the wide variety of coals with different combustion performance and ash qualities, and also to designs which perform with alternate fuels. Moreover, there are individual system practices and preferences which require variances and special design consideration. Cycle and load range requirements vary not only from one system or station to another but also with the progress of time.

On the other hand, the size of the United States utility industry also requires a large output of equipment. The number of units which are to be designed, built, erected and put into operation each year is formidable. The trend to larger unit sizes also concentrates responsibility and risks and requires the backing of increasingly larger economic and technical resources.

Designs and techniques must therefore skillfully combine the flexibility to meet the variety of requirements with the assurance of performance. The latter takes on added importance with increasing unit sizes.

Extrapolation Versus Experience

The rapid increase in unit sizes and the accelerated acceptance of supercritical pressure cycles raises a question often

[11] See Chapter 22, Controls and Instruments, for additional information.

overlooked: *how rapidly does the industry dare to widely accept designs extrapolated from past experience?* Let us remember that about three years elapse from order date to commercial operation. Reliable and meaningful experience then requires at least another two years, and considerably longer periods are necessitated if long term factors such as creep, corrosion and fatigue are to be safely evaluated.

Among critical parameters for unit size increases are larger furnaces and new or modified firing equipment. Pressure parts are also affected: sizes, numbers, supports, all may involve new or modified designs.

The problem of balancing the need and extent of extrapolation from past experience with the need and extent of conservative concepts and elements proved by past experience is certainly one of the highly instrumental forces which finally shape the offered product. These decisions again emphasize the individual response to an individual challenge, the value and importance of farsighted judgment and engineering leadership.[12]

Boiler Requirements

Let us now summarize the main requirements which the character and operation of electric power production demands for the basic design of boilers. They must be (1) fully compatible for a *wide* range of sizes, (2) suitable for *largest* sizes, (3) adaptable to either high subcritical or to supercritical pressure cycles, (4) flexible to meet various fuel conditions and combinations, (5) compatible for large scale manufacturing and (6) competitive with other boilers and other types of thermal converters.

We may well take the position that *availability* is and always has been one of the primary requirements of all central station components. This is certainly so. As a matter of fact, one of the basic contributions of the furnace wall systems used in boilers of the controlled circulation type operating in the 2400 psig range is increased availability.

With the trend to larger and larger units, availability assumes even greater importance. This is because one of the economic incentives for such units is first cost saving with only slight or marginal heat rate improvement. The cost of unscheduled outages of large units soon becomes prohibitive and challenges the ingenuity and skill of the boiler designer and manufacturer to improve the reliability of *all* components.

Availability does not depend upon the equipment alone. We must recognize that maximum availability can be achieved only by the properly directed and combined efforts of manufacturers and users. Design and production techniques are important but so are operating and maintenance practices.

There are a number of contributions which the boiler designer and manufacturer may make in supporting the goal of maximum availability. These include (1) development effort for all new or modified components based on a record of sustained successful operation under central station conditions, (2) assembly of proved components into soundly designed systems which are properly arranged and composed of carefully chosen materials, and (3) careful attention to quality control of materials and manufacturing techniques during shop fabrication and field erection.

Only by intense effort along these lines

---

[12] For an interesting elaboration of this point of view, see "Engineering Is . . . . ." by Ronald B. Smith, *Mechanical Engineering*, Vol. 86, May 1964, pp. 44–46.

can we expect to insure the availability so necessary to justify the installation of large supercritical pressure boilers.

Characteristics of Central Station Boilers

As emphasized previously we achieve technological advancement by a combination of judicious balancing of extrapolation from past experience and exercise of farsighted judgment. There must be room for both daring innovation and maximum use of accumulated engineering experience. Using this philosophy of engineering design, we find that the benchmark for supercritical pressure boilers rests on an understanding of the factors which contributed to the success of C-E Controlled Circulation Boilers operating on subcritical pressure cycles.[13]

We have already noted the characteristic requirements of the central station industry in the United States to install larger and larger units. The dominant operating pressure level of boilers installed in the decade preceding this writing has been 2400 psig or higher. Looking back in time, we note that prior to 1955 only two units had been purchased for the 2400 psig level. Yet in the following eight years, the utility industry purchased a total of 118 units at this pressure, more than half of which were Controlled Circulation Boilers.

Figure 25–6 shows the distribution of these boilers according to size and illustrates two distinct trends. The group shown in the lower crosshatched section ranged from 100,000 to 200,000 kw in 1955 and gradually increased in size to a range of approximately 200,000 to 400,000 kw in 1963. The group in the upper section represents substantially larger units ordered during the same period and has an average

size in excess of 500,000 kw. The first boiler of 1,000,000 kw equivalent capacity was ordered in 1961. For the purposes of this analysis it may be considered typical of the 500,000 kw group since it is actually composed of two twin furnaces.

Primary and reheat steam temperatures have a bearing on the present usage of supercritical pressure cycles. A review of the history of the central station industry shows a direct correlation between improvements in thermal efficiency and primary steam conditions. Until the advent of the supercritical pressure cycle, increase in steam pressure was generally paralleled by increase in steam temperature, and indeed this was true of the Philo unit which was designed for a primary steam temperature

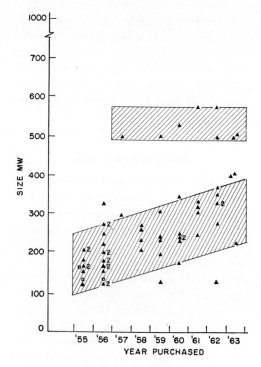

Fig. 25–6.   Controlled   Circulation   Boilers, 2400 psig throttle pressure

---

[13] For additional information, see Chapter 24, Controlled Circulation Boilers.

of 1150 F and the first Eddystone unit which has operated at 1200 F. Other factors, however, were also at work. At the same time that capital savings resulted in the installation of larger and larger units, as we have noted, there was a gradual retreat from previously used primary steam temperatures.

A study of steam temperatures accompanying installations using 2400 psig throttle pressures discloses that 1050 F was overwhelmingly selected as the primary temperature from 1951 through 1958. The trend since that time has been in the direction of 1000 F primary temperature, and we may conclude that this is a well established—but surely not exclusive—pattern. Again, experience has proved to be the arbiter. First, the initial cost of boilers and turbines for the higher temperature level proved to be less attractive as experience accumulated. In addition, even though accurate and conservative methods of superheater metal selection are used, problems do arise during sustained elevated temperature operation because of the adverse effects of certain fuel constituents on unit availability. Some central station owners therefore decided to reduce primary steam temperatures while continuing to lower capital cost through larger units. Other utilities chose to take advantage of the thermal gain from higher primary steam temperature and maintained the established 1050 F level.

Furnace Wall System

Let us now compare the major boiler pressure part systems at subcritical and at supercritical pressure on the basis of their temperature performance at full load for the same primary and reheat steam temperature as shown in Figure 25–7.

In the controlled circulation unit for

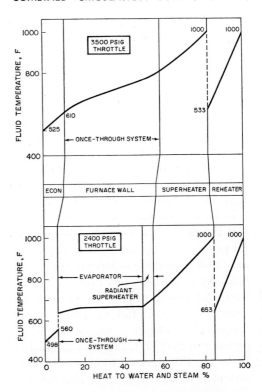

Fig. 25–7. Boiler fluid temperatures, subcritical and supercritical pressures

2400 psig the economizer system, the superheater system and the reheater system all utilize once-through flow at the temperature ranges shown. In the furnace wall system the subcooled water from the economizer is heated to saturation temperature and gradually transformed to saturated steam at a constant temperature. The furnace wall system in Controlled Circulation Boilers has a specific organization which consists of a characteristic furnace tube layout, a steam drum with particular internals, and a unique arrangement of downcomers with circulating pumps and valves and inlet headers with orifices.

When proceeding now to supercritical pressure at 3500 psig, we note that the economizer system, the superheater system and the reheater system must still use once-through flow in the same manner as does the subcritical unit. Their design must merely adjust to slightly different temperature conditions at higher pressures. The only pressure part systems basically affected are the furnace wall where *only* single phase fluid exists and the steam drum which is not needed because separation is neither possible nor required. Temperatures increase steadily but slowly as heat is added to the fluid.

From the foregoing we can understand that the distinctive features of supercritical pressure design are related to the furnace wall system for supercritical pressure fluid. By containing this fluid within the basic wall design of controlled circulation units, we can take full advantage of the successful development and operating experience of the C-E Controlled Circulation Boiler. In this manner the pressure parts system as well as the fuel, air and gas handling systems and structural arrangements may follow the pattern of this proved design, as shown in Figure 25–8.

The sound principles and the simplicity of the furnace enclosure walls have always been among the strongest assets of the Controlled Circulation Boiler. The walls are made up of panels with parallel tube circuits, all arranged in a single upward pass. They are fed from furnace wall inlet headers at the lower end and terminate in outlet headers at the upper end.

The first commercial installation of a welded furnace wall for an American central station boiler occurred at the Kearny

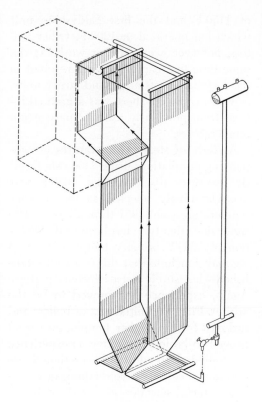

Fig. 25–8.   Furnace wall system, Controlled Circulation Boiler

Generating Station of Public Service Electric & Gas Company. The panels of this controlled circulation unit were fabricated by a patented method of fusion welding. More than a decade of experience has given evidence of the practicality and economic soundness of this basic procedure for shop fabrication of tube panels in large quantities. Their long term reliability has been demonstrated under a wide variety of operating conditions.[14]

[14] A summary of this experience is found in an article entitled "High Quality Welding Used in Modern Utility Power Boilers" by R. M. Losee, *Welding Journal*, Vol. 42, March 1963, pp. 193–200. For earlier information on the background of panel construction of welded furnace walls, see "New Kearny Station in Service", *Combustion*, Vol. 24, May 1953, pp. 40–43 and two articles in *Combustion*, Vol. 27, June 1956, pp. 44–47: "The Cromby Story — Case History in Panel Construction" by W. C. Norris and Walter Rupinski plus "Field Experience on the No. 2 Boiler — Cromby Generating Station" by E. F. Sheehan. Related areas of this topic are discussed in this volume in a section on strength of furnace walls in Chapter 10, Stress Analysis and Structural Design, and there is a description of a fusion panel welder for panel wall construction in Chapter 11, Manufacture and Machine Design, section on manufacturing case studies.

Panel wall construction is accompanied by rigorous quality control during fabrication and improved techniques of field erection. It has made possible considerable design simplification.

Circulating Pumps

Development of circulating pumps for protection of furnace walls predates the 1940 award of a contract by Montaup Electric Company to Combustion Engineering to design and build the first high capacity, high pressure, forced circulation boiler to be installed in the United States. Cooperation and teamwork with major pump manufacturers have been responsible for a continuous and significant development of boiler circulating pumps. Reliability of these pumps is equal to that of other pumps installed in central stations, and Controlled Circulation Boilers are being designed and placed in service without spare circulating pumps. Pumps of the injection, wet and canned type have been successfully used. Over a twenty year period we note that approximately 500 boiler circulating pumps were placed in commercial operation.

Tangential Firing

While we have associated ourselves with the principles of tangential firing from the very beginning, several new aspects are introduced when these principles are applied to very large units.

The use of the furnace as a mixing chamber for the large quantities of pulverized fuel and air, introduced tangentially in a combustion chamber, has always been one of the strongest arguments for this firing method. The growth of furnace sizes has reinforced the weight of this argument because of the formidable dis-

tribution problem of fuel and air around a very large outside furnace circumference. The use of a single "fireball" establishing general contact with all four corners of each furnace envelope regardless of load, supports attainment and control of full combustion efficiency by evening out the distribution imbalances which any piping and duct arrangement must necessarily introduce. Under firing conditions this mixing and ignition action is an immeasurably valuable assist to the operator in safeguarding the equipment.[15]

One of the characteristics of large Combustion Engineering reheat units has always been the combination of tilting burners with tangential firing, providing a remarkable and highly practical facility to vary furnace heat absorption. It is this flexibility of furnace performance provided by tilting burners which adds a safety margin to the design of these very large furnaces, based as they must be on extrapolation of experience and on engineering judgment.

The change of heat absorption along the height of the enclosure wall in a typical pulverized coal fired furnace, as effected by tilt, is shown in Figure 25–9. This also indicates a further asset of tangential firing: the comparatively small variation of absorption rate around the wall circumference in areas of high mean values. This lends particular support to the problem of balancing internal flow to heat absorption in the multitude of parallel tubes in larger and larger furnaces found in modern steam generating units.

Adapting the European Engineering Heritage

We have just looked into the American background and experience that accrued to Combustion Engineering as the result of

---

[15] Additional information may be found in Chapter 17, Fuel Burning Systems.

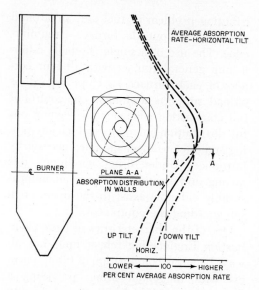

Fig. 25–9. Furnace heat absorption pattern, tangential firing

the development of a particular forced circulation design, the Controlled Circulation Boiler. We have considered the influence of primary steam temperature, described furnace wall systems and construction of panel walls, mentioned the development of boiler circulating pumps and discussed the significance of tangential firing. Now we shall take another look at the Sulzer Monotube Boiler, which was previously described in the first section of this chapter.

An examination of the boiler designs originating in Europe prior to 1953, when Sulzer Brothers and Combustion Engineering entered into a licensing agreement, quite forcefully underlines our earlier remarks concerning the *interaction between environment and technological advancement*. In Europe the widely different economic conditions and fuel situations within comparatively small national electric power systems imposed a highly individual development. The pacesetters for application of high steam temperatures and pressures, surprisingly enough, had

been industrial plants which often combined power generation and process steam requirements in rather advanced and highly efficient backpressure cycles. As early as 1939 a briquette factory operated a once-through reheat boiler generating 200,000 lb of steam per hour at 2150 psig, and some years after the end of World War II a supercritical pressure boiler was installed in a German chemical plant. The largest Sulzer Monotube central station boilers in operation in 1953 provided steam at 1225 psig, 970 F without reheat for 50,000 kw turbines and were the first installation of the single boiler-turbine-generator concept in Europe. A typical central station contract of the period is represented by a boiler designed to burn brown coal and supply steam at 1660 psig, 985 F for a 75,000 kw turbine-generator.

Not only were European unit sizes and steam cycle conditions quite different from those used by the United States central station industry but we must also recognize that many aspects of boiler design, particularly those relating to furnace wall enclosures, were based on markedly differing concepts. All boiler furnaces were conceived as being essentially steel supported brick chambers with widely spaced tube systems supported in front of the refractory lined inside surface. These tube systems were tied back through the brick to the steel supporting structure and were designed to move relative to the surrounding brick wall. Because of this comparative freedom for expansion of tube systems, they could be and were designed with highly individual shapes and functions.

A particular development of Sulzer Brothers was the arrangement and control of evaporator or heat absorbing tube systems for once-through subcritical pressure boilers. These systems were combined with a portion of water heating surface in a continuous meandering ribbon of parallel tube circuits as shown in Figure 25–10. The advantages were the capability of stable operation independent of load, the avoidance of external unheated downcomers and the problem of distributing steam-water mixtures in headers, plus the retention of a reasonable amount of design freedom for surface arrangement.

The Eddystone Experience

The merging of European and American technical experience took place most dramatically in the design of the first supercritical pressure boiler for the Eddystone Station of Philadelphia Electric Company. Here we were faced with the *exciting challenge* of building a boiler which at the time of its announcement established new records for steam capacity, steam pressure and steam temperature. The basic design criterion was to take maximum advantage of all of the most recent technological advances that could be justified in a project with the specific goal of building and operating the most efficient power plant in the world.

Yet in retrospect we recall Eddystone not only as a *technical venture* but also as a *human experiment* in cooperation and mutual assistance. Memories of personalities, committee meetings and progress reports remain vivid — of knowledge that boiler designers gained from turbine designers, of the new appreciation of integrated control systems that went beyond usual equipment boundaries, of engineers whose efforts transcended international and corporate interests as they sought solutions to problems that leapfrogged frontiers then existing in steam power technology.[16]

Under these auspices the concept and basic layout of the supercritical pressure boiler crystallized. With candor and willingness to put facts on the table, we joined with engineers of Sulzer Brothers and Philadelphia Electric Company to transform the important European know-how obtained from the design and operation of once-through Sulzer Monotube Boilers to the specific conditions of the Eddystone

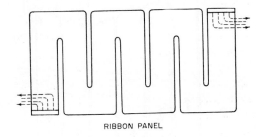

RIBBON PANEL

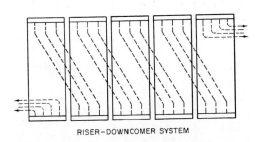

RISER–DOWNCOMER SYSTEM

Fig. 25–10. Once-through evaporator tube systems, Europe, 1954

---

16 For a detailed account of the original design concepts, see three papers published in *Trans. ASME*, Vol. 79, 1957: "Engineering the Eddystone Plant for 5000-lb, 1200-deg Steam" by J. H. Harlow, pp. 1410–1430; "The Eddystone Superpressure Unit" by C. B. Campbell, C. C. Franck, Sr. and J. C. Spahr, pp. 1431–1446; and "Engineering the Eddystone Steam Generator for 5000 psig, 1200 F Steam" by E. M. Powell, pp. 1447–1457. Operating experience is discussed and assessed in an editorial and a series of eleven special articles in *Electrical World*, "The Eddystone Story — Unit 1 Extends Power Plant Technology", March 11, 1963, pp. 87–110.

supercritical pressure plant. Our own experience within the mainstream of boiler development for American central stations was a most valuable base from which to proceed. High pressure Controlled Circulation Boilers with tangential firing in skincased twin furnaces made up of welded panel walls were being built to serve 250,-000 kw turbines, and units of similar design were already in operation at equivalent electrical ratings of 200,000 kw.

Among the major design extrapolations for the first Eddystone supercritical pressure boiler were the furnace enclosure and the bypass system. The high primary and reheat steam temperatures made it necessary to use a large amount of radiant superheater surface in the upper portion of the furnace while covering the lower region with waterwall surface at a considerably lower fluid temperature level. In boilers of the once-through design there is a continuous rise in fluid temperature along every foot of tube in which heat is absorbed. These requirements plus the decision to adapt ribbon tube panels to furnace enclosures called for an extraordinary amount of ingenuity and engineering skill. Figure 25–11 shows the furnace wall system made up of tangent small diameter tubing backed by skin casing. Ribbon tube panels in vertical and horizontal arrangement were used in this top supported boiler in which special provisions had to be made in the design of the buckstay system to accomodate cubical expansion.[17]

The bypass system likewise involved engineering challenges to handle the very large steam flow and large quantities of energy bypassing three turbine sections en route from the boiler to the condenser. Unprecedented design parameters had to be established and several new components

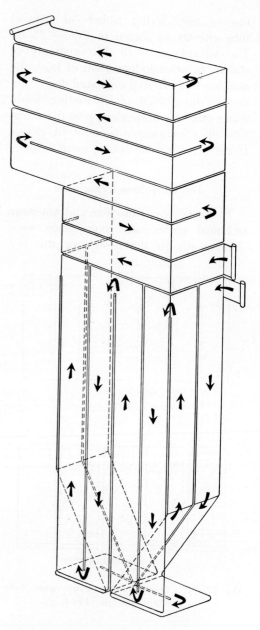

Fig. 25–11.   Furnace wall system, first Eddystone supercritical pressure boiler

[17] For a better understanding of Eddystone Station, see the description and illustrations included in Chapter 1, Visualizing the Steam Power Plant, section entitled, What Is a Boiler?

were developed. The availability of Sulzer bypass valves and control equipment which had been tested in European operating experience lent considerable help in designing the bypass system.

Lessons from Operation

Two C-E Sulzer Monotube Boilers went into operation at subcritical pressures in 1958, and by the middle of 1959 the first two supercritical pressure units were also in service. Full scale central station operating experience in the United States now became available for the first time, and we were able to compare actual performance with that predicted earlier in engineering studies and laboratory tests.

Among the satisfying results we found were that the physical and thermal properties for supercritical pressure fluid were sufficiently accurate to permit design of heating surfaces even though these values had been obtained by extrapolation from then known experimental data. Extensive research work in metallurgy for improved alloy steels to withstand supercritical pressures and temperatures proved to be sound. While methods to obtain ultrapure makeup water and to remove contaminants from feedwater during plant operation worked out successfully, some unanticipated problems arose as a result of deposition of copper oxides on turbine blades. We found solutions by combining know-how in chemistry, metallurgy and mechanical engineering.

Yet surprisingly enough one of the greatest benefits we gained from the design and operation of this first generation of once-through boilers was the redis-covery of the scope and essential qualities of *design engineering*. It is all too easy to become complacent about and take for granted existing engineering standards and the contributions that designers and draftsmen make to the design process. In the final analysis, however, lines and lettered instructions on drawings and blueprints become physical reality in such things as structural steel supports, tubing of various configurations, piping, controls and instruments.

Design has been aptly defined as that *engineering effort which creates the means to perform a given function in the most efficient manner.* To accomplish this, general concepts must be made specific by incorporating relevant past experience and standards and developing new practices *only* where the old are found to be inadequate or uneconomic. Ultimately these are translated into drawings expressed in terms of definite dimensions and specified materials which are subsequently fabricated and erected. But it was first in the drafting room that the combination of ribbon tube panel with skin casing and bracing had to be worked out. And it was there that pipes and valves for the bypass system had to be detailed and fitted into the station layout. Only then could we come to the full realization, comprehension and understanding of the design of a supercritical pressure boiler.[18]

In engineering, the first phase of design is justified only by the second phase, that of *operation*. Now the designer *lives* with his creation. He sees and listens. His "brain children" are tested. His hand senses the temperature of the skin casing and his ear is conscious of the muffled vibration aris-

[18] The engineering design process can be made more meaningful if the reader attempts to understand such books as *Engineering Design — A Systematic Approach* by Robert Matousek, Interscience (John Wiley), 1963, 264 pages and *The Design of Engineering Systems* by W. Gosling, Wiley, 1932, 247 pages.

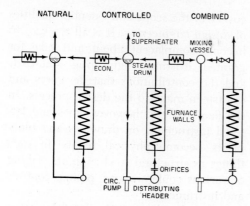

ing from the tremendous amount of thermal energy released in the boiler furnace. His eyes survey the maze of closely spaced headers and tubes in the roof enclosure and the extensive bypass piping. The failures of the equipment he helped to design are expressed in the oppressive silence of a power plant not earning a return but losing money by standing idle.

All of this design and operating experience is a part of *engineering development*, a prelude to technological advancement.

Fig. 25–12.   Similarity of boiler types

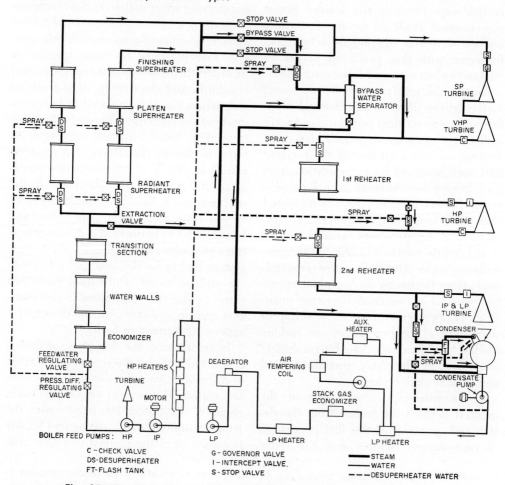

Fig. 25–13.   Bypass system, first Eddystone supercritical pressure boiler

It reminded us again that *purchase and design of a boiler is followed by operation by human beings in a power plant environment.* The direct personal experiences that we lived through there were translated from the mind to the engineering conference and then through the drafting room and manufacturing plants to a new generation of supercritical pressure units, the Combined Circulation Boiler. Having gone full cycle, that is, from original concept to investigation to design to operation and back to new concept, *we experienced one of the greatest human rewards of being an engineer: the exciting potential of engineering effort when challenged to reach new frontiers.*

A Retrospective View

Let us now review what we learned from the first generation of supercritical pressure boilers. The requirement of a turbine bypass system to establish flow through furnace walls for their protection during startup and at very low loads had been met successfully, but the attendant complications threatened to become a handicap as boiler sizes continued to increase. While panel ribbon furnace construction had been transformed sufficiently to meet the needs of the first generation, it contributed serious design, manufacturing and erection problems.

We therefore concentrated our design efforts on the turbine bypass system with the intention of substantially reducing its size or eliminating its need entirely. We reviewed the design and manufacturing techniques used in furnace wall construction for Controlled Circulation Boilers and decided to adapt them to the needs of the second generation of supercritical pressure boilers.

The result of this study and re-evaluation has since been designated the C-E Combined Circulation Boiler. It has a furnace wall system of the same basic design as Combustion Engineering natural and controlled circulation boilers so that all heated circuits have single pass upward flow in welded tube panels with a common inlet temperature. Figure 25–12 shows the similarity of these systems.

The subcritical pressure *controlled* circulation system protects the heated circuit by recirculation, adding saturated water to the steam being generated in the tube. The supercritical pressure *combined* circulation system also protects the heated circuit by recirculation, adding supercritical pressure fluid to the once-through flow in such a manner that the combined flow always protects the tube. At startup and low loads the system requires more than once-through flow and is protected by recirculation or combined flow; at higher loads once-through flow alone can provide the required protection. The drum which separates the steam-water mixture at subcritical pressure levels is replaced by a mixing vessel with a recirculating line at supercritical pressures.

At Eddystone the minimum flow requirements to protect the furnace walls during startup necessitated a turbine bypass system capable of dissipating the equivalent of as much as 100,000 kw of *thermal* energy. The complications introduced by this system can be seen in Figure 25–13 by following the flow from the bypass valve located beyond the finishing superheater to the bypass water separator where the flow divides with water going directly to the condenser and steam passing successively through the first and second reheaters en route to the condenser. How this system has been simplified is shown in Figure 25–14 which illustrates the startup system for a 3500 psig Combined Circulation Boiler. In the latter the system consists of shutoff and throttling valves arranged between the furnace wall and superheater which can be bypassed through a low pressure system with a water separator. This arrangement permits the furnace wall system to operate at its proper pressure while allowing the superheater to operate at a lower pressure level during startup. The system also lends itself to variable pressure operation through the superheater and turbine over any specified load range.

What the Combined Circulation Boiler Does

The C-E Combined Circulation Boiler has been developed to strengthen the advantages of once-through boilers designed to operate in the supercritical pressure region. Recirculation during startup and low loads is provided by a boiler circulating pump, and this maintains the whole furnace enclosure at an essentially even temperature level regardless of load. Furnace wall protection no longer requires a turbine bypass, although advantages to other parts of the power plant cycle may still justify the inclusion of a startup system. The result is that all pressure part components for the economizer, furnace walls, superheaters and reheaters can be designed in a similar manner for both 2400 and 3500 psig. This can be seen by comparing the cross sections of two units with an equivalent 500,000 kw output, Figure 25–15 showing a 2400 psig Controlled Circulation Boiler (with circulating pump about one third of the way from the bottom on the left) and Figure 25–16, a 3500 psig Combined Circulation Boiler (with

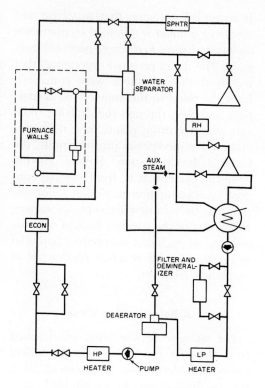

Fig. 25–14. Cycle flow diagram, Combined Circulation Boiler

circulating pump dotted in phantom view at about the same elevation on the right).

There are several characteristics of 2400 psig controlled circulation units that must be accomplished by other means in a 3500 psig combined circulation unit. In subcritical pressure operation, the drum water level establishes a barrier beyond which water cannot pass except in the form of steam. In supercritical pressure operation a water level cannot exist and in the absence of any other barrier the turbine valves may be subjected to temperature shocks from high pressure water during attempted hot starts. Supercritical pressure boilers therefore require barriers in the form of valves which will protect the turbine.

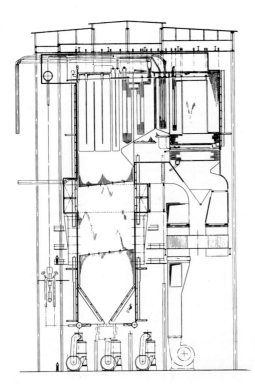

Fig. 25—15. Side elevation, C-E Controlled Circulation Boiler, 500 Mw, 2400 psig, 1000/1000 F

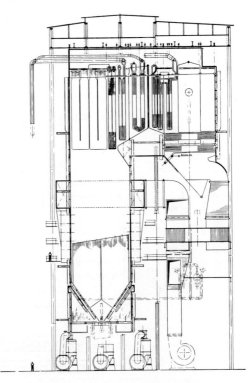

Fig. 25—16. Side elevation, C-E Combined Circulation Boiler, 500 Mw, 3500 psig, 1000/1000 F

Controlled circulation units can also easily provide low pressure steam during startup. This is important for thermal protection of the turbine in order to avoid large temperature differentials during hot starts. There is no counterpart of this in a supercritical pressure boiler where the furnace wall system must always be kept at supercritical pressure to avoid instability by the presence of steam-water mixtures. This again calls for a barrier between the furnace wall and superheater together with a system to produce low pressure, controlled enthalpy steam for temperature matching during startup.

Outlook and New Challenges

Rather than describe equipment in detail, we have to this point made an attempt to place a decade of engineering development in the design and operation of supercritical pressure boilers into the perspective of human response and challenge within the larger environment of the Amercan electric utility industry. These have not been the words of detached observers but rather those of engineers directly participating in the development.[19]

As a charted summary of this experi-

[19] Those desiring additional explanations and illustrations will find two American Power Conference papers by W. W. Schroedter of interest: "A New Steam Generator for Supercritical Pressure", *Proceedings*, Vol. 24, 1962, pp. 301–316 and "Engineering the Bull Run Steam Generator", Vol. 25, 1963, pp. 359–385.

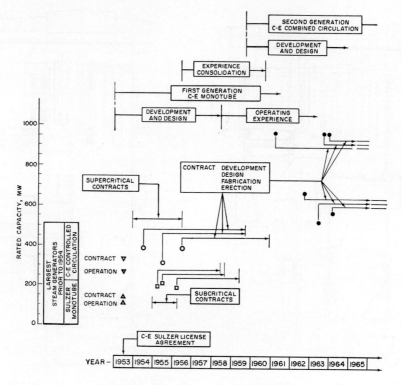

Fig. 25–17.   Chronological development, C-E supercritical pressure boilers

ence, Figure 25–17 places the events of this development in a timetable which covers the emergence of the first and second generations of supercritical pressure boilers and reflects the size growth of individual units during this period. This chart is best comprehended by starting in the lower left hand corner and working up to the upper right hand corner. Boilers are rated in equivalent electrical megawatt capacity as indicated on the vertical axis of Figure 25–17.

As reference points we have shown the largest Sulzer Monotube and C-E Controlled Circulation Boilers under contract and in operation in 1953 when the technical license agreement between Sulzer Brothers and Combustion Engineering was initiated. That was the year which marked

the beginning of preliminary design and development laboratory research for the first generation of C-E Sulzer Monotube Boilers. Close coordination of sales and engineering efforts in the next three years, 1954–1956, resulted in the award of contracts for both subcritical and supercritical pressure units, and there was a commitment of major engineering, development laboratory and production resources to these projects. Accordingly, with efforts for development, design, fabrication and erection of these boilers under way, we judged it prudent to wait to accumulate and consolidate actual operating experience before embarking on the design of additional units of larger size.

By 1958 the main design concepts and all component engineering lay behind us.

Considerable manufacturing and erection experience had accumulated, and the first subcritical pressure boiler was ready for operation. *The first stirrings of the restless engineering mind in search for product improvement were already discernible among us.* In 1959 more operating experience from subcritical pressure units became available and the operation of the first supercritical pressure boilers had begun. Three years had now passed since the last contract for a supercritical pressure steam generating unit had been awarded. A full and comprehensive technological study was now launched — a searching analysis of the next steps to be taken — and there the development of the second generation of supercritical pressure boilers began.

As time went by, we considered and studied many different avenues of approach. Gathering information from the various areas of experience and evaluating facts and figures with the aid of engineering judgment began to clarify the multifaceted problem. Although more operating experience did become available, we found that not all of it pointed in the same direction. Some of it even produced more questions than answers. Nevertheless, by 1960 the adaptations of concepts and principles to be used for second generation units had been formulated, and studies for their most practical *and economical* execution were under way. The period of experience consolidation had come to an end. We had selected the path, our direction was clear. Late that year we were ready and eager to join our associates in the sales department to seek the first contracts for the second generation of units: the C-E Combined Circulation Boiler.

With the coming of 1961 and the winning of the first contract — the then largest supercritical pressure boiler in the world — another period of detailed development and design had been touched off. *Again we found taking place those interactions between specific projects and engineering development in which neither stands still and both advance together.* Now once more we witnessed new challenges and new responses. We eagerly awaited the first operating experience to see if it confirmed or necessitated modifications of our earlier predictions. Looking forward in anticipation of future developments, we found ourselves experiencing once again the genuine excitement and satisfactions that are an integral part of an engineering career in a dynamic and ever challenging power industry.[20]

---

[20] This spirit has been captured in two books by Philip Sporn: *Energy — Its Production, Conversion and Use in the Service of Man*, 1963, 69 pages and *Foundations of Engineering*, 1964, 143 pages, both published by The Macmillan Company (Pergamon Press).

Manufacture and shipment of shop assembled boilers

26

Shop Assembled Boilers[1]

SHOP ASSEMBLY of boilers has increased markedly in recent years. This concept has been applied to fire tube and natural and controlled circulation water tube boiler types. Although the majority of the water tube units have been designed for pressurized firing of oil or gas, stoker fired and waste heat units have also been pre-assembled in the shops of manufacturers.

The most significant advantage is lower installed cost as compared with a field erected unit. This differential is due to the development of standard designs with maximum use of standardized fabrication procedures and minimum field installation costs.

Shop assembled boilers are furnished with integrated auxiliary equipment. The lower capacity units are shipped completely packaged with fuel burning equipment, safety and combustion controls, and boiler trim. Because of shipping clearance limitations it is not always possible or desirable to furnish the higher capacity boilers in a single package. The forced draft fan and driver, for example, may become so large physically that it is necessary to ship this equipment as a separate package designed for simple connection in the field. With higher capacity and higher pressure units it may also be desirable to use heat recovery equipment which is shipped as a separate, though thoroughly integrated, package. It is possible to design some larger boiler types so that they can be shipped in component assemblies, thus retaining many of the advantages of shop assembly.

Inherent design and shipping clearance limitations relegate the fire tube units to top operating pressures and capacities of approximately 250 psig and 20,000 lb of steam per hour respectively. They are seldom furnished with superheaters. Because of the relatively low operating pressures, heat recovery equipment is not justified nor desirable. The basically different design concept of the water tube boiler permits a substantially wider range of operating conditions than can be obtained with fire tube units.

Design Considerations

The natural circulation water tube boiler designed for pressure firing of oil or gas has found wide acceptance in industry. Shipping clearances determine the allowable height-width dimensions of an assembled unit. Usually the allowable shipping depth is greater than can be effectively used. One of the problems of the designer is therefore to use the available height and width to best advantage. The unit must be arranged with an adequate furnace for efficient combustion of the fuel and the boiler surface selected for optimum trans-

[1] Material contributed by S. F. Mumford.

fer of heat, consistent with reasonable draft loss.

The burner-furnace design must be properly coordinated, and burners have been developed specifically for shop assembled boilers. These burners, which have a relatively narrow flame pattern, are designed to burn the fuel completely within the necessarily limited, though sufficient, clearance dimensions from the burner centerline to the furnace walls.

Extensive use of water cooled surface in the furnace is typically found in shop assembled boilers. This heat absorbing surface that "sees" the flame determines the temperature of the combustion gases leaving the furnace. Liberal use of water cooling on the furnace sides, roof and floor not only reduces the furnace temperature but also the maintenance of any furnace refractory that may be used. A supplementary advantage for shop assembled units is that this water cooled surface, properly arranged, can be effectively used to retain the refractory backing in place during shipment.

The amount of furnace volume or heat release rate per cubic foot of furnace volume bears no direct relationship to the furnace exit temperature; the amount of water cooled furnace surface or the heat release rate per square foot of effective radiant absorbing surface is the valid criterion for determining furnace conditions. Size and furnace configuration for these package boilers result in a ratio of radiant surface to furnace volume which is greater than for the larger field erected units. This permits considerably higher furnace liberation rates per cubic foot of furnace volume for the package designs.

The boiler exit temperature is a function of the arrangement of furnace and boiler surface and of the superheater, if a superheater is installed. Comparing rela-

tive performance or contemplated maintenance of competitive boilers on the amount of boiler surface alone is a fallacy that should be avoided. Such yardsticks are possibly valid when comparing identical boiler types delivering saturated steam at low pressure, but when applied to shop assembled units they negate the advantages of well integrated boiler design. Similarly, the exit temperature from the boiler or heat recovery equipment, if installed, and the excess air required to burn the fuel determine the thermal efficiency of the unit.

Therefore, if a specification for an assembled boiler is to be prepared, it is far more logical and to the best interest of both the purchaser and manufacturer to prepare a performance specification indicating precisely the conditions of operation and what is expected of the steam generating and accessory equipment, rather than a restrictive specification covering many details and minor items which will not necessarily assure the ultimate user of obtaining the most suitable unit for his particular application. This applies not only to the assembled boiler package but especially to the burner and control equipment, and to the accessory equipment as well.

Generally the enclosing casing structure, including the integral base plate of shop assembled boilers, serves several functions. It is designed to withstand the maximum positive pressure encountered under forced draft operation without permanent deflection. It is designed to eliminate objectionable gas leakage under maximum pressure conditions. Also it must have sufficient structural strength for the necessary handling and lifting during manufacture, in transit and at the installation site. Permanent or detachable lifting lugs are invariably provided to facilitate this necessary handling. Many oil and gas fired assembled units require only a suitably reinforced concrete slab or curb for foundation.

Outdoor installation of shop assembled boilers with an enclosure or shelter over the burners and controls is quite common. For such applications the enclosing casing structure is arranged so that water cannot accumulate in any areas and arranged or protected so that corrosion on the inner surface will not occur as a result of condensation of the constituents of the flue gas. Protection against corrosion can be achieved by the use of a heat resistant coating applied to the inside of the casing or by insulating the outside of the casing such that the metal temperature is held above the dew point of the flue gas.

Fuel Burning Equipment and Controls

The majority of shop assembled boilers are fired by oil or gas. The burner or burners, forced draft fan, limit and combustion controls, and flame safeguard device are invariably furnished as an integrated package which, depending on physical size and arrangement, may be shipped attached to the boiler and in one or more separate components.

Burners

Normal fuels for these water tube shop assembled boilers are No. 6 oil or gas. Oil burners are of the gun type, steam atomizing to attain wide turndown. Gas burners are of gun or ring type and are also suitable for a wide turndown with reasonable gas supply pressures. Most burners are designed to burn either oil or gas but not in combination. By relatively simple changes conversion from one fuel to another can be accomplished. Although some burners are available to burn two fuels separately or in combination, insur-

ance requirements and the complication and expense of control equipment involved should be carefully evaluated against the actual need for such an arrangement.

Low capacity boilers are supplied with a single burner. For installations of higher capacity boilers two burners are usually furnished, not primarily to increase the operating range but rather to maintain steam pressure and avoid a purging cycle when one of the burners is cleaned. This has also been accomplished by installing two burners in a single register. The furnace cross sectional area, dictated to some extent by the allowable shipping clearance dimensions, may also indicate a superior arrangement using two burners with small throats as against a single burner with a larger throat.

Standard packaged oil pump and heater sets are available. These are suitable for single or multiple boiler applications.

Forced Draft Fan

With smaller capacity units, without heat recovery, the forced draft fan may be located below, on either side, or attached to and supported on the windbox. With higher capacity boilers the physical size of the fan usually makes location below the windbox impossible and direct attachment to the side or front impractical, although field attachment and support on the top of the windbox is feasible in some cases. With an air preheater the higher static fan is placed ahead of this heat recovery equipment, automatically removing it from the windbox area. Usually the forced draft fan wheels for these assembled boilers are of the non-overloading type and are operated at a speed of 1750 rpm. The tolerances on volume and static are adequate but held to a minimum. Excessive tolerances have an adverse effect on air control at the low end of the operating range and will reduce the acceptable turndown ratio.

Controls and Their Selection

A number of varying factors tend to complicate the selection of control equipment and safety devices which will suit exactly the requirements of all potential users. Yet the practice of custom engineering each individual control system entails the loss of all of the advantages of using standardized equipment. To insure the retention of these benefits, packaged control systems are offered in standard, performance-proved combinations of various components. Thus the selective process requires only an engineered evaluation of the system requirements and selection of the standard control combination which best meets these requirements.

Among the factors which will influence the ultimate control selection are local codes and ordinances, insurance regulations, initial and operating costs, the nature of the boiler load, the type of fuel to be burned and the degree of training and availability of operating and maintenance personnel. Despite the complexity of the selection the problem may be reduced to three basic considerations: (1) whether the firing cycle should be fully or semi-automatic, (2) the number and type of limit controls and, (3) whether the combustion control should be of the positioning or metering type.

For fully automatic operation the steps necessary to start up and shut down the boiler automatically are programed by the flame safeguard controls with electric timer and necessary relays. However an operator must restart the burner on flame failure or extended power failure. With semi-automatic operation the boiler will shut down automatically (and sound an alarm) but an operator must perform some of the steps in starting up the boiler. The semi-automatic system should incorporate means to prevent ignition until the furnace has been properly purged and to shut off the gas-electric ignitor after the recommended trial-for-ignition period.

The advantage of the fully automatic arrangement is that it permits infinite load variation by recycling automatically at loads below the burner turn down range. However, if plant load requirements are such that operation below the burner turn down range is infrequent, semi-automatic operation should be adequate. In addition to the lower initial cost, reduced hazards and lower maintenance because of the simpler equipment, the semi-automatic arrangement encourages familiarity by requiring the operator to perform some operations himself.

Limit Controls

The purpose of limit controls is to insure safe operating conditions. When a limit is exceeded the control automatically shuts down the burner. Experience has indicated that an excessive number of limit controls can cause nuisance shut downs. Since explosion hazards are directly related to the number of burner reignitions, it is therefore important to reduce the number of these limit-control devices to significant malfunctions such as low water, inadequate fuel supply conditions or loss of air supply. The proper use of alarms, such as a low water alarm, can forewarn the operator so that corrective action can be taken before an automatic shutdown becomes mandatory.

Combustion Controls

The function of the combustion control is to match firing rate to steam demand while maintaining substantially constant steam pressure and to provide optimum fuel-air ratio at all firing rates. While flame safeguard and limit controls are usually electrically actuated, the actuation of the combustion control may be electric or pneumatic. The type of control may be either metering or positioning.

Positioning Type. The principal components of a simple positioning type combustion control are a master steam pressure controller, a characterizable fuel control valve and a fan damper or fan vanes. The master pressure controller is set to maintain steam pressure essentially constant at some predetermined value generally referred to as the set point. Deviations from the set points are sensed by the master which acts to change the position of the fuel control valve and the fan damper simultaneously and in a preset relationship. Fuel control valves of the self-compensating type give reasonable assurance that for each increment of force applied to move the valve, the change in fuel flow will be the same regardless of limited changes in pressure ahead of the valve. Such a system is simple and it can act to preserve continuously the proper fuel-air ratio providing the designed resistances to the flow of fuel and air are maintained.

Metering Type. In addition to the three principal components of the positioning control, a full metering system contains a device which will measure fuel flow and transmit a loading corresponding to the measured flow, a similar device for measuring and transmitting an air flow signal and fuel-air ratio relay. The master pressure controller, set to maintain steam pressure constant, senses deviations from the set point and acts to move in parallel both the fuel control valve and fan damper. Measured changes in fuel flow and relative air flow are transmitted to the fuel-air ratio relay which acts to preserve the desired ratio of these two quantities for most efficient combustion over the operating range. It is also possible to match steam flow against air flow to minimize the effect of changes in the calorific value or viscosity of the fuel. A full metering system is obviously more complex, and therefore not as easily understood by the operator, and the cost is greater. It is capable of finer adjustment of fuel-air ratio but frequently has a relatively limited range depending upon method of measuring air flow.

Combined Types. Combustion control systems are available which combine some of the functions of the positioning and metering systems. Usually components are added to the basic positioning system to assure a constant fuel flow for a given position of the fuel valve, to assure a constant air flow for a given position of the fan damper or to preserve the proper fuel-air ratio.

To assure the most suitable arrangement of fuel burning equipment it is essential to know complete and exact information on operating conditions, including the nature of the load, characteristics of available current and fuel and any special conditions for the particular installation. A precise description of what is required of the equipment, rather than a detailed and frequently restrictive specification, will usually result in a better application. An integrated arrangement is essential because of the interdependence of the burner, pilot, fan and combustion and safety controls.

Feedwater Control

Automatic regulation of feedwater flow to a water tube shop assembled boiler is necessary. For a reasonably steady load characteristic single element actuation from steam drum water level is usually adequate. For fluctuating loads a means for anticipating load changes, such as a steam flow element, is usually provided. Regardless of the method of actuation of the feed valve, it is desirable to maintain a constant feed pressure upstream of the valve, especially for multiple boiler installations.

Heat Recovery Equipment

For the higher pressure and higher capacity shop assembled boilers operated at high load factor, heat recovery equipment can frequently be economically justified. Under these conditions packaged economizers and air preheaters can increase overall boiler efficiency and effect substantial fuel savings by recovering heat from the flue gases leaving the generating surface. This heat recovery equipment is shipped as a complete but separate package. It is arranged close to the boiler gas outlet on the same elevation or above the boiler it serves, depending on the individual plant arrangement. Gas breechings and ducts from the boiler outlet to the stack usually are shipped as component assemblies, as are the feed line from the economizer to the steam drum or the air duct from the preheater to the windbox.

With low pressure boilers the exit gas temperature leaving the generating surface is low enough to assure reasonable efficiency. As the operating pressure increases, however, the saturated steam temperature, and therefore, the boiler exit temperature also increases, thus tending to justify the application of heat recovery equipment.

With a relatively low capacity boiler or a higher capacity boiler operating at low load factor, the initial investment cost of heat recovery equipment and associated additional breechings, ducts or piping should be evaluated relative to the possible fuel savings. As the capacity and load factor increase, the application of heat recovery equipment becomes more attractive.

A counterflow arrangement of flue gas and feedwater for an economizer, or of flue gas and combustion air for an air preheater, results in the most effective use of the heat recovery surface. With high sulfur fuels the possibility of corrosion of the cold end surfaces should be taken into account when contemplating the use of either an economizer or air preheater.

For either a regenerative or tubular type air preheater the operating temperature of the cold end metal subjected to possible corrosion is essentially an average between the entering air and leaving gas temperatures. Means are available for raising this metal temperature to eliminate or minimize corrosion. This can be accomplished by bypassing some of the combustion air or preheating all of the combustion air to a limited degree. The design can be selected for a higher gas exit temperature with an attendant efficiency reduction. The degree and frequency of part load operation is most significant in establishing the optimum air heater selection. Packaged regenerative air preheaters are designed with reversible and replaceable cold end layers fabricated of corrosion resistant material to minimize maintenance.

Since the gas side transfer rate in an economizer is relatively low compared with the water side rate, the metal temperature of the cold end of a counterflow economizer is only slightly above the entering feed temperature. With high sulfur fuels it is usually not advisable to consider an economizer unless the feedwater temperature is above 250 F.

There are many applications where the above limitations do not apply, and for these applications the use of heat recovery equipment can result in considerable fuel savings. Obviously the savings will increase with the higher capacity and higher pressure shop assembled boilers operated at high load factor.

Stoker Firing

To burn a solid fuel properly the furnace of a stoker fired boiler must be arranged for sufficient grate area and adequate distance for flame travel to the relatively cold convection generating surface. To prevent slagging in the convection surface ample waterwall cooling is provided in the furnace to reduce the gas temperature below the softening temperature of the ash. Because of these considerations the furnace, and therefore the complete shop assembled stoker fired boiler, is substantially larger for a given output than one designed for oil or gas firing only.

Conservatism in specifying design conditions such as grate heat release rate does not necessarily assure the optimum selection for an actual application. For example, stokers do not have the inherent turn down range of properly designed oil or gas burners. Setting a low grate release rate for an infrequent peak condition can result in an oversize unit which cannot maintain good combustion conditions at the frequently used low end of the operating range. Similarly, the low end of the operating range should be very carefully considered in selecting forced and induced draft fans. Fans should be adequate for the design or peak condition but the addition of substantial and unnecessary tolerances may result in a fan that is too large for good control of flows at part load rates. These are typical examples of the possible adverse effects of oversizing equipment and

are of special importance when applied to shop assembled units.

The degree of complete packaging is obviously reduced for stoker fired units. However, the preassembled concept is applicable. Depending on capacity, the boiler, stoker, forced draft fan, induced draft fan and, as required, air preheater and dust collector have been furnished as packages to minimize field erection time and expense.

Waste Heat Boilers

Although the shop assembled idea has been applied primarily to fuel fired boilers, it is also applicable to waste heat boilers.[2] Unless there is some special consideration, such as auxiliary firing, these units are built without a furnace preceding the boiler convection surface. The volume of the furnace of a fuel fired boiler is normally greater than the volume occupied by the boiler convection surface. Therefore, depending on the design and arrangement, considerable additional volume is available for installation of boiler surface in a shop assembled waste heat boiler.

There are many other significant differences between boilers designed to recover heat from waste gases and direct fired boilers. The temperature and quantity of waste gas and the constituents in the gas vary widely depending on the source.

The temperature of the gas entering the boiler is substantially lower than the flame temperature of a fired unit. Therefore, for a given heat recovery a greater quantity of gas is involved. Since most oil or gas fired shop assembled boilers are pressure fired, the forced draft fan overcomes resistances to gas flow throughout the boiler. With many waste heat units these resistances are overcome by an induced draft fan.

[2] See Chapter 23, Natural Circulation Boilers, section on waste heat boilers, for additional applications and design considerations.

Because of the relatively large volume of gases to be handled it is desirable to design for nominal draft losses to minimize the horsepower requirements of the induced draft fan driver.

The constituents in waste gases must be carefully evaluated in establishing the design of waste heat boilers. The chemical analysis, dust loading and slagging characteristics will affect the arrangement of the boiler surface and casing and setting. The magnitude and rate of fluctuations in gas flow to the boiler have a very marked effect on the optimum arrangement and type of boiler and on any automatic boiler controls.

Although the normal application of such boilers is to recover heat from waste gases, a supplementary and occasionally primary reason for their installation is to reduce the gas temperature to a point where certain constituents can be recovered or dust carryover collected before discharge to the atmosphere.

In spite of the fact that many of the design criteria are different from those for fuel fired boilers, the advantages of shop assembly are equally valid.

Economics

The principal reason for the continuing increased use of shop assembled boilers is low installed cost. Although each application should be individually evaluated, it is usually found that equivalent capacity in oil or gas fired shop assembled designs can be purchased for 60 to 75 per cent of the investment required for a field erected unit, depending on the equipment selected and local conditions at the plant site. There is also a trend to install several shop assembled units instead of a single large field erected unit. In such cases the investment cost differential may be less, but other factors, such as limited available head room

for the installation of a field erected boiler or much shorter delivery requirements of shop assembled units, may also be important considerations.

Role of Standardization

Standardization is the key to reduced costs. Standard boilers are pre-engineered. In setting up a line of standard boilers it is necessary initially to consider all possible variables involved. Design conditions such as capacity and operating pressure are varied in increments. Physical variables such as terminal connection locations may be varied to some limited extent. Different types of burning and control equipment may be used to suit given applications.

To make standard units suitable for a wide market some degree of inherent flexibility is necessary. However, this flexibility must be exactly defined to retain the advantages of the standardization concept. Although the engineering cost for a whole line of standard boilers is greater than that required for several individual boilers, this cost becomes very nominal when distributed over a large number of standard units.

Savings in Manufacturing

The largest part of the savings with standard shop assembled boilers, however, is in manufacturing. It is far simpler and requires considerably less time to process the necessary fabricating information into the shop. This is essential since many shop assembled units are sold for very short delivery. Many parts are manufactured for a large number of boilers and are then taken from stock as needed.

Standard shop assembled boilers are built under controlled conditions which permits a high quality product at low cost. The assigned shop personnel are thoroughly familiar with the optimum sequence of assembly and special techniques used in shop assembly. The mechanics involved become expert in their particular operations. Tools, equipment, jigs and gages are bought or made for their one exacting requirement. The degree of initial fabrication is carefully integrated with the sequence and method of assembly. Techniques are used that would not be feasible in the field. The enclosed shop assembly area is arranged for optimum materials flow both of parts fabricated for individual units and for parts and materials to be taken from stocks. Likewise, delays due to adverse weather conditions are not encountered.

The cost of many of the basic materials that make up the standard shop-assembled boiler package are less since they are purchased in carload lots to take advantage of price differentials and stored for use as needed. Similarly, quantity purchasing of frequently used accessory and trim items also reduces the cost to the manufacturer. The shipping charges for an assembled unit are less than the sum of charges for knocked down shipment.

Aside from the obvious elimination of field erection costs there are supplementary advantages that further reduce the installation costs and time. Most units require only a simple concrete slab foundation. Shop assembled units are relatively compact so that a smaller area is required for installation than would otherwise be needed for units of the conventional field erected type. Since the boiler is shipped assembled, no erection space or material storage space is required at the installation site.

Shipment

The majority of shop assembled boilers are shipped by railroad, but truck and barge shipments are also used. Initially the cross section of many units was limited by standard railroad clearances. These limiting clearances are based on restrictions that exist on some routes at given points and are not universally applicable. Shipments to certain areas, depending on the location of manufacturer, can considerably exceed standard limiting heights and widths. In other areas special routings avoid local restrictions. The higher capacity standard units invariably exceed standard railroad clearances and must be checked to establish the shipping route from the shop to the site for each individual application.

Truck shipment has been used for short distances or in combination with rail shipment. Barge shipment for multiple units is feasible under some conditions.

As the capacity and therefore the physical size of a boiler increases to the point where it is no longer feasible to ship the boiler as a complete assembly, it is possible to apply the shop assembly concept to components of the boiler unit. The degree to which this can be applied depends on the physical arrangement of the boiler and its dimensions.

For example the side furnace walls of a natural circulation boiler can be arranged to be shop assembled and shipped with tubes attached to inlet and outlet headers. Depending upon the wall construction used, the insulation and casing may be an integral part of this assembly. After the walls are set in place the supply and relief tubes are field installed.

This same idea can be applied to some controlled circulation boilers to a greater degree. Not only the furnace walls, in several sub-assemblies, but the complete convection section may also be shipped as an assembly to reduce the cost and time of field erection.

27

Boilers and Recovery Units for Pulp and Paper Industry [1]

STEAM GENERATION plays a most important role in the pulp and paper making process. Starting from the tree, the pulp and paper industry makes paper from the cellulose fibers which amount to about 50 per cent of this primary raw material. Steam is generated by burning the remainder in the form of bark and waste liquor. The wood is converted into pulp by chemical methods, and steam generation is an integral part of the operation in which the chemicals are recovered. Supplementary steam and power for the conversion of pulp to paper may be obtained from power boilers burning conventional fuels if there is insufficient supply from bark boilers and chemical recovery units.

From the point of view of thermodynamic cycles the pulp and paper industry offers many interesting possibilities in heat balance.[2] For example, Fig. 27–1 shows a steam flow diagram for a mill having a daily capacity of 360 tons of bleached foodboard. In an ideal situation it would be possible to generate all power required by means of back-pressure tur-

bines without resorting to purchased power or condensing turbines.

Choice of steam conditions is dependent upon specific combinations of process and generating equipment, but the upward trend is unmistakable. At the end of World War II steam conditions of 600 psig and 750 F were considered high. By contrast, an increasing number of units now operate at 1200 psig, 900 F.

Function of Pulp Mills

Wood pulp is prepared from a wide variety of hard and soft woods obtained in many geographical areas. Although pulp is the raw material of the papermaker, not every pulp mill produces paper. Conversely, there are many paper mills that do not produce the pulp from which they manufacture paper and related products.

The principal function of the pulp mill is to separate the cellulose fiber from other substances in the wood. After this separation is completed, the pulp mill then cleans, refines and otherwise treats the fibers so that they can be used to make

[1] Material contributed by Edmond L. Smith and E. H. Kennedy.
[2] See Chapter 2, Elements of Power Plant Design, and Chapter 5, Thermodynamic Cycles for Power Plants.

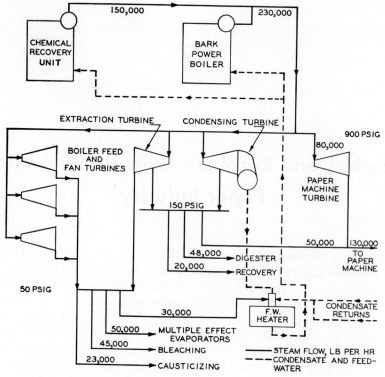

Fig. 27–1. Steam flow diagram for mill producing bleached foodboard

paper or paperboard.[3] The rejected portion of the wood, mostly ligneous in character, is either discarded or may be treated and used as a fuel.

The first step in a pulping operation is to prepare the logs after their delivery to the mill. If they are transported by truck or railroad, removal of noncombustible surface dirt and sand is desirable. Some mills accomplish this as a part of a log handling system in which the logs are dropped into a water sluiceway and transported for a short distance, thereby being cleaned while being moved. Where logs are floated to the mill site or stored in water at the site, special provisions for

surface cleaning are not always required.

Debarking is the second step in the preparation of the logs. There are three common methods. One is hydraulic, in which high pressure water jets are directed at the logs, and the bark is separated by the impact of the water. A second is dry drum debarking, where logs are fed into large rotating horizontal drums and bark is removed by physical impact as the logs tumble over one another. A third is wet drum debarking, which is similar to the foregoing except that water in the form of low pressure sprays is used in the drums as a soaking agent.

---

[3] See the colored pictorial diagram showing the processes for pulp and paper manufacture.

Bark Power Boilers[4]

Whatever the method of handling the logs and separating the bark, the waste product to be disposed of is likely to be a wet one. Typical analyses of wood refuse as received by the boiler room for burning are shown in Table 27–1.

The moisture content can be as high as 75 to 80 per cent. Whenever it exceeds an average of 55 per cent, the bark is either pressed to remove the excess water or is mixed with drier material to give a product which can be burned with some degree of regularity.

After the bark has been separated from the logs and is of acceptable moisture content, it may be burned in a power boiler, either alone or in combination with other fuels. As shown in Fig. 27–2, the modern approach is to use a spreader stoker[5] to project the bark into a furnace through distributors or burner registers located high enough to allow drying of the bark before it reaches the grate at the bottom of the furnace. Turbulence is provided by blowing tangentially directed streams of preheated air at high velocity through rows of nozzles at various furnace levels. All of the bark passes through

[4] This section prepared by M. O. Funk.

[5] For additional information, see Chapter 18, Stokers.

Table 27–1 Analyses of Wood Refuse Burned as Fuel*

	Jack Pine	Birch	Maple	Eastern Hemlock
Proximate analysis, per cent				
Ash	2.1	2.0	4.3	2.5
Volatile	74.3	78.5	76.1	72.0
Fixed carbon	23.6	19.2	19.6	25.5
Ultimate analysis, per cent				
Carbon	53.4	57.4	50.4	53.6
Hydrogen	5.9	6.7	5.9	5.8
Sulfur	0.0	0.0	0.0	0.0
Nitrogen	0.1	0.3	0.5	0.2
Ash	2.0	1.8	4.1	2.5
Oxygen (by difference)	38.6	33.8	39.1	37.9
Btu per lb (bone dry)	8930	8870	8190	8885
Ash analysis				
SiO_2	16.0	3.0	9.9	10.0
Al_2O_3	6.3	0.0	3.8	2.1
Fe_2O_3	5.0	2.9	1.7	1.3
CaO	51.6	58.2	55.5	53.6
$CaCO_3$	4.9	13.0	1.4	9.7
MgO	5.5	4.2	19.4	13.1
MnO	1.6	4.6	1.0	1.2
P_2O_5	2.8	2.9	1.1	2.1
K_2O	4.1	6.6	5.8	4.6
Mn_2O	3.1	1.3	2.2	1.1
TiO_2	0.2	Trace	Trace	Trace
SO_3	2.6	3.2	1.4	1.4
Fusion point of ash, F				
Initial	2450	2710	2650	2760
Softening	2750	2720	2820	2770
Fluid	2760	2730	2830	2780
Weight, lb per cu ft, bone dry	29	37–44	31–42	26–29

Average moisture of about 50 per cent as received at firing equipment

*Adapted from information compiled by the Steam Power Committee of the Canadian Pulp and Paper Association.

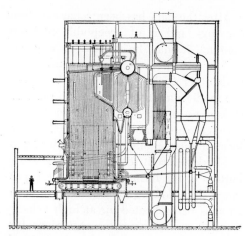

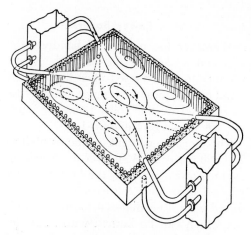

Fig. 27–2.   Combination firing of bark, natural gas, oil and coal

Fig. 27–3.   Turbulent zone of furnace of bark burning boiler

this highly turbulent high temperature gas zone, shown in Fig. 27–3, where a large portion burns rapidly in suspension. Only the larger particles fall to the grate.

The furnace envelope for this method of bark burning may be completely water cooled and have either a dumping or continuous ash discharge grate at the bottom. The entire bark burning process is carried out at high combustion rates and high furnace temperatures.

Auxiliary fuels can be burned in combination with bark to meet steam requirements. Within certain limitations, coal, oil or gas may be burned simultaneously with bark to increase steam and power generation. This means that the power plant for a pulp and paper mill can be made up of bark power boilers and chemical recovery units, as shown in the colored pictorial diagram of the interacting processes for making pulp and paper.

When coal is the auxiliary fuel, spreader stokers or pulverizers are employed.[6] The choice is usually an economic one. In areas where fuel costs are high, the increased

boiler efficiencies that can be realized with pulverized coal will generally offset higher first cost. Conversely, in areas with low fuel costs, the lower first cost of the stoker unit will generally offset the lower efficiencies. Other conditions, such as use factor, purchased power costs and proportions of fuels to be burned will also affect the choice of coal firing method.

For auxiliary liquid fuels, oil or gas burners are located in furnace side walls above the level of the bark distributors and arranged for tangential firing. The elevations of the distributors and the auxiliary burners are selected to compensate for the difference in the quantities and temperatures of gas from each fuel. In addition to helping to maintain a more uniform steam temperature, high location of auxiliary burners affords protection to the grates should there be occasion to burn oil or gas without the firing of bark.

One important consideration in the simultaneous firing of coal and bark is the ash properties of the respective fuels. When mixed and burned in a common

---

[6] For more details, see Chapter 16, Pulverizers and Chapter 18, Stokers.

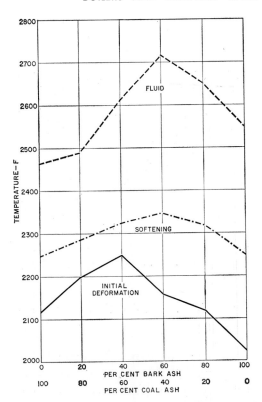

Fig. 27–4. Fractional ash fushion temperatures of mixtures of compatible bark and coal that may be fired simultaneously

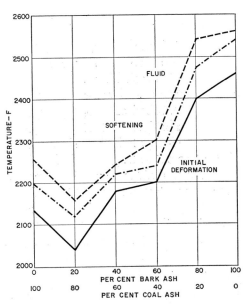

Fig. 27–5. Fractional ash fusion temperatures of mixtures of incompatible bark and coal

Fig. 27–6. Boiler designed to burn incompatible mixtures of bark and pulverized coal. Spreader stoker for bark burning is located in extension of pulverized coal furnace

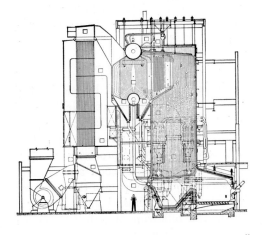

furnace, the resulting ash will have a pronounced effect on grate performance, furnace slagging and cleanliness, and boiler availability. Fig. 27–4 shows a fractional ash analysis suitable for simultaneous firing, while Fig. 27–5 illustrates ash properties which are noncompatible if coal and bark are fired from about the same point in the same furnaces. Under the latter circumstances, it is still possible to burn coal and bark in combination by employing tangential burners for the coal and constructing an extension to the pulverized coal furnace in which bark is fired on a dump grate spreader stoker, as shown in Fig. 27–6.[7]

---

[7] An informative article on combination firing, "Steam Generators for Multiple Fuel Firing," by M. O. Funk appeared in *Combustion,* Vol. 30, October 1958, pp. 49–54.

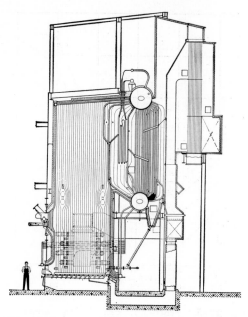

Fig. 27–7. Combination firing of bark, saw-dust, shavings, hogged wood and oil

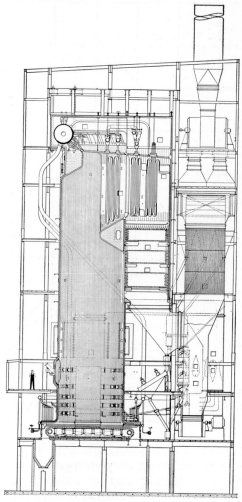

Fig. 27–8. Combination firing of bark, oil and natural gas

Quite naturally there are limits which must be applied to the simultaneous burning of bark and other fuels. These are set by load characteristics, extent of bark preparation and feeding regulation, proportions of various fuels to be burned, characteristics of auxiliary multiple fuels and size of boiler. Typical installations of multiple fuel firing are shown in Figs. 27–7 and 27–8.

Preparation of Pulp

Pulp may be prepared by mechanical or chemical processes or combinations of the two. The straight *mechanical* process is utilized for making groundwood, while the principal *chemical* processes are further defined as sulfite, soda and sulfate. The *semichemical* pulps are the result of a combination of chemical and mechanical action. The following description relates only to the kraft or alkaline chemical pulp-

ing process. Description of other major pulping processes will be found later in this chapter.

The various steps in the preparation of pulp can best be followed by referring to the colored pictorial process diagram. The logs pass through the large barking drums. Stripped logs then go to the chippers where they are reduced to a size suitable for use in the digester. The chips are screened for removal of slivers and

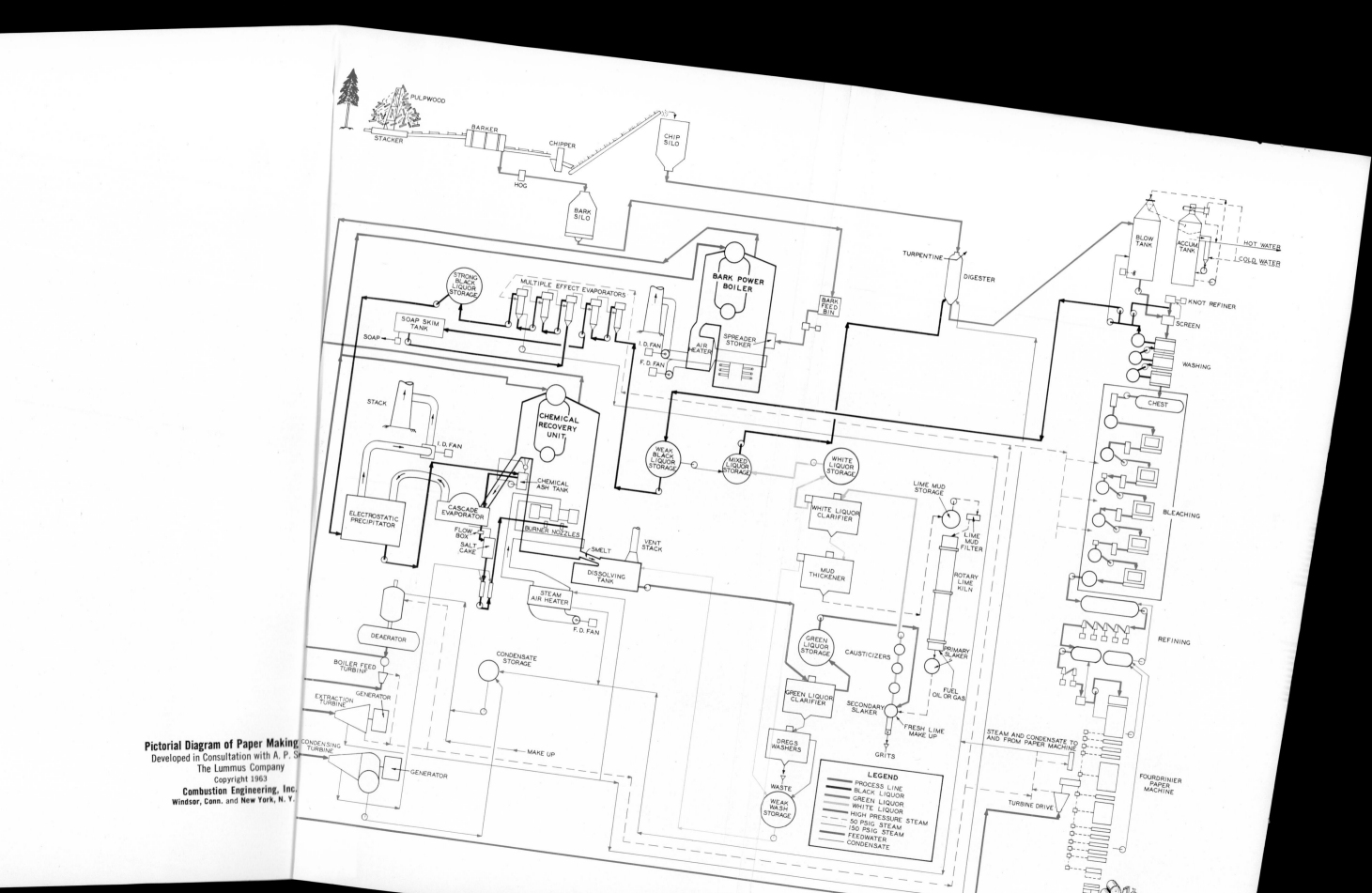

PULPWOOD

STACKER BARKER CHIPPER CHIP SILO

HOG

BARK SILO

TURPENTINE DIGESTER

BLOW TANK ACCUM. TANK HOT WATER COLD WATER

STRONG BLACK LIQUOR STORAGE

MULTIPLE EFFECT EVAPORATORS

BARK POWER BOILER

BARK FEED BIN

KNOT REFINER

SOAP SKIM TANK

SOAP

I. D. FAN AIR HEATER SPREADER STOKER

F. D. FAN

SCREEN

WASHING

STACK

I. D. FAN

CHEMICAL RECOVERY UNIT

CHEST

WEAK BLACK LIQUOR STORAGE MIXED LIQUOR STORAGE WHITE LIQUOR STORAGE

LIME MUD STORAGE

ELECTROSTATIC PRECIPITATOR

CHEMICAL ASH TANK

CASCADE EVAPORATOR

WHITE LIQUOR CLARIFIER

BLEACHING

FLOW BOX BURNER NOZZLES

SALT CAKE SMELT VENT STACK

LIME MUD FILTER

DISSOLVING TANK

MUD THICKENER

ROTARY LIME KILN

STEAM AIR HEATER

DEAERATOR

F. D. FAN

REFINING

CONDENSATE STORAGE

GREEN LIQUOR STORAGE CAUSTICIZERS

PRIMARY SLAKER

BOILER FEED TURBINE

EXTRACTION TURBINE GENERATOR

GREEN LIQUOR CLARIFIER

SECONDARY SLAKER

FUEL OIL OR GAS

FRESH LIME MAKE UP

STEAM AND CONDENSATE TO AND FROM PAPER MACHINE

CONDENSING TURBINE

MAKE UP

DREGS WASHERS

GRITS

FOURDRINIER PAPER MACHINE

GENERATOR

WASTE

WEAK WASH STORAGE

TURBINE DRIVE

LEGEND

PROCESS LINE
BLACK LIQUOR
GREEN LIQUOR
WHITE LIQUOR
HIGH PRESSURE STEAM
50 PSIG STEAM
150 PSIG STEAM
FEEDWATER
CONDENSATE

Pictorial Diagram of Paper Making
Developed in Consultation with A. P. S
The Lummus Company
Copyright 1963
Combustion Engineering, Inc.
Windsor, Conn. and New York, N. Y.

sawdust and then conveyed to chip bins. A cook is prepared by filling the digester with wood chips, then adding makeup liquor, along with a suitable quantity of white liquor.

At this point it should be explained that pulp mill operators refer to many chemical solutions as liquors. In the alkaline pulp mill, the characteristic colors have given rise to the common terminology: *black liquor*, the liquids after the digester and up to the recovery unit; *green liquor*, the solution produced in the dissolving tank; and *white liquor*, the causticized green liquor which constitutes the active chemical solution for cooking the wood in the digesters.

Wood digestion is one of the few major chemical processes that has thus far offered firm resistance to conversion from the batch to continuous operation. During the past several years, however, the perfection of continuous digesters has led to more widespread use of a continuous method of digestion in the production of certain types of pulp. Despite this, the bulk of chemical pulp is still cooked on a batch basis in large spherical or cylindrical steel pressure vessels known as digesters. In commercial practice, the volume of the digester is sufficient to prepare from six to twenty tons of pulp per cook.

After the digester has been loaded with wood chips, the cover is bolted to a flanged opening at the top. The vessel and contents are then brought up to a cooking pressure of approximately 150 psig. Large quantities of steam are required to bring the digester up to pressure. Because of this heavy intermittent demand, boilers for the pulp and paper industry must be designed for high peak capacities and must be equipped with suitable controls to respond to these conditions of fluctuating loads.

The digester charge is steamed or cooked for a period varying from two to six hours, depending on the grade of pulp desired. The steaming promotes circulation of the caustic cooking liquors and penetration of wood chips. This reaction of the chemicals on the ligneous substances in the wood causes a separation to take place, the cellulose generally resisting the chemical action. After the charge has been properly cooked, it is blown at full pressure to the blow tank where the heat in excess of atmospheric conditions flashes into steam, which in turn is condensed to hot water for process use. The blow tank serves as a stock storage balance necessary between batch operation in the preceding digesters and the continuous operation in the following multistage washers. The blow tank proves equally essential with the newer continuous digesters on account of the complexity of digester operation. In the blow tank, water is used to wash the cellulose fiber free of spent cooking liquors and dissolved residue. A further countercurrent washing process produces clean pulp ready for further refinement and subsequent conversion to paper.

The black liquor washed from the pulp is discharged to the weak liquor tanks, where it has a solids content ranging from 12 to 20 per cent. From the weak liquor tanks, the black liquor goes to multiple-effect evaporators, which remove about 80 per cent of the water. It then flows to the chemical recovery unit by way of the precipitator and a cascade evaporator.

Chemical Recovery Unit

Several important changes in the black liquor take place in the recovery unit, the first of which is the vaporization of the water not removed by multiple-effect evaporation. When the final traces of water are driven off, a char is formed in the furnace. This char, which is a light black ash, is the so-called dry solids constituent of the black liquor. When bone dry, it exists as a fine dark brown granular powder.

Another action of the recovery unit is to fuse the inorganics and thus form the *smelt*, which is continuously drained into the dissolving tank through water-cooled spouts near the bottom of the furnace. In the kraft or alkaline process, sodium sulfate (salt cake) is added as a makeup chemical after the black liquor passes through the cascade evaporator. This sodium sulfate, in the presence of carbon and a reducing atmosphere, is converted to sodium sulfide. The two principal inorganic materials then present, sodium carbonate and sodium sulfide, combine as a mixture which is fluid at high temperatures within the furnace. This fluid mixture, referred to as smelt, goes to the dissolving tank to form the green liquor. After the recovery of chemical in the dissolving tank, the green liquor is pumped to the causticizing room. Here it is reacted with lime in causticizers to form white liquor for the digesters.

A third action of the recovery unit is to burn the carbonaceous matter in the dry solids. Part of the heat thus generated is used for maintaining the endothermic chemical reactions taking place in the furnace, while the balance is used for generating steam in the waste heat boiler section above the furnace. Heated air is supplied to the furnace through suitable ports or nozzles.

The intense heat in the furnace causes some sublimation of the sodium compounds present. For this reason, the hot gases of combustion are laden with sublimed chemicals which tend to condense

Fig. 27–9.   Tubular   cascade   evaporator

and collect on the cooler heating surfaces of the boiler, superheater and economizer. The dry chemicals which form deposits throughout the boiler must be removed by soot blower action and returned to the furnace.

Not all of the chemical ash in the flue gas is deposited in the boiler. As much as 10 per cent of the inorganic portion of the total dry solids fed to the furnace may be retained in the gas leaving the boiler. Supplementary equipment following the boiler is therefore necessary to keep the stack losses low and improve the overall recovery of chemical. Fig. 27–9 shows a tubular cascade evaporator that partially scrubs the gas stream and at the same time lowers the flue gas temperature by evaporating water from the black liquor.

Black liquor enters the cascade evaporator near the gas inlet. The liquor level in the tank is automatically maintained so that the tubular surface will be completely coated with liquor as the rotors slowly revolve. This rotation produces a mild pumping action which circulates liquor within the tank. Ash and solid material remain suspended in the circulating liquor. As the wetted tubes come into contact with the hot gas, and by reason of the involved path which the gas must follow, a thorough intermingling of gas and liquor takes place. This action tends to clean the gas of entrained matter and simultaneously evaporate the water in the liquor.

Since a considerable portion of the ash entrained in the gas is the product of sublimation and condensation of sodium salts, the size of many of the ash particles is extremely fine, some of it in the submicron range. Although physically soluble in water, the dust is extremely difficult to wet, and the sodium salts appear to be highly ionized, requiring an electrical field to effectively remove them from the gas stream. Most recovery units are therefore equipped with an electrostatic precipitator for recovering the chemicals still remaining in the gas stream after the direct contact evaporator. The dust collected by the precipitator is mixed with the incoming black liquor and flows to the cascade evaporator, salt cake mixing tank and the furnace.

Basic C–E Recovery Unit Design

The basic C–E recovery unit design stems from the work of the late F. H. Rosencrants in the mid-1930's. It was at this time that the design incorporating the cascade evaporator located directly behind the boiler was conceived. A tower arrangement of boiler and furnace was selected in order to minimize the number of gas turns and to arrange boiler tubes essentially parallel to gas flow, thus reducing the amount of lancing required.

By the use of vertical slag screens located immediately over the furnace the accumulation of chemical could be dropped directly to the hearth below. With ash handling equipment located below the rear boiler passes, the chemical not trapped in the furnace was swept into the liquor in the cascade evaporator. Thus it was possible to return the recovered chemicals to the furnace without manual labor. This design also provided for a completely water-cooled furnace without exposed refractory except for the hearth.

The elements of this chemical recovery unit design were the cascade evaporator, the tower arrangement, the water-cooled furnace, vertical tube-bank arrangement, preheated air and concentrated liquors. The result was a continuous-duty chemical recovery unit requiring little maintenance and a minimum of lancing attention. A cross section of the first C–E recovery unit which was installed in 1938 is shown in Fig. 27–10.

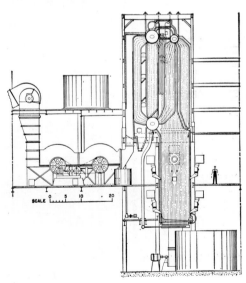

Fig. 27–10. First C–E Chemical Recovery Unit installed in 1938

The current design of the C–E recovery unit is shown in Fig. 27–11. This is a completely integrated unit comprising furnace and pressure parts, superheater, economizer, soot blowers, tubular cascade evaporator, salt-cake feeding and mixing equipment, fans, air and gas systems, dissolving tank, liquor pumps, controls and instruments. The lower structure, extending from the hearth to the sloping roof, is considered the furnace. The walls of this furnace are formed of closely spaced tubes having extended metal fins. For very high pressures, tangent tube construction is used with skin casing.

In these designs there are no exposed refractory surfaces, except for the chrome refractory hearth. In operation even this refractory is covered by a layer of chilled smelt as a result of the flat watercooled hearth design. The lower section of the furnace is completely sealed by metal strips continuously welded to adjacent tube fins. The only openings below the primary air nozzle are those provided for the smelt spouts, which are located ap-

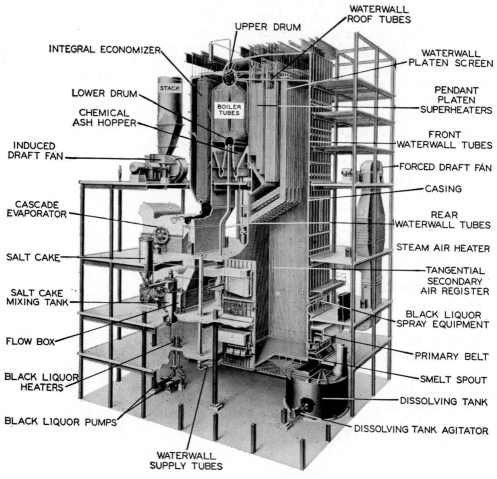

Fig. 27–11. Cutaway view of C–E Chemical Recovery Unit

proximately a foot above the centerline of the floor tubes. Although there is a thin layer of chrome ore over the tubes, the heat transfer rate is such that a layer of chilled smelt from three to six inches deep forms on the hearth. With this protective covering of hard smelt, molten smelt does not come in contact with any refractory surface, except when the initial covering layer is formed.

The lower portion of the furnace, as shown in Fig. 27–12, is divided into three overlapping zones between which there are no distinct lines of demarcation. In the *reduction zone*, immediately above the hearth, a reducing atmosphere is maintained to burn the organic residue out of the accumulated black ash and to secure the maximum conversion of chemical into smelt. The *drying zone* is the one in which a major portion of the moisture is evaporated from the black liquor as it is sprayed into the furnace. The heat for this evaporation process is obtained from burning the organic compounds out of the liquor in the *reduction zone* and from completing combustion of unburned gas and secondary air supplied in the *oxidation zone* just above the drying zone.

Primary air is introduced near the bottom of the furnace through a single row of nozzles in each of the four walls. At this same level there is a larger opening at each corner for the insertion of oil or gas guns. Auxiliary fuel, however, is generally required only when starting up or shutting down the recovery unit unless the mill steam demand is such that additional steam has to be generated in the recovery unit. At a level about fifteen feet above the furnace hearth, additional openings are provided for the black liquor spray guns. The number of openings varies with the size of the recovery unit, with as many as twelve being used on very large units. The spray guns are mounted on rocker bars and oscillate in the vertical plane. They are connected by means of flexible hoses to a liquor header encircling the furnace. Secondary air is introduced at the four corners of the furnace several feet above the liquor spray openings. Specially designed registers inject the combustion air tangent to an imaginary circle in the center of the furnace. This action tends to rotate the combustion gas stream and create intensive turbulence in the oxidation zone of the furnace. Velocities are such that secondary air penetrates

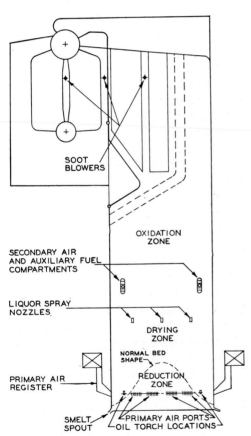

Fig. 27–12. Location of reduction, drying and oxidation zones in furnace of chemical recovery unit

deeply into the furnace, and turbulence thus produced assures uniform and complete combustion of unburned gas originating in the reduction zone.

The upper part of the furnace contains the screen tubes and superheater. The superheater elements consist of tubes tangent to each other so as to form a panel. Extremely wide transverse spacing between adjacent panels assures low draft loss through the superheater. The most important contribution of the tangent superheater design is the elimination of hand lancing because slag does not build up to any degree on the elements.

Pulping Processes

As noted earlier in this chapter, pulp is produced by three methods, namely, mechanical, chemical or a combination of the two. Moreover, there are many processes known for making chemical pulps. A brief description of the major chemical pulping processes is included in this section. Alkaline pulping, the most widely used chemical process, is further discussed in connection with mill capacity and its relationship to the selection and size of the recovery unit.

Mechanical Pulping — Groundwood

Mechanical pulping is significant because of the large tonnages produced. Newsprint is composed of approximately 75 to 80 per cent groundwood, blended with 20 to 25 per cent chemical pulp. Book papers also use a large percentage of groundwood.

In the straight mechanical process, no effort is made to separate the lignin from the cellulose. The wood, after it is stripped of bark, is merely subjected to an abrasive action which reduces it to pulp. The groundwood pulp is then blended with the necessary quantity of chemical pulp before conversion to paper.

Semichemical Pulping

A number of processes are used for producing pulps by a combination of chemical and mechanical treatment. The preponderance of hardwoods in many areas where pulp is produced has led to widespread adoption of the *semichemical* process for hardwood pulping. The process results in relatively high yields and high strength characteristics of the pulp. The pulp is most commonly used in its unbleached form in the manufacture of cardboard cartons and as a corrugating medium.

Sodium is the base employed for semichemical digestions. The name derives from the fact that digestion time is quite short as compared to full chemical cooks; that is, usually only long enough to soften the wood chips. The short cooking period is followed by a series of mechanical steps, generally referred to as refining stages, after which the pulp is suitable for forming a sheet. There are many variations of semichemical pulping.

Recovery of chemicals is feasible in the semichemical process. Many kraft mills produce semichemical pulps, and in this case, the semichemical waste liquors are mixed with the kraft black liquor and burned in a conventional recovery unit. This is known as "cross recovery". The semichemical waste liquor contains sodium and sulfur and replaces all or part of the salt cake used for makeup in the kraft cycle. Because of higher yields in the semichemical processes, the amount of liquor solids derived from the digestion step is considerably lower than that obtained from a full chemical cook. Generally speaking, there is only about one third the amount of liquor produced per ton of pulp; moreover, the heating value of the liquor solids is about 60 to 70 per cent of that of kraft liquor solids.

Semichemical mills can operate apart from a kraft mill and still recover waste liquors. The Sivola process, described later in this chapter, can be used to regenerate the cooking liquors in conjunction with a kraft type recovery unit. A semichemical mill utilizing this method is in operation in Heinola, Finland.

Chemical Pulping

Historically, *sulfite pulping* is the oldest chemical pulping process in existence today. The first sulfite pulp was produced in this country during the year 1867.

Sulfite mills generally employ an acidic liquor to dissolve the ligneous and other noncellulosic substances from the wood. For the manufacture of cooking liquors, burners or roasters are first used to produce sulfur dioxide from sulfur. This gas after being cooled is then passed through towers where it comes in contact with a base material so as to make a readily soluble aqueous solution. Both the burning and cooling processes must be controlled to minimize the possibility of forming sulfur trioxide.

For many years sulfite pulping made use of calcium as the basic element in the cooking acid. In more recent years, however, the ammonium radical and the elements magnesium and sodium have been substituted for calcium. The majority of the sulfite mills still use a calcium base cooking acid and discard the liquid effluent from the digesters.

Calcium Base Sulfite Pulp. In calcium base sulfite pulping, the cooking acid is a fortified calcium bisulfite. Raw materials for making this acid are sulfur, limestone or dolomite, and water, all of which are readily available.

Considerable progress has been made toward the utilization of the waste liquors resulting from calcium base pulping. These efforts have been exerted mainly along two lines: the concentration of the waste liquor in order that it may be disposed of by burning, and the development of other uses of the waste material based on its various physical and chemical properties. Waste calcium base liquor is rich in sugars and complex long chain organic compounds. Ethyl alcohol can be produced from waste liquor by converting the sugars with yeast. The residue of this process serves as a feed for livestock. A few pulp mills synthesize vanillan from waste liquor.

As a fuel, the solid matter in waste calcium base liquor will have a higher heating value of about 8000 Btu per pound. When concentrated to the range of 50 to 60 per cent solids, the liquor becomes a low grade fuel, varying from about 4000 to 5000 Btu per pound, as fired, depending upon the degree of concentration.

Several mills are now burning waste sulfite liquor, using Rosenblad switching-type evaporators for concentration. This waste liquor is burned in suspension similar to heavy fuel oil. The liquor is first heated and then introduced to the furnace through steam or mechanical atomizing burners. The ash content of this waste material is relatively low, usually around 10 per cent, and its melting point is in the order of 2500 F. Calcium base liquor is burned at one midwestern pulp mill, using pulverized coal as an auxiliary fuel in a completely water-cooled furnace. If no auxiliary fuel is to be used, the liquor must be burned in a refractory or partially water-cooled furnace.

To date no practical system has been devised for the recovery of calcium and sulfur in waste calcium base sulfite liquor. The raw materials are abundant and inexpensive. All approaches to recovery of these chemicals have proved economically disproportionate to the relatively small cost of raw materials. The increasing problems of stream pollution, however, have influenced the development of other bases for sulfite pulping wherein chemical recovery is practical and pollution may thus be curtailed.

Magnesia Base Sulfite Pulp. Although magnesium bisulfite was used briefly in the preparation of the cooking acid in the world's first sulfite mill in 1874, it was not until 1936 that interest in this country was revived in the use of magnesia as a base for making pulping acids. This interest was stimulated by the fact that pure magnesium base waste liquor, unlike sodium and calcium base liquor, could be burned under controlled conditions to form magnesium oxide with the liberation of sulfur dioxide. These two compounds could then be further reacted to reform the cooking acid. Thus, a cyclic sulfite process was conceived which offered recovery of the cooking chemicals.[8]

Ammonia Base Sulfite Pulp. The use of ammonia as a base in sulfite pulping was stimulated by the greatly increased and more economical production of ammonia during and since World War II. One advantage claimed for ammonia base pulping is shorter cooking time as compared to calcium base pulping. The process is similar to calcium base pulping and consists essentially of substituting ammonia solution for lime solution in the sulfur dioxide absorption towers, resulting in the formation of ammonium bisulfite.

Ammonia is purchased as anhydrous ammonia in tank car lots, and sulfur dioxide is produced in a conventional sulfur burner. The system is not cyclic, insofar as the ammonia base is concerned; however, the waste ammonia base liquor can be concentrated and burned with ultimate recovery of sulfur dioxide.

Sodium Base Sulfite Pulp. Sodium has been widely exploited as a possible base for sulfite pulping. Much work has been done in this country and abroad to develop a practical method of sodium sulfite pulping with ultimate recovery of the cooking chemicals. The principal problem involved in such a scheme is the conversion of the products of the recovery furnace to chemical solutions that can be reused for digestion. A large part of this development can also be attributed to the increased desire on the part of mills to pulp hardwoods. The sulfite semichemical process is generally a variation of sodium base sulfite pulping, and is now used extensively in this country.

In June, 1952, the first successful full scale installation of a sodium sulfite chemical recovery system was placed in operation in Rauma, Finland. Known as the *Sivola process*, after its developer, it is the most flexible of any of the sodium base sulfite recovery processes. Its flexibility is based on the fact that a wide range of cooking chemicals can be produced, thereby offering the pulp mill a choice of cooking methods. Many types of pulps can be produced utilizing the same basic chemical recovery scheme.

---

[8] For additional information, see two articles in *Chemical Engineering*, Vol. 65, Sept. 8, 1958: "Magnesia Pulping Breaks Pollution Stalemate", pp. 60–62, and "Magnesia Process Buttons Up Sulfite Pulping", pp. 114–117.

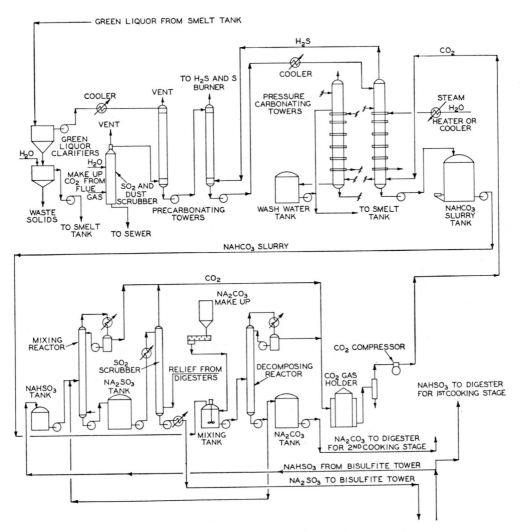

Fig. 27–13. Flow diagram of Sivola recovery process

The Sivola process may be installed and operated independently, or it may be integrated with the conventional kraft or soda recovery system. Primary chemical recovery is done in the same type of chemical recovery unit employed by the vast sulfate pulp industry.

In the Sivola recovery system, the green liquor produced by the primary chemical recovery unit is first carbonated under controlled conditions with carbon dioxide. The carbon dioxide is derived from other steps within the recovery system. This carbonation converts the sodium sulfide and sodium carbonate in the green liquor to sodium bicarbonate. The sodium bicarbonate is then decomposed to sodium carbonate, part being used to make sodium bisulfite cooking acid and the remainder for a second alkaline cooking stage. Several alternates are available, depending upon the type of pulp desired, and, subsequently, upon the cook to be employed.

The various steps in the Sivola recovery process are shown diagrammatically in Fig. 27–13.

Soda and Sulfate Pulp. The *alkaline pulping* processes, as distinguished from the acid or neutral processes, employ sodium hydroxide (caustic soda) or a combination of sodium hydroxide and sodium sulfide as the active chemicals to dissolve the ligneous part of the wood. This carbonaceous matter, which is separated from the cellulose fibers, is burned in smelting furnaces connected to waste heat boilers. Practically all of the inorganic chemical is recovered.

The soda process, the oldest of the alkaline pulping methods, derives its name from the use of caustic soda as the cooking liquor. In North America, the first mills were located in Pennsylvania, and were started in 1880. A diagrammatic outline of this process is shown in Fig. 27–14.

The sulfate mill derives its name from the makeup chemical employed, sodium sulfate. The first producing installation in North America was established in 1907. Since that time, the major expansion of the pulp industry has been centered about the use of the sulfate or kraft alkaline

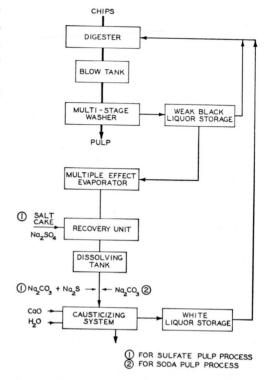

Fig. 27–14. Flow diagram of soda and sulfate processes. As indicated, these differ only in the makeup chemicals used.

pulping process which is also shown diagrammatically in Fig. 27–14.

The soda and sulfate mills employ practically the same arrangement of equipment to manufacture pulp. They differ only in the makeup chemicals employed, the stage in the process at which they are supplied in preparing the cooking liquids, and the grade of pulp produced. The soda mill uses sodium carbonate (soda ash) as the makeup chemical, adding it directly to the causticizing tanks, thereby producing caustic soda by the reactions between the recovered chemical solution, the make-up sodium carbonate and the lime, in accordance with the following:

$$Na_2CO_3 + CaO + H_2O \rightarrow CaCO_3 + 2NaOH$$

Insofar as cooking is concerned, the principal difference between the soda and sulfate process lies in the presence of sodium sulfide in the cooking liquor. The sodium sulfide acts as a buffer in the cooking reaction and governs the characteristics of the pulp produced. In the recovery of chemicals, the degree of conversion of sodium sulfate to sodium sulfide is one of the measures of chemical efficiency of the recovery unit. Sulfate pulp has a longer fiber than soda pulp, because it is usually made from long fibered soft woods, and paper manufactured therefrom has a high degree of strength. Kraft is a term usually applied to sulfate mills. Sulfate pulp can be treated to give it qualities which formerly were considered to be available only in soda and sulfite pulps.

Mill Capacity and Its Relation to Black Liquor Heating Value

The capacity of a mill in terms of tons of paper or pulp produced per day is the unit commonly used for rating the installed equipment. Thus recovery units are rated in tons per day. The rated capacity of a recovery unit is its ability to vaporize the water, burn the carbon and reduce the chemical contained in the black liquor resulting from the production of a specified number of tons of air-dried pulp per day. Air-dried pulp, as distinguished from the bone-dry pulp, contains about ten per cent moisture.

Black liquor at any station in the mill between the blow tank and chemical recovery unit is a mixture of water with organic compounds from the wood and the residual inorganic compounds employed for the cook. A complete analysis of black liquor, as a mixture, is difficult to make; however, chemically, it is considered to consist primarily of the sodium salt of lignosulfonic acid. A typical ultimate analysis of the original solid matter in a hardwood kraft liquor shows the following:

Total carbon	38.40 per cent
Hydrogen	3.70
Total sulfur	4.30
Total sodium	21.56
Inert mineral oxides	0.00
Total oxygen and nitrogen	32.04 (by difference)
Total	100.00

The general practice followed in the past to rate recovery units in tons of capacity made necessary a specific knowledge of the pulp yield from the digester and, subsequently, the solids per ton washed from the pulp, along with the higher heating value of the liquor solids resulting from the pulping operation.

The present method is to use the dry-solids-per-ton measurment, taking an average value of 3000 lb of dry solids per ton of air-dried pulp. The calorific value of the dry solids in black liquor varies from 5200 Btu per pound for soda liquor, up to 7200 Btu per pound for rich kraft liquors. When pulping southern pine, a substance called soap forms during the digestion process and appears in the black liquor. Since this soap has a heating value in the range of 14,000 Btu per pound, it will tend to raise the average heating value of the liquor. Many mills, however, remove the soap and process it into a substance known as tall oil. The average value for sulfate black liquor solids with soap removed is 6500 Btu per pound. Addition of salt cake will lower the heating value proportionately, since salt cake (sodium sulfate) has no heating value.

Although recovery units are alternatively rated in terms of the total pounds of dry solids burned per 24 hours, the heating value of the solids is important in determining the size of the furnace and the boiler heating surface. The solids content of the liquor furnished to the recovery unit also affects the overall de-

sign. This explains the reason why a so-called 400-ton recovery unit for one mill may vary from the size and design of a 400-ton installation in another mill.

Recovery Unit Heat Balance

A heat balance is a useful engineering tool for predicting steam output of a chemical recovery unit. By comparison to power boilers, a recovery unit heat balance is more complicated. Chemicals in the fuel, addition of salt cake, chemical reaction in the furnace and reclaiming of chemicals for use in the pulp mill cycle are all factors which add complexity to the recovery unit heat balance. Fig. 27–15 shows the system boundaries which must be taken into consideration in the calculations.

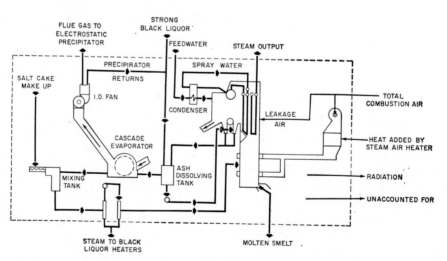

Fig. 27–15. System boundaries for recovery unit heat balance

An example of conditions for a recovery unit heat balance study is as follows:

Quantity dry solids	One pound
Moisture content in black liquor	53.8 per cent
Higher heating value per pound dry solids	6210 Btu
Salt cake added per pound dry solids	0.05 lb
Ambient air temperature to unit	80 F
Temperature of black liquor to unit	200 F
Temperature of gas leaving evaporator	300 F

Dry solids analysis — per cent	
Carbon	38.40
Hydrogen	3.70
Sulfur	4.30
Sodium	21.56
Oxygen and nitrogen (by difference)	32.04
Inert mineral oxides	0.00
Temperature basis	80 F

Under these conditions the heat input and the heat distribution are as follows:

Heat input	Btu
Heating value of black liquor	6210
Sensible heat in black liquor	157
Heat in steam to liquor heaters	39
Heat in preheating air from air heater	237
Total heat input	**6643**

Heat distribution	Btu
Water vapor loss — all sources	1419
Dry gas loss	290
Reduction of salt cake makeup	139
Heat of reaction correction	483
Heat in fusion and sensible heat in smelt	229
Radiation	75
Unaccounted for	248
Heat available for steam	3760
Total heat distribution	**6643**

Chemical Reduction and Steam Production

Although the chemical recovery unit bears much similarity to a power boiler in its general appearance and makes use of many of the same physical components, its distinctive process function places the heat absorbing surfaces in a different category. The recovery of chemical is the primary object, while resulting steam generation is of secondary importance.

A recovery unit of modern design consists of an integrated arrangement of evaporating, burning, reducing, dissolving, mixing and steam generating areas. All of these are carefully controlled and regulated to form an important element of the mill for producing pulp. Steam is a parallel product of the chemical recovery process, and it serves the same function and has the same importance as steam generated in boilers fired by other fuels. The design of a chemical recovery unit is a carefully balanced combination of chemical process requirements and modern steam generating practice to effect maximum chemical reduction and recovery, along with the highest possible steam production and minimum operating and maintenance costs.

28

Marine Boilers [1]

THE GREAT NUMBER of limitations and unique requirements which apply to shipboard power plants make the marine boiler a very specialized form of steam generator. Since most ships are designed for specific trades, propulsion machinery for a certain ship must be selected to meet the operating conditions encountered in the trade that the vessel will serve.

Generally, marine boilers must meet the following conditions:

High level of dependability
Limited space
Wide range of steam output capacities
Ability to change load rapidly
Good accessibility
Limited weight

Service Requirements

The design of a marine boiler properly starts with a review and study of the service requirements for the particular ship under consideration. The steam conditions and evaporating rates are set by the ship designer after he has completed an economic evaluation of all propulsion plant cycles which could be used. The heat balances, calculated at various steady steaming conditions, establish certain plant operating conditions which the boiler must meet. In this connection, it must be recognized that boiler performance is a parameter in the heat balance calculations. For example, the boiler efficiency can be set at a given amount for any one evaporating rate, but heat balance calculations at other evaporating rates must be based upon the corresponding boiler efficiencies as set by the performance characteristic of a particular boiler design. Some types of ships will have a weight allowance specified for the boilers.

Normal power is a specified characteristic of a given merchant ship and generally corresponds to 100 per cent rating of the boiler. For naval vessels 100 per cent boiler rating corresponds to *full power*.

In addition to the conditions set by the quantities which are readily defined by numerical values, the operating conditions which will be encountered in service have a direct influence upon the boiler design. Although two ships might have the same shaft horsepower (shp) and the same evaporating rates for the boilers, one ship might be in a trade which called for prolonged periods of steady steaming, and in contrast, the other ship might be in a service which required the boilers to

[1] Material contributed by W. C. Freeman and E. W. Ludt.

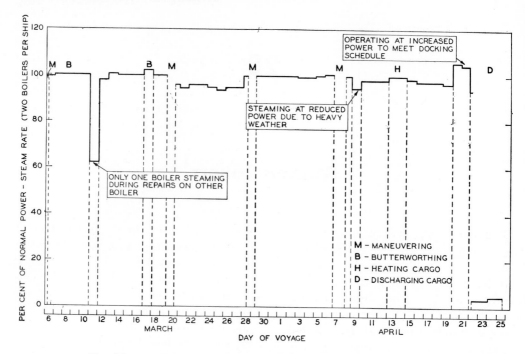

Fig. 28—1.   Variations of boiler output during voyage of tanker

be frequently changing load. As examples, the former would be typical of a tanker and the latter, a dredge or a ferry boat.

Fig. 28–1 shows the variations of boiler output which were experienced during a round trip voyage between Philadelphia and the Persian Gulf by a tanker of 45,000 tons deadweight (dwt).

By analyzing the boiler load variations during a voyage, it is possible to make a graph showing the load pattern for the boilers on that particular trade. In designing new ships, it is customary to plot these graphs with averages compiled over an extended period from data of ships that have been in the same trade that the new vessels will serve. Fig. 28–2 illustrates the boiler load pattern which might be experienced by a dry cargo ship during a single round trip voyage between the West Coast of the United States and the Orient.

Obviously a ferry boat boiler has a load pattern that is much different from that of a tanker, and the boiler on a dry cargo ship has a load pattern far different from the boiler on a destroyer. Although the design of a ship and its machinery must take into consideration possible changes

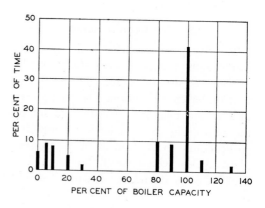

Fig. 28—2.   Boiler load pattern during voyage of dry cargo ship

in trade conditions, it is the prime objective to get the optimum design for the trade in which the vessel will initially serve. In this connection, it is fortunate that most marine boilers have the inherent characteristic of being versatile to a degree. Therefore, if trade conditions bring about changes in the boiler load pattern, the boiler usually will be able to meet the new conditions within the limits as determined by the other machinery components of the propulsion plant.

The load pattern can be an important factor in deciding some of the principal characteristics of the boiler design, and it will also determine some of the detail features which must be included. Consideration must also be given to various other service conditions, such as ship sailing schedule and quality of operating personnel. The following listing gives some of the boiler design features which may be decided entirely, or in part, by service conditions:

Number of boilers per ship
Number of burners per boiler
Type of burners
Furnace dimensions
Overall boiler dimensions
Extent of control systems
Instrumentation
Size of steam drum
Type of steam separators
Relative amount of waterwall generating surface

It is the careful study of anticipated operating conditions which enables the boiler designer to produce a unit which will deliver optimum results in service.

Up to this point there has been no discussion of the extremely basic condition of space limitation which actually dictates the boiler design on many ships. To the boiler designer it would be ideal

if space could be provided in the fireroom so that the optimum boiler design could be installed. Table 28–1 and Fig. 28–3 show the principal dimensions of one standard series of boiler designs. While the ship owner and naval architect usually try to design the ship so that, as nearly as possible, space will be provided for the optimum boiler design, it is almost inevitable that space restrictions will be imposed. The space problem must be considered constantly by the boiler designer from the outset of the preliminary ship design to the time when the boilers are

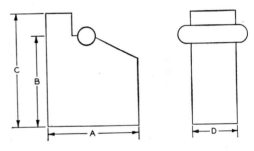

Fig. 28–3. Dimensions applicable to Table 28–1

Table 28–1* Principal Dimensions for a Standard Design of Marine Boilers for 600 psig, 800 F Steam Conditions

Normal Power Evaporation	Principal Dimensions			
Lb Per Hr	"A"	"B"	"C"	"D"
35000	19'–3''	18'–0''	24'–3''	10'–0''
40000	19'–3''	18'–0''	24'–3''	10'–9''
45000	19'–3''	18'–0''	24'–3''	11'–11''
50000	19'–3''	18'–0''	24'–3''	12'–8''
51000	20'–4''	20'–1''	27'–4''	10'–4''
55000	20'–4''	20'–1''	27'–4''	10'–9''
60000	20'–4''	20'–1''	27'–4''	11'–6''
70000	20'–4''	20'–1''	27'–4''	13'–0''
80000	20'–4''	20'–1''	27'–4''	14'–1''

* This table is based on two-drum bent tube boilers with 150 per cent overload capacity and furnace release rates of 70,000 Btu per cu ft hr.

installed and accessibility has been satisfactorily proved.

In many ships the very nature of the purpose of the ship establishes limiting dimensions for the fireroom space. For example, the train ferry must have as many continuous decks as possible and this feature immediately sets a limit upon the height allowed for the boiler space. For many ship types the strength members of the ship hull present the most common reason for limiting the boiler dimensions.

Selection of Design

After the service conditions have been properly evaluated, the boiler designer proceeds to determine the physical characteristics of the design which will best meet requirements. Ideally, the preliminary design should be completed in time to be used by the ship designer when he establishes the machinery arrangement and the layout of the main hull structurals in way of the fireroom. Space is generally the first item to be considered. If the optimum boiler design — the one which has the arrangement and physical characteristics most suitable for the service conditions and performance requirements — has any dimension that is definitely in excess of the space allowed, then a compromise must be made. In designing the boiler furnace, the major factors to be considered are as follows:

Burner accessibility and clearances
Gas flow and flame travel
Circulation
Interrelationship of the furnace dimensions with the main generating bank dimensions
Amount of waterwall surface
The burners must be located in posi-

tions that will be readily accessible from the firing aisle. Each burner of a particular type and manufacture has its own operating characteristics, and the furnace must be suitable for those characteristics. The prescribed minimum burner clearances must be carefully maintained in order to avoid flame impingement against the furnace walls, floor or screen generating tubes.

In selecting the dimensions of the furnace, provisions must be incorporated to cause the proper flow pattern for the combustion gases within the furnace and into the tube bank. It would be ideal if the gas flow could be controlled to the extent that the mass flow rate and the gas temperature both would be uniform at all points where the gas enters the screen tube bank. Generally it is not possible to achieve this theoretical condition, and therefore the boiler designer must be guided by the results of past experience obtained during the testing and operating service of designs similar to the one under consideration. It is particularly important to provide adequate distances between the burners and the screen tube bank so that the flame front will not go beyond the furnace and into the tube bank.

In selecting the preliminary design for a marine boiler, it is usually unnecessary to make detailed calculations on the circulation of the boiler circuits, providing the design is reasonably similar to previous designs of the same general type for which complete circulation calculations have been performed. It is important to note that the maximum circulation effect is obtained when the majority portion of the heat absorbed is applied to the lowermost portion of a tube.[2] Therefore, locating the burners in the lower part of the

---

[2] See Chapter 7, Fluid Flow, for additional information on boiler circulation.

furnace serves to meet the requirements of circulation performance as well as providing the best arrangement for operating the burners.

Most types of boilers have the arrangement and dimensions of their generating banks related to some degree to furnace dimensions. For example, in early designs of two drum bent tube boilers, limitations on the draft loss through the main bank would frequently set the main bank dimensions, and the furnace height would be fixed accordingly. With some boiler designs, the furnace dimensions can be set at the optimum point, and the main bank dimensions are essentially independent. This is made possible by having the distributing header located several feet away from the lower drum, as discussed later in this chapter in the section on bent tube boilers.

In most instances boilers are now designed with the maximum amount of waterwall heating surface. For a long period of time it was customary to fit waterwall tubes into the side, roof and rear furnace walls, but as higher rates of boiler evaporation were required, waterwall tubes also became feasible in the burner wall.

Development of Marine Boilers

In tracing the history of the development and application of marine boilers, it is interesting to note that some of the basic requirements have always applied, although from time to time the emphasis has shifted from one requirement to another. At the outset, space and weight limitations were not considered to be as important as other factors, and yet at later stages the emphasis on those items brought about the development of new types of boilers. Generally, it has been the economic or military need for increased propulsion power that has instigated the advances in boiler design.

The earliest types of marine boilers consisted of relatively large pressure vessels, with furnaces located underneath them.[3] The addition of tubes to these boilers was brought about through an early recognition of the neccessity for greater steam output. These tubes formed multiple passages for the products of combustion and provided considerable surface which served to increase efficiency, owing to the greater amount of heat extracted from the gases passing through them. Thinner and lighter plates with staybolts were substituted for heavy unstayed surfaces to reduce weight even though pressures were increased.

It soon became apparent that the exterior furnaces were far from satisfactory, and these were then placed inside the boiler shell. The exterior of the boiler had now developed into an approximate cube and its flat exterior, no matter how heavily stayed, placed very low limits on the pressure that could be carried and also left much to be desired from a maintenance and safety standpoint. The internal furnaces and tubes, however, were cylindrical and entirely satisfactory for the pressure demands of their time. It is interesting to note that by 1870 marine boiler pressures had reached only 60 psig, and by 1900 they had increased to about 300 psig.

Scotch Marine Boilers

To overcome the structural weaknesses and at the same time reduce cost of fabrication, the boiler shell was made cylindrical (replacing the earlier box-like

---

[3] An excellent historical account of early marine boiler designs is given in *Naval Boilers* by Robert F. Latham, published by U.S. Naval Institute, Annapolis, Md., 1956.

construction), and provision was made to install one or more combustion chambers between the two flat sides of the shell. Combustion chambers were fitted at the exterior of the front and rear shell plates to cause the combustion gases to flow in succession from furnace outlets into the first pass of fire tubes and then through the following passes of fire tubes. As finally developed, this boiler — known as the *Scotch marine boiler* — met with the almost instant approval of marine engineers. While minor changes have been made throughout the years, its design has remained much the same and its qualities of ruggedness, reliability, ease of maintenance, and ability to stand abuse made it — until recent decades — the most popular boiler in the marine field.

Scotch marine boilers are either single or double end, with from one to four furnaces for each end. Perhaps the most familiar one is the single end type as shown in Fig. 28–4. The boiler shown is coal fired with a spreader stoker and is fitted with two furnaces. A close inspection of the illustration will show two separate combustion chambers, each stayed to the other. Tubes used as flues for returning products of combustion from the combustion chambers to the smokebox, covering the upper front of the boiler, are also shown.

Even though the Scotch marine boiler proved to be popular and well-suited for shipboard installations, the fact that its pressure was limited to 300 psig retarded progress. There was a realization that advanced boiler designs with greater generating capacity, higher pressure and increased efficiency were needed to meet the changing requirements brought about by the development of turbine propulsion machinery. Stiff commercial competition among merchant fleets as well as various

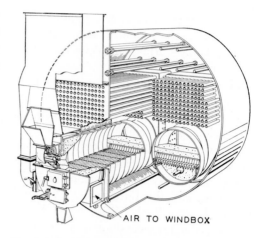

AIR TO WINDBOX

Fig. 28–4. Scotch marine boiler fired by spreader stoker

naval powers made these developments most urgent. Marine engineers began to adapt various types of water tube boilers to fit into the restricted space available for installations on shipboard. Some of these proved highly advantageous with respect to heat transfer and weight and offered a variety of designs suitable for pressures in excess of the maximum of firetube types. Thus new possibilities were presented for the utilization of steam aboard ship.

Sectional Header Boilers

One of the early water tube boilers was the cross drum type which had generating tubes extending between a row of rear headers arranged vertically and connected to the drum, and a row of uptake headers at the front of the boiler. Vertical waterwall tubes were arranged at both sides of the furnace. At a later stage of development, the downtake headers in the steam drum were relocated to the front of the boiler and that basic arrangement is known today as the *cross-drum sectional-header* boiler. The ready access provided by handhole plates in the headers makes it possible to turbine-clean the water sides of the main bank generating tubes without the need for a man to enter the steam drum. This boiler is appreciably heavier than other more modern boiler designs. During World Wars I and II, the sectional-header boiler was used for many kinds of merchant ships. The design is ideally suited for mass production.

The C-E Type SM Sectional Header Boiler as shown in Fig. 28–5 is designed for capacities up to about 150,000 lb of steam per hour and pressures up to 850 psig. Steel corner columns incorporated into the casing members form a boxlike structure which supports the boiler. Insulated casing encloses the entire unit. Where it is necessary to have good accessibility, the casing panels are portable and are held in place by bolted batten bars. At other locations the casing panels are welded in place. Generally, the side and rear walls of the furnace are fitted with vertical waterwall tubes. Superheaters may be either interdeck or overdeck, depending on the steam temperature required. Fig. 28–6 shows a typical interbank superheater for a sectional-header boiler.

Fig. 28–7 shows the general arrangement of a cross-drum sectional-header boiler design as installed in the SS *Atlantic Seaman* and two duplicate sister ships, which were put into service in 1950 and 1951. Each ship has two boilers, and each boiler has a normal power evaporation rate of 65,000 lb per hour with a steam condition of 650 psig and 1020 F at the superheater outlet.

The two boilers in the SS *Surveyor*, an ocean survey vessel built in 1959 for the U. S. Coast and Geodetic Survey Department, are also of sectional-header design, and the general arrangement is shown in Fig. 28–8. Each boiler has a normal power evaporation rate of 17,500 lb per hour with steam conditions of 410 psig, 750 F at the superheater outlet.

Bent Tube Boilers

Just as the need for increased steaming capacities within fixed space and weight limitations spurred the development of the earlier water tube type boilers, so did the same need precipitate the advance to boiler designs of the *bent tube* type. This designation covers a wide range of boiler designs which are characterized by the ability to raise steam pressure within a short period of time. This means smaller tube diameters, fewer headers, increased furnace ratings and wider application of water cooled furnaces. In addition to bent tube type, the boilers of this category became known as multidrum type, express type, and by various names corresponding to the designers of particular arrangements.

The most compelling reasons for the development of higher capacity boilers came from the naval designers who, at about the end of the nineteenth century, were charged with developing the torpedo boats which were the forerunners of modern destroyer type vessels.

With advanced designs available for naval vessels, it was a quite logical step to utilize adaptations of those designs for higher powered passenger ships. Thus during the 1930's, the two-drum bent tube design was developed for application to merchant ships with power plants ranging up to about 10,000 shp.

After World War II, ship operators and boiler designers became acutely aware of the fact that marine boiler designs would have to be modified in order to avoid some of the difficulties that were being encountered with the prewar designs.

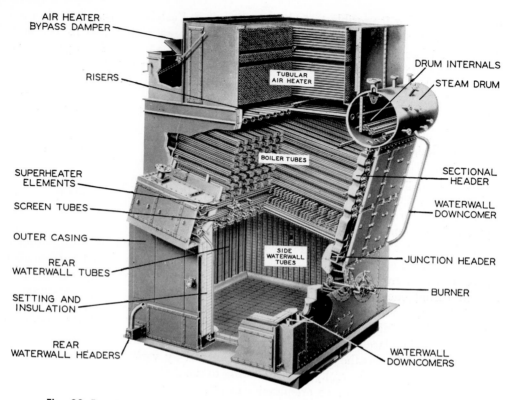

Fig. 28–5. C-E Type SM Sectional Header Boiler, principal parts identified

Fig. 28–6. Interbank superheater for sectional header boiler

During the War, of course, emphasis had been upon standardization and multiple production, and time was not available for the development of improved designs.

Another factor which prompted the development of new boiler designs stemmed from competitive and economic pressures which compelled shipowners to look toward higher steam pressures and temperatures, and also propulsion plants of greater power, as means of achieving more profitable operation. It was also realized that ship boilers would have to be designed to burn efficiently the fuel oils that would be available. Due to improved refining processes coupled with the natural motivations of profitable marketing, it was to be expected that the crude oil was to be processed to the fullest and the resulting residual oil which normally goes to bunkers of ships would be progressively of lower quality. The prewar boilers were particularly vulnerable to fireside damage caused by slag deposits.

A comprehensive analysis of these problems led to the development of the C–E

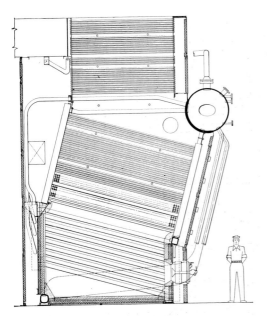

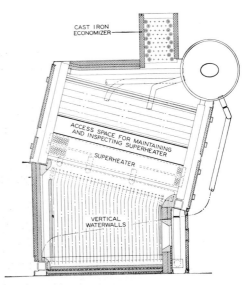

Fig. 28—7. C-E Sectional Header Boiler for SS Atlantic Seaman

Fig. 28—8. C-E Sectional Header Boiler for SS Surveyor

V2M Vertical Superheater Boiler. A typical arrangement of this design is shown in Fig. 28–9. By providing a separate drum or header, called a distributing header, at the lower end of the screen tubes, it is possible to set the floor of the furnace independently of the location of lower drum and main bank. This allows greater latitude in establishing optimum furnace dimensions and also permits the superheater tubes to be parallel to the generating tubes. The access space within the superheater contributes to ease of maintenance and inspection.

The V2M-8 Vertical Superheater boiler shown in Fig. 28–10 features an arrangement which achieves a completely water cooled furnace, thus eliminating costly refractory maintenance problems. The burners are located in the roof, enabling operation from the main level of the furnace room while the boilers themselves are set on a lower level. This results in simpler foundations and a lower center of gravity for the power plant.

Simplification of the boiler casing is achieved by means of a cubic configuration which results in a more uniform expansion of pressure parts as the boiler is brought up to steaming condition. The waterwall tubes are standardized so that fewer shapes are required. The superheater headers are of a unique design which includes a flat tube sheet, thus permitting superheater tubes to enter the headers on a straight run without complicated bends. The V2M-8 Vertical Superheater boiler design includes long retractable soot blowers at the superheater, and the boiler can be designed for cast iron economizers or air heaters.

Moore McCormack Lines C4-S-60a vessels are equipped with V2M-8 Vertical Superheater boilers, each of which is designed for the following operating conditions:

Normal evaporation rate	61,400 lb per hr
Overload evaporation rate	73,700 lb per hr
Superheater outlet pressure, normal power	865 psig
Superheater outlet temperature, normal power	955 F
Feedwater temperature	281 F
Boiler efficiency, normal power	88 per cent

Controlled Circulation Boilers

All of the marine boilers described to this point are dependent upon natural forces to maintain the circulation flow within the boiler. Natural circulation is obtained by the difference in hydraulic head between the saturated water in the

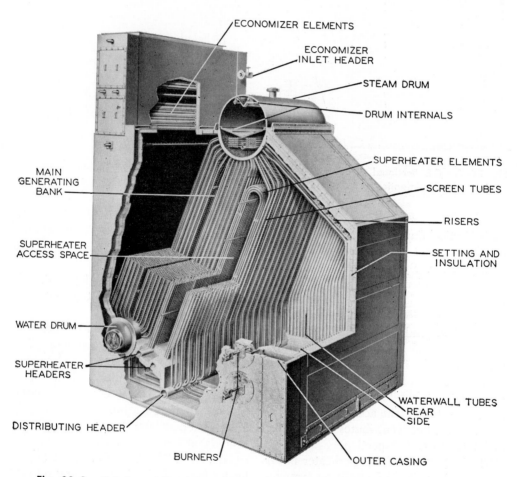

Fig. 28–9.   C-E Type V2M Vertical Superheater Boiler, principal parts identified

downcomers and the relatively less dense mixture of steam and water in the steam generating tubes. For the lower range of steam pressures, natural circulation forces are usually quite adequate but at higher pressures, it becomes desirable and advantageous to provide a more positive means of maintaining the circulation.

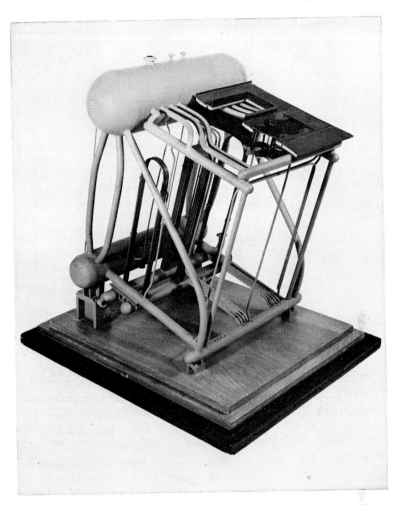

Fig. 28–10. C-E Type V2M-8 Vertical Superheater Boiler

Over the years many boiler designs featuring various systems of forced circulation have been invented. The C–E Controlled Circulation Marine Boiler presents an ideal design for shipboard steam plants in the higher pressure range. A diagram of a typical arrangement illustrating the principle of operation for this boiler is shown in Fig. 28–11. It will be noted that the economizer is the same as used on natural circulation boilers.[4]

With its features of positive circulation, compactness, relatively light weight, suitability for high pressure and temperature, and adaptability to limited space conditions, the controlled circulation boiler can offer important advantages for advanced design marine steam practice. A C–E

[4] For additional information, see Chapter 24, Controlled Circulation Boilers.

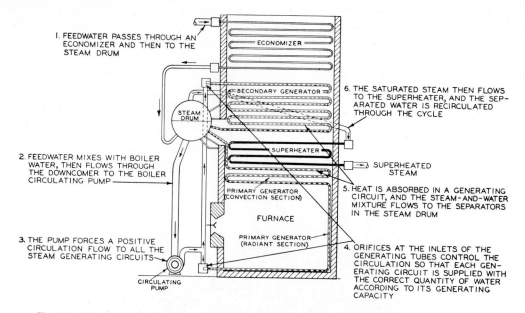

1. FEEDWATER PASSES THROUGH AN ECONOMIZER AND THEN TO THE STEAM DRUM

2. FEEDWATER MIXES WITH BOILER WATER, THEN FLOWS THROUGH THE DOWNCOMER TO THE BOILER CIRCULATING PUMP

3. THE PUMP FORCES A POSITIVE CIRCULATION FLOW TO ALL THE STEAM GENERATING CIRCUITS

ECONOMIZER

SECONDARY GENERATOR

STEAM DRUM

SUPERHEATER

PRIMARY GENERATOR (CONVECTION SECTION)

FURNACE

PRIMARY GENERATOR (RADIANT SECTION)

CIRCULATING PUMP

6. THE SATURATED STEAM THEN FLOWS TO THE SUPERHEATER, AND THE SEPARATED WATER IS RECIRCULATED THROUGH THE CYCLE

SUPERHEATED STEAM

5. HEAT IS ABSORBED IN A GENERATING CIRCUIT, AND THE STEAM-AND-WATER MIXTURE FLOWS TO THE SEPARATORS IN THE STEAM DRUM

4. ORIFICES AT THE INLETS OF THE GENERATING TUBES CONTROL THE CIRCULATION SO THAT EACH GENERATING CIRCUIT IS SUPPLIED WITH THE CORRECT QUANTITY OF WATER ACCORDING TO ITS GENERATING CAPACITY

Fig. 28–11. Diagrammatic arrangement of C-E Controlled Circulation Marine Boiler

Controlled Circulation Marine Boiler for superheater outlet conditions of 2000 psig, 1050 F is shown in Fig. 28–12.

Furnace Design Principles

The configuration of a marine boiler furnace is determined by a number of factors. First of all, some of the furnace dimensions are set by the type of boiler under consideration. Fireroom space limitations, service requirements and burner arrangement also influence the furnace layout. The furnace arrangement must also conform to certain criteria which are prerequisites for proper thermal and circulation performance. Since the generating tubes enclosing the furnace work at higher rates of heat input than any other generating tubes in the boiler, necessary provisions for circulation are largely determined by the waterwall and screen tubes. The amount of waterwall surface determines the furnace exit gas tempera-

ture which, in turn, is most significant in the design of the superheater. Practical requirements must also be considered. The burners must be located where they are easily operated.

The type of sectional header boiler built for Liberty ships is an example of an all refractory furnace. The furnace sides, rear and front walls are entirely refractory, and the screen tubes directly above the furnace are the only generating tubes adjacent to the combustion space. Such an arrangement was quite suitable for the lower pressure and temperature steam conditions, and it also offered the advantage of presenting a simplified construction which helped to expedite the production of World War II shipyards.

For other designs of sectional header boilers, and particularly those suitable for operation at 450 psig and 750 F, it was customary to fit a vertical waterwall at the rear of the boiler and to have either inclined or vertical waterwalls on the sides of the boiler. With the inclined waterwall, all tubes can be identical which is an advantage that simplifies the spare parts inventory. On the other hand, the vertical waterwall arrangement offers the advantage of improved circulation, and this is most important for sectional header boilers which operate at pressures higher than 450 psig.

Two-drum bent tube boilers are always furnished with watercooled surfaces on the side and roof, and for the majority of designs a rear waterwall is included. In some cases waterwalls are fitted in the front wall. Since the burners must occupy

Fig. 28–12. C-E Controlled Circulation Marine Boiler, USS Timmerman

space in the burner wall, it is usually not feasible to include a front waterwall for boilers in the lower capacity range.

Heat Absorption by Waterwalls[5]

Waterwalls absorb a substantial portion of the heat released in a furnace. Frequently furnace conditions are judged on the basis of heat released per cubic foot of furnace volume. A much better criteria for evaluating furnace conditions is the heat released per square foot of effective projected radiant absorbing surface. The rate at which heat is absorbed by radiation by each square foot of absorbing surface is a function of the rate at which heat is released. The difference between these values is the rate at which heat is not absorbed by radiation. The furnace temperature is dependent upon the heat not absorbed by furnace radiation, that is, the heat remaining in the gases leaving the furnace and passing into the boiler generating surface.

For example, an oil fired sectional-header boiler has both side and rear watercooled walls. As will be noted from Table 28–2 the furnace release rate per cubic foot of furnace volume is 71,000 Btu per hour, and the release rate per square foot of effective projected radiant absorbing surface is 162,000 Btu per hour. If the waterwalls were omitted from this boiler, and air heater or boiler surface were added to maintain the same efficiency and therefore the same firing rate for a given evaporation, the release rate per cubic foot of furnace volume would remain unchanged but the release rate per square foot of effective radiant absorbing surface would increase to 378,000

Btu per hour. The furnace temperature would rise from 2430 to 2700 F.

To attain the same furnace temperature of 2430 F without water cooling on the furnace walls, it would be necessary to increase the boiler width by 133 per cent. The furnace release rate per cubic foot of furnace volume would be considerably reduced but would not be indicative of actual furnace loading.

An indication of the heat absorbed by the component parts of boilers, identified as A and B in Table 28–2, is shown in Fig. 28–13. With waterwalls installed in Boiler A, 42.2 per cent of the heat is absorbed in the furnace by radiation, whereas only 32.5 per cent is absorbed in the furnace by radiation in Boiler B. Although a greater percentage is absorbed in Boiler A, the rate per square foot of absorbing surface is considerably less. The first row of boiler tubes generates steam at a high rate, since heat is applied by radiation and convection. From Fig. 28–13 it will be noted that 20 per cent of the total heat is absorbed in the first row of the boiler with watercooled furnace walls, 13.1 per cent by radiation and 6.9 per cent by convection. In the boiler without furnace wall cooling, 32 per cent of the total heat is absorbed in the first row, 21.9 per cent by radiation, 8.1 per cent by convection. Therefore, the use of watercooled furnace walls not only reduces furnace temperature and brickwork maintenance but also reduces the rate at which steam is generated in the first row of steam generating tubes. In most marine boilers this is the critical row from the circulation standpoint.

---

[5] This section has been adapted from ASME Paper 51–SA–53, "Some Developments in Marine Boiler Design" by S. F. Mumford. Excerpts from this paper were published in *Combustion*, Vol. 23, July 1951, pp. 50–55.

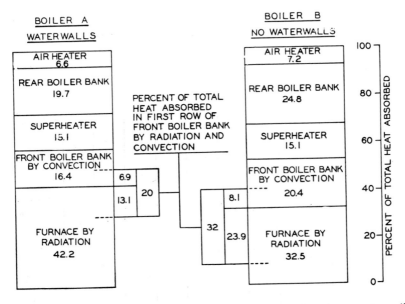

Fig. 28-13. Heat absorption in marine boilers with and without waterwalls

Table 28-2 Effect of Furnace Wall Cooling on Furnace Temperature

Oil fired sectional header boiler	A With side and rear walls cooled	B No wall cooling	C Same as B with width increased by 133 per cent
Release rate Btu per hr cu ft furnace volume	71,000	71,000	30,500
Btu per hr sq ft effective projected radiant absorbing surface	162,000	378,000	162,000
Absorption rate Btu per hr sq ft effective projected radiant absorbing surface	63,000	116,000	63,000
Gas temperature leaving furnace, F	2430	2700	2430

Superheaters

Superheaters consist essentially of a series of tubular elements connected to headers. The saturated steam enters the inlet header from piping connected to the steam drum. In a single pass superheater the saturated steam flows from the saturated header through the superheater elements into the superheater outlet header. In the multipass superheater, the headers are diaphragmed to allow the steam to make as many passes necessary to assure good steam distribution through all elements.

Fig. 28-14 shows the percentage of heat absorbed in component parts of a number of marine boilers designed for a broad range of capacities and superheater outlet conditions. It can be observed that

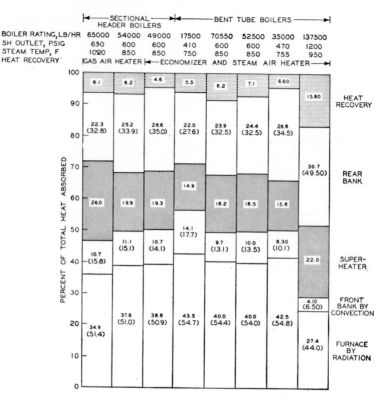

Fig. 28–14. Heat absorption in component parts of marine boilers

the amount of heat absorbed in the superheater increases with higher steam pressures and temperatures.

Marine superheater design requires a judicious balancing of economic and practical factors. There must be a sufficiently large temperature difference between the combustion gas passing over the superheater surface and the steam within the surface to result in a superheater of economic proportions. At the same time there are practical limitations on superheater metal temperatures, and provision must be made to arrange superheater elements to resist slag accumulation. Screen tubes are located ahead of superheaters to obtain reasonable metal temperatures while at the same time allowing a certain amount

of direct radiation to be absorbed by the superheater tubes. This results in a flatter steam temperature curve at the superheater outlet.

Some boiler designs have the superheater in back of the main generating bank. Such an arrangement requires a relatively greater amount of heating surface and an elaborate system for controlling superheater outlet temperature. Another arrangement incorporates a second furnace which allows the steam temperature to be controlled by varying the firing rate of the superheater furnace. Such a boiler design permits a wide range of control but there are inherent complications in the operating procedures.

Most two-drum bent tube boilers are

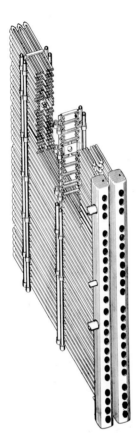

Fig. 28–15. Typical horizontal superheater arrangement

designed with the superheater within the generating bank and with either horizontal or vertical superheaters. For the horizontal superheater, the superheater elements are generally supported from clamps or brackets attached to adjacent generating tubes. A typical arrangement is shown in Fig. 28–15. Positive means must be provided to keep superheaters clear of slag deposits. Modern designs include access spaces within the superheater banks in order to permit convenient access for inspection, cleaning and maintenance.

The vertical superheater, as shown earlier in Fig. 28–9, has advantageous features which result in reduced main-

tenance and optimum service efficiency. Since the elements are arranged parallel to boiler tubes, clear lanes between generating and superheater tubes present the best arrangement for effective action of the soot blowers. With the superheater tubes in a vertical position, it is difficult for slag to accumulate. Bulky supports are eliminated since it is possible to support each superheater tube from the superheater headers which are outside of the gas pass. Small slip spacers attaching superheater elements and adjacent generating tubes maintain the upper ends of the superheater elements in the correct lateral position.

Desuperheaters

For most modern marine boilers all of the steam generated by the boiler is passed through the superheater, and auxiliary steam requirements are met by desuperheating the required quantity of auxiliary steam. This arrangement is necessary in order to maintain at all times a flow of steam through the superheater since the superheater is located in a relatively high temperature gas zone, and overheating may occur if any substantial proportion of steam were taken directly from the steam drum to the auxiliary steam line. To provide low temperature steam for auxiliaries and for other purposes, such as heating, Butterworthing (a special system for steam cleaning cargo tanks) and evaporators, steam from the superheater outlet is passed through a *desuperheater* which absorbs some of the heat in the superheater steam.

Desuperheaters can be of the internal or the external types. The internal type consists of tubular elements with necessary terminal connections to be installed within the drum of the boiler. Fig. 28–16 shows a typical arrangement of an internal type desuperheater as installed in the boilers of a large tanker. It will be noted that the unit is arranged so that it may be passed through the drum manhole as a complete assembly. The external type consists of a direct or indirect heat exchanger mounted in the steam line, with feedwater most generally used as the cooling medium.

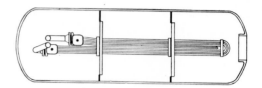

Fig. 28–16.   Internal type desuperheater

Steam Temperature Controls

For high temperature applications it may be desirable to design for a constant steam temperature over a relatively wide load range, as indicated by the superheat characteristic Curve A in Fig. 28–17, or for nominal temperature applications to limit the steam temperature at infrequent overload ratings, as shown by Curve B. Extensions of characteristic curves in dashed line show expected temperatures without control.

A typical arrangement which will provide close control of steam temperature and in so doing protect the last passes of the superheater, turbine and connecting steam piping is shown in Fig. 28–18. An air operated control valve is actuated by the steam temperature at the superheater outlet. Below the set temperature all steam generated passes through the orificed line, the control valve being closed. When the temperature tends to rise above the set temperature, the control valve opens to permit a portion of the steam to flow to the desuperheater and have its temperature reduced. The control valve is provided with a hand jack for manual operation.

The same general arrangement is used to accomplish the limiting type temperature control, as shown in Curve B of Fig. 28–17, except that the automatic control valve is operated manually. At high boiler ratings when the temperature starts to exceed the predetermined maximum, the

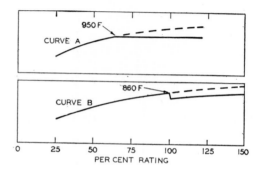

Fig. 28–17.   Superheater characteristic curves

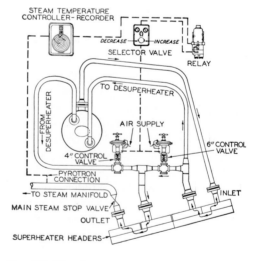

Fig. 28–18.   Steam temperature control arrangement for marine boiler

control valve is opened fully, accounting for the temperature drop just beyond normal rating and the continuing rise to maximum rating.

Heat Recovery Equipment for Marine Boilers

The general classification, *heat recovery equipment,* covers heat exchangers which are located such that heat is absorbed from the combustion gases after the gases have passed through the superheater and steam generating sections of the boiler. Tubular air heaters, Ljungstrom regenerative-type air heaters and economizers are the most usual types for marine boilers. Figs. 28–19 and 28–20 indicate the effect of heat recovery equipment on the heat balance of two different types of marine propulsion power plants.

Some designers have proposed various other combinations of indirect heat exchangers, such as an arrangement whereby heat is absorbed from the stack gas in one heat exchanger and then subsequently transferred to the combustion air through the medium of a secondary fluid and a second heat exchanger. In still another arrangement, the heat recovery equipment consists of a gas turbine which absorbs heat from the combustion gases and converts the heat energy which, in turn, can be used to drive the forced draft fan or compressor. This refers to pressure-fired boilers in which the combustion air is delivered to the burners at a pressure of several atmospheres, in contrast to the much lower pressures used for conventional boilers. This type of boiler is primarily for application to naval vessel propulsion plants.

The boiler drum pressure is a most important factor for the design of the heat recovery equipment since the water in the generating tubes is essentially at the saturation temperature corresponding to drum pressure and that temperature represents the theoretical limit to which the generating tube bank can cool the combustion gases. In other words, for 640 psig drum pressure, the water in the generating tubes is 525 F and, therefore, if the main generating bank were provided with an infinite amount of heating surface, the gas temperature leaving could be reduced only to 525 F. In consideration of various practical limitations it is customary to proportion the boiler design such that the gas temperature leaving the main bank is about 150 deg F above saturation temperature. With increase in the operating pressure, a greater proportion of heat must be absorbed by heat recovery equipment as indicated by Table 28–3 which shows saturation temperatures corresponding to various drum pressures.[6] Under optimum conditions the heat recovery equipment cools the stack gas to a temperature level consistent with reasonable efficiency.

Table 28–3

Drum Pressure psig	Corresponding Saturation Temperature F
250	406
450	459
600	489
850	527
1200	568
1500	596
2000	636

Economizers

The marine *economizer* consists of a series of horizontal tubular elements by means of which heat is recovered from

[6] This table is based on the C–E Steam Tables, which may be obtained from the General Offices of Combustion Engineering, Inc., Windsor, Conn.

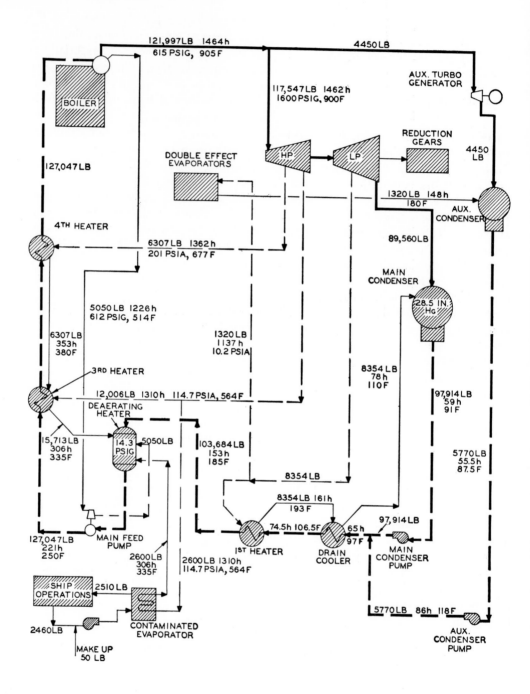

Fig. 28–19.   Heat balance diagram for 17,500 shp marine power plant equipped with regenerative type air heater

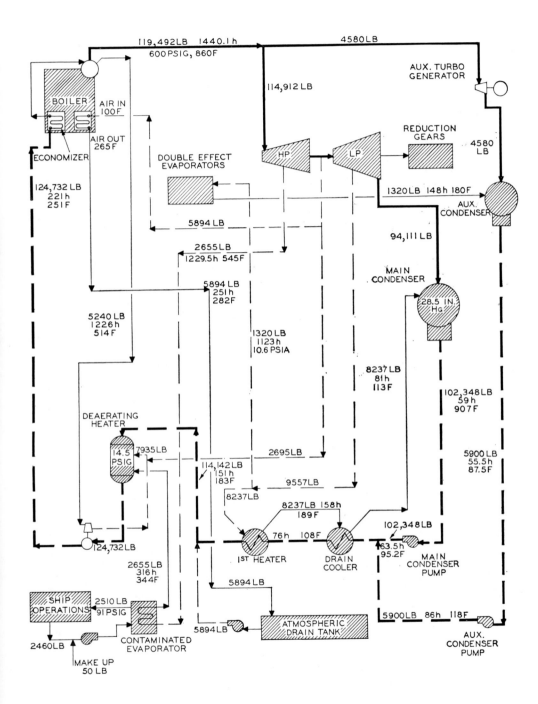

Fig. 28−20. Heat balance diagram for 17,500 shp marine power plant equipped with economizer and steam air heater

combustion gas leaving the boiler and added to the incoming feedwater. The amount of heat absorbed in an economizer is dependent on the temperature difference between gas and water, the heat transfer rate and the amount of heating surface. It is the usual practice to utilize some form of extended surface on tubes to increase the heating surface per foot of tube length.

Economizers can be considered to fall into two categories: *bare tube* and *extended surface* types. The bare tube usually takes in varying sizes which can be arranged to form hairpin or multiloop elements.

Due to the fact that the coefficient of heat transfer is relatively low on the gas side of an economizer tube as compared to that on the waterside, it is desirable to have some form of extended heating surface on the outside of the tube so as to increase the overall rate of heat transfer. Many different configurations of extended surface are used, and each has characteristics of a specific standard adopted by a particular boiler manufacturer. In turn, each type of extended-surface economizer has a heat transfer rate that is peculiar to the shape and finish of the surface, the material employed and the method of fabrication. Fig. 28–21 shows one of the most widely used types of economizer extended surface.

Most marine economizers are designed for counter flow of gas and water, that is, water down through elements and gas up outside of elements. This is done in order to take advantage of the greater temperature difference between the gas and water. Usually the average temperature difference is in the range of 200 to 250 deg F. Under these conditions the heat transfer rate cannot be increased

without incurring a substantial resistance to gas flow, and the use of extended surface to increase the heating surface per lineal foot is desirable. Whatever the arrangement of economizer, ample provision must be made to assure that the heating surface can be kept free of deposits. The coexistence of deposits and moisture will cause corrosion, and accordingly the spacing of the elements, the

Fig. 28–21. View of economizer elements with circumferential fins

quantity and effectiveness of the soot blowers, and the design of the breeching above the economizers must all be carefully considered.

Moisture can come from a number of sources, as follows:
1. Down the stack
2. Leaks in economizers or boiler pressure parts
3. Condensation of moisture in gases

Although a leak in an economizer pressure part cannot go long undetected, a tremendous amount of corrosion-erosion damage can result in a very short time if a leak is allowed to persist. Therefore, it is advantageous to design economizers with the minimum of joints and handhole plates consistent with proper provision for replacing an element. Generally, the header-tube joint is made up as a full welded joint or, as an alternate construction, the elements are welded to nipples in the headers.

While the economizer is designed principally for steady steaming conditions, proper consideration must be given to the design of the elements so that steam will not be generated within the economizer during maneuverings. This means that there must be suitable water velocities and pressure drops which will assure adequate circulation in each element. Under most conditions there is sufficient differential between saturation and feedwater temperatures to prevent the generation of steam. However, there may be some maneuvering conditions, such as the sequence from *stop* to *full ahead*, in which steaming may become a problem. This is particularly true if the water level is high at the start of the maneuver and the boiler control system is of the single element (water level) type.

Usually an economizer is installed at the boiler outlet adjacent to the steam drum with elements parallel to the drum. In most fireroom arrangements sufficient space is available for a good economizer arrangement. However, to obtain the required economizer heat absorption, the economizer length, width and number of tubes high may have to be varied to obtain the best arrangement for the space conditions available and meet thermal performance conditions. In addition, the gas pressure loss permitted and water pressure drop must be considered. There are a few instances where the economizer tube length, that is, distance between tube sheets, is slightly more or less than the boiler bank width or depth.

Today it is common practice to design marine economizers so that they can be bypassed if a leak occurs, thereby allowing the boiler to remain in service until the necessary repairs can be made. This means that the economizer must withstand entering gas temperatures without any feedwater flow through the economizer tubes. With the economizer bypassed, the loss in efficiency results in an increased fuel firing rate, and increasing draft losses cause a higher fan load. Another important consideration, which applies to most merchant ship boiler designs, is that there is generally an increase of total steam temperature due to the higher gas flow and increased furnace temperature.

Air Heaters

Use of *air heaters* in marine practice to improve the performance of steam generating units orginated prior to 1880. At that time the heaters were practically all of the tubular type and consisted of various arrangements of vertical or horizontal banks with short or long tubes. In some the gas was passed through the tubes, while in others the tubes served as a passage for the air. Most marine air heaters are of the horizontal type which is preferred because of its simplicity and the ease of incorporating it into the boiler arrangement.

Tubular Air Heaters. The tubular type consists of a suitable number of horizontal tubes expanded into and supported by tube sheets. The number, size, spacing and arrangement of the tubes are dependent upon the available space and the amount of heat the air heater must recover from the flue gas. The tubes and tube sheets are enclosed in a steel plate casing. The tubes are grouped in a suitable number of banks to allow for the installation of soot blowers and to provide access for cleaning. A tubular air heater is fitted to the sectional-header boiler shown previously in Fig. 28–5.

Air heaters have utilized tubes over a quite wide range. However, for most installations it is found that the smaller tube size allows for good tube arrangement with low box volume to minimize space occupied. This permits suitable tube spacing for effective cleaning of the gas passage area. At the same time there is a satisfactory heat transfer rate with an air pressure loss through tubes in keeping with design requirements.

Air heaters are usually arranged with an in-line tube bank so as to gain the advantages of better cleaning and lower gas-side draft loss. The staggered type arrangement, although it provides slightly better thermal performance because of the higher heat transfer rate, also results in a higher draft loss and is more difficult to clean.

In marine installations most tubular air heaters are installed immediately above the boiler gas exit where the unit can be fitted into the boiler design. For a two pass heater, air both enters and exits at the rear side of the boiler, presenting an efficient arrangement for transporting air to the fuel burners. Fig. 28–22 shows the arrangement of a tubular air heater with a spreader-stoker-fired marine boiler.

The installation of air heaters usually results in exit gas temperatures exceeding 300 F at the normal operating conditions. With air inlet temperatures of 100 F and with counterflow arrangement this results in a tube metal temperature of approximately 200 F in the air inlet area. Under low boiler load conditions such as in port or in maneuvering, the exit gas temperature will drop because of the decreased firing rate, and the tube metal temperature may fall below the dew point, resulting in air heater tube deterioration caused by sulfuric acid formation. Under some conditions sulfuric acid may condense on air heater surface even when metal temperatures are in excess of 300 F.

Excessive moisture in flue gas contributes to air heater maintenance. The vapor may come from the following sources:

Fuel

Leak in boiler or economizer

Improperly drained soot blower lines

Soot blower leaks

Residue from water washing

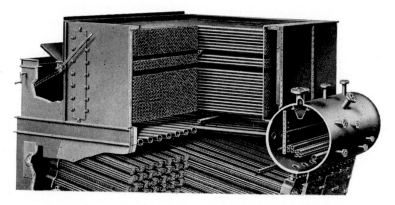

Fig. 28–22.   Tubular air heater located on top of sectional header marine boiler

To minimize the effect of low exit gas temperature it is the practice to incorporate in the design an air heater bypass which under low load conditions prevents all or a portion of the air from entering the air heater by means of a damper arrangement.

Regenerative Air Heaters.[7] The regenerative air heater was first conceived by Dr. Frederik Ljungstrom in connection with design work being conducted with Alfred Nobel about 1885. The principle was applied to an air heater about 1917 when Dr. Ljungstrom was concerned with a design for steam turbine drive for locomotive work. The first marine installation was made in the SS *Asturias* in 1934.

Regenerative air heaters for marine service are designed for horizontal or vertical flow of the air and stack gases. This type of heat exchanger is made of heating elements which are contained in a slowly turning rotor of cellular construction. As the rotor turns, heat is absorbed continuously by the heating elements from the flue gas, while a like amount of heat is released simultaneously to the combustion air, as these fluids flow axially through the rotor. The rotor is enclosed in a gas tight housing which is fitted at each end to make connections with the air and flue gas ducts. Dampered integral air and flue gas bypass ducts are incorporated in the four corners of the structure. The air bypasses in parallel afford means of controlling cold end heating element temperature during operation at reduced steaming rate. The flue gas bypasses in parallel, in combination with the air bypasses, afford means of limiting overall pressure loss at steaming rates above that corresponding to normal power. The components are evident in Fig. 28–23 showing a typical regenerative air heater for marine service.

In counterflow air heaters the part where the flue gas enters and air leaves is the hot end, and conversely the part where the air enters and the flue gas leaves is the cold end. These terms apply to the structure as a whole as well as the rotor and heating elements.

The heating elements are stacked in the rotor in layers, usually two but seldom more than three. This feature permits replacement of the elements of the cold layer, which are those subject to possible deterioration, without disturbing the main body of heat transfer surface. The elements of the cold layer are packed in baskets convenient for handling. Fig. 28–24 shows a typical cold layer basket, each basket being reversible so that portions of the element thinned by corrosion can be turned away from the zone of corrosion. Reversibility nearly doubles the useful element life. The elements of the cold layer are fabricated from corrosion-resistant low alloy steel as are also the baskets containing them. Heating elements of the hot layer can be shop packed in baskets or in the rotor. Shop packing simplifies field installation and assures control over tightness of the pack.

Cleaning devices driven by power are furnished with the regenerative air heater to remove dust deposits from the heating surface. These cleaning devices are usually installed in the gas outlet and air inlet ducts integral with the air heater. The gas side cleaner is normally used at sea for soot blowing, while the air side cleaner is primarily reserved for use in

---

[7] Much of the material in this section is adapted from ASME Paper 55-S-32, "Rotary Regenerative Heaters for Shipboard Installations," by W. E. Hammond, C. E. Hoch and R. P. Giblon.

Fig. 28–23. Regenerative air heater for marine service

Fig. 28–24. Cold layer basket showing heating surface of regenerative air heater

port. The air side cleaner blows the soot back into the furnace, thus avoiding objectionable smoke and dust which is prohibited by harbor ordinances. The need for soot blowing can readily be determined through an observation port which permits inspection of the heating surface while the air heater is in operation.

The regenerative type of heat exchanger is small and light. This results from the fundamental nature of counterflow heat transfer which permits significant reduction in heating surface.

A factor to be considered in the selection of air heaters is that of metal temperature. In the regenerative type, tests and experience have demonstrated that the actual metal temperature is 20 to 30 deg F *above* the average of the air and gas temperatures.[8] By contrast, in a tubular type air heater the measured temperatures of tube metal ranged from 10 to 120 deg F *below* the mean of the air and gas temperature.[9] This fact is of material significance in the selection of air preheaters if corrosion and plugging are to be avoided, and it demonstrates one of the reasons why regenerative heaters may be operated with materially lower leaving gas temperature than tubular types.

Installation of a regenerative type air heater aboard ship presents no problem. The vertical flow air heater can be located directly above the boiler outlet or in the area above the boiler and connected with conventional duct work. From the top of the air heater on the gas side an uptake is led to the stack in the usual manner. Forced draft fans may be located conventionally and connected to the air side of the heater by means of duct work. Various arrangements can be utilized to suit the conditions. Cooling air to be introduced to the casing can be taken from the forced draft fan discharge duct ahead of the heater. Fig. 28–25 illustrates a typical shipboard arrangement of a regenerative type air heater.

Steam Air Heaters. The selection of the heat recovery equipment to be incorporated in the design of a boiler is influenced by the boiler operating condi-

[8] H. Karlsson and W. E. Hammond, "Air Preheater Design As Affected by Fuel Characteristics," *Trans. ASME,* Vol. 75, 1953, pp. 711–722.
[9] E. F. Rothemich and G. Parkmakian, "Tubular Air Heater Problem," *Trans. ASME,* Vol. 75, 1953, pp. 723–728.

tions and the efficiency required of the boiler unit. These are related to the specification of a suitable steam cycle for a marine installation. The most suitable steam cycle for one installation may not be advantageous to another. Therefore for certain installations an air heater may be best suited. Where feed temperature and pressure conditions permit, an economizer or a combination of an economizer and a steam air heater are used to obtain the boiler efficiency required.

One of the methods used to improve the steam cycle efficiency is by means of the feedwater heating system, and here the steam air heater serves the purpose of utilizing steam extracted from the feedwater heater or auxiliary exhaust. This reduces the flow of steam to the condenser and improves cycle efficiency. Another method used is to extract low pressure bleed steam from the main turbines.

A steam air heater is comprised of small diameter tubes about ⅝ in. OD, usually with extended surface. They have sufficient size for the steam flow involved and are connected to inlet and outlet header boxes. The bleed or exhaust steam enters the inlet header box and flows inside the tubes, while the combustion air flows around the tubes.

In the condensing of the bleed steam or auxiliary exhaust, heat is transferred to the air used for combustion. Since the condensing steam film coefficient of heat transfer is high, extended surface is used to advantage. Closely pitched tubes and fins can be utilized, as both the air and

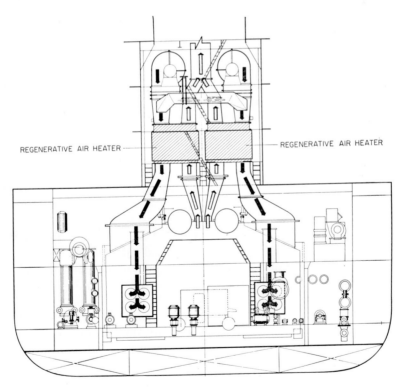

REGENERATIVE AIR HEATER

REGENERATIVE AIR HEATER

Fig. 28–25. Arrangement of regenerative air heaters aboard ship

heating fluids are clean, eliminating entirely the necessity for cleaning.

In most steam air heater installations, bleed steam at 10 to 45 psig is used. While a feedwater heater uses steam at relatively high pressure, the steam air heater uses auxiliary exhaust or low pressure bleed steam. Utilizing the lower pressure bleed steam is a good method of improving cycle efficiency.

Another point to be considered is that the auxiliary exhaust can be utilized to an advantage in a steam air heater while boilers are steaming in port, thereby improving low load boiler operating conditions. Suitable air temperature for good combustion is readily maintained, whereas with a tubular or regenerative type air heater a bypass system around the heater is necessary to avoid low stack temperatures.

Steam air heaters do not improve the boiler efficiency since the heater does not serve to reduce the gas temperature at the boiler outlet. The steam air heater, however, is effective by improving the overall marine plant efficiency. For this reason it is the practice to use the steam air heater with an economizer, as the economizer will absorb heat from the boiler gases and thereby reduce stack temperatures to meet the required boiler efficiency.

Fuel Burning

Fuel Oil

Oil burners for marine boilers must have features and operational characteristics which are consistent with the service requirements of the propulsion plant. First of all, a marine burner must be capable of properly burning the oil within a furnace of minimum dimensions. Likewise, the design of the furnace and the location of the burners must go hand in hand with the inherent characteristics of the particular type of burner selected for a given application. The burner must also be capable of producing efficient firing over a wide range of oil flow rates and be able to change load rapidly to meet the maneuvering requirements. For ships which maneuver a substantial proportion of the operating time, it is essential that the boilers be fitted with burners of a type which is able to vary the firing rate over a wide range without the need of changing atomizer tips.

Before the fuel oil can be burned, it is necessary that the oil be changed from a liquid to an atomized condition and simultaneously mixed with an ample supply of air to permit combustion. A burner actually consists of two parts: the atomizer or burner barrel which serves to deliver a flow of atomized oil to the furnace, and the register which serves to supply a flow of air to the furnace. The burner barrel contains a sprayer plate, or whirl chamber, and an orifice tip which set together to produce the spray of fine oil particles.[10]

The straight mechanical type of oil burner consists of a burner atomizer which converts the potential energy of the oil pressure into a flow of atomized oil particles. The register is designed to introduce and mix the air with the oil spray produced by the atomizer. The oil flow is regulated by varying the supply pressure. On some installations this is accomplished manually, and on others it is automatically performed. Air flow is regulated by manual adjustment of the forced

---

[10] See Chapter 22, Fuel Burning Systems, for additional information on burner design.

draft fan output or by the automatic adjustment of the combustion control. This type of burner has a range or turndown ratio of between 1.5 and 3.0, depending on the pressure of the fuel oil service system.

The return flow type of burner functions with a constant pressure oil supply, and the atomizer barrel contains a passage which permits a portion of the oil to return to the fuel oil service pump suction. Fig. 28–26 shows a return flow type atomizer. The firing rate is varied by regulating the control valve in the return line. This type of burner achieves a much wider range than the straight mechanical burner.

The steam atomizing type burner utilizes a flow of steam which mixes in the atomizer tip with the oil flow. A portion of the energy in the steam serves to break up the oil particles, and better atomization results. This type of burner has a high turndown ratio and offers the advantage of being able to burn efficiently low quality fuel.

Most ship boilers have one of the burner types just described. Various other burner designs have been developed but none has been given acceptance to the extent of being used for a great number of marine boiler installations. Some auxiliary boilers are fitted with rotary cup type burners. Such a burner utilizes a motor drive to supply the energy for atomizing the oil.

Coal

While the vast majority of shipboard boilers are fired by oil fuel, there remain some ship trades where the economic conditions make it desirable to burn coal. Modern coal fired marine boilers are fitted with stokers. Many types of stokers, including chain grate, underfeed, overfeed and spreader types, have been used for marine service. The spreader stoker has proved itself over a long period of operation to be best suited and most efficient in meeting the requirements. It has the capacity to burn a wide range of bituminous coals and the ability to respond quickly to load changes. These features make spreader stokers attractive for vessels that will continuously serve in trades which have a readily available source of coal.[11]

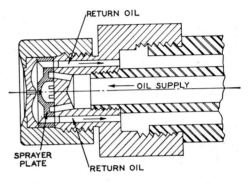

Fig. 28–26. Return flow atomizing burner

Fig. 28–27 shows the firing aisle of a ship having boilers equipped with spreader stokers. The spreader stoker usually consists of two or three units mounted on a stoker front which is built into the boiler casing. Each unit has a coal hopper which drops the coal into a feeder. The feeder consists of a bladed rotor, the speed of which can be controlled to regulate the coal flow. The feeder can be controlled manually or by automatic combustion control. The coal is fed into the furnace by the distributing rotor. The heavier coal particles burn on the grate and the finer particles burn in suspension.

[11] See Chapter 18, Stokers, for additional information on stoker design.

The spreader stoker maintains a thin layer of fuel on the grate, and that makes it possible for the boiler to respond rapidly to variations in load. When the boiler load demand decreases, the automatic control reduces the rotor speed, thereby reducing the amount of fuel feed.

Boiler Casings

The primary function of a boiler casing, Figs. 28–28 and 28–29, is to contain the products of combustion in such a way that the gases flow from the furnace through the steam generating, super-heater and heat recovery tube banks, and out the breeching. Although both single and double-cased designs may be used, the function of containing the products of combustion should take place in that casing which is immediately exterior to the refractory and insulation wall. In other words, for a double-cased boiler the inner casing should be designed and erected so that as nearly as possible there is a gas tight barrier between the firesides and the spaces exterior to that inner casing.

The vast majority of modern boilers are built double cased. In this arrangement air pressure in the space between the inner and outer casings is greater than the pressure within the furnace. Accordingly if there are any open joints in the inner casing, there will be a flow of air into the furnace instead of an outward flow of gas and soot. However, this advantage should not be overexploited to the extent of disregarding the maintenance of a tight inner casing. Boiler efficiency will be impaired and other detrimental effects will accrue if the flow of air through inner casing leaks is allowed to become substantial.

Design of Inner Casing

The inner casing, or the only casing in a single-cased boiler, must be designed to

Fig. 28–27.   Firing aisle of a marine boiler fired by a spreader stoker

Fig. 28–28.   Exterior view of marine boiler showing casing arrangement

accommodate the refractory and insulation. These materials must be arranged to protect the casing from exposure to gases and must insulate the casing from high temperatures. Structural members should preferably be located outside the inner casing. Whenever this is not possible, as may be the case for some supports of furnace insulation and refractory, alloy material should be used if there is any possibility of exposure to high temperature.

The space between inner and outer casings of a double-cased boiler provides a convenient duct system by which the air for combustion can flow to the burners. The arrangement presents considerable flexibility to the design of the forced draft system since there can be a wide choice of locations for the air inlet connection. Those sections of the air space which are not used to sustain the main flow of combustion air are provided with a flow of cooling air which ultimately discharges into the windbox. Thus all of the inner casing is pressurized. Since the air flow absorbs a large proportion of the heat given off by the inner casing, there

is a reduction in the radiation losses and boiler efficiency is improved.

For propulsion plants utilizing the heat cycle incorporating a steam air heater, it is generally possible to mount the steam air heater on the casing immediately above or adjacent to the windbox. The cooling air is provided by a separate duct leading directly from the forced draft fan discharge.

In laying out the arrangement of casing, calculations must be made to determine that the air pressure drop values are not excessive and that the velocities and flow pattern of the air in the windbox will be suitable for the even distribution of air to the registers. In determining the dimensions of the air space, allowance must be made for the restrictions imposed by downcomers, structural members and fittings such as soot blower sleeves.

Methods of Support

For most designs of bent-tube boilers, the weight of the pressure parts, and the included water, is carried by the water drum saddles and waterwall header saddles. Economizers and tubular type air

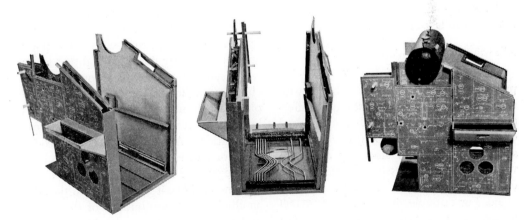

Fig. 28–29. Details of boiler casing as shown by model

heaters are generally supported by the boiler casing, although for some of the higher powered ships, it has been expedient to locate the heat recovery unit apart from the boiler, where the ship structure provides support. Such an arrangement may be necessary to obtain a better layout of the breeching when there is a narrow fidley which limits the space directly above the boiler. The Ljungstrom air heater is usually located on a deck or platform above the boiler, and support is provided by the ship structure. It is customary, however, for a steam air heater to be supported by the boiler casing.

For some types of boilers the casing structure must also support the pressure parts, and this requires that heavier structurals be included at the points of loading. The sectional header type boiler has column-type supports built into each corner of the casing.

The loadings from connecting piping, particularly main steam piping, can produce excessive stresses in the boiler connections. According to accepted procedure the boiler manufacturer specifies the maximum allowable forces and moments which can be taken by the connections, and the shipbuilder designs the piping so that the limits will not be exceeded.

Allowances for Expansion

During the course of designing a boiler, problems of expansion must be considered constantly. The substantial differences in temperature which are imposed on the boiler parts in going from *cold* or *secured condition* to *steaming condition* would result in excessive stresses if the expansions were not allowed to take place. For example, in a boiler of 75,000 lb per hour normal power evaporation rate, with 600 psig, 850 F steam conditions, the steam drum might move upwards approximately ⅝ in. in going from cold condition to steaming condition. At the same time, the length of the drum might be extended by ½ in. These figures are typical, but for a given design the actual amounts are dependent upon the particular arrangement of boiler parts. The expansions must be accommodated, and furthermore they must be controlled so that the movements are always in the directions for which expansion joints have been provided. For some of the pressure parts, such as circulators, the expansion is absorbed within the part itself by providing sufficient bends to give flexibility. The sliding joint is a very effective device for allowing relative movement between a pressure part and the adjacent casing.

Access and Inspection

In order to incorporate the highest degree of accessibility consistent with the other design requirements, the various inspection, maintenance, and repair procedures which may have to be performed should be taken into consideration in the design as the layout of pressure parts and casing is developed. Increasing importance is being placed upon features which will permit a degree of inspection while the boiler is steaming. For example, some boilers are being fitted with view ports and permanently installed lighting units which enable the engineer on watch to check periodically for leaking handhole plates. Such an arrangement in the windbox makes it possible to detect oil accumulations. A view port at the economizer or air heater will enable a check on the degree of fouling of those surfaces. In some designs, it is arranged so that the handhole plates are outside of the casing in order that they can be inspected by simply removing an asbestos blanket.

Sometimes when a boiler is too hot for a man to get inside, it is desirable to be able to make inspections of the firesides. A periscope-type device can be entered into the tube bank through a sleeve provided in the casing and a visual examination of heating surfaces, baffles and other parts can be made.

Refractory and Insulation

The foregoing discussions of furnace and boiler design serve to describe the extenuating conditions which the refractory lining in the furnace must withstand. There are many types of refractory products and all are characterized by the following:

Ability to maintain structural and thermal characteristics at operating temperatures.

Ability to radiate heat.

Ability to offer maximum resistance to chemical reactions.

Ability to act as a barrier which will retain products of combustion within the furnace space.

In the past, it was quite customary for refractory and insulating materials to be identified solely by trade names, but in recent years a more scientific approach has been made so that refractory specifications now are quite definite in listing the physical and chemical characteristics. Fig. 28–30 shows the most appropriate temperature ranges for which the various refractory materials should be properly applied.[12]

Controls and Instrumentation

It is essential that the shipboard boiler plant be fitted with adequate instruments to enable the operating personnel to raise steam, maintain design conditions for steady steaming, secure the boiler units and to detect promptly malfunctions and failures. It is customary to have most boiler instruments situated on a gage board which also contains the combustion and feedwater controls. Duplicate instruments for principal variables are provided at the main throttle station gage board.

Shipboard boiler controls can properly be classified into two basic groups: controls of the type which regulate continuously and those of the type which act to perform a prescribed operation when a limiting condition has been exceeded.

Regulating type controls include the following:

Combustion

Boiler water level

Fuel oil temperature

Fuel oil viscosity

Blowdown

Superheat temperature

Combustion controls of the pneumatic or electric types are widely used for merchant type ships, while naval vessels use pneumatic controls exclusively. Different systems that are available offer varying degrees of automatic control. Generally, the combustion control system maintains constant steam pressure by controlling the flow of air and oil to the boiler. The more advanced combustion controls transmit the air and oil loadings simultaneously but with a slight lag between air and oil, so that with an increasing boiler load, the air will lead the oil, and on a decrease in boiler load, the oil will lead the air. Such an arrangement makes it possible to

[12] More detailed information on refractories may be found in a paper entitled "Present Day Trends in Modern Marine Boiler Refractories" by Christian E. Nelson presented before a joint meeting of the Metropolitan Sections of the Society of Naval Architects and Marine Engineers and the Society of Marine Port Engineers, New York, February 28, 1956.

TEMPERATURE CLASSIFICATION OF REFRACTORIES

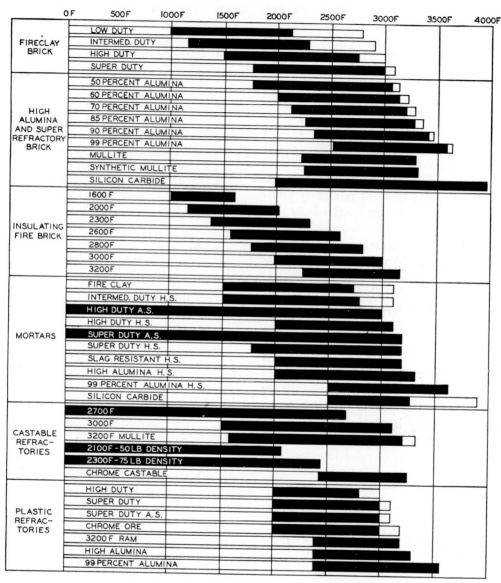

Fig. 28–30. Temperature ranges for various refractory materials

minimize the emission of smoke during maneuvering.

In years past many ships were fitted with feedwater regulator control systems which operated solely as a function of drum water level. As boiler steam conditions and evaporation rates were advanced to meet the requirements of higher powered propulsion plants, it was found necessary to have a two-element type control. In this type, impulses of drum water level and steam flow are combined to give a better response during maneuvering conditions. The two-element system is installed on many cargo ships and has been proven as a reliable system.

Some types of ships, namely naval vessels and higher powered passenger ships, are fitted with three-element type feedwater controls. In the three-element system, drum level, feedwater flow and steam flow are measured and transmitted to the regulating valve in the feed line. In this system the relative difference in flow between steam flow from the boiler and feedwater flow to the boiler is used as an impulse to give a greater degree of control.

There are many controls which serve to operate or present a warning signal when a dangerous condition is approached. Controls of this type include the following:

    High water level alarm
    Low water level alarm
    Low stack temperature alarm
    Fuel oil shutoff for forced draft fan failure

Common Attributes of Marine and Stationary Practice

The special considerations required for the design of marine boilers have been discussed in this chapter. Many of these relate to the differences in operating conditions encountered in land and marine practice. For example, the output of a marine power plant is basically a function of the speed and the displacement of a ship, and there is no exact counterpart to this in industrial power plants and central stations.

It is important to realize, however, that the same fundamentals apply to both marine and land power plant practices.[13] Where common problems have materialized, as in the need for developing improved firing methods, similar solutions have been found and applied in both areas. On the other hand, space and height limitations are of primary concern to the marine boiler designer.

Marine boilers operate successfully at very much higher heat release rates and smaller box volumes than field-erected stationary boilers. This is partly accounted for by the nature of marine power plant operation. For one thing, feedwater is of high quality, since at sea makeup is furnished by evaporators. In addition, two or more boilers are generally installed, and although they operate at rated capacity while the ship is at sea, at least one can be shut down for inspection and maintenance while in port. This is in marked contrast to the operating conditions in some types of industrial and central station power plants which have what amounts to an almost continuous base load. Under these conditions there are rarely periods of low load demand, and boilers may be operated for sustained periods of a year or longer between shutdowns for inspection and maintenance.

[13] See Chapter 2, Elements of Power Plant Design; Chapter 5, Thermodynamic Cycles for Power Plants; Chapter 19, Fundamentals of Boiler Design.

Fig. 28–31   Model of automated marine boiler

Fig. 28–31 shows a model of a marine boiler in which both the superheater arrangement and the control configuration for automatic operation reflect experience of a similar nature in central station design and operation.

Over the years both marine and station-ary power plant designers have benefited greatly by the interchange of technical information. Where the problems have been similar, the solutions have been comparable. Where the problems and situations have been different, each field has retained its distinctive characteristics.[14]

[14] Two interesting papers bearing on this subject may be consulted in the Engineering Societies Library, New York: "Comparison of Land and Marine Steam Power Plant Practice" by M. L. Ireland, Jr., F. A. Ritchings and S. Crocker, ASME Paper 53–A–99, and "The Distinguishing Aspects of Marine Engineering" by G. L. West, Jr., ASME Paper 59–A–202.

29

High Temperature Water Boilers[1]

HEATING SYSTEMS utilizing high temperature water have received wide acceptance since the end of World War II. These systems usually operate in a pressure range from 120 to 300 psig, resulting in supply temperatures to the distribution system of from 350 F to 420 F. The higher temperature range effects economies in that water flow rates and resulting pumping costs are reduced and system heat exchangers can be made smaller. On the other hand, the lower temperatures permit lighter and less expensive materials.

High temperature water systems are closed systems. Makeup is required only to restore the amount of water that leaks out of the system at valve stems, pump shafts and similar packed joints. Obviously the average water temperature in the system will vary within limits, depending on the load, and as a result an expansion drum is used to permit expansion or contraction of the water volume. The small amount of makeup required to hold water level in the expansion drum above a predetermined low level limit is added intermittently and automatically by a small makeup pump.

For heat consumers such as unit heaters, radiant panels and coils of absorption refrigeration equipment, high temperature water may be used directly. As with steam, it is used indirectly for domestic hot water. Low pressure steam or low pressure hot water, if required, may be produced, in suitable heat exchangers.

Principal Types of Systems

To maintain pressure in the system two methods have been used, steam pressurization and gas pressurization. Gas pressurization is commonly called mechanical pressurization. Gas identifies the type of fluid used for pressurization, whereas mechanical indicates a method used to pressurize the fluid.

In the gas or mechanical pressurized system, nitrogen is employed to maintain a pressure above the water level in the expansion drum. This pressure is maintained independent of the heating load by means of suitable controls which add or bleed off the gas as changes in water level occur.

In a steam pressurized system, the water is heated to saturation temperature corresponding to operating pressure. Reduction in pressure from the boiler outlet to the expansion drum due to friction losses and difference in elevation (the drum is usually located higher than the boiler outlet) permits a small amount of water to

---

[1] Material contributed by S. F. Mumford, J. L. Hutchings, Jr., and E. R. Shequine.

flash into steam. The steam is collected in the upper part of the drum and maintains a pressure cushion on the entire system.

Gas Pressurized System

Although the physical layout and size of individual installations vary, the basic components and usually the basic arrangement of the systems are similar. A typical diagrammatic arrangement of a gas pressurized system is shown in Fig. 29–1 with the graphs at the bottom indicating the pressure-temperature relationship at various points in the system. Return water, t_r, is heated in the boiler and delivered to the system at supply temperature, t_s. The water gives up its heat to the system load which is usually divided in several zones and is returned to the suction of the circulating pump at t_r. The circulating pumps are selected with sufficient head to overcome both the system and boiler resistance. Pressure higher than saturation pressure corresponding to the boiler outlet temperature is maintained in the system by means of gas pressure superimposed on the system at the expansion tank. The ex-

pansion tank floats on the line. Water temperature at the boiler outlet is used as an index for combustion control.

Steam Pressurized System

The basic steam pressurized system is shown diagrammatically in Fig. 29–2 with a similar graph to indicate pressure-temperature relationship throughout the system. Water at return temperature, t_r, is heated in the boiler and delivered to the expansion drum at supply temperature, t_s, which is essentially equal to saturation temperature corresponding to operating pressure in the expansion drum. The circulating pumps taking suction from the drum circulate the hot water through the system. The water gives up its heat to the load and is returned to the boilers at temperature t_r. The circulating pumps are selected for sufficient head to overcome both the system and boiler resistance.

The fuel firing rate of all operating boilers is controlled by pressure in the common drum. If pressure tends to fall below the set pressure, fuel firing of all operating boilers is equally increased; and

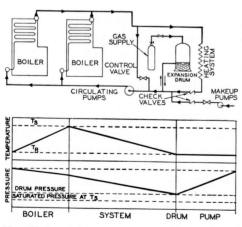

Fig. 29–1. Schematic arrangement of gas pressurized system including pressure-temperature relationships at various points

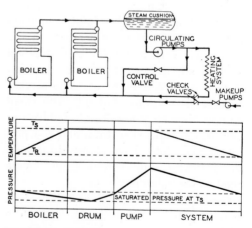

Fig. 29–2. Schematic arrangement of steam pressurized system including pressure-temperature relationships at various points

conversely, if pressure tends to increase above the set value, a similar reduction occurs.

For each of these systems a bypass around the heating load is provided. During initial start up it may be desirable to completely bypass the system. For partial load operation, especially when several heating zones are not operative, it may be desirable to bypass a portion of the total water circulated through the boilers, in which case the temperature of the water entering the boilers would be between the normal return and supply temperature.

High Temperature Water Versus Steam

The decision to use high temperature water or steam for heating or process work will depend upon the size, arrangement and type of load. For large heating systems and certain process applications, high temperature water usually has certain advantages over steam.

A steam heating system requires greater net plant output because of the losses associated with the change of phase of the heating medium, i.e., steam to condensate. These losses, which are primarily trap and vent losses or flash off from condensate, can account for 10 to 25 per cent of the net plant output. Since high temperature water exists as a liquid throughout the system, these losses do not occur, and as a result the required capacity of hot water boilers is less than steam boilers for a given system output.

Maintenance costs for high temperature water systems are less because of the elimination of high maintenance items such as steam traps, pressure reducing valves and condensate equipment. In the closed high temperature water system, oxygen is eliminated on initial operation, and therefore the problem of pipe corrosion and replacement of return lines does not exist.

Since makeup for a high temperature water system is negligible, blowoff is unnecessary with normal operation. Makeup equipment can be very simple and inexpensive, usually consisting of a small water softener, a pair of makeup pumps and provision for intermittent addition of water-treatment chemicals to the heating system.

Generally high temperature water distributing lines, both supply and return, are of the same diameter, being smaller than the steam distributing mains and larger than the condensate return lines of a steam system. Piping cost of the two systems will depend on the actual distribution system, with high temperature water piping costs becoming relatively less with larger systems or longer distribution lines. Underground high temperature water lines can follow ground contours, thus simplifying the piping design.

A high temperature water system has substantially greater heat storage capacity than a steam system. As a result, fluctuating loads in the system tend to be damped out so that they do not directly or immediately affect boiler loads. The boilers therefore operate at a more constant rate which improves their operating efficiency and the efficiency of the heating system as well.[2]

Because of the heat storage capacity the heating system acts as an accumulator, permitting extremely close control of temperature and the ability to readily meet infrequent peak loads. Close control of temperature is often of considerable importance in process equipment, resulting in improved product quality or increased production. The ability to meet infrequent peak loads by utilizing this heat storage

[2] See Chapter 2, Elements of Power Plant Design, for a chart, Fig. 2–4, showing the characteristically flat boiler load curves of a high temperature water installation.

may allow the installed capacity of the heating system to be reduced.

High Temperature Water Boilers

The term "boiler" as applied to the hot water heating units is somewhat of a misnomer because under normal operating conditions very little or no steam is generated. However, these units are usually designed in accordance with the ASME Boiler Code and are operated in substantially the same manner as steam boilers. The absence of steam generation is noteworthy in that natural circulation effects are negligible with respect to assisting boiler and overall system circulation. In effect the boiler has a forced circulation system of the once-through type. Both fire tube and water tube steam boilers have been modified and used with some degree of success for hot water service, but boilers designed specifically for such forced circulation service are especially suitable and have been used in the majority of large installations.

Regardless of the type of boiler, the possibility of steam formation exists under certain special load conditions and during transient conditions. This is especially true in steam pressurized systems where water is being delivered from the boiler at essentially saturated temperature. The circulation system within the boiler should be designed so that natural circulation effects resulting from this steam will be in a direction so as to assist the normal flow in the individual tube circuits. Otherwise a vapor binding condition can occur with subsequent overheating of tubes.

Arrangement of Boiler

Fig. 29–3 shows a cross section view through a typical high temperature water boiler. In this design, water entering at the inlet nozzle (lower rear) is distributed by

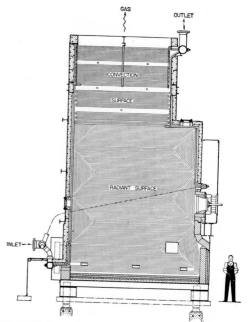

Fig. 29–3. Side elevation of high temperature water boiler designed for oil or gas firing and fully water cooled

means of a manifold outside the boiler casing to two inlet headers, one located at the bottom of the rear wall for feeding the furnace rearwall and sidewall tubes and the other located immediately above the burner windbox for feeding the furnace front wall and roof tubes. The convection bank is formed by a continuation of the front and rear wall tubes, and all tubes terminate in the outlet header at the top.

In order to maintain water velocities in the tubes of sufficient magnitude to prevent sedimentation and to avoid temperature stratification and steam blanketing in the horizontal tube sections, the tube circuits are relatively few in number and correspondingly longer than those in conventional steam boilers. The quantity of water circulated is roughly proportional to the boiler design capacity. However, fuel burning equipment requirements do not permit reducing the furnace width, and number of tube circuits, in direct proportion to the boiler size. Therefore, to maintain adequate water velocities in the tubes for the smaller size boilers, the front wall tubes and their inlet header are eliminated as shown in Fig. 29–4.

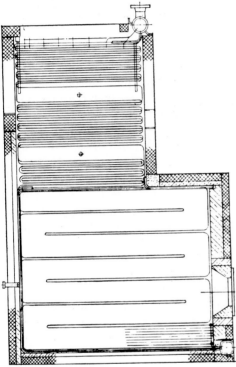

Fig. 29–4. Side elevation of high temperature water boiler with no front wall tubes and lower capacity

Where the system is designed for a temperature drop of 125 to 175 deg F between supply and return temperatures, the boiler pressure drop can be held to 10 psi or less. This low pressure drop eliminates the need for separate boiler circulating pumps and results in a simpler and more economical arrangement from the standpoint of initial operating costs.

Capacity and Circulation

The capacity of the boiler to heat water is contingent on the quantity of water circulated through the boiler and the change in temperature of the water as it passes through the boiler. In single boiler installations this presents no problem because it is a simple matter to circulate all of the cold system return water through the boiler and restore it to the designed system supply temperature. However, in multiple boiler installations it is necessary to provide proper distribution of the system return water to the various boilers in use so that each can carry its proper share of the total heating load. The boilers are usually fed from a common system return manifold so their inlet temperatures are the same and they should deliver water at the same design outlet temperature. The result is that for proper load distribution the flow through each boiler should be directly proportional to its rated capacity.

In the boiler shown in Fig. 29–3, orifice plates are installed at the inlets of all tubes in order to control the distribution within the boiler. These orifices can also provide proper distribution of the system return water to the various boilers in use. In a heating plant where all boilers are identical, the symmetry of the installation assists in obtaining the desired distribution. If, on the other hand, the boilers are of different sizes and dissimilar physical characteristics, a careful study of the entire circulation system is necessary to obtain optimum results.

The once-through type high temperature water boiler, with substantially no steam generation, requires neither a steam drum nor does it trap dissolved solids entering with the feedwater as is the case with a steam boiler. It is therefore unnecessary to provide a blowdown connection on the boiler. A strainer or sediment trap is usually installed in the boiler inlet line in order to prevent the introduction of solid impurities such as dirt or mill scale into the boiler. This is especially desirable during initial startup or when cutting in new distribution zones.

Furnace Design

Referring to Figs. 29–3 and 29–4, it may be seen that the controlled circulation principle permits an optimum furnace arrangement including a maximum amount of water cooling on the furnace walls and roof. The furnace floor can also be water-cooled for oil and gas firing. With forced-draft type oil or gas burners, the fuel burns very rapidly and requires very little furnace volume for proper combustion. Under these conditions, the heat release rate per square foot of effective projected radiant surface is the best criterion of furnace performance.

Load Conditions and Efficiency

Load conditions require careful consideration when selecting the boilers and fuel burning equipment. The heating system must have a capacity to meet a maximum load condition which, for most installations, occurs only once or twice a year and then for periods of short duration. Even where several boilers are installed, they are operated at below 50 per cent of maximum rating much of the time, and their average annual load factor can be 25 per cent or less. Frequently, extra capacity is initially built into the heating plant to provide for future expansion of the distribution system. Because of this low load factor, boiler efficiency at maximum rating should not be overemphasized. Efficiencies of 80 per cent with No. 6 oil firing and 76 per cent with bituminous coal or natural gas are normal and com-

pare favorably with the efficiency of steam heating boilers.

The majority of installations made to date have heat loads consisting mostly of space heating. The use of high temperature water in absorption-type refrigeration equipment for summer air conditioning is gaining in popularity and will effect an improvement in load factor. Certain industrial processes utilizing hot water will require continuous operation of the boilers at full load. In these cases, the foregoing considerations regarding efficiency and subsequent recommendations regarding sizing of fuel burning equipment would obviously not apply.

Fuel Burning Equipment

High temperature water boilers of standard design are available for use with oil or gas burners or for coal firing by means of spreader stokers. Fuel burning equipment is substantially the same as that furnished for steam boilers except that oil burners are usually of the mechanical instead of steam atomizing type in order to minimize steam losses and makeup feed requirements. Air puff type soot blowers are usually employed on hot water boilers for the same reasons. Pulverized coal firing becomes practical for boilers rated from 100 million Btu per hour upwards and in special cases where the coal is not suitable for stoker firing.

It is essential that the fuel burning equipment be selected to give good combustion with a minimum of manual adjustment at low ratings. Oversizing of the equipment can be just as detrimental as undersizing. Mechanical draft fans should have tolerances of no more than 15 to 25 per cent above maximum load requirements of volume and static pressure respectively.

Except for certain unusual fuels, the

use of preheated air will not result in any significant improvement in furnace combustion conditions with gas, oil or stoker firing, and in the latter case will increase grate maintenance. The cost of an air preheater to improve boiler efficiency is usually not justified by the fuel savings, and, particularly at low loads, the air preheater introduces additional corrosion problems.

Controls

Some degree of automatic control is highly desirable for high temperature water boilers. It will generally result in better combustion conditions in the furnace. Of greater importance, the automatic controls release the boiler attendant from the monotony of routine boiler operation and permit better utilization of manpower.

Generally, high temperature water boilers are installed to meet space heating requirements, and rapid load changes are not often experienced. A simple positioning type combustion control is adequate for the smaller single-burner shop assembled boilers and stoker-fired units. For larger multi-burner boilers, a metering system is preferable. The addition of complexity to a control system does not necessarily guarantee additional efficiency or economy of operation. In fact, the reverse may very well be the case. The simple system which is easily understood and maintained by the operating personnel will result in more consistent performance.

On steam pressurized systems a master controller acting from expansion drum pressure serves to load all boilers equally as required with the proper water flow distribution. If the system is mechanically pressurized there is substantially no relationship between expansion drum pressure and heating load. Therefore, water temperature leaving the boiler must be used as an index for setting the boiler firing rate, and each boiler should be equipped with its own master controller.

The smaller single-burner boilers can be furnished with completely automatic package burners which, in addition to modulating the firing rate through the burner turndown range, will cycle the burner on and off as the heating load drops below the minimum firing rate of the burner. The high heat storage in hot water systems makes them particularly suitable for on-off firing without excessive cycling. Flame safeguard systems are necessary for the completely automatic units and are also frequently installed on the larger boilers.

Inasmuch as the boiler is dependent on a pump for circulation, a safety device should be provided to stop the fuel input in the event circulation drops below a predetermined point. This can be incorporated as a part of the boiler water flow meter if installed, or can be actuated by the pressure drop within the boiler itself.

Circulating Pumps

The heart of high temperature water heating systems is the circulating pump. Standard horizontal process type centrifugal pumps are available which will give reliable service under normal operating conditions. Fig. 29–5 shows a cross section of a type of pump commonly used for this service.

Economic considerations dictate that the friction loss in the pipe system be held to values which can be overcome by use of a single stage, 1750-rpm pump. At this pump speed, suitable packing is available for sealing the pump shaft. Mechanical seals have also been developed which will give satisfactory performance. It is essential that the mechanical seal be arranged for adequate cooling and to pre-

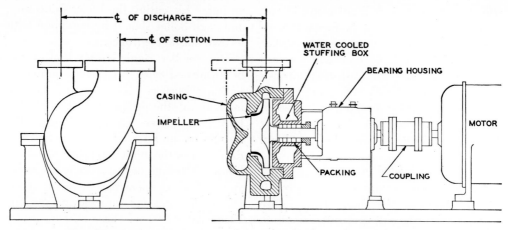

Fig. 29—5.   Typical circulating pump for high temperature water boiler

vent the accumulation of sediment at its face.

The pump casing should be constructed of cast steel. Alloy steel should be used for the impeller, shaft, sleeves, and pump trim in order to avoid corrosion from the constituents in boiler water and in chemical cleaning compounds. In order to prevent vapor binding and cavitation at the pump suction, it is essential that the pump have low net positive suction head characteristics.

30

Flash Drying Systems[1]

THE REMOVAL of moisture from various process materials is one of the oldest of operations. It was originally used in connection with food preservation, but today its widest applications are found in connection with many industrial processes. In fact, there are but relatively few materials now produced that do not require at least a degree of drying during some stage of manufacture. The field of drying by conventional methods is described in a complete manner in technical literature. This is an old art on which much valuable research has been done. Furthermore it is comparatively easy to collect detailed performance data during a drying cycle which may range from several minutes to several hours.

Dryers

Standard Types

Several so-called standard types of dryers have been developed over a period of years. They are generally classified as rotary, tunnel, spray or drum types. Each has severe limitations, and each is therefore confined to a narrow and specific field of application. Some materials, however, may be dried equally well in two or more types. None of them can simultaneously dry and grind materials. Where high evaporative capacities are required, the necessary equipment is large. As a result, the ultimate selection of a specific type is usually governed by consideration of building space, fuel available, and many other variable limiting factors. To overcome these, as well as other limitations, it is desirable to approach the problem in another manner.

Developments

Air-swept pulverizers have been manufactured by the Raymond Division of Combustion Engineering, Inc. since the early 1890's. In the early application of these, the finely ground material was removed from the mill by air at room temperature. This method of operation was entirely satisfactory as long as the feed remained relatively dry. However, with increased moisture content the capacity fell off rapidly. The use of preheated air followed, and was first applied to C-E Raymond Roller Mills for grinding coal. It was next used with C-E Raymond Impact Mills for grinding coal and other materials. This use of preheated air made it possible to maintain mill capacity with greatly increased moisture content in the feed, and represented a real advance in the field of drying.

The development of Flash Drying is

[1] Material contributed by A. R. Jenny and C. W. Gordon.

comparatively recent, dating back only to about 1930. Fundamental theory is simple and easily understood. The drying cycle requires less than ten seconds and, as a result, intermediate measurement during the process is difficult. Flash Drying has proved its value and efficiency in a number of successful installations handling a wide range of material. Flash Drying is the registered trademark for C-E Raymond Drying Systems.

Further advances were made through the development of conditioned wet feed. This was accomplished by adding a mixer to the system for the purpose of blending previously dried material and the incoming wet filter cake. With this arrangement it is now possible to dry materials having an initial moisture content as high as 85 per cent.

Flash Drying is applicable to materials in which the desired particle size has already been established in the original wet feed. With these, disintegration is all that is required to obtain efficient drying. The C-E Raymond Cage Mill has been developed for use with applications of this type.

Flash Drying of materials which require neither grinding nor disintegration is accomplished in the Raymond Air Stream System.

Applications in which large particle sizes are required fall outside the practical range of Flash Drying. Similarly, higher-moisture-content slurries are usually handled more satisfactorily in conventional spray dryers.

The C-E Raymond Flash Drying and Incineration Systems were developed simultaneously with the Flash Drying Systems. They have been extensively applied to the drying and incineration of such wastes as sewage sludge and furfural.

Drying — Theory and Practice

Definitions

Prior to discussing the theory of drying, it is necessary to define a few terms.

(a) *Dewatering* is the mechanical removal of moisture through the use of screens, presses, vacuum filters, centrifuges or similar devices.

(b) *Dehydration* is the removal of moisture by mechanical means, or by the application of heat. The term is usually limited to moisture removal from food products at low temperature.

(c) *Drying* is the removal of moisture by the application of heat. The term has no accepted limitations, and will be used in this text to the exclusion of the term dehydration.

Dewatering

Before drying is undertaken, the extent to which dewatering may be employed for moisture removal should be fully developed, as it is by far the most economical method available. Many processes that would be unprofitable, when drying alone is used, become economically attractive if dewatering plus drying is substituted. This is best illustrated by a study of Table 30–1. For example, assume that a distillery slop which contains 95 per cent moisture is first passed through a set of screens, then a dewatering press, and finally a dryer. It will be seen from the tabular values that with each 100 lb of dry solids, when entering the screens, there are 1900 lb of water. In passing through them, the moisture content is reduced to 85 per cent, corresponding to 566 lb of water per 100 lb of dry solids. In going through the dewatering press, this moisture content is still further reduced to 65 per cent, or 186 lb of water per 100 lb of dry solids. Thus, by dewatering, the maximum moisture that must be evapo-

Table 30—1   Table of Moisture Content

Showing the Number of Pounds of Water for each 100 Pounds of Dry Solids at Various Percentages of Moisture (Wet Basis)

Mois-ture %	Water lb	Mois-ture %	Water lb	Mois-ture %	Water lb	Mois-ture %	Water lb	Mois-ture %	Water lb
1	1.01	21	26.6	41	69.5	61	156	81	425
2	2.04	22	28.2	42	72.3	62	163	82	455
3	3.10	23	29.9	43	75.5	63	170	83	490
4	4.16	24	31.6	44	78.6	64	178	84	525
5	5.26	25	33.3	45	82.0	65	186	85	566
6	6.40	26	35.1	46	85.0	66	194	86	615
7	7.54	27	37.0	47	88.7	67	203	87	670
8	8.70	28	38.9	48	92.3	68	212	88	735
9	9.90	29	40.7	49	96.0	69	222	89	810
10	11.10	30	42.9	50	100.0	70	234	90	900
11	12.36	31	44.8	51	104	71	245	91	1010
12	13.64	32	47.0	52	108	72	256	92	1150
13	14.94	33	49.4	53	113	73	270	93	1328
14	16.28	34	51.5	54	117	74	285	94	1565
15	17.65	35	53.9	55	122	75	300	95	1900
16	19.1	36	56.1	56	127	76	316	96	2400
17	20.4	37	58.8	57	133	77	335	97	3233
18	22.0	38	61.2	58	138	78	354	98	4900
19	23.5	39	64.0	59	144	79	376	99	9900
20	25.0	40	66.6	60	150	80	400	100	....

rated, in this case, through the application of heat has been reduced from 1900 lb to 186 lb per 100 lb of dry solids.

Principles of Flash Drying

By its very nature, Flash Drying creates conditions that produce the most rapid and efficient removal of moisture. There are four fundamental factors which govern the extent, as well as the rapidity, of evaporation:

1. Moisture dispersion
2. Temperature differential
3. Agitation
4. Particle size

Moisture Dispersion. Rapid drying requires the maximum possible exposure of moist surface. Filter cakes, as received, have very unfavorable drying characteristics. They are best conditioned by blending with previously dried material in the mixer, and a fluffy product, in which the moisture has been dispersed over several times the original area, is thus obtained. This conditioned feed is now ready for delivery to the dryer. In general, the most efficient drying of filter cake is accomplished through use of dry return. There are other materials whose physical state is such, when wet, that the use of dry return is not required. In still others, particularly heat-sensitive products, the use of dry return is not desirable.

Temperature Differential. High gas temperatures are required for rapid drying as well as for high thermal efficiency. The rate of heat transfer from the gas to the moisture in the particle of material to be dried is roughly proportional to the difference between the initial temperature and the saturation temperature of the drying medium. In the operation of a Flash Drying system the material to be dried is commingled with the heated gas for a period of a few seconds and then separated from it. During this short time interval the temperature is dropped to approximately that of wet-bulb by the moisture pickup from the wet feed. These operational characteristics result in several important operational advantages for the Flash Dryer over other available types.

First, the material passes quickly and uniformly through the system, and no particles remain lodged in it. In other dryers, some of the material may be retained for long periods of time, becoming bone-dry, and in such condition it is subject to scorching and overheating. Second, it is possible to use higher initial drying-medium temperatures than with any other system. The use of these temperatures is made possible by the fact that the product never exceeds the wet-bulb temperature, owing to the extremely rapid drying action. It is for this reason that Flash Drying is particularly well adapted to the difficult task of drying organic materials whose nature may be such as to be subject to heat damage which would result in the destruction of valuable ingredients, or properties, and in the production of disagreeable odors. Although dried product may be recirculated, it has received an additional burden of moisture in the mixer, and is thus protected from damage during its next passage through the circuit.

Agitation. Maximum agitation results in rapid drying. In the Flash Dryer this is accomplished through the use of a mill, along with high gas velocities. The necessity for this arrangement is occasioned by the fact that, when a particle gives up its moisture to a hot gas, an envelope of vapor

is formed around it. The envelope tends to prevent continued vaporization by setting up a momentary condition of local equilibrium. To maintain rapid operation of the drying process, it is necessary continuously to remove this vapor film. Violent agitation of gas and moist particles in the mill at the initial stage, and high turbulent velocity of the mixture during the finishing stages, provide the means for almost instantaneous moisture removal.

Particle Size. As outlined above, drying is accomplished by removing moisture from the surface of the particle. Therefore, to secure drying penetration it is necessary for the internal moisture to reach the surface by capillary action. It is possible that a small amount of heat may find its way into the particle by radiation, and thus vaporize some of the contained water. However, the behavior of particles of varying size definitely indicates that penetration is slight and that capillary movement must be depended on. Thus, operations requiring simultaneous grinding and drying are particularly favorable ones for Flash Drying application. Other materials that have at least one small dimension are readily dried. Distillers' spent grain is an example of this latter type. Some materials give up the last few percentages of moisture reluctantly. With these, additional drying effect can be secured by employing multistage drying.

Performance

The performance of a Flash Dryer is based on certain psychrometric laws and is graphically shown by the curves in Fig. 30–1. For purposes of illustration, assume the drying operation to start at a point A with gas entering the dryer at a temperature of 1300 F dry-bulb, and 0.02 lb water per lb dry gas (absolute humidity). The drying now proceeds along the line of wet-bulb 160 F to the vent gas condi-

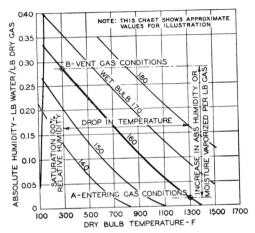

Fig. 30—1. Chart showing psychrometric laws upon which Flash Drying performance is based

tion of 300 F dry-bulb at point *B*. The absolute humidity has now been increased to 0.29 lb per lb of dry gas, and this gain represents the moisture picked up from the wet solids. The drop in dry-bulb temperature from 1300 F to 300 F represents the exchange of sensible heat to latent heat of vaporization in the moisture content of the gas. All during this heat interchange process, the solids subjected to drying have remained at the wet-bulb temperature of 160 F, and if such a temperature does not adversely affect the substance, the latter will leave the system unchanged. By using a drying medium temperature upward from 1000 F, the vent wet-bulb temperature can be held to between say 140 F and 180 F. Assays of various substances such as sewage sludge, spent grain, gluten feeds, and blood, both before and after drying, have failed to disclose chemical changes within the

limits of accuracy on sampling and analytical procedure. Cultures, yeasts, and similar materials have shown a degradation of from 5 to 15 per cent when Flash Drying is used. These results, obtained through the simple theory outlined, are particularly significant in that living organisms must be retained and thus there is a greater degree of heat sensitivity than in the preceding group of materials. The foregoing facts, however, hold true only if no heat is added after the commencement of drying and the particles are removed from the cooled drying medium before complete moisture removal is effected. The two principles on which this type of operation is based are:

1. A body of heated gas will retain the same wet-bulb temperature while being partially or fully saturated with moisture, provided the total heat remains unchanged.
2. A particle suspended in a body of hot gas assumes the wet-bulb temperature of the gas, provided some moisture remains in the particle.

In actual practice, Flash Drying does not strictly follow these laws. In fact, the product temperature is frequently below the wet-bulb temperature, and it is not overheated, nor is its quality impaired. This action may be strikingly illustrated by dropping bits of white paper into the mixer. These will pass through the dryer in about six seconds and are recovered with the dried product, uncharred and without heat discoloration.

Practical Application

In the foregoing, certain laws directly relating to Flash Drying have been discussed. However, before the practical application of these laws can be made to design and performance calculations, it is necessary to know the following governing factors:

a. Capacity — pounds of finished product per hour
b. Initial moisture content — per cent
c. Final moisture content — per cent
d. Combined moisture — per cent
e. Final particle size
f. Maximum permissible product temperature
g. Melting point of product
h. Type of heat available
i. Source of available heat

In addition to these data, the following information must be determined:

A. Initial gas temperature
B. Vent gas temperature

The initial gas temperature will depend on the heat sensitivity of the material. The vent gas temperature is a function of the final moisture content of the finished product. These temperatures are available if the material has been previously dried. If not, then a laboratory test must be conducted, because neither can be accurately predicted in advance.

Typical Calculations

With all these data available, the next step is to calculate the weight of gas required for drying. This may be accomplished by making a simple heat balance, equating heat input to heat output. It is then relatively easy to calculate the weight of entering hot air or gas for a given drying duty.[2]

The general equation for vent temperature above 212 F used in calculating the air required for a given evaporation is obtained as follows:

Heat input (A) = Heat absorbed in evaporating water (B) + Heat losses (C)

(A) Heat input
E = pounds of gas entering dryer per hour
c_p = specific heat of gases entering dryer
T_E = temperature of gases entering dryer, F
T_v = temperature at vent, F
60 F = ambient temperature

Then the sensible heat above 60 F of the gases entering the dryer, which is the heat input, will be
$$\text{Heat input} = E \times c_p \times (T_E - 60) \text{ Btu}$$

(B) Heat absorbed
M = pounds of water to be evaporated per hour
60 F — ambient temperature
Assume that the water is raised from 60 F to 212 F and then changed from the liquid to the gaseous state at standard pressure.
$$\text{Heat absorbed} = M [1.0 (212 - 60) + 970.3]$$
$$= 1122.3 M \text{ Btu}$$

(C) Heat losses
  1. Radiation
The dryer radiation is assumed to be 5 per cent of heat input
$$\text{Radiation} = 0.05 E \times c_p \times (T_E - 60) \text{ Btu}$$
  2. Vent
  (a) Heat above 212 F in evaporated moisture
$$M \times 0.47 \times (T_v - 212)$$
  (b) Heat in entering gases
$$E \times c_p \times (T_v - 60)$$
  (c) Infiltration
Assume infiltration is 10 per cent of entering gases
Assume infiltration is 50 per cent saturated at 60 F. There are 38.8 grams of water vapor per pound (7000 grains) of dry air under these conditions.
$$\text{Dry air loss} = 0.10 E \times 0.24 \times (T_v - 60)$$
$$= 0.024 E (T_v - 60)$$

$$\text{Moisture} = \frac{38.8}{7000} \times 0.10 E \times 0.47$$
$$\times (T_v - 60) = 0.00026 E (T_v - 60)$$

[2] The method of calculation and accompanying curves were developed by R. G. Tucker.

The vent loss is the sum of (A), (B) and (C).

Vent loss $= 0.47$ M $(T_V - 212)$
$$+ (c_p + 0.02426)(T_V - 60) E$$

3. Product

DS = pounds dry solids in product
W = pounds water retained in product
T_P = product temperature
0.2 = specific heat of dry solids

Product loss $= DS \times 0.2 \times (T_P - 60)$
$$+ W \times 1.0 \times (T_P - 60)$$
$$= (0.2\,DS + W)(T_P - 60)$$

(D) Heat balance

As noted previously, (A) = (B) + (C)

$E \times c_P (T_E - 60) = 1122.3$ M $+ 0.05$ E
$$\times c_p (T_E - 60) + 0.47\,M\,(T_V - 212)$$
$$+ (c_p + 0.02426)(T_E - 60) E$$
$$+ (0.2\,DS + W)(T_P - 60)$$

Simplifying, combining terms and solving for E

$$E = \frac{(1022.66 + 0.47\,T_V)\,M + (0.2\,DS + W)\,(T_P - 60)}{(0.95\,T_E - T_V + 3)\,c_p - 0.02426\,T_V + 1.455}$$

The preceding equation was based upon the assumption that the vent temperature is in excess of 212 F. For temperatures below this point, slight modifications must be made, based upon the steam tables and simple thermodynamic relationships. Enthalpies must be adjusted from the thermodynamic base of 32 F to the assumed ambient temperature of 60 F. To raise the temperature of water from liquid at 60 F to vapor at vent temperature, the following equation applies.

Heat required = (enthalpy of vapor)
— (enthalpy of liquid at 60 F)
= (enthalpy of saturated water vapor at 32 F
+ 0.42 Btu per deg F)
— (enthalpy of liquid at 60 F)

Using values from C-E steam tables
Heat required $= 1075.1 + 0.42 (T_V - 32)$
$$- 28.07$$
$$= 1033.6 + 0.42\,T_V$$

Substituting the appropriate values for the heat absorbed and the heat losses in the vent under (D) above, the following equation is obtained for quantity of gas entering dryer per hour for vent temperature below 212 F.

$$E = \frac{(1033.6 + 0.42\,T_V)\,M + (0.2\,DS + W)\,(T_P - 60)}{(0.95\,T_E - T_V + 3)\,c_p - 0.02426\,T_V + 1.455)}$$

Entering gas quantities are of course easily converted to heat input required and vent quantity.

The computation is greatly simplified by the use of the following three curves:
Fig. 30–2 — Air flow at vent required for drying
Fig. 30–3 — Drying efficiency
Fig. 30–4 — Specific volume of vent gases

To illustrate use of curves and calculations the following example may be helpful

Material	Corn gluten
Initial moisture	70 per cent
Final moisture	10 per cent
Capacity	2000 lb final product per hr
	1800 lb dry solids per hr
Type of fuel fired	Direct oil (No. 3)

Assume

Inlet temperature	1000 F
Vent temperature	250 F
Feed temperature	60 F
Product temperature	170 F
Specific heat of product	0.25
Furnace and combustion losses	10 per cent

Water evaporation for design

Wet feed at 30 per cent solids

1800/0.30 =   6000 lb per hr

Product at 10 per cent moisture   2000 lb per hr
Actual water evaporation   4000 lb per hr
Sensible heat absorbed by product
$2000 \times 0.25 (170 - 60) =$
    55,000 Btu per hr

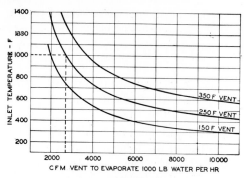

Fig. 30–2. Required air flow at vent for drying

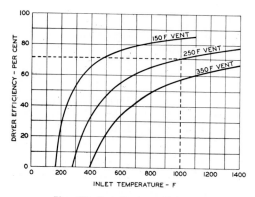

Fig. 30–3. Drying efficiency

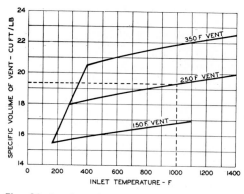

Fig. 30–4. Specific volume of vent gases

Since it requires 1122 Btu per pound to receive water at 60 F and evaporate it at 212 F, 55,000 Btu per hour can be converted to equivalent water evaporation.

$$\frac{55,000}{1122} = 49 \text{ lb water per hour equivalent}$$

Actual water	=	4000 lb per hr
Equivalent to heat product		49
Total water evaporation for design		4049

Air flow required for drying
Refer to Fig. 30–2
Find inlet 1000 F in left hand margin
Follow horizontally to curve for 250 F vent
Project downward to find that 2690 cfm at exit conditions is required to evaporate 1000 lb water per hour.

Air flow for 4049 lb per hr

$$2690 \times \frac{4049}{1000} = 10,890 \text{ cfm at exit condi-}$$

tions without safety factor
Furnace heat input
Refer to Fig. 30–3 for drying efficiency
Find inlet 1000 F on horizontal scale
Move vertically to curve for 250 F vent temperature
Move to left and read efficiency = 71.3 per cent
Dryer heat input

$$\frac{4049 \times 1122}{0.713} - 6,380,000 \text{ Btu per hr}$$

This does not allow for furnace and combustion losses which are assumed to be 10 per cent

$$\frac{6,380,000}{0.90} = 7,090,000 \text{ Btu per hr total}$$
furnace heat input without safety factor.

To convert vent cfm to lb per hr, refer to Fig. 30–4 to find specific volume.
For inlet 1000 F and vent 250 F
Specific volume is 19.35 cu ft per lb

$$10,890 \text{ cfm} \times \frac{60}{19.35} = 33,800 \text{ lb vent gases}$$

per hour without safety factor
Pounds of entering gases per hour
Simply subtract water evaporation and air infiltration from vent quantity.

By definition, air infiltration is 10 per cent of entering air.

Total vent = 33,800 lb per hr
Less water evaporated 4,000
29,800 lb per hr

But by definition this is 110 per cent of entering quantity

$$\frac{29,800}{1.10} = 27,100 \text{ lb per hr enters without safety factor}$$

These calculations then provide the quantities necessary to complete the design and selection of the drying system and its auxiliaries.

Flash Drying Systems

C-E Raymond Systems are designed to accomplish drying under three distinct conditions:

A. Drying without disintegration
B. Drying with disintegration
C. Drying and pulverizing

These systems are manufactured in three types:

  a. Single stage
  b. Multistage
  c. Counterflow

and may be now classified as follows:

A. Drying without disintegration —
  single stage, multistage, counterflow
B. Drying with disintegration —
  single stage, multistage, counterflow
C. Drying and pulverizing —
  single stage, multistage

Typical applications of the three are:

A. Drying without disintegration
  Coal (⅜ in. and smaller)
  Amine crystals
  Sodium chloride
  Potassium persulfate
  Wheat flour
  Ammonium sulfate
  Potassium perchlorate
  Wood flour

  Pharmaceuticals
  Synthetic resins
B. Drying with disintegration
  Distillers' spent grain
  Sodium sulfate and sulfite
  Sewage sludge
  Corn gluten
  Gypsum sludge
  Clay
  Calcium carbonate sludge
  Filter cakes
  Silica gel catalyst
  Dicalcium phosphate
C. Drying and pulverizing
  Clay
  Diatomaceous earth
  Copper sulfate
  Gypsum
  Steamed bone
  Aluminum stearate
  Carboxylmethylcellulose
  Potassium perchlorate
  Synthetic resins
  Food products

Essential Elements

Flash Drying Systems are designed to perform specific functions and to be installed within given building areas. They are composed of standard elements arranged to suit the given conditions. The primary elements in the system are as follows:

A. Air heater
  Direct or indirect type
  Steam, gas, oil or coal fired
B. Wet feeder
  Roll or conveyor type
C. Mixer
  High-speed or low-speed
D. Agitator
  Cage or impact mill
E. Collection system
  Cyclone, air piping and fan
F. Dry divider
G. Cooling and transport system
  Air piping and fan
H. Instruments and controls
  Some Flash Drying Systems require all

the above elements, while others may omit one or more of them.

Operation of Flash Drying Systems

Flash Drying Systems are simple in design and are therefore relatively easy to operate. The amount of material in the system at any given time is a matter of only a few pounds, in contrast with the so-called conventional types of dryers in which the quantity of material in process may amount to tons. It is this difference in weight flowing through the system which makes it possible to adjust conditions so as to obtain a closer control of the final moisture content in the finished product.

Best results are obtained when a close study is made of the wet feed supply. The variations in feed rate should not exceed plus or minus 10 per cent when a uniform final moisture content is desired. This final moisture content is a direct function of the cyclone collector temperature. An increase in this temperature will lower the moisture content, while a decrease in temperature will increase the final moisture. Response to temperature changes is rapid because of the small amount of material under process in the system at any given time.

Heat Supply

Heat for the drying system is always supplied by an air heater. Although this may be manually operated, automatic temperature control is preferred. The automatic control feature regulates the furnace heat input so as to maintain a constant cyclone exit temperature. A uniform final moisture content in the finished product results from maintaining a constant cyclone exit temperature. To serve Flash Drying Systems, conventional air heaters are used. These may be direct or

indirect fired. In other cases, extended surface steam air heaters are used.

Direct-Type Heater. Flash Drying frequently uses rather high inlet air temperatures, 1200 to 1300 F being common. For such service, conventional direct-fired units burning oil or gas are commonly used. Typical designs are illustrated in Figs. 30–5 and 30–6. Direct stoker fired air heaters are also used under some conditions.

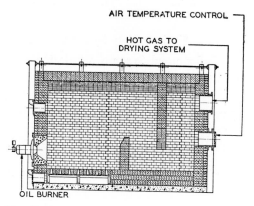

Fig. 30—5. Direct type of air heater for oil or gas firing

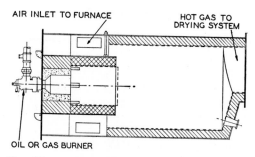

Fig. 30—6. Package design of direct type air heater

Indirect Air Heaters. If low-temperature indirect heat is desired, extended surface steam air heaters may be most economical. Air temperatures are limited to a maximum of about 20 deg F less than saturation temperature of the steam supply. For indirect heat at higher temperatures, it is customary to employ indirect-fired units using gas-to-air heat exchangers. These may be gas, oil or coal fired.

Wet Feeder

The wet feeder may be an integral part of the Flash Drying System, such as a feed roll on an impact mill. In other instances, it may be a part of the dewatering system, such as in the case of the conveyor belt from a vacuum filter. In any event, a variable-speed drive should be provided, in order that the rate of feed may be changed as required. Variations in wet feeder arrangement are illustrated in the several flow diagrams discussed later in this chapter.

Mixer

The mixer is used to condition the incoming wet feed by blending it with previously dried material. A product is thus obtained which can be easily picked up by the hot gas stream. The mixer is of the double-paddle type, designed for high or low-speed operation, and acts as a conveyor to deliver the conditioned feed to the agitator inlet.

Agitator and Collection System

The agitator may be either a cage or an impact mill, depending on the character of the material to be handled. Flow is usually induced by a vent fan connected to the cyclone outlet. The wet material is fed into the hot gas stream, and this mixture then enters the agitator axially. Rotating parts provide the necessary violent agitation, so that the drying action is practically instantaneous. As a result, the product leaves the agitator almost completely dried, but mixed with the gas. This mixture now enters the cyclone collector, where separation occurs, and the finished product is removed by means of a rotary air lock, while the moisture-laden gas is discharged to the atmosphere through the vent fan. In some systems, a portion of the vent gas may be returned to the furnace, to act as a tempering medium.

Dry Divider

When dry return is needed for conditioning the incoming wet feed, the finished product is proportioned in a dry divider. This proportioning may be either automatically or manually controlled. The automatic dry divider consists of a timer to actuate a thrustor, which, in turn, positions a splitter damper in the rotary-air-lock discharge. This timer is manually set to hold the damper in position to discharge all the dry product to the mixer for a portion of the cycle, and then to the discharge conveyor for the remainder of the cycle. The proper setting is determined by observing the physical condition of the feed in the mixer.

Cooling and Transport System

Temperature of the finished product from a Flash Drying System is from 50–150 deg F below cyclone temperature. Thus, sewage sludge dried with a cyclone temperature of 300 F will have a product temperature of approximately 170 F. Before sacking, it will be necessary to reduce this temperature to about 100 F. Many other types of finished products may also require prepacking cooling, and this is economically accomplished through the use of an air cooling and transport system. In this system, the warm finished product is discharged into an air stream, and simultaneously cooled and transported to a cyclone in the storage or packing room.

Air at room temperature is frequently cool enough for this purpose. In some cases, however, it may be necessary to pass the air through cooling coils in order that it may be cool enough to effect the necessary temperature reduction in the finished product. However, each problem requires careful analysis, and all factors must be weighed before the equipment is selected.

Methods of Drying

Drying without Disintegration

In some drying applications, only relatively low temperatures are required because the necessary reduction in moisture is small. These systems are usually composed of the four basic operating elements in their simplest form. The necessary temperature of the drying medium is obtained in a steam air heater. The feed is introduced through a variable-speed wet feeder of the screw-conveyor type. A cyclone with rotary air lock acts to separate the dried finished product from the moisture-laden gas, and this is then removed from the system by the vent fan. An arrangement of this type, for drying certain chemical salts, is shown in Fig. 30–7.

A modification of the foregoing system, using larger quantities of heat because of necessary increased drying effect, is shown in Fig. 30–8. In this one, the product is composed of finely divided particles carrying a relatively high percentage of surface moisture, such as coal slurry from a mine washery. Again, the four basic elements of the Flash Drying System are used. The increased temperature and quantity of drying medium are secured in this case through the use of a stoker-fired, direct-type air heater.

Instruments and Controls

A recording temperature controller for the final vent temperature is usually pro-

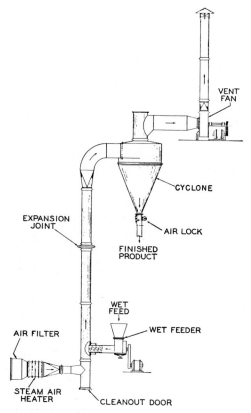

Fig. 30–7.   A simple system for drying without disintegration

vided. This instrument is generally arranged to vary furnace fuel input so as to maintain a constant vent temperature which is necessary for uniform final moisture.

An indicating or recording temperature instrument is needed for the entering hot air temperature. This is not usually a controlling-type instrument.

In some cases indicating draft gages are provided for several important points in the system. The above instrumentation, which is relatively simple, is thoroughly practical and provides the operator with the essential facts for easy and efficient operation.

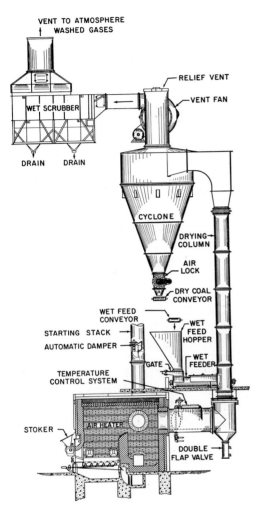

Fig. 30–8. A modified simple drying system for increased drying effect

There are many variations of the simple system described above. Some products are most advantageously dried in two or more stages, while others may require a counterflow type of system for best results. When a counterflow system is used, expensive secondary dust collection is sometimes eliminated.

Drying with Disintegration

Systems of this type are largely used for products in which the particle size is established in the wet feed. The requirements in these cases are to dry the material and to reestablish the particle size. A system of this type, designed to dry spent grain, sewage sludge and similar materials, is shown in Fig. 30–9. The system arrangement is similar to the one in Fig. 30–8, except for the addition of the cage-type agitator. The wet feed, after it has been dewatered, is supplied to the mixer in the form of a filter cake. After conditioning, through the admixture of dry return, it is simultaneously disintegrated and thoroughly mixed with the heated drying medium in passing through the agitator to the cyclone collector. The particle size is reestablished through dis-

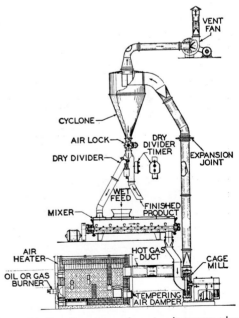

Fig. 30–9. A system for simultaneous drying and disintegration

integration, and the proportion of finished product to dry return is regulated by the automatic dry divider. With some products, a continuous size classification is required. This classification is obtained by incorporating a Raymond mechanical air separator which continually returns the oversized products to the system for additional treatment.

Drying and Pulverizing

These systems are used when a finely divided finished product is required. Clay, aluminum stearate, and other similar materials are processed in the arrangement of equipment illustrated by Fig. 30–10. The reduction in particle size is obtained through the use of an impact pulverizer, together with its feeder, in place of the mixer and cage type of agitator shown in Fig. 30–9. The vented gas from the system, instead of going directly from the cyclone collector to the vent fan, is first passed through some form of dust-collec-

tor so as to effect additional product recovery. These collectors may be of the bag-filter type or any other available type that will provide the necessary degree of recovery. When the material to be processed is in the form of filter cake, then a mixer, dry divider and dry return are added, so that properly conditioned feed is supplied to the pulverizer.

Flash Drying and Incineration Systems

Sewage-treatment plants have been in service for many years. The term *treatment* is used advisedly because the end products of these plants are a treated water effluent and a quantity of harmful solid matter. The water effluent can be discharged into streams, without nuisance danger. The solid matter, on the other hand, is usually dewatered on sand drying beds and under certain conditions can be used as fertilizer or fill even though it retains a large quantity of pathogenic bacteria.

As a result of the demand for some form of suitable disposal plant to render this solid matter harmless, the C-E Raymond Flash Drying and Incineration System was developed. This system, which is a combination of the principles of Flash Drying with those relating to the burning of fuel in suspension, has been widely accepted and is serving communities ranging in size from 6000 to 3,600,000 population.

Fertilizer

As a first step this system produces a fine dried fertilizer. The actual chemical value of this product will depend on the type of sludge treatment used. For example, activated sludge contains approximately 6 per cent nitrogen, while digested sludge contains only 2.5 per cent.

In many plants, the entire output is sold

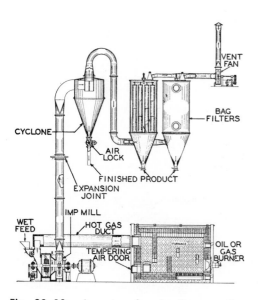

Fig. 30–10. A system for simultaneous drying and pulverization

as fertilizer, and the present output of those that are Raymond-equipped is more than 200,000 tons per year. In these the heat for drying is supplied by digester gas produced in the plant or by some supplementary fuel such as oil or coal.

Incineration

Some sewage is so low in nitrogen that the plant management elects to incinerate it. The end product is then an excellent fill, in the form of a sterile ash.

The C-E Raymond Flash Drying and Incineration System is illustrated by the flow sheet in Fig. 30–11. The operation is similar to previously described Flash Drying Systems with the exception that the dried sludge may be either delivered to a storage bin by an air transport system and sacked as fertilizer, or it may be discharged to the furnace and burned. In the latter case, the dried material is delivered to the sludge burner. Air for combustion is also delivered to the burner, the fuel is burned in suspension, and the heat thus generated is used in the drying

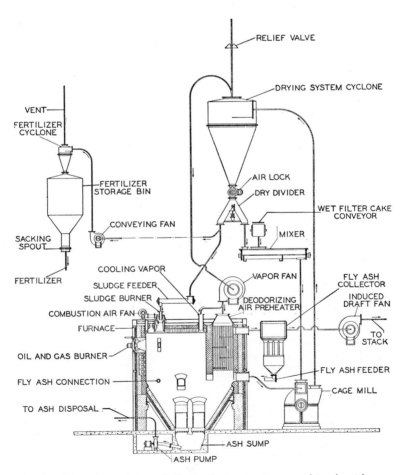

Fig. 30–11. Flow sheet of Flash Drying system combined with an incinerator system

process. The major portion of the ash drops to the furnace bottom, and from here it is pumped to the site where fill is required. The fly ash carryover is trapped in a high-efficiency mechanical collector and returned to the furnace for disposal.

Deodorization

The gas that has been in contact with the sludge during the drying process has become odorous. In some plant locations it would create a nuisance if discharged directly to the atmosphere. To avoid this the gas is subjected to heat treatment in the deodorizing preheater, where it is first reheated to about 700 F and then by mixing with the products of combustion further increased in temperature to 1200–

1300 F. This heat treatment destroys objectionable sludge odors.

Variations

There are many variations of this standard system, since each municipality has problems peculiar to its particular location. One effective variation is to combine this system with a standard garbage and refuse incinerator, thereby disposing of all municipal wastes in one plant. Fig. 30–12 shows such an arrangement. It combines the well known C-E Raymond Flash Drying System for Sewage Sludge with a mixed refuse incinerator employing the equally well known C-E Traveling Grate Stoker.

The dual disposal of mixed refuse and

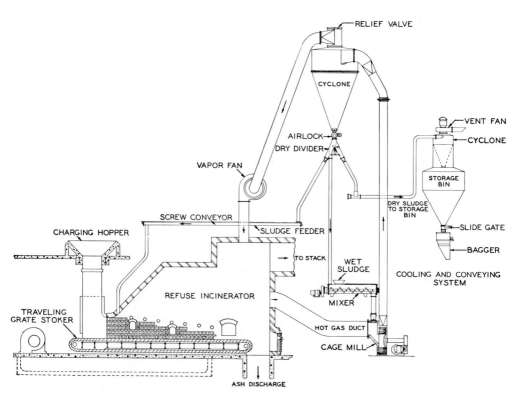

Fig. 30–12. Cross section of Flash Drying system and traveling grate refuse incinerator

sewage sludge at the same plant site effects economies in both first cost and operating costs of the disposal equipment. It enables the smaller communities to provide for modern disposal facilities whereas perhaps they could not afford separate facilities from the standpoint of first cost or operating costs.[3]

Other Applications

This system is not limited to sewage sludge; it can be applied also to many other waste fuels. For example, it is successfully used in drying and burning the residue from the production of furfural (cotton-seed hulls, rice hulls, and corn cobs) and at the same time in producing all the steam necessary to support opera-

tion of the process. Drying and burning finely divided wood waste is another outstanding application.

The field of application for Flash Drying Systems is extremely broad. However, because of wide variations in products handled, it is frequently necessary to establish specific control data through carefully supervised laboratory tests.

In the foregoing, broad principles necessary to operation have been pointed out, and the design of equipment used in the various arrangements has been discussed. The coordination of basic theory with practical tests has resulted in many successful installations in which standardized equipment elements are arranged to meet specific finished-product requirements.

[3] See Chapter 31, Refuse Incinerators, for further details of incinerator design and application.

Municipal incinerator installation

31

Refuse Incinerators[1]

DISPOSAL OF REFUSE MATERIAL is a problem in many communities and industries, and the modern incinerator is one of the most effective ways of burning these wastes economically and inoffensively. The principles of incinerator design, particularly for the larger municipal and industrial applications, are similar to those employed in stokers and boilers described elsewhere in this book.[2] Likewise, combustion of refuse materials obeys the same physical laws as do other fossil fuels and may be calculated in a similar manner.

Incineration is used in many applications for disposal of a wide variety of refuse materials. Although it is common practice to classify refuse ingredients under several categories, many of these require highly specialized furnaces or are either small in size or have a limited field of usefulness. What follows will be confined to municipal and industrial incinerator designs which are closely related to conventional steam power plant practice.

Refuse Characteristics

Modern food processing and packaging techniques have had a pronounced effect upon the characteristics of refuse. In years past garbage accounted for 65 per cent or more of the volume of refuse, often re-

sulting in an overall moisture content in excess of 50 per cent. This approaches the point where auxiliary fuel is required to sustain combustion with suitable furnace temperatures.

Municipal collections now may average 10 per cent or less garbage, with an overall moisture content of 15 to 20 per cent. This refuse is characterized by large quantities of paper bags, crates and similar dry combustible material. Although much bulkier it is more easily burned in incinerators of adequate design.

Industrial refuse has also changed with the greatly increased use of plastics and other synthetic materials, many of which have high heating values with little or no moisture or ash to burden them in the furnace. Table 31–1 indicates the heating values for a wide variety of materials which commonly appear in both municipal and industrial refuse.

The highly variable appearance of refuse is belied by its chemical analysis, which is quite uniform, as much of it is produced from wood and similar cellulose raw materials. Laboratory tests as well as theoretical calculations show that the average heating value of such cellulose by-products is about 8000 Btu per pound of combustible. The major variables comprise

[1] Material contributed by H. G. Meissner and E. R. Shequine.
[2] See Chapter 19, Fundamentals of Boiler Design, and Chapter 18, Stokers, for more detailed information.

the moisture and ash or inert ingredients, and these are not difficult to determine on a test basis.

Table 31–1 Municipal and Industrial Refuse — Typical Heating Values of Components

Domestic Refuse	Moisture	BTU as fired
Paper, cardboard, cartons, bags......	3	7,660
Wood crates, boxes, scrap	7	7,825
Brush, branches	17	7,140
Leaves	30	4,900
Grass	50	3,820
Garbage	75	1,820
Greenstuff	50	3,470
Greens	50	4,070
Rags-cotton-linen	10	6,440

Industrial Scrap Refuse

Boot, shoe trim and scrap	8,500
Sponge waffle and scrap	8,500
Butyl soles scrap	11,500
Cement wet scrap	11,500
Rubber	12,420
Tire cord scrap	12,400
Rubber scorched scrap	19,700
Tires, bus and auto	18,000
Gum scrap	19,700
Latex coagulum	19,700
Latex waste, coagulum waste	12,000
Leather scrap	10,000
Waxed paper	12,000
Cork scrap	12,400
Paraffin	16,803
Oil waste, fuel oil residue..................	18,000

Plastic and Synthetic Refuse

Cellophane plastic	12,000
Polyethylene	19,840
Polyvinyl chloride	17,500
Vinyl scrap	17,500
Aldehyde sludge	18,150
Solvent naptha	18,500
Carbon disulfite	8,000
Benzine	10,000

Miscellaneous

Carbon to CO_2	14,093
Carbon to CO	4,347
Sulfur	3,983
Methane	23,879

Combustion Calculations for Refuse Incinerators

Combustion calculations for refuse can be made on the same basis as used for other fuels, that is by converting the refuse weights to Btu fired per hour, for which the air and gas weights are quite uniform and easily determined. The curves in Fig. 31–1 are plotted by using the above data. The moisture variable may be estimated from known characteristics or by weighing and drying a representative sample of refuse.

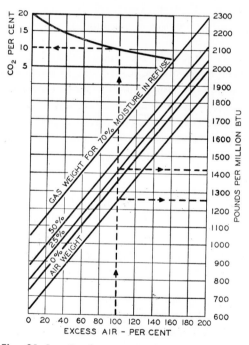

Fig. 31–1. Combustion products of refuse— air and gas weights for various excess air and moisture contents

The major design factors such as grate and furnace dimensions, air and gas quantities, fan and stack requirements are developed in the following example from the above starting point. It will be noted that this is the same procedure that is used in the design of furnaces for burning other fuels.[3] It is based on the knowledge that theoretical combustion air requirements of a wide variety of combustible materials, including most of the ingredients in refuse, are quite uniform per million Btu fired.

Assume an average municipal refuse having a moisture and ash-free heating value of 8000 Btu per pound, containing 25 per cent moisture and 12.5 per cent ash and other inert or non-combustible matter such as cans, bottles and tramp iron. Many incinerator specifications call for the burning of a given number of tons per day, without stating the number of hours of operation, which may vary from one to three shifts. The total refuse to be fired per day must be reduced to pounds per hour when the operating period has been determined, and then to Btu per hour for use in the following calculations.

For this example, consider the combustion of 100 tons of refuse per day, operating on a three-shift basis. This is the equivalent of 8340 lb per hr. In order to avoid excessive slagging and to minimize furnace maintenance, a flame temperature on the order of 2000 F is desirable. Under these conditions, as shown in Fig. 31–2, 100 per cent excess air is required for satisfactory operation.

The gas weight generated per pound of refuse comprises the combustion air plus the water evaporated from the refuse as it enters the furnace, plus the combustible portion of the refuse. The ash and other inert material remain on the grate and do not affect the gas weight that must be taken into consideration.

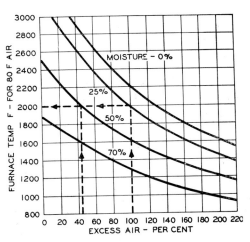

Fig. 31–2. Furnace gas temperature in a refractory furnace in terms of excess air and moisture content

The incinerator grate area is determined by dividing the total Btu input by the allowable grate heat release expressed in Btu per square foot per hour. This is an empirical value established by tests and experience to assure satisfactory performance while avoiding excessive size and cost of grate mechanisms. For typical municipal refuse, 300,000 Btu per sq ft per hr is considered satisfactory. This is equivalent to 60 lb per sq ft per hr of 5000 Btu per lb refuse.

The furnace volume is similarly determined by dividing the total Btu per hour input by the allowable furnace heat release established in similar manner. For incinerator applications a suggested value is 20,000 Btu per cu ft per hr.

Typical Example

The following tabulation shows how the above procedure is used in practice for an incinerator having a capacity of 100 tons per day.

[3] See Chapter 21, Combustion and Boiler Calculations.

Combustion Calculations

Heat content (moisture and ash-free basis)	8000	Btu per lb
Moisture	25	per cent
Ash and other noncombustible matter	12.5	per cent
As-fired heating value 8000 [1 − (0.25 + 0.125)]	5000	Btu per lb
Firing rate — 100 tons per day (100 × 2000/24)	8340	lb per hr
Firing rate — heat content (5000 × 8340)	41,720,000	Btu per hr
Excess air required according to Fig. 31–2, to burn refuse at 2000 F flame temperature	100	per cent
Theoretical combustion air requirement based on heat value of 8000 Btu per lb of cellulose*	5	lb
Total air weight per pound of combustible (theoretical air + excess air)	10	lb
Total air weight per million Btu (1,000,000 × 10/8000)	1250	lb
Weight of water per pound of refuse 0.25/[1 − 0.25]	0.333	lb
Weight of water per pound of combustible 0.333/[1.0 − 0.125]	0.38	lb
Total gas weight per pound of combustible equals air weight + water weight + one pound combustible	11.38	lb
Total gas weight per million Btu of combustible (1,000,000 × 11.38/8000)	1420	lb
Grate area, assuming heat release rate at 300,000 Btu per sq ft per hr (41,720,000/300,000)	139	sq ft
Combustion rate (300,000/50)	60	lb per sq ft per hr
Furnace volume, assuming heat release rate of 20,000 Btu per cu ft per hr (41, 720, 000/20,000)	2085	cu ft
Furnace height (2085/139) or (300,000/20,000)	15	ft
Total air weight, 100 per cent excess air (1250 × 41.7)	52,100	lb per hr
Air volume, including furnace leakage, at 100 F		
Weight of air at 100 F, atmospheric pressure, is 0.0709 lb per cu ft (52,100/0.0709 × 60)	12,300	cu ft per min

* "A Field Study of Performance of Three Municipal Incinerators," Institute of Engineering Research, University of California, Berkeley, California, Series 37, Issue 6, November 1951, p. viii.

Air supplied by forced draft and overfire fans at 85 per cent of above	10,450	cu ft per min
Gas weight leaving furnace (1420 ×41.7)	59,400	lb per hr
Gas volume corresponding to above weight at 2000 F	61,200	cu ft per min

Gas Velocities in Furnace

Vertical gas velocity above fuel bed (61,200/139)	440	ft per min
Horizontal gas velocity at furnace outlet for 8 ft furnace width (61,200/8 × 15)	510	ft per min
Cross-sectional area in duct or chimney at gas velocity of 2000 ft per min (61,200/2000)	30.6	sq ft

Adaptability of Calculations

This method of selection and sizing of furnaces, flues, dust collectors, fans and stacks refers all incinerators to the common denominator of heat input. Thus comparison of different installations is facilitated. Furnace temperatures (with both refractory and waterwalls, tempering air or water sprays for gas cooling) and similar data are then readily determined. Note Fig. 31–2 and Fig. 31–3 which show furnace temperature with various excess air and moisture contents, and Fig. 31–4

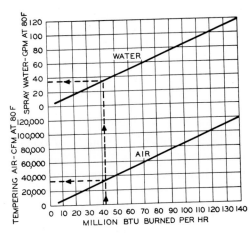

Fig. 31–4. Tempering air or water spray requirements for gas cooling

which gives the water and air requirements for gas cooling. Calculations for these charts are based on standard combustion and heat transfer formulas.

Utilization of Incinerator Heat

Heat utilization from incineration has been considered a difficult and unpredictable art, and it is only in the past few years that serious thought has been given to this matter. The heat output from a properly designed and operated incinerator is no more irregular than that from some of the refuse fuels such as hogged

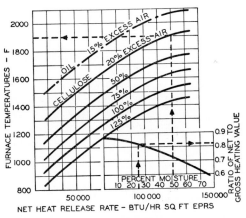

Fig. 31–3. Furnace gas temperature in a waterfall furnace in terms of excess air and moisture content

wood and bark, which are now used to fire large high-pressure industrial boilers. Two factors which have expedited this revived interest in heat utilization are the increase in heat value in commonly available refuse and development of the various types of continuous flow incinerators.

Generation of steam should be considered only when there is a nearby need for steam. In the case of installation of incinerator-fired boilers, auxiliary gas or oil burners should be provided in order to insure continuity of steam supply. Incinerator operation may vary from eight to twenty-four hours and from five to seven days per week. Collections may be interrupted because of storms, and during these periods the refuse may be exceptionally wet, resulting in a reduction of burning capacity and steam generation.

Municipal Incinerator Uses

The most common example of the use of heat energy from incinerators is for supplying hot water, steam and, on rare occasions, electric power to the plant itself. Depending upon the circumstances the utilization may be as simple as bypassing a portion of the combustion gases to a boiler to heat hot water or as complex as an isolated electric generating plant with superheaters and heat recovery equipment in the boiler and a turbine-generator for producing power. There may be some situations in which the amount of steam or power generated is sufficient to consider outside sale. A great deal of engineering judgment and extensive economic studies enter into decisions relating to the use of incinerator heat energy.

Industrial Incinerator Uses

The foregoing generalizations apply primarily to municipal incinerators. There are many circumstances in industrial

plants where heat energy from incineration of refuse materials may be coordinated with the plant output of process steam or electricity. Under these conditions the incinerator becomes an integral part of an industrial power plant.

As an example the waste material in a certain industrial plant comprises a number of liquid and solid combustibles from rubber goods manufacture as well as a considerable amount of normal refuse such as cafeteria garbage, rubbish, paper and wood products. There is also the usual complement of cans, bottles, metal scrap and ash or other inert materials. The heat value of these ingredients ranges from 8000 to 20,000 Btu per pound.

A plant survey showed that this refuse totaled about 80 tons for an average day, equivalent to 6670 lb per hr, and analysis on a weighted basis resulted in an average heating value of about 10,000 Btu, or a total of 1600×10^6 Btu per day. For the 24 hr operation proposed, the available heat output is 66.7×10^6 Btu per hr. Auxiliary fuel oil is provided for in the furnace design which is shown in Fig. 31–5.

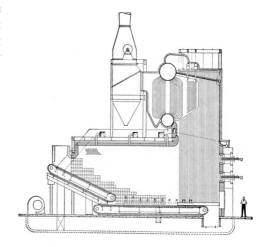

Fig. 31–5.   Incinerator   stoker   and   waste heat boiler for industrial plant

The incinerator and boiler unit is located next to the present boiler plant, with a bin-and-crane system for handling and storage. Mixing of the heterogeneous solid and liquid matter is accomplished here.

The overall boiler efficiency is estimated from Fig. 31–6 to be 70 per cent and the heat added per pound of steam is 1100 Btu. The boiler output is 42,500 lb per hr or 6.52 lb of steam per pound of refuse.

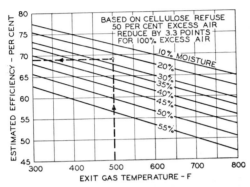

Fig. 31–6. Estimated boiler efficiency with refuse firing

If the efficiency when firing oil is assumed to be 82 per cent, then each ton of refuse fired will replace 114 gal of fuel oil, and the 80 tons per day will save about 9120 gal of oil. Added advantages of this project include reduced hauling costs for refuse disposal and improved public relations by eliminating present air pollution.

As a generalization it might be stated that each ton of municipal refuse is capable of generating 6000 to 7000 lb of steam. Industrial waste running higher in heating value will produce proportionately more steam.

Waterwall Construction for Incinerators

Although incinerators are commonly visualized as a form of refractory-lined combustion chamber, the modern incinerator frequently employs partial waterwall

construction, especially if steam generation is involved. When heat is absorbed by waterwalls rather than radiated back from refractory furnace walls, excess air may be reduced. With smaller quantities of air to handle, fan requirements, boiler draft loss and fly ash carryover are all reduced. This means substantial reduction in the sizes of the forced and induced draft fans, duct work and dust collectors. An example of extended waterwall construction is shown in Fig. 31–5 discussed previously.

Incinerator — High Temperature Water Boiler

High temperature water boilers as shown in Fig. 31–7 fit in well as a means of utilizing the heat from incineration, provided that an auxiliary fuel such as gas or oil is included to take care of weekends or other periods when suitable refuse

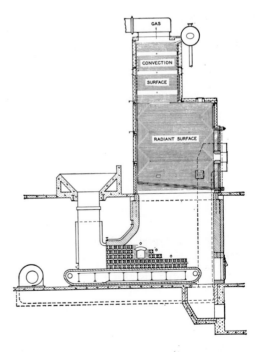

Fig. 31–7. High temperature water boiler combined with refuse incinerator

is not available. These boilers[4] are available in standardized capacities of 12,000,000 to 50,000,000 Btu per hr or more, corresponding to incinerator capacities of 30 to 120 tons per 24 hours.

This type of boiler-incinerator combination is especially suitable for such applications as central heating plants for large buildings, shopping centers, or military bases, all of which may have considerable refuse to burn. It is also applicable for supplying steam for vulcanizing equipment, ovens or tanks with heating coils, calender rolls, heating platens, drying kilns, evaporators or similar industrial processes in plants where there may be a supply of combustible refuse.

Incinerator — Flash Drying System

The combination of refuse incinerator and sewage disposal plants is becoming increasingly popular as the hot gas from the furnace can be used in Flash Drying equipment[5] and the sludge may be returned for incineration when desired. Noxious gas can be passed into the hot furnace for dissociation of objectionable fumes before discharge to the atmosphere.

The handling of mixed refuse and sewage sludge at the same plant site effects economies in both first cost and operating expenses. Many smaller communities can now provide for modern disposal facilities at a cost far below separate sewage and incinerator plants.

General Types of Incinerators

There are two general types of incinerators, designated as the batch feed and continuous feed designs respectively. The batch feed type is similar in some respects to the hand-fired coal burning furnace in

that the refuse is introduced into the furnace at intervals. In the continuous feed design, the hopper is kept full and the action of the stoker beneath removes the refuse at a more or less steady rate, similar to the action in a coal stoker.

Batch Feed Design

Batch feed furnaces are generally confined to the smaller plants, the unit capacities seldom exceeding 150 tons per day or 12,500 pounds per hour. As in the case of hand-fired coal furnaces there is some loss in capacity when a fresh charge is deposited on the fire, as well as when the ash residue is being removed. The heat output from the batch furnaces is therefore somewhat less uniform than the continuous feed types, and excess capacity must be provided to make up for this periodic loss in burning rate.

Continuous Feed Design

The principal type of continuous feed incinerator is the traveling grate. In contrast to the batch feed types, the refuse is fed to the furnace at a relatively uniform and continuous rate from the bottom of a hopper by the action of the stoker mechanism. The fuel-air ratio and heat output are more easily controlled, and automatic regulating devices have been used successfully to adjust the above functions as well as the furnace temperature and draft, outlet gas tempering sprays, and similar items. A typical installation incorporating an inclined drying stoker and a horizontal burning stoker is shown in Fig. 31–8.

Refuse Handling

Refuse from both industrial and municipal sources is very bulky, 12 to 13 lb per

---

[4] See Chapter 29 for more detailed information on high temperature water boilers.
[5] See Chapter 30, Flash Drying Systems, for more detailed information.

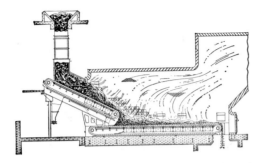

Fig. 31—8. Combination of an inclined drying stoker and a horizontal burning stoker

cu ft compared with 40 to 60 lb per cu ft for coal or similar solid fuels. This requires special handling and storage facilities, both for collections and plant site. For the smaller installations, the trucks frequently dump directly on the charging floor, from where the refuse is pushed into the furnaces either manually or by small bulldozers. This system limits the incinerator operation to the time when refuse is collected, since it must be burned as re-ceived because of the lack of storage space on the charging floor. The furnaces must therefore be sized to burn all the daily delivery in an eight to ten hour period.

The larger and more modern plants are installing cranes and storage bins large enough to handle accumulation of refuse for one or two days. Trucks dump directly into one side of the bin, and the crane with clamshell or grapple bucket conveys the refuse from bin to charging hopper as needed. One arrangement for refuse handling with use of a traveling crane is shown in Fig. 31–9.

Incinerator Combustion Control

As pointed out earlier, municipal refuse is essentially a cellulose fuel and has the typical surface burning characteristics of such fuels. In other words, refuse burns from the top down, whereas in many circumstances coal burns from the bottom up.

Air distribution in the furnace should

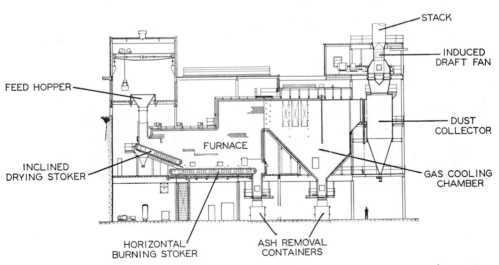

Fig. 31—9. Refuse incinerator installation, mechanical handling equipment shown in upper left and gas cooling chamber located just to right of center

be approximately in proportion to the ratio of volatile and fixed carbon in the refuse. Experience has shown that about one third of the air should be introduced through the grates for the purpose of cooling. Of the remainder, one third should be blown in jets through the side walls on to the surface of the fuel bed, thereby directing oxygen to that area where it can be of the greatest aid to combustion. The final third of the air should be introduced in jets through the roof in order to create turbulence, hasten the burning of volatile matter and add sufficient excess air to reduce furnace outlet temperatures to acceptable levels.

This relatively large percentage of overfire air should be introduced at sufficient velocity to create the necessary turbulence without stirring up the fuel bed and thereby creating fly ash carryover. It is also desirable that all combustion be completed in the furnace where the overfire air is introduced.

Combustion control equipment, including draft gages and temperature recorders, should be provided to regulate the total air flow and measure gas temperatures, which are major factors in reducing unburned carbon in the residue and fly ash emission. A typical arrangement of equipment, showing application of overfire air, is illustrated in Fig. 31–10.

Air pollution control must be provided, either with baffled dry or wet bottom settling chambers or by use of mechanical dust collectors or scrubbers. For the mech-

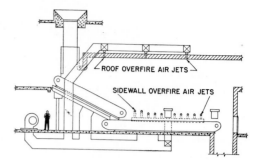

Fig. 31–10. Application of overfire air jets to an incinerator stoker

anical collectors, the gas must be cooled to 800 F or less by tempering the air or water sprays to permit use of carbon steel elements. Such an installation is shown in Fig. 31–9, where both air and water are provided under automatic control.

When a boiler section is included, the gas is cooled in generating the steam or hot water, and a dust collector may be used. The draft loss through such equipment must be included in the induced-draft fan requirements.

Similarity of Incinerator and Boiler Design

The close similarity between incinerator and boiler furnace design, which has been stressed throughout this chapter should be kept constantly in mind. The mechanical engineer should use his knowledge of instrumentation and materials handling to further the automatic operation of incinerators, especially when the heat output is to be put to practical use.

Appendix A

Combustion Calculation Charts

THIS APPENDIX supplements information on graphical combustion methods appearing in Chapter 21, Combustion and Boiler Calculations. More detailed information can be found in the First Edition of *Combustion Engineering*, Otto de Lorenzi, editor, Chapter 25, Performance Calculations, Section on Heat Balance, pp. 25–18 through 25–39.

These and related charts originally appeared in a series of articles by W. S. Patterson and A. L. Nicolai published in *Combustion* in 1941, 1942 and 1944. They are available in slightly revised form from the General Offices of Combustion Engineering, Inc. Windsor, Conn., under the title "Combustion Calculations by Graphical Methods."

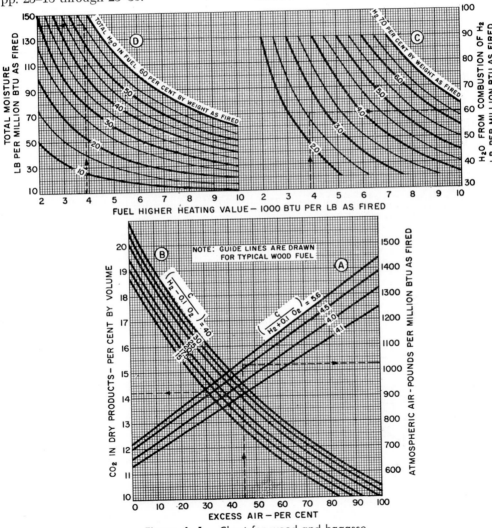

Figure A–1. Chart for wood and bagasse.

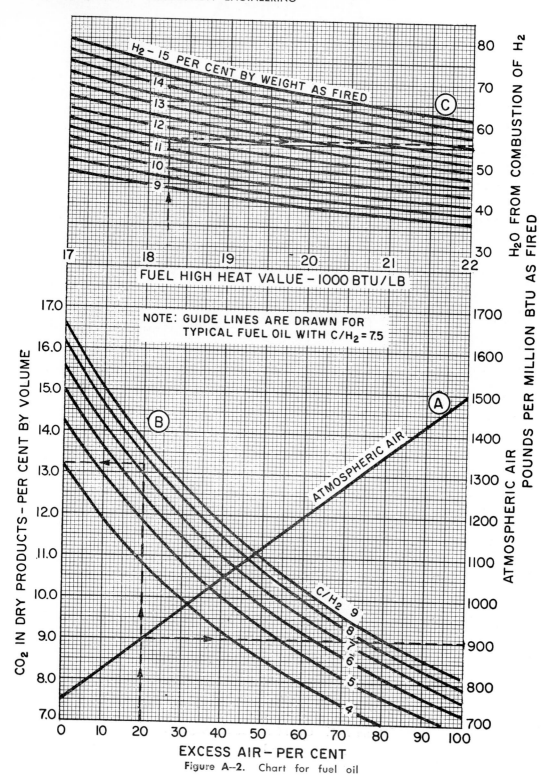

Figure A–2. Chart for fuel oil

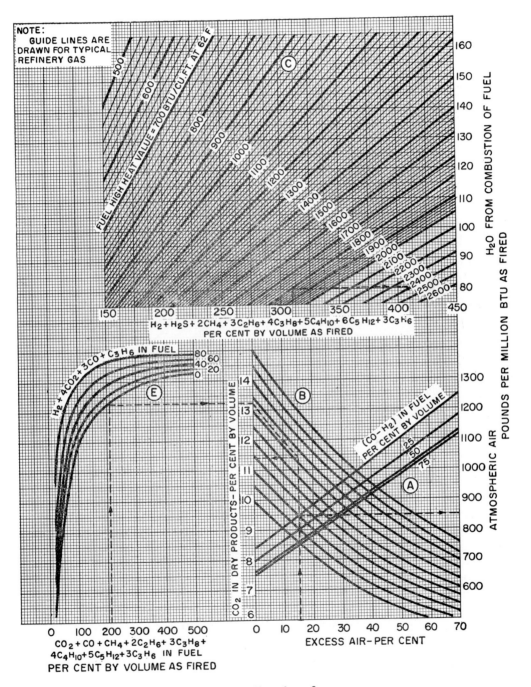

Figure A–3.   Chart for refinery gas

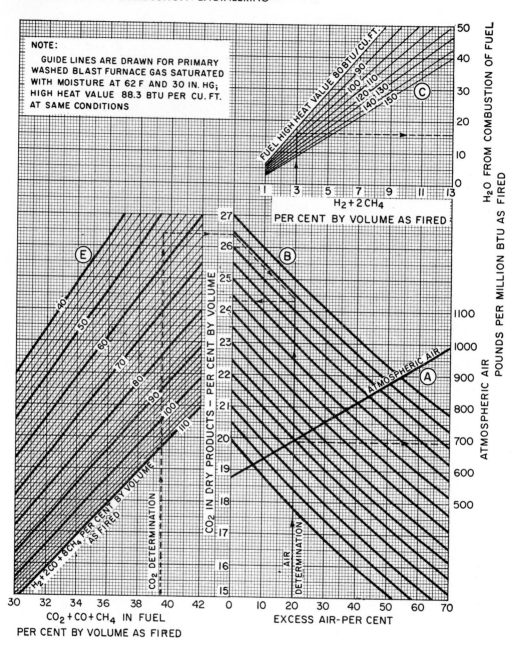

Figure A–4.   Chart for blast furnace gas

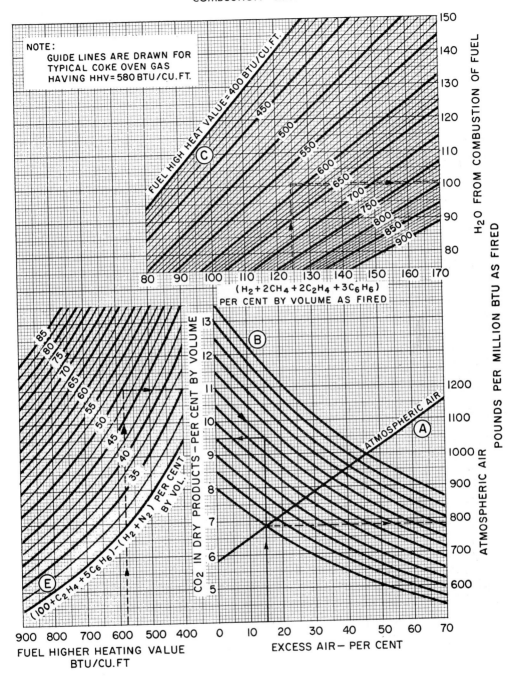

Figure A-5. Chart for coke oven gas

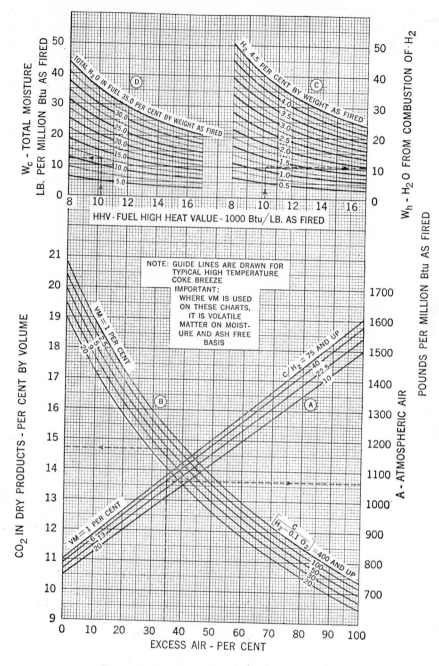

Figure A–6. Chart for coke and coke breeze

Appendix B

Absolute Humidity — The weight of water vapor in a gas water-vapor mixture per unit volume of space occupied, as, for example, grains or pounds per cubic foot.

Accumulator — A pressure vessel containing water and steam, which is used to store the heat of steam for use at a later period and at some lower pressure.

Acid Cleaning — The process of cleaning the interior surfaces of steam generating units by filling the unit with a dilute acid accompanied by an inhibitor to prevent corrosion, and subsequently draining, washing and neutralizing the acid by a further wash of alkaline water.

Acid Sludge — Oil refinery waste fuel from acid treatment of unrefined petroleum.

Acidity — Represents the amount of free carbon dioxide, mineral acids and salts (especially sulfates of iron and aluminum) which hydrolize to give hydrogen ions in water and is reported as milliequivalents per liter of acid, or ppm acidity as calcium carbonate, or pH, the measure of hydrogen ion concentration.

Adiabatic Temperature — The theoretical temperature that would be attained by the products of combustion provided the entire chemical energy of the fuel, the sensible heat content of the fuel, and combustion air above the datum temperature were transferred to the products of combustion. This assumes:

   a) combustion is complete,

   b) there is no heat loss,

   c) there is no dissociation of the gaseous compounds formed, and

   d) inert gases play no part in the reaction.

Aeration — The process of mixing air with pulverized fuel in a transport pipe or storage bin.

Agglomerating — A caking characteristic of a coal that, in the volatile matter determination, causes it to give a coke residue in the form of an agglomerate button.

Agglomeration — Groups of fine dust particles clinging together to form a larger particle.

Agglutinating — A characteristic of coal that causes it to form a button having measurable bonded strength when mixed with certain amounts of inert material and heated in the absence or near absence of air.

Air Atomizing Oil Burner — A burner for firing oil in which the oil is atomized by compressed air which is forced into and through one or more streams of oil breaking the oil into a fine spray.

Air-Cooled Wall — A refractory wall of hollow construction through which air passes.

Air Deficiency — Insufficient air, in an air-fuel mixture, to supply the oxygen theoretically required for complete oxidation of the fuel.

Air Dried — Condition of coal after sample has been exposed to 85 F to 95 F air until weight is constant.

Air-Fuel Ratio — The ratio of the weight, or volume, of air to fuel.

Air Heater or Air Preheater — Heat transfer apparatus through which air is passed and heated by a medium of higher temperature, such as the products of combustion or steam.

(a) *Regenerative Air Preheater* — An air heater in which heat is first stored up in the structure itself by the passage of the products of combustion, and which then gives up the heat so stored to the subsequent passage of air.

(b) *Recuperative Air Heater* — An air heater in which the heat from products of combustion passes through a partition which separates the products from the air.

(1) *Tubular Air Heater* — An air heater containing a group of tubular elements through the walls of which heat is transferred from a flowing heating medium to an air stream.

(2) *Plate Air Heater* — An air heater containing passages formed by spaced plates through which heat is transferred from a flowing heating medium to an air stream.

Air Infiltration — The leakage of air into a setting or duct.

Air Puff Blower — A soot blower automatically controlled to deliver intermittently jets or puffs of compressed air for removing ash, refuse or soot from heat absorbing surfaces.

Air Resistance — The opposition offered to the passage of air through any flow path.

Air Seal — A closure obtained by using air as the securing medium, as air under pressure to prevent the entrance of pulverized material between the shaft and yoke of ball pulverizers.

Air Swept Pulverizer — A pulverizer through which air flows and from which pulverized fuel is removed by the stream of air.

Air Transport System — A fuel transport system utilizing air as the conveying medium.

Air Vent — A valved opening in the top of the highest drum of a boiler or pressure vessel for venting air.

Alkalinity — Represents the amount of carbonates, bicarbonates, hydroxides and silicates or phosphates in the water and is reported as grains per gallon, or ppm as calcium carbonate.

Allowable Working Pressure — The maximum pressure for which the boiler was designed and constructed.

Ambient Air — The air that surrounds the equipment. The standard ambient air for performance calculations is air at 80 F, 60 per cent relative humidity, and a barometric pressure of 29.921 in. Hg, giving a specific humidity of 0.013 lb of water vapor per lb of air.

Ambient Temperature — The temperature of the air surrounding the equipment.

Analysis, Proximate — Analysis of a solid fuel determining moisture, volatile matter, fixed carbon and ash expressed as percentages of the total weight of sample.

Analysis, Ultimate — Chemical analysis of solid, liquid or gaseous fuels. In the case of coal or coke, determination of carbon, hydrogen, sulfur, nitrogen, oxygen and ash.

Angle of Repose — The maximum angle which the inclined surface of a pile of loosely divided material can make with the horizontal.

Anthracite — ASTM coal classification by rank: Dry fixed carbon 92 per cent or more and less than 98 per cent; and dry volatile matter 8 per cent or less and more than 2 per cent on a mineral matter free basis. Known as "hard coal".

Arch Bar — A cast iron or steel bar for supporting brickwork.

Armored Wall — A wall of a furnace consisting of spaced tubes which are covered on the furnace side with abutting metallic blocks.

As-Fired Fuel — Fuel in the condition as fed to the fuel burning equipment.

Ash — The incombustible solid matter in fuel.

Ash-Free Basis — The method of reporting fuel analysis whereby ash is deducted and other constituents are recalculated to total 100 per cent.

Ash Pit — A pit or hopper located below a furnace where refuse is accumulated and from which it is removed at intervals.

Ash Sluice — A trench or channel used for transporting refuse from ash pits to a disposal point by means of water.

Aspect Ratio — A ratio used in calculating resistance to flow in a rectangular elbow; the ratio of width to depth.

Aspirating Burner — A burner in which the fuel in a gaseous or finely divided form is burned in suspension, the air for combustion being supplied by bringing into contact with the fuel, air drawn through one or more openings by the lower static pressure created by the velocity of the fuel stream.

Aspirator — A device which utilizes the energy in a jet of fluid to create suction.

As-Received Fuel — Fuel in the condition as received at the plant.

Atomizer — A device by means of which a liquid is reduced to a very fine spray.

Attrition — The reduction in size of dust particles caused by abrasion.

Automatic Lighter — A means for starting ignition of fuel without manual intervention. Usually applied to liquid, gaseous or pulverized fuel.

Auxiliary Air — Additional air, either hot or cold, which may be introduced into the exhauster inlet or burner lines to increase the primary air at the burners.

Available Draft — The draft which may be utilized to cause the flow of air for combustion or the flow of products of combustion.

Availability Factor — The fraction of the time during which the unit is in operable condition.

Axial Fan — Consists of a propeller or disc type of wheel within a cylinder discharging the air parallel to the axis of the wheel.

B

Backing Ring — A ring of steel or other material placed behind the welding groove when joining tubes or pipes by welding, to confine the weld metal.

Baffle — A plate or wall for deflecting gases or liquids.

Baffle-Type Collector — A device in gas paths utilizing baffles so arranged as to deflect dust particles out of the gas stream.

Bag Filter — A device containing one or more cloth bags for recovering particles from the dust laden gas or air which is blown through it.

Bag-Type Collector — A filter wherein the cloth filtering medium is made in the form of cylindrical bags.

Bagasse — Sugar cane from which the juice has been essentially extracted.

Balanced Draft — The maintenance of a fixed value of draft in a furnace at all combustion rates by control of incoming air and outgoing products of combustion.

Banking — Burning solid fuels on a grate at rates sufficient to maintain ignition only.

Bare Tube Superheater — A superheater in which all of the heating surface consists of the external surface of the tubes.

Bare Tube Wall — A furnace wall having bare tubes.

Base Load — Base load is the term applied to that portion of a station or boiler load that is practically constant for long periods.

Beaded Tube End — The rounded exposed end of a rolled tube when the tube metal is formed over against the sheet in which the tube is rolled.

Bellows Seal — A seal in the shape of a bellows used to prevent air or gas leakage.

Bin System — A system in which fuel is pulverized, stored in bins, and subsequently withdrawn through feeders to the burners in amounts sufficient to satisfy load demands.

Bird Nesting — Accumulations of porous masses of loosely adhering refuse and slag particles in the first tube bank in a water tube boiler.

Bituminous Coal — ASTM Coal classification by rank on a mineral matter free basis and with bed moisture only:

Low Volatile: Dry fixed carbon 78 per cent or more and less than 86 per cent; and dry volatile matter 22 per cent or less and more than 14 per cent.

Medium Volatile: Dry fixed carbon 69 per cent or more and less than 78 per cent; and dry volatile matter 31 per cent or less and more than 22 per cent.

High Volatile (A): Dry fixed carbon less than 69 per cent; and dry volatile matter more than 31 per cent— Moist Btu 14,000 or more.

High Volatile (B): Moist Btu 13,000 or more and less than 14,000.

High Volatile (C): Moist Btu 11,000 or more and less than 13,000.

    (either agglomerating or non-weathering)

Black Liquor — Liquid byproduct fuel extracted from resinous woods in a wood pulp manufacturing process and containing the chemicals used to accomplish the extraction.

Blast Furnace Gas — Lean combustible byproduct gas resulting from burning coke with a deficiency of air in a blast furnace.

Blister — A raised area on the surface of solid metal produced by pressure thereon while the metal is hot and plastic due to overheating.

Block — Usually a rectangular-shaped casting of metal or of high heat-conducting material made to fit closely on or cast to furnace wall tubes, providing a substantially smooth surface on the furnace side. Also a refractory shape used as a furnace lining and cooled by air.

Blowback — The difference between the pressure at which a safety valve opens and at which it closes, usually about three per cent of the pressure at which valve opens.

Blowdown — Removal of a portion of boiler water for the purpose of reducing concentration, or to discharge sludge.

Blower — A fan used to force air under pressure.

Blowhole — A local area in a burning fuel bed through which a disproportionately large quantity of air passes.

Boiler — A closed pressure vessel in which a liquid, usually water, is vaporized by the application of heat.

Water Tube — A boiler in which the tubes contain water and steam, the heat being applied to the outside surface. Also, see *Steam Generating Unit.*

Bent Tube — A water tube boiler consisting of two or more drums connected by tubes, practically all of which are bent near the ends to permit attachment to the drum shell on radial lines.

Horizontal — A water tube boiler in which the main bank of tubes are straight and on a slope of 5 to 15 deg from the horizontal position.

Sectional Header — A horizontal boiler of the longitudinal or cross-drum type, with the tube bank comprised of multiple parallel sections, each section made up of a front and rear header connected by one or more vertical rows of generating tubes and with the sections or groups of sections having a common steam drum.

Box Header — A horizontal boiler of the longitudinal or cross drum type consisting of a front and a rear inclined rectangular header connected by tubes.

Cross Drum — A sectional header or box header boiler in which the axis of the horizontal drum is at right angles to the center lines of the tubes in the main bank.

Longitudinal Drum — A sectional header or box header boiler in which the axis of the horizontal drum or drums is parallel to the tubes in a vertical plane.

Low Head — A bent tube boiler having three drums with relatively short tubes in the rear bank.

Fire Tube — A boiler with straight tubes, which are surrounded by water and steam and through which the products of combustion pass.

Horizontal Return Tubular — A fire-tube boiler consisting of a cylindrical shell, with tubes inside the shell attached to both end closures. The products of combustion pass under the bottom half of the shell and return through the tubes.

Locomotive — A horizontal fire-tube boiler with an internal furnace, the rear of which is a tube sheet directly attached to a shell containing tubes through which the products of combustion leave the furnace.

Vertical — A fire-tube boiler consisting of a cylindrical shell, with tubes connected between the top head and the tube sheet which forms the top of the internal furnace. The products of combustion pass from the furnace directly through the vertical tubes.

Scotch — In stationary service, a fire tube boiler consisting of a cylindrical shell, with one or more cylindrical internal furnaces in the lower portion and a bank of tubes attached to both end closures. The fuel is burned in the furnace, the products of combustion leaving the rear to return through the tubes to an uptake at the front head — known as dry-back type.

In marine service, this boiler has an internal combustion chamber of water-leg construction covering the rear end of the furnace and tubes, in which the products of combustion turn and enter the tubes — known as wet-back type.

Boiler Convection Bank — A group of two or more rows of tubes forming part of a water tube boiler circulatory system and to which heat is transmitted mainly by convection from the products of combustion.

Boiler Horsepower — The evaporation of 34½ lb of water per hour from a temperature of 212 F into dry saturated steam at the same temperature. Equivalent to 33,472 Btu per hour.

Boiler Slag Screen — A screen formed by one or more rows of widely spaced tubes constituting part of, or positioned in front of, a water tube boiler convection bank, and functioning to lower the temperature of the products of combustion and to serve as an ash cooling zone.

Boiler Water — A term construed to mean a representative sample of the circulating boiler water, after the generated steam has been separated and before the incoming feed water or added chemical becomes mixed with it so that its composition is affected.

Boiling — The conversion of a liquid into vapor with the formation of bubbles.

Boiling Out — The boiling of a highly alkaline water in boiler pressure parts for the removal of oils, greases, etc.

Bond — A retaining or holding high-temperature cement for making a joint between brick or adjacent courses of brick.

Breeching — A duct for the transport of the products of combustion between parts of a steam generating unit or to the stack.

Bridgewall — A wall in a furnace over which the products of combustion pass.

Bridging — The accumulation of refuse and slag partially or completely blocking spaces or apertures between heat absorbing tubes.

British Thermal Unit — The mean British thermal unit is 1/180 of the heat required to raise the temperature of one lb of water from 32 F to 212 F at a constant atmospheric pressure. It is about equal to the quantity of heat required to raise one lb of water 1 deg F. A Btu is essentially 252 calories.

Brown Coal — Lignitic coal lowest in classification according to rank. Moist (bed moisture only) Btu less than 8300, unconsolidated in structure.

Bubble — A small volume of steam inclosed within a surface film of water from which it was generated.

Buckstay — A structural member placed against a furnace or boiler wall to restrain the motion of the wall.

Buckstay Spacer — A spacer for separating a pair of channels which are used as a buckstay.

Bulge — A local distortion or swelling outward caused by internal pressure on a tube wall or boiler shell caused by overheating. Also applied to similar distortion of a cylindrical furnace due to external pressure when overheated provided the distortion is of a degree that can be driven back.

Bunker C Oil — Residual fuel oil of high viscosity commonly used in marine and stationary power plants. (No. 6 fuel oil)

Burner — A device for the introduction of fuel and air into a furnace at the desired velocities, turbulence and concentration to establish and maintain proper ignition and combustion of the fuel.

Burner Windbox — A plenum chamber around a burner in which an air pressure is maintained to insure proper distribution and discharge of secondary air.

Bypass Temperature Control — Control of vapor or air temperature by diverting part or all of the heating medium from passing over the heat absorbing surfaces, usually by means of a bypass damper.

Byproduct Coke — Coke manufactured with attendant recovery of byproducts in ovens that are heated externally.

C

Caking — Property of certain coals to become plastic when heated and form large masses of coke.

Calorie — The mean calorie is 1/100 of the heat required to raise the temperature of one gram of water from 0 C to 100 C at a constant atmospheric pressure. It is about equal to the quantity of heat required to raise one gram of water one deg C. Another definition is: A calorie is 3600/860 joules, a joule being the amount of heat produced by a watt in one second.

Calorific Value — The number of heat units liberated per unit of quantity of a fuel burned in a calorimeter under prescribed conditions.

Calorimeter — Apparatus for determining the calorific value of a fuel.

Capacity Factor — The ratio of the average load carried to the maximum design capacity.

Carbon — The principal combustible constituent of all fossil fuels.

Carbonization — The process of converting coal to carbon by removing other ingredients.

Carbon Loss — The loss representing the unliberated thermal energy occasioned by failure to oxidize some of the carbon in the fuel.

Carryover — The chemical solids and liquid entrained with the steam from a boiler.

Casing — A covering of sheets of metal or other material such as fire-resistant composition board used to enclose all or a portion of a steam generating unit.

Caustic Embrittlement — See embrittlement cracking.

Central Station — A power plant or steam heating plant generating power or steam for sale.

Centrifugal Fan — Consists of a fan rotor or wheel within a scroll type of housing discharging the air at right angle to the axis of the wheel.

Chain Grate Stoker — A stoker which has a moving endless chain as a grate surface, onto which coal is fed directly from a hopper.

Checker Work — An arrangement of alternately spaced brick in a furnace with openings through which air or gas flows.

Chemical Feed Pipe — A pipe inside a boiler drum through which chemicals for treating the boiler water are introduced.

Cinder — A particle of gas borne partially burned fuel larger than 100 microns in diameter.

Cinder Catcher — Apparatus for separating and collecting cinders from the products of combustion.

Cinder Return — Apparatus for the return of collected cinders to the furnace, either directly or with the fuel.

Cinder Trap — A dust collector having staggered elements in the gas passage which concentrates larger dust particles. A portion of the gas passes through the elements with the concentrated dust into a settling chamber, where change in direction and velocity drops out most of the coarser particles.

Circular Burner — A liquid, gaseous or pulverized fuel burner having a circular opening through the furnace wall.

Circulation — The movement of water and steam within a steam generating unit.

Circulation Ratio — The ratio of the water entering a circuit to the steam generated within that circuit in a unit of time.

Circulator — A pipe or tube to pass steam or water between upper boiler drums usually located where the heat absorption is low. Also used to apply to tubes connecting headers of horizontal water tube boilers with drums.

Classifier — That part of a pulverizer system which rejects coarse particles from the air stream conveying pulverized fuel.

Cleanout Door — A door placed so that accumulated refuse may be removed from a boiler setting.

Clinker — A hard compact congealed mass of fused furnace refuse, usually slag.

Clinker Chill — Any water cooled wall surface, the major portion of which is in contact with the edges of the fuel bed.

Closed Fireroom System — A forced draft system in which combustion air is supplied by elevating the air pressure in the fireroom.

Coal — Solid hydrocarbon fuel formed by ancient decomposition of woody substance under conditions of heat and pressure.

Coal Burner — A burner for use with pulverized coal.

Coal Gas — Gas formed by the destructive distillation of coal.

Coal Tar — Black viscous liquid, one of the byproducts formed by distillation of coal.

Coke — Fuel consisting largely of the fixed carbon and ash in coal obtained by the destructive distillation of bituminous coal.

Coke Breeze — Fine coke screenings usually passing a ½ in. or ¾ in. screen opening.

Coke Oven Gas — Gas produced by destructive distillation of bituminous coal in closed chambers. Heating value, 500–550 Btu per cu ft.

Coking — The conversion by heating in the absence or near absence of air, of a carbonaceous fuel, particularly certain bituminous coals, to a coherent, firm, cellular carbon product known as coke.

Collection Efficiency — The ratio of the weight of dust collected to the total weight of dust entering the collector.

Collector — A device used for removing gas borne solids from flue gas.

Colloid — A finely divided organic substance which tends to inhibit the formation of dense scale and results in the deposition of sludge, or causes it to remain in suspension, so that it may be blown from the boiler.

Colloidal Fuel — Mixture of fuel oil and powdered solid fuel.

Combustible — The heat producing constitutents of a fuel.

Combustible in Refuse — Combustible matter in the solid refuse resulting from the incomplete combustion of fuel. It may occur in the flue dust discharged from the stack or collected in hoppers, as well as in ash-pit refuse.

Combustible Loss — The loss representing the unliberated thermal energy occasioned by failure to oxidize completely some of the combustible matter in the fuel.

Combustion — The rapid chemical combination of oxygen with the combustible elements of a fuel resulting in the production of heat.

Combustion Rate — The quantity of fuel fired per unit of time, as pounds of coal per hour, or cubic feet of gas per minute.

Compartment — One of two or more air chambers under the stoker from which air can be passed in controlled quantities.

Concentration —
  (1) The weight of solids contained in a unit weight of boiler feedwater
  (2) The number of times that the dissolved solids have increased from the original amount in the feedwater to that in the boiler water due to evaporation in generating steam.

Condensate — Condensed water resulting from the removal of latent heat from steam.

Condenser Boiler — A boiler in which steam is generated by the condensation of a vapor.

Continuous Blowdown — The uninterrupted removal of concentrated boiler water from a boiler to control total solids concentration in the remaining water.

Continuous Tube Element — An integral heat absorbing assembly consisting of one tube, or a series of tubes welded together, without the use of intermediate flanges or headers.

Convection — The transmission of heat by the circulation of a liquid or a gas such as air. Convection may be natural or forced.

Corner Firing — A method of firing liquid, gaseous or pulverized fuel in which the burners are located in the corners of the furnace.

Corrosion — The wasting away of metals due to chemical action. In a boiler, usually caused by the presence of oxygen, carbon dioxide or an acid.

Cracked Residue — The fuel residue obtained by cracking crude oils.

Cracking — The thermal decomposition of complex hydrocarbons into simpler compounds or elements.

Cross Tube Burner — A form of burner so arranged with respect to furnace wall tubes that the length of the burner opening is at right angles to the line of the tubes.

Crude Oil — Unrefined petroleum.

Crusher — A machine to reduce lumps of solid fuel to a desired maximum size.

Culm — The fine refuse from anthracite production.

Cyclone — A device which uses centrifugal action for separation of materials of different densities.

D

Damper — A device for introducing a variable resistance for regulating the volumetric flow of gas or air.

  (a) *Butterfly Type* — A single blade damper pivoted about its center.

  (b) *Curtain Type* — A damper, composed of flexible material, moving in a vertical plane as it is rolled.

  (c) *Flap Type* — A damper consisting of one or more blades each pivoted about one edge.

  (d) *Louvre Type* — A damper consisting of several blades each pivoted about its center and linked together for simultaneous operation.

  (e) *Slide Type* — A damper consisting of a single blade which moves substantially normal to the flow.

Damper Loss — The reduction in the static pressure of a gas flowing across a damper.

Deaeration — Removal of air and gases from boiler feed water prior to its introduction to a boiler.

Deflector — A device for changing direction of a stream of air or of a mixture of pulverized fuel and air.

Degasification — Removal of gases from samples of steam taken for purity tests. Removal of carbon dioxide from water as in the ion exchange method of softening.

Delayed Combustion — A continuation of combustion beyond the furnace. (See also secondary combustion).

Design Load — The load for which a steam generating unit is designed, usually considered the maximum load to be carried.

Design Pressure — The maximum allowable working pressure permitted under the rules of the ASME Boiler Code.

Design Steam Temperature — The temperature of steam for which a superheater is designed.

Deslag — To remove slag which has adhered to heat absorbing surfaces.

Desuperheater — Apparatus for reducing and controlling the temperature of a superheated vapor.

  (a) *Shell and Tube Type* — A desuperheater consisting of a pressure vessel containing tubular elements through the walls of which heat is transferred.

(b) *Spray Type* — A superheater in which a lower temperature fluid is injected at relatively high velocity in an atomized state into the superheated vapor to reduce its temperature by direct contact with the atomized fluid.

(c) *Submerged Type* — A desuperheater consisting of tubular elements located in the boiler circulation below the water line.

Dew Point — The temperature at which condensation starts.

Diffuser — As applied to oil or gas burners, a metal plate with openings so placed as to protect the fuel spray from high velocity air while admitting sufficient air to promote the ignition and combustion of fuel. Sometimes termed impeller.

Direct-Fired Boiler — Commonly used to denote a boiler and furnace fired by pulverized coal directly from the pulverizing mills.

Direct-Fired System — A system in which fuel is pulverized in proportion to the load demand and conveyed directly from the pulverizers to the burners.

Discharge Tube — A tube through which steam and water are discharged into a drum. Also a riser or releaser.

Disengaging Surface — The surface of the boiler water from which steam is released.

Dissolved Gases — Gases which are in solution in water.

Dissolved Solids — Those solids in water which are in solution.

Distillate Fuels — Liquid fuels distilled usually from crude petroleum, except residuals such as No. 5 and No. 6 fuel oil.

Distillation Zone — The region, in a solid fuel bed, in which volatile constituents of the fuel are vaporized.

Distilled Water — Water produced by vaporization and condensation with a resulting higher purity.

Divided Furnace — An arrangement in which the furnace is divided into two or more parts.

Division Wall — The wall, or walls, in a furnace to provide two or more parts.

Downcomer — A tube in a boiler of water wall system through which fluid flows downward.

Draft — The difference between atmospheric pressure and some lower pressure existing in the furnace or gas passages of a steam generating unit.

Draft Differential — The difference in static pressure between two points in a system.

Draft Gage — A device for measuring draft, usually in inches water gage.

Draft Loss — The difference in the static pressure of a gas between two points in a system, both of which are below atmospheric pressure, and caused by resistances to flow. Usually measured in inches water gage.

Drain — A valved connection at the lowest point for the removal of all water from the pressure parts.

Drum — A cylindrical shell closed at both ends designed to withstand internal pressure.

Drum Baffle — A plate or series of plates or screens placed within a drum to divert or change the direction of the flow of water or water and steam.

Drum Internals — All apparatus within a drum.

Drum Operating Pressure — The pressure of the steam maintained in the steam drum or steam-and-water drum of a boiler in operation.

Dry Ash — Refuse in the solid state, usually in granular or dust form.

Dry Ash-Free Basis — The method of reporting fuel analysis with ash and moisture eliminated and remaining constituents recalculated to total 100 per cent.

Dry-Bottom Furnace — A pulverized-fuel-fired furnace in which the ash particles are deposited on the furnace bottom in a dry nonadherent condition.

Dry Bulb Temperature — The temperature of the air indicated by thermometer not affected by the water vapor content of the air.

Dry Fuel Basis — The method of reporting fuel analysis with moisture eliminated and other constituents recalculated to total 100 per cent.

Dry Gas — Gas containing no water vapor.

Dry Gas Loss — The loss representing the difference between the heat content of the dry exhaust gases and their heat content at the temperature of ambient air.

Dry Mineral-Matter-Free Basis — The method of reporting fuel analysis with moisture and ash, plus other mineral matter eliminated and remaining constituents recalculated to total 100 per cent.

Dry Pipe — A perforated or slotted pipe or box inside the drum and connected to the steam outlet.

Dry Steam — Steam containing no moisture. Commercially dry steam containing not more than one half of one per cent moisture.

Dual Flow Oil Burner — A burner having an atomizer, usually mechanical, having two sets of tangential slots, one set being used for low capacities and the other set for high capacities.

Dulong's Formula — A formula for calculating the approximate heating value of solid fuels from the ultimate analysis.

Dump Grate Stoker — One equipped with movable ash trays, or grates, by means of which the ash can be discharged at any desirable interval.

Dust — Particles of gas borne solid matter larger than one micron in diameter.

Dust Collecting Fan — A centrifugal fan which concentrates dust and skims the dust into a cyclone or hopper.

Dustless Unloader — A device for wetting dust so the particles are adherent to each other, to prevent dissipation by atmospheric current while conveying.

Dust Loading — The amount of dust in a gas, usually expressed in grains per cu ft or lb per thousand lb of gas.

Dutch Oven — A furnace that extends forward of the wall of a boiler setting. It usually is of all-refractory construction with a low roof, although in some cases the roof and side walls are water cooled.

E

Earthquake Bracing — Diagonal bracing between columns designed to withstand violent lateral motion of the structure.

Ebullition — The act of boiling or bubbling.

Economizer — A heat recovery device designed to transfer heat from the products of combustion to a fluid, usually feedwater.

Efficiency — The ratio of output to the input. The efficiency of a steam generating unit is the ratio of the heat absorbed by water and steam to the heat in the fuel fired.

Electrostatic Precipitator — A device for collecting dust, mist or fume from a gas stream, by placing an electrical charge on the particle and removing that particle onto a collecting electrode.

Element — An integral heat absorbing assembly which with other similar or identical units can be assembled into a heat recovery device such as a boiler, superheater, economizer or air heater.

Elutriator — A device used to determine particle size based on the principle that a definite size range of particles will be borne by definite fluid velocities.

Embrittlement Cracking — A form of metal failure that occurs in steam boilers at riveted joints and at tube ends, the cracking being predominantly intercrystalline.

Endothermic Reaction — A reaction which occurs with the absorption of heat.

Entrainment — The conveying of particles of water or solids from the boiler water by the steam.

Equalizer — Connection between parts of a boiler to equalize pressures.

Erosion — The wearing away of refractory or of metal parts by the action of slag or fly ash.

Evaporated Makeup — Distilled water used to supplement returned condensate for boiler feedwater.

Evaporation Rate — The number of pounds of water evaporated in a unit of time.

Evasé Stack — An expanding connection on the outlet of a fan or in an air flow passage for the purpose of converting kinetic energy to potential energy, i.e., velocity pressure into static pressure.

Excess Air — Air supplied for combustion in excess of that theoretically required for complete oxidation.

Exhauster — A fan connected to the outlet of a pulverizer and used to draw pulverizer air through a pulverizer and in some cases to augment the pulverizer air by the addition of primary air.

Exothermic Reaction — A reaction which occurs with the evolution of heat.

Expansion Joint — The joint to permit movement due to expansion without undue stress.

Explosion Door — A door in a furnace or boiler setting designed to be opened by a predetermined gas pressure.

Extended Surface — Heating surface in the form of fins, rings, or studs added to heat absorbing elements.

External-Mix Oil Burner — A burner having an atomizer in which the liquid fuel is struck, after it has left an orifice, by a jet of high velocity steam or air.

External Treatment — Treatment of boiler feed water prior to its introduction into the boiler.

Externally Fired Boiler — A boiler in which the furnace is essentially surrounded by refractory or water-cooled tubes.

F

Fan Performance — A measure of fan operation in terms of volume, total pressures, static pressures, speed, power input, mechanical and static efficiency, at a stated air density.

Feed Pipe — A pipe through which water is conducted into a boiler.

Feedwater — Water introduced into a boiler during operation. It includes makeup and return condensate.

Feedwater Treatment — The treatment of boiler feedwater by the addition of chemicals to prevent the formation of scale or eliminate other objectionable characteristics.

Filter — Porous material through which fluids or fluid-and-solid mixtures are passed to separate matter held in suspension.

Filter (Cloth) — A porous fabric which separates dust from a gas stream allowing the gas to pass through.

Fin — A strip of steel welded longitudinally to a tube.

Fineness — The percentage by weight of a standard sample of a pulverized material which passes through a standard screen of specified mesh when subjected to a prescribed sampling and screening procedure.

Fines — Sizes below a specified range.

Fin Superheater — A superheater made up of elements with extended surface of fin form.

Fin Tube — A tube with one or more fins.

Fin Tube Wall — Spaced waterwall tubes on which flat metal extensions are welded in a plane parallel to the wall.

Fire Box — The equivalent of a furnace. A term usually used for the furnaces of locomotive and similar types of boilers.

Fire Point — The lowest temperature at which, under specified conditions, fuel oil gives off enough vapor to burn continuously when ignited.

Fire Tube — A tube in a boiler having water on the outside and carrying the products of combustion on the inside.

Firing Door — A door in a furnace through which coal or other solid fuel is introduced into the furnace.

Fishtail Burner — A burner consisting of a diverging chamber having a rectangular outlet which is materially longer than wide.

Fixed Ash — That portion of the ash derived from the original vegetation including all intimately contained minerals.

Fixed Carbon — The carbonaceous residue less the ash remaining in the test container after the volatile matter has been driven off in making the proximate analysis of a solid fuel.

Flame Detector — A device which indicates if fuel, such as liquid, gaseous, or pulverized, is burning, or if ignition has been lost. The indication may be transmitted to a signal or to a control system.

Flame-Propagation Rate — Speed of travel of ignition through a combustible mixture.

Flammability — Susceptibility to combustion.

Flareback — A burst of flame from a furnace in a direction opposed to the normal flow, usually caused by the ignition of an accumulation of combustible gases.

Flare Type Burner — A circular burner from which the fuel and air are discharged in the form of a cone.

Flashing — Steam produced by discharging water at saturation temperature into a region of lower pressure.

Flash Point — The lowest temperature at which, under specified conditions, fuel oil gives off enough vapor to flash into momentary flame when ignited.

Flat Flame Burner — A burner terminating in a substantially rectangular nozzle, from which fuel and air are discharged in a flat stream.

Flue — A passage for products of combustion.

Flue Dust — The particles of gas-borne solid matter carried in the products of combustion.

Flue Gas — The gaseous products of combustion in the flue to the stack.

Fluidizing — Causing a mass of finely divided solid particles to assume some of the properties of a fluid, as by aeration.

Fluid Temperature — The temperature at which a standard ash cone fuses down into a flat layer on the test base, when heated in accordance with a prescribed procedure.

Fluxing — The addition of chemicals to reduce the ash fluid temperature.

Fly Ash — The fine particles of ash which are carried by the products of combustion.

Foaming — The continuous formation of bubbles which have sufficiently high surface tension to remain as bubbles beyond the disengaging surface.

Forced Circulation — The circulation of water in a boiler by mechanical means external to the boiler.

Forced-Draft Fan — A fan supplying air under pressure to the fuel burning equipment.

Fouling — The accumulation of refuse in gas passages or on heat absorbing surfaces which results in undesirable restrictions to the flow of gas or heat.

Fracture — The breaking of dust particles into smaller sizes.

Free Ash — Ash which is not included in the fixed ash.

Free Moisture — Same as surface moisture.

Friability — The tendency of a coal to crumble or break into small pieces.

Front Discharge Stoker — A stoker so arranged that refuse is discharged from the grate surface at the same end as the coal feed.

Fuel — A substance containing combustible used for generating heat.

Fuel-Air Mixture — Mixture of fuel and air.

Fuel-Air Ratio — The ratio of the weight, or volume, of fuel to air.

Fuel Bed — Layer of burning fuel on a furnace grate.

Fuel Bed Resistance — The static pressure differential across a fuel bed.

Fuel Oil — A liquid fuel derived from petroleum or coal.

Fume — Suspended particles in gas, ranging, from 0.1 microns to 1 micron.

Furnace — An enclosed space provided for the combustion of fuel.

Furnace Arch — A substantially horizontal structure extending into the furnace, to serve as a deflector of the gases.

Furnace Cooling Factor — Furnace cooling factor is the heat available per sq ft of heat absorbing surface in the furnace. That surface is the projected area of tubes and extended metallic surfaces on the furnace side including walls, floor, roof, partition walls, and platens and the area of the plane of the furnace exit which is defined as the entrance to the convection tube bank.

Furnace Draft — The draft in a furnace, measured at a point immediately in front of the highest point at which the combustion gases leave the furnace.

Furnace Slag Screen — A screen formed by one or more rows of tubes arranged across a furnace gas outlet, serving to create an ash cooling zone for the particles suspended in the products of combustion leaving the furnace.

Furnace Volume — The cubical contents of the furnace or combustion chamber.

Fused Slag — Slag which has coalesced into homogeneous solid mass by fusing.

Fusibility — Property of slag to fuse and coalesce into a homogeneous mass.

Fusible Plug — A hollowed threaded plug having the hollowed portion filled with a low melting point material, usually located at the lowest permissible water level.

Fusion — The melting of ash.

G

Gage Cock — A valve attached to a water column or drum for checking water level.

Gage Pressure — The pressure above atmospheric pressure.

Gasification — The process of converting solid or liquid fuel into a gaseous fuel such as the gasification of coal.

Generating Tube — A tube in which steam is generated.

Grains Per Cubic Foot — The term for expressing dust loading in weight per unit of gas volume (7000 grains equals one pound).

Granular Ash — Small particles of dry ash.

Grate — The surface on which fuel is supported and burned, and through which air is passed for combustion.

Gravity — Weight index of fuels: liquid petroleum products expressed either as specific, Baumé, or API (American Petroleum Institute) gravity; weight index of gaseous fuels as specific gravity related to air under specified conditions; or weight index of solid fuels as specific gravity related to water under specified conditions.

Grindability — Grindability is the characteristic of coal representing its ease of pulverizing and is one of the factors used in determining the capacity of a pulverizer. The index is relative, the larger values, such as 100, represent coals easy to pulverize like Pocahontas and smaller values such as 40 represent coals difficult to pulverize.

H

Handhole — An opening in a pressure part for access, usually not exceeding 6 in. in longest dimension.

Hand Lance — A manually manipulated length of pipe carrying air, steam, or water for blowing ash and slag accumulations from heat absorbing surfaces.

Hardness — A measure of the amount of calcium and magnesium salts in a boiler water. Usually expressed as grains per gallon or ppm as Calcium Carbonate.

Hard Water — Water which contains calcium or magnesium in an amount which requires an excessive amount of soap to form a lather.

Heat Available — The thermal energy above a fixed datum that is capable of being absorbed for useful work. In boiler practice, the heat available in a furnace is usually taken to be the higher heating value of the fuel corrected by subtracting radiation losses, unburned combustible, latent heat of the water in the fuel or formed by the burning of hydrogen, and adding the sensible heat in the air for combustion, all above ambient temperatures.

Heat Balance — An accounting of the distribution of the heat input and output.

Heating Surface — That surface which is exposed to the heating medium for absorption and transfer of heat to the heated medium.

(a) *Boiler and waterwall heating surface* — This heating surface shall consist of all of the heat-transfer apparatus in contact on one side with the water or wet steam being heated and on the other side with gas or refractory being cooled, in which the fluid being heated forms part of the circulating system; this surface shall be measured on the side receiving heat.

Waterwall heating surface in the furnace, including walls, floor, roof, partition walls, and platens, consisting of bare or covered tubes, shall be measured as the sum of the projected areas of the tubes and the extended metallic surface on the furnace side.

Continuation of furnace tubes beyond the furnace gas outlet shall be included as boiler heating surface and this surface shall be measured on that portion of the circumferential and the extended metallic surface receiving heat.

All other boiler surfaces, including furnace screen tubes, shall be measured on that portion of the circumferential and the extended metallic surface receiving heat. Surface shall not be included in more than one category.

(b) *Superheater and reheater surface —* This heating surface shall consist of all of the heat-transfer apparatus in contact on one side with steam being heated and on the other side with gas or refractory being cooled; this surface shall be measured on the side receiving heat.

Radiant superheating or radiant reheating surface in the furnace, including walls, floor, roof, partition walls, and platens, shall be measured as the sum of the projected areas of the tubes and the extended metallic surfaces on the furnace side.

Continuation of superheater tubes beyond the furnace gas outlet shall be included as convection superheater surface and this surface shall be measured on that portion of the circumferential and the extended metallic surface receiving heat.

All other superheater and reheater surface, including screen tubes, shall be measured on the basis of the circumferential and the extended metallic surface receiving heat.

Heat Release — The total quantity of thermal energy above a fixed datum introduced into a furnace by the fuel, considered to be the product of the hourly fuel rate and its high heat value, expressed in Btu per hour per cubic foot of furnace volume.

High Velocity Thermocouple — A single-shielded furnace gas temperature measuring instrument arranged so that furnace gases are drawn over the junction of the thermocouple at high velocities.

Hogged Fuel — Wood refuse after being chipped or shredded by a machine known as a "hog".

Hopper — A chamber or bin used for holding solid fuel or refuse.

Hopper Bottom Furnace — A furnace bottom with one or more inclined sides forming a hopper for the collection of ash and for the easy removal of same.

Horizontal Firing — A means of firing liquid, gaseous or pulverized fuel, in which the burners are so arranged in relation to furnace as to discharge the fuel and air into the furnace in approximately a horizontal direction.

Hydrostatic Test — A strength and tightness test of a closed pressure vessel by water pressure.

I

Ignition — The initiation of combustion.

Ignition Arch — A refractory arch, or surface, located over a fuel bed to radiate heat and increase the rapidity of ignition.

Ignition Temperature — Lowest temperature of a fuel at which combustion becomes self-sustaining.

Illuminants — Light oil or coal compounds that readily burn with a luminous flame such as ethylene, propylene and benzene.

Impact Plate — A plate against which a stream of coal is impinged for the purpose of pulverization.

Inches Water Gage (in. w.g.) — Usual term for expressing a measurement of relatively low pressures or differentials by means of a U-tube. One inch w.g. equals 5.2 lb per sq ft or 0.036 lb per sq in.

Induced-Draft Fan — A fan exhausting hot gases from the heat absorbing equipment.

Inert Gaseous Constituents — Incombustible gases such as nitrogen which may be present in a fuel.

Inherent Moisture — Sometimes called the bed moisture; is moisture so closely held by the coal substance that it does not produce wetness.

Inhibitor — A substance which selectively retards a chemical action. An example in boiler work is the use of an inhibitor, when using acid to remove scale, to prevent the acid from attacking the boiler metal.

Initial Deformation — The temperature at which a standard ash cone exhibits the first signs of rounding or bending of the apex when heated in accordance with a prescribed procedure.

Injector — A device utilizing a steam jet to entrain and deliver feed water into a boiler.

Inlet Boxes — An integral part of the fan enclosing the fan inlet or inlets to permit attachment of the fan to the duct system.

Insulation — A material of low thermal conductivity used to reduce heat losses.

Integral Economizer — A segregated portion of a water tube boiler in which the feed water is preheated before its admixture with the circulating boiler water.

Interbank Superheater — A superheater located in a space between tube banks of a bent tube boiler.

Interdeck Superheater — A superheater located in a space between tube banks of a straight tube boiler.

Intermittent firing — A method of firing by which fuel and air are introduced into and burned in a furnace for a short period, after which the flow is stopped, this succession occurring in a sequence of frequent cycles.

Internally Fired Boiler — A fire tube boiler having an internal furnace such as a Scotch, locomotive fire-box, vertical tubular, or other type having a water-cooled plate-type furnace.

Internal Furnace — A furnace within a boiler consisting of a straight or corrugated flue, or a fire-box substantially surrounded with water cooled heating surface except the bottom.

Internal-Mix Oil Burner — A burner having a mixing chamber in which high velocity steam or air impinges on jets of incoming liquid fuel which is then discharged in a completely atomized form.

Internal Treatment — The treatment of boiler water by introducing chemicals directly into the boiler.

Intertube Economizer — An economizer, the elements of which are located between tubes of a boiler convection bank.

Intertube Superheater — A superheater, the elements of which are located between tubes of a boiler convection bank.

Inverted Loop Tube — A substantially vertical U-bend element, which is suspended so that the U-bend is at the top.

Ion — A charged atom or radical which may be positive or negative.

Jumper Tube — A short tube connection for bypassing, routing, or directing the flow of liquid as desired.

L

Lagging — A covering, usually of insulating material, on pipe or ducts.

Leakage — The uncontrolled quantity of fluid which enters or leaves through the enclosure of air or gas passages.

Ligament — The minimum cross section of solid metal in a header, shell or tube sheet between two adjacent holes.

Lighting-Off Torch — A torch used for igniting fuel from a burner. The torch may consist of asbestos wrapped around an iron rod and saturated with oil or may be a small oil or gas burner.

Lignite — A consolidated coal of low classification according to rank — moist (bed moisture only) Btu less than 8300.

Lining — The material used on the furnace side of a furnace wall. It is usually of high grade refractory tile or brick or plastic refractory material.

Liquid Ash Removal — The method of intermittently or continuously drawing off ash in a molten condition from the bottom of a furnace.

Liquid Slag — Slag in a fluid state.

Live Steam — Steam which has not performed any of the work for which it was generated.

Live Steam Reheater — A heat exchanger of the shell and tube type for reheating steam between expansion stages of a prime mover or between prime movers at different pressures, using steam at substantially boiler pressure.

Load Factor — The ratio of the average load in a given period to the maximum load carried during that period.

Low-Heat Value — The high heating value minus the latent heat of vaporization of the water formed by burning the hydrogen in the fuel.

M

Makeup — The water added to boiler feed to compensate for that lost through exhaust, blowdown, leakage, etc.

Manifold — A pipe or header for collecting a fluid from, or the distributing of a fluid to, a number of pipes or tubes.

Manufactured Gas — Fuel gas manufactured from coal, oil, etc., as differentiated from natural gas.

Mass Blower — A single or multi-jet soot blower with a large nozzle area for discharging a relatively large volume of the blowing medium in a short time.

Maximum Continuous Load — The maximum load which can be maintained for a specified period.

Mechanical Atomizing Oil Burner — A burner which uses the pressure of the oil for atomization.

Mechanical Draft — The negative pressure created by mechanical means.

Mechanical Efficiency — The ratio of power output to power input.

Mechanical Stoker — A device consisting of a mechanically operated fuel feeding mechanism and a grate, and is used for the purpose of feeding solid fuel into a furnace, distributing it over the grate, admitting air to the fuel for the purpose of combustion, and providing a means for removal or discharge of refuse.

    Overfeed Stoker — A stoker in which fuel is fed onto grates above the point of air admission to the fuel bed. Overfeed stokers are divided into four classes, as follows:

(a) A *front feed inclined grate stoker* is an overfeed stoker in which fuel is fed from the front onto a grate inclined downwards toward the rear of the stoker.

(b) A *double inclined side feed stoker* is an overfeed stoker in which the fuel is fed from both sides onto grates inclined downwards toward the center line of the stoker.

(c) A *chain* or *traveling grate* is an overfeed stoker having a moving endless grate which conveys fuel into and through the furnace where it is burned, after which it discharges the refuse.

(d) A *spreader stoker* is an overfeed stoker that discharges fuel into the furnace from a location above the fuel bed and distributes the fuel onto the grate.

Underfeed Stoker — A stoker in which fuel is introduced through retorts at a level below the location of air admission to the fuel bed. Underfeed stokers are divided into three general classes, as follows:

(a) A *side ash discharge underfeed stoker* is a stoker having one or more retorts which feed and distribute solid fuel onto side tuyeres or a grate through which is admitted air for combustion and over which the ash is discharged at the side parallel to the retorts.

(b) A *rear ash discharge underfeed stoker* is a stoker having a grate composed of transversely spaced underfeed retorts, which feed and distribute solid fuel to intermediate rows of tuyeres through which is admitted air for combustion. The ash is discharged from the stoker across the rear end.

(c) A *continuous ash discharge underfeed stoker* is one in which the refuse is discharged continuously from the normally stationary stoker ash tray to the ash pit, without the use of mechanical means other than the normal action of the coal feeding and agitating mechanism.

Meta-Anthracite — Highest coal classification according to rank. Dry fixed carbon 98 per cent or more and dry volatile matter 2 per cent or less, on a mineral matter free basis.

Micron — One millionth of a meter, or 0.000,039 in. or 1/25,400 in. The diameter of dust particles is often expressed in microns.

Micron Efficiency Curve — A curve showing the actual collection efficiency for each specific micron size.

Mill Drying — The evaporation of moisture from the fuel within the pulverizer.

Mineral-Matter-Free Basis — The method of reporting coal analysis whereby the ash plus other minerals which are in the original coal are eliminated and the other constituents recalculated to total 100 per cent.

Moisture in Steam — Particles of water carried in steam usually expressed as the percentage by weight.

Moisture Loss — The loss representing the difference in the heat content of the moisture in the exit gases and that at the temperature of the ambient air.

Monolithic Baffle — A baffle of poured or rammed refractory material.

Mud or Lower Drum — A pressure chamber of a drum or header type located at the lower extremity of a water tube boiler convection bank which is normally provided with a blowoff valve for periodic blowing off of sediment collecting in the bottom of the drum.

Multifuel Burner — A burner by means of which more than one fuel can be burned, either separately or simultaneously, such as pulverized fuel, oil or gas.

Multipass Arrangement — Heat absorbing surfaces so baffled as to provide two or more passes in series.

Multiple Retort Stoker — An underfeed stoker consisting of two or more retorts, parallel and adjacent to each other, but separated by a line of tuyeres, and arranged so that the refuse is discharged at the ends of the retorts.

Multiple-Shielded High-Velocity Thermocouple — A multiple-shielded furnace gas temperature measuring instrument arranged so that furnace gases are drawn over the junction of the thermocouple at high velocities.

Multiport Burner — A burner having a number of nozzles from which fuel and air are discharged.

N

Natural Circulation — The circulation of water in a boiler caused by differences in density.

Natural Gas — Gaseous fuel occurring in nature.

Net Fan Requirements — The calculated operating conditions for a fan, excluding tolerances.

Neutral Atmosphere — An atmosphere which tends neither to oxidize nor reduce immersed materials.

Nozzle — A short flanged or welded neck connection on a drum or shell for the outlet or inlet of fluids; also a projecting spout through which a fluid flows.

O

Oil Heating and Pumping Set — A group of apparatus consisting of a heater for raising the temperature of the oil to produce the desired viscosity, and a pump for delivering the oil at the desired pressure.

Open Furnace — A furnace, particularly as applied to chain or traveling grate stoker firing, containing essentially no arches.

Orsat — A gas-analysis apparatus in which certain gaseous constituents are measured by absorption in separate chemical solutions.

Overdeck Superheater — A superheater located above the tube bank of a straight tube boiler.

Overfire Air — Air for combustion admitted into the furnace at a point above the fuel bed.

Overfire Air Fan — A fan used to provide air to a combustion chamber above the fuel bed.

Oxidizing Atmosphere — An atmosphere which tends to promote the oxidation of immersed materials.

Oxygen Attack — Corrosion or pitting in a boiler caused by oxygen.

P

Packaged Steam Generator — A boiler equipped and shipped complete with fuel burning equipment, mechanical draft equipment, automatic controls and accessories.

Particle Size — A measure of dust size, expressed in microns or per cent passing through a standard mesh screen.

Pass — A confined passageway, containing heating surface, through which a fluid flows in essentially one direction.

Peak Load — The maximum load carried for a stated short period of time.

Peat — An accumulation of compacted and partially devolatilized vegetable matter with high moisture content, an early stage of coal formation.

Pendant Tube Superheater — An arrangement of heat absorbing elements which are substantially vertical and suspended from above.

Perfect Combustion — The complete oxidation of all the combustible constituents of a fuel, utilizing all the oxygen supplied.

Perforated Plates — Steel plates having holes so distributed as to provide a flow restriction and as a result, improve uniformity of gas velocity distribution when placed across either gas entrance or exit to precipitators or both.

Petrographic Analysis — The determination of the structural, mineralogical and chemical character of slags.

Petroleum — Naturally occurring mineral oil consisting predominately of hydrocarbons.

Petroleum Coke — Solid carbonaceous residue remaining in oil refining stills after distillation process.

pH — The hydrogen ion concentration of a water to denote acidity or alkalinity. A pH of 7 is neutral. A pH above 7 denotes alkalinity while one below 7 denotes acidity. This pH number is the negative exponent of 10 representing hydrogen ion concentration in grams per liter. For instance a pH of 7 represents 10^{-7} grams per liter.

Pitot Tube — An instrument which will register total pressure and static pressure in a gas stream, used to determine its velocity.

Pitting — A concentrated attack by oxygen or other corrosive chemicals in a boiler, producing a localized depression in the metal surface.

Platen — A plane surface receiving heat from both sides and constructed with a width of one tube and a depth of two or more tubes, bare or with extended surfaces.

Plastic Slag — Slag in a viscous state.

Plenum — An enclosure through which gas or air passes at relatively low velocities.

Plugging — An expression used to describe the building up of dust particle formations to the extent that gas passages are sealed.

Pneumatic Conveying — The transportation of fuel through a conduit by air.

Precipitate — To separate materials from a solution by the formation of insoluble matter by chemical reaction.

Precipitation — The removal of solid or liquid particles from a fluid.

Precipitator — An ash separator and collector of the electrostatic type.

Preheated Air — Air at a temperature exceeding that of the ambient air.

Pressure Drop — The difference in pressure between two points in a system, at least one of which is above atmospheric pressure, and caused by resistance to flow.

Pressure-Expanded Joint — A tube joint in a drum, header or tube sheet expanded by a tool which forces the tube wall outward by driving a tapered pin into the center of a sectional die.

Pressure System Pulverizer — A pulverizer located on the discharge side of primary air blower.

Primary Air — Air introduced with the fuel at the burners. In direct-fired systems this may be the same as pulverizer air, although in some cases the pulverizer air is augmented by air bypassed around the pulverizer or bled in at the exhauster suction.

Primary Air Fan — A fan to supply primary air for combustion of fuel.

Priming — The discharge of steam containing excessive quantities of water in suspension from a boiler, due to violent ebullition.

Producer Gas — Gaseous fuel obtained by burning solid fuel in a chamber where a mixture of air and steam is passed through the incandescent fuel bed. This process results in a gas, almost oxygen free, containing a large percentage of the original heating value of the solid fuel in the form of carbon monoxide and hydrogen.

Products of Combustion — The gases, vapors, and solids resulting from the combustion of fuel.

Proximate Analysis — See analysis, proximate.

Puff — A minor combustion explosion within the boiler furnace or setting.

Pulverized Fuel — Solid fuel reduced to a fine size.

Pulverized-Fuel Feeder — An apparatus for the controlled delivery of pulverized fuel from a storage bin.

Pulverizer — A machine which reduces a solid fuel to a fineness suitable for burning in suspension.

1. **High speed** (over 800 rpm)
   (a) *Impact pulverizer* — A machine wherein the major portion of the reduction in particle size of the fuel to be pulverized is effected by fracture of larger sizes by sudden shock, impingement, or collision of the fuel with rotating members and casing.
   (b) *Attrition pulverizer* —A machine wherein the major portion of the reduction in particle size is by abrasion, either by pulverizer parts on coal, or by coal on coal.
2. **Medium speed** (between 70 and 300 rpm)
   (a) *Roller pulverizer* — A machine having grinding elements consisting of conical or cylindrical rolls and a bowl, bull-ring, mating rings, or table, any of which may be the rotating member, the fuel to be pulverized being reduced in size by crushing and attrition between the rolls and the rings.
   (b) *Ball pulverizer* — A machine in which the grinding elements consist of one or more circular rows of metal balls arranged in suitable raceways, wherein the fuel to be pulverized is reduced in size by crushing and attrition between the balls and raceways.
3. **Low speed** (under 70 rpm)
   (a) *Ball or tube pulverizer* — A machine having a rotatable cylindrical or conical casing charged with metal balls or slugs and

the fuel to be pulverized, reduction in particle size being effected by crushing and attrition due to continuous relative movement of the charge on rotation of the casing.

Pulverizer Air — Air which is passed through a pulverizer to dry and convey the pulverized fuel to the burners in direct-fired systems, or to the cyclone in storage systems. (Gas is sometimes used for the same purpose in storage systems.)

Pulverizer Exhauster — A fan connected to the outlet of a pulverizer and used to draw pulverizer air through a pulverizer and in some cases to augment the pulverizer air by the addition of primary air.

Purge Meter Interlock — A flow meter so arranged that an air flow through the furnace above a minimum amount must exist for a definite time interval before the interlocking system will permit an automatic ignition torch to be placed in operation.

Purity — The degree to which a substance is free of foreign materials.

Pyrites — A compound of iron and sulfur naturally occurring in coal.

R

Radiation Loss — A comprehensive term used in a boiler-unit heat balance to account for the conduction, radiation, and convection heat losses from the settings to the ambient air.

Rank — Method of coal classification based on the degree of progressive alteration in the natural series from brown coal to meta-anthracite. The limits under classifications according to rank are on a mineral matter free basis.

Rated Capacity — The manufacturer's stated capacity rating for mechanical equipment, for instance, the maximum continuous capacity in pounds of steam per hour for which a boiler is designed.

Rate of Blowdown — A rate normally expressed as a percentage of the water fed.

Raw-Fuel Feeder — A machine for the controlled delivery of raw fuel.

Raw Water — Water supplied to the plant before any treatment.

Rear Discharge Stoker — A stoker so arranged that refuse is discharged from the grate surface at the end opposite the coal feed.

Recessed Tube Wall — A refractory furnace wall with slots in which waterwall tubes are placed so that the tubes are partially exposed to the furnace.

Reciprocating Grate — A grate element which has reciprocating motion, usually for the purpose of fuel agitation.

Recirculating Line — Piping and connections on a heat exchanger through which fluid is returned from the outlet to the inlet.

Recirculation — The reintroduction of part of the flowing fluid to repeat the cycle of circulation.

Recirculator Tube — A connection between upper and lower waterwall headers to return water to the lower header.

Reducing Atmosphere — An atmosphere which tends to promote the removal of oxygen from a chemical compound.

Reduction — Removal of oxygen from a chemical compound.

Refractory Wall — A wall made of refractory material.

Refinery Gas — The commercially noncondensible gas resulting from fractional distillation of crude oil, or the cracking of crude oil or petroleum distillates. Refinery gas is either burned at the refineries or supplied for mixing with city gas.

Register — The apparatus used in a burner to regulate the direction of flow of air for combustion.

Reheated Steam — Superheated steam which derives its superheat from a reheater.

Reheater — Heat transfer apparatus for heating steam after it has given up some of its original heat in doing work.

Reheating — The process of adding heat to steam to raise its temperature after it has done part of its intended work. This is usually done between the high-pressure and low-pressure sections of a compound turbine or engine.

Reinjection — The procedure of returning collected fly ash to the furnace of a boiler for the purpose of burning out its carbon content.

Relative Humidity — The ratio of the weight of water vapor present in a unit volume of gas to the maximum possible weight of water vapor in unit volume of the same gas at the same temperature and pressure.

Residual Fuels — Products remaining from crude petroleum by removal of some of the water and an appreciable percentage of the more volatile hydrocarbons.

Resistance — Impediment to gas flow, such as pressure drop or draft loss through a dust collector. Usually measured in inches water gage.

Retort — A trough or channel in an underfeed stoker, extending within the furnace, through which fuel is forced upward into the fuel bed.

Retractable Blower — A soot blower in which the blowing element can be mechanically extended into boiler setting and retracted.

Return-Flow Oil Burner — A mechanical atomizing oil burner in which part of the oil supplied to the atomizer is withdrawn and returned to storage or to the oil line supplying the atomizer.

Riffle — A device for diverting material into two or more equal parts, comprising a number of narrow sloping chutes of equal width, having a common inlet and having adjacent chutes diverging to separate outlets; a laboratory device. Also used on some exhauster outlets to divide mixtures of pulverized coal and air.

Rifled Tube — A tube which is helically grooved on the inner wall.

Ringelmann Chart — A series of four rectangular grids of black lines of varying widths printed on a white background, and used as a criterion of blackness for determining smoke density.

Riser Tube — A tube through which steam and water passes from an upper waterwall header to a drum.

Rolled Joint — A joint made by expanding a tube into a hole by a roller expander.

Rotary Oil Burner — A burner in which atomization is accomplished by feeding oil to the inside of a rapidly rotating cup.

Rotary Valve — A device having a parted cylinder which rotates on cylindrical faces to form a pressure seal, used for discharging dust from a hopper.

Run of Mine — Unscreened bituminous coal as it comes from the mine.

S

Saturated Air — Air which contains the maximum amount of water vapor that it can hold at its temperature and pressure.

Saturated Steam — Steam at the temperature corresponding to its pressure.

Saturated Water — Water at its boiling point.

Saturated Temperature — The temperature at which evaporation occurs at a particular pressure.

Scale — A hard coating or layer of chemical materials on internal surfaces of boiler pressure parts.

Screen Analysis — A method of determining the size of dust particles by passing dust through sieves of standard mesh.

Screen Collector — A collector using screens of cloth or wire to filter out dust.

Screw Feed — A means of introducing fuel by rotation of a screw.

Seal — A device to close openings between structures to prevent leakage.

Seal Weld — A weld used primarily to obtain tightness and prevent leakage.

Secondary Air — Air for combustion supplied to the furnace to supplement the primary air.

Secondary Combustion — Combustion which occurs as a result of ignition at a point beyond the furnace. (See also delayed combustion.)

Sectionally Supported Wall — A furnace or boiler wall which consists of special refractory blocks or shapes that are mounted on and supported at intervals of height by metallic hangers; also known as suspended wall.

Sedimentation — Particle size determination by settling time in a liquid.

Segregation — The tendency of refuse of varying compositions to deposit selectively in different parts of the unit.

Semi-Anthracite — A coal classification according to rank. Dry fixed carbon 86 per cent or more and less than 92 per cent and dry volatile matter 14 per cent or less and more than 8 per cent, on a mineral-matter-free basis.

Semi-Fused Slag — Hard slag masses consisting of particles which have partly fused together.

Separately Fired Heater — Heat transfer

apparatus receiving heat from an independently fired furnace.

Service Water — General purpose water which may or may not have been treated for a special purpose.

Settling Velocities — The velocity at which the dust will fall out of dust laden gas under the influence of gravity only.

Shell — The cylindrical portion of a pressure vessel.

Screen — A perforated plate, cylinder or meshed fabric, usually mounted on a frame, for separating coarser from finer parts.

Scrubber — An apparatus for the removal of solids from gases by entrainment in water.

Separator — A mechanical device for the removal of slate from coal, or an electromagnetic device for the removal of magnetic ores or tramp iron from coal.

Shredder — A machine for cutting, scraping, or tearing material into shreds.

Side Dump Stoker — A stoker so arranged that refuse is discharged from a dump plate at the side of the stoker.

Silt — Finely divided anthracite obtained as a residue from cleaning process.

Single Retort Stoker — An underfeed stoker using one retort only in the assembly of a complete stoker. A single furnace may contain one or more single retort stokers.

Single Stage Furnace — A furnace consisting of one combustion chamber.

Sinuous Header — A header of a sectional header type boiler in which the sides are curved back and forth to suit the stagger of the boiler tubes connected to the header faces.

Skimmer Cyclone — The cyclone with an arrangement at its inner periphery for skimming off dust which is more or less concentrated at that point.

Slack — Screenings, or fine coal; maximum top size seldom above 2½ in.

Slacking — Breaking down of friable coals due to changes in moisture contents.

Slag — Molten or fused refuse.

Slag Blower — A soot blower usually of the retractable type for removing slag from heat absorbing surfaces by blowing the surfaces.

Slag Spout — The extension trough through which molten ash flows from the furnace.

Slag Tapping — The removal of molten slag from a furnace either intermittently or continuously.

Slag Tap Furnace — A pulverized-fuel-fired furnace in which the ash particles are deposited and retained on the floor thereof in molten condition, and from which the molten ash is removed by tapping either continuously or intermittently; also known as wet-bottom furnaces.

Slip Seal — A seal between members designed to permit movement of either member by slipping or sliding.

Sludge — A soft water-formed sedimentary deposit which normally can be removed by blowing down.

Slug — A large "dose" of chemical treatment applied internally to a steam boiler intermittently. Also used sometimes instead of "priming" to denote a discharge of water out a boiler steam outlet in relatively large intermittent amounts.

Smoke — Small gas borne particles of carbon or soot, less than one micron in size, resulting from incomplete combustion of carbonaceous materials and of sufficient number to be observable.

Soft Water — Water which contains little or no calcium or magnesium salts, or water from which scale forming impurities have been removed or reduced.

Softening — The act of reducing scale forming calcium and magnesium impurities in water.

Softening Temperature — The temperature at which a standard ash cone fuses down to a spherical mass when heated in accordance with a prescribed procedure.

Soot — Unburned particles of carbon derived from hydrocarbons.

Soot Blower — A mechanical device for discharging steam or air to clean heat absorbing surfaces.

Spaced Tube Wall — A water tube wall with space between the tubes.

Spalling — The breaking off of the surface of refractory material as a result of internal stresses.

Specific Heat — The quantity of heat, expressed in Btu, required to raise the temperature of one pound of a substance one degree F.

Spectroscopic Analysis — Identification of chemical elements by characteristic emission and absorption of light rays.

Splash Plate — An abrasion-resistant metal plate, forming the back of an elbow in a pulverized fuel and air line, against which the fluidized material strikes and is dispersed for the purpose of obtaining uniform distribution in the succeeding line or burner.

Splitter — Plates spaced in an elbow of a duct so disposed as to guide the flow of fluid through the elbow with uniform distribution and to minimize pressure drop.

Sponge Ash — Accumulation of dry ash particles into soft structures having a spongy appearance.

Spontaneous Combustion — Ignition of combustible material following slow oxidation without the application of high temperature from an external source.

Spray Angle — The angle included between the sides of the cone formed by liquid fuel discharged from mechanical, rotary atomizers and by some forms of steam or air atomizers.

Sprayer Plate — A metal plate used to atomize the fuel in the atomizer of an oil burner.

Spray Tower — A duct through which liquid particles descend countercurrent to a column of gas; a fine spray is used when the object is to concentrate the liquid, a coarse spray when the object is to clean the gas by entrainment of the solid particles in the liquid droplets.

Stack — A vertical conduit, which due to the difference in density between internal and external gases, creates a draft at its base.

Stack Effect — That portion of a pressure differential resulting from difference in elevation of the points of measurement.

Standard Air — Dry air weighing 0.075 lb per cu ft at sea level (29.92 in. barometric pressure) and 70 F.

Standard Flue Gas — Gas weighing 0.078 lb per cu ft at sea level (29.92 in. barometric pressure) and 70 F.

Static Efficiency — The mechanical efficiency multiplied by the ratio of static pressure differential to the total pressure differential, from fan inlet to fan outlet.

Staybolt — A bolt threaded through or welded at each end, into two spaced sheets of a firebox or box header to support flat surfaces against internal pressure.

Steam — The vapor phase of water substantially unmixed with other gases.

Steam and Water Drum — A pressure chamber located at the upper extremity of a boiler circulatory system in which the steam generated in the boiler is separated from the water and from which steam is discharged at a position above a water level maintained therein.

Steam Atomizing Oil Burner — A burner for firing oil which is atomized by steam. It may be of the inside or outside mixing type.

Steam Binding — A restriction in circulation due to a steam pocket or a rapid steam formation.

Steam-Cooled Wall — A wall partly or completely covered with superheater or reheater tubes.

Steam Dome — A receptacle riveted or welded to the top sheet of a fire tube boiler through and from which the steam is taken from the boiler.

Steam-Free Water — Water containing no steam bubbles.

Steam Generating Unit — A unit to which water, fuel, and air are supplied and in which steam is generated. It consists of a boiler furnace, and fuel burning equipment, and may include as component parts water walls, superheater, reheater, economizer, air heater, or any combination thereof. Also, see *boiler*.

Steaming Economizer — An economizer so designed that some of the fluid passing through it is evaporated.

Steam Jet Blower — A device which utilizes the energy of steam flowing through a nozzle or nozzles to induce a flow of air to be supplied for combustion.

Steam Jet Exhauster — A similar device used to create draft.

Steam Purity — The degree of contamination. Contamination usually expressed in ppm.

Steam Quality — The per cent by weight of vapor in a steam and water mixture.

Steam Scrubber — A series of screens, wires, or plates through which steam is passed to remove entrained moisture.

Steam Separator — A device for removing the entrained water from steam.

Steam Washer — A device in a steam drum in which steam is mixed or brought into contact with water having a lower concentration than boiler water, to reduce the solids concentration in the entrained moisture.

Sticky Ash — Ash which is at a temperature between initial deformation and softening temperature.

Stoke's Law — For particles about 1 to 150 microns, the terminal or settling velocity is proportional to the square of the radius of the particle, the difference of densities of the particle and fluid, acceleration of gravity and the reciprocal of the viscosity of the fluid.

Straightening Vanes — Vanes inserted in gas ducts to direct the flow of gas parallel to the walls.

Stratification — Non-homogeneity existing transversely in a gas stream.

Stud Plate — A small steel plate welded to a tube to support refractory.

Stud Tube Wall — A wall containing water tubes covered with refractory which is held in place by stud anchors attached to the tubes.

Sub-Bituminous Coal — Coal classification according to rank:

   A. Moist Btu 11,000 or more and less than 13,000.

   B. Moist Btu 9500 or more and less than 11,000.

   C. Moist Btu 8500 or more and less than 9500.

Suction System Pulverizer — A pulverizer in which the internal pressure is below atmospheric. It is generally located on the inlet of the primary air exhauster.

Sulfate-Carbonate Ratio — The proportion of sulfates to carbonates, or alkalinity expressed as carbonates, in boiler water. The proper maintenance of this ratio has been advocated as a means of inhibiting caustic embrittlement.

Superheat — To raise the temperature of steam above its saturation temperature. The temperature in excess of its saturation temperature.

Superheat Control — Regulation of vapor temperature over a range of operating conditions.

Superheated Steam — Steam at a higher temperature than its saturation temperature.

Superheater — A group of tubes which absorb heat from the products of combustion to raise the temperature of the vapor passing through the tubes above the temperature corresponding to its pressure.

   (a) *Convection superheater* — A superheater so arranged and located to absorb heat from the products of combustion mainly by convection.

   (b) *Radiant superheater* — A superheater so arranged and located to absorb heat mainly by radiation.

Superheater Outlet Pressure — The steam pressure at the point where it leaves the superheater.

Supply Tube — A tube which carries water to the inlet water header; also known as downcomer tube.

Surface Blowoff — Removal of water, foam, etc., from the surface at the water level in a boiler.

Surface Combustion — The non-luminous burning of a combustible gaseous mixture close to the surface of a hot porous refractory material through which it has passed.

Surface Moisture — That portion of the moisture in the coal which comes from external sources as water seepage, rain, snow, condensation, etc.; sometimes designated as free moisture.

Surge — The sudden displacement or movement of water in a closed vessel or drum.

Suspended Arch — An arch in which the refractory blocks or shapes are suspended by metallic hangers.

Suspended Solids — Undissolved solids in boiler water.

Suspended Wall — Same as sectionally supported wall.

Swell — The sudden increase in the volume of the steam in the water steam mixture below the water level.

Swinging Load — A load that changes at relatively short intervals.

T

Tangential Firing — A method of firing by which a number of burners are so located in the furnace walls that the center lines of the burners are tangential to an imaginary circle. Corner firing is usually included in this type.

Tangent Tube Wall — See tube-to-tube wall.

Tap — The action of removing molten slag from a slag-tap furnace through a tap hole.

Tap Hole — A hole through which molten slag is removed from a slag-tap furnace.

Telescopic Blower — A long retractable soot blower with element made up of two or more sections which telescope mechanically.

Tempering Air — Air at a lower temperature added to a stream of preheated air to modify its temperature.

Tempering Moisture — Water added to certain coals which, as received, have insufficient moisture content for proper combustion on stokers.

Tertiary Air — Air for combustion supplied to the furnace to supplement the primary and secondary air.

Theoretical Air — The quantity of air required for perfect combustion.

Theoretical Draft — The draft which would be available at the base of a stack if there were no friction or acceleration losses in the stack.

Therm — A unit of heat applied especially to gas. One therm equals 100,000 Btu.

Thermal Probe — A liquid-cooled tube used as a calorimeter in a furnace to measure heat absorption rates.

Thermal Sleeve — A spaced internal sleeve lining of a connection for introducing a fluid of one temperature into a vessel containing fluid at a substantially different temperature, used to avoid abnormal strains.

Tie Bar — A structural member designed to maintain the spacing of furnace waterwall tubes.

Tile — A preformed, burned refractory, usually applied to shapes other than standard brick.

Total Air — The total quantity of air supplied to the fuel and products of combustion. Per cent total air is the ratio of total air to theoretical air, expressed as per cent.

Total Moisture — The sum of inherent moisture and surface moisture in coal.

Total Pressure — The sum of the static and velocity pressures.

Total Solids Concentration — The weight of dissolved and suspended impurities in a unit weight of boiler water, usually expressed in ppm.

Transport System — The pump and piping, blow tank and piping, or screw conveyor, used to transport the pulverized fuel from the cyclone to the pulverized-fuel bin in storage systems.

Traveling Grate Stoker — A stoker similar to a chain grate stoker with the exception that the grate is separate from but is supported on and driven by chains. Only enough chain strands are used as may be required to support and drive the grate.

Treated Water — Water which has been chemically treated to make it suitable for boiler feed.

Tube — A hollow cylinder for conveying fluids.

Tube Cleaner — A device for cleaning tubes by brushing, hammering, or by rotating cutters.

Tube-To-Tube Wall — A waterwall in which the tubes are substantially tangent to each other with practically no space between the tubes; also known as tangent tube wall.

Tube Turbining — The act of cleaning a tube by means of a power driven rotary device which passes through the tube.

Tubular-Type Collector — A collector utilizing a number of essentially straight-walled cyclone tubes in parallel.

Thimble — A small thimble-like filter made of porous material used for obtaining a sample of dust from a gas stream.

Turbidity — The optical obstruction to the passing of a ray of light through a body of water, caused by finely divided suspended matter.

Turbulent Burner — A burner in which fuel and air are mixed and discharged into the furnace in such a manner as to produce turbulent flow from the burner.

Tuyeres — Forms of grates, located adjacent to a retort, through which air is introduced.

Two Stage Furnace — A multistage furnace consisting of a primary and a secondary furnace only.

U

Unaccounted-For Loss — That portion of a boiler heat balance which represents the difference between 100 per cent and the sum of the heat absorbed by the unit and all the classified losses expressed as per cent.

Ultimate Analysis — see analysis, ultimate.

Unfired Pressure Vessel — A vessel designed to withstand internal pressure, neither subjected to heat from products of combustion nor an integral part of a fired pressure vessel system.

Use Factor — The ratio of hours in operation to the total hours in that period.

V

Vacuum Dust Unloader — A suction system used for conveying dust from various points to an accumulation point.

Vane — A fixed or adjustable plate inserted in a gas or air stream used to change the direction of flow.

Vane Control — A set of movable vanes in the inlet of a fan to provide regulation of air flow.

Vane Guide — A set of stationary vanes to govern direction, velocity and distribution of air or gas flow.

Velocity Pressure — The measure of the kinetic energy of a fluid.

Vent — An opening in a vessel or other enclosed space for the removal of gas or vapor.

Vertical Firing — An arrangement of a burner such that air and fuel are discharged into the furnace, in practically a vertical direction.

Viscosity — Measure of the internal friction of a fluid or its resistance to flow.

Vitreous Slag — Glassy slag.

Volatile Matter — Those products given off by a material as gas or vapor, determined by definite prescribed methods.

Volume of Air — The number of cubic feet of air per minute expressed at fan outlet conditions.

W

Wall Blower — A short retractable blower for cleaning by mass blowing of adjacent wall heat absorbing surfaces.

Wall Box — A structure in a wall of a steam generator through which apparatus, such as soot blowers, extends into the setting.

Washer — An apparatus utilizing water (or other liquid media) for the removal of inorganic extraneous matter from coal or for the removal of solids from gases.

Waste Fuel — Any byproduct that is waste from a manufacturing process.

Waste Heat — Sensible heat in non-combustible gases, such as gases leaving furnaces used for processing metals, ores or other materials.

Water Column — A vertical tubular member connected at its top and bottom to the steam and water space respectively of a boiler, to which the water gage, gage cocks, and high and low level alarms may be connected.

Water-Cooled Baffle — A baffle composed essentially of closely spaced boiler tubes.

Water-Cooled Wall — A furnace wall containing water tubes.

Water Gas — Gaseous fuel consisting primarily of carbon monoxide and hydrogen made by the interaction of steam and incandescent carbon.

Water Hammer — A sudden increase in pressure of water due to an instantaneous conversion of momentum to pressure.

Water Level — The elevation of the surface of the water in a boiler.

Water Screen — A screen formed by one or more rows of water tubes spaced above the bottom of a pulverized fuel furnace, and serving to create an ash cooling zone.

Water Tube — A tube in a boiler having the water and steam on the inside and heat applied to the outside.

Weep — A term usually applied to a minute leak in a boiler joint which forms droplets (or tears) of water very slowly.

Wet Bulb Temperature — The lowest temperature which a water wetted body will attain when exposed to an air current. This is the temperature of adiabatic saturation.

Wetness — A term used to designate the percentage of water in steam. Also used to describe the presence of a water film on heating surface interiors.

Wetting — The process of supplying a water film to the water side of a heating surface.

Wide-Range Mechanical Atomizing Oil Burner — A burner having an oil atomizer with a range of flow rates greater than that obtainable with the usual mechanical atomizers.

Windbox — A chamber below the grate or surrounding a burner through which air under pressure is supplied for combustion of the fuel.

Windbox Pressure — The static pressure in the windbox of a burner or stoker.

Z

Zone Control — The control of air flow into individual zones of a stoker.

SELECTED TERMS FROM GLOSSARY OF ELECTRIC UTILITY TERMS, EDISON ELECTRIC INSTITUTE, 1961

Auxiliary Equipment (Generating Station) — Accessory equipment necessary for the operation of a generating station. This would include pumps, stokers, fans, pulverizers, etc.

Average Demand — See demand, average.

Base Load — The minimum load over a given period of time.

Base Load Station — A generating station which is normally operated to take all or part of the base load of a system and which, consequently, operates essentially at a constant output.

BTU (British Thermal Unit) — The standard unit for measuring quantity of heat energy, such as the heat content of fuel. It is the amount of heat energy necessary to raise the temperature of one pound of water one degree Fahrenheit.

Capability — The maximum load which a generating unit, generating station, or other electrical apparatus can carry under specified conditions for a given period of time, without exceeding approved limits of temperature and stress.

Capability Margin — The difference between net system capability and system maximum load requirements (peak load). It is the margin of capability available to provide for scheduled maintenance, emergency outages, system operating requirements, and unforeseen loads. On a regional or national basis, it is the difference between aggregate net system capability of the various systems in the region or nation and the sum of system maximum (peak) loads without allowance for time diversity between the loads of the several systems. However, within a region, account is taken of diversity between peak loads of systems that are operated as a closely coordinated group.

Capacity — The load for which a generating unit, generating station, or other electrical apparatus is rated as stated usually by manufacturer's name plate ratings. Sometimes used synonymously with *capability*. See *name plate rating*.

> **Dependable** — The load-carrying ability for the time interval and period specified when related to the characteristics of the load to be supplied. Dependable capacity of a station is determined by such factors as capability, operating power factor, and portion of the load which the station is to supply.

> **Peaking** — Generating units or stations which are available to assist in meeting that portion of peak load which is above base load.

> **Purchase** — The amount of firm power available for purchase from a source outside the system to supply energy or reserve capacity.

> **Reserve**

>> **Cold** — Thermal generating units available for service but not maintained at operating temperature.

>> **Hot** — Thermal generating units available, up to temperature and ready for service, although not actually in operation.

>> **Spinning** — Generating units connected to the bus and ready to take load.

> **Thermal** — The manufacturer's rating of a thermal electric generating unit or the sum of such ratings for all units in a station or stations.

Capacity Factor — The ratio of the average load on a machine or equipment for the period of time considered to the capacity rating of the machine or equipment.

Coal Equivalent of Fuels Burned — The quantity of coal (tons) of stated kind and heat value which would be required to supply the Btu equivalent of all fuels burned. In determining this coal equivalent, the Btu content of other fuels is generally divided by the representative heat value per ton of coal burned.

Coal Rate — The weight in pounds of coal (including the coal equivalent of other fuels) burned for electric generation divided by the resulting net generation. It is generally expressed as pounds of coal per net kilowatt-hour. See also *heat rate*.

Conventional Fuels — The fossil fuels: coal, oil, or gas.

Demand — The rate at which electric energy is delivered to or by a system, part of a system, or a piece of equipment expressed in kilowatts, kilovolt-amperes or other suitable unit at a given instant or averaged over any designated period of time. The primary source of "Demand" is the power-consuming equipment of the customers. See *load*.

> **Annual Maximum** — The greatest of all demands of the load under consideration which occurred during a prescribed demand interval in a calendar year.

> **Annual System Maximum** — The greatest demand on an electric system during a prescribed demand interval in a calendar year.

> **Average** — The demand on, or the power output of, an electric system or any of its parts over any interval of time, as determined by dividing the total number of kilowatt hours by the number of units of time in the interval.

> **Billing** — The demand upon which billing to a customer is based, as specified

in a rate schedule or contract. It may be based on the contract year, a contract minimum, or a previous maximum and, therefore, does not necessarily coincide with the actual measured demand of the billing period.

Coincident — The sum of two or more demands which occur in the same demand interval.

Instantaneous Peak — The maximum demand at the instant of greatest load, usually determined from the readings of indicating or graphic meters.

Integrated — The demand averaged over a specified period, usually determined by an integrating demand meter or by the integration of a load curve. It is the average of the continuously varying instantaneous demands during a specified demand interval.

Maximum — The greatest of all of the demands of the load under consideration which has occurred during a specified period of time.

Non-Coincident — The sum of two or more individual demands which do not occur in the same period interval. Meaningful only when considering demands within a limited period of time, such as a day, week, month, a heating or cooling season, and usually for not more than one year.

Demand Charge — The specified charge to be billed on the basis of the billing demand, under an applicable rate schedule or contract.

Demand Interval — The period of time during which the electric energy flow is averaged in determining demand, such as 60-minute, 30-minute, 15-minute or instantaneous.

Depreciation — The amounts provided for the prospective retirement of depreciable plant in the course of its service life.

Among the causes to be given consideration are wear and tear, decay, action of the elements, inadequacy, obsolescence, changes in the arts, changes in demand and requirements of public authorities.

Dispatching — The operating control of an integrated electric system involving operations such as:

(1) The assignment of load to specific generating stations and other sources of supply to effect the most economical supply as the total or the significant area loads rise or fall.

(2) The control of operations and maintenance of high-voltage lines, substations and equipment, including administration of safety procedures.

(3) The operation of principal tie lines and switching.

(4) The scheduling of energy transactions with connecting electric utilities.

Distribution — The act or process of distributing electric energy from convenient points on the transmission or bulk power system to the consumers. Also a functional classification relating to that portion of utility plant used for the purpose of delivering electric energy from convenient points on the transmission system to the consumers, or to expenses relating to the operation and maintenance of distribution plant.

Diversity — That characteristic of variety of electric loads whereby individual maximum demands usually occur at different times. Diversity among customers' loads results in diversity among the loads of distribution transformers, feeders and substations, as well as between entire systems. (See also *load diversity.*)

Diversity Factor — The ratio of the sum of the non-coincident maximum demands of two or more loads to their coincident maximum demand for the same period.

Energy, Electric — As commonly used in the electric utility industry, electric energy means kilowatt hours.

Dump — Energy generated by water power that cannot be stored or conserved when such energy is beyond the immediate needs of the producing system.

Economy — Energy produced and supplied from a more economical source in one system, substituted for that being produced or capable of being produced by a less economical source in another system.

Interchange — Kilowatt hours delivered to or received by one electric utility system from another for economy purposes. They may be returned in kind at a later time or may be accumulated as energy balances until the end of a stated period. Settlement may be by payment or on a pooling basis.

Net for Distribution — On an electric system or company basis this means the kilowatt hours available for total system or company load. Specifically it is the sum of net generation by the system's own plants, purchased energy and net interchange (in less out).

Off-Peak — Energy supplied during periods of relatively low system demands as specified by the supplier.

On-Peak — Energy supplied during periods of relatively high system demands as specified by the supplier.

Surplus — Energy generated that is beyond the immediate needs of the producing system. This energy is frequently obtained from spinning reserve and sold on an interruptible basis.

Generating Station (Generating Plant) — A station at which are located prime movers, electric generators, and auxiliary equipment for converting mechanical, chemical and nuclear energy into electric energy.

Generating Unit — An electric generator together with its prime mover.

Generation, Electric — This term refers to the act or process of transforming other forms of energy into electric energy; or to the amount of electric energy so produced, expressed in kilowatt hours.

Gross — The total amount of electric energy produced by the generating units in a generating station or stations.

Net — Gross generation less kilowatt hours consumed out of gross generation for station use.

Generator, Electric — A machine which transforms mechanical energy into electrical energy.

Generator, Steam — Equipment which burns fuel and changes water into steam.

Heat Rate — A measure of generating station thermal efficiency, generally expressed in Btu per net kilowatt hour. It is computed by dividing the total Btu content of fuel burned for electric generation by the resulting net kilowatt hour generation.

Load — The amount of electric power delivered or required at any specified point or points on a system. Load originates primarily at the power consuming equipment of the customers. See *demand*.

Connected — Connected load is the sum of the capacities or ratings of the electric power consuming apparatus connected to a supplying system, or any part of the system under consideration.

Load Curve — A curve on a chart showing power (kilowatts) supplied, plotted against time of occurrence, and illustrating the varying magnitude of the load during the period covered.

Load Diversity — Load diversity is the difference between the sum of the maxima of two or more individual loads and the coincident or combined maximum load, usually measured in kilowatts.

Load Factor — The ratio of the average load in kilowatts supplied during a designated period to the peak or maximum load occurring in that period.

Loss (Losses) — The general term applied to energy (kilowatt hours) and power (kilowatts) lost in the operation of an electric system. Losses occur principally as energy transformations from kilowatt hours to waste heat in electrical conductors and apparatus.

   Average — The total difference in energy input and output or power input and output (due to losses), averaged over a time interval and expressed either in physical quantities or as a percentage of total input.

   Energy — The kilowatt hours lost in the operation of an electric system.

   Line — Kilowatt hours and kilowatts lost in transmission and distribution lines under specified conditions.

   Peak Per Cent — The difference between the power input and output, as a result of losses due to the transfer of power between two or more points on a system at the time of maximum load, divided by the power input.

   System — The difference between the system net energy or power input and output resulting from characteristic losses and unaccounted-for between the sources of supply and the metering points of delivery on a system.

Megawatt (MW) — 1000 kilowatts.

Name Plate Rating — The full load continuous rating of a generator and its prime mover or other electrical equipment under specified conditions as designated by the manufacturer. It is usually indicated on a name plate attached mechanically to the individual machine or device. Name plate rating is generally less than, but for older equipment may be greater than, demonstrated capability of the installed machine.

Network — A system of transmission or distribution lines so cross connected and operated as to permit multiple power supply to any principal point on it.

Peak — See *demand, maximum.*

Peak Capability — See *capability.*

Peak Load — See *demand, maximum.*

Peak Load Station — A generating station which is normally operated to provide power during maximum load periods.

Peaking Capacity — See *capacity, peaking.*

Power (Electric) — The time rate of generating, transferring or using electric energy, usually expressed in kilowatts.

Prime Mover — The engine, turbine, water wheel or similar machine which drives an electric generator.

Production — The act or process of generating electric energy. Also a functional classification relating to that portion of utility plant used for the purpose of generating electric energy, or to expenses relating to the operation or maintenance of production plant, or the purchase and interchange of electric energy.

Pumped Storage — An arrangement whereby a reservoir is filled with water by pumping during offpeak periods when low cost steam energy is available or when water is being spilled at other hydro plants. This method of operating a hydro plant stores water which can be used at a more appropriate time or saves water which would otherwise be lost.

Station Use (Generating) — The kilowatt hours used at an electric generating station for such purposes as excitation and operation of auxiliary and other facilities essential to the operation of the station. Station use includes electric energy supplied from house generators, main generators, the transmission system, and any other sources for this purpose. The quantity of energy used is the difference between the gross generation plus any supply from outside the station and the net output of the station.

Steam-Electric Generating Station — An electric generating station utilizing steam for the motive force of its prime movers.

Summer Peak — The greatest load on an electric system during any prescribed demand interval in the summer (or cooling) season, usually between June 1 and September 30.

System, Electric — The physically connected generation, transmission, distribution and other facilities operated as an integral unit under one control, management or operating supervision.

System Net Input — Net available energy that is put into a utility's system for sale within its own service area or otherwise used by the utility within its own service area. It is the net energy generated in a system's own plants, plus energy received from other systems, less energy delivered to other systems.

System Output — The net generation by the system's own plants plus purchased energy, plus or minus net interchange energy.

Thermal — A term used to identify a type of electric generating station, capacity, or capability, or output in which the source of energy for the prime mover is heat.

Total Fuel Expense (After Residual Credit) — Total cost (including freight and handling) of coal, oil, gas, nuclear or other fuel used in the production of electric energy, less fuel portion of steam transfer credit, and residual credits, such as net credits from the disposal of ashes, cinders, and nuclear byproducts.

Transmission — The act or process of transporting electric energy in bulk from a source or sources of supply to other principal parts of the system or to other utility systems.

Transmission Line — A line used for bulk transmission of electricity between a generating or receiving point and major substations or delivery points.

Turbine-Generator — A rotary-type unit consisting of a turbine and an electric generator.

Turbine (Steam) or (Gas) — An enclosed rotary type of prime mover in which heat energy in steam or gas is converted into mechanical energy by the force of a high velocity flow of steam or gases directed against successive rows of radial blades fastened to a central shaft.

Utility Generation — Electric generation by electric systems.

Utilization Factor — The ratio of average load (kilowatts) over a designated period of time to the net capability in the same period of time. This ratio represents the average use made of the net capability of equipment over a specific period of time. See also *load factor* and *capacity factor*.

Wheeling Service — The use of the transmission facilities of one system to transmit power of and for another system.

Winter Peak — The greatest load on an electric system during any prescribed demand interval in the winter or heating season, usually between December 1 of a calendar year and March 31 of the next calendar year.

Appendix C

Engineering Data and Conversion Factors

INSTANTANEOUS SPECIFIC HEAT

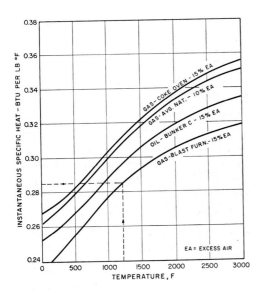

Fig. C–1. Values of instantaneous specific heat

    Coke oven gas
    Natural gas
    Bunker C oil
    Blast furnace gas

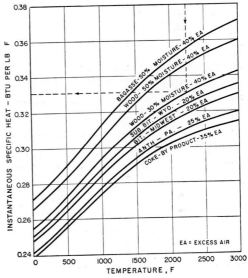

Fig. C–2. Values of instantaneous specific heat

    Bagasse
    Wood
    Subbituminous coal
    Bituminous coal
    Anthracite
    Coke

Table C–1 CONVERSION FACTORS*

To Obtain	Multiply	By
Acres	Sq miles	640
Ampere-hr	Coulombs	2.7777×10^{-4}
Amperes	Faradays/sec	96500
Angstrom units	Centimeters	1×10^{8}
Angstrom units	Microns	1×10^{4}
Atmospheres	Bars	0.98692
Atmospheres	Cm of Hg @ O C	0.013158
Atmospheres	Dynes/sq cm	9.8692×10^{-7}
Atmospheres	Ft of H_2O @ 39.2F	0.029499
Atmospheres	Grams/sq cm	9.6784×10^{-4}
Atmospheres	In. of Hg @ 32F	0.033421
Atmospheres	In. of H_2O @ 39.2F	0.0024583
Atmospheres	Kg/sq meter	9.67841×10^{-5}
Atmospheres	Pounds/sq in.	0.068046
Atomic mass units	Electron-volts	1.0739×10^{-9}
Atomic mass units	Ergs	670.33
Atomic mass units	Grams	6.0247×10^{23}
Atomic mass units	Million electron volts (Mev)	1.0739×10^{-3}
Atoms U-235 fissioned (@ 200 Mev/fission)	Kw-hr	1.1236×10^{17}
Atoms U-235 fissioned (@ 200 Mev/fission)	Megawatt-days	2.696×10^{21}
Barns	Sq cm	1×10^{24}
Bars	Atmospheres	1.013
Btu	Calories	3.9685×10^{-3}
Btu	Electron-volts	1.5188×10^{-22}
Btu	Ergs	9.4805×10^{-11}
Btu	Ft-lb	0.0012854
Btu	Fissions (@ 200 Mev/fission)	3.037×10^{-14}
Btu	Hp-hr	2545.0
Btu	Joules	9.478×10^{-4}
Btu	Kg-cal	3.9685
Btu	Kw-hr	3413.0
Btu	Megawatt-days	8.189×10^{7}
Btu	Watt-hr	3.4130
Btu/cu ft	Kg cal/cu meter	0.112370
Btu/(cu ft)(hr)	Kw/liter	9.6644×10^{4}
Btu/hr	Ergs/sec	3.4138×10^{-7}
Btu/hr	Mech. hp	2545.1
Btu/hr	Kw	3413.0
Btu/kw hr	Kg cal/kw hr	3.9685
Btu/(hr)(ft)(deg F)	Cal/(sec)(cm)(deg C)	241.90
Btu/(hr)(ft)(deg F)	Watts/(cm)(deg C)	57.803
Btu/(hr)(sq ft)	Cal/(sec)(sq cm)	13,273.0
Btu/(hr)(sq ft)(deg F)	Kg-cal/(hr)(sq m)(deg C)	0.205
Btu/(hr)(sq ft)(deg F per in.)	Kg-cal/(hr)(sq m)(deg C per cm)	0.080639
Btu/lb	Joules/gram	0.430
Btu/lb	Kg cal/kg	1.8
Btu/(lb)(deg F)	Cal/(gram)(deg C)	1.000
Btu/(lb)(deg F)	Joules/(gram)(deg C)	0.23889
Btu/sq ft	Kg-cal/sq meter	0.36867
Calories	Btu	251.98
Calories	Electron-volts	3.8276×10^{-20}
Calories	Ergs	2.3889×10^{-8}

To Obtain	Multiply	By
Calories	Ft-lb	0.32389
Calories	Joules	0.23889
Calories	Watt-hr	860.01
Calories/(cu cm)(sec)	Kw/liter	0.23888
Calories/gram	Btu/lb	0.55556
Calories/(gram)(deg C)	Btu/(lb)(deg F)	1.0
Calories/(sec)(cm) (deg C)	Btu/(hr)(ft)(deg F	4.1336×10^{-3}
Calories/(sec)(sq cm)	Btu/(hr)(sq ft)	7.5341×10^{-5}
Calories/(sec)(sq cm) (deg C)	Btu/(hr)(sq ft) (deg F)	1.355×10^{-4}
Centimeters	Angstrom units	1×10^{-8}
Centimeters	Inches	2.540
Centimeters	Microns	1×10^{-4}
Centimeters	Mils	0.0025400
Centimeters of Hg @ 0 C	Atmospheres	76.0
Centimeters of Hg @ 0 C	Bars	75.01
Centimeters of Hg @ 0 C	Ft of H_2O @ 39.2 F	2.242
Centimeters of Hg @ 0 C	Grams/sq cm	0.07356
Centimeters of Hg @ 0 C	In. of H_2O @ 4 C	0.1868
Centimeters of Hg @ 0 C	Lb/sq in.	5.1715
Centimeters/deg C	In./deg F	4.5720
Centimeters/(sec)(sec)	Gravity (at sea level)	980.665
Centimeters of H_2O @ 39.2 F	Atmospheres	1033.24
Centimeters of H_2O @ 39.2 F	Lb/sq in.	70.31
Centimeters^{-2}	(Meters)$^{-2}$ (of buckling)	1×10^{-4}
Centimeters^{-2} (of buckling)	Microbucks	1×10^{-6}
Centipoises	Centistokes	(Density of liquid)
Centipoises	Poises	100
Centistokes	Centipoises	1/(density of liquid)
Cents	Reactivity change	$100/\beta$
Cents/million Btu (thermal)	Mills/kw-hr (electrical)	29.30 x eff.
Circular mils	Sq cm	1.9735×10^{5}
Circular mils	Sq in.	1.2732×10^{6}
Circular mils	Sq mils	1.2732
Circumferences	Radians	0.15916
Coulombs	Ampere-hr	3600
Coulombs	Faradays	96,500
Cu Centimeters/sec	Cu ft/min	472.0
Cu ft	Cu meters	35.314
Cu ft	Gal (Imp., liq.)	0.16054
Cu ft	Gal (U.S.A., liq.)	0.13368
Cu ft	Liters	3.532×10^{-2}
Cu ft/min	Cu centimeters/sec	0.0021186
Cu ft/min	Gal (U.S.A., liq.)/sec	8.0192
Cu ft/lb	Cu meters/kg	16.02
Cu ft/sec	Gal/min	0.0022280
Cu ft/sec	Liters/min	0.0005886
Cu in.	Cu centimeters	0.061023

* Compiled by H. R. Towse from various sources.

To Obtain	Multiply	By
Cu in.	Gal (Imp.)	277.4
Cu in.	Gal (U.S.A., liq.)	231.0
Cu in.	Liters	61.03
Cu yards	Cu meters	1.3079
Curies	Disintegrations/min	4.5045×10^{-13}
Curies	Disintegrations/sec	2.7027×10^{-11}
Cycles/sec	Radians/sec	0.15916
Degrees	Radians	57.296
Disintegrations/sec	Curies	3.70×10^{10}
Disintegrations/sec	Rutherfords	1×10^{6}
Dollars	Reactivity change	$1/\beta$
Dollars/day	Mills/hr	24×10^{-3}
Dollars/year	Mills/hr	8.766
Doubling time	Period (of an exponential)	0.69315
Dynes	Grams	980.66
Dynes	Pounds, avoir.	444820.0
Dynes/sq cm	Atmospheres	1.0133×10^{6}
Dynes/sq cm	Cm of Hg @ 0 C	1.3332×10^{4}
Dynes/sq cm	Grams/sq cm	980.66
Dynes/sq cm	Lb/sq in.	68947
Electron rest-energy units (mc^2)	Million electron volts (Mev)	1.9569
Electron-volts	Btu	6.584×10^{21}
Electron-volts	Calories	2.6126×10^{19}
Electron-volts	Ergs	6.2419×10^{11}
Electron-volts	Grams	5.6099×10^{32}
Electron-volts	Mass units (atomic)	9.3116×10^{8}
Ergs	Electron-volts	1.6021×10^{-12}
Ergs	Fissions (at 200 Mev/fission)	3.2041×10^{-4}
Ergs	Ft-lb	13558000.0
Ergs	Gram-centimeters	980.66
Ergs	Joules	1×10^{7}
Ergs	Mass units (atomic)	1.4918×10^{-3}
Ergs absorbed/gram of air	Roentgens	83.8
Ergs/gram absorbed by any given material	Rads	100
Ergs/sec	Mech. hp	7.457×10^{9}
Ergs/sec	Kw	1×10^{10}
Faradays	Coulombs	1.0362×10^{-5}
Feet	Meters	3.281
Ft of air @ 1 Atm and 60 deg F	Lb/sq in.	1.89×10^{3}
Ft of H_2O @ 39.2 F	Atmospheres	33.899
Ft of H_2O @ 39.2 F	In. of Hg @ 32 F	1.1330
Ft of H_2O @ 39.2 F	Lb/sq in.	2.3066
Ft/min	Centimeters/sec	1.9685
Ft/(sec)(sec)	Centimeters/(sec)(sec)	0.03281
Ft/(sec)(sec)	Gravity (sea level)	32.174
Fissions (@ 200 Mev/fission)	Btu	3.29×10^{13}
Fissions (@ 200 Mev/fission)	Calories	1.305×10^{11}
Fissions (@ 200 Mev/fission)	Ergs	3.121×10^{3}
Fissions (@ 200 Mev/fission)	Kw-hr	1.1236×10^{17}
Fissions (@ 200 Mev/fission)	Megawatt-days	2.696×10^{21}
Fissions (@ 200 Mev/fission)	Watt-sec	3.1211×10^{10}
Fissions/sec	Watts	3.121×10^{10}
Ft-lb	Btu	777.98
Ft-lb	Calories	3.0874
Ft-lb	Ergs	7.3756×10^{-8}
Ft-lb	Joules	0.73756
Ft-lb	Kg-meters	7.233
Ft-lb	Kw-hr	2.6552×10^{6}
Ft-lb	Mech. hp-hr	1.980×10^{6}
Ft-lb/min	Btu/min	778.0
Ft-lb/min	Kg cal/min	3087.4
Ft-lb/min	Kw	44,254.0
Ft-lb/min	Mech. hp	33,000
Gal (Imperial)	Barrels (petroleum, U.S.A.)	35
Gal (Imperial)	Gal (U.S.A., liquid)	0.83268
Gal (Imperial, liquid)	Liters	0.220
Gal (U.S.A., liquid)	Barrels (petroleum, U.S.A.)	42
Gal (U.S.A., liquid)	Cu ft	7.4805
Gal (U.S.A., liquid)	Gal (Imperial)	1.2010
Gal (U.S.A., liquid)	Liters	0.2642
Gal (U.S.A., liquid/min	Cu meters/hr	4.4029
Gal (U.S.A., liquid/sec	Cu ft/min	0.12468
Grains	Grams	15.432
Grains	Pounds (avoir.)	7000
Grains/gal (U.S.A., liquid)	Parts per million	0.0584
Grams	Atomic mass units (Amu)	1.6599×10^{-24}
Grams	Dynes	1.020×10^{-3}
Grams	Electron-volts	1.7825×10^{-33}
Grams	Grains	6.480×10^{-2}
Grams	Pounds (avoir.)	453.5924
Grams U–235 fissioned (@ 200 Mev/fission)	Btu	1.28×10^{-8}
Grams U–235 fissioned (@ 200 Mev/fission)	Calories	5.09×10^{-11}
Grams U–235 fissioned (@ 200 Mev/fission)	Ergs	1.217×10^{-18}
Grams U–235 fissioned (@ 200 Mev/fission)	Kw-hr	4.384×10^{-5}
Grams U–235 fissioned (@ 200 Mev/fission)	Megawatt-days	1.052
Grams U–235 fissioned (@ 200 Mev/fission)	Watt-sec	1.217×10^{-11}
Gram-cm/sec	Watts	10197
Grams/(cm)(sec)	Centipoises	0.01
Grams/sq cm	Atmospheres	1033.3
Grams/sq cm	Cm of Hg @ 0 C	13.595
Grams/sq cm	In. of Hg @ 32 F	34.531
Grams/sq cm	Lb/sq in.	70.30
Gravity (sea level)	Ft/(sec)(sec)	0.03108
Half life	Mean life (for radioactive decay)	0.693
Inches	Centimeters	0.3937
Inches	Microns	3.9370×10^{-5}
Inches	Mils	0.001
Inches of Hg @ 32 F	Atmospheres	29.921
Inches of Hg @ 32 F	Ft of H_2O @ 39.2 F	0.88265
Inches of Hg @ 32 F	Lb/sq in.	2.0360

To Obtain	Multiply	By
Inches of Hg @ 0 C	In.of H_2O @ 4 C	0.07355
Inches of H_2O @ 4 C	In. of Hg @ 0 C	13.60
Inches of H_2O @ 39.2 F	Lb/sq in.	27.673
Joules	Btu	1054.8
Joules	Calories	4.186
Joules	Ergs	1×10^{-7}
Joules	Fissions (@ 200 Mev/fission)	3.2041×10^{-11}
Joules	Ft-lb	1.35582
Joules	Kw-hr	3.6000×10^6
Joules	Mech. hp-hr	2.6845×10^6
Joules	Watt-sec	1
Joules/gram	Btu/lb	2.3255
Kg	Pounds (avoir.)	0.45359
Kg	Slugs	14.594
Kg	Tons (metric)	1000
Kg-cal	Ergs	2.388×10^{-11}
Kg-cal (mean)	Btu (mean)	0.2520
Kg-cal (mean)	Joules	2.389×10^{-4}
Kg-cal (mean)	Kw-hr	860.01
Kg-cal (mean)	Mech. hp-hr	641.3
Kg-cal/cu meter	Btu/cu ft	8.899
Kg-cal/(hr)(sq meter) (deg C)	Btu/(hr)(sq ft) (deg F)	4.88
Kg-cal/(hr)(sq meter) (deg C per cm)	Btu/(hr)(sq ft) (deg F per in.)	12.40
Kg-cal/kg	Btu/lb	0.5556
Kg-cal/kw hr	Btu/kw hr	0.2520
Kg-cal/min	Kw	14.33
Kg-cal/min	Mech. hp	10.70
Kg/cu meter	Lb/cu ft	16.018
Kg/(hr)(meter)	Centipoises	3.60
Kg/liter	Lb/gal. (U.S.A., liquid)	0.11983
Kg/meter	Lb/ft	1.488
Kg/sq cm	Atmospheres	1.0332
Kg/sq cm	Lb/sq in.	0.0703
Kg/sq meter	Lb/sq in.	703.07
Kw	Btu/sec	1.055
Kw	Ergs/sec	1×10^{-10}
Kw	Ft-lb/sec	0.00135582
Kw	Kg-cal/min	0.06972
Kw	Mech. hp	0.7457
Kw-hr	Btu	2.930×10^{-4}
Kw-hr	Fissions (@ 200 Mev/fission)	8.9058×10^{-18}
Kw-hr	Ft-lb	3.7662×10^{-7}
Kw-hr	Grams of U–235 fissioned	23,000
Kw-hr	Joules	2.7778×10^{-7}
Kw-hr	Kg-cal	0.0011628
Kw-hr	Mech. hp-hr	0.7457
Kw-hr	Megawatt-days	24×10^3
Kw-hr	Lb water evaporated from and at 212 F	0.2843
Liters	Gal. (Imperial)	4.546
Liters	Gal. (U.S.A., liquid)	3.78533
Mean life (= 1/disintegration constant)	Half life	1.443
Mech. hp	Btu/sec	1.4145
Mech. hp	Ergs/sec	1.3412×10^{-10}
Mech. hp	Ft-lb/min	3.0303×10^{-5}
Mech. hp	Ft-lb/sec	0.0018182
Mech. hp	Kg-cal/min	0.093557
Mech. hp	Kw	1.3410
Mech. hp	Watts	0.0013410
Mech. hp-hr	Btu	0.00039292
Mech. hp-hr	Joules	3.725×10^{-7}
Mech. hp-hr	Kg-calories	0.0015593
Mech. hp-hr	Kw-hr	1.3410
Megawatt-days	Btu	1.2208×10^{-8}
Megawatt-days	Fissions (@ 200 Mev/fission)	3.7108×10^{-22}
Megawatt-days	Kw-hr	41.667×10^{-6}
Megawatt-days	Mech. hp-hr	3.107×10^{-5}
Meters	Inches	0.0254
Meters	Microns	1×10^{-6}
Meters^{-2}	Cm^{-2} (of buckling)	1×10^4
Meters^{-2} (of buckling)	Microbucks	1×10^{-2}
Microbucks	(Meters)$^{-2}$ (of buckling)	1×10^2
Microbucks, $\mu\beta$	Cm^{-2} (of buckling)	1×10^6
Microns	Centimeters	1×10^4
Microns	Inches	25,400
Microns	Mils	25.4
Miles (nautical)	Km	0.54
Miles (Int. nautical)	Miles U.S.A., statute)	0.8690
Milliliters/gram	Cu ft/lb	62.42621
Millimeters	Microns	0.001
Million electron volts (Mev)	Atomic mass units	931.16
Million electron volts (Mev)	Btu	6.584×10^{15}
Million electron volts (Mev)	Calories	2.6126×10^{13}
Million electron volts (Mev)	Ergs	624190
Million electron volts (Mev)	Kw-hr	2.2472×10^{19}
Million electron volts (Mev)	Megawatt-days	5.3916×10^{23}
Million electron volts (Mev)	Rest energy of electron $= mc^2$	0.5110
Million electron volts (Mev)	Watt-sec	6.2419×10^{12}
Mev absorbed/cu cm of standard air	Roentgens	0.000677
Mev absorbed/gram of air	Roentgens	5.24×10^{-7}
Mills/kw-hr (electric)	Cents/million Btu (thermal)	0.03413/ efficiency
Mils	Centimeters	393.7
Mils	Inchs	1000
Mils	Microns	0.03937
Minutes	Radians	3437.75
Neutrons/cm (= nvt)	Neutrons/kilobarn	1×10^{21}
Neutrons produced by U-235 fission	Btu	8.16×10^{13}
Neutrons produced by U-235 fission (@ 200 Mev/fission)	Kw-hr	2.7865×10^{17}
Neutrons produced by U-235 fission (@ 200 Mev/fission)	Megawatt-days	6.69×10^{21}

To Obtain	Multiply	By
Neutrons produced by U-235 fission (@ 200 Mev/fission)	Watt-sec	7.74×10^{10}
Number of molecules	Moles (gram)	0.60248×10^{24}
Ounces (avoir.)	Grains (avoir.)	0.0022857143
Ounces (avoir.)	Grams	0.035274
Ounces (U.S.A., liquid)	Gal. (U.S.A., liquid)	128.0
Parts per million	Grains per gal. (U.S.A., liquid)	17.118
Period	e-folding time	1.0
Poises	Centipoises	0.01
Poundals	Pounds (avoir.)	32.174
Pound-ft	Dyne-cm	7.3756×10^{-8}
Pounds	Dynes	2.248×10^{-6}
Pounds	Grains	0.00001429
Pounds	Slugs	32.174
Pounds (avoir.)	Grams	0.002205
Pounds (avoir.)	Kg	2.2046
Pounds/(sec)(ft)	Centipoises	0.000672
Pounds of H$_2$O evap. from and at 212 F	Kw-hr	3.5173
Pounds/cu ft	Pounds/gal	7.48
Pounds/gal	Grams/cu cm	8.3454
Pounds/hr	Kg/min	132.28
Pounds/(hr)(ft)	Centipoises	2.42
Pounds/(sec)(ft)	Centipoises	0.000672
Pounds/sq inch	Atmospheres	14.696
Pounds/sq inch	Bars	14.504
Pounds/sq inch	Cm of Hg @ 0 C	0.19337
Pounds/sq inch	Dynes/sq cm	0.000014504
Pounds/sq inch	Ft of H$_2$O @ 39.2 F	0.43352
Pounds/sq inch	Grams/sq cm	0.014223
Pounds/sq inch	Inches of Hg @ 32 F	0.491
Pounds/sq inch	Inches of H$_2$O @ 39.2 F	0.0361
Pounds/gal. (U.S.A., liquid)	Kg/liter	8.3452
Pounds/sq inch	Kg/sq cm	14.223
Pounds/sq inch	Kg/sq meter	0.0014223
Pounds/gal. (U.S.A., liquid)	Pounds/cu ft	0.1337
Pounds/gal. (U.S.A., liquid)	Pounds/cu inch	231
Radians	Degrees	0.017453
Radians	Revolutions	6.283
Radians/sec	Cycles/sec	6.2832

To Obtain	Multiply	By
Rutherfords	Curies	37,000
Rutherfords	Disintegrations/min	1.6667×10^{-8}
Rutherfords	Disintegrations/sec	0.000001
Slugs	Pounds (avoir.)	0.03108
Sq centimeters	Barns	1×10^{-24}
Sq centimeters	Circular inches	5.0671
Sq centimeters	Circular mils	5.067×10^{-6}
Sq centimeters	Sq inches	6.4516
Sq ft	Acres	43560
Sq ft	Sq meters	10.764
Sq inches	Circular inches	0.7854
Sq inches	Circular mils	7.854×10^{-7}
Sq inches	Sq centimeters	0.15500
Sq meters	Sq ft	0.0929
Sq mils	Circular mils	0.7854
Sq mils	Sq cm	155,000
Sq mils	Sq inches	1,000,000
Thermal neutron flux in fuel (average)	Kw/kg U-235	2.43×10^{10}
Tonnes	Tons, metric	1.0
Tons (metric)	Tons (short)	0.9072
Tons (short)	Tons (metric)	1.1023
Viscosity in centipoises	Poises	100
Viscosity in grams/(sec)(cm)	Poises	1.0
Viscosity in lb/(hr)(ft)	Centipoises	2.4192
Viscosity in lb/(sec)(ft)	Centipoises	0.000672
Viscosity in kg/(hr)(meter)	Centipoises	3.60
Watts	Btu/hr	0.29293
Watts	Fissions/sec	3.204×10^{-11}
Watts	Ft-lb/sec	1.3558
Watts	Joules/sec	1.0
Watt-hr	Btu	0.2930
Watt-hr	Calories	1.1628×10^{-3}
Watt-hr	Ft-lb	3.7662×10^{-4}
Watt-hr	Joules	2.778×10^{-4}
Watts/(cm)(deg C)	Btu/(hr)(ft)(deg F)	0.01730
Watts/sq cm	Btu/(hr)(sq ft)	3.1534×10^{-4}
Watts/(sq cm)(deg C)	Btu/(hr)(sq ft)(deg F)	5.676×10^{-4}
Watt-sec	Btu	1054.8
Watt-sec	Calories	4.186
Watt-sec	Gram-cm	9.8066×10^{-5}
Watt-sec	Joules	1.0

PROPERTIES OF HIGH PRESSURE SUPERHEATED STEAM

Psia		900 F	1000 F	1100 F	1200 F
1250	v	0.5980	0.6558	0.7113	0.7644
	h	1437.7	1497.1	1555.4	1612.6
	s	1.5813	1.6235	1.6620	1.6975
1800	v	0.3986	0.4425	0.4834	0.5224
	h	1416.0	1480.6	1542.0	1601.8
	s	1.5290	1.5748	1.6155	1.6526
2400	v	0.2836	0.3205	0.3538	0.3848
	h	1388.5	1460.8	1526.9	1589.8
	s	1.4810	1.5323	1.5761	1.6152
3206.2	v	0.1980	0.2290	0.2564	0.2816
	h	1353.4	1434.8	1507.3	1575.1
	s	1.4293	1.4872	1.5351	1.5773
3500	v	0.1762	0.2058	0.2313	0.2546
	h	1340.7	1424.5	1496.6	1563.3
	s	1.4127	1.4723	1.5201	1.5615

Psia		900 F	1000 F	1100 F	1200 F
4000	v	0.1462	0.1743	0.1979	0.2192
	h	1314.4	1406.8	1482.9	1552.1
	s	1.3827	1.4482	1.4987	1.5417
5000	v	0.1036	0.1303	0.1513	0.1696
	h	1256.5	1369.5	1455.0	1529.5
	s	1.3231	1.4034	1.4602	1.5066
6000	v	0.0755	0.1013	0.1207	0.1370
	h	1192.5	1330.5	1427.2	1507.7
	s	1.2642	1.3622	1.4263	1.4765
8000	v	0.0458	0.0673	0.0844	0.0985
	h	1074.4	1250.8	1369.8	1463.9
	s	1.1614	1.2867	1.3657	1.4243
10,000	v	0.0353	0.0495	0.0635	0.0760
	h	1012.9	1181.0	1313.3	1419.7
	s	1.1050	1.2243	1.3122	1.3784

Values from 1250 to 3206.2 psia from "Steam Tables" © 1940, Combustion Engineering, Inc.

Values for 3500, 4000, 5000 psia from "Thermodynamic Properties of Steam" by J. H. Keenan and F. G. Keyes, © 1936, courtesy of John Wiley & Sons.

Values for 6000, 8000 and 10000 psia from "Properties of Steam at High Pressures—An Interim Steam Table" © 1956, courtesy A.S.M.E.

PROPERTIES OF WATER AND SATURATED STEAM

From "Steam Tables," copyright 1940. Combustion Engineering, Inc.

Absolute Pressure Lb./Sq. in.	Sat. Temp. Degrees Fahr.	Sp. Volume Sat. Liquid	Sp. Volume Sat. Vapor	Enthalpy Sat. Liquid	Enthalpy Sat. Vapor
1	101.76	0.01614	333.79	69.72	1105.2
5	162.25	0.01641	73.600	130.13	1130.8
10	193.21	0.01659	38.462	161.17	1143.3
14.696	212.00	0.01672	26.828	180.07	1150.4
15	213.03	0.01672	26.320	181.11	1150.7
20	227.96	0.01683	20.110	196.16	1156.1
25	240.07	0.01692	16.321	208.41	1160.4
30	250.34	0.01700	13.763	218.83	1164.0
35	259.28	0.01708	11.907	227.92	1167.0
40	267.24	0.01715	10.506	236.02	1169.7
45	274.45	0.01721	9.408	243.38	1172.0
50	281.01	0.01727	8.522	250.09	1174.0
55	287.07	0.01732	7.792	256.30	1175.8
60	292.71	0.01738	7.179	262.10	1177.5
65	297.97	0.01743	6.654	267.51	1179.1
70	302.92	0.01748	6.210	272.61	1180.5
75	307.60	0.01752	5.820	277.44	1181.9
80	312.03	0.01757	5.476	282.02	1183.1
85	316.25	0.01761	5.169	286.40	1184.3
90	320.27	0.01766	4.898	290.57	1185.4
95	324.13	0.01770	4.653	294.58	1186.4
100	327.83	0.01774	4.433	298.43	1187.3
105	331.38	0.01778	4.232	302.13	1188.2
110	334.79	0.01782	4.050	305.69	1189.0
115	338.08	0.01785	3.882	309.13	1189.8
120	341.26	0.01789	3.728	312.46	1190.6
125	344.34	0.01792	3.586	315.69	1191.3
130	347.31	0.01796	3.455	318.81	1192.0
135	350.21	0.01799	3.333	321.86	1192.7
140	353.03	0.01803	3.220	324.83	1193.3
145	355.76	0.01806	3.114	327.71	1193.9
150	358.43	0.01809	3.016	330.53	1194.4
155	361.02	0.01812	2.921	333.27	1195.0
160	363.55	0.01815	2.834	335.95	1195.5
165	366.01	0.01818	2.752	338.55	1195.9
170	368.42	0.01821	2.674	341.11	1196.3
175	370.77	0.01824	2.601	343.61	1196.7
180	373.08	0.01827	2.532	346.07	1197.2
185	375.34	0.01830	2.466	348.47	1197.6
190	377.55	0.01833	2.404	350.83	1198.0
195	379.70	0.01836	2.344	353.13	1198.4
200	381.82	0.01839	2.288	355.40	1198.7
210	385.93	0.01844	2.183	359.80	1199.4
220	389.89	0.01850	2.086	364.05	1199.9
230	393.70	0.01855	1.9989	368.16	1200.4
240	397.40	0.01860	1.9176	372.16	1200.9
250	400.97	0.01866	1.8431	376.04	1201.4
260	404.43	0.01870	1.7742	379.78	1201.8
270	407.79	0.01875	1.7101	383.43	1202.2
280	411.06	0.01880	1.6504	386.99	1202.5
290	414.24	0.01885	1.5947	390.47	1202.9
300	417.33	0.01890	1.5426	393.85	1203.2
310	420.35	0.01894	1.4938	397.16	1203.5
320	423.29	0.01899	1.4479	400.40	1203.8
330	426.16	0.01903	1.4048	403.56	1204.0
340	428.96	0.01908	1.3640	406.65	1204.2
350	431.71	0.01912	1.3255	409.70	1204.4
360	434.39	0.01917	1.2889	412.67	1204.5
370	437.01	0.01921	1.2545	415.58	1204.6
380	439.59	0.01925	1.2217	418.45	1204.7
390	442.11	0.01930	1.1904	421.27	1204.8
400	444.58	0.0193	1.1609	424.02	1204.9
410	447.00	0.0194	1.1327	426.74	1205.0
420	449.38	0.0194	1.1058	429.42	1205.0
430	451.72	0.0195	1.0800	432.05	1205.0
440	454.01	0.0195	1.0554	434.63	1205.0
450	456.27	0.0195	1.0318	437.18	1205.0
460	458.48	0.0196	1.0092	439.69	1205.0
470	460.66	0.0196	0.9875	442.17	1205.0
480	462.80	0.0197	0.9668	444.60	1205.0
490	464.91	0.0197	0.9466	447.00	1204.9
500	467.00	0.0197	0.9274	449.40	1204.9
510	469.05	0.0198	0.9090	451.75	1204.8
520	471.07	0.0198	0.8912	454.07	1204.7
530	473.05	0.0199	0.8741	456.35	1204.6
540	475.02	0.0199	0.8576	458.62	1204.5
550	476.94	0.0199	0.8416	460.83	1204.4
560	478.85	0.0200	0.8263	463.04	1204.3
570	480.73	0.0200	0.8114	465.22	1204.1
580	482.58	0.0201	0.7968	467.37	1204.0
590	484.41	0.0201	0.7831	469.50	1203.8
600	486.21	0.0201	0.7695	471.59	1203.6
620	489.75	0.0202	0.7438	475.72	1203.3
640	493.21	0.0203	0.7197	479.79	1202.9
660	496.58	0.0204	0.6969	483.77	1202.5
680	499.87	0.0204	0.6757	487.64	1202.1
700	503.09	0.0205	0.6552	491.49	1201.6
725	507.01	0.0206	0.6314	496.2	1200.9
750	510.83	0.0207	0.6091	500.8	1200.2
775	514.57	0.0208	0.5882	505.3	1199.5
800	518.20	0.0209	0.5685	509.7	1198.8
825	521.75	0.0210	0.5500	514.0	1198.0
850	525.23	0.0210	0.5326	518.3	1197.2
875	528.62	0.0211	0.5162	522.4	1196.4
900	531.94	0.0212	0.5006	526.6	1195.6
925	535.20	0.0213	0.4858	530.6	1194.7
950	538.38	0.0214	0.4717	534.6	1193.8
975	541.50	0.0215	0.4583	538.5	1192.9
1000	544.56	0.0216	0.4456	542.4	1191.9
1050	550.52	0.0218	0.4219	550.0	1190.0
1100	556.26	0.0219	0.4002	557.4	1187.8
1150	561.81	0.0221	0.3804	564.6	1185.6
1200	567.19	0.0223	0.3620	571.7	1183.2
1250	572.39	0.0225	0.3453	578.6	1180.8
1300	577.43	0.0227	0.3294	585.4	1178.3
1350	582.32	0.0229	0.3147	592.1	1175.8
1400	587.07	0.0231	0.3011	598.6	1173.2
1450	591.70	0.0233	0.2885	605.0	1170.5
1500	596.20	0.0235	0.2765	611.4	1167.7
1550	600.59	0.0237	0.2653	617.7	1164.8
1600	604.87	0.0239	0.2548	623.9	1161.9
1650	609.05	0.0241	0.2448	630.0	1158.8
1700	613.12	0.0243	0.2354	636.1	1155.7
1750	617.11	0.0245	0.2265	642.1	1152.5
1800	621.00	0.0247	0.2180	648.0	1149.3
1850	624.82	0.0249	0.2099	653.9	1145.9
1900	628.55	0.0252	0.2022	659.9	1142.4
1950	632.20	0.0254	0.1949	665.8	1138.8
2000	635.78	0.0257	0.1879	671.7	1135.2
2050	639.29	0.0259	0.1812	677.6	1131.4
2100	642.73	0.0262	0.1748	683.4	1127.6
2150	646.11	0.0265	0.1685	689.2	1123.5
2200	649.42	0.0267	0.1626	695.0	1119.4
2250	652.67	0.0270	0.1569	700.8	1115.3
2300	655.87	0.0274	0.1514	706.7	1111.0
2350	659.00	0.0277	0.1462	712.6	1106.5
2400	662.02	0.0280	0.1410	718.5	1101.4
2450	665.12	0.0283	0.1360	724.6	1096.3
2500	668.10	0.0287	0.1313	730.7	1091.0
2550	671.03	0.0291	0.1264	736.7	1085.6
2600	673.91	0.0295	0.1219	743.1	1080.1
2650	676.75	0.0300	0.1173	749.5	1074.5
2700	679.54	0.0305	0.1123	756.1	1068.3
2750	682.28	0.0310	0.1077	763.0	1061.8
2800	684.98	0.0316	0.1032	770.0	1054.6
2850	687.65	0.0322	0.0986	777.5	1046.6
2900	690.26	0.0329	0.0941	785.2	1038.1
2950	692.83	0.0337	0.0895	793.6	1028.9
3000	695.37	0.0346	0.0849	802.6	1019.3
3050	697.84	0.0357	0.0804	812.9	1007.7
3100	700.29	0.0372	0.0752	824.6	994.0
3150	702.69	0.0392	0.0691	841.3	976.3
3200	705.04	0.0443	0.0596	871.3	946.6
3206.2	705.34	0.0541	0.0541	910.3	910.3

Appendix D

Properties of Steam

THERE IS an ancient as well as a continuing relationship between the thermodynamic properties of steam and the design of boilers and power plant prime movers. Research in this field knows neither professional nor national boundaries. Most of the activity involves extremely precise physical measurements and mathematical formulation of these physical relationships as workable tables for hand calculation or complex correlations for computer use. Contributors to research relating to properties of steam have ranged from the American and British physicists, Josiah Willard Gibbs and Hugh L. Callendar, to the French experimentalist, Henry Victor Regnault, the German thermodynamicist, Richard Mollier and the contemporary Russian science professors, M. P. Vukalovich and N. B. Vargaftik. Mechanical engineers in industry and in engineering colleges have provided the stimulus for much of the steam table research of the past century and have used the results in the design of power plants of ever advancing steam conditions.

One of the earliest written records of interest in the properties of steam appears in the *Philosophical Transactions* of 1741 of the Royal Society of London. It pre-sents the results of experimental work conducted by John Payne and reported under the impressive title of "A Narrative of a New Invention of Expanding Fluids, by Their Being Conveyed into Certain Ignified Vessels, Where They Are Immediately Rarefied into an Elastic Impelling Force, Sufficient to Give Motion to Hydraulo-pneumatical and Other Engines, for Raising Water, and Other Uses, &c." The contemporary reader should find the following selected observations of interest.[1]

1. That a pot or vessel, of the size and shape here mentioned, will (being kept to a dark red heat, and the water regularly dispersed) rarefy or expand 50 gallons of water, wine measure, per hour.

2. That a cube inch of water will make in practice 4000 inches of steam; or that the elastic steam of one cube inch of water is sufficient to exclude the air out of a vessel that is in content 4000 inches.

3. That the above 50 gallons will produce 46,000,000 cube inches of elastic steam per hour, which is per minute 770,000. . . .

6. That by an experiment made at a fire engine, 40 gallons of water per hour, made into elastic steam in this method, will effectually give motion to a 24 inch cylinder fire engine.

7. That, by true experiments made at Wedgbury and Newcastle on Tyne, one hun-

---

[1] The original paper may be found in Vol. 41, Part 2, 1739–1741, pp. 821–828.

dred weight, containing 112 lb of pit coals, will, and is sufficient in this method to expand or rarefy 90 gallons of water per hour into an elastic steam or vapour.

8. That, by the best accounts and observations I could get and make, they consume under their boilers to make the same quantity of steam, three hundred weight of pit coal, at 112 lb to the hundred, in working a fire engine one hour. . . .

James Watt also aided in the early understanding of the properties of steam and conducted many experiments on his own and in collaboration with James Southern.[2] Perhaps the outstanding 19th century experimental contributions were made by Henry Victor Regnault, a physical chemist whose work in measuring physical properties of steam and many other substances encompassed three volumes.[3] The course of thermodynamic research and development was greatly influenced by this experimental work as exemplified by acknowledgments in two widely used 19th century textbooks, *A Manual of the Steam Engine and Other Prime Movers* by W. J. M. Rankine and *Technical Thermodynamics* by Gustav Zeuner. Richard Mollier, who succeeded Zeuner as professor of thermodynamics at the Technischen Hochschule in Dresden, represents a link between the experimental contributions of Regnault and the conceptual formulations of Josiah Willard Gibbs. Mollier first proposed the familiar enthalpy-entropy diagram that commonly bears his name, this being but one of his several pioneering developments using graphical methods for the solution of thermodynamic problems.[4]

An outstanding British contributor to the theoretical and experimental understanding of the properties of steam was Hugh L. Callendar whose systems of equations to represent these properties first appeared in the *Proceedings* of the Royal Society in 1900 and were subsequently adapted by Mollier for a set of German steam tables published in seven editions between 1906 and 1932. In Great Britain *The Callendar Steam Tables* made their initial appearance in 1915 followed by *The Enlarged Callendar Steam Tables* in 1924.

There was comparatively little research in steam properties in the United States prior to an informal conference held at Harvard University on June 23, 1921. Under the leadership of Professor Lionel S. Marks and George Orrok, an influential consulting engineer in the steam power field as well as an active member of

---

[2] This is discussed in a British book published in 1822 under the title, *The Articles, Steam and Steam Engines, Written for the Encyclopaedia Britannica* by John Robison, with notes and additions by James Watt and *A Letter on Some Properties of Steam* by John Southern. Additional information on the contribution of Watt to steam table research may be found in *The Steam Engine Explained and Illustrated* by Dionysius Lardner, Seventh Edition, London, 1840, pp. 90–96.

[3] These were published in Paris in 1847, 1862 and 1870 under the title of *Relation des expériences pour déterminer les principales lois et les données numériques qui entrent dans le calcul des machines à vapeur*.

[4] The original reference for what is now known as the Mollier diagram is "Neue Diagramme zur technischen Warmelehre", *Zeitschrift des VDI*, Vol. 48, Feb. 20, 1904, pp. 271–275. See also *International Journal of Heat and Mass Transfer*, Vol. 7, January 1964, Special Issue — Centenary Tribute to Richard Mollier, and an article by L. M. K. Boelter and Eldon L. Knuth, "The Works of Richard Mollier," which appeared in the February 1964 issue of the same publication, pp. 125–132.

ASME, the fourteen participants in this conference discussed the possibility of obtaining accurate data for considerably higher steam conditions.[5] As a result ASME organized a Special Research Committee on Thermal Properties of Steam and obtained contributions of $85,000 from manufacturers of steam power equipment and the principal electric utilities to underwrite an eight year study of steam properties. Most of the experimental work was done at the Massachusetts Institute of Technology under Frederick G. Keyes and at the Harvard Engineering School under Harvey N. Davis, and this was linked to the development of a set of steam tables begun by Joseph H. Keenan as a member of the turbine engineering department of the General Electric Company. In 1928 Keenan joined the faculty of Stevens Institute of Technology, whose presidency had been assumed by Davis, and their work continued there under the support and sponsorship of the same ASME Special Research Committee.

With research along similar lines known to be under way in Great Britain and Germany, the time was opportune for international collaboration. The appropriate call in the tradition of technical journalistic leadership was sounded by Fred R. Low, a past president of ASME and the distinguished editor of *Power*, in an appeal published in the March 26, 1929 issue under the editorial title, "The Physical Properties of Steam."

". . . It would be a great thing for science and for the engineering profession if all the outstanding workers in this field from all over the world could be brought together for a comparison of methods and results, an analysis of their differences and their probable causes.

"If agreement upon a set of values could be arrived at by such a conference of experts, we should have a basis worthy of international acceptance on which each country or organization could predicate its own formulas, diagrams and tables upon whatever coordinates, in whatever units and with whatever arrangement it desired."

The First International Steam Tables Conference met in London later that year with representatives from the United Kingdom, Czechoslovakia, Germany and the United States. A notable achievement was the adoption of the first International Skeleton Steam Tables, even though these were very limited in scope and range. The second conference was held in Berlin in 1930 followed by the Third International Conference in 1934 which met in Washington, D.C., New York City and Cambridge, Mass. The major achievement of the latter was the acceptance of the definitive International Skeleton Steam Tables of 1934, these being accompanied by estimates of accuracy or tolerances and including the designation of fundamental units, definitions and conversion relationships. A Fourth International Steam Tables Conference had been planned for 1939 but was abandoned because of economic conditions and the outbreak of World War II.

If engineers in general accepted the 1934 Skeleton Tables (upon which were based the more complete steam tables such as those by Keenan and Keyes published in the United States in 1936, the 1939 British tables by G. S. Callendar and A. C. Egerton, the 1950 revised tables of the Japan Society of Mechanical Engi-

---

[5] A historical summary of steam tables published in the United States prior to 1921 appears in an article by A. M. Greene, "Early U.S. Steam Tables," *Mechanical Engineering*, Vol. 56, 1934, pp. 715–717, 764.

neers and the 1952 German VDI tables by W. Koch and E. Schmidt), there remained some restless stirrings such as the continuing research efforts on steam properties conducted in Russia. American readers first learned of this in March 1953 through publication in *Combustion* of an article by H. Erythropel entitled "New Steam Table Up to 700 C". By coincidence the editor of *Combustion* was a former protégé and colleague of Fred R. Low, and it was the knowledge which Alfred D. Blake had of the earlier international steam table conferences, plus his recognition of the significance of the German technical literature, that prompted him to do two things immediately after the November 1, 1952 issue of *Zeitschrift des VDI* arrived on his desk. He requested W. W. Schroedter to translate the Erythropel article which told of unprecedented experimental work up to steam conditions of 1112 F, 4266 psia as set forth in the 1951 Russian steam tables prepared by M. P. Vukalovich. He also asked Glenn R. Fryling to prepare the article for publication and to write an editorial for the March 1953 issue of *Combustion,* suggesting that it include a look backward and a look forward. The following excerpts from the editorial entitled "International Steam Table Conferences" are pertinent to this account of the historical evolution of research on properties of steam.

"As steam conditions in central stations push higher and higher, the validity of steam tables, and particularly their reliability for use in heat balance computations, becomes of ever increasing importance. In the past The American Society of Mechanical Engineers has shown considerable interest in comprehensive research of the properties of

steam, as also have mechanical engineering groups in other countries. Some means should be found to reconvene interested steam table authorities into a Fourth International Steam Table Conference. Its benefits would be in keeping with the following comments from an editorial [written by Alfred D. Blake] in these columns in September 1934:

"'It has been said that engineering knows no national borders, yet economic conditions in different countries exert a strong influence on engineering practice. On the other hand, the properties of steam are universal, and, granting equal accuracy of observations, discrepancies in the results of different investigators must be attributable to methods. That the values are likely to be brought into line for all practical purposes represents a monumental accomplishment well worth the money and effort put into the work.'"

This appeal for a Fourth International Steam Table Conference was followed a month later by a discussion of papers on central station turbines at the American Power Conference in which Blake reported that one utility and several equipment manufacturers were making studies for topping a midwestern station with a 4500 psig, 1200 F unit employing two stages of reheat.[6] Formal public announcement that this pioneering commercial supercritical pressure unit was to be located at the Philo Station of Ohio Power Company was made on May 21, 1953, and a little more than a year later, on August 29, 1954, Philadelphia Electric Company announced plans to build an even larger unit operating at 5000 psig, 1200 F.

To its credit ASME responded to the obvious need for additional research on steam properties to supplement the limited amount of experimental and extrapolated data upon which to design boilers and turbines for supercritical pressure operation in central stations. Invitations were

[6] This is as reported in *Combustion,* Vol. 24, April 1953, p. 49. The actual design and operating temperature was 1150 F.

extended to hold another international conference which was renamed the Fourth International Conference on Properties of Steam and scheduled for Philadelphia in September 1954 coincidental with the meeting of the International Electrotechnical Commission. Professors F. G. Keyes and J. H. Keenan of Massachusetts Institute of Technology, both of whom had participated in the three preceding International Steam Table Conferences, made these pertinent observations in a paper originally prepared for delivery at the Philadelphia conference.

"It was the cherished hope of the conferees in 1934 that the limits of temperature range, 550 C (1032 F) and of pressure, 350 atm (5000 psia) attained in the investigation of water substance would serve all requirements in the science and art of power production for the lifetime of the youngest conference participants. The hope has not been realized, for now we envisage the need for accurate data at even higher temperatures and greater pressures.

"Nor is this all, for we require far more exact and verified data for the viscosity and thermal conductivity of water substance than exist at present. Finally, it is now highly desirable that a comprehensive investigation be pursued on the relation of the international scale of temperature to the thermodynamic scale. . . ."[7]

The limits for the International Skeleton Steam Tables were set at the 1954 Philadelphia meeting at 15,000 psia, 1500 F, and Russia was invited to participate in the Fifth International Conference on Properties of Steam which was held in London in July of 1956. The main technical recommendation of the Fifth Conference was the adoption of the International

MKS system of units for all future work. The Sixth International Conference on the Properties of Steam met in New York in October 1963, and from it emerged the adoption of skeleton tables of the values of (a) thermodynamic properties of saturated water and saturated steam; (b) specific volume of compressed water and superheated steam; and (c) specific enthalpy of compressed water and superheated steam. The values in the skeleton tables cover pressure and temperature ranges of from 0 to 1000 bars (14,500 psia) and from 0 to 800 C (1470 F). In November 1964 a supplementary release provided skeleton tables of the transport properties of water substance, including the viscosity of compressed water and superheated steam and the thermal conductivity of compressed water and superheated steam.[8]

At a meeting of the Thermal Conductivity Panel of the Sixth International Conference on the Properties of Steam held in Paris in June of 1964, during which the Skeleton Tables of Viscosity and Thermal Conductivity of Water Substance were drawn up, J. A. Tillinghast of the American delegation spoke of future work on properties of steam. He indicated that the ASME Research Committee on Properties of Steam expected publication of new tables for use by steam plant engineers in units of pounds force per square inch and Btu per pound. The view of the Committee was that properties of water substance would then be adequately defined for the next decade or longer. These remarks were supplemented by Professor J. Kestin of the American delegation, who told of the projected National Reference Data System

---

[7] This was subsequently published under the title, "The Present Status of Steam Properties," in *Mechanical Engineering*, Vol. 77, February 1955, pp. 127–132.

[8] See "Sixth International Conference on the Properties of Steam — A Report" by J. Kestin, *Trans. ASME*, Vol. 87, Series A, 1965, pp. 87–92.

under the management of the U.S. National Bureau of Standards. The general aim would be to collect, correlate and store information on all physical properties of all substances. Rather than publish a large number of detailed tables, the system would be organized around a center in which computers would be used not only to work out correlations but also to store and retrieve information. This center, containing a large number of tapes with provision for easy access, could ultimately provide answers to specific questions transmitted from a distance via communications networks. The overall program for correlating physical property data would be a cooperative one involving government, universities and private industrial organizations.

As of the time of this writing (Spring 1965) the only detailed tables based on the skeleton tables adopted by the Sixth International Conference on the Properties of Steam are those published in Great Britain and Russia. These are *Steam Tables 1964* (Physical Properties of Water and Steam, 0–800 C and 0–1000 bars) prepared by R. W. Bain and published by Her Majesty's Stationery Office, 1964, 147 pages and *Tables of the Thermodynamic Properties of Water and Steam* by M. P. Vukalovich, Seventh Edition, Moscow, 1963, 401 pages. These tables originated in the Moscow Power Institute and cover a range of 0.01 to 970 bars and 0 to 1000 C.

Many American companies have now adapted steam tables for reproduction on digital computers and regularly use these formulations in programmed design calculations. Pending completion of detailed tables under preparation by the ASME Research Committee on Properties of Steam, the detailed tables for use in hand calculations remain *Thermodynamic Properties of Steam* by Joseph H. Keenan and Frederick G. Keyes as published by John Wiley, 89 pages, 1936 and supplemented by "Properties of Steam at High Pressures — An Interim Steam Table" issued as a separate pamphlet by ASME, five pages, 1956.

Another set of tables based on the Skeleton Tables adopted by the Third International Steam Tables Conference of 1934 and a 1940 ASME paper by Erich F. Leib[9] is that issued by Combustion Engineering, Inc. as "Steam Tables — Properties of Saturated and Superheated Steam", Third Edition, 1940, 38 pages. These tables were published in their entirety in the First Edition of *Combustion Engineering* and are available to engineering students and practicing engineers without charge from the General Offices of the corporation in Windsor, Connecticut. Distribution is also made through educational institutions and interested industrial and governmental organizations.

Acknowledgment. The assistance of two ASME staff members, Miss J. Meyer, who helped trace the history of ASME participation in steam properties research, and Prof. S. R. Beitler, who made available information on the International Conferences on Properties of Steam, is greatly appreciated. W. W. Schroedter also deserves credit for helping to locate information on the contributions of Richard Mollier.

---

[9] This was subsequently published in *Trans.* ASME, Vol. 63, 1941, pp. 157–176, as "Thermodynamic Properties of Vapors."

The Sixth International Conference on the Properties of Steam[10]

The First International Steam Tables Conference was held in London in July 1929, and was followed in June 1930 by the Second Conference, held in Berlin. After these two Conferences there were published[11] small Skeleton Tables of Properties of Steam, giving agreed values to which were attached tolerances to cover the differences between the experimental values reported by different investigators.

At the Third Conference, held in New York in September 1934, the Skeleton Tables were reviewed and extended. From that date until the present Sixth Conference the Skeleton Tables remained unchanged. Those Tables were presented in the Report of the Third Conference published in *World Power* 1935 24 (No. 142).

There was a tentative decision at the Third Conference to hold the next Conference in Prague in 1938. The disturbed situation in Europe at the time prevented this, and no further international gathering was held until a conference was convened in Philadelphia in 1954. At that conference the properties of steam were discussed on a wider basis, and it was decided that future work should include consideration of the transport properties of steam. A new title was consequently adopted, the 1954 conference taking the name of the Fourth International Conference on the Properties of Steam and accepting the offer of The American Society of Mechanical Engineers to act as the International Secretariat.

At the Fifth International Conference on the Properties of Steam held in London in July 1956, the Delegations from the Federal Republic of Germany (BRD), the Union of Soviet Socialist Republics (USSR), the United Kingdom (UK) and the United States of America (USA) were asked to form a Commission, with the task of preparing new Skeleton Tables of the properties of water and steam for submission to the Sixth International Conference.

The Commission so formed, having met informally in London in 1957, held its first formal meeting in Moscow in July 1958, adopting there the title of International Coordinating Committee on the Properties of Steam. The second formal meeting was held in Munich in July 1962, and the third in Providence, Rhode Island, and New York in October 1963.

At Moscow, the situation regarding experimental data was generally reviewed, a procedure was set up for the formal submission of data for further consideration, and the intervals and contents of the Skeleton Tables of Thermodynamic Properties were decided upon.

At Munich, the International Coordinating Committee considered draft Skeleton Tables of Thermodynamic Properties submitted by BRD, USSR, UK and USA, together with proposals from Czechoslovakia and Japan. Agreement was reached on a set of tables of thermodynamic properties, subject to certain further re-

---

[10] Prepared under the Editorship of R. W. Haywood, University of Cambridge. The Conference was held in New York City, October 7–10, 1963.

[11] *Mechanical Engineering*, February, 1930, Vol. 52, p. 120 and April, 1931, Vol. 53, p. 289.

finements, and on a procedure for the preparation of draft Skeleton Tables of Transport Properties through the use of certain forms of equations.

After the Munich meeting, the refining of the Skeleton Tables of Thermodynamic Properties was completed and a proposal circulated before the meeting of the International Coordinating Committee in Providence. Further preparatory work on transport properties was also carried out.

At its meetings in Providence and New York, the International Coordinating Committee drew up a Report for presentation to the Sixth International Conference meeting in New York, and the proposals contained in that Report were submitted for the approval of the Conference.

This *Official Release* records the decisions reached by the Conference in regard to revised and extended Tables of Thermodynamic Properties of Water Substance and to the future work of the International Conference on the Properties of Steam.

Thermodynamic Properties of Water Substance

The Conference adopted the Skeleton Tables contained in Supplement A herewith, namely

Table 1.1 Thermodynamic properties of saturated water and saturated steam,

Table 1.2 Specific volume of compressed water and superheated steam,

Table 1.3 Specific enthalpy of compressed water and superheated steam

as the *International Skeleton Tables of the Thermodynamic Properties of Water Substance, 1963.*

The Conference also resolved that the

material contained in Supplement B herewith, relating to the gas constant and to the units used in these Tables, should be published with the Tables.

In adopting these Tables, the Conference recorded its appreciation of the large amount of work carried out on its behalf by the United Kingdom Commission in relation to the Thermodynamic Properties of Steam, with particularly warm thanks to Mr. R. W. Bain.

Submission of Experimental Data

The Conference recorded its thanks to all those who had submitted experimental data on the properties of water and steam. It expressed its particular gratitude to the Soviet Delegation for the large amount of such data that was presented for the consideration of the International Coordinating Committee at its meetings in Moscow, Munich and Providence.

Future Organization and Work of the International Conference

With the ending of the Sixth Conference, the *International Conference on the Properties of Steam* remained in being as a standing body, and its future organization and work were defined by the Sixth Conference in the following resolution:

Recognizing the excellent work done by the International Coordinating Committee, the need for continuation of this type of work, and the need to formulate data from this Conference into universally accepted computer formulations, it is resolved that:

(1) The International Coordinating Committee, created by the Fifth International Conference on the Properties of Steam to prepare for this Sixth International Conference, be dissolved with ex-

pression of this Conference's deep appreciation of its efforts and the success of its work.

(2) The Seventh International Conference on the Properties of Steam shall be convened about five years hence. The date, place and agenda shall be determined by a *Steering Committee* of the Federal Republic of Germany, the Union of Soviet Socialist Republics, the United Kingdom and the United States of America. In due time, this Steering Committee shall appoint any persons to such committees as it may deem desirable for the purpose of preparing for the work of the Seventh Conference.

(3) A new Committee be named, to be known as the *International Formulation Committee* of the Sixth International Conference on the Properties of Steam. This Committee shall consist of six national formulation teams, each consisting of two members and each named by and representing respectively Czechoslovakia, the Federal Republic of Germany, Japan, the Union of Soviet Socialist Republics, the United Kingdom and the United States of America. This Formulation Committee is charged by this Conference to:

(a) Develop at the earliest practical date a formulation, for use with computers, of the properties of steam as they are represented by the International Skeleton Tables of 1963. This formulation shall provide values that are, at all points, within the tolerances stated in the International Skeleton Ta-

bles of 1963, and shall be thermodynamically consistent.

(b) Give a statement of the tolerances applicable to this formulation in the various ranges covered.

(4) When the work described in (3) above has been completed, the Secretariat shall circulate the formulation and the statement for the approval of those National Delegations present at this Conference, and the Delegations shall then register their vote with the Secretariat either in the affirmative or in the negative. If no vote is received from a Delegation within six weeks of the date of circulation, that Delegation shall be considered to have voted in the affirmative. If the formulation and statement receive the affirmative vote of not less than 60% of the voting Delegations, they shall be published with the authority of this Conference as an internationally recognized formulation.

(5) When the International Formulation Committee has completed the work described in (3) above, it shall disband.

(6) The American Society of Mechanical Engineers be requested to continue to act in the capacity of Secretariat for the International Conference on the Properties of Steam.[12]

(7) This Conference recommends to all countries interested in the properties of steam the formation of National Coordinating Committees in their own countries, and directs that the Secretariat shall, amongst its other duties, disseminate information to the proper officer of each such National Coordinating Committee as

[12] Full reports of the meetings of the International Coordinating Committee in Moscow (1958), Munich (1962) and Providence (1963), of the Fifth Conference in London (1956) and of the Sixth Conference in New York (1963) are contained in the Reports and Proceedings of those gatherings issued by the Secretariat of the International Conference on the Properties of Steam, The American Society of Mechanical Engineers, United Engineering Center, 345 East 47th Street, New York 17, N.Y., USA.

shall have communicated its address to the Secretariat.

Supplement B, Specific Gas Constant, Reference State, Units and Conversion Factors

Molar Gas Constant[13]

The value given by the "NAS-NRC Committee on Fundamental Constants" and recorded in "New Values for the Physical Constants," *Technical News Bulletin* (National Bureau of Standards of USA) 1963 (October) *47*, 175, is

$$(8.314\ 3 \pm 0.001\ 2)\ \text{J/mole K}$$

Molar Mass of H_2O[14]

In the *Comptes Rendus de la Vingt et Unième Conférence (Montréal, 1961)* of the *International Union of Pure and Applied Chemistry* (Butterworths Scientific Publications, London) the molar masses of H and O are given as

$$(1.007\ 97 \pm 0.000\ 01)\ \text{g/mole}$$

and

$$(15.999\ 4 \pm 0.000\ 1)\ \text{g/mole, respectively.}$$

Consequently the molar mass of H_2O is

$$(18.015\ 34 \pm 0.000\ 10)\ \text{g/mole.}$$

Note: The above molar gas constant and molar masses are all on the new unified scale on which the molar mass of carbon 12 is exactly 12 g/mole.

Specific Gas Constant for H_2O

From the above it follows that, for H_2O

$$R = (461.51 \pm 0.07)\ \text{J/kg K}$$

where, following the Report of the NAS-NRC Committee on Fundamental Constants, the deviations indicated are "error limits" and are three times the standard deviations.

Temperature

The Kelvin degree is so defined that the thermodynamic absolute temperature at the triple-point of water substance is indicated exactly by 273.16 *K*.

If one temperature be indicated by T_K K, t_C C, T_R R and t_F F the numerical values are interrelated exactly by

$$t_C = T_K - 273.15,$$
$$t_F = T_R - 459.67,$$
$$t_F = 32 + 1.8\,t_C.$$

In the Skeleton Tables the temperatures are given on the International Practical Scale of Temperature of 1948, which provides a closely approximate realization of the Thermodynamic Celsius Temperature, t_C C. The effects of the error in this approximation are less than the tolerances tabulated.

Pressure

The unit used is the bar

$$1\ \text{bar} = 10^6\ \text{dyn/cm}^2 = 10^5\ \text{N/m}^2$$
$$= 10^5\ \text{pascal} = 10^5\ \text{Pa}$$

Specific Volume

The unit used is the cm^3/g

$$1\ \text{cm}^3/\text{g} = 10^{-3}\ \text{m}^3/\text{kg}$$

---

[13] See also "Report to the Joint IUPAP-IUPAC Commission on Nuclidic Masses and Atomic Constants," by E. R. Cohen and J. W. M. Dumond. (Presented in Vienna, Austria, July 1963).
[14] See also "Report of the International Commission on Atomic Weights (1961)" by A. E. Cameron and Edward Wickers, *J. Amer. Chem. Soc.* 1962 *84*, 4175.

Specific Enthalpy

The unit used is the J/g

$$1 \text{ J/g} = 10^7 \text{ erg/g} = 10^3 \text{ J/kg} = 1 \text{ kW s/kg}$$
$$= 10 \text{ bar cm}^3/\text{g}$$

NOTE: Reference state. At the Fifth International Conference on the Properties of Steam, 1956, it was decided to adopt the liquid phase at the triple-point of water substance as the state for which the specific internal energy and the specific entropy are each made exactly zero.

Conversion to Other Units

The above data link the units used in the Tables with the units of the Système International d'Unités. Conversion to other important units can be achieved by the use of appropriate and evident combinations of the following exact equations:

$$1 \text{ lb} = 0.453\ 592\ 37 \text{ kg}$$
$$1 \text{ ft} = 0.304\ 8 \text{ m}$$
$$1 \text{ deg R} = (5/9) \text{ deg K}$$
$$1 \text{ kgf} = 1 \text{ kp} = 9.806\ 65 \text{ N} = 9.806\ 65 \text{ kg m/s}^2$$
$$1 \text{ lbf} = (9.806\ 65/0.304\ 8) \text{ poundal} = (9.806\ 65/0.304\ 8) \text{ lb ft/s}^2$$
$$1 \text{ cal}_{IT} = 4.186\ 8 \text{ J}$$
$$1 \text{ Btu} = (2.326 \times 453.592\ 37) \text{ J}$$
$$1 \text{ atm} = 1.013\ 25 \text{ bar}$$

All the numbers used in these equations are exact and are given by the International Organization for Standardization (ISO/R 31). The equations for the International Table calorie and the British Thermal Unit are those made definitive by the Fifth International Conference on the Properties of Steam, 1956. The equations for the pound and the foot are in exact accord with more recent legislation in the USA and in the UK.

Supplementary Release on Transport Properties[15]

After the Sixth International Conference on the Properties of Steam, held in New York in October, 1963, the Secretariat issued an *Official Release*. This recorded the decisions reached by the Conference in regard to revised and extended Tables of *Thermodynamic Properties* of Water Substance and to the future work of the International Conference on the Properties of Steam. Study of the current state of knowledge in relation to the *Transport Properties* of Water Substance was not completed at the Sixth Conference. To complete this work the Conference set up a small international Panel, comprising representatives from France, the German Federal Republic, the Union of Soviet So-

cialist Republics, the United Kingdom, and the United States of America. This Panel met in Paris in June, 1964, and there drew up for the first time internationally agreed Skeleton Tables of Viscosity and Thermal Conductivity of Water Substance, which were accompanied by formulae suitable for interpolation in those Tables.

In accordance with a resolution of the Sixth Conference, this material was circulated to and approved by the Heads of all National Delegations attending the Sixth Conference. This *Supplementary Release on Transport Properties* is now issued by the Secretariat under the full authority of the Sixth Conference, and presents in the accompanying Appendices the *Interna-*

---

[15] Issued in November 1964 under the editorship of R. W. Haywood.

tional *Skeleton Tables of the Transport Properties of Water Substance, 1964.* For convenience, the lettering of the Supplements and numbering of the Tables follow in sequence upon those appearing in the Official Release.[16]

Correlating Formulae Suitable for Interpolation in Table 2

The values appearing in Table 2 may be reproduced within the stated tolerances by the use of the appropriate formulae given below, wherein

μ denotes coefficient of viscosity,

ρ denotes density,

p denotes absolute pressure,

p_s denotes absolute pressure at saturation,

t denotes temperature (deg C) on the International Practical Scale of Temperature (1948),

and T denotes absolute temperature (deg K), determined for the present purpose by writing $(T/K) = (t/C) + 273.15$.

2.1 Viscosity of superheated steam at 1 bar pressure in the temperature range 100 C to 700 C

$$\frac{\mu_1}{\text{micropoise}} = 0.407 \left(\frac{t}{C}\right) + 80.4$$

Tolerance: $100 < \frac{t}{C} \leq 300 : \pm 1\%$

$\qquad\qquad 300 < \frac{t}{C} \leq 700 : \pm 3\%$

2.2 Viscosity of superheated steam from 1 bar pressure to saturation pressure in the temperature range 100 C to 300 C

$$\frac{\mu - \mu_1}{\text{micropoise}} = -\frac{\rho}{(\text{g/cm}^3)}\left[1858 - 5.90\left(\frac{t}{C}\right)\right]$$

where μ_1 is given by (2.1).

Tolerance for μ : $\pm 1\%$

2.3 Viscosity of superheated and supercritical steam from 1 bar pressure to 800 bar pressure in the temperature range 375 C to 700 C

$$\frac{\mu - \mu_1}{\text{micropoise}} = 353.0\,[\rho/(\text{g/cm}^3)]$$
$$+ 676.5\,[\rho/(\text{g/cm}^3)]^2$$
$$+ 102.1\,[\rho/(\text{g/cm}^3)]^3$$

where μ_1 is given by (2.1).

Tolerance for μ : $\pm 4\%$

2.4 Viscosity of liquid water along the saturation line from 0 C to 300 C

$$\frac{\mu}{\text{micropoise}} = 241.4 \times 10^{247.8\{[(T/K)-140]^{-1}\}}$$

Tolerance: $\pm 2.5\%$

2.5 Viscosity of liquid water from saturation pressure to 800 bar pressure in the temperature range from 0 C to 300 C

$$\frac{\mu}{\text{micropoise}} = 241.4 \times 10^{247.8\{[(T/K)-140]^{-1}\}}$$
$$\times \left[1 + \frac{(p - p_s)}{10^6\,\text{bar}}\phi\right]$$

where $\phi = 1.0467 \left(\frac{T}{K} - 305\right)$

Tolerance: $1 < \frac{p}{\text{bar}} \leq 350 : \pm 2.5\%$

$\qquad\qquad 350 < \frac{p}{\text{bar}} \leq 800 : \pm 4\%$

---

[16] A full report of the Panel meeting in Paris is contained in the *Official Report* of that meeting, issued by the Secretariat of the International Conference on the Properties of Steam, The American Society of Mechanical Engineers, United Engineering Center, 345 East 47th Street, New York, New York, 10017, USA.

Correlating Formulae Suitable for Interpolation in Table 3

The values appearing in Table 3 may be reproduced within the stated tolerances by the use of the appropriate formulae given below, wherein:

λ denotes thermal conductivity,

ρ denotes density,

p denotes absolute pressure,

p_s denotes absolute pressure at saturation,

t denotes temperature (deg C) on the International Practical Scale of Temperature (1948),

t_s denotes saturation temperature (deg C),

T denotes absolute temperature (deg K), determined for the present purpose by writing $(T/K) = (t/C) + 273.15$,

and $T_0 = 273.15\ K$.

3.1 Thermal conductivity of superheated steam at 1 bar pressure in the temperature range from 100 C to 700 C

$$\frac{\lambda_1}{\text{milliwatt/m K}} = 17.6 + 5.87 \times 10^{-2} \left(\frac{t}{C}\right)$$
$$+ 1.04 \times 10^{-4} \left(\frac{t}{C}\right)^2$$
$$- 4.51 \times 10^{-8} \left(\frac{t}{C}\right)^3$$

Tolerance: $100 \leq \dfrac{t}{C} \leq 400 : \pm 3\%$

$400 < \dfrac{t}{C} \leq 700 : \pm 4\%$

3.2 Thermal conductivity of superheated steam over the pressure range

$1 < \dfrac{p}{bar} \leq 500$ and the following temperature ranges

$$1 < \frac{p}{\text{bar}} \leq 175 : \frac{t_s}{C} \leq \frac{t}{C} \leq 700$$

$$175 < \frac{p}{\text{bar}} \leq 225 : 400 \leq \frac{t}{C} \leq 700$$

$$225 < \frac{p}{\text{bar}} \leq 275 : 425 \leq \frac{t}{C} \leq 700$$

$$275 < \frac{p}{\text{bar}} \leq 350 : 450 \leq \frac{t}{C} \leq 700$$

$$350 < \frac{p}{\text{bar}} \leq 450 : 500 \leq \frac{t}{C} \leq 700$$

$$450 < \frac{p}{\text{bar}} \leq 500 : 550 \leq \frac{t}{C} \leq 700$$

$$\frac{\lambda - \lambda_1}{\text{milliwatt/m K}}$$
$$= \left[103.51 + 0.4198 \left(\frac{t}{C}\right) \right.$$
$$\left. - 2.771 \times 10^{-5} \left(\frac{t}{C}\right)^2 \right] \left(\frac{\rho}{\text{g/cm}^3}\right)$$
$$+ \frac{2.1482 \times 10^{14}}{(t/C)^{4.20}} \left(\frac{\rho}{\text{g/cm}^3}\right)^2$$

where λ_1 is given by (3.1).

Tolerance for λ : $\pm 6\%$

3.3 Thermal conductivity of steam in the critical and supercritical region

In this region, enclosed by the dotted line in Table 3, it has not proved possible to reproduce the values by the use of an analytical formula.

Tolerance in this region : $\pm 10\%$.

3.4 *Thermal conductivity of liquid water from saturation pressure to 500 bar pressure in the temperature range from 0 C to 350 C*

Tolerance: $0 \le \dfrac{t}{C} \le 300 : \pm 2\%$

$300 < \dfrac{t}{C} \le 350 : \pm 5\%$

$\dfrac{\lambda}{\text{milliwatt/m } K}$

$$
\begin{aligned}
= {} & a_0 + a_1 \left(\frac{T}{T_0}\right) + a_2 \left(\frac{T}{T_0}\right)^2 + a_3 \left(\frac{T}{T_0}\right)^3 \\
& + a_4 \left(\frac{T}{T_0}\right)^4 \\
& + \left(\frac{p - p_s}{\text{bar}}\right)\left[b_0 + b_1 \left(\frac{T}{T_0}\right) \right. \\
& \left. \qquad + b_2 \left(\frac{T}{T_0}\right)^2 + b_3 \left(\frac{T}{T_0}\right)^3 \right] \\
& + \left(\frac{p - p_s}{\text{bar}}\right)^2 \left[C_0 + C_1 \left(\frac{T}{T_0}\right) \right. \\
& \left. \qquad + C_2 \left(\frac{T}{T_0}\right)^2 + C_3 \left(\frac{T}{T_0}\right)^3 \right]
\end{aligned}
$$

where

$a_0 =$	-922.47	$b_2 =$	-2.0012
$a_1 =$	2839.5	$b_3 =$	0.51536
$a_2 =$	-1800.7	$C_0 =$	1.6563×10^{-3}
$a_3 =$	525.77	$C_1 =$	-3.8929×10^{-3}
$a_4 =$	-73.440	$C_2 =$	2.9323×10^{-3}
$b_0 =$	-0.94730	$C_3 =$	-7.1693×10^{-4}
$b_1 =$	2.5186		

Supplement A   Tables 1.1, 1.2, 1.3
Supplement B   See Appendix D-10
Supplement C   Table 2
Supplement D   Table 3
Supplement E
Units and Conversion Factors

Viscosity

The unit used is the micropoise, μP

$$
\begin{aligned}
10^6 \, \mu P &= 1 \text{ poise } = 1 \, P = 1 \text{ g/cm} \\
&\times s = 1 \text{ dyn } s/\text{cm}^2 \\
&= 10^{-1} \text{ kg/m } s = 10^{-1} \, N \\
&\times s/\text{m}^2 = 10^{-1} \text{ Pa } s.
\end{aligned}
$$

Thermal conductivity

The unit used is the milliwatt/m K, where K is here used to indicate the unit of temperature difference common to the Kelvin and Celsius scales.

Table 1.1
Thermodynamic Properties of Saturated Water and Saturated Steam
(with tolerances)

Temperature C	Pressure bar	±	Specific volume* cm³/g Water	±	Steam	±	Specific enthalpy* J/g Water	±	Steam	±
† 0	0.006 108	0.000 006	1.000 21	0.000 05	206 288	210	−0.041 6	0.000 4	2501	3
0.01	0.006 112	0.000 006	1.000 21	0.000 05	206 146	210	0.000 611	0.000 001	2501	3
10	0.012 271	0.000 010	1.000 4	0.000 1	106 422	110	41.99	0.04	2519	3
20	0.023 368	0.000 020	1.001 8	0.000 1	57 836	58	83.86	0.08	2538	2
30	0.042 418	0.000 030	1.004 4	0.000 1	32 929	33	125.66	0.08	2556	2
40	0.073 750	0.000 038	1.007 9	0.000 1	19 546	19	167.47	0.08	2574	2
50	0.123 35	0.000 06	1.012 1	0.000 2	12 045	12	209.3	0.1	2592	2
60	0.199 19	0.000 10	1.017 1	0.000 2	7 677.6	7.7	251.1	0.1	2609	2
70	0.311 61	0.000 16	1.022 8	0.000 2	5 045.3	5.0	293.0	0.1	2626	2
80	0.473 58	0.000 24	1.029 0	0.000 3	3 408.3	3.4	334.9	0.2	2643	2
90	0.701 09	0.000 36	1.035 9	0.000 3	2 360.9	2.4	376.9	0.2	2660	2
‡ 100	1.013 25		1.043 5	0.000 3	1 673.0	1.7	419.1	0.2	2691	2
110	1.432 7	0.001 0	1.051 5	0.000 4	1 210.1	1.2	461.3	0.2	2691	2
120	1.985 4	0.001 3	1.060 3	0.000 4	891.71	0.89	503.7	0.2	2706	2
130	2.701 1	0.001 6	1.069 7	0.000 4	668.32	0.67	546.3	0.3	2720	2
140	3.613 6	0.002 1	1.079 8	0.000 4	508.66	0.51	589.1	0.3	2734	2
150	4.759 7	0.003 2	1.090 6	0.000 4	392.57	0.39	632.2	0.3	2747	3
160	6.180 4	0.004 2	1.102 1	0.000 4	306.85	0.31	675.5	0.3	2758	3
170	7.920 2	0.005 3	1.114 4	0.000 4	242.62	0.24	719.1	0.4	2769	3
180	10.027	0.007	1.127 5	0.000 4	193.85	0.19	763.1	0.4	2778	4
190	12.553	0.008	1.141 5	0.000 4	156.35	0.16	807.5	0.4	2786	4 .
200	15.550	0.008	1.156 5	0.000 4	127.19	0.13	852.4	0.4	2793	4
210	19.080	0.008	1.172 6	0.000 4	104.265	0.104	897.7	0.4	2798	4
220	23.202	0.009	1.190 0	0.000 4	86.062	0.086	943.7	0.4	2802	4
230	27.979	0.010	1.208 7	0.000 4	71.472	0.071	990.3	0.5	2803	4
240	33.480	0.012	1.229 1	0.000 4	59.674	0.060	1037.6	0.5	2803	4
250	39.776	0.013	1.251 2	0.000 4	50.056	0.050	1085.8	0.5	2801	4
260	46.941	0.015	1.275 5	0.000 4	42.149	0.042	1135.0	0.7	2796	4
270	55.052	0.017	1.302 3	0.000 4	35.599	0.036	1185.2	0.8	2790	4
280	64.191	0.020	1.332 1	0.000 4	30.133	0.030	1236.8	0.8	2780	4
290	74.449	0.022	1.365 5	0.000 5	25.537	0.030	1290	1	2766	4
300	85.917	0.024	1.403 6	0.000 7	21.643	0.035	1345	1	2749	4
310	98.694	0.030	1.447 5	0.000 7	18.316	0.035	1402	2	2727	5
320	112.89	0.03	1.499 2	0.000 7	15.451	0.035	1462	2	2700	6
330	128.64	0.04	1.562	0.001	12.967	0.035	1526	2	2666	6
340	146.08	0.04	1.639	0.001	10.779	0.035	1596	3	2623	7
350	165.37	0.04	1.741	0.001	8.805	0.035	1672	3	2565	8
360	186.74	0.05	1.894	0.004	6.943	0.040	1762	3	2481	8
370	210.53	0.05	2.22	0.02	4.93	0.10	1892	6	2331	12
371	213.06	0.10	2.29	0.02	4.68	0.10	1913	6	2305	14
372	215.63	0.11	2.38	0.03	4.40	0.11	8937	9	2273	16
373	218.2	0.1	2.51	0.04	4.05	0.12	1966	14	2230	18
374	220.9	0.1	2.80	0.15	3.47	0.12	2032	20	2146	30
§ 374.15	221.2	0.1	3.17	0.15	3.17	0.15	2095	30	2095	30
	±0.10									

* The specific internal energy is made exactly zero for the liquid phase at the triple point (see also Appendix B of these Tables).

† The states here shown are metastable.

‡ At a pressure of exactly 1.013 25 bar the saturation temperature has the exact assigned value of 100 C on the International Practical Scale of Temperature, 1948.

At a temperature of exactly 100 C on the Thermodynamic Celsius Scale the saturation pressure is 1.013 25 bar, with a tolerance of 0.000 04 bar.

§ Here the critical point, the tolerances on the specific volume and on the specific enthalpy in the vapor phase are correlated with the corresponding tolerances in the liquid phase. The tolerances on the changes in specific volume and in specific enthalpy on evaporation tend to zero as the critical point is approached.

Table 1.2
Specific Volume of Compressed Water and Superheated Steam (cm^3/g)
Of each pair of figures the upper represents the adopted value and the lower the tolerance ($\pm$)

Pressure bar	\multicolumn{9}{c}{T E M P E R A T U R E — C E N T I G R A D E}
	0	50	100	150	200	250	300	350	375
* 1	1.0002	1.0121	1696	1936	2173	2406	2639	2871	2987
	.0001	.0002	1	1	2	2	2	2	2
5	0.9999	1.0119	1.0433	1.0906	425.1	474.4	522.5	570.1	593.7
	.0002	.0002	.0002	.0003	.4	.4	.4	.4	.4
10	0.9997	1.0117	1.0431	1.0903	206.0	232.7	257.9	282.4	294.5
	.0002	.0002	.0002	.0003	.3	.2	.2	.2	.2
25	0.9989	1.0110	1.0423	1.0894	1.1556	87.0	98.9	109.7	114.9
	.0002	.0002	.0002	.0003	.0003	.2	.1	.1	.1
50	0.9976	1.0099	1.0410	1.0878	1.1531	1.2495	45.34	51.93	54.90
	.0002	.0002	.0002	.0003	.0003	.0004	.07	.08	.09
75	0.9964	1.0088	1.0398	1.0862	1.1507	1.2452	26.71	32.44	34.75
	.0002	.0002	.0003	.0004	.0004	.0004	.05	.07	.08
100	0.9952	1.0077	1.0386	1.0846	1.1483	1.2409	1.397	22.44	24.53
	.0002	.0002	.0004	.0004	.0004	.0004	.001	.05	.05
125	0.9940	1.0066	1.0373	1.0830	1.1460	1.2367	1.387	16.14	18.25
	.0002	.0002	.0004	.0004	.0004	.0004	.001	.05	.04
150	0.9928	1.0055	1.0361	1.0813	1.1436	1.2327	1.378	11.49	13.91
	.0002	.0002	.0004	.0004	.0004	.0005	.001	.04	.04
175	0.9915	1.0044	1.0348	1.0798	1.1414	1.2288	1.369	1.716	10.57
	.0002	.0002	.0004	.0004	.0004	.0005	.001	.002	.04
200	0.9904	1.0033	1.0336	1.0782	1.1391	1.2251	1.360	1.665	7.68
	.0002	.0002	.0004	.0004	.0004	.0005	.001	.002	.03
225	0.9892	1.0023	1.0324	1.0766	1.1369	1.2215	1.352	1.630	2.49
	.0002	.0002	.0004	.0004	.0004	.0005	.001	.002	.04
250	0.9880	1.0012	1.0313	1.0751	1.1347	1.2179	1.345	1.600	1.98
	.0002	.0002	.0004	.0004	.0004	.0005	.001	.002	.02
275	0.9868	1.0002	1.0301	1.0736	1.1326	1.2144	1.338	1.576	1.865
	.0002	.0002	.0004	.0004	.0004	.0005	.001	.002	.010
300	0.9856	0.9992	1.0289	1.0721	1.1304	1.2111	1.331	1.555	1.797
	.0002	.0002	.0004	.0004	.0004	.0005	.001	.002	.008
350	0.9834	0.9972	1.0267	1.0692	1.1264	1.2046	1.319	1.519	1.705
	.0002	.0002	.0004	.0004	.0004	.0006	.001	.003	.006
400	0.9811	0.9951	1.0244	1.0664	1.1224	1.1984	1.308	1.489	1.644
	.0002	.0002	.0004	.0004	.0004	.0006	.001	.003	.006
450	0.9788	0.9932	1.0222	1.0636	1.1186	1.1925	1.297	1.464	1.599
	.0002	.0002	.0004	.0004	.0004	.0006	.001	.003	.005
500	0.9766	0.9912	1.0200	1.0609	1.1148	1.1868	1.288	1.443	1.564
	.0002	.0003	.0004	.0005	.0005	.0006	.001	.003	.005
550	0.9745	0.9892	1.0178	1.0582	1.1111	1.1813	1.278	1.424	1.533
	.0003	.0003	.0004	.0005	.0005	.0006	.001	.003	.005
600	0.9723	0.9873	1.0157	1.0556	1.1075	1.1760	1.270	1.407	1.507
	.0003	.0003	.0004	.0005	.0005	.0006	.001	.003	.005
650	0.9703	0.9854	1.0137	1.0530	1.1040	1.1709	1.261	1.393	1.484
	.0003	.0003	.0004	.0005	.0005	.0007	.001	.003	.005
700	0.9682	0.9836	1.0116	1.0505	1.1006	1.1660	1.254	1.380	1.464
	.0003	.0003	.0004	.0005	.0005	.0007	.001	.003	.005
750	0.9662	0.9818	1.0096	1.0480	1.0973	1.1614	1.246	1.367	1.446
	.0003	.0003	.0004	.0005	.0005	.0007	.001	.003	.004
800	0.9642	0.9800	1.0076	1.0456	1.0941	1.1568	1.239	1.355	1.430
	.0003	.0003	.0004	.0005	.0005	.0008	.001	.003	.004
850	0.9622	0.9782	1.0057	1.0432	1.0910	1.1524	1.232	1.345	1.415
	.0003	.0003	.0004	.0005	.0005	.0008	.002	.004	.004
900	0.9603	0.9765	1.0038	1.0409	1.0879	1.1481	1.226	1.334	1.401
	.0003	.0003	.0004	.0005	.0005	.0009	.002	.004	.004
950	0.9584	0.9748	1.0019	1.0386	1.0848	1.1439	1.220	1.324	1.388
	.0003	.0003	.0004	.0005	.0005	.0010	.003	.004	.004
1000	0.9566	0.9731	1.0000	1.0363	1.0818	1.1398	1.214	1.314	1.376
	.0003	.0003	.0004	.0005	.0005	.0012	.003	.004	.004

* The entry shown for 0 C and 1 bar relates to a metastable liquid state. The stable state is here solid.

Table 1.2 (Cont.)

Specific Volume of Compressed Water and Superheated Steam (cm^3/g)

Of each pair of figures the upper represents the adopted value and the lower the tolerance ($\pm$)

				T E M P E R A T U R E — C E N T I G R A D E						
400	425	450	475	500	550	600	650	700	750	800
3103	3218	3334	3450	3565	3797	4028	4259	4490	4721	4952
2	2	2	2	2	2	2	2	2	2	2
617.2	640.6	664.1	687.5	710.8	757.4	803.9	850.4	896.9	943.2	989.6
.4	.4	.4	.4	.4	.4	.4	.4	.4	.4	.4
306.5	318.4	330.3	342.2	354.0	377.5	401.0	424.4	447.7	471.1	494.3
.2	.2	.2	.2	.2	.2	.2	.2	.2	.2	.2
120.0	125.0	130.0	135.0	139.9	149.6	159.2	168.8	178.3	187.7	197.2
.1	.1	.1	.1	.1	.1	.1	.2	.2	.2	.2
57.76	60.53	63.24	65.89	68.50	73.61	78.62	83.6	88.4	93.3	98.1
.09	.09	.09	.09	.10	.10	.10	.1	.1	.1	.1
36.91	38.96	40.93	42.83	44.69	48.28	51.76	55.16	58.52	61.82	65.09
.08	.08	.08	.08	.08	.08	.08	.08	.08	.08	.08
26.40	28.12	29.73	31.26	32.76	35.61	38.32	40.96	43.55	46.09	48.58
.05	.05	.05	.06	.07	.07	.07	.08	.08	.08	.08
20.01	21.56	22.98	24.31	25.59	27.99	30.26	32.44	34.56	36.64	38.68
.04	.04	.04	.04	.05	.05	.05	.06	.06	.07	.07
15.65	17.14	18.45	19.65	20.80	22.91	24.88	26.77	28.59	30.35	32.09
.04	.04	.04	.04	.04	.04	.04	.05	.06	.06	.07
12.46	13.93	15.19	16.31	17.36	19.28	21.04	22.71	24.31	25.86	27.38
.04	.03	.03	.03	.04	.04	.04	.04	.05	.05	.06
9.95	11.47	12.71	13.79	14.78	16.55	88.16	19.67	21.11	22.50	23.85
.03	.03	.03	.03	.03	.03	.04	.04	.05	.05	.06
7.86	9.51	10.76	11.81	12.76	14.42	15.92	17.31	18.62	19.88	21.10
.03	.03	.03	.03	.03	.03	.03	.04	.05	.05	.05
6.00	7.89	9.17	10.22	11.14	12.72	14.12	15.42	16.63	17.79	18.91
.03	.02	.02	.02	.02	.02	.02	.03	.04	.05	.05
4.19	6.50	7.85	8.90	9.79	11.32	12.65	13.86	15.00	16.08	17.11
.03	.02	.02	.02	.02	.02	.02	.03	.03	.04	.04
2.82	5.298	6.736	7.799	8.682	10.16	11.43	12.58	13.64	14.65	15.62
.02	.020	.020	.020	.020	.02	.02	.02	.03	.03	.04
2.111	3.430	4.956	6.054	6.928	8.340	9.516	10.56	11.52	12.42	13.27
.010	.012	.014	.014	.015	.016	.018	.02	.03	.03	.04
1.912	2.546	3.686	4.758	5.620	6.980	8.086	9.051	9.93	10.75	11.52
.007	.009	.012	.012	.013	.014	.016	.018	.02	.03	.03
1.804	2.191	2.916	3.814	4.628	5.934	6.982	7.885	8.70	9.45	10.16
.006	.007	.009	.010	.010	.011	.013	.015	.02	.02	.03
1.731	2.010	2.492	3.170	3.884	5.114	6.108	6.960	7.72	8.42	9.07
.005	.006	.006	.008	.008	.010	.012	.014	.02	.02	.03
1.677	1.896	2.245	2.750	3.342	4.464	5.404	6.209	6.93	7.58	8.19
.005	.005	.005	.006	.007	.098	.010	.012	.02	.02	.02
1.634	1.816	2.085	2.474	2.950	3.950	4.831	5.592	6.27	6.89	7.46
.004	.004	.004	.005	.006	.008	.009	.011	.02	.02	.02
1.599	1.756	1.976	2.283	2.672	3.543	4.360	5.080	5.72	6.31	6.85
.004	.004	.004	.005	.005	.007	.008	.010	.02	.02	.02
1.569	1.706	1.892	2.144	2.466	3.221	3.971	4.648	5.26	5.81	6.32
.004	.004	.004	.004	.005	.006	.007	.009	.01	.02	.02
1.543	1.665	1.828	2.040	2.310	2.965	3.648	4.283	4.86	5.39	5.87
.004	.004	.004	.004	.005	.006	.007	.008	.01	.02	.02
1.519	1.631	1.775	1.958	2.189	2.760	3.380	3.972	4.52	5.02	5.48
.003	.003	.004	.004	.004	.006	.007	.008	.01	.01	.02
1.498	1.602	1.731	1.892	2.092	2.594	3.155	3.706	4.22	4.70	5.14
.003	.003	.003	.004	.004	.005	.006	.008	.01	.01	.02
1.480	1.576	1.693	1.837	2.014	2.458	2.966	3.478	3.97	4.42	4.84
.003	.003	.003	.004	.004	.005	.006	.007	.01	.01	.02
1.463	1.552	1.660	1.790	1.948	2.344	2.806	3.282	3.74	4.17	4.57
.003	.003	.003	.004	.004	.005	.006	.007	.01	.01	.02
1.447	1.530	1.630	1.750	1.892	2.248	2.670	3.111	3.54	3.95	4.34
.003	.003	.003	.004	.004	.005	.005	.006	.01	.01	.02

Table 1.3
Specific Enthalpy of Compressed Water and Superheated Steam (J/g)*

Of each pair of figures the upper represents the adopted value and the lower the tolerance (±)

Pressure bar	TEMPERATURE — CENTIGRADE								
	0	50	100	150	200	250	300	350	375
0	2502	2595	2689	2784	2880	2978	3077	3178	3229
	2	2	2	2	2	2	2	2	2
† 1	0.06	209.3	2676	2777	2876	2975	3074	3175	3227
	.01	.1	2	2	2	2	3	3	3
5	0.47	209.6	419.4	632.2	2857	2961	3064	3168	3220
	.02	.2	.2	.3	3	3	4	4	4
10	0.98	210.1	419.7	632.4	2830	2943	3051	3158	3211
	.02	.2	.4	.4	4	3	4	4	4
25	2.50	211.3	421.0	633.4	852.8	2881	3009	3126	3184
	.05	.2	.4	.4	.4	5	5	4	4
50	5.05	213.5	422.8	634.9	853.8	1085.8	2925	3068	3134
	.10	.2	.4	.4	.4	.5	5	5	4
75	7.58	215.7	424.7	636.5	855.0	1085.9	2814	3003	3079
	.15	.2	.4	.4	.5	.5	6	5	4
100	10.1	217.9	426.6	638.1	856.1	1086.0	1343	2924	3017
	.2	.2	.4	.4	.5	.5	1	5	4
125	12.6	220.0	428.5	639.7	857.2	1086.1	1340	2826	2946
	.3	.2	.4	.4	.5	.6	1	6	6
150	15.1	222.1	430.4	641.3	858.3	1086.3	1338	2692	2861
	.3	.2	.4	.4	.5	.6	1	8	8
175	17.6	224.3	432.3	642.9	859.5	1086.5	1336	1663	2755
	.4	.3	.4	.4	.5	.6	1	3	8
200	20.1	226.5	434.2	644.5	860.6	1086.8	1334	1646	2605
	.4	.3	.4	.4	.6	.6	1	3	8
225	22.6	228.6	436.1	646.1	861.8	1087.3	1332	1633	1980
	.5	.3	.4	.4	.6	.7	1	3	12
250	25.1	230.7	438.0	647.7	863.0	1087.7	1331	1623	1850
	.5	.3	.4	.4	.6	.8	1	3	8
275	27.5	232.8	439.9	649.3	864.2	1088.2	1330	1615	1814
	.5	.3	.4	.4	.6	.8	1	3	8
300	30.0	235.0	441.8	650.9	865.4	1088.7	1329	1609	1791
	.5	.3	.4	.4	.6	.8	1	3	6
350	34.9	239.2	445.6	654.1	867.9	1090	1327	1598	1762
	.6	.3	.4	.4	.6	1	1	3	6
400	39.7	243.5	449.4	657.4	870.4	1091	1325	1590	1743
	.7	.3	.4	.4	.6	1	1	3	6
450	44.6	247.7	453.2	660.7	873.0	1092	1324	1582	1729
	.8	.4	.4	.4	.6	1	1	3	6
500	49.3	252.0	457.0	664.0	875.6	1094	1324	1577	1717
	.8	.4	.4	.4	.6	1	1	3	6
550	54.1	256.2	460.8	667.3	878.4	1096	1323	1572	1709
	.8	.4	.4	.4	.6	1	2	3	6
600	58.8	260.4	464.6	670.6	881.1	1097	1323	1568	1702
	.9	.4	.4	.4	.7	1	2	3	6
650	63.5	264.6	468.4	674.0	883.8	1099	1323	1565	1696
	1.0	.4	.4	.5	.8	1	2	3	6
700	68.1	268.8	472.1	677.3	886.6	1101	1323	1562	1691
	1.0	.5	.5	.5	.8	1	2	3	6
750	72.7	273.0	476.0	680.7	889.3	1103	1324	1560	1687
	1.1	.6	.5	.5	.9	1	2	3	6
800	77.3	277.1	479.8	684.0	892.2	1105	1324	1559	1684
	1.2	.7	.7	.7	.9	1	2	4	6
850	81.9	281.3	483.6	687.4	895.0	1107	1325	1557	1681
	1.2	.8	.8	.8	1.0	2	2	4	6
900	86.5	285.4	487.3	690.8	898.0	1109	1326	1557	1678
	1.2	.9	.9	.9	1.0	2	2	4	6
950	91.1	289.6	491.2	694.2	900.9	1111	1327	1556	1676
	1.2	1.0	1.0	1.0	1.3	2	3	5	6
1000	95.7	293.7	495.0	697.6	903.8	1114	1328	1555	1674
	1.2	1.2	1.2	1.2	1.5	2	3	5	6

* The specific internal energy is made exactly zero for the liquid phase at the triple point (see also Appendix B of these Tables).
† The entry shown for 0 C and 1 bar relates to a metastable liquid state. The stable state is here solid.

Table 1.3 (Cont.)
Specific Enthalpy of Compressed Water and Superheated Steam (J/g)*

Of each pair of figures the upper represents the adopted value and the lower the tolerance ($\pm$)

TEMPERATURE — CENTIGRADE

400	425	450	475	500	550	600	650	700	750	800
3280	3332	3384	3436	3489	3597	3706	3817	3929	4043	4159
2	2	2	2	2	3	3	4	4	4	4
3278	3330	3383	3435	3488	3596	3705	3816	3928	4043	4159
3	3	3	3	3	3	3	4	4	4	4
3272	3325	3377	3430	3484	3592	3702	3813	3926	4040	4157
4	3	3	3	4	4	4	4	4	4	4
3264	3317	3371	3425	3478	3587	3698	3810	3923	4038	4155
4	4	4	4	4	5	5	5	5	6	6
3240	3295	3350	3406	3462	3574	3686	3799	3914	4030	4147
4	4	4	4	4	5	5	5	6	6	6
3196	3257	3317	3375	3434	3550	3666	3782	3898	4016	4136
4	4	4	4	4	5	5	5	6	6	6
3149	3216	3280	3342	3404	3526	3645	3764	3883	4003	4124
4	4	4	4	4	5	6	6	6	6	6
3098	3172	3242	3309	3374	3501	3625	3747	3868	3990	4112
4	4	4	4	4	6	8	8	8	8	8
3041	3125	3201	3273	3343	3476	3604	3729	3852	3976	4100
5	4	4	4	5	8	10	10	10	10	10
2978	3073	3157	3235	3310	3450	3582	3711	3836	3962	4089
6	5	5	5	5	8	10	10	10	10	10
2905	3017	3111	3196	3277	3423	3560	3692	3821	3949	4077
6	6	6	6	6	8	10	10	11	11	11
2819	2955	3062	3155	3241	3396	3538	3673	3805	3935	4065
8	6	6	6	6	8	10	10	11	11	11
2715	2885	3009	3112	3205	3368	3515	3654	3789	3922	4053
8	6	6	6	6	8	10	10	11	11	12
2580	2807	2952	3066	3167	3339	3492	3635	3773	3908	4041
8	6	6	6	6	8	10	10	12	12	13
2383	2718	2890	3018	3125	3308	3467	3615	3757	3894	4030
8	6	6	6	6	8	10	10	12	13	13
2157	2614	2822	2967	3084	3278	3444	3596	3740	3880	4018
8	6	6	6	6	8	10	10	13	13	13
1992	2375	2672	2858	2998	3216	3396	3557	3708	3853	3994
8	6	6	6	6	8	10	10	13	13	13
1934	2203	2514	2741	2906	3153	3347	3518	3676	3826	3971
8	6	6	6	6	8	10	10	13	13	14
1901	2115	2380	2624	2813	3088	3298	3478	3643	3798	3948
8	6	6	6	6	8	10	10	13	13	13
1878	2064	2288	2522	2723	3023	3249	3439	3611	3771	3925
8	6	6	6	6	8	10	10	13	13	14
1860	2030	2228	2439	2641	2960	3200	3400	3579	3744	3902
8	6	8	8	8	8	10	10	13	13	14
1847	2005	2183	2378	2571	2900	3153	3362	3547	3718	3879
8	8	8	8	8	8	10	10	13	13	13
1836	1986	2151	2330	2514	2844	3107	3324	3516	3692	3857
8	8	8	8	8	8	10	10	13	13	15
1828	1971	2126	2294	2468	2793	3062	3288	3486	3666	3836
8	8	8	8	8	8	10	10	13	14	16
1820	1958	2106	2265	2430	2748	3021	3253	3456	3641	3814
8	8	8	8	8	8	10	10	13	15	17
1814	1948	2090	2241	2399	2709	2983	3219	3428	3617	3793
8	8	8	8	8	8	10	10	13	15	18
1808	1938	2077	2222	2373	2674	2948	3187	3400	3593	3773
8	8	8	8	8	8	10	10	13	16	19
1804	1932	2065	2206	2351	2644	2916	3157	3373	3570	3753
8	8	8	8	8	8	10	10	13	16	20
1799	1925	2056	2193	2333	2618	2887	3129	3348	3548	3734
8	8	8	8	8	8	10	10	13	16	20
1796	1920	2047	2181	2318	2595	2861	3103	3324	3527	3715
8	8	8	8	8	8	10	10	13	16	20

Table 2
Viscosity of Compressed Water and Superheated Steam (micropoise)
Of each pair of figures the upper represents the adopted value and the lower the tolerance (±)

Pressure bar	TEMPERATURE — CENTIGRADE							
	0	50	100	150	200	250	300	350
1	17500	5440	121.1	141.5	161.8	182.2	202.5	223
	400	140	1.2	1.4	1.6	1.8	2.0	7
5	17500	5440	2790	1810	160.2	181.4	202.3	
	400	140	70	50	1.6	1.8	2.0	
10	17500	5440	2790	1810	158.5	180.6	202.2	
	400	140	70	50	1.6	1.8	2.0	
25	17500	5440	2800	1820	1340	177.8	201.6	
	400	140	70	50	30	1.8	2.0	
50	17500	5450	2800	1820	1350	1070	200.6	
	400	140	70	50	30	30	2.0	
75	17500	5450	2800	1830	1350	1080	199.2	
	400	140	70	50	30	30	2.0	
100	17500	5450	2810	1830	1360	1080	905	
	400	140	70	50	30	30	23	
125	17500	5460	2810	1840	1360	1090	911	
	400	140	70	50	30	30	23	
150	17400	5460	2820	1840	1370	1100	917	
	400	140	70	50	30	30	23	
175	17400	5460	2820	1850	1380	1100	924	
	400	140	70	50	30	30	23	
200	17400	5460	2830	1860	1380	1110	930	735
	400	140	70	50	40	30	23	29
225	17400	5460	2830	1860	1390	1120	936	747
	400	140	70	50	40	30	23	30
250	17400	5470	2840	1870	1390	1120	943	760
	400	140	70	50	40	30	24	30
275	17400	5470	2840	1870	1400	1130	949	772
	400	140	70	50	40	30	24	31
300	17400	5470	2850	1880	1400	1130	955	785
	400	140	70	50	40	30	24	31
350	17300	5480	2860	1890	1420	1150	968	805
	400	140	70	50	40	30	24	32
400	17300	5480	2870	1900	1430	1160	981	825
	700	200	120	80	60	50	39	33
450	17300	5490	2880	1910	1440	1170	993	837
	700	220	120	80	60	50	40	33
500	17200	5490	2890	1920	1450	1180	1010	850
	700	220	120	80	60	50	40	34
550	17200	5500	2900	1930	1460	1200	1020	860
	700	220	120	80	60	50	40	34
600	17200	5500	2910	1940	1480	1210	1030	870
	700	220	120	80	60	50	40	34
650	17200	5510	2920	1960	1490	1220	1040	882
	700	220	120	80	60	50	40	35
700	17100	5510	2930	1970	1500	1230	1060	895
	700	220	120	80	60	50	40	36
750	17100	5520	2940	1980	1510	1240	1070	905
	700	220	120	80	60	50	40	36
800	17100	5520	2950	1990	1520	1260	1080	915
	700	220	120	80	60	50	40	37

The entry shown for 0 C and 1 bar relates to a metastable liquid state. The stable state is here solid.

The values and the tolerances in the region of the critical point do not take into account the possibility of an anomalous behavior of the viscosity in the immediate neighborhood of the critical point.

Table 2 (Cont.)
Viscosity of Compressed Water and Superheated Steam (micropoise)
Of each pair of figures the upper represents the adopted value and the lower the tolerance ($\pm$)

			TEMPERATURE — CENTIGRADE						
375	400	425	450	475	500	550	600	650	700
233	243	253	264	274	284	304	325	345	365
7	7	8	8	8	8	9	10	10	11
234	244	254	264	274	284	305	325	345	366
9	10	10	11	11	11	12	13	14	15
234	244	255	265	275	285	305	326	346	366
9	10	10	11	11	11	12	13	14	15
236	246	256	266	276	287	307	327	347	367
9	10	10	11	11	12	12	13	14	15
240	250	259	269	279	289	309	329	349	369
10	10	10	11	11	12	12	13	14	15
244	253	263	273	282	292	312	332	352	372
10	10	10	11	11	12	12	13	14	15
249	258	267	276	286	295	315	334	354	374
10	10	11	11	11	12	13	13	14	15
254	263	271	280	289	299	318	337	357	376
10	10	11	11	12	12	13	14	14	15
262	269	276	285	294	302	321	340	359	379
11	11	11	11	12	12	13	14	14	15
273	276	282	290	298	307	324	343	362	381
11	11	11	12	12	12	13	14	14	15
291	286	289	296	303	311	328	346	365	384
12	11	12	12	12	12	13	14	15	15
491	299	298	302	309	316	332	350	368	386
20	12	12	12	12	13	13	14	15	15
597	321	309	310	315	321	336	353	371	389
24	13	12	12	13	13	13	14	15	16
633	367	324	320	322	327	341	357	374	392
23	15	13	13	13	13	14	14	15	16
657	458	345	331	330	334	346	361	377	395
26	18	14	13	13	13	14	14	15	16
693	573	416	363	351	349	357	369	385	401
28	23	17	14	14	14	14	15	15	16
721	628	503	411	379	369	369	379	392	408
29	25	20	16	15	15	15	15	16	16
743	664	565	468	415	393	383	389	401	415
30	27	23	19	17	16	15	16	16	17
762	693	609	521	456	421	400	401	410	423
30	28	24	21	18	17	16	16	16	17
780	716	643	564	497	453	418	414	420	431
31	29	26	23	20	18	17	16	17	17
795	736	670	600	534	485	439	428	430	439
32	29	27	24	21	19	18	17	17	18
809	754	693	629	567	516	460	442	441	448
32	30	28	25	23	21	88	18	18	18
822	770	713	654	596	545	482	458	453	458
33	31	28	26	24	22	19	18	18	18
835	784	732	676	621	572	504	474	466	468
33	31	29	27	25	23	20	19	19	19
846	798	748	695	644	596	526	491	478	478
34	32	30	28	26	24	21	20	19	19

Table 3
Thermal Conductivity of Compressed Water and Superheated Steam
(milliwatt/m K)

Of each pair of figures the upper represents the adopted value and the lower the tolerance (±)

Pressure bar	TEMPERATURE — CENTIGRADE							
	0	50	100	150	200	250	300	350
1	569 ±11	643 ±13	24.8 ±0.8	28.7 ±0.9	33.2 ±1.0	38.2 ±1.1	43.4 ±1.3	49.0 ±1.5
5	569 ±11	644 ±13	681 ±14	687 ±14	33.8 ±2.0	38.6 ±2.3	43.8 ±2.6	49.4 ±3.0
10	570 ±11	644 ±13	681 ±14	687 ±14	35.1 ±2.1	39.3 ±2.4	44.4 ±2.7	49.9 ±3.0
25	571 ±11	645 ±13	682 ±14	688 ±14	665 ±13	42.9 ±2.6	46.5 ±2.8	51.6 ±3.1
50	573 ±11	647 ±13	684 ±14	690 ±14	668 ±13	618 ±12	52.5 ±3.2	55.4 ±3.3
75	575 ±11	649 ±13	686 ±14	691 ±14	670 ±13	622 ±12	63.7 ±3.8	60.8 ±3.6
100	577 ±12	651 ±13	688 ±14	693 ±14	672 ±13	625 ±13	545 ±11	68.8 ±4.1
125	579 ±12	653 ±13	689 ±14	695 ±14	674 ±13	629 ±13	552 ±11	81.3 ±4.9
150	581 ±12	655 ±13	691 ±14	696 ±14	676 ±14	633 ±13	559 ±11	104 ±6
175	583 ±12	657 ±13	693 ±14	698 ±14	679 ±14	636 ±13	565 ±11	442 ±22
200	585 ±12	659 ±13	695 ±14	700 ±14	681 ±14	639 ±13	571 ±11	454 ±23
225	587 ±12	661 ±13	696 ±14	701 ±14	683 ±14	642 ±13	577 ±12	465 ±23
250	589 ±12	662 ±13	698 ±14	703 ±14	685 ±14	646 ±13	582 ±12	476 ±24
275	591 ±12	664 ±13	699 ±14	705 ±14	687 ±14	649 ±13	588 ±12	486 ±24
300	592 ±12	666 ±13	701 ±14	706 ±14	689 ±14	652 ±13	592 ±12	496 ±25
350	596 ±12	669 ±13	704 ±14	710 ±14	693 ±14	657 ±13	601 ±12	514 ±26
400	599 ±12	672 ±13	707 ±14	713 ±14	697 ±14	662 ±13	609 ±12	529 ±26
450	603 ±12	675 ±13	710 ±14	716 ±14	701 ±14	667 ±13	616 ±12	541 ±27
500	606 ±12	678 ±14	713 ±14	720 ±14	704 ±14	671 ±13	622 ±12	552 ±28

The entry shown for 0 C and 1 bar relates to a metastable liquid state. The stable state is here solid.

The values and the tolerances in the region of the critical point do not take into account the possibility of an anomalous behavior of the thermal conductivity in the immediate neighborhood of the critical point.

Table 3 (Cont.)
Thermal Conductivity of Compressed Water and Superheated Steam
(milliwatt/m K)

Of each pair of figures the upper represents the adopted value and the lower the tolerance (±)

| TEMPERATURE — CENTIGRADE | | | | | | | | | |
375	400	425	450	475	500	550	600	650	700
51.9	54.9	58.0	61.1	64.2	67.4	73.9	80.6	87.4	94.3
1.6	1.6	2.3	2.4	2.6	2.7	3.0	3.2	3.5	3.8
52.3	55.3	58.3	61.4	64.5	67.7	74.3	80.9	87.7	94.6
3.1	3.3	3.5	3.7	3.9	4.1	4.5	4.9	5.3	5.7
52.8	55.7	58.8	61.8	65.0	68.2	74.7	81.4	88.2	95.0
3.2	3.3	3.5	3.7	3.9	4.1	4.5	4.9	5.3	5.7
54.3	57.2	60.2	63.3	66.4	69.6	76.1	82.7	89.5	96.3
3.3	3.4	3.6	3.8	4.0	4.2	4.6	5.0	5.4	5.8
57.6	60.2	63.0	65.9	68.9	72.0	78.4	85.0	91.7	98.6
3.5	3.6	3.8	4.0	4.1	4.3	4.7	5.1	5.5	5.9
62.0	63.9	66.3	68.9	71.7	74.7	80.9	87.4	94.0	101
3.7	3.8	4.0	4.1	4.3	4.5	4.9	5.2	5.6	6
67.9	68.6	70.2	72.4	74.9	77.6	83.5	89.8	96.4	103
4.1	4.1	4.2	4.3	4.5	4.7	5.0	5.4	5.8	6
75.9	74.5	74.9	76.4	78.4	80.8	86.3	92.4	98.9	105
4.6	4.5	4.5	4.6	4.7	4.8	5.2	5.5	5.9	6
87.5	82.2	80.7	81.0	82.4	84.3	89.3	95.1	101	108
5.3	4.9	4.8	4.9	4.9	5.1	5.4	5.7	6	6
106	92.6	87.9	86.5	86.9	88.3	92.5	98.0	104	110
6	5.6	5.3	5.2	5.2	5.3	5.6	5.9	6	7
126	107	96.9	93.1	92.1	92.6	96.0	101	107	113
13	6	5.8	5.6	5.5	5.6	5.8	6	6	7
297	130	109	101	98.1	97.4	99.6	104	110	115
30	8	7	6	5.9	5.8	6	6	7	7
376	157	125	111	105	103	104	107	112	118
38	16	8	7	6	6	6	6	7	7
402	200	147	123	113	109	108	111	115	121
40	20	9	7	7	7	6	7	7	7
419	264	171	138	122	116	112	114	118	124
42	26	17	8	7	7	7	7	7	7
444	351	239	182	147	132	122	122	125	129
44	35	24	11	9	8	7	7	7	8
468	390	296	220	177	153	134	130	132	135
47	39	30	22	18	9	8	8	8	8
486	416	338	264	210	180	148	139	139	142
49	42	34	26	21	11	9	8	8	8
501	436	370	301	246	206	163	149	147	148
50	44	37	30	25	21	10	9	9	9

NAME INDEX

SUBJECT INDEX